ELECTRICAL MEASUREMENTS

ELECTRICAL MEASUREMENTS

FORREST K. HARRIS, Ph.D.

Physicist at the National Bureau of Standards
and Professorial Lecturer in Electrical Engineering
at the George Washington University

JOHN WILEY & SONS, INC.

New York · London · Sydney

SEVENTH PRINTING, JUNE, 1966

Library of Congress Catalog Card Number: 51—13122

Printed in the United States of America

PREFACE

This book is the direct outgrowth of a course of lectures on electrical measurements given over a ten-year period to students of electrical engineering and of physics at the George Washington University. Some share of the responsibility for the appearance of this book must be accepted by the students who have taken this course. It was as a result of their urging that the long task of committing these lectures to a written form was begun. The author does not blame them for this; he also finds note-taking a very tiresome business. These students have helped materially in many details by classroom discussions and by their work on assigned problems. Many laboratory problems also have come to the author's attention during the past quarter-century at the National Bureau of Standards, either while doing his own work or when looking over some other worker's shoulder. The author has attempted to combine the viewpoints of the laboratory and of the classroom, and to keep in mind the needs and questions of laboratory workers as well as students.

The volume of material on measurements which must be discussed in a book that makes any attempt at thoroughness is so great that the scope of its content must be limited to only a portion of the field; and the author has chosen to restrict the discussion primarily to direct-current and low-frequency measurements. Also, in beginning such a discussion, a certain degree of sophistication on the part of the reader must be assumed. It is therefore supposed that the reader is a student of electrical engineering or of physics, who already has some acquaintance with the theory of electricity and of electric circuits, or is a laboratory worker who has had equivalent training. It is further supposed that the reader has a background of mathematics through the calculus and that he has had sufficient laboratory experience to know something about the manipulation of electrical instruments and apparatus. Finally it will be supposed that the measurements he wishes to undertake are such that he is not content to accept without question the uncorrected indication of any instrument that comes to hand. Thus the discussion will seek to emphasize the nature and magnitude of the errors encountered in practical measurements and the means that may be taken to minimize or correct them, as well as to present the devices and arrangements by which various types of measurements are made.

In considering the subject of electrical measurements a variety of viewpoints is possible. At one extreme, measurements constitute a system of philosophy in which cause and effect can be kept in orderly array. (This viewpoint is more easily maintained at the desk than in the laboratory.) At the other extreme, measurements may be considered a contest in which the adversary is what has been called "the law of the natural cussedness of inanimate objects." An intermediate and more profitable point of view may be taken in which the measurement is a challenge such that, as the worker strives for more certainty in his results, he is confronted with problems of increasing difficulty arising chiefly from the characteristics of the apparatus and instruments he must use. These problems being solved, the worker may perhaps find himself a step nearer to the final impassable barrier set by nature—the granularity of energy. All these viewpoints occur at one time or another in varying degree to anyone who works in the field of measurements, and to some extent each will be apparent in this book.

The author believes that the art of measurement is as much a matter of one's attitude and way of thinking as it is a collection of devices and techniques whereby one can push buttons or turn knobs and so learn how big something is or how nearly alike two things are. At the risk of being considered a bit pedantic, the author suggests that there may be profit to the reader in approaching the subject as an exercise in mental discipline rather than simply as a collection of embalmed facts or as a compendium of recipes for getting things measured.

The problems and difficulties of precise measurement increase very rapidly as accuracy requirements are increased. If the relation between accuracy of results and difficulty of measurement could be expressed as an analytic function it would surely be found to have a strong exponential term. In most fields, measurements to an accuracy of a few per cent are readily achieved by simple means if one uses reasonable care in selecting suitable methods and instruments. If accuracy requirements are a per cent or better, careful selection of method and apparatus is essential; one must make sure that the instruments are of good quality, he must apply corrections to their indications where necessary, and frequently he must also consider the effects of the measuring equipment on the thing that is being measured. If the accuracy requirements are of the order of a tenth of a per cent, one has about reached the limit to which the indications of deflecting instruments can be read, and usually he must apply corrections in the most painstaking manner, taking into account, among other things, the effects of ambient conditions on the measuring apparatus. If accuracy requirements are increased beyond this point, special methods and techniques must be employed which permit a comparison between the thing being measured and some standard whose characteristics have been studied and whose stability is known within limits that are closer than the accuracy requirements of the measurement being undertaken. These remarks apply of course only to quantities that are of normal magnitude. Where the thing to be measured is either very large or extremely small, the difficulties encountered in its precise measurement increase much more rapidly than has been indicated above.

In brief, the laboratory worker who uses instruments as tools and measurements as a means of obtaining information, as well as the student of the theory of measurements, must be alert to the limitations and possibilities of various devices and techniques, to the end that the accuracy or repeatability required by the job at hand may be attained without wasting time and effort on matters that are not significant. It is hoped that this book will serve as an aid in the development of a background that is essential to the worker in this field.

ACKNOWLEDGMENTS

In collecting information on a subject so general as electrical measurements many sources must be consulted, and, since portions of the present text have been prepared from rough lecture notes, it is inevitable that published material will sometimes be used without proper acknowledgment of its source. I regret any such inadvertences and wish to make a general acknowledgment of my indebtedness to the authors of the vast body of literature that has grown up around the subject. Books which have been extensively consulted include the following:

Cullwick, *Fundamentals of Electromagnetism* (Macmillan, 1939).

Curtis, *Electrical Measurements* (McGraw-Hill, 1937).

Drysdale and Jolley, *Electrical Measuring Instruments* (Benn, 1924).

Edgecumbe and Ockenden, *Industrial Electrical Measuring Instruments* (Pitman, 1933).

Gerszonowicz, *Galvanómetros y Oscilógrafos* (Univ. Montevideo, 1943).

Golding, *Electrical Measurements and Measuring Instruments* (Pitman, 1946).

Hague, *Alternating-Current Bridge Methods* (Pitman, 1946).

Hague, *Instrument Transformers* (Pitman, 1936).

Keinath, *Die Technik elektrischer Messgeräte* (Oldenbourg, 1928).

Kennelly, *Electrical Vibration Instruments* (Macmillan, 1923).

Kerchner and Corcoran, *Alternating-Current Circuits* (Wiley, 1951).

Knowlton, *Electrical Power Metering* (McGraw-Hill, 1934).

Laws, *Electrical Measurements* (McGraw-Hill, 1938).

Marshall, *Measurements in Electrical Engineering* (Swift, 1943).

Michels, *Advanced Electrical Measurements* (Van Nostrand, 1941).

Palm, *Elektrische Messgeräte und Messeinrichtungen* (Springer, 1948).

Reich, *Theory and Applications of Electron Tubes* (McGraw-Hill, 1939).

Rider, *The Vacuum-Tube Voltmeter* (Rider, 1941).

Stout, *Electrical Measurements* (Edwards, 1949).

Terman, *Radio Engineers' Handbook* (McGraw-Hill, 1943).

Other source material in the form of unpublished notes was freely made available by friends and colleagues at the National Bureau of Standards and elsewhere. Such assistance from H. B. Brooks, B. L. Dunfee, F. L. Hermach, R. L. Sanford, F. B. Silsbee, J. L. Thomas, F. D. Weaver, and F. Wenner is gratefully acknowledged. Most of the drawings were prepared by Johanna Van Gelder. Data for several of the tables and figures were computed by R. McAuliff and T. Zapf. T. W. Cushing was of great assistance in reading proof and in preparing the index. I have also bedeviled most of the people just mentioned for criticism and advice on portions of the manuscript. Dr. F. B. Silsbee, Dr. F. M. Defandorf, and Mr. F. L. Hermach have read the entire manuscript and have made many helpful suggestions which have been incorporated in the text. Similar assistance was given on parts of the text by Dr. Charles Moon and Messrs. Irvin L. Cooter and Chester Peterson of the National Bureau of Standards, Professor H. N. Hayward of the University of Illinois, Mr. Ralph Kotter of the Massachusetts Institute of Technology and formerly of the National Bureau of Standards, Mr. John A. Miller of the Weston Electrical Instrument Corporation, Messrs. D. A. Young and C. A. Wentz of the Westinghouse Electric Corporation, and Mr. Norman Bonn of the Rubicon Company. To all these friends, whose contributions have made this book possible, I wish to express my deep appreciation, not only for their help and encouragement but also for their continued friendship in spite of the harassment inflicted on them.

The generous cooperation of the Allen B. Du Mont Laboratories, the General Electric Company, the General Radio Company, the Leeds and Northrup Company, the Rubicon Company, the Westinghouse Electric Corporation, and the Weston Electrical Instrument Corporation in making figures and technical data available for use in this book is also gratefully acknowledged.

Finally, since neither effort nor friends have been spared in trying to make this book authoritative in its field, I will be grateful to any readers who are kind enough to call to my attention such errors as they may discover and such sins of omission or commission as may come to their attention.

In closing this manuscript I wish to acknowledge in a special way my debt to the five friends and teachers who, more than any others, have tried to give me some insight into the subject of electrical measurements. It is therefore with respect and affection that I dedicate this book to Homer L. Dodge, who introduced me to the subject of electrical measurements; to William B. Kouwenhoven, who guided me during my apprenticeship in graduate school and who also befriended me in an hour of extreme peril; to Herbert B. Brooks, who showed me the necessity of careful precise work; to Frank Wenner, who showed me how much fun measurements could be; and to Francis B. Silsbee, who, when I told him that I had been asked to teach electrical measurements, expressed the hope that now I might perhaps learn something of the subject.

Forest K. Harris

National Bureau of Standards
Washington, D. C.
April 13, 1951

CONTENTS

CHAPTER 1

THE ART OF MEASUREMENT

Choice of Method

A number of important steps are always involved in a measurement. First a method must be chosen that makes use of available apparatus to obtain the desired result with whatever accuracy is required. This necessitates consideration of the reliability of the instruments or apparatus to be used, the effects of various conditions which will be encountered in the experiment, the time needed for setting up and operating the necessary equipment, and the accuracy that may be desired or attainable in the final result. The method chosen should be as simple as possible consistent with the requirements of the task. It is quite frequently desirable to avoid apparatus and methods whose inherent accuracy is higher than is required for the job at hand, if their use and manipulation are so time consuming or otherwise expensive that the choice is economically unsound. It is usually profitable to consider carefully the various methods that can be used in a particular task, before actually starting the measurement. The questions, "Is there another and better way of doing this?" and "Is this method basically sound and applicable?" should always be asked and answered before time is taken to assemble the apparatus and make the measurement by a particular method. The appropriate choice of apparatus and experimental method becomes easier as the worker's experience becomes broader in his field.

The method and apparatus having been chosen, it is important that they be intelligently used. The function of each piece of apparatus and its method of operation should be thoroughly understood. The sketching of a preliminary wiring diagram will frequently save time in assembly and may prevent blunders in connecting apparatus. Measuring instruments and other apparatus should first be inspected to ensure that they are in good working order, and the setup should be carefully checked before it is energized. Skill in the manipulation of apparatus and in the taking of data is acquired by actual practice. Meticulous care and a questioning attitude are essential if reliable results are to be obtained.

Recording of Data

Data which will form the basis of a written report, or which are of sufficient value to be preserved, should be carefully recorded, preferably in a bound notebook. In some instances it may be preferable to record data on loose-leaf forms so that related information can be assembled later and permanently bound together. The practice of jotting data down on scratch paper for later transcription or of trusting to memory for their preservation is an almost certain way of losing important or significant results. Records of data should not only be complete as regards observations, but should include a wiring diagram of the circuit used, with each instrument or other piece of apparatus identified (preferably with make, model, and serial number), so that the setup can be exactly duplicated at any future time, and so that, if any piece of apparatus proves to be defective or incorrectly calibrated, its influence on the experimental results can be determined. Any unusual behavior of apparatus should be noted on the data sheet, and, if recorded data are rejected or discarded, the reasons for the action should be recorded at the time. In brief, the laboratory worker should strive to make the record of his experiment complete enough that either he or some other worker will be able to tell later just what was done and, if necessary, duplicate the work.

Significant Figures

In computing results, sample computations together with the formulas used should be included as an aid in analyzing or reconstructing the experiment. Where corrections are applied to the readings of instruments it is generally better to record actual readings, and to apply the corrections as a separate recorded step. In making numerical computations it is unnecessarily time consuming and fatiguing to use more digits than are actually significant in the values entering the computation. To avoid the necessity for manipulating surplus digits in arithmetic operations and the added opportunities for mistakes as a result of the extra manipulations, numerical values should always be rounded off at the point where they cease to have a real meaning in terms of the conditions of measurement.

In stating numerical values of observed or computed quantities, certain conventions as to significant figures have been generally accepted and are convenient aids in reducing the labor of computation.

1. In any statement of a measured quantity no digit should be retained that does not convey some actual information; i.e. the last digit given should represent the point of uncertainty. Unless otherwise stated, it

may be assumed for convenience that the last stated digit is uncertain by one unit. For example, a statement that a length is 103.1 meters would mean that the length has been measured to within 0.1 meter and its value is 103.1 ± 0.1 meters; or, stated more precisely, it lies between 103.0 and 103.2 meters.

2. To avoid misunderstanding in summarizing results, and for convenience in handling where multiplication or division is involved, zeros which serve merely to show the location of the decimal point should not be used in the stated number. It is simpler and better to indicate the location of the decimal point by an exponential form, using an appropriate power of 10. Thus if we were to express 103.1 meters in centimeters it would be better to write it as 1.031×10^4 cm, rather than as 10,310 cm. Similarly 0.01031 kilometer would be better expressed as 1.031×10^{-2} km.[1]

3. In "rounding off" a value by dropping non-significant figures, the last retained digit should be increased by 1 if the first discarded digit[2] is 5 or more. For example, if the value 20.652 were rounded to three significant figures it should be written as 20.7; 20.648 would round off to 20.6.

4. In addition or subtraction no digit need be retained in the result whose position with respect to the decimal point is to the right of the last significant digit of the number whose final significant digit is farthest to the left. For example, the numbers 103.24 and 0.0081 should be added as $103.24 + 0.01 = 103.25$, or subtracted as $103.24 - 0.01 = 103.23$. No digit farther to the right of the decimal point would have any significance.[3]

5. In multiplication or division we need to retain in each factor only a number of digits which will produce in that factor a percentage uncertainty

[1] It will, of course, be realized that, where a series of numbers must be added or subtracted, they must first be reduced to the same units and must be expressed in terms of a common power of 10.

[2] The case in which the discarded digit is 5 and no further figures follow it is considered by many workers to be special. A rule which is much used is to round off to the even number. Thus 20.65 would be rounded to 20.6, while 20.75 would be rounded to 20.8. By such a device the rounding will, on the average, be increased to the next higher digit about as often as it will be decreased to the lower value. To a limited extent this improves the value obtained on averaging.

[3] It will be apparent that the difference between two numbers that are nearly equa will be known with a lower percentage accuracy than either of the original numbers. For this reason methods of measurement and of computation which involve the difference between nearly equal numbers are generally to be avoided where the accuracy requirement on the remainder is high, since this places very severe accuracy requirements on the minuend and subtrahend. For one particular class of measurements (substitution methods), however, such a method is especially suitable, and it is much used for comparing an unknown with an accurately known standard of approximately equal value, since moderate accuracy in the difference measurement will establish the value of the unknown to very nearly the full accuracy of the standard.

which is no greater than the uncertainty of the factor having the fewest significant figures. For example, the product of 103.24 and 0.0081 may be written as $103 \times 0.0081 = 0.83$; or, better, $1.03 \times 10^2 \cdot 8.1 \times 10^{-3} = 8.3 \times 10^{-1}$. Here the factor 0.0081 is known to only about 1% and the product cannot be more certain, so that the factor 103.24 need not be considered more closely than 1% (or 103).

6. In multiplications and divisions where the accuracy of the result need not be better than about $\frac{1}{4}$%, a 10-in. slide rule is adequate. If accuracy requirements are closer, longhand or machine methods or logarithms should be used.

7. In computing with logarithms, no more digits need be retained in the mantissa of the logarithm than are significant in the numerical factors which enter the computation. Thus, in a computation, the Briggsian logarithm of 103.2 should be written as 2.0137, not as 2.013679.

8. In taking an average of four or more values, an additional figure beyond those of the individual values may be retained as having possible significance.

9. A number representing a precision index or probable error need never be stated to more than two significant figures.

Experimental Accuracy

Whenever results are reported, some estimate of their accuracy should be made and stated in the report,[4] and the basis of this accuracy statement should appear on the data or computation sheets. An estimate of the accuracy of a measurement is not always easy to make, and frequently requires more skill and understanding than does the actual manipulation of apparatus or the observation of data. It will therefore be well to consider the question of accuracy at some length.

There are certain fundamental standards that by universal agreement are accepted as the basis of our system of measurements, that are by definition the units in terms of which measurements are made, and that are therefore *exact*. All other standards are ultimately derived from them by some process of measurement and are more or less uncertain in magnitude, since no matter how carefully they may be determined, they are subject to errors that are inherent in all measurements. Thus all measurements which are made of any quantity whatever are subject not

A detailed discussion concerning the writing of technical reports is not appropriate to this text. Simple, clear language is always much to be desired. The writer should keep in mind that his reader may not be technically trained, and may even be a person to whom English is a second and somewhat unfamiliar language. This latter point should be kept particularly in mind when writing a report or paper for formal publication.

only to the errors of the immediate determination but also to the uncertainties in all the standards on which the measurement is based or in terms of which it is made. The only possible exceptions would be measurements made by direct comparison with the fundamental standards. Such measurements would be subject only to the experimental errors or uncertainties inherent in the immediate comparison. Generally, laboratory determinations are many steps removed from the fundamental standards and are therefore uncertain by whatever amount has accumulated in all the intermediate steps between the measurement in question and the fundamental standard or standards from which it is derived. We may say then that we can never exactly determine the magnitude of any physical quantity by any experimental procedure. To a greater or lesser extent there are errors in all measurements. It is the task of a person engaged in measurements to hold these errors and uncertainties within whatever limits are consistent with the requirements of the task at hand.

The fundamental units that form the basis of electrical measurements are the meter, the kilogram, the second, and one electrical unit (which may be chosen arbitrarily). The meter is defined as the distance between two marks on a particular metal bar under specified conditions; the kilogram is defined as the mass of a particular metal cylinder. Both these fundamental standards are carefully preserved at the International Bureau of Weights and Measures at Sèvres, France. Our fundamental standard of time, the second, is defined as the 1/86,400 part of a mean solar day. We shall later define the fundamental electrical unit which is needed to derive the remaining electrical units.

The electrical units in terms of which measurements are made are defined in terms of the exact fundamental units but are physically realized by experimental means, and we must therefore start in any measurement with the uncertainties that are included in the values assigned to the physical reference standards available in the laboratory. The primary standards maintained by the National Bureau of Standards (and by the national laboratories of other countries) are known in value to within a few parts per million. Values for resistance standards and for standard cells that are used as laboratory reference standards can be established to within one or two thousandths of a per cent. Working standards of resistance and voltage are readily available whose assigned values include uncertainties of less than 0.01%. The highest grades of laboratory standard ammeters, voltmeters, and wattmeters are guaranteed by their makers to be initially within 0.1%. Portable indicating instruments that are used in general laboratory measurements are available in a number of quality grades, and their guaranties range from 0.2% to $\frac{3}{4}$%. Switchboard and panel instruments fall, for the most part, in the 1 or 2% classes.

Thus the inherent uncertainty that must be accepted at the start of a measurement depends largely on the apparatus or instruments available or selected for use in the experimental setup. Further uncertainties will arise from experimental procedures and techniques that are used, and it will be our task to study the techniques, instruments, and apparatus for electrical measurements to the end not only that we may understand their operation and application but also that their uncertainties may be evaluated in the various situations that arise in laboratory work. We shall, however, first discuss very briefly the general question of experimental uncertainties and some of the means that are available for their evaluation.

Accuracy and Precision

In the measurement of any physical quantity our observations are influenced by a multitude of contributing factors that should be considered as the parameters or variables of the natural phenomenon by means of which the measurement is made. For example, if we were measuring the resistance of a certain piece of wire, its temperature, the distribution of current throughout its length and cross section, its previous history as regards heat treatment or cold working, any tension to which it might be subjected at the time of measurement, and many other factors (some important, others relatively minor) would influence the value of resistance obtained from the measurement. Ideally, then, a measurement should involve fixing the magnitudes of all the parameters that exert an influence on the phenomenon so that, these magnitudes being known, the magnitude of the desired quantity can be determined. Repeated observations of the magnitude of a quantity will disagree among themselves as a result of the experimenter's failure to keep the parameters sufficiently well fixed, or his failure to apply proper corrections for them, or as a result of the action of parameters which are unknown to him or are beyond his control. These uncontrolled or unknown influences will act to disturb the observations and to make the resulting value obtained for the quantity depart more or less from the *exact* value that could be assigned if all the parameters were completely known and defined. Thus there is no way in which we can arrive experimentally at a completely true value of a quantity; all we can do is to approximate the truth by the "best" value that can be deduced from the available experimental data.

If we were to assume that the influences of the various parameters beyond our control, as well as the uncontrollable residue of the parameters we try to hold fixed, act in a completely random fashion, we could deduce certain helpful results from probability considerations. In general, combinations of circumstances that produce large deviations of the observed from the true value of a quantity will occur less frequently than those which produce small deviations; i.e. since each influence may produce either positive or negative deviations, there will in general be a tendency for the effects of these influences to cancel one another rather than to be additive. Under such idealized conditions, it would follow that the greater the number of observations the greater the likelihood of obtaining equal numbers of positive and negative deviations of approximately equal size. Then on a strict probability basis we would be tempted to say that the *true* value of a measured quantity is the average of an infinite number of observed values taken under such conditions that the various parameters contributing to deviations act in a completely free and random fashion.

The weakness (or rather the fallacy) in the above argument is that we can never be sure that the parameters are acting in the random manner specified. It may well be that certain of the parameters influence the measurement in a non-random fashion. Perhaps our meter-stick is too short, or the scale calibration of our ammeter is in error by a significant amount that is unknown to us and therefore uncorrected. Such an influence would introduce a constant deviation in our measurements, superposed on the random deviations. Under these circumstances our average would approach, not the "true" value, but one that differs from truth by the amount of the constant deviation. Thus we can never be completely certain that the value of a quantity deduced from experimental data is correct in the sense that it is the "true" one. The most we can do is to arrive at a "best" value, taking into account such parameters as we can control and for whose effects we can apply corrections. It has been well said[5] that "Absolute certainty is the privilege of uneducated minds."

In terms of the "true" value of a quantity as stated above, we can define the *accuracy* of a measurement as its approach to truth, the deviation of the measured from the true value being an accuracy index. On the other hand, the *precision* of a measurement is simply its repeatability, the index of precision being stated in terms of the deviation of a single observation or group of observations from a mean value. Thus, while the terms *accuracy* and *precision* are often used as though they were interchangeable, they should be distinguished; *accuracy* being a measure of the approach to a *true* value, whereas *precision* is merely a measure of *consistency* or repeatability.

Random Errors

After corrections have been applied for all the parameters whose influences we know, there is left a residue of deviations to which, if they

[5] Keyser, *Mathematical Philosophy*, p. 120, Dutton, 1922.

are assumed to be random, the laws of chance may be applied. One must always keep in mind in such a treatment that all we can do is to arrive at the value which is most probable on the basis of the data available to us. The laws of probability take no account of an *unknown but constant* error superposed on the deviations that are truly random. Procedures are available that make it possible to state from a limited group of data the most probable value of a quantity, the probable uncertainty of a single observation, and the probable limits of uncertainty of the "best" value derived from the data. The study of the laws of chance[6] describing the behavior of random events is beyond the scope of the present work. We shall simply state certain useful results derived from these laws. Their development and proof can be found in textbooks on the theory of errors.[7] In the present discussion we shall be concerned only with *precision.*

1. The *arithmetic mean* (or average) of a series of similar observations of a quantity is usually the *best* value that can be obtained from them.[8]

2. The *root-mean-square* of the deviations of a set of observations from the arithmetic mean of the set, called the *standard deviation,* is the best measure of the dispersion of the set. It can be expressed as $\sigma = \sqrt{\frac{\Sigma d_m^2}{n}}$, where σ is the standard deviation, d_m is the deviation of any individual observation from the mean of the group, and n is the number of observations in the group.

3. The probable deviation (usually called the probable error) of a single observation is defined as that deviation from the mean of the group for which the probability that it will be exceeded is equal to the probability that it will not be exceeded. This index of precision is given approximately by the formula $r = 0.6745\sigma$, r being the probable deviation of a single observation and σ the standard deviation. If the number (n) of observations is small, a somewhat better value of the probable deviation

[6] Originally developed to enable gentlemen gamblers to divide fairly the unplayed residue of stakes at the close of a card game which was presumed to be honest.

[7] An excellent discussion of the theory of errors at an elementary level will be found in Crumpler and Yoe, *Chemical Computations and Errors*, Wiley, 1940.

[8] There is sometimes a strong temptation to discard a single value that differs rather markedly from the others of the series. Such a procedure can usually be justified only if it is known that the result of an observation was incorrectly recorded, or that the apparatus was not functioning properly when the observation was made, or that the rejection is warranted by some similar and equally cogent reason. The mere fact that a result differs by more than one wishes from the others of a set is almost never a sufficient reason for discarding it unless some real explanation can be found for the difference.

is given by the formula $r = 0.6745\sigma\sqrt{\frac{n}{n-1}}$, which is equivalent to $r = 0.6745\sqrt{\frac{\Sigma d_m^2}{n-1}}$.

4. A deviation of $4r$ from the mean will occur as a result of truly random influences less than once in a hundred times; i.e. the probability that the deviation will be no more than $4r$ is 0.993. Since it is very improbable that a deviation of $4r$ will occur as a result of random influences, the appearance of such a deviation is usually considered to have a *real* significance. It may indicate that the quantity being measured has changed by a significant amount, that a significant change in the conditions of measurement has occurred but has not been detected, that a new parameter has been introduced, or that a mistake[9] has been made.

5. The *probable error*[10] (R) of the arithmetic mean of a group of observations (which we will understand to be the probable deviation of the mean of the group from the mean of an infinite number of observations taken under similar conditions) is[11] $R = \frac{r}{\sqrt{n}}$, or $R = 0.6745\sqrt{\frac{\Sigma d_m^2}{n(n-1)}}$, the symbols having the same meanings as before.

6. The probable error of a result which is computed from measured values depends on the functional relation which exists between the data and the result. Suppose $A = f(x, y, z, \cdots)$, $x, y, z, \cdots$ being independent, and suppose further that the probable deviations of $x, y, z, \cdots$ are $r_x, r_y, r_z, \cdots$. Then the probable deviation of A is

$$r_A = \sqrt{\left(\frac{\partial f}{\partial x}\right)^2 r_x^2 + \left(\frac{\partial f}{\partial y}\right)^2 r_y^2 + \left(\frac{\partial f}{\partial z}\right)^2 r_z^2 + \cdots}$$

Certain of the more common cases are listed on page 10:

[9] It is the practice of some experimenters to discard values that deviate by more than $4r$ from the mean of the group. Such a procedure is somewhat arbitrary and should be used with extreme caution. However, the appearance of such a large deviation is a sufficient reason for examining the data and procedure for possible mistakes.

[10] It cannot be too frequently emphasized that R is a measure of precision but not of accuracy.

[11] It should be noted that the probable uncertainty of the arithmetic mean of a number of observations decreases only rather slowly as their number is increased. For example, the probable error of the mean of a hundred observations is almost a third as great as the probable errors of the mean of ten observations taken under similar conditions.

a. A sum (or difference): If $A = x \pm y$, then $r_A = \sqrt{r_x^{\,2} + r_y^{\,2}}$.[12]

b. A product: If $A = K \cdot xy$, then $r_A = K\sqrt{y^2 r_x^{\,2} + x^2 r_y^{\,2}}$.

c. A quotient: If $A = K\dfrac{x}{y}$, then $r_A = \dfrac{K}{y}\sqrt{r_x^{\,2} + \dfrac{x^2}{y^2} r_y^{\,2}}$.

d. A power: If $A = Kx^n$, then $r_A = nKx^{n-1} \cdot r_x$.

e. A logarithm: If $A = K \log_\varepsilon x$, then $r_A = \dfrac{K}{x} \cdot r_x$.

f. An exponential: If $A = Ka^x$, then $r_A = k(\log_\varepsilon a)a^x \cdot r_x$.

Systematic Errors

The accuracy of a result obtained by measurements depends on the reduction of systematic (or non-random) errors. This is often more difficult than the reduction or evaluation of accidental (or random) errors. Systematic errors are frequently hidden, and may not be disclosed by direct observations or by statistical procedures based on measurements which are merely repetitive and which are made in the same way each time. A knowledge on the part of the experimenter of the characteristics of the measured thing and of the measuring apparatus is the best safeguard against systematic errors of unknown origin. However, measurements are often prompted by a need for information about the characteristics of the thing measured. In such cases a few simple precautions and procedures may prove helpful in disclosing the presence and origin of such errors. One of the most useful precautions is that of checking the data for evidence of changes that are larger than may reasonably be ascribed to chance. The appearance of changes that are more than four times the probable error of individual observations taken under conditions presumed to be identical may be evidence of a change in systematic errors, and the cause should be determined if possible. A procedure that is generally applicable in measurements of something whose characteristics are not completely known is to change deliberately as many operating or environmental conditions as feasible and note the effect of each such change on

[12] It may be pointed out that, if one of the contributing factors has a large and the other a small uncertainty, their contributions to the result are very different. Thus if $r_y = r_x/2$ its contribution to r_A will be about 10% of the contribution of r_x. It therefore appears that, if a result were to be obtained by summing the values of two observed quantities and the uncertainty of one of them is half the uncertainty of the other, it would be almost a complete waste of time to attempt to improve the value having the smaller uncertainty unless something were first done to improve the value having the greater uncertainty. Similar analyses can readily be made of the relative significance of small and large uncertainties for other cases that can be expressed analytically.

the results. Such procedures can also be used to determine the influence of some necessary change in an operating or environmental condition, by deliberately exaggerating the change and noting the trend of the response. Correspondingly, systematic errors in the measuring equipment may often be disclosed by repeated measurements under different conditions, or with different apparatus, or, where possible, by an entirely different method.

Laboratory Practices

Certain precautions should always be observed to ensure the safe, efficient use of laboratory instruments and equipment.[13] There are some considerations that apply in general to the electrical circuit used, regardless of the instruments and the type of measurement undertaken. In making electrical connections, see that contact surfaces are clean, nuts or binding posts are firmly tightened, wires or cables have sufficient cross section for the expected current, and insulation is appropriate for the voltage in use. Sliding contacts should be cleaned occasionally with a lint-free cloth, either dry or moistened with a solvent[14] such as benzol or varsol. Sliding contacts will remain in good operating condition longer if lubricated. If the contact pressure is high a solid grease, such as Vaseline, may be used. For light contacts[15] a highly refined, neutral mineral oil is better. In either case only a very light coating is needed. When soft-soldering connections or other parts of an electrical circuit, only rosin or a solution of rosin in alcohol should be used. Almost all prepared fluxes are sufficiently corrosive to damage the components of delicate apparatus. Leads which are attached to instruments should never be left hanging down over the edge of a table, or stretched between tables or across the floor where they may be accidentally caught with a hand or foot and the instrument pulled to the floor. They should be twisted in pairs to each instrument to reduce the effects from magnetic fields produced by current in the leads. Where a large alternating current is used (say 25 amp or more), a current transformer and an instrument having a 5-amp range are generally preferable to a high-range instrument, both to avoid large currents in the neighborhood of measuring instruments and to isolate the measuring from the supply circuit. Similarly for alternating voltages in excess of a few hundred volts a voltage transformer should be used in preference to a high-range voltmeter. Before a circuit is energized all

[13] The discussion which follows is largely abstracted from a more general discussion of the same subject by Weaver, *Instruments*, **23**, 1236 (1950).

[14] The practice of using carbon tetrachloride in cleaning electrical contacts is deprecated. Technical CCl_4 usually contains traces of free chlorine which, in the presence of moisture, may form hydrochloric acid, resulting in corrosion at a later time.

[15] Where an extremely light pressure is involved between noble-metal contacts, no lubricant should be used.

components should be checked to ensure that connections are properly made and that the ranges of apparatus are ample for the quantity to be measured. Protective resistors should be inserted where necessary. When opening a circuit connected to measuring equipment, it is advisable where possible to first reduce the supply voltage to a low value. The conductors or leads to equipment should be removed one at a time, making the first break at the terminal nearest the power source, and afterward removing the terminal connected to the equipment. This program should be reversed when connecting equipment, making the connection at the power terminal last. Consistency in following this procedure may prevent short circuits at exposed terminals. Power circuits are usually protected by fuses or circuit breakers, but these protective devices do not guarantee that instruments and other equipment will not be damaged if the circuit is shorted by the careless handling of leads or switches. Where there is a chance of electrical shocks, the operator should be particularly careful. Currents as small as 10 or 20 milliamperes can be dangerous, depending on the physical condition of the victim and the current path through his body. Under certain conditions, depending on skin resistance, one may receive a fatal shock from equipment operated from a 110-volt source. The cases of some equipment are provided with ground terminals which, if properly connected, will protect the operator from some of the hazards of electrical shock.

There are other precautions that the laboratory worker should observe, which apply directly to the instruments rather than to the general circuit. Where a multirange instrument is used, the position of the range switch should be checked before closing the circuit. Failure to do so may result in a bent pointer or a burned-out coil. When a measurement is to be made under conditions that will produce a high initial current and a much smaller steady-state current (for example, a tungsten-filament lamp bank) it may be advisable to protect the current coils of instruments against the initial high current by a short-circuiting switch. When delicate instruments, such as microammeters or pivoted galvanometers, must be moved, they should be protected against mechanical damage, by shorting the terminals to provide heavy overdamping. Where a coil clamp or arrestment is provided, it should always be set when the instrument is moved. All instruments should be handled carefully, especially those used as laboratory reference standards. Pivoted instruments should never be placed where they may be exposed to vibration. One severe shock, such as a hammer blow on a bench or table where an instrument is sitting, can permanently damage its pivots or jewels.[16]

[16] Where bearing injury is suspected as a result of shock or vibration, an immediate check should be made. A method for checking this point is described below.

Instruments being prepared for shipment should be wrapped in heavy paper to exclude dust, and surrounded by several inches of cushioning material such as excelsior in a strong box or packing case. The top of a wooden packing case should be fastened with screws rather than nails to avoid instrument damage resulting from blows of a hammer or nail puller. It is advisable to invert pivoted instruments in the packing case so that the upper guide bearing, rather than the lower load-carrying bearing and pivot, may receive any damaging shocks that occur during shipment. This precaution should also be observed when the instruments are to be transported by car in a padded tray. When instruments are not in use they should be stored in cases or cabinets that are free from dust, acid fumes, excessive heat, moisture, and vibration.

When adjustments or repairs on instruments are needed, it is well to keep in mind that only the manufacturer or his authorized agent is really well qualified to make major repairs. If it is necessary to open an instrument case, this should be done in a room where there is a minimum of dust or chemically corrosive vapors, and in an area free from iron filings. It is a good practice to make periodic tests (at least once a year) of laboratory instruments by comparing them with reference instruments. Such tests should reveal any significant changes in their calibrations. If high accuracy is needed, the instruments should be checked against reference standards that are known to be reliable, or should be sent for checking to a measurements laboratory having such standards.

A knowledge of some of the sources of trouble in instruments (other than errors in calibration) may be helpful in increasing the accuracy of measurements. Some of the conditions that interfere with the normal turning of the moving system of an instrument are a warped or loosened scale, fibers extending upward from a paper scale, iron filings or other obstructions in the air gap, a bent pointer or damping vane, a flat pivot or broken jewel, a moving system that is too tight or too loose in its bearings. After any of these sources of error has been corrected, the instrument should be retested. Obstructions can often be detected by a "jumping" of the pointer as the operating current of the instrument is very slowly increased or decreased to produce a gradual change in the deflection. If, during such a test the pointer is set to a scale mark and the instrument is lightly tapped, pivot friction will be revealed by a slight change in the pointer position. Where pivot friction is present its effect on instrument readings can be temporarily minimized by gently tapping the case. Hard tapping will defeat its purpose and may result in damage to the bearing. Errors resulting from friction and from mechanical unbalance may be expected if the instrument is used in a position other than the one in which it was designed to operate. Where the moving system vibrates in operation because of mechanical resonance at the operating frequency, errors may be expected. This condition can often be corrected by changing the balancing weights on the moving system and rebalancing it. Inelastic yield in the springs, indicated by a zero shift after the instrument has been deflected up-scale for a considerable time, constitutes a source of error for which a correction cannot easily be applied. Such a spring should be replaced by the manufacturer if the amount of the zero shift is significant.

Poor electrical contacts at switches or elsewhere in a circuit can cause considerable annoyance and may constitute a source of error. Where this condition cannot be alleviated by cleaning and oiling the contacting surfaces, it may be necessary to replace the contacts with silver or some other good contact material. For rugged service, where large currents are involved and there is considerable wear as a result of high wiping pressure at movable contacts, silver inlays in the contacting areas may be helpful. Where possible one should avoid locating instruments in an area where there are strong magnetic fields, or near large masses of metal, particularly if the instrument is not magnetically shielded. Strong fields from machinery, conductors, and even other instruments may produce significant errors of indication; and the presence of neighboring masses of metal, for example a metal table top on which the instrument is placed, may produce appreciable eddy-current errors in some types of instruments. Iron in the neighborhood of an unshielded permanent-magnet instrument may act as a magnetic shunt and change the instrument indication by a considerable amount. It must be remembered that some types of instruments require considerable power for their operation and that significant changes in circuit conditions may result from the insertion of instruments. In accurate measurements allowance must be made for such effects. Also, if the instrument or other apparatus is required to dissipate an appreciable amount of power, its resulting temperature rise may cause an error in the values it indicates.

All these and other sources of error to which the observer must be alert will be considered later in detail, together with the means for their correction or elimination. It will be well for the reader to keep constantly in mind the necessity for evaluating all possible sources of error in order that the measurements he makes may be carried out expeditiously, but with whatever accuracy is appropriate to the particular task that he has undertaken.

CHAPTER 2

ELECTRICAL UNITS

A very considerable number of systems of electrical units[1] have been used at various times in electrical work. Some are chiefly of historical interest, and some are employed principally in theoretical discussions, while others are or have been used in measurements and have been found acceptable for this purpose on either a limited or an international basis, sometimes backed by the authority of law, sometimes merely as a matter of convenience. In many textbooks one system or another (or even a combination of systems) has been used without clearly stating which one and without any analysis of the considerations involved. Too frequently the reader is left without a definite knowledge of what system of units is being employed. It is therefore expedient to acquaint ourselves with some of the more important and generally used systems so that, in reading the literature of the science, we may recognize and understand the meaning of the various systems that we are likely to encounter, and have some conception of the comparative sizes of the units in which electrical magnitudes are expressed. However, before we examine the systems of electrical units it will be profitable to discuss briefly some of the general considerations involved in defining or constructing any system of units.

Fundamental and Derived Quantities

When we make a measurement, we arrive by some experimental procedure at an expression of the magnitude of the quantity being measured. In order to state the magnitude of the quantity we must first fix the size of the unit in which it is to be measured. The magnitude of the quantity can then be expressed in terms of the chosen unit and a numerical multiplier. If we were concerned only with physical quantities of a single kind

[1] Varner describes eight systems of electrical units and six systems of mechanical units in his book, *The Fourteen Systems of Units*, O.S.C. Cooperative Association, Corvallis, Oregon, 1948.

(for example, lengths) we could, if we wished, select for our unit any magnitude that seemed convenient (inch, rod, meter, nautical mile, etc.). However, when we have to measure two or more quantities of different kinds, which experience tells us are related, we do not usually choose the size of our units with complete independence. We find it convenient, although it is not absolutely necessary, to use the physical equation which expresses the relation between the quantities, since only in this way can we avoid the necessity of using awkward numerical constants when we must express a quantity of one kind that we have derived from measurements of quantities of another kind. For example, if we were to choose the sizes of our units independently, we could measure the edge of a cubical box in inches and express its volume in liters, but we would need a numerical constant (conversion factor) in order to do so. The physical equation expressing the relation between the volume (V) of a cube and the length (L) of its edge is known to be $V =$ a constant $\times L^3$, and if the volume (derived from a measurement of length, L, in inches) is to be expressed in liters, the value of the constant needed in the equation is 0.0164. However, if we express the volume in cubic inches the numerical constant needed is unity. For *convenience*, then, we can use the equation relating length and volume to assign a unit of volume (an inch cube) such that *unity* is the numerical constant needed to derive a statement of the volume from a length measured in inches. Thus we avoid the use of a conversion factor which is annoying to look up and even more troublesome to remember.

We can generalize from this illustration and say that, where we have a number of quantities of different kinds which are connected by physical equations expressing relations between some of them, we can use these equations to set up a system of units such that conversion factors other than unity can usually be avoided in deriving expressions for quantities of one kind from measurements made on related quantities. If we have M kinds of quantities to evaluate and N *independent* physical equations which express relations between them, we can choose the sizes of the units of only $M - N$ of the quantities, and then use the N defining equations to fix the sizes of units of the remaining quantities so that numerical constants other than unity are not usually needed[2] to express any one of our quantities in terms of measurements made on any combination of the related quantities.[3] A system of units which is constructed in such a way

[2] Where numerical factors (such as π, or simple numbers) appear in the defining equations, they must of course be taken into account in assigning values to the units.

[3] This is equivalent to the mathematical statement that in a system of N independent equations in M variables there can be only $M - N$ independent parameters.

is said to be a *consistent system*. The $M - N$ units of the set which are independently chosen may be considered *fundamental*, whereas the remaining N units are *derived*.

There is no rule other than convenience by which we can decide which particular set of $M - N$ units of a consistent system shall be considered fundamental, and which derived. As an example, the English system of mechanical units with which we are most familiar uses units of length, force, and time (foot, pound, second) as fundamental, all other units, such as mass, velocity, and work, being derived from them through equations based on the physical laws which state their interrelations.[4] On the other hand, in the metric system we almost invariably use length, mass, and time (meter, kilogram, second; or centimeter, gram, second) as our fundamental units, while the unit of force (newton in the mks system, or dyne in the cgs system) is derived. Thus we see that our choice of the fundamental units in terms of which we will define the other units of a consistent system is arbitrary. In setting up any system of units, the choice should be one which makes for convenience in our measuring procedures, but there is no one choice which is *exclusively* correct. We can state further that for a particular system the number of units which we will consider to be fundamental is also arbitrary to the extent that it depends only on the number of different quantities we wish to measure or express, and the number of defining equations that are available or convenient for expressing their relations.

It is also convenient for purposes of analysis to identify our fundamental quantities by assigning to them the role of "dimensions"[5] which can be used to describe the nature of the derived units of the system through the defining equations. In the example cited above (the mechanical system in which length, force, and time are fundamental) we could assign the symbols L, F, T to our basic quantities and express any other mechanical quantity in terms of them. Acceleration is $\frac{\text{length}}{(\text{time})^2}$, or LT^{-2}; mass is $\frac{\text{force}}{\text{acceleration}}$, or $FL^{-1}T^2$. In the system in which length, mass, and time are fundamental, we can use the dimensional symbols L, M, T. Then, in terms of our dimensional symbols, acceleration is LT^{-2}, and force is LMT^{-2}. We are at liberty to use either system that appears to be

[4] An alternative system of English units which is somewhat less familiar in terms of everyday life is the one which uses length, mass, and time (foot, slug, second) as the fundamental units, whereas force (in pounds) is considered a derived unit.

[5] This statement means only that the quantities which are chosen as dimensions are the independent parameters in terms of which our system of equations will be expressed, and therefore are designated by a special "dimensional" symbol or letter.

convenient in any particular case. It cannot be said that one is right and the other wrong, as both are self-consistent.

The Electrical Quantities

There are six electrical quantities with which we are concerned in electrical measurements, and which must be defined in terms of units of appropriate size before measurements can be made. These electrical quantities are (1) charge, or quantity of electricity; (2) current; (3) potential difference, or electromotive force; (4) resistance; (5) capacitance; and (6) inductance.[6] To assist us in defining these quantities, we will make use of four familiar physical equations which state certain electrical relationships: (1) $E = IR$; (2) $E = \mathscr{L}\frac{dI}{dt}$; (3) $Q = CE$; and (4) $I = \frac{dQ}{dt}$. It may be observed that, in terms of these defining equations,[7] two of the units are at our disposal; and that, having fixed the values of these, the other four can be derived in terms of the stated relations.[8]

[6] There are in addition certain related magnetic quantities, the values of whose units can be assigned in terms of one or more of the electrical units. Magnetic quantities will also be considered at an appropriate place.

Inductance will be designated by the symbol $\mathscr{L}$ in the present discussion because the symbol L (usually reserved for this purpose) is needed as the dimensional symbol for *length*. Elsewhere in this book we shall use the standard symbol L for inductance.

[7] We assume that the unit of time is fixed by some other independent means.

[8] The size of the units in the particular system which we are defining will, of course, depend on the values which are assigned to the parametric units. It must also be realized that we have considerable freedom in selecting the particular defining equations which we will use in setting up a system of units and the form in which we state them. Those listed above are convenient to use and familiar in form. While a particular set of defining equations may determine a system of units without ambiguity, other sets of independent defining equations which describe relations between the same magnitudes (or related magnitudes) could serve equally well. For example, comprehensive systems of units (in which the magnetic units are also included) could be constructed from the following system of equations:

(1) force $= Q\mathscr{E}$; (2) force $= Q$ (velocity $\times B$); (3) $Q = \int \rho\, dv$;

(4) curl $H = 4\pi i + \frac{\partial D}{\partial t}$; (5) curl $\mathscr{E} = -\frac{\partial B}{\partial t}$; (6) divergence $D = 4\pi\rho$;

(7) $B = \mu H$; (8) $D = \epsilon\mathscr{E}$. [See Hall, *J. Franklin Inst.*, **225**, 205 (1938).]

Through force, velocity, and volume we have introduced three mechanical units (say length, mass, and time). We have also introduced nine electrical and magnetic units: (1) Q = charge; (2) $\mathscr{E}$ = electric field intensity; (3) B = magnetic induction, or flux density; (4) ρ = electric charge density; (5) H = magnetizing force; (6) i = current density; (7) D = displacement, or electric flux density; (8) μ = permeability;

At this point we could, of course, be quite arbitrary in choosing a starting place for defining a system of electrical units. For example, we could say that the resistance unit shall be the resistance of a certain coil of wire and that the unit of voltage shall be the emf of a certain cell which we will keep in the laboratory. We could then proceed to define a complete and consistent system of units based on our own particular units of resistance and of voltage, the associated units for the other four electrical quantities being assigned through use of the four defining equations. However, unless there was universal agreement on what particular coil and cell would represent our resistance and voltage units, endless confusion would result when electrical workers attempted to compare experimental results, or even to communicate with one another about their work. Historically, just such confusion existed in the early days among electrical experimenters, when various individuals set up their own units more or less independently. It was soon realized that agreement would have to be reached concerning the size of the units, and that such agreement would have to be on an international basis to facilitate the free exchange of information between workers. Thus the need was recognized for universal agreement on the electrical units and their magnitudes, even before commercial applications existed which would make such agreement imperative.

Since most electrical measurements involve the use of some associated mechanical quantity—force, power, energy, etc.—and since in many cases it is only by the measurement of some mechanical effect that we can conveniently estimate the magnitude of an electrical quantity, it is to be expected that we would make use of an established system of mechanical units to fix the sizes of the units in which electrical quantities are to be measured, and that we would add equations expressing relations between electrical and mechanical units to the group of defining equations which we will use in constructing systems of units. The work of Gauss (1833) and of Weber (1851) showed that it was possible to measure electrical quantities in terms of mechanical units, and Weber pointed out the possibility of defining a complete system of electrical units and assigning their values in terms of mechanical units. The actual values assigned to the units, based on Weber's experimental work, were never widely

---

(9) ϵ = permittivity. Thus we have twelve units and eight defining equations, so that we may choose four units as fundamental and eight as derived. It is usually convenient, and therefore customary, to select three mechanical units (usually length, mass, and time) and one electrical unit as fundamental and to define the other units in terms of them. There is, however, no electrical unit which is universally accepted as the fourth fundamental unit. Indeed, in different systems different units may be used, as we shall see.

accepted; but the principles which Weber employed form the basis of the system of electrical units which is in use today.

The British Association Ohm

Pioneer work looking toward the establishment of a generally useful system of units which would at the same time be on a sound scientific basis was done by the British Association for the Advancement of Science. In 1861 this body appointed a committee, under the chairmanship of Maxwell, to consider electrical units and standards. This committee may be said to have laid the foundation for the system of units which is universally used in practical work today. After examining the possible systems of units which had been proposed, the committee decided (1863) to base the electrical units on the centimeter-gram-second (cgs) system of mechanical units, using the electromagnetic system proposed by Weber. The committee also sponsored research for obtaining experimental values for some of the proposed units. In 1864 the committee issued a *British Association unit of resistance*, based on work by Maxwell and others, intended to represent 10^9 units of resistance in the cgs electromagnetic system. In terms of this unit, numerical values were assigned to wire-wound resistance standards, and a number of copies of the "BA Ohm" were distributed to various laboratories by the committee as a means of promoting uniformity on an international basis.

The cgs Systems

Before proceeding further with a discussion of the history and present status of the electrical units, let us examine the basis on which our system of units was formulated. In order to define a system of electrical units in terms of mechanical units we must use one or more defining equations in which relations between electrical and mechanical quantities are stated. We can also make use of equations stating relations between the electrical quantities themselves, and so define the quantities in which we are interested.

Once it is agreed that we are to define our electrical units in terms of a mechanical system of units, we find that there are two convenient starting points. We may start with the mechanical force between charges at rest and formulate an electrostatic system of units, or between charges in motion (electric currents) and develop an electromagnetic system of units. Such force equations are available in Coulomb's law for the electrostatic case, and in Ampère's law for the electromagnetic case. However, the use of either will involve not only three mechanical quantities but also another electrical quantity in addition to one of the six that we wish to define. The force between charges at rest depends not only on the magnitude of the charges and the distance between them but also on the permittivity of the medium in which the charges are located. Similarly the force between electric currents depends on the permeability of the medium.[9] Thus the introduction of the appropriate law of force, as a defining equation introduces three mechanical quantities and one additional electrical quantity. We have then a total of ten quantities and, with our four electrical defining equations, a total of five independent equations, leaving us with five parameters. Now the values of the units of our three mechanical quantities have been independently established through purely mechanical considerations so that, unless we wish to assign arbitrary values to the units of two of the electrical quantities, we shall need another independent equation which relates mechanical and electrical quantities but which does not introduce any additional parameters. Such an equation is available in the relation between charge, potential difference, and mechanical work ($E = \text{work}/Q$), which reduces the parameters of our system to four. This is the point at which all classical derivations of systems of electrical units arrive, and it seems quite appropriate to base a system of electrical units on four fundamental units, three of which may be mechanical while the fourth must be electrical.[10] Having four fundamental units from which all the remaining electrical units may be derived, we shall need four dimensions (parameters) if the derived units are to be stated in dimensional (parametric) form.[11]

[9] In using Coulomb's law or Ampère's law to fix the size of electrical units we may, for definiteness, assume that no material medium is present and that the hypothetical measurement which is used to define the size of the unit is performed in vacuum or free space. Consequently we are free to assign any particular convenient numerical value to the permittivity or permeability of free space. We cannot, of course, arbitrarily assign values to both since they are related quantities (viz. $1/\mu_v\epsilon_v = c^2$, where μ_v and ϵ_v are respectively the permeability and permittivity of free space, and c is the velocity of light in free space). It must not be assumed, however, that the assignment of such properties as permittivity or permeability to free space requires the existence of a "material ether" as a mechanism by which charges or currents produce action at a distance. Since action at a distance without any intervening mechanical device for its propagation is a concept which we must necessarily accept, it is perhaps better to consider the permittivity of free space simply as a factor which is needed to state the relation between charge density and the intensity of the electric field which it produces; similarly the permeability of free space is a factor which is used in describing the relation between electric currents and the resulting magnetic field intensity.

[10] The fourth unit may be considered a connecting link between the mechanical and electrical systems.

[11] Up to this point we have not specified which four of the units shall be considered fundamental and which six derived. Indeed, as we have already seen, the choice is arbitrary and may be dictated by convenience if we like. If we were to select our dimensions (or parameters) on the criterion of convenience, it might be well to make such a choice that the dimensional (or parametric) statements of the derived units

The mechanical units which we shall use as fundamental in defining the cgs systems, their sizes, and their corresponding dimensional symbols are:

Length—centimeter—L
Mass—gram—M
Time—second—T

The derived mechanical units that we will need are

Force—dyne—LMT^{-2}
Work—erg—L^2MT^{-2}

The cgs Electrostatic System. This system of electrical units is based on the force between charges at rest. We can first define *unit charge* by means of Coulomb's law of force (force $= Q_1Q_2/\epsilon r^2$), where Q_1 and Q_2 are equal point charges, r is their separation, and ϵ is the permittivity of the homogeneous medium in which the charges are located. Our definition can be stated as follows: A unit charge is that point charge which, when placed 1 centimeter from an equal point charge in free space (vacuum), will exert on it a force of 1 dyne. Now in general we can say that the permittivity of a medium can be equated to the product of two factors $\epsilon = \epsilon_r \cdot \epsilon_v$, where ϵ_v is the permittivity of free space, and ϵ_r is the relative or specific permittivity of the medium under consideration, and therefore a pure number. For free space, of course, the relative permittivity ϵ_r is unity since it is the basis of reference in terms of which ϵ_r is defined, and since ϵ_v, the permittivity of free space, is to be one of our fundamental units we may also assign the value unity to it. We can then write Coulomb's law in dimensional or parametric form as

$$LMT^{-2} = \frac{Q^2}{\epsilon_v L^2}$$

from which we can write the dimensional expression for charge as

$$Q = \epsilon_v^{1/2} M^{1/2} L^{3/2} T^{-1}$$

The unit of *potential difference* may be defined in terms of mechanical work: Unit potential difference is the potential difference which must

---

would be as simple as possible. However, it has been traditional practice to use length, mass, and time as the mechanical dimensions and to select for the electrical dimension (ϵ_v), the permittivity of free space, when stating the units of an electrostatic system in parametric form; and to select (μ_v), the permeability of free space, for electromagnetic systems. These parameters are not entirely convenient to use, since they both involve fractional exponents, which can be avoided by employing other electrical quantities as parameters, as we shall see later. However, since they are the conventional dimensions which appear throughout the literature, we shall use them in the present development.

exist between two points in order that 1 erg of work be done in moving unit charge from one point to the other. To obtain the dimensional expression for potential difference, we use the relation

$$\text{potential difference} = \frac{\text{work}}{\text{charge}}$$

or

$$E = \frac{ML^2T^{-2}}{\epsilon_v^{1/2}M^{1/2}L^{3/2}T^{-1}} = \epsilon_v^{-1/2}M^{1/2}L^{1/2}T^{-1}$$

Having established two of the cgs electrostatic units in terms of mechanical units and permittivity, we may derive all the others by using our electrical defining equations. The cgs electrostatic unit of *current* is 1 cgs electrostatic unit of charge per second. We have

$$I = \frac{\text{charge}}{\text{time}} = \frac{Q}{T} = \epsilon_v^{1/2}M^{1/2}L^{3/2}T^{-2}$$

The unit of *resistance* can be defined through Ohm's law as the resistance across which unit potential difference will appear when carrying an unvarying unit current. We have

$$R = \frac{E}{I} = \frac{\epsilon_v^{-1/2}M^{1/2}L^{1/2}T^{-1}}{\epsilon_v^{1/2}M^{1/2}L^{3/2}T^{-2}} = \epsilon_v^{-1}L^{-1}T$$

The unit of inductance may be defined as the inductance across which unit potential difference would appear when the current is changing at the rate of 1 unit per second. We have $E = \mathscr{L}(dI/dt)$ and, since dI/dt is dimensionally the same as I/T,

$$\mathscr{L} = \frac{\epsilon_v^{-1/2}M^{1/2}L^{1/2}T^{-1}}{\epsilon_v^{1/2}M^{1/2}L^{3/2}T^{-2}/T} = \epsilon_v^{-1}L^{-1}T^2$$

The unit of capacitance can be defined as the capacitance across which unit charge will cause unit potential difference to appear. We have[12] $Q = CE$ or

$$C = \frac{Q}{E} = \frac{\epsilon_v^{1/2}M^{1/2}L^{3/2}T^{-1}}{\epsilon_v^{-1/2}M^{1/2}L^{1/2}T^{-1}} = \epsilon_v L$$

The cgs Electromagnetic System. If, instead of basing our system of units on the force between point charges at rest, we define a system based

[12] It may be noted that the unit of capacitance is dimensionally a length multiplied by ϵ_v. Now in the cgs electrostatic system ϵ_v is assigned the value of unity, and length is expressed in centimeters. Hence cgs electrostatic units of capacitance are frequently referred to as "centimeters" of capacitance. This practice is deprecated since it tends to conceal the fact that the unit of permittivity and its dimensions are also involved. The cgs electrostatic units are often conveniently designated in a short form by using the prefix *stat* with the practical name for the electrical quantity; viz. statfarad, statvolt, statcoulomb, etc.

on the field of force resulting from an electric current, we can construct a system whose magnitudes differ from those of the electrostatic system defined above. Also it will be more convenient to use the *permeability* of free space, μ_v (rather than its permittivity, ϵ_v), as the fourth parameter to be added to our fundamental mechanical units of length, mass, and time. We will start with Ampère's law,[13] which in the case of sections of a pair of infinitely long, straight, parallel conductors in free space (each carrying a constant current I) can be stated as

$$\text{force} = \frac{2\mu_v I^2 b}{a}$$

where a is their separation and b is the length of the section on which the force is measured. From this equation we can define the cgs electromagnetic unit of current as that current which, when flowing in straight, parallel wires spaced 1 cm apart in free space (vacuum) will exert a force of 2 dynes[14] on each other per centimeter length of the circuit. The dimensions of current, in terms of our parameters M, L, T, μ_v, are obtained from the equation by writing

$$\text{force} = MLT^{-2} = \mu_v I^2$$

from which $I = \mu_v^{-1/2} M^{1/2} L^{1/2} T^{-1}$

Now we may say that the dimensions of current (or of any other electrical quantity) are equivalent, regardless of the system in which it is defined. Then we may equate the dimensions of current in the cgs electrostatic and the cgs electromagnetic systems and write

$$\mu_v^{-1/2} M^{1/2} L^{1/2} T^{-1} = \epsilon_v^{1/2} M^{1/2} L^{3/2} T^{-2}$$

so that $\mu_v^{-1/2} \epsilon_v^{-1/2} = LT^{-1}$, which are the dimensions of velocity; i.e.

$$\frac{1}{\sqrt{\mu_v \epsilon_v}} = \frac{\text{distance}}{\text{time}} = \text{velocity (dimensionally)}$$

[13] A classical approach to the definition of unit current in the cgs electromagnetic system is to use a magnetic analogue of Coulomb's law to define a unit magnetic pole, and then to use this with Ampère's law to define unit current. This derivation is unfortunate for two reasons: (1) a unit pole situated t a point and isolated in space is a concept that cannot be realized either practically or theoretically; and (2) alternative definitions of unit pole which are not compatible and which have different dimensions have been widely used. These definitions lead to alternative statements of Coulomb's law in which the permeability of free space μ_v appears either in the numerator or in the denominator of the equation for the force between unit poles, depending on which definition is used. Because of this inconsistency in the definitions of magnetic units Coulomb's law should be avoided as a basis for any electromagnetic system of units. A consistent system of magnetic units will be defined at a later time.

[14] Note that we have allowed for the numerical factor 2 in the equation so that our units will still form a consistent system.

Experimentally, when the ratio of any particular cgs electrostatic unit to the corresponding cgs electromagnetic unit is measured, it is found to be very nearly either 3×10^{10} cm/sec (within the experimental error, the *velocity of light in free space*) or some integral power of this quantity. It is worth remarking in this connection that the bases of our two systems are "electricity at rest" and "electricity in motion." It would be natural to expect that the ratio of magnitudes of the units in the two systems would be some function of the velocity of propagation of an electrical disturbance (i.e. the velocity of light) as, indeed, would be predicted from Maxwell's theory.

If we proceed to define all the units in the cgs electromagnetic system as we have already done in the cgs electrostatic system, it will be found that in every case the ratio of the units involves some power of the product $\mu_v^{1/2}\epsilon_v^{1/2}$, and therefore some power of the velocity of light. This will be seen from Table 1.

TABLE 1

Unit	Symbol	Defining Equations esu	Defining Equations emu	Dimensions esu	Dimensions emu	Ratio of Units, number of emu in one esu
Charge	Q	force $= \dfrac{Q_1Q_2}{\epsilon_v r^2}$	$Q = It$	$\epsilon_v^{1/2}M^{1/2}L^{3/2}T^{-1}$	$\mu_v^{-1/2}M^{1/2}L^{1/2}$	$\dfrac{1}{3 \times 10^{10}}$
Current	I	$I = \dfrac{dQ}{dt}$	force $= \mu_v I^2$	$\epsilon_v^{1/2}M^{1/2}L^{3/2}T^{-2}$	$\mu_v^{-1/2}M^{1/2}L^{1/2}T^{-1}$	$\dfrac{1}{3 \times 10^{10}}$
Potential difference	E	work $= EQ$		$\epsilon_v^{-1/2}M^{1/2}L^{1/2}T^{-1}$	$\mu_v^{1/2}M^{1/2}L^{3/2}T^{-2}$	3×10^{10}
Resistance	R	$E = IR$		$\epsilon_v^{-1}L^{-1}T$	$\mu_v LT^{-1}$	9×10^{20}
Inductance	$\mathscr{L}$	$E = \mathscr{L}\dfrac{dI}{dt}$		$\epsilon_v^{-1}L^{-1}T^2$	$\mu_v L$	9×10^{20}
Capacitance	C	$Q = CE$		$\epsilon_v L$	$\mu_v^{-1}L^{-1}T^2$	$\dfrac{1}{9 \times 10^{20}}$

Practical Units

It happens that the units in the cgs electromagnetic system are of an inconvenient size for practical use. The practical units, based on the cgs electromagnetic units, are made larger or smaller than the corresponding cgs units by an appropriate power of 10, to bring those which are most used in experimental work to convenient magnitudes.

When the British Association Committee on electrical units decided that the practical unit of resistance (the ohm) should be 10^9 cgs electromagnetic units of resistance, it also decided that the practical unit of potential difference (the volt) should be 10^8 cgs electromagnetic units of potential difference. These two magnitudes being fixed, the other four follow from the relations which must exist between them: through Ohm's law the practical unit of current (the ampere) must be assigned the value of 10^{-1} cgs electromagnetic unit, and similarly for the others. We can therefore make up Table 2, showing the magnitudes of the practical units in terms of the corresponding cgs electromagnetic units.

TABLE 2

Unit	Name	Symbol	Number of cgs emu in One Practical Unit	Defining Equation
Charge	Coulomb	Q	10^{-1}	$Q = It$
Current	Ampere	I	10^{-1}	$E = IR$
Potential difference	Volt	E	10^{8}	(Arbitrary)
Resistance	Ohm	R	10^{9}	(Arbitrary)
Inductance	Henry	$\mathscr{L}$	10^{9}	$E = \mathscr{L}\dfrac{dI}{dt}$
Capacitance	Farad	C	10^{-9}	$Q = CE$

International Units

The Committee on Electrical Units and Standards of the British Association assigned to wire-wound resistance standards and to the electromotive force of standard cells numerical values which were believed at that time to be adequate approximations of the theoretical values,[15] and made these standards available to laboratory workers in the interest of securing uniformity on an international scale.

The British Association unit of resistance was generally accepted for a number of years, but in 1878 Rowland[16] found that it differed from its intended absolute[17] value by about 1.5%. The basic principle of the BA units was given international status by the Paris Electrical Congress in 1881, but it appeared desirable at that time to specify *reproducible*

[15] See Table 2 and also p. 20 above.

[16] Rowland, *Am. J. Sci.*, **115**, 430 (1878).

[17] Here and elsewhere the term *absolute* in connection with a unit or measurement signifies that the quantity in question is defined or derived from the mechanical units. It does not, however, imply that there is no error involved or that perfection has been attained. The most recent absolute determination of the ohm is believed to represent its intended value within 10 parts in a million [see Thomas *et al.*, *NBS J. Research*, **43**, 352 (1949)].

standards which could be set up independently in any laboratory. It was found experimentally that the ohm was closely represented by the resistance at 0°C of a column of mercury of uniform cross section, 106.3 cm long and having a mass of 14.4521 gm (i.e. about 1 sq mm in cross section). For a reproducible standard of current the silver voltameter was developed, current being measured by the rate at which silver is deposited electrolytically from a silver nitrate solution, the rate corresponding to 1 amp being 0.001118 gm/sec under specified conditions.

The International Electrical Congress in Chicago (1893) gave international sanction to these reproducible standards, and on July 12, 1894, the Congress of the United States passed Public Bill No. 105, making the "international" units, embodied in the reproducible standards and defined in terms of the cgs electromagnetic system, the "legal units of electrical measure in the United States."

As improvements in measuring technique were developed, it became apparent that the units defined by the *reproducible* standards were not exactly equal to the units based on the cgs electromagnetic system. The London International Congress on Electrical Units and Standards (1908) recognized this difference and, to avoid confusion, designated as *international units* those based on the "mercury ohm" and the "silver ampere" (i.e. the reproducible standards), as distinguished from the *absolute units*, which were exact decimal multiples of the cgs electromagnetic units.

An International Technical Committee on which Great Britain, France, Germany, and the United States were represented carried out measurements at the National Bureau of Standards in Washington, D. C., in 1910, and assigned definite numerical values in terms of the "international units" to standard resistors and standard cells of each of the collaborating countries. From that time forward the units were maintained in each country by its national laboratory, in terms of the group of resistors and of standard cells, the values of which had been assigned in international units by the 1910 determination.

Absolute Units

Actually the need for basic standards which could be reproduced in isolated laboratories disappeared shortly after the creation of the "mercury ohm" and the "silver ampere," as a result of the establishment and growth of national laboratories: the Physikalisch-Technische Reichsanstalt of Germany in 1887, the National Physical Laboratory of Great Britain in 1899, the National Bureau of Standards of the United States in 1901, and other national laboratories at later dates. Furthermore, the development of improved techniques of measurement has made it possible to evaluate absolute units with an accuracy equal to or better than that with which the international units could be reproduced by the "mercury ohm" and the "silver ampere." Also, comparisons made in the decade following 1910 indicated that the units maintained in the various countries were drifting relative to one another by small but definite amounts. In the interest of preserving uniformity in the units, an amendment to the *Convention of the Meter* was drawn up, placing the responsibility for the establishment and maintenance of the electrical units in the *International Committee on Weights and Measures*, and in the *International Bureau of Weights and Measures*, which it supervises. The United States ratified this amendment in 1923. In 1927 this International Committee appointed an Advisory Committee, composed principally of representatives of the larger national laboratories, and in 1929 accepted their recommendation that the "absolute system, derived from the centimeter-gram-second system, should replace the international system of units for all measurements in science and industry."

The International Committee, empowered to fix the ratios between the corresponding units in the international and absolute systems, awaited the results of determinations going on in various national laboratories of the ratios between the international units (as maintained by them in terms of the 1910 ohm and volt) and the corresponding cgs electromagnetic units. Reports from the national laboratories were reviewed in 1937 and again in 1939, and arrangements were made for introducing the new units on January 1, 1940. The outbreak of war in September 1939 prevented the execution of these plans, but in October 1946 the International Committee met again and chose January 1, 1948, as the date for putting the new units into effect. The change was made at the appointed time, and the absolute system of electrical units is now in use as the system on which electrical measurements are based.

The "international" units maintained by the various national laboratories have not been exactly the same,[18] so that the conversion factors required in 1948 for transferring values to the absolute system are slightly different in different countries. The changes in values resulting from the

[18] The units were of course very closely the same for all countries at the time of the international assignment of values to the standards in 1910, but, since each country separately maintained its own group of standards, the "international" units for the various countries unavoidably drifted apart to a greater or less degree, depending on the physical standards themselves (the 1-ohm coils and the standard cells) and the details of the way in which their values were maintained. For details of the methods used in maintaining the ohm and volt at the National Bureau of Standards, and for further information concerning the establishment of the absolute units, see *NBS Circ.* C475, by F. B. Silsbee. This circular was freely used in the preparation of the present chapter.

shift from international units (as maintained by the National Bureau of Standards) to the absolute units are given in Table 3.

TABLE 3

FACTORS FOR CONVERTING THE VALUE OF AN ELECTRICAL QUANTITY IN INTERNATIONAL UNITS (NBS) TO ITS VALUE IN ABSOLUTE UNITS

Quantity	Unit	Conversion Factor*
Resistance	Ohm	1.000 495
Electromotive force	Volt	1.000 330
Current	Ampere	0.999 835
Charge	Coulomb	0.999 835
Inductance	Henry	1.000 495
Capacitance	Farad	0.999 505
Energy	Joule	1.000 165
Power	Watt	1.000 165

* These are the factors by which the numeric representing the value of a quantity expressed in terms of an international unit is to be multiplied to obtain the numeric representing the value of the same quantity where expressed in terms of the corresponding absolute unit.

Although the factors in the table are carried out to six places beyond the decimal point, the last figure is not significant, but has been rounded off in conformity with the decisions of the International Committee on Weights and Measures.

The mks System of Units

In connection with the definition of the practical units as decimal multiples of the cgs electromagnetic units,[19] it should be noted that, if we had used the meter, kilogram, and second as our fundamental mechanical units rather than the centimeter, gram, and second in defining the electromagnetic units, and had we at the same time assigned the value 10^{-7} instead of unity as the permeability of free space,[20] then the magnitudes of the six electrical units so defined would be identical with their values in the *Practical* system of units. This system was first proposed by Giorgi in 1901 and is known as the Giorgi-mks system. Giorgi's system has been favored by many workers as the basic system of units rather than

[19] See p. 23.

[20] We are of course completely at liberty to choose whatever value we please as the permeability of free space (or for any other one unit) when we are setting up our system. We must be careful, however, that we do not arbitrarily assign any more magnitudes than are permitted by the inter-relations fixed by the defining equations. Thus we are free to assign one magnitude in addition to length, mass, and time, and our choice of the value for the permeability of free space is one of convenience.

the cgs system; and the mks system was adopted in 1935 by the International Electrotechnical Commission, which, however, left the fourth unit (in addition to the meter, kilogram, and second) for later decision. In 1938 the Advisory Committee on Electrical and Magnetic Magnitudes and Units (of the IEC) recommended the adoption of the value 10^{-7} for the permeability of free space (μ_v) (in the unrationalized or classical system) as the fourth unit connecting the electrical to the mechanical units. An additional statement by the committee is worth quoting in this connection: "The Committee recognizes that any one of the following practical units, ohm, ampere, volt, henry, farad, coulomb, weber, already in use may equally serve as the fourth fundamental unit, because it is possible to derive each unit and its dimensions from any four others mutually independent." The system of absolute units adopted internationally on January 1, 1948, as our present working units is then equivalent to the Giorgi-mks system of units, so that the *mks unit o, current* is identical with the *absolute ampere*, etc.

Other Systems of Units

It is perhaps worth while to call attention to some of the other systems of electrical units which have been extensively used by writers in discussing electrical theories and phenomena.

In the *Gaussian system* of units, all electrical quantities are in the cgs electrostatic system, while all magnetic quantities are in the cgs electromagnetic system. Such a mixed system of units has some advantages with respect to convenience in the size of the units and has been widely used. It necessitates a numerical factor in equations which state relations between electrical and magnetic quantities. For example, one would write

$$\text{curl } H = \frac{1}{c}\left(4\pi I + \frac{\partial D}{\partial t}\right), \quad \text{curl } \mathscr{E} = -\frac{1}{c}\frac{\partial B}{\partial t}, \quad \text{and} \quad \mathscr{F} = \frac{4\pi NI}{c}$$

where H is intensity of magnetization, I is current, D is electric flux density, $\mathscr{E}$ is electric field intensity, B is magnetic flux density, $\mathscr{F}$ is magnetomotive force, and c (our numerical factor) is 3×10^{10}.

In some of the physical equations which must be used in electrical theory and engineering, 4π appears as a numerical factor. By changing the sizes of certain of the units, this factor can be removed from the equations which are frequently used and relegated to relations which are less common. Such a device is called *rationalization.* Two of the equations used as illustrations in the preceding paragraph would appear as

$$\text{curl } H = \frac{1}{c}\left(I + \frac{\partial D}{\partial t}\right), \quad \text{and} \quad \mathscr{F} = \frac{NI}{c}$$

Another equation, cited earlier in the discussion, would be changed from divergence $D = 4\pi\rho$ to divergence $D = \rho$. Two methods of rationalization have been used. If the sizes of the units of mass, length, time, permittivity, and permeability are left unchanged, practically all the other units are changed in size. The units of charge and current must be decreased by the factor $\sqrt{4\pi}$; the units of potential difference, magnetomotive force, magnetic flux, and similar quantities are increased by the factor $\sqrt{4\pi}$; the units of resistance and inductance are increased by the factor 4π; and the unit of capacitance is decreased by the factor 4π in rationalizing any system of units. The Gaussian system of units, rationalized by this procedure, is known as the *Heaviside-Lorentz* system of units.

Another method of rationalization (sometimes called subrationalization), which accomplishes the same result so far as the physical equations of electricity and magnetism are concerned without, however, producing such a general disturbance in the sizes of the various units, involves the increase of the unit of permittivity by the factor 4π, and the simultaneous decrease of the unit of permeability by the same factor. In this case the six electrical quantities which are of primary interest to us in measurements are left unchanged, as are the magnetic units of flux and flux density, whereas the units of magnetomotive force $\mathscr{F}$ and of magnetizing force H are increased by the factor 4π. This is the device which is used in the *rationalized mks system* of units, in which the fundamental mechanical units are the meter, kilogram, and second, while the permeability of free space μ_v is $4\pi \times 10^{-7}$.[21]

Establishment and Maintenance of the Absolute Units

The first step in establishing the ohm by absolute measurement is the construction of a mutual- or self-inductor whose dimensions can be measured with great accuracy and whose form is such that its inductance can be very precisely calculated in absolute henries from these measurements and from the permeability of the space surrounding the winding. An experiment is then performed in which a resistance is measured in terms of this inductance and a known frequency (i.e. by comparing a resistance with an impedance). Since the inductance is known in absolute

[21] The question of the use of rationalized units would appear to be one of convenience and perhaps of esthetics as well. Suppression of the factor 4π in certain fundamental equations gives them a more symmetrical form and one which is perhaps more easily remembered. Moreover, in either rationalized system the 4π appears in those equations which relate to systems having spherical or circular symmetry, whereas it is absent from equations which relate to linear or orthogonal systems. In carrying out computations, however, the factor 4π must ultimately be used, in connection with one unit or another.

units the value of the resistance is established in absolute units in terms of inductance and time.[22]

To establish the absolute unit of electromotive force a current balance is constructed, made up of a system of fixed and moving coils of accurately known dimensions. The force developed between the fixed and movable coils of the apparatus by the current in them is balanced by the force of gravity acting on a known mass. From this force, together with the measured dimensions and relative positions of the coils and the permeability of the space in which they act, the value of the current can be calculated in absolute units in terms of length, mass, time, and permeability. (Time enters this calculation through the acceleration of gravity.) A resistor in series with the coils, carrying the same current, is adjusted[23] until its potential drop just balances the emf of a standard cell. The emf of the standard cell in absolute units is then equal to the product of the value of the resistance in absolute ohms times the calculated value of the current in absolute amperes.

Absolute determinations of the ohm and ampere are very tedious and costly experiments to perform, taking months and requiring both very special apparatus and the highest possible quality of experimental techniques. Consequently they are repeated only rather infrequently. During the intervals between absolute determinations, the values of the *ohm* and the *volt* are maintained at the National Bureau of Standards (and at the national laboratories of other countries) by primary groups of carefully constructed standard resistors and standard cells. At the National Bureau of Standards these groups consist of ten resistors and twenty-five cells respectively. Each member of the group is individually compared directly with the one used in the absolute determination, so that values are obtained for each member and for the mean of the primary group. Frequent intercomparisons are made between the individual members of the group to detect any change or unsteadiness in the value of an individual relative to the mean of the group. If successive measurements should reveal a change or drift in value, indicating that a particular individual had become defective, another high-quality standard would be substituted for the defective one, and the assigned value of the mean would be adjusted accordingly.

[22] The actual measurements in the ohm and ampere determination are of such nature as to require the highest types of experimental skill. For details of such measurements, made at the National Bureau of Standards, see:

Curtis, Moon, and Sparks, *NBS J. Research*, **21,** 375 (1938).

Curtis, Driscoll, and Critchfield, *NBS J. Research*, **28,** 133 (1942).

Thomas, Peterson, Cooter, and Kotter, *NBS J. Research*, **43,** 291 (1949).

[23] In the actual experiment the resistance may be held constant and the current adjusted.

Certain of the standards are selected and used as *reference standards*, on the assumption that their values will remain constant during the interval between intercomparisons. The mean of the entire group (taking into account any substitutions that may have been necessary) is assumed to remain constant during the longer interval between absolute determinations. As an additional check, international intercomparisons are made from time to time at the International Bureau of Weights and Measures in Sèvres, France. There standards sent by each of the large national laboratories are compared with one another so that each national laboratory may know how well its units of resistance and electromotive force agree with those of other countries. Further contributory evidence as to the constancy of the units maintained in this way has been obtained at the National Bureau of Standards by periodic comparisons with secondary resistance standards of radically different construction (such as resistors of pure platinum or gold), and standard cells made up to different specifications (e.g. with different acidity of the electrolyte or with a large proportion of deuterium oxide in place of water). While it is conceivable (but not very probable) that a group of similar standards, maintained under nearly identical conditions, could all drift in value by the same amount so that their individual changes could not be detected by intercomparisons between members of the group, the possibility is far more remote that an identical drift in value would occur in standards whose material and construction differ from those of the primary group. Therefore the absence of time variation in the differences between the members of the primary group and between the primary and secondary standards must be accepted as strong evidence that the primary standards are themselves stable and that the units are being maintained at a constant value.

It should be noted that the "mercury ohm" has only very rarely been used as a laboratory reference standard, as it is far from ideal for this purpose. Since the time that the value of the international ohm was established in terms of the "mercury ohm," the unit has been maintained at the National Bureau of Standards in terms of standards constructed of resistance-alloy wire and kept under more or less carefully controlled conditions. The "silver ampere" was equally inconvenient as a laboratory reference standard and served merely to establish the value of the international volt. In fact no physical reference standard ampere can be maintained in a laboratory. Consequently the second reference standard which is necessary, together with the reference standard of resistance, for deriving all the other units, is the *Weston normal cell*,[24] which in 1910 was assigned the value 1.018300 international volts under certain specified conditions, in terms of the "silver ampere" and the "mercury ohm."

[24] See discussion on p. 185 for details concerning standard cells.

When the values of the ohm and volt were reassigned in 1948 to conform to the absolute system, all the derived electrical quantities were changed correspondingly. However, it should be noted that the changes from the international to the absolute units were so small that many ordinary engineering measurements have not been affected. Precise measurements, of course, may be affected, and the electrical worker should make sure of the units in which his resistors, standard cells, inductors, and capacitors are calibrated wherever the required accuracy is 0.1% or better.

Dissemination of the Standards

The National Bureau of Standards has the duty of maintaining standards but has no authority to enforce the use of accurate measuring apparatus by others. Such "police powers" are retained by the separate state governments. However, the voluntary submission, for periodic tests, of electrical standards by the public utility commissions of various states, by electrical manufacturers and utility companies, by privately operated testing and research laboratories, and by university and college laboratories serves to disseminate the values of the units and to keep the electrical measurements of the entire country on a uniform basis. It should be noted that, although only the values of the ohm and the volt are maintained by primary groups of standards, the measurement of any electrical quantity is possible through an appropriate combination of these two standards together with a standard of time. Hence the electrical units are disseminated by the National Bureau of Standards on a national scale, not only by the certification of standard resistors and standard cells, but also by the testing of high-grade laboratory standard ammeters, voltmeters, wattmeters, watthour meters, potentiometers, etc., together with appropriate range-extending apparatus, and by the measurement and certification of precision inductors and capacitors. The various intermediate steps which are taken by the National Bureau of Standards between the establishment of the absolute standard of resistance and voltage and the testing of electrical instruments and apparatus are shown in the block diagram of Fig. 1.

Dimensions and Dimensional Checks

In our discussion of the definitions of electrical units in the two cgs systems, a tabulation of the dimensions of each unit was made in terms of length, mass, time, and one other quantity. It has been stated that the choice of the fourth quantity is arbitrary, as are the three mechanical quantities which were chosen as fundamental. In the electrostatic system it was convenient to use the permittivity of free space, and in the electromagnetic system the permeability of free space, as our fourth fundamental

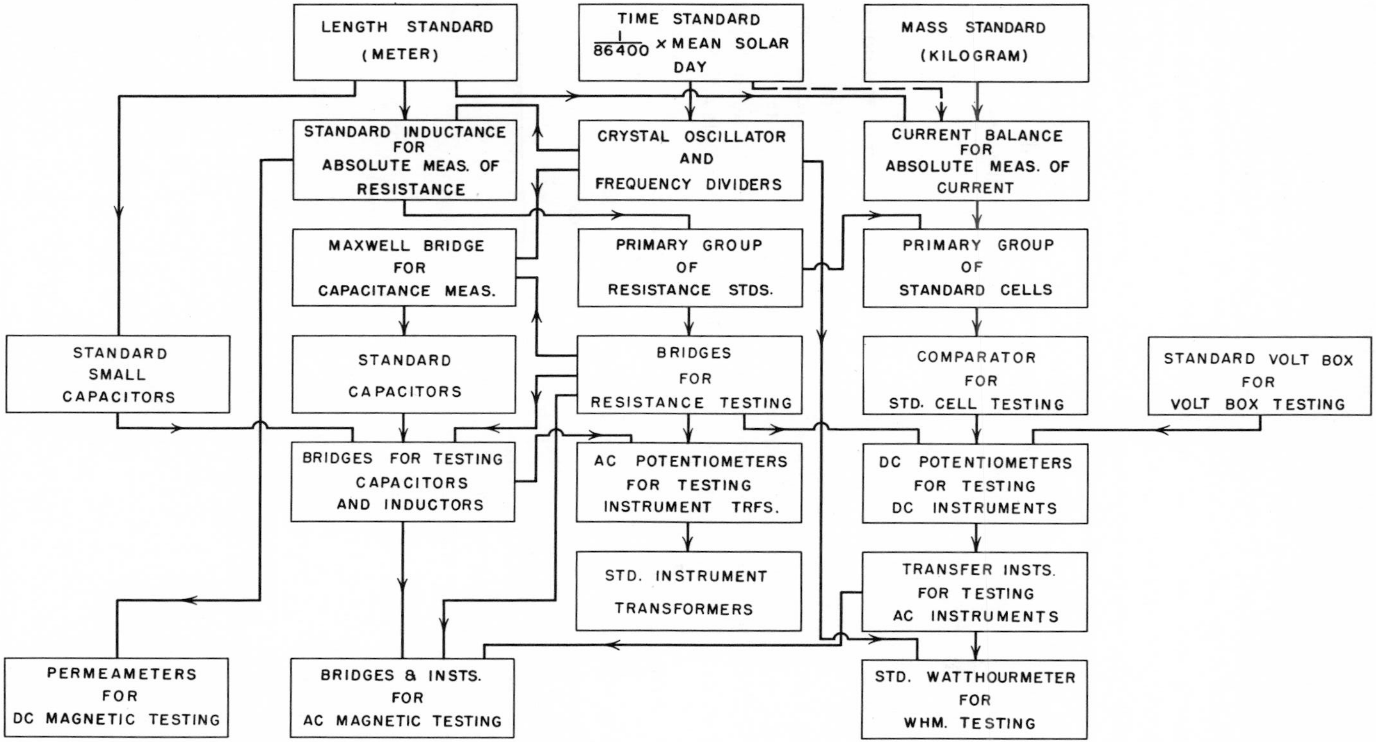

LENGTH STANDARD
(METER)
TIME STANDARD
1/86400 × MEAN SOLAR DAY
MASS STANDARD
(KILOGRAM)
STANDARD INDUCTANCE FOR ABSOLUTE MEAS. OF RESISTANCE
CRYSTAL OSCILLATOR AND FREQUENCY DIVIDERS
CURRENT BALANCE FOR ABSOLUTE MEAS. OF CURRENT
MAXWELL BRIDGE FOR CAPACITANCE MEAS.
PRIMARY GROUP OF RESISTANCE STDS.
PRIMARY GROUP OF STANDARD CELLS
STANDARD SMALL CAPACITORS
STANDARD CAPACITORS
BRIDGES FOR RESISTANCE TESTING
COMPARATOR FOR STD. CELL TESTING
STANDARD VOLT BOX FOR VOLT BOX TESTING
BRIDGES FOR TESTING CAPACITORS AND INDUCTORS
AC POTENTIOMETERS FOR TESTING INSTRUMENT TRFS.
DC POTENTIOMETERS FOR TESTING DC INSTRUMENTS
STD. INSTRUMENT TRANSFORMERS
TRANSFER INSTS. FOR TESTING AC INSTRUMENTS
PERMEAMETERS FOR DC MAGNETIC TESTING
BRIDGES & INSTS. FOR AC MAGNETIC TESTING
STD. WATTHOURMETER FOR WHM. TESTING

FIG. 1.

quantity simply because these happened to appear directly in the physical equations used to express a basic relation between mechanical and electrical quantities. In establishing our system of definitions, Coulomb's law of force between point charges made use of space permittivity as a connecting link between the mechanical and electrical quantities with which we were dealing. Similarly, in Ampère's law of force between currents, space permeability was used as the connecting link. Although such a connecting link between mechanical and electrical quantities is needed, we are by no means restricted to either space permittivity or permeability as a fourth dimensional concept. A number of other choices are possible, and some are certainly more convenient for the dimensional checking of physical equations than ϵ_v or μ_v, since either of these choices requires the use of fractional exponents.

If, for example, we choose charge as our fourth dimensional unit together with length, mass, and time, we can avoid the use of fractional exponents altogether in stating the dimensions (or parameters) of any electrical quantity. Thus we have in the L, M, T, Q system of parameters: charge has the dimension Q; current, being charge per unit time, has the dimensions $T^{-1}Q$; potential difference, being work per unit charge, has the dimensions $L^2MT^{-2}Q^{-1}$; resistance, defined by Ohm's law, has the dimensions $L^2MT^{-1}Q^{-2}$; inductance $\left(\text{from the relation } E = \mathscr{L}\dfrac{dI}{dt}\right)$ has the dimensions L^2MQ^{-2}; capacitance (from the relation $Q = CE$) has the dimensions $L^{-2}M^{-1}T^2Q^2$. To obtain the dimensions of space permittivity in terms of these parameters we may use Coulomb's law (force $= Q^2/\epsilon_v L^2$), and ϵ_v has the dimensions $L^{-3}M^{-1}T^2Q^2$. Space permeability can be obtained similarly from Ampère's law (force $= \mu_v I^2$), so that μ_v has the dimensions LMQ^{-2}. The dimensions of the product $\mu_v\epsilon_v$ are then

$$LMQ^{-2} \cdot L^{-3}M^{-1}T^2Q^2 = L^{-2}T^2 = \frac{1}{(\text{velocity})^2}$$

as we have previously seen.

The dimensions of some of the more important magnetic quantities may be simply derived, using laws connecting them with quantities whose dimensions have already been stated.[25] For example, we know that a voltage is induced in a conductor by a change in flux linkages in accordance with the equation $E = N(d\phi/dt)$, N being the *number* of turns of the conductor linking with the flux, and $d\phi/dt$ being the time rate of change of magnetic flux. Since N is a pure number (and therefore dimensionless) we may write, for the dimensions of ϕ,

$$\phi = ET = L^2MT^{-2}Q^{-1} \cdot T = L^2MT^{-1}Q^{-1}$$

[25] For definitions of the magnetic quantities the reader may refer to Chapter 9.

Flux density B is flux per unit area. Dimensionally, this is

$$B = \frac{\phi}{L^2} = MT^{-1}Q^{-1}$$

Also we know that $B/H = \mu$ for any substance. Now $\mu = \mu_r \cdot \mu_v$, where μ_r is relative permeability and is dimensionless since it is the ratio of permeability in the medium to the permeability of free space μ_v. Hence, dimensionally

$$H = \frac{B}{\mu_v} = \frac{MT^{-1}Q^{-1}}{LMQ^{-2}} = L^{-1}T^{-1}Q$$

Also we know that the magnetizing force H is the magnetomotive force per unit length. Then the dimensions of magnetomotive force are

$$H \cdot L = T^{-1}Q$$

It may be noted that the dimensions of magnetomotive force are identical with those of current, as they should be since magnetomotive force can be defined by current-turns.

For convenient reference the dimensions of various electrical and magnetic quantities are listed in Table 4 in terms of the $LMTQ$ system of dimensional parameters.

TABLE 4

Quantity	Dimensions	Quantity	Dimensions
Charge	Q	Permittivity	$L^{-3}M^{-1}T^2Q^2$
Current	$T^{-1}Q$	Permeability	LMQ^{-2}
Potential difference (voltage)	$L^2MT^{-2}Q^{-1}$	Magnetic flux (ϕ)	$L^2MT^{-1}Q^{-1}$
		Flux density (B)	$MT^{-1}Q^{-1}$
Resistance	$L^2MT^{-1}Q^{-2}$	Magnetomotive force ($\mathscr{F}$)	$T^{-1}Q$
Inductance	L^2MQ^{-2}		
Capacitance	$L^{-2}M^{-1}T^2Q^2$	Magnetizing force (H)	$L^{-1}T^{-1}Q$

It is generally true that every term of an exact physical equation must have the *same* dimensions,[26] since a physical equality can compare only quantities which are physically similar. We can make use of this axiom

[26] Bridgman points out that equations may be created for which this is not true (see Bridgman, *Dimensional Analysis*, p. 42, Yale University Press, 1931) and gives as an example the expression $V + S = gt + \frac{1}{2}gt^2$, which may be obtained by adding the equations $V = gt$ and $S = \frac{1}{2}gt^2$. However, such an expression, obtained by the combination of two dissimilar physical equations, must be considered an algebraic rather than a physical equation, since it is a composite statement of facts which are not necessarily related. While one should be aware that such an expression can result from algebraic manipulations of more than one physical equation, the chance of its occurrence in the solution of a physical problem is so remote that this occurrence should be a warning that some extraneous matter has been introduced in the course of the operations which led to the expression.

in checking the accuracy of derived formulas. If we substitute the dimensions of each quantity involved in the relationship, *the dimensions of every term must be the same.* This procedure by no means guarantees the correctness of the formula in question, but, if a dimensional check shows that all the terms do not have the same dimensions, then we may be sure that the formula is incorrect in some particular. The dimensions missing from a term will often afford a clue concerning the nature of an error which has been made. However, it should be kept in mind that the information gained is usually of a purely negative character. Although an error is indicated if all terms do not have the same dimensions, the mere fact that all the terms of an expression do have the same dimensions does not prove the validity of the formula. Also, no information of any sort concerning numerical coefficients is available from such a dimensional check, since pure numbers are dimensionless and are not significant in a comparison of dimensions.

We will take some examples. In a certain bridge for capacitance measurements, we find that the expression for the phase defect angle of a capacitor is $\tan \delta = \omega CR$. Now $\tan \delta$ is dimensionless, being the numerical ratio of two sides of a triangle $(L \cdot L^{-1})$. Hence, if our formula is correct, the product ωCR must also be dimensionless. Now

$\omega = 2\pi \times$ frequency, and has the dimension T^{-1},
C has the dimensions $M^{-1}L^{-2}T^2Q^2$,
R has the dimensions $ML^2T^{-1}Q^{-2}$,

so that the dimensions of ωCR are $T^{-1} \cdot M^{-1}L^{-2}T^2Q^2 \cdot ML^2T^{-1}Q^{-2}$. It will be seen that these dimensions cancel out, so that the combination is dimensionless; i.e. our formula checks dimensionally since both terms are dimensionless. It may be noted that the dimensions of ωC are identical with the dimensions of $1/R$. This is to be expected since $\omega C = 1/\text{reactance}$, and reactance and resistance are equivalent dimensionally. Our dimensional check could have been made without recourse to the mechanical dimensions by noting that ωCR is equivalent to (resistance/reactance) and is therefore dimensionless.

As another example let us say that for a certain network we have derived for current the expression

$$I = \frac{\omega \mathscr{L} E}{\sqrt{\left(\omega^2 \mathscr{L}^2 + \dfrac{R}{\omega C}\right)^2 + \omega^2 \mathscr{L} R^2}}$$

Since the left-hand side of the equation is a current, the right-hand member must also have the dimensions of current $(T^{-1}Q)$ if the equation is correct. On substituting dimensions we have

$$\frac{T^{-1}\cdot ML^2Q^{-2}\cdot ML^2T^{-2}Q^{-1}}{\sqrt{\left(T^{-2}\cdot M^2L^4Q^{-4}+\dfrac{ML^2T^{-1}Q^{-2}}{T^{-1}\cdot M^{-1}L^{-2}T^2Q^2}\right)^2+T^{-2}\cdot ML^2Q^{-2}\cdot M^2L^4T^{-2}Q^{-4}}}$$

$$= T^{-1}Q\left(\frac{1}{\sqrt{1+\dfrac{1}{ML^2Q^{-2}}}}\right)$$

We see that the equation does not check dimensionally since the dimensions of current, outside the parentheses, are multiplied by the factor $\left(\dfrac{1}{\sqrt{1+\dfrac{1}{ML^2Q^{-2}}}}\right)$, which is not dimensionless. A factor ML^2Q^{-2} is needed in the numerator of the last term under the radical in order to make the equation homogeneous dimensionally. Our original expression for current is therefore incorrect, and its derivation should be examined for an error which probably involves the omission of an inductance (i.e. an electrical quantity or combination of quantities having the dimensions ML^2Q^{-2}) in the final term of the denominator. As before, we could make the check without recourse to mechanical dimensions if we recall that $\omega\mathscr{L}$ and $1/\omega C$ are both reactances and therefore have the dimensions of resistance. For our dimensional check we may substitute R for $\omega\mathscr{L}$ and for $1/\omega C$, wherever they occur. Thus we may write

$$I = \frac{ER}{\sqrt{(R^2+R^2)^2+\omega R^3}} = \frac{E}{R}\left(\frac{1}{\sqrt{1+\dfrac{\omega}{R}}}\right)$$

Now E/R has the dimensions of current, but is multiplied by an expression which is not dimensionless and must be incorrect. Also, inspection shows that if $\mathscr{L}$ were inserted in the last term under the radical the quantity inside the parentheses would become dimensionless.

It is possible to make dimensional checks of many expressions without resorting to the mechanical dimensions, and, wherever it is apparent that this procedure will require less work, it should be done. Occasionally an expression may be encountered in which the relations between the electrical quantities are not immediately apparent. In such a case the mechanical dimensions should be used in making a dimensional check.

Conversion of Units

It is frequently necessary to express the value of a physical quantity in terms of different units or to modify an equation by changing the units of one or more quantities in the equation. For example, it may be necessary to express a length of 3 in. in centimeters, or to write Ohm's law in terms of volts, microamperes, and ohms rather than volts, amperes, and ohms. To avoid mistakes, particularly when dealing with unfamiliar quantities or complicated conversions, a systematic procedure is generally helpful in carrying out the conversion.

A measured physical quantity (such as the height of a cylinder) is expressed as a number and a unit, e.g. 3 in., and may be considered the number of times the unit is applied in some way to obtain the measured value. Since the value of the quantity is independent of the units in which the measurement is made, we may write, for two systems of units, the equivalence $N_1U_1 = N_2U_2$, in which U is the value of a unit quantity and N is the number of times it is applied to obtain the measured quantity in the respective systems.

To determine the number of units of a different size, when we know the number of units of a particular size in a given quantity, the relationship between the different units must be known. This is usually expressed as an equivalence $1U_1 = fU_2$ (e.g. 1 in. = 2.54 cm). If we multiply both sides of this equivalence by N_1, we have $N_1U_1 = (N_1f)U_2$. Hence $N_2 = N_1f$, so that the number, N_2, of units of size U_2 in a given quantity is f times the number of units of size U_1 in the same quantity, f being defined by a known equivalence. This equivalence, $1U_1 = fU_2$, may be written as $1 = 1U_1/fU_2$, and the quantity under consideration may be multiplied by this fraction or its reciprocal without changing its value (since the fraction is itself equal to unity). Thus,

$$N_1U_1 = N_1U_1 \times \frac{fU_2}{1U_1} = (N_1f)U_2$$

as has already been stated.

We have then a convenient and easily applied method for carrying out the first of two types of conversion, that of expressing the value of a quantity in different units. The method consists in writing the number or letter symbol and the unit of the quantity, and multiplying it by appropriate known ratios of units (expressed as fractions equal to unity) which are so chosen that the undesired units cancel each other in pairs, until the quantity is expressed in the desired units. The mechanism is best illustrated by simple examples:

1. A length of 3 in. $= 3\,\cancel{\text{in.}} \times \dfrac{2.54\text{ cm}}{1\,\cancel{\text{in.}}} = 7.62\text{ cm.}$

2. A current density of J amp per sq cm

$$= \frac{J\,\cancel{\text{amp}}}{\cancel{\text{cm}^2}} \times \frac{10^6\ \mu\text{a}}{1\,\cancel{\text{amp}}} \times \frac{\overline{2.54}^2\,\cancel{\text{cm}^2}}{1\text{ in.}^2} = 6.45 \times 10^6\,\frac{\mu\text{a}}{\text{in.}^2}.$$

3. A force of 1 newton $= \dfrac{1\ \text{kg-meter}}{\text{sec}^2} \times \dfrac{100\ \text{cm}}{1\ \text{meter}} \times \dfrac{1000\ \text{gm}}{1\ \text{kg}}$

$$= \frac{10^5\ \text{gm-cm}}{\text{sec}^2} = 10^5\ \text{dynes}.$$

It should be noted that in the last example the conversion was made by expressing the quantity in parametric units and by using appropriate ratios of these units. Generally, the ratios (or equivalences) of only a few basic units need be known.

Now a physical equation expresses in algebraic form a relation between the magnitudes of physical quantities. In an ordinary physical equation each letter symbol represents the number of units of a physical quantity, and the units must be specified unless a consistent system of units is used. It is frequently desirable to use mixed units which do not belong to a consistent system and to modify the equation accordingly, the modified equation being valid only for the specified units. Since $N_1 = N_2/f$, it is necessary (if the size of a unit is to be changed) to substitute for the letter symbol of that quantity (representing the number of units of size U_1), wherever it appears in the equation, a new letter symbol divided by the conversion factor, f, given above. The new letter symbol will represent the number of new units of size U_2 for which the modified equation is valid.

The same type of method also may be used to carry out the second type of conversion, that of modifying an ordinary physical equation by changing the units of one or more quantities without correspondingly changing the units of the remaining quantities in the equation. The procedure consists in writing a letter symbol for the number of new units of the quantity, also writing the new unit, and then multiplying by appropriate ratios of units (expressed as fractions equal to unity) until only the old unit and a multiplying factor remain. This factor, which includes the letter symbol for the number of new units, is then substituted for the letter symbol of that quantity in the old units, wherever it appears in the equation. Again the method may be illustrated by examples.

1. Suppose that we have Ohm's law, $V = IR$, where V, I, R are the number of volts, amperes, and ohms respectively (a consistent system of units), and we wish to modify the equation so that the current is expressed in microamperes with the other units unchanged. We may write

$$I'\ \mu\text{a} \times \frac{1\ \text{amp}}{10^6\ \mu\text{a}} = \frac{I'}{10^6}\ \text{amp}$$

Then $V = I'R/10^6$, where I' is in microamperes, with R and V in ohms and volts as in the original equation.

2. Suppose we have $R = \rho l/A$, where R is in ohms, ρ in ohm-centimeters, l in centimeters, and A in square centimeters, and we wish ρ' to be in microhm-inches. We may write

$$\rho' \text{ microhm-in.} \times \frac{2.54 \text{ cm}}{1 \text{ in.}} \times \frac{1 \text{ ohm}}{10^6 \text{ microhms}} = \rho' \times \frac{2.54}{10^6} \text{ ohm-cm}$$

Then

$$R = 2.54 \times 10^{-6} \frac{\rho' l}{A}$$

where ρ' is in microhm-inches, with the other units unchanged.

CHAPTER 3

DIRECT-CURRENT GALVANOMETERS

A galvanometer is an instrument for detecting the presence of small currents or voltages in a closed circuit or for measuring their magnitudes. The ordinary uses of the galvanometer include four distinct types of measurement in each of which the quantity to be measured is different.[1]

1. We may be interested in the current, or change in current, in a circuit which includes the galvanometer. For example, in the measurement of insulation resistance by a direct deflection method, we need to know the current sensitivity of the galvanometer.

2. The voltage or change in voltage is to be measured (or detected) in the circuit to which the galvanometer is connected. The voltage in the galvanometer branch of a bridge or potentiometer circuit is an example. In this very large class of measurements, the voltage sensitivity rather than the current sensitivity of the galvanometer is of interest.

3. The quantity of electricity suddenly passed through the galvanometer is to be measured. An example is the comparison of capacitors by ballistic throw, when they are discharged in turn through the galvanometer. Here the ballistic (or quantity) sensitivity is important, the quantity $q = \int i\,dt$ being passed impulsively through the circuit containing the galvanometer.

4. We may measure the time integral of emf, $\int e\,dt$, in the circuit. This is done in the comparison of magnetic fields by ballistic throw, when the flux linkages are suddenly changed in a search coil in series with the galvanometer. This may be called the microvolt-second (or flux-linkage) sensitivity.

All these sensitivities can be derived from the *current sensitivity* together with certain galvanometer and circuit parameters. Hence a statement of

[1] F. Wenner, General Design of Critically Damped Galvanometers. *NBS Bull.*, **13**, 213 (1916).

current sensitivity is indispensable in describing the performance of a galvanometer, although we are generally not directly interested in the response of a galvanometer to a current through it. In this chapter we will examine only the current and voltage sensitivities of galvanometers. Consideration of ballistic sensitivities will be treated separately later.

The principle of operation of a galvanometer requires the interaction of two magnetic fields, one of which is produced by the current being measured. The result of this interaction is a torque tending to produce a deflection. The magnitude of this torque is a function of the galvanometer current. This torque must be opposed by a restoring torque whose magnitude is a function of the displacement of the moving system. The restoring torque may result from (1) the elastic action of a spring or suspension; (2) gravitational action on an unsymmetrically distributed mass; or (3) the reaction of a magnet in a magnetic field. Combinations of these forces are sometimes used to supply the restoring torque.

The indicating system, under the influence of these opposing torques, takes up an equilibrium position from which the magnitude of the current may be determined. Inertial and damping forces, which act whenever the indicating system moves, determine the manner in which it approaches the equilibrium position but *have no effect* on the position of equilibrium itself.

History

The discovery by Oersted in 1819 of the effect of an electric current on a magnetic needle may be said to represent the earliest use of the galvanometer principle and led to the development of the *tangent* galvanometer, described by Pouillet in 1837. This galvanometer consisted of a magnetic needle pivoted at the center of a narrow circular coil. In this type of galvanometer the displacing torque results from the interaction of the field from the current in the coil, with the field of the needle; and the opposing torque results from the action of the earth's magnetic field on the needle. The equilibrium position of the needle is along the resultant between the field of the coil and the horizontal component of the earth's field. The magnitude of the current may be determined from the equilibrium position of the needle, and from the knowledge of the coil constants and the magnitude of the horizontal component of the earth's field. Such a galvanometer is necessarily sensitive to variations in the local field resulting from the presence of magnetic materials in the neighborhood, or from current-carrying conductors near the galvanometer. The tangent galvanometer is no longer used as a practical instrument.

The *moving-magnet* galvanometer, described by Thomson in 1858, was a logical development from the tangent galvanometer. As in the tangent galvanometer, the displacing torque results from the interaction of the field of the needle with that of coils carrying the current to be measured, but in this instrument the magnetic needle is shielded from the action of local fields external to the current coils of the galvanometer. The restoring torque is supplied by the elastic properties of a fine quartz filament from which the moving element (magnets and mirror) is suspended. The shielding, consisting of an iron cylinder or a series of coaxial cylinders enclosing the galvanometer, cannot be completely effective, so that the instrument is somewhat sensitive to local fields. Also, because of the small forces involved the suspension is delicate. Consequently, although this instrument can be built to have very high sensitivities and is therefore still found in some laboratories, it is almost never used in any type of engineering measurement.

The *moving-coil* galvanometer (Sturgeon, 1836) was first described at about the same time as the tangent galvanometer. In this type of galvanometer the displacing torque results from the action of the field of a fixed, permanent magnet on the field produced by current in a suspended coil. The restoring torque is supplied by the elastic properties of a fine metal wire which suspends the coil in the magnet field and which usually also carries current to the coil. This galvanometer was first improved by the introduction of a fixed soft-iron core or armature (Thomson, 1867) within the coil, and later by the addition of pole pieces to the magnet (d'Arsonval, 1882). Two advantages result from the use of an armature and properly shaped pole pieces: (1) the coil moves in a uniform radial field; and (2) since the air gap between the pole pieces and the armature can be made comparatively narrow, the field in which the coil moves can be made large. With few exceptions, modern d-c galvanometers are of the d'Arsonval type.

Operating Principles

In a moving-coil (d'Arsonval) galvanometer the current-carrying element is in the form of a coil of one or more turns, usually rectangular in shape, suspended so that it is free to turn about its vertical axis of symmetry. This coil is usually arranged to move in a uniform, radial, horizontal magnetic field in the air gap between the pole pieces and armature of a permanent magnet. As shown in Fig. 1, the coil is suspended so that it can rotate in this air gap.

If we assume a uniform radial horizontal field B, the force acting on a vertical element (dl) of wire carrying a current (i) is $dF = iB\,dl$. If l is the vertical side of the coil, and if there are N turns of wire in the coil, the force acting on the coil side in each air gap is $F = BiNl$. If the horizontal coil width is b, then the turning moment of the forces acting on the coil is $\mathscr{T} = BNlbi = Gi$, where $G = BNlb$. It will be noted that the area of the coil times the number of turns in the winding (Nlb) is a constant describing the coil itself. This product is sometimes referred to as the "area-turns" of the coil.

The torque ($\mathscr{T}$) of the turning couple is opposed by the "elastic" torque resulting from the twist in the suspension supporting the coil. Under the action of these torques, the coil will assume an equilibrium position at an angle θ with the position of zero restoring torque such that $U\theta = Gi$, where U is the elastic constant of the suspension—the restoring torque per unit angle of twist—and is a function of its cross section, length, and modulus of elasticity.

If we define the *current sensitivity* of the galvanometer as the deflection produced by unit current we have $S_i = \theta/i = G/U$. We have assumed here that the current has a constant value and that the equilibrium is established as a steady-state condition.

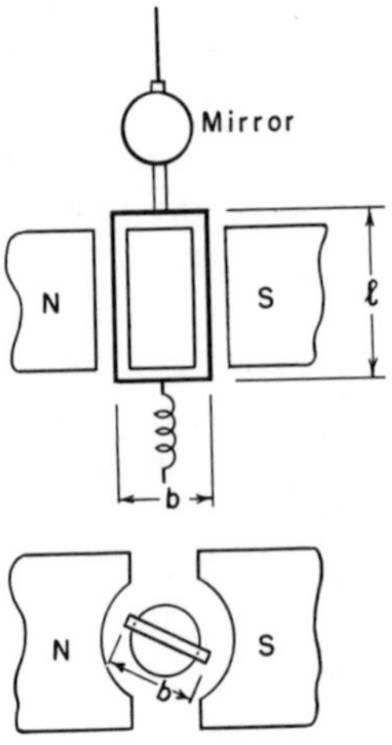

FIG. 1.

Equation of Motion

In order to state both the equilibrium condition and the manner in which the moving coil approaches its equilibrium position, we must examine the equation of motion of the galvanometer. It should be emphasized that this equation (that of a damped harmonic oscillator) will, with a suitable interpretation of the constants, be applicable to the behavior of the moving system of any indicating instrument. Indeed, it applies to any mechanical system which moves in damped harmonic motion under the combined action of elastic, inertial, and damping forces. It is therefore one of the more important equations of engineering mathematics. As we examine in detail the steps in its solution for our particular case, it will be well to keep in mind that our procedure is typical of a large class of engineering problems.

As we have already seen, the *displacing* torque acting to produce coil motion is Gi, where G is a function of coil area-turns and of the magnetic field in which the coil rotates. The current at any instant in the coil is i. In general, the current in the circuit is not constant during the motion of the coil. If the coil moving in the magnetic field is considered as a motor, it will be seen that the motion must generate a back emf e such that the mechanical power in the motor is $-ei$. But the mechanical power is also the torque (Gi) multiplied by the angular velocity $(d\theta/dt)$. From this we have $e = -G(d\theta/dt)$. We shall assume in the following discussion that the voltage E impressed on the circuit is constant. If the resistance of the circuit is R (also a constant), then $i = \frac{E}{R} - \frac{G}{R}\frac{d\theta}{dt}$, and the displacing torque is $\frac{EG}{R} - \frac{G^2}{R}\frac{d\theta}{dt}$.

The mechanical couples which oppose the motion are: (1) the *restoring* torque $U\theta$, dependent on the elastic properties of the suspension and proportional to the angular displacement θ of the coil; (2) the *damping* torque $K(d\theta/dt)$, dependent on frictional forces and proportional to the angular velocity $(d\theta/dt)$ of the coil;[2] and (3) the *inertial* torque $P(d^2\theta/dt^2)$ proportional to the angular acceleration $(d^2\theta/dt^2)$ of the coil, P being the moment of inertia of the coil about its axis of rotation.

We may now write the equation of motion of the galvanometer by equating opposing torques, thus:

$$P\frac{d^2\theta}{dt^2} + K\frac{d\theta}{dt} + U\theta = \frac{GE}{R} - \frac{G^2}{R}\frac{d\theta}{dt}$$

or on rearranging

$$P\frac{d^2\theta}{dt^2} + \left(K + \frac{G^2}{R}\right)\frac{d\theta}{dt} + U\theta = \frac{GE}{R}$$

It will be noted from the latter grouping of terms that damping may be considered as made up of two parts: (1) mechanical damping, $K(d\theta/dt)$, which depends on galvanometer construction; and (2) electromagnetic damping, $\frac{G^2}{R}\frac{d\theta}{dt}$, which is a function of circuit resistance also. For the formal solution of the equation we will combine the two damping constants, $K + (G^2/R) = A$.

(*a*) *Transient Term.* We have now a linear, second-degree differential equation whose solution is the sum of a "complementary function" (representing a transient condition) and a "particular integral" (representing the steady-state condition). Using a method of differential equations, we will introduce the D operator,[3] $\mathrm{D} = d/dt$. The

[2] This assumed proportionality of damping (or friction) to the first power of angular velocity is not always strictly true, but is a close enough approximation for most purposes.

[3] See A. Murray, *Differential Equations*, Chapter VI, or any elementary textbook on differential equations.

complementary equation is $(PD^2 + AD + U)\theta = 0$, for which the auxiliary equation is

$$Pm^2 + Am + U = 0, \quad \text{and} \quad m = \frac{-A \pm \sqrt{A^2 - 4PU}}{2P}$$

$$= \frac{-A}{2P} \pm \sqrt{\frac{A^2}{4P^2} - \frac{U}{P}}$$

There are three possible cases, depending on the value of the discriminant $\left(\sqrt{\frac{A^2}{4P^2} - \frac{U}{P}}\right)$ of the auxiliary equation:

(1) $m_1 \neq m_2$ and real if $\frac{A^2}{4P^2} > \frac{U}{P}$;

(2) $m_1 = m_2$ and real if $\frac{A^2}{4P^2} = \frac{U}{P}$; and

(3) $m_1 \neq m_2$ and complex if $\frac{A^2}{4P^2} < \frac{U}{P}$.

For cases 1 and 3 the complementary function is $\theta = C_1\varepsilon^{m_1 t} + C_2\varepsilon^{m_2 t}$, and for case 2 $\theta = \varepsilon^{mt}(C_1 + C_2 t)$. The transient term has been obtained by setting the displacing torque equal to zero and solving the resulting equation of motion without the action of outside forces. We will consider the three possible cases later, but will first obtain the particular integral.

(*b*) *Steady-State Term.* If we reduce our original equation to standard form, we have

$$\left(D^2 + \frac{A}{P}\,D + \frac{U}{P}\right)\theta = \frac{GE}{RP}$$

or, since D may be treated as an algebraic operator,

$$\theta = \frac{GE/RP}{D^2 + \frac{A}{P}D + \frac{U}{P}}$$

Now, from the auxiliary equation for m it will be seen that $A/P = -(m_1 + m_2)$, and that $U/P = m_1 m_2$. Then, on substitution and reduction to partial fractions, we have

$$\frac{1}{D^2 - (m_1 + m_2)D + m_1 m_2} \equiv \frac{\alpha}{D - m_1} + \frac{\beta}{D - m_2}$$

From this identity $1 = D(\alpha + \beta) - (m_2\alpha + m_1\beta)$, and on equating coefficients

$$\left.\begin{aligned} \alpha + \beta &= 0 \\ m_2\alpha + m_1\beta &= -1 \end{aligned}\right\} \text{ so that } \left\{\begin{aligned} \alpha &= \frac{1}{m_1 - m_2} \\ \beta &= -\frac{1}{m_1 - m_2} \end{aligned}\right.$$

and

We may now write the particular integral

$$\theta = \frac{1}{m_1 - m_2} \cdot \frac{1}{D - m_1}\left(\frac{GE}{RP}\right) - \frac{1}{m_1 - m_2} \cdot \frac{1}{D - m_2}\left(\frac{GE}{RP}\right)$$

$$= \frac{GE}{RP(m_1 - m_2)}[\varepsilon^{m_1t} \int \varepsilon^{-m_1t}\, dt - \varepsilon^{m_2t} \int \varepsilon^{-m_2t}\, dt]$$

since the impressed voltage (E) and the total circuit resistance (R) are both assumed to be constant. But $\varepsilon^{mt} \int \varepsilon^{-mt}\, dt = -1/m$, and the particular integral becomes

$$\theta = \frac{GE}{RP(m_1 - m_2)} \cdot \left(\frac{1}{m_2} - \frac{1}{m_1}\right) = \frac{GE}{RP(m_1m_2)} = \frac{GE}{RU}$$

since $m_1m_2 = U/P$.

This represents the steady-state solution to the galvanometer equation after sufficient time has elapsed that the transient term has disappeared. It will be noted that this solution checks our previous expression for the steady state since $E/R = I$, the final current after motion has ceased in the galvanometer coil and no back emf is being generated. The particular solution also gives us the *voltage sensitivity* of the galvanometer, $S_e = \theta/E = G/RU = S_i/R$, in terms of the *current sensitivity*, where R is the total circuit resistance, including that of the galvanometer itself.

(*c*) *General Solution.* If we now call the final deflection θ_F, where $\theta_F = GE/RU$, we are prepared to write the general solution to the galvanometer equation of motion by combining the complementary function and the particular integral, i.e. the transient and the steady-state terms. We have[4] $\theta = \theta_F + C_1\varepsilon^{m_1t} + C_2\varepsilon^{m_2t}$, in which we must determine the constants of integration. These constants will depend on the boundary conditions of the problem. In our case they will be defined in terms of the initial condition of the moving system.

The case which is of the greatest interest to us is the one in which the

[4] This is, of course, the solution for cases 1 and 3 ($m_1 \neq m_2$). The solution for case 2 ($m_1 = m_2 = m$) will be considered later.

galvanometer coil is initially at rest in its equilibrium position, for which we have at a time

$$t = 0 \begin{cases} \theta = 0 & (1) \\ \dfrac{d\theta}{dt} = 0 & (2) \end{cases}$$

as the boundary conditions of the problem. From condition 1 we have $0 = \theta_F + C_1 + C_2$, and from condition 2, by differentiation, $0 = m_1C_1 + m_2C_2$. If these equations be solved for C_1 and C_2, we have

$$C_1 = \frac{m_2\theta_F}{m_1 - m_2}, \quad \text{and} \quad C_2 = \frac{m_1\theta_F}{m_2 - m_1}$$

Finally we have for the galvanometer equation

$$\theta = \theta_F \left(1 - \frac{m_2}{m_2 - m_1}\,\varepsilon^{m_1t} + \frac{m_1}{m_2 - m_1}\,\varepsilon^{m_2t}\right)$$

UNDERDAMPED MOTION. As we shall see later the most important case of galvanometer motion is the one in which the discriminant of the auxiliary equation is negative and the motion is a damped oscillation. We shall consider this case first. Here $A^2 < 4PU$, so that m_1 and m_2 are conjugate complex quantities. Let

$$\begin{pmatrix} m_1 = -a + jb \\ m_2 = -a - jb \end{pmatrix} \quad \text{where} \quad \begin{pmatrix} a = \dfrac{A}{2P} \\ b = \sqrt{\dfrac{U}{P} - \dfrac{A^2}{4P^2}} \end{pmatrix}$$

We have

$$\frac{-m_2}{m_2 - m_1} = \frac{a + jb}{-2jb}, \quad \text{and} \quad \frac{+m_1}{m_2 - m_1} = \frac{-a + jb}{-2jb}$$

Then

$$\theta = \theta_F\left[1 + \frac{(-a - jb)}{2jb}\,\varepsilon^{(-a+jb)t} - \frac{(-a + jb)}{2jb}\,\varepsilon^{(-a-jb)t}\right]$$

$$= \theta_F\left[1 + \frac{\varepsilon^{-at}}{2jb}\left(a\{\varepsilon^{-jbt} - \varepsilon^{jbt}\} - jb\{\varepsilon^{jbt} + \varepsilon^{-jbt}\}\right)\right]$$

$$= \theta_F\left[1 + \frac{\varepsilon^{-at}}{2jb}(-2aj \sin bt - 2bj \cos bt)\right]$$

$$= \theta_F\left[1 - \frac{\varepsilon^{-at}}{b}(a \sin bt + b \cos bt)\right]$$

Now let

$$\frac{a}{\sqrt{a^2 + b^2}} = \cos \phi, \quad \text{and} \quad \frac{b}{\sqrt{a^2 + b^2}} = \sin \phi$$

so that

$$\phi = \tan^{-1} \frac{b}{a}$$

Then we have

$$\theta = \theta_F \left[1 - \frac{\sqrt{a^2 + b^2}}{b} \varepsilon^{-at} (\sin bt \cos \phi + \cos bt \sin \phi)\right]$$

$$= \theta_F \left[1 - \frac{\sqrt{a^2 + b^2}}{b} \varepsilon^{-at} \sin \left(bt + \tan^{-1} \frac{b}{a}\right)\right]$$

Here the transient term represents an oscillatory motion of diminishing amplitude. It may be seen that the frequency of oscillation is $b/2\pi$, whence the period

$$T = \frac{2\pi}{b} = \frac{2\pi}{\sqrt{\dfrac{U}{P} - \dfrac{A^2}{4P^2}}}$$

If there were no damping, i.e. if $A = 0$, the period would by definition be the *free period*

$$T_0 = \frac{2\pi}{\sqrt{\dfrac{U}{P}}} = 2\pi \sqrt{\frac{P}{U}}$$

Now

$$\sqrt{a^2 + b^2} = \sqrt{\frac{A^2}{4P^2} + \frac{U}{P} - \frac{A^2}{4P^2}} = \sqrt{\frac{U}{P}} = \frac{2\pi}{T_0}$$

from which

$$\frac{\sqrt{a^2 + b^2}}{b} = \frac{T}{T_0}$$

Also

$$\frac{b}{a} = \frac{2\pi}{T} \cdot \frac{2P}{A} = \frac{4\pi P}{AT}$$

and we may write

$$\theta = \theta_F \left[1 - \frac{T}{T_0} \varepsilon^{-\frac{At}{2P}} \sin \left(\frac{2\pi t}{T} + \tan^{-1} \frac{4\pi P}{AT}\right)\right]$$

It may be noted at this point that the free period (without damping) is defined in terms of the ratio of two of the intrinsic (design) constants of the galvanometer, $\dfrac{P}{U} = \dfrac{\text{moment of inertia}}{\text{stiffness of suspension}}$, and that the period is increased either by increasing the moment of inertia or by using a weaker suspension. In cases where it is important to keep the period small in order that the response may be as rapid as possible, U/P must be kept large. We may also note that the *actual* period is in all cases larger than the *free* period; i.e. the oscillations are slower in the presence of damping than without it. However, an inspection shows that the change in period is small if the damping is small, for then

$$\frac{T}{T_0} = \sqrt{1 + \left(\frac{a}{b}\right)^2} = \frac{1}{\sqrt{1 - \dfrac{A^2}{4PU}}} \approx 1 + \frac{A^2}{8PU}$$

If then $T = T_0 + \Delta T$, we have $\dfrac{\Delta T}{T_0} \approx \dfrac{A^2}{8PU}$, which is small if A is small.

CRITICALLY DAMPED MOTION. The expression derived above for damped oscillatory motion (the underdamped galvanometer) is not in its most useful form. Before transforming it we will consider the case of the *critically damped* galvanometer, for which the motion just ceases to be oscillatory. If the discriminant of our auxiliary equation vanishes, we have

$$\frac{A_c^2}{4P^2} - \frac{U}{P} = 0, \quad \text{or} \quad \frac{A_c}{2P} = \sqrt{\frac{U}{P}} = \frac{2\pi}{T_0}$$

A_c being the damping constant corresponding to critical damping. Here $m_1 = m_2 = m = -A_c/2P$, and the solution of the galvanometer equation is $\theta = \theta_F + (C_1 + C_2 t)\varepsilon^{mt}$, the particular integral being the same as before since the damping has no effect on the steady-state solution. Assuming the same boundary conditions

$$\left.\begin{pmatrix} \theta = 0 \\ \\ \dfrac{d\theta}{dt} = 0 \end{pmatrix}\right\} \text{when } t = 0$$

we have

$$C_1 + \theta_F = 0; \qquad mC_1 + C_2 = 0$$

Then

$$C_1 = -\theta_F, \quad \text{and} \quad C_2 = m\theta_F = \frac{-A_c\theta_F}{2P}$$

so that

$$\theta = \theta_F\left[1 - \varepsilon^{-A_c t/2P}\left(1 + \frac{A_c t}{2P}\right)\right] = \theta_F\left[1 - \left(1 + \frac{2\pi t}{T_0}\right)\varepsilon^{-2\pi t/T_0}\right]$$

It will be noted that in this case there is no oscillatory motion, and that the deflection approaches its final value asymtotically.

RELATIVE DAMPING. If we now define *relative damping*, $\gamma = A/A_c$, then for *any damping whatever*

$$A = \gamma A_c = \gamma \frac{4\pi P}{T_0}$$

Also, as we have seen,

$$\frac{T}{T_0} = \frac{1}{\sqrt{1 - \dfrac{A^2}{4PU}}} = \frac{1}{\sqrt{1 - \dfrac{A_c^2\gamma^2}{4PU}}}$$

and since $A_c^2 = 4PU$,

$$\frac{T}{T_0} = \frac{1}{\sqrt{1-\gamma^2}}$$

and

$$\tan^{-1}\frac{4\pi P}{AT} = \tan^{-1}\sqrt{\frac{1}{\gamma^2} - 1} = \sin^{-1}\sqrt{1-\gamma^2}$$

We may now write the equation of motion of the underdamped galvanometer in terms of the relative damping

$$\theta = \theta_F\left[1 - \frac{1}{\sqrt{1-\gamma^2}}\,\varepsilon^{-\frac{2\pi t}{T_0}\gamma}\sin\left(\frac{2\pi t}{T_0}\sqrt{1-\gamma^2} + \sin^{-1}\sqrt{1-\gamma^2}\right)\right]$$

It may be noted that this equation describes the galvanometer motion in terms of working constants, relative damping, free period, and sensitivity (the latter being implied in θ_F), whereas our former expression required a knowledge of intrinsic or design constants as well.

LOGARITHMIC DECREMENT. The time required for the deflection to reach a maximum value may be obtained by setting $d\theta/dt = 0$. When this is done we have

$$\sqrt{1-\gamma^2}\cos\left(\frac{2\pi t_m}{T_0}\sqrt{1-\gamma^2} + \sin^{-1}\sqrt{1-\gamma^2}\right)$$
$$= \gamma\sin\left(\frac{2\pi t_m}{T_0}\sqrt{1-\gamma^2} + \sin^{-1}\sqrt{1-\gamma^2}\right)$$

which may be written as

$$\tan\left(\frac{2\pi t_m}{T_0}\sqrt{1-\gamma^2} + \sin^{-1}\sqrt{1-\gamma^2}\right) = \frac{\sqrt{1-\gamma^2}}{\gamma}$$

Then

$$\frac{2\pi t_m}{T_0}\sqrt{1-\gamma^2} = \tan^{-1}\frac{\sqrt{1-\gamma^2}}{\gamma} - \sin^{-1}\sqrt{1-\gamma^2} = N\pi$$

where N may be any integer. If N is an even number, we have a minimum value of deflection since our initial value at $t = 0$ represents a minimum. When N is an odd integer, t_m corresponds to a maximum value of deflection. Our first maximum deflection then corresponds to

$$\frac{2\pi t_1}{T_0}\sqrt{1-\gamma^2} = \pi$$

from which

$$t_1 = \frac{T_0}{2\sqrt{1-\gamma^2}}$$

The value of the first maximum deflection is

$$\theta_1 = \theta_F\left[1 - \frac{1}{\sqrt{1-\gamma^2}}\,\varepsilon^{-\pi\gamma/\sqrt{1-\gamma^2}}\sin\left(\pi + \sin^{-1}\sqrt{1-\gamma^2}\right)\right]$$

$$= \theta_F\left(1 + \varepsilon^{-\pi\gamma/\sqrt{1-\gamma^2}}\right)$$

Therefore,

$$\frac{\theta_1}{\theta_F} = 1 + \varepsilon^{-\pi\gamma/\sqrt{1-\gamma^2}}, \quad \text{or} \quad \frac{\theta_1 - \theta_F}{\theta_F} = \varepsilon^{-\pi\gamma/\sqrt{1-\gamma^2}}$$

so that

$$\log_\varepsilon \frac{\theta_1 - \theta_F}{\theta_F} = \frac{-\pi\gamma}{\sqrt{1-\gamma^2}}$$

Similarly, the first minimum, occurring at a time $t = T = T_0/\sqrt{1-\gamma^2}$, is

$$\theta_2 = \theta_F\left(1 - \varepsilon^{-2\pi\gamma/\sqrt{1-\gamma^2}}\right)$$

If we take the ratio of successive extreme excursions from the steady-state position, we have

$$\frac{\theta_F - \theta_2}{\theta_1 - \theta_F} = \frac{\varepsilon^{-2\pi\gamma/\sqrt{1-\gamma^2}}}{\varepsilon^{-\pi\gamma/\sqrt{1-\gamma^2}}} = \varepsilon^{-\pi\gamma/\sqrt{1-\gamma^2}}$$

from which

$$-\log_\varepsilon \frac{\theta_F - \theta_2}{\theta_1 - \theta_F} = \frac{\pi\gamma}{\sqrt{1-\gamma^2}} = \lambda = -\log_\varepsilon \frac{\theta_1 - \theta_F}{\theta_F}$$

Now λ is the quantity which, in damped harmonic motion, is known as the *logarithmic decrement* of the deflections, and is usually defined as the Naperian logarithm of the ratio of successive swings of the oscillating system. It will be noted from the expressions above that it can equally well be defined as the logarithm of the ratio of the initial overshoot to the final deflection of a galvanometer. It may be further noted that we have derived a simple relation between logarithmic decrement and relative damping, namely $\lambda = \pi\gamma/\sqrt{1-\gamma^2}$. Using this relation, we can put our equation for damped motion into a form commonly found in the literature:

$$\theta = \theta_F \left[1 - \frac{T}{T_0}\, \varepsilon^{-2\lambda t/T} \sin\left(\frac{2\pi t}{T_0} + \tan^{-1}\frac{\pi}{\lambda}\right)\right]$$

Actually, although the latter equation appears to be simpler in form, no real simplification has been achieved. The labor of computing values of θ has not been reduced. Furthermore, we have replaced a simple physical concept (relative damping) with one which is more abstract (logarithmic decrement). In view of these considerations we shall confine our further attention to the galvanometer equation expressed in terms of relative damping.

OVERDAMPED MOTION. Before we proceed with a discussion of the *underdamped* galvanometer we will, for the sake of completeness, write the equation of the overdamped galvanometer. For damping greater than critical the roots of our auxiliary equation are real:

$$\frac{A^2}{4P^2} > \frac{U}{P}, \quad \text{and} \quad \gamma > 1;$$

so that

$$\begin{cases} m_1 = -\dfrac{A}{2P} + \sqrt{\dfrac{A^2}{4P^2} - \dfrac{U}{P}} = \dfrac{2\pi}{T_0}(-\gamma + \sqrt{\gamma^2 - 1}) \\[2ex] m_2 = -\dfrac{A}{2P} - \sqrt{\dfrac{A^2}{4P^2} - \dfrac{U}{P}} = \dfrac{2\pi}{T_0}(-\gamma - \sqrt{\gamma^2 - 1}) \end{cases}$$

These values may be substituted in the general solution of the galvanometer equation, whereupon we have

$$\theta = \theta_F \left[1 - \frac{\gamma + \sqrt{\gamma^2 - 1}}{2\sqrt{\gamma^2 - 1}}\, \varepsilon^{-2\pi t(\gamma - \sqrt{\gamma^2 - 1})/T_0} + \frac{\gamma - \sqrt{\gamma^2 - 1}}{2\sqrt{\gamma^2 - 1}}\, \varepsilon^{-2\pi t(\gamma + \sqrt{\gamma^2 - 1})/T_0}\right]$$

for the overdamped galvanometer.

It may be seen from the discussion which follows that the overdamped case is of little practical importance in current or voltage measurements[5] and is a condition to be avoided in such measurements if one wishes to read θ_F.

[5] It will be shown in Chapter 8 that for some types of measurement the overdamped condition has very decided advantages.

In Fig. 2 galvanometer motion is plotted against time for a series of values of relative damping. In order to make these curves completely general, the time t is stated in terms of the free period T_0 of the galvanometer, and the deflection in terms of the final deflection θ_F. The family

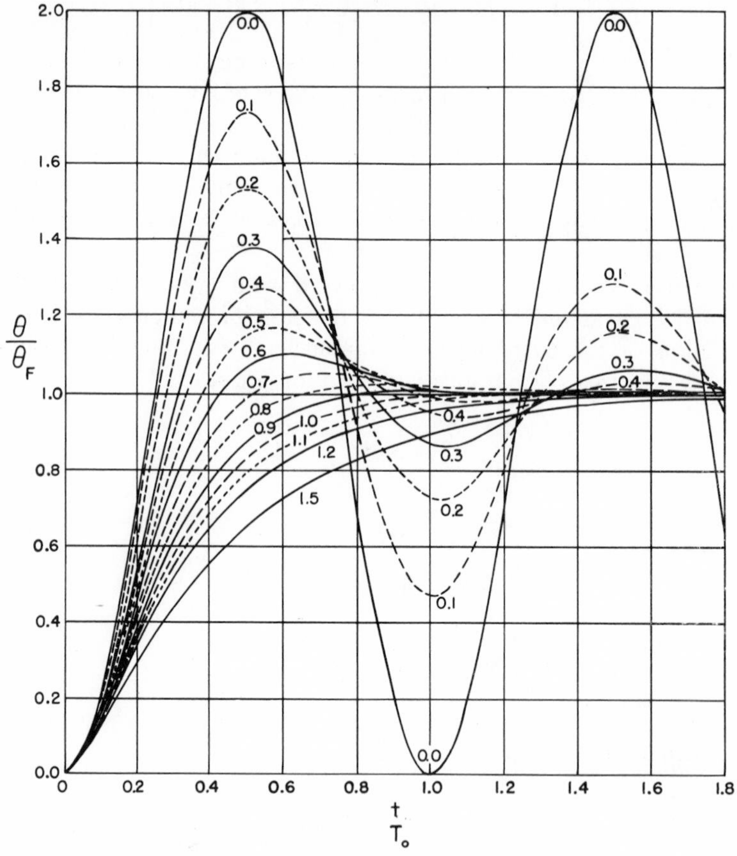

FIG. 2.

of curves therefore applies to any galvanometer, regardless of its free period and other constants.

Reading Time a Function of Damping

An inspection of this family of curves shows that (1) the actual period increases slowly for small damping and then more rapidly as critical damping is approached; (2) although for small damping the oscillation persists for a considerable time, it very quickly becomes negligible as damping approaches the critical value; and (3) for damping greater than critical the approach is slower, the motion becoming more sluggish as γ increases. It is immediately apparent that if the deflection must be read, in order to estimate the magnitude of a current or an emf, one should not use the overdamped condition since the time required to arrive at the final value is unnecessarily long because of the sluggish motion.

Let us inquire what damping is required to make the reading time minimum. If we assume that we are interested in reading the galvanometer to a precision Δ, we require only that the deflection arrive and *remain* within a band $\theta_F \pm \Delta\theta$ as shown in Fig. 3. It is apparent that

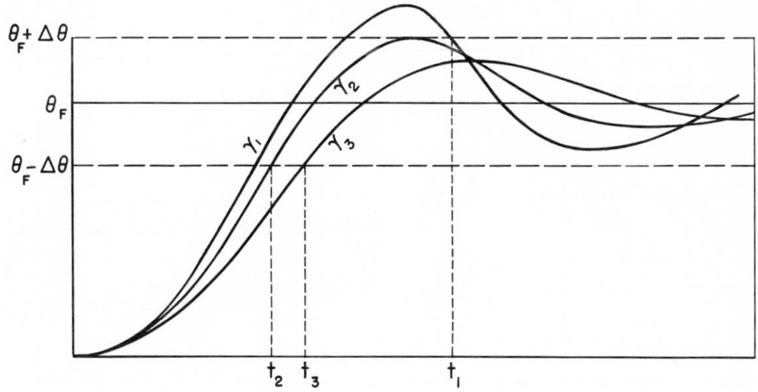

FIG. 3.

the minimum reading time t_2 occurs when the first maximum of the deflection is $\theta_F + \Delta\theta$, corresponding to the relative damping γ_2. If the damping is less (γ_1), the first maximum lies outside the band $\theta_F \pm \Delta\theta$, and the reading time ($t_1$) is greater. If the damping is greater (γ_3), the first maximum is within the band, but the time (t_3) at which the deflection first reaches the lower limit $\theta_F - \Delta\theta$ is greater. Figure 4 shows how reading time (plotted as t/T_0) varies with damping for reading precisions of 10, 1, and 0.1% of the final value. It will be noted that, if the reading is to be within 10%, minimum reading time is attained for a relative damping $\gamma = 0.6$, the reading time being 37% of the free period. For an accuracy of 1%, the optimum damping is $\gamma = 0.83$ and the time is 67% of the free period. For a reading accuracy of 0.1%, the optimum damping is $\gamma = 0.91$ and the time is equal to the free period. Since one does not usually read galvanometer deflections closer than 1%, it appears that if minimum reading time is to be the use criterion the optimum damping is around 0.8 of critical.[6]

[6] A detailed study of related problems has been made by Gerszonowicz, *Galvanómetros y Oscilógrafos*, Vol. 1, p. 31, Montevideo, 1943.

Another advantage accrues from the use of the galvanometer at a damping somewhat less than critical, and this second advantage is decidedly more important than the actual saving in time. With the damping as much as 20% less than critical the initial maximum is appreciably greater (about 1%) than the final value. The deflection can be observed to "overshoot" and then settle back to its final value. The observation of this overshoot assures the user that the galvanometer coil

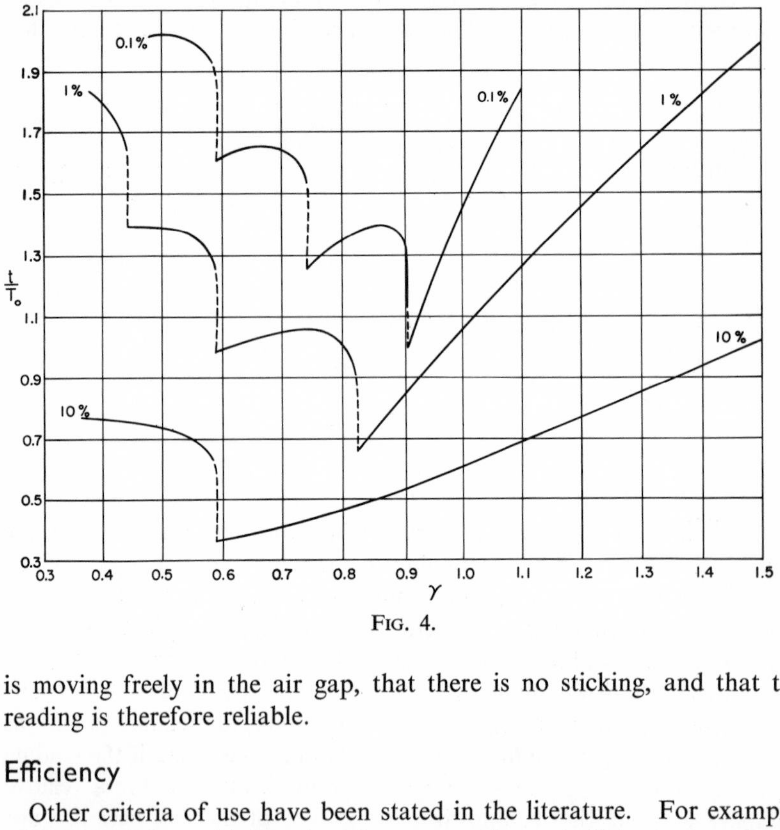

FIG. 4.

is moving freely in the air gap, that there is no sticking, and that the reading is therefore reliable.

Efficiency

Other criteria of use have been stated in the literature. For example, White (1904) has said that the galvanometer is most efficient as a voltage-measuring device if it operates at critical damping. That is, in a circuit whose resistance is such as to produce critical damping, a greater fraction of the available energy is put into producing deflection than for any other circuit condition. That this statement is only approximately true will be seen from the following discussion.[7] In order to arrive at an expression for efficiency we will consider the galvanometer as an electric motor which,

[7] This discussion is based on unpublished notes of Dr. F. Wenner.

in deflecting, converts electrical energy into mechanical energy and stores it in the suspension.

In using the galvanometer to detect or measure a small voltage in a circuit of comparatively low resistance, the torque acting to produce deflection is influenced by the back emf which the coil generates and by the resistance of the coil and suspensions, since in a low-resistance circuit these will have a considerable effect on the current which flows in the circuit. If we consider the power available in the circuit, its source being the emf to be measured, we see that it must be used either to heat the resistance of the circuit or to move the galvanometer coil. The only part of this power which is useful to us is that which the galvanometer, acting as a motor, converts to mechanical power in twisting the suspension, i.e. in producing deflection. Now the current at any instant is $i = (E - e)/R$, where E is the external emf available in the circuit, e is the back emf generated by the motion of the galvanometer coil, and R is the total circuit resistance, including that of the galvanometer. The power appearing as heat is i^2R, and the power converted to mechanical power is ei. The mechanical power may be written as $(eE - e^2)/R$ if we substitute for i, and if we take its maximum value with respect to e we have

$$\frac{d}{de}\left(\frac{eE - e^2}{R}\right) = \frac{1}{R}(E - 2e) = 0$$

from which $e = E/2$ at the maximum.

The maximum power available for mechanical work, i.e. the maximum rate at which the energy available from the circuit can be converted into mechanical energy and stored as potential energy in the suspension, is

$$\frac{1}{R}\left(\frac{E^2}{2} - \frac{E^2}{4}\right) = \frac{E^2}{4R}$$

The energy that is actually stored in the suspension at the completion of the deflection is

$$\frac{U\theta_F^{\,2}}{2} = \frac{G^2E^2}{2R^2U}, \quad \text{since} \quad \theta_F = \frac{GE}{RU}$$

Now, since $T_0 = 2\pi\sqrt{P/U}$, we may write $U = 4\pi^2P/T_0^{\,2}$; and the stored energy becomes $G^2E^2T_0^{\,2}/(2\pi R^2 \cdot 4\pi P)$. Also

$$\gamma = \gamma_0 + \frac{G^2}{A_cR}$$

and, since $A_c = 4\pi P/T_0$, we may write

$$\gamma - \gamma_0 = \frac{G^2T_0}{4\pi PR}$$

Making this substitution, we have finally that the potential energy stored in the suspension is

$$\frac{E^2(\gamma - \gamma_0)T_0}{2\pi R}$$

Now this potential energy is stored in the suspension during the time required for the galvanometer to deflect from its zero position to its first passage through θ_F. Let this time be T_d. The maximum amount of energy which can be made available during the time T_d is $E^2T_d/4R$. The ratio of the energy stored during the interval T_d to the maximum energy available may be considered to be the efficiency with which the galvanometer, acting as a motor, converts electrical energy into mechanical energy. Thus the efficiency is

$$\text{eff} = \frac{2}{\pi}\frac{T_0}{T_d}(\gamma - \gamma_0)$$

Actually we are not usually concerned with the deflection to better than 1%, so that in practice we may define T_d as the time required for the galvanometer deflection to arrive at a value within 1% of the final deflection. We can thus include the critically damped case as well as the underdamped condition.

In Fig. 5, T_d/T_0 and efficiency are plotted against γ. It will be seen that the motor efficiency of a galvanometer is maximum at a damping somewhat less than critical and that the maximum is greater, the lower the value of the open-circuit damping γ_0. Actually, the criterion of "greatest efficiency" leads to an optimum value of damping not greatly different from the criterion of "minimum reading time." For most high-sensitivity galvanometers which have an appreciable open-circuit damping the motor efficiency will not be far from its maximum value if we operate at a relative damping of about 0.8.

Determination of Relative Damping

The external circuit resistance (CDRX) needed to produce critical damping is usually stated by the maker, and the user is thus provided with an approximate value to which it is desirable to adjust the resistance connected to the terminals of the galvanometer for "best" operation. However, it should be borne in mind that the critical damping resistance will be changed if the galvanometer suspension is repaired or replaced, since relative damping is a function of the elastic properties of the suspension, among other things. Also, we can benefit by adjusting the damping to a value somewhat lower than critical (for which the resistance is somewhat higher). Fortunately it is possible to determine quickly and simply both the open-circuit damping and the circuit resistance required for *any* desired damping.

It will be recalled that in originally formulating the equation of motion we combined two damping terms. One of these (K) represented open-circuit damping. The other (G^2/R) represented electromagnetic damping

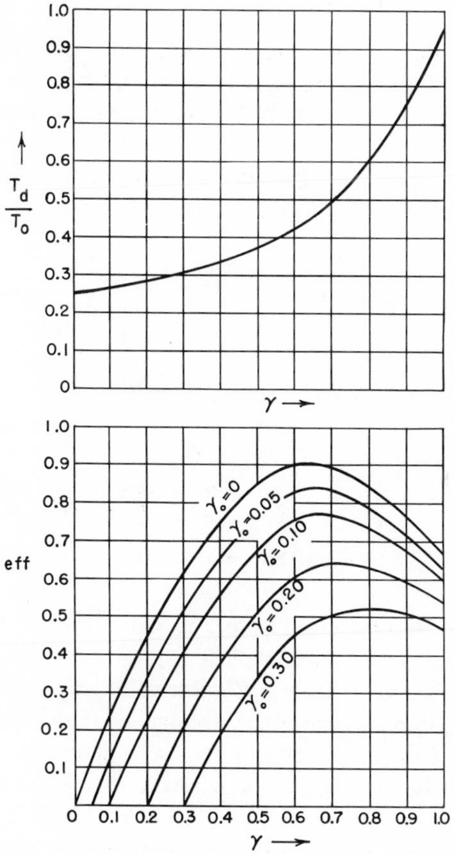

FIG. 5.

resulting from the back emf generated in the coil acting in a circuit of resistance R. Thus, any damping (A_1) can be expressed as $A_1 = K + (G^2/R_1)$. If this expression be divided by A_c, the damping constant associated with critical damping, we have

$$\gamma_1 = \frac{A_1}{A_c} = \frac{K}{A_c} + \frac{G^2}{R_1 A_c} = \gamma_0 + \frac{G^2}{R_1 A_c}$$

where γ_0 is the relative damping on open circuit. Similarly, $\gamma_x = \gamma_0 + (G^2/R_x A_c)$ is the relative damping associated with any circuit resistance (R_x). If we rearrange these equations and divide the first by the second, we have

$$\frac{\gamma_1 - \gamma_0}{\gamma_x - \gamma_0} = \frac{R_x}{R_1} \quad \text{or} \quad R_x = R_1 \frac{\gamma_1 - \gamma_0}{\gamma_x - \gamma_0}$$

This equation enables us to compute the circuit resistance (R_x) needed for any value of relative damping (γ_x) in terms of the open-circuit damping, and the damping associated with a particular, arbitrarily selected circuit resistance.

γ_0 and γ_1 can be experimentally determined, using the circuit shown in Fig. 6. The values of resistances R_a and R_b must be such that only a

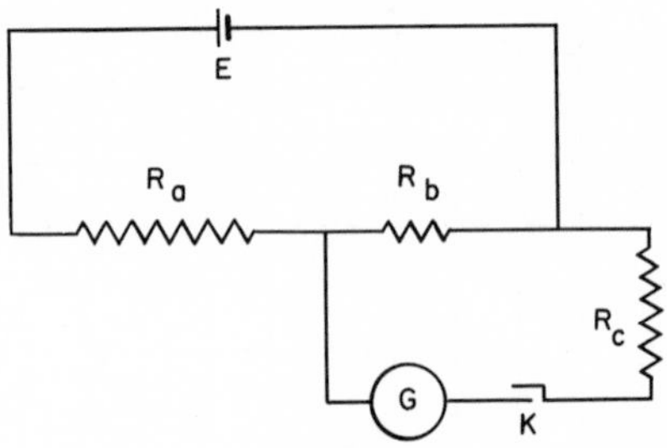

FIG. 6.

very small voltage is introduced into the galvanometer circuit. This voltage, $R_bE/(R_a + R_b)$, should be sufficient to give a deflection of 10 cm or more on the galvanometer scale. If a low value, say 1 ohm, is assigned to R_b, R_a can be computed from the voltage E of the battery and the voltage sensitivity of the galvanometer to give a deflection of convenient size. Since R_a will be very large compared to R_b, the resistance of the galvanometer circuit will be $R = R_b + R_c + R_g$. The only restriction that need be imposed on R is that it be greater than the critical damping resistance of the galvanometer so that, when the key K is closed, the first maximum deflection will be greater than the final deflection by a measurable amount. (An overshoot of 10 to 20% will be found convenient to work with.) It is helpful if R_c be made adjustable, so that the overshoot can be adjusted. If now, with R_a, R_b, and R_c set at the desired values and the galvanometer at rest at zero deflection, the key is closed, the initial maximum (θ_1) and the final deflection (θ_F) (after the oscillatory motion has died out) may be observed. Then the key may be opened and the initial overswing past zero (θ_2) may be observed on open circuit.

From the last two observations (θ_F, θ_2) the open-circuit damping (γ_0) may be computed by the formula

$$-\log_\varepsilon \frac{\theta_2}{\theta_F} = \frac{\pi\gamma_0}{\sqrt{1-\gamma_0^2}}$$

and from the first and second observations (θ_1, θ_F) the total damping (γ_1)

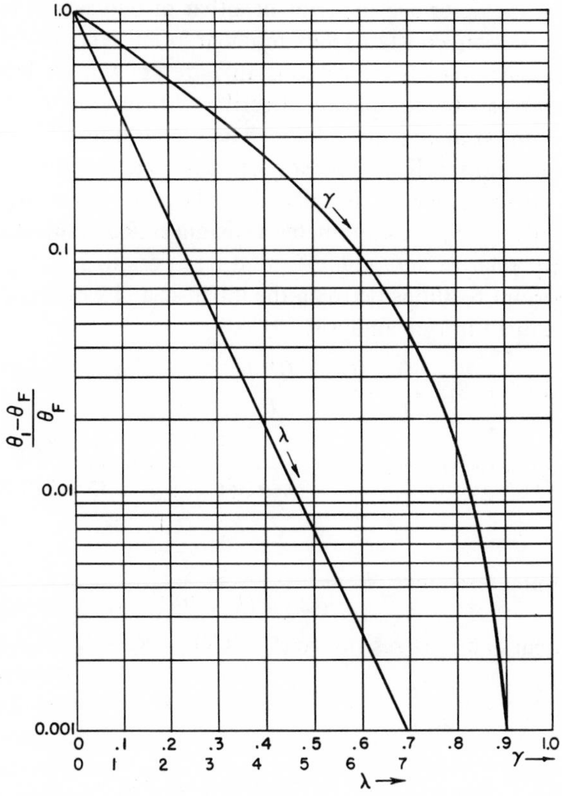

FIG. 7.

corresponding to the circuit resistance $R_1 = R_b + R_c + R_g$ may be computed by the formula

$$-\log_\varepsilon \frac{\theta_1 - \theta_F}{\theta_F} = \frac{\pi\gamma_1}{\sqrt{1-\gamma_1^2}}$$

Figure 7 shows the relation between relative overshoot and relative damping, or, alternatively, logarithmic decrement. With these values

(γ_0, γ_1, and R_1) the circuit resistance (R_x) corresponding to any damping (γ_x) may be computed by the formula

$$R_x = R_1 \frac{\gamma_1 - \gamma_0}{\gamma_x - \gamma_0}$$

Galvanometer Constants

Relations between Design and Working Constants. Galvanometer performance can be described in terms of either of two sets of constants. If the intrinsic, design constants (P, moment of inertia; A, damping; U, torsion constant; and G, motor constant) are known, the behavior of the galvanometer can be completely described for any condition of use and it becomes an *absolute* instrument. These constants are not usually known accurately and are, for the most part, tedious to determine. Hence galvanometer performance is usually described in terms of *working* constants [sensitivity, S; galvanometer resistance, R_g; critical damping resistance, R_c (or relative damping, γ); and free period, T_0].

Certain important relations between the intrinsic and working constants have been developed in our analysis.

Current sensitivity, $S_i = \dfrac{\theta}{I} = \dfrac{G}{U} = \dfrac{BNlb}{U}$

Critical damping resistance, $R_c = \dfrac{G^2}{2\sqrt{PU}(1-\gamma_0)} = \dfrac{G^2 T_0}{4\pi P(1-\gamma_0)}$

If $\gamma_0 \ll 1$,

Critical damping resistance, $R_c \approx \dfrac{G^2}{2\sqrt{PU}} \approx \dfrac{G^2 T_0}{4\pi P}$

External critical damping resistance (CDRX) $= R_c - R_g$

Free period, $T_0 = 2\pi \sqrt{\dfrac{P}{U}}$

Actual period, $T = \dfrac{T_0}{\sqrt{1-\gamma^2}}$, for relative damping γ

The voltage sensitivity may also be readily derived. After the steady state is established $U\theta = GE/R$, so that voltage sensitivity, $S_e = \theta/E = G/UR$. At critical damping the voltage sensitivity is

$${}_cS_e = \frac{G}{UR_c} = \frac{2(1-\gamma_0)\sqrt{PU}}{GU} = \frac{T_0}{\pi G}(1-\gamma_0) \approx \frac{T_0}{\pi G} \quad \text{if} \quad \gamma_0 \ll 1$$

For a galvanometer of a given type and period, such that we can consider P, U, T_0, and B fixed, coils can be interchanged; i.e. we may vary the size of wire and the number of turns in the coil. We will assume that the cross section of the coil is fixed and that the space factor of the winding is constant; i.e. the fraction of the total cross section taken up by the conductors is independent of the size of the wire. Then we may say that Na = constant C_1, where N = turns and a = cross section of wire. The coil resistance is then

$$R_g = \frac{NC_2}{a} = \frac{C_1C_2}{a^2}$$

where C_2 is a constant whose value depends on the resistivity of the wire and the dimensions of the coil. We can write

$$a^2 = \frac{C_1C_2}{R_g}, \quad \text{and} \quad N = \sqrt{\frac{C_1}{C_2}} \cdot \sqrt{R_g}$$

The current sensitivity is

$$S_i = \frac{G}{U} = \frac{BNlb}{U} = \frac{Blb}{U}\sqrt{\frac{C_1}{C_2}} \cdot \sqrt{R_g} = C_i\sqrt{R_g}$$

If we assume that the circuit resistance is maintained at the value needed for critical damping

$$R_c = \frac{G^2}{2\sqrt{PU}(1-\gamma_0)} = \frac{(Blb)^2N^2}{2\sqrt{PU}(1-\gamma_0)} = \frac{(Blb)^2}{2\sqrt{PU}(1-\gamma_0)} \cdot \frac{C_1}{C_2} R_g = C_d R_g$$

At critical damping the voltage sensitivity is

$${}_cS_e = \frac{S_i}{R_c} = \frac{C_i}{C_d} \cdot \frac{1}{\sqrt{R_g}} = \frac{C_e}{\sqrt{R_g}}$$

From these relations we can state that, if the field in the air gap (B) and the free period (T_0) are fixed in value, then (1) the current sensitivity of the galvanometer is proportional to $\sqrt{R_g}$; (2) the voltage sensitivity is inversely proportional to $\sqrt{R_g}$; and (3) the circuit resistance required to maintain critical damping is proportional to the coil resistance. Reference to the equation connecting circuit resistance and relative damping establishes (2) and (3) for any constant value of damping since the open-circuit damping (γ_0) is not a function of R_g.

If a high current sensitivity is desired in a particular type of galvanometer whose air-gap flux and whose free period are fixed, we should use a high coil resistance (many turns of fine wire). On the other hand, if high voltage sensitivity is desired in a particular type of galvanometer, the coil resistance should be low (few turns of coarse wire), providing the circuit resistance is adjusted to keep the relative damping at a constant value. In any case the circuit resistance needed for constant damping with our "fixed type" of galvanometer is directly proportional to the coil resistance.

Parameters Controlling Performance. From the relations between intrinsic and working constants it will be apparent that there are a number of parameters whose variations control the performance of the galvanometer.

CIRCUIT RESISTANCE. Shunt or series resistance may be used to change damping. Such changes affect voltage sensitivity but do not of themselves affect current sensitivity. The addition of series resistance decreases the deflection resulting from a given emf in the circuit. Current sensitivity is unaffected since it is defined in terms of current in the galvanometer coil, but a shunt resistance does, of course, decrease the response of the instrument to a given current *in the circuit.*

FIELD STRENGTH. If the field in the air gap is changed, the sensitivities and the critical damping resistance are affected. A decrease in the field decreases the current sensitivity, decreases the critical damping resistance, and decreases damping resulting from a given circuit resistance. Magnetic shunts are sometimes used in high-sensitivity galvanometers to control performance.

SUSPENSIONS. A change in the stiffness of the suspension changes sensitivity, critical damping resistance, and period. A decrease in U increases the current sensitivity, the period, and the critical damping resistance (increasing the relative damping of a given circuit resistance).

Approximate values of torsional moments for suspensions may be computed from the formulas

$$\frac{M_t}{\theta} = \frac{\pi d^4 F}{32l} \text{ for wire of circular cross section}$$

and

$$\frac{M_t}{\theta} = \frac{\gamma b h^3 F}{l} \text{ for rectangular cross section}$$

where M_t = torsional moment required to twist the suspension through an angle θ in radians.

l = length of suspension.

d = diameter of circular wire.

b = width and h = thickness of suspension of rectangular cross section.

F = torsional modulus of the suspension material.

$$\gamma = 0.141 \quad 0.228 \quad 0.281 \quad 0.312 \quad 0.333$$

$$\text{for} \quad \frac{b}{h} = 1 \quad 2 \quad 4 \quad 10 \quad \infty.$$

If we assume a constant length and cross section for the suspension (i.e. a constant resistance), we find from the above formulas that the stiffness of the suspension is greatest when its cross section is circular, and that the stiffness measured by the torque required to twist it through a fixed angle decreases as its width is made large compared to its thickness, as shown in Table 1.

TABLE 1

Cross Section	*Stiffness*
Circular	1
$b = h$	0.88
$b = 2h$	0.72
$b = 4h$	0.44
$b = 10h$	0.20

Phosphor-bronze, 14K gold, 24K gold, and copper ribbon are used as suspension material. For very delicate suspensions quartz fibers are sometimes used, the current leads to the moving coil being loosely coiled gold ligaments which increase the suspension stiffness by 10% or less. Very fine tungsten wire is sometimes used. It is instructive to compare the stiffness of various types and sizes of suspensions on the basis of a constant length. Table 2 gives such a comparison for suspensions having circular sections.

TABLE 2

Material	*Diameter,* microns	*Torsional* Modulus,* dynes/cm²	*Torque per Radian for* 10-*cm Length,* dyne-cm/radian
Fused quartz	3	6.6×10^{11}	5×10^{-5}
" "	5	5.8 "	3×10^{-4}
" "	10	4.8 "	5×10^{-3}
" "	15	4.2 "	2×10^{-2}
" "	20	3.9 "	6×10^{-2}
" "	30	3.5 "	3×10^{-1}
" "	50	3.3 "	2
Tungsten	10	15×10^{11}	1.5×10^{-2}
Copper	18 (0.7 mil)	4.2×10^{11}	4×10^{-2}
"	25 (1 mil)	"	1.8×10^{-1}
"	37 (1.5 mil)	"	1
Gold (24K)	18	2.6×10^{11}	3×10^{-2}
"	25	"	1.1×10^{-1}
"	37	"	6×10^{-1}
"	50 (2 mil)	"	1.6
Phosphor-bronze	60	5×10^{11}	6.4
"	80	"	20

* Values for torsional modulus of fused quartz from Reinkober, *Phys. Zeits.*, **38,** 112 (1937). Values for other materials from various sources.

Keinath states[8] that Siemens and Halske use 60- to 80-micron phosphor-bronze wire rolled to a thickness of 18 to 25 μ and a width of 250 μ (0.25 mm) as suspension material. The corresponding moments of torque for these thicknesses would be 2 to 6 dyne-cm/radian for a 10-cm length.

Leeds and Northrup list[9] (Table 3) the characteristics of a number of suspension materials after rolling to flat ribbons. (The characteristics of the corresponding wire before rolling will be found in Table 2 for some cases.)

TABLE 3

Material	*Unrolled Diameter,* mils	(*For 10-cm Length*) *Torsion after Rolling,* dyne-cm/radian	*Resistance,* ohms for 10 cm
Gold (14K)	1.5	0.16	14.0
,,	2	0.49	7.0
,,	2.5	1.40	5.0
,,	3	2.05	3.5
,,	4	7.30	1.8
Gold (24K)	0.7	0.006	9
,,	1	0.022	4
,,	1.5	0.049	2.5
,,	2	0.22	1.0
Copper	0.7	0.006	8.0
,,	1	0.02	3.5
,,	1.3	0.034	3.0
,,	1.5	0.049	2.2
,,	2	0.22	0.9

In these cases the rolling is continued until the strip shows the desired value of torsion when tested.

Changes in U are possible in some galvanometers without a change in the suspension, by the introduction of either a magnetic or a gravitational control force. The former is used by the General Electric Company in a fluxmeter. The latter is used in a high-sensitivity galvanometer designed by Wenner. In this galvanometer the suspension is taut and the center of mass is deliberately displaced from the axis of rotation. A gravity control is thus added which may be varied in magnitude as the galvanometer is tilted from its level position so that the axis of rotation makes an angle with the vertical. The variation in U is sufficient to change the period from 5 to 15 seconds with a corresponding gain in current sensitivity of 9 times.[10] (In this galvanometer a magnetic shunt is also

[8] Keinath, *Die Technik elektrischer Messgeräte*, vol. 1, p. 28.

[9] Data in Table 3 are reproduced by permission of the Leeds and Northrup Company, from *Notes on Moving Coil Galvanometers*, p. 10, 1947.

[10] It should be noted that the usable voltage sensitivity has been increased by only 3 times, since the resistance needed to maintain a constant relative damping is proportional to the period and is increased by a factor of 3.

provided with which critical damping resistance may be adjusted as needed. This latter adjustment of course changes sensitivity at the same time.)

DAMPING. This may be increased by attaching an auxiliary short-circuited loop to the coil or by winding the coil on a metal form which acts as a short-circuited turn. In either case the moment of inertia is increased so that the period as well as the damping is affected.

MOMENT OF INERTIA. The moment of inertia may be changed by altering the weight or shape of the moving coil, thus changing the free period and the damping.

It will be seen that the adjustments tabulated above are not independent. Usually more than one effect results from any change made on a parameter. In general the design of a galvanometer is a compromise which must result from the multiple effects, on the working constants, of any change in the intrinsic constants. For example, if we increase B in order to increase sensitivity, then the circuit resistance needed for critical damping is increased since $R_c \propto B^2$, and a circuit of fixed resistance which was previously properly damped will be more highly damped. A decrease in U to increase sensitivity will increase the damping of a given circuit resistance, and will at the same time increase the period of the galvanometer, making the response both slower and more sluggish. If we wish to increase sensitivity while retaining the damping characteristics of a particular circuit it is necessary to adjust both B and U. However, even this compromise will increase the period.

Zero Stability of Sensitive Galvanometers

We have already seen that in a taut-suspension galvanometer an unsymmetrical weight distribution results in a gravity-control factor when the axis of rotation is not vertical. If this factor is in a direction to oppose the elastic control from the suspension, then, as the gravity and elastic controls approach each other in magnitude, U would become vanishingly small and the zero would become unstable since no restoring torque would be available to return the moving system to its zero position after a displacement. Most laboratory galvanometers are therefore constructed so that the moving system is carried by the upper suspension only, while the lower suspension is loosely coiled so that it serves as a current lead but does not contribute appreciably to the control torque. In this way the response is made relatively insensitive to galvanometer level. However, because of the limited clearances in the air gap the possible tilt is limited to small values such that the coil will move freely in the air gap. This construction is practical therefore only for galvanometers that can be rather carefully leveled. It is not feasible for galvanometers in which the level may change through more than a small angle. In portable galvanometers, and in galvanometers intended for marine applications, taut suspensions must be used in order to keep the coil centered in the air gap. Here special care must be taken to balance the moving system about the axis of rotation and so reduce gravity control to a negligible factor for departures of the axis from the vertical.

A second cause of instability is the presence of magnetic impurities in the coil. In a truly radial field magnetic impurities would be unimportant, but this ideal is never completely realized. The combination of traces of magnetic material in the coil together with the unavoidable irregularities in the air-gap field produces a torque which may become an appreciable control factor in sensitive galvanometers (where U is small). The higher the sensitivity of the instrument, the greater becomes the tendency to instability resulting from magnetic contamination of the coil. In modern sensitive galvanometers precautions are taken to eliminate magnetic impurities from the copper with which the coil is wound and from the enamel with which it is insulated. Silk is never used for insulation as it contains traces of magnetic material. In this connection it is important to note that all possible precautions should be taken to avoid magnetic contamination when opening a galvanometer for repair or adjustment. Such work should be done in a clean, dust-free place since dust (particularly in an industrial area) is very apt to carry magnetic contamination.

A third factor which must be considered is the possibility of inelastic yield in the suspension. This depends on the modulus of the suspension material and the fiber stress at which it operates. As finer suspensions are used to increase sensitivity one may approach the elastic limit of the suspension material, in which case the inelastic yield may be quite pronounced. As a result the zero may be shifted when the moving system returns from a deflection. In some galvanometer designs which aim at very high sensitivity, fine quartz filaments are used for suspensions because of their good elastic properties. The current leads to the galvanometer are very fine, loosely coiled gold ligaments which provide only a small fraction of the control torque.

Another effect which is closely allied to zero instability, and which may be just as troublesome in a galvanometer having high voltage sensitivity, is the presence of parasitic thermal emf's either in the galvanometer itself or in the circuit to which it is connected. In sensitive galvanometers materials must be avoided which have an appreciable thermal emf against copper. In some cases the entire electrical circuit of the galvanometer, including the suspensions, is of copper. Generally disturbances from thermal emf in the galvanometer can be reduced by thermal insulation. The galvanometer should not be exposed to air currents or to radiation from a source of heat. Sometimes, where the location makes such exposure unavoidable, the instrument may advantageously be wrapped in cotton batting, leaving exposed only the portion of the window required by the optical system. Of course this does not eliminate disturbances from parasitic thermal emf in circuits connected to the galvanometer, and, where high voltage sensitivity is required, precautions must be taken to eliminate such parasites from the entire galvanometer circuit.

Sensitivity Limit

It was first pointed out by Ising[11] in 1926 that a theoretical limit to galvanometer sensitivity is set by the Brownian motion of the moving system. Even though the galvanometer is so located that it is entirely free from mechanical or electrical disturbances, and from zero instability in the usual sense of the word, its moving system will still show a small continuous random motion as a result of continuous bombardment by the molecules of the air around it. In the usual case these motions are exceedingly small, but their presence can be demonstrated by means of the amplifying device which will be described later. The conditions controlling this residual motion were stated more precisely by Barnes and Silverman[12] in 1934. In any mechanical system which is constrained by some force to motion about an equilibrium position, it can be shown that there is a mean kinetic energy of $\frac{1}{2}KT$ associated with each degree of freedom of the system. This is a necessary consequence of the law of equipartition of energy.

In the particular case of the galvanometer, the moving system has one degree of freedom, that of rotation about its equilibrium position. If θ be the angular deflection from the equilibrium position, we must expect that the moving system will oscillate with a Brownian movement of such magnitude that $\frac{1}{2}U\bar{\theta}^2 = \frac{1}{2}KT = W$, where $\bar{\theta} =$ the mean (rms) deflection, U is the control force, and $\frac{1}{2}KT$ is the average kinetic energy per degree of freedom, of an air molecule at the temperature T. Now at ordinary room temperature (20°C) W is approximately 2×10^{-14} erg, and we can write

$$\bar{\theta} = \sqrt{\frac{2W}{U}} = \sqrt{\frac{4 \times 10^{-14}}{U}}$$

This can be expressed in terms of the working constants of the galvanometer: relative damping, γ; circuit resistance, R; and the galvanometer

[11] Ising, Natural Limit for the Sensibility of Galvanometers, *Phil. Mag.* (7th Series), **1**, 827 (1926).

[12] Barnes and Silverman, Brownian Movement as a Natural Limit to All Measuring Processes, *Rev. Mod. Physics*, **6**, No. 3 (July, 1934).

current $\bar{i}$ corresponding to the deflection $\bar{\theta}$. We have seen that the current sensitivity

$$S_i = \frac{G}{U} = \frac{\delta\theta}{\delta i} = \frac{\bar{\theta}}{\bar{i}}$$

and that for any damping $A = (G^2/R) + K$. If we divide this latter expression by the critical damping constant $A_c = 4\pi P/T_0$, we may write

$$\frac{G^2}{RA_c} = \frac{A}{A_c} - \frac{K}{A_c}, \quad \text{or} \quad G^2 = \frac{4\pi P}{T_0} R(\gamma - \gamma_0)$$

Now

$$S_i = \frac{G}{U} = \sqrt{\frac{4\pi PR}{T_0 U^2}(\gamma - \gamma_0)}$$

and since $P/U = T_0^2/4\pi^2$ we may write

$$S_i = \sqrt{\frac{T_0}{2\pi} \cdot \frac{R}{U} \cdot 2(\gamma - \gamma_0)}$$

But

$$\bar{i} = \frac{\bar{\theta}}{S_i} = \sqrt{\frac{2W}{U} \cdot \frac{2\pi}{T_0} \cdot \frac{U}{R} \cdot \frac{1}{2(\gamma - \gamma_0)}} = \sqrt{\frac{2\pi W}{T_0 R(\gamma - \gamma_0)}}$$

If $\bar{i}$ is in amperes and R in ohms, we must express W in joules, so that we may say

$$\bar{i} = \sqrt{\frac{2\pi \cdot 2 \times 10^{-21}}{T_0 R(\gamma - \gamma_0)}} = 1.12 \times 10^{-10} \sqrt{\frac{1}{T_0 R(\gamma - \gamma_0)}} \text{ ampere}$$

Also, since the corresponding voltage in the galvanometer circuit is $\bar{e} = \bar{i}R$, we have

$$\bar{e} = 1.12 \times 10^{-10} \sqrt{\frac{R}{T_0(\gamma - \gamma_0)}} \text{ volt}$$

It will be obvious that one cannot discriminate between a deflection $\bar{\theta}$ (the rms random departure of the moving element from its equilibrium position) caused by Brownian movement and the same deflection caused by the presence of an emf $\bar{e}$ in the galvanometer circuit. We must therefore inquire into the frequency of occurrence of purely random deflections of various magnitudes. On this basis it will be possible to decide whether a particular deflection which we observe results from the action of molecular forces or from the presence of a *measurable* voltage in the galvanometer circuit.

The probability that a particular deflection $\theta \geq a\bar{\theta}$ can be deduced from the laws of probability.[13] This probability is plotted in Fig. 8 for various values of a. From the figure and table it will be seen that the "Brownian" deflection will exceed $\bar{\theta}$ about $\frac{1}{3}$ of the time, and that it will exceed $3.3\bar{\theta}$ only $\frac{1}{1000}$ of the time. The chance that it will exceed $4\bar{\theta}$ is so small as to be entirely negligible. We can therefore say that if the

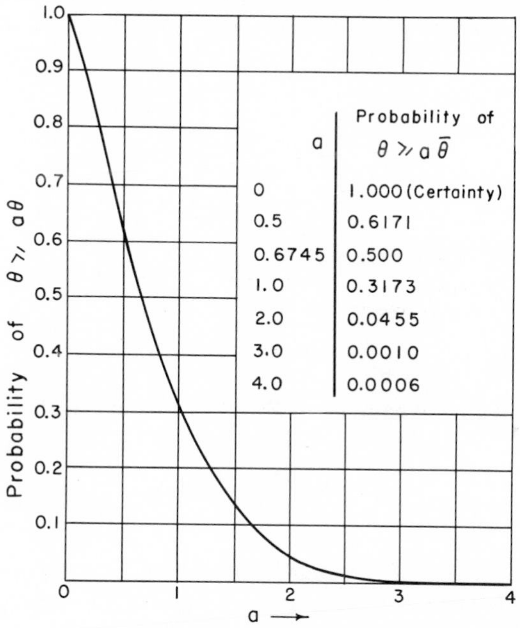

FIG. 8.

observed deflection is as much as $4\bar{\theta}$ we can be certain that it is caused by an emf in the circuit, or we say that an emf of $4\bar{e}$ can be detected with certainty. The selection of this value ($4\bar{e}$) is, of course, arbitrary; and it

[13] If we observe the random Brownian motion of the galvanometer over a long time, the magnitude of the deflection $|\theta|$ will be greater than the average $|\theta_{avg}|$ half the time and less than the average half the time. In other words the probability that the average deflection will be exceeded at any particular instant is $\frac{1}{2}$. It can be shown that the rms deflection $\bar{\theta}$ is about $\frac{3}{2}$ as great as the average θ_{avg}. This can be more exactly stated as $\bar{\theta} = 1.4826\ldots\theta_{avg}$. [See Deming and Birge, Statistical Theory of Errors, *Rev. Mod. Physics*, **6**, No. 3, 125 (July 1934).] The probability of $\theta \geqslant \bar{\theta}$ can be evaluated from a table of values of the probability integral $\left(\frac{2}{\pi}\int_0^{\theta/\theta_{avg}} \varepsilon^{-t^2}\,dt\right)$ and is found to be $P = 0.3173$. In other words the rms deflection $\bar{\theta}$ will be exceeded nearly $\frac{1}{3}$ of the time. The probability of $\theta \geqslant a\bar{\theta}$ can be similarly evaluated for any value of a.

will be apparent that if the galvanometer deflection is continuously recorded, so that a running average of the deflection can be taken, we can, over a fairly short time interval, detect with certainty the presence in the circuit of an emf smaller than $4\bar{e}$, perhaps even as small as $\bar{e}$ if the observations be continued for a sufficient time. However, the value $e_{\min} \approx 4 \times 10^{-10} \sqrt{R_c/T_0}$ volt is a sufficiently good approximation to the smallest emf that can be detected with certainty by a single observation with a *critically damped* galvanometer whose period is T_0 and whose

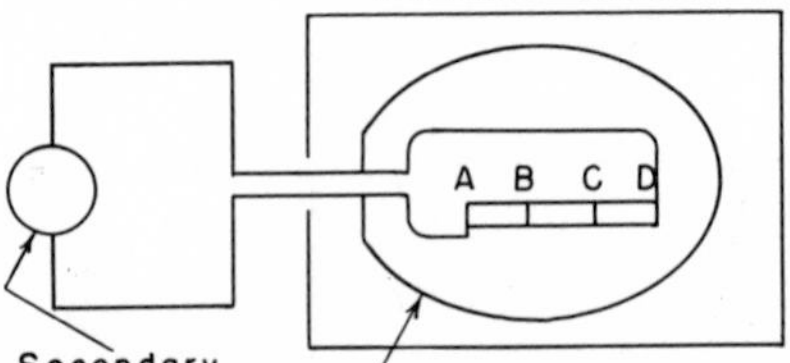

FIG. 9.

circuit resistance at critical damping is R_c. For example, if $R_c = 100$ ohms and $T_0 = 4$ sec,

$$e_{\min} = 4 \times 10^{-10} \sqrt{\frac{100}{4}} = 2 \times 10^{-9} \text{ volt}^{14}$$

Actually, the magnitude of the Brownian motion of a galvanometer is usually exceedingly small. If we assume a value of $U = 10^{-6}$ dyne-cm/radian, such as might be characteristic of a delicate quartz-fiber suspension, the relation $\frac{1}{2}U\theta^2 = 2 \times 10^{-14}$ erg leads to a value of $\bar{\theta} = 2 \times 10^{-4}$ radian, or 0.2 mm on a scale at a meter distance.

Amplification of Deflection. (*a*) THE THERMO-RELAY of Moll and Burger[15] may be used to amplify small deflections of a moderately sensitive galvanometer to the limit fixed by its Brownian motion.

The thermo-relay, shown schematically in Fig. 9, consists of a strip thermocouple in an evacuated glass tube. The parts AB and CD are of constantan, and the part BC is of manganin. If a strong beam of light

[14] It may be noted that a similar physical limit exists to the attainable sensitivity of any measuring device. This limit may be set by Brownian motion, or by one of the related effects such as the Shot effect (the small, irregular changes in magnitude of current in a vacuum tube resulting from random fluctuations of emission from the cathode) or the Johnson effect (an emf resulting from thermal agitation of electrons in a conductor) (see Barnes and Silverman, *op. cit.*).

[15] Moll and Burger, *Phil. Mag.*, **50**, 624 (1925).

from a primary galvanometer strikes the strip *BC* exactly at its midpoint, thermojunctions *B* and *C* will be heated to the same temperature. The resultant thermal emf will be zero, and the secondary galvanometer in the relay circuit will not be deflected. A small deflection of the primary galvanometer will displace the light spot toward one of the junctions (*B* or *C*). The temperature of this junction will be raised above that of the other, and the resultant thermal emf will deflect the secondary galvanometer. The response time of the relay is small (about 2.5 sec) as a result of the low heat capacity of the strip (thickness = 0.001 mm). Amplification may be made sufficient to attain the Brownian limit of sensitivity with a moderately sensitive primary galvanometer having a stable zero and

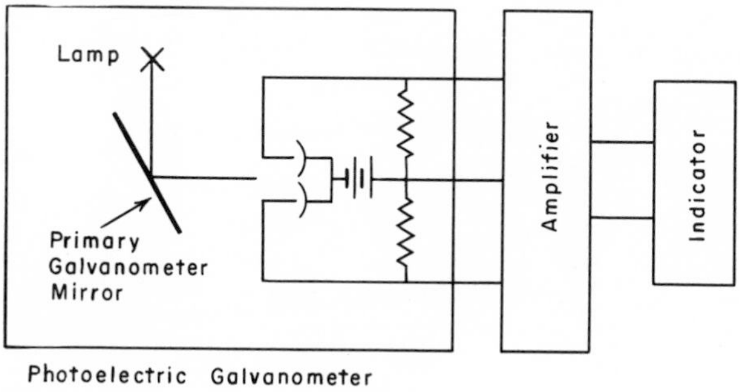

FIG. 10.

mounted so that it is entirely free from mechanical disturbances. If the displacement of the light spot over the thermocouple strip is not more than 1 mm, the deflections of the secondary galvanometer are proportional to those of the primary instrument.

(*b*) THE PHOTOELECTRIC GALVANOMETER, recently described as a commercial instrument (Rubicon, *Bull.* 360) uses the photoelectric effect to amplify the deflections of a stable taut-suspension galvanometer. As shown in Fig. 10, the light beam from the primary galvanometer is focused on a double-cathode photocell. The displacement of the galvanometer light beam produces a signal in the photocell bridge circuit which is approximately 3×10^6 times the emf applied to the primary instrument. This signal may be further amplified for indication on a secondary galvanometer, for operating a recorder or for control applications. For effective operation mechanical stability of the optical system and thermal stability of the galvanometer are very important. These features have been attained by rigid mounting of the optical assembly and galvanometer element to heavy Duralumin plates which also serve as portions of a thermal shield enclosing the entire assembly.

Commercial Galvanometers

Tables 4 to 10 list the working constants of commercial galvanometers, including most of those found in recent catalogs of two American[16] manufacturers and one European[17] manufacturer. It will be noted that in most cases only the voltage or current sensitivity is given, depending on whether the instrument was designed primarily for voltage or current applications. However, since the voltage is always assumed to be impressed on a circuit consisting of the galvanometer together with its external critical damping resistance, both sensitivities can be computed from data given in the table for any particular instrument.

TABLE 4

POINTER-TYPE GALVANOMETERS, PORTABLE, FIXED SCALE, TAUT SUSPENSIONS

R_g, ohms	T_0, sec	Sensitivity		Scale Factor		Critical Damping Resistance (External), ohms
		Voltage, scale div. per μv	Current, scale div. per μa	Voltage, μv per scale div.	Current, μa per scale div.	
10	1.5		0.3		3.5	100
10	2	0.01	..	100	..	8
30		..	0.33	..	3	70
300		..	1	..	1	1,000
1,100		..	2	..	0.5	3,500
12	2.5	0.016	..	64	..	20
25	3	..	1	..	1	110
250		..	4	..	0.25	1,800
2,500		..	8	..	0.125	10,000
16	4.5	0.022	..	46	..	30

Attention is called to the tabulation of scale factor, in addition to the sensitivity, which has been defined in the preceding discussion as the ratio of "response" to "stimulus." Scale factor may be defined as the stimulus necessary to evoke standard response and represents the numeric by

16 Leeds and Northrup Company, Philadelphia, Pa.; Rubicon Company, Philadelphia, Pa.

17 Kipp und Zonen, Delft, Holland (American representative, James G. Biddle, Philadelphia, Pa.).

TABLE 5

PORTABLE, MIRROR-LAMP-INTEGRAL SCALE, TAUT SUSPENSION

R_g, ohms	T_0, sec	Sensitivity		Scale Factor		CDRX, ohms
		Voltage, scale div. per μv	Current, scale div. per μa	Voltage, μv per scale div.	Current, μa per scale div.	
13	2	0.4	..	2.5	..	13
25		0.18	..	5.5	..	50
200		..	30	..	0.03	600
350		..	80	..	0.012	2,500
1,100	2.5	..	40	..	0.025	8,000
1,100		..	140	..	0.007	8,000
23	3	0.04	..	25	..	80
300		..	25	..	0.04	2,000–10,000
500		..	250	..	0.004	6,000
1,000		..	40	..	0.025	15,000
1,100		..	200	..	0.005	10,000
30	4	0.67	..	1.5	..	40
40	5	..	100	..	0.01	225
60		..	200	..	0.005	600
500		..	670	..	0.0015	10,000
1,500	6	..	1,700	..	0.0006	40,000

TABLE 6

PORTABLE, MIRROR-DETACHED SCALE, TAUT SUSPENSION

13	2	0.57	..	1.75	..	12
25		0.25	..	4	..	50
200		..	50	..	0.02	600
350		..	100	..	0.01	2,000
1,100	2.5	..	170	..	0.006	8,000
350	3	..	200	..	0.005	3,000
500		..	330	..	0.003	6,000
1,100		..	330	..	0.003	10,000
30	4	1	..	1	..	40
40	5	..	140	..	0.007	225
60		..	250	..	0.004	600
500		..	1,000	..	0.001	10,000
1,500	6	..	2,000	..	0.0005	40,000

TABLE 7

PLATFORM OR WALL TYPE, MIRROR-DETACHED SCALE, SLACK SUSPENSION

R_g, ohms	T_0, sec	Sensitivity		Scale Factor		CDRX, ohms
		Voltage, mm per μv	Current, mm per μa	Voltage, μv per mm	Current, μa per mm	
21	1.5	2	..	0.5	..	40
500		..	125	..	0.008	2,500
500	3	..	330	..	0.003	500
10	5	5	..	0.2	..	25
12		2	..	0.5	..	50
15		10	..	0.1	..	20
16		5	..	0.2	..	40
25		10	..	0.1	..	50
40		..	200	..	0.005	300
50		..	400	..	0.0025	500
500	6	..	2,000	..	0.0005	7,000
650		..	2,000	..	0.0005	10,000
16	7	20	..	0.05	..	10
500		..	3,300	..	0.0003	10,000
17	7.5	10	..	0.1	..	25
12	8	20	..	0.05	..	10
115		..	70	..	0.014	10,000
30	9	2	..	0.5	..	60
12	10	10	..	0.1	..	15
650	11	..	1,000	..	0.001	3,000
35	12	0.67	..	1.5	..	165
2,500		..	2,000	..	0.0005	30,000
650	13	..	10,000	..	0.0001	30,000
500	14	..	10,000	..	0.0001	22,000
1,000		..	1,000	..	0.001	10,000
8,000	18	..	5,000	..	0.0002	46,000
800	20	..	25,000	..	0.00004	70,000
800	40	..	100,000	..	0.00001	100,000

TABLE 8

MARINE TYPE, MIRROR-DETACHED SCALE, TAUT SUSPENSION, ELECTROMAGNETIC FIELD

270	2	..	50	..	0.02	100,000

TABLE 9

PLATFORM TYPE, MIRROR-DETACHED SCALE, MAGNETIC SHUNT-VARIABLE SENSITIVITY, TAUT SUSPENSION

R_g, ohms	T_0, sec	Sensitivity		Scale Factor		CDRX, ohms	
		Voltage, mm per μv	Current, mm per μa	Voltage, μv per mm	Current, μa per mm		
55	1.3	1.7–0.8	100–170	0.6–1.25	0.01–0.006	1–160	
75	2.5	5–2	360–600	0.2–0.5	0.0028–0.0017	1–200	
340	3.5	1.25–0.14	1,250–10,000	0.8–7	0.0008–0.0001	700–70,000	Quartz-fiber suspension
340	7	2.5–0.25	6,000–50,000	0.4–4	0.00017–0.00002	2,000–200,000	

TABLE 10

SAME AS TABLE 9, EXCEPT SLACK QUARTZ-FIBER SUSPENSION

20	1.3	4–2	75–140	0.25–0.5	0.013–0.007	1–50
30	3	0.8–0.3	250–670	0.12–0.35	0.004–0.0015	1–200
45	3	4–1	500–2,000	0.25–1.0	0.002–0.0005	80–200
35	7	16–6	800–2,500	0.06–0.17	0.0012–0.0004	15–400
50	7	6–2.2	1,700–6,700	0.16–0.45	0.0006–0.0015	200–3,000

which scale reading must be multiplied in order to convert the reading to a value in the electrical unit used. This figure has, at various times, been called reciprocal sensitivity, figure of merit, and (through loose usage) sensitivity. The term *scale factor* is used here as a means of avoiding the confusion which results from having reciprocal relations which are both called sensitivity. It will be seen that the term "scale factor" is descriptive of that property of the galvanometer which is the reciprocal of its sensitivity. This nomenclature has the added advantage that a large number will correspond to a high sensitivity, and similarly a large number is associated with a large scale factor. Units used in the table are current in microamperes, voltage in microvolts, and a standard deflection in millimeters. For instruments having separate, detached scales the standard deflection is 1 mm on a scale distant 1 meter from the galvanometer mirror, while for instruments having integral, attached scales the standard deflection is 1 scale division.

Galvanometer Selection. In selecting a galvanometer for a particular measurement job, a number of factors should be considered. Many experimental difficulties may be avoided or minimized if a suitable galvanometer is used.

RESISTANCE. Generally speaking, a high-resistance galvanometer is used with a high-resistance circuit and a low-resistance galvanometer with a low-resistance circuit. However, an exact match between galvanometer and circuit resistance is never necessary and is usually undesirable.

SENSITIVITY. This should be sufficient for the work at hand but should not greatly exceed the requirements of the measurement, for high sensitivity usually implies small restoring force, long period, a more delicate instrument generally, and perhaps zero instability. Where high current sensitivity is required a high-resistance galvanometer is indicated, and where high voltage sensitivity is needed a low-resistance instrument is implied, subject in either case to the damping requirements imposed by the circuit in which the instrument will operate.

DAMPING. Where possible for current and voltage measurements the relative damping should be somewhat less than, or at most equal to, critical. For most applications, a relative damping of about 0.8 can be taken as an optimum value. In general, a galvanometer should be selected whose critical damping resistance is matched reasonably well to the resistance of the circuit in which it will be used. Where this is impossible the operator should plan to use whatever parallel or series resistance is needed to secure proper damping.

PERIOD. To conserve reading time it is desirable that the period of the galvanometer be as short as possible, subject to the limitations imposed by sensitivity requirements. In cases where measured voltage or current is not steady, its variations are more easily followed with a short-period instrument.

FREEDOM FROM MECHANICAL DISTURBANCES. The moving system should be well balanced about its axis of rotation. Where disturbances must be expected the galvanometer mounting should incorporate suitable anti-shock or anti-vibration elements. Precautions should likewise be taken against air currents and sources of heat in selecting a location for the galvanometer. If taut-suspension galvanometers are properly balanced, they are in general less responsive than slack-suspension instruments to mechanical disturbances.

ZERO STABILITY. This may be expected to decrease with increasing sensitivity, both because the residual imperfections, such as lack of symmetry or the presence of magnetic impurities, exercise a larger share of the control as the stiffness of the suspension is decreased, and because the fiber stress in the suspension material may approach its elastic limit for delicate suspensions. Where high voltage sensitivity is required the design of the galvanometer and of the operating circuit must be such as to reduce thermal emf's to a minimum.

STRAY FIELD EFFECTS. The d'Arsonval galvanometer is usually relatively free of trouble from this source. Its coil operates in a field so strong that changes in the local external field have only a small effect on the field in the air gap. However, this consideration is of great importance in types of instruments whose operating field is not so high that stray fields are negligible. In such cases the use of an astatic system or of magnetic shielding is indicated. Moving-magnet galvanometers are sensitive to external fields and must be very carefully shielded.

VISIBILITY AND ACCESSIBILITY OF MOVING SYSTEM. The window in the galvanometer case, through which the moving system may be observed, should be of sufficient size that the mechanical clearance of the coil in the air gap may be seen. In this way the necessary leveling adjustments can be made without opening the galvanometer case. Furthermore, the construction should be such as to facilitate repairs. For the most part such repairs involve either the replacement or the adjustment of the suspensions or the mirror. The design should preferably permit the easy removal from the instrument of the entire moving system (including the suspensions) as a unit for such repairs.

COIL CLAMPING. Any slack-suspension galvanometer has a delicate moving system that must be protected from mechanical injury when the instrument is moved. A suitable device should be provided for clamping the coil and holding it rigidly in place during transport. This coil clamp must be such that it is easily applied and released by an adjustment accessible from outside the case and must not interfere with normal operation. A zero adjustment accessible from outside the case is a necessity. This is usually a device by which the upper suspension abutment can be rotated. It is important that this adjustment be centered on the axis of rotation of the moving system, since the air-gap clearances are usually so small that very little lateral motion of the coil can be tolerated.

OPTICAL CONSIDERATIONS. The system used for reading deflections should provide good definition, both to make full use of available sensitivity and to avoid operator fatigue. Two systems are commonly used: (1) the image of a lamp filament (or of a target illuminated by a lamp) is projected on a scale; or (2) the image of a scale is focused in a telescope.

The lamp and scale system has the advantage of convenience if the level of general illumination at the observer's position is low enough to make the image of the source stand out bright and easily legible on the scale. The telescope and scale system is often advantageous in a brightly lighted room where there would be insufficient contrast between projected image and general illumination to make the first system feasible. In using a telescope, operator fatigue will be minimized if the image is sharply focused with the observer's eye relaxed "as though the object seen were at a great distance." Care must be taken that the adjustment focusing the telescope cross wires to maximum sharpness is made under the same *relaxed* condition to avoid both parallax and eye strain. Coincidence of the two images (scale and cross wires) can be tested by moving the head laterally with respect to the eyepiece. If the image of the scale shifts relative to the cross wires the focusing has *not* been properly done. In either case the observed image should be sharply focused and as free as possible from aberrations. This requires not only a mirror of good quality on the galvanometer but also high quality throughout the optical train, including the galvanometer window. Image doubling can often be avoided by using a non-tarnishing aluminum front-surface mirror on the galvanometer and by providing a mirror of the same type (or a right-angle prism) where, for convenience, the line of sight must be turned through an angle.

Galvanometer Types. PLATFORM GALVANOMETER. A modern sensitive galvanometer is shown in Fig. 11. The zero adjustment, accomplished by rotating the upper suspension abutment, and the coil-clamping mechanism are accessible through the top of the case. It will be noted that the window in the case is large enough to permit coil clearance in the air gap to be seen. The mechanism for adjusting the zero and that for the coil arrestment can be seen in the photograph in which the case is removed. The moving system of the galvanometer is supported from a rigid frame which can be removed as a unit for repair or replacement of suspensions. This frame and the loosely coiled lower suspension can be seen in the final picture, in which the magnet and pole pieces have been removed and a portion of the base has been cut away.

In many laboratory tasks a portable taut-suspension galvanometer having an internal optical system has adequate sensitivity and is more convenient to use than the sensitive type illustrated in Fig. 11. In this type of galvanometer it is very important that the moving system be carefully balanced, both to minimize response to mechanical disturbances and to ensure that the zero position of the system be unaffected by small departures from the horizontal of the table or platform on which the galvanometer rests. If the moving system is not well balanced, the zero

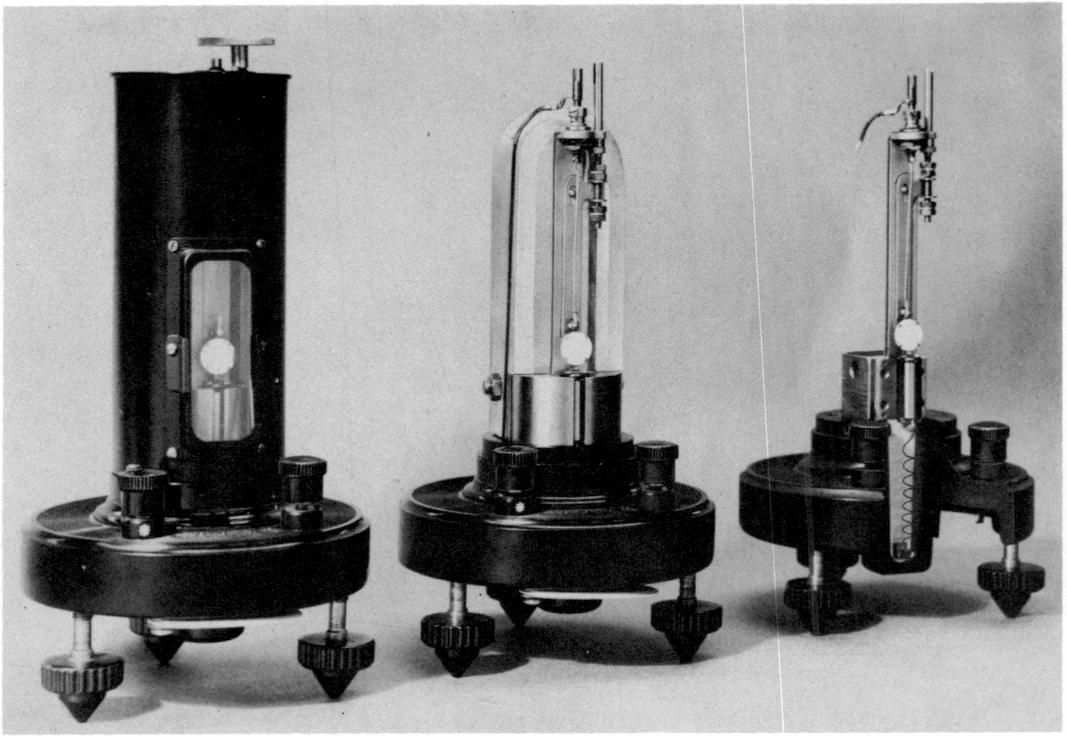

FIG. 11. Sensitive moving-coil galvanometer. (Courtesy of Leeds and Northrup Company.)

of the galvanometer may change enough with position to require very careful leveling of its supporting platform.

PORTABLE GALVANOMETERS. The effective pointer length of an internal indicating system is limited by the physical dimensions of the instrument case. Thus unless a special optical system is used the response of the galvanometer, as observed on the scale, must be estimated on the basis of an optical path somewhat shorter than the length of the instrument. Hence the observable response may be considerably less than that of a shelf-type galvanometer having the same angular coil motion per unit current but having a standard 100-cm optical path. Various methods

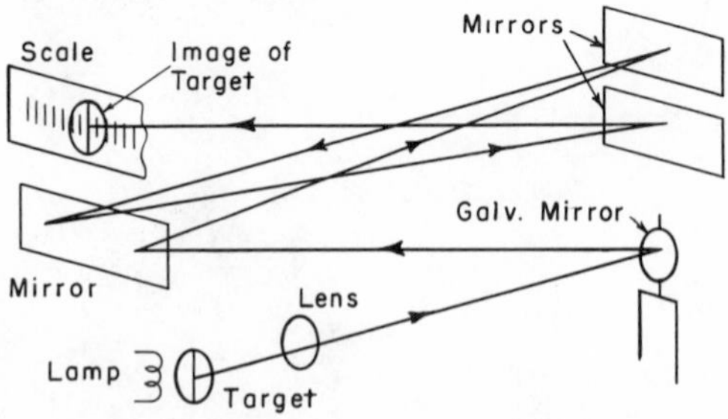

FIG. 12. Optical system of Rubicon spotlight galvanometer.

have been employed to increase the effective pointer length in portable galvanometers. One of these, used by the Rubicon Company, is shown schematically in Fig. 12. A series of plane mirrors is arranged so that the optical path between the galvanometer mirror and the scale traverses the length of the galvanometer enclosure five times, and totals about 75 cm in a physical space of 15 cm. Front-surface mirrors must be used, and the quality of the optical system must be high throughout in order that the target image on the scale be sharp and clearly defined.

Another type of optical system, used in the Leeds and Northrup Company's Model E portable galvanometer, accomplishes a similar result by means of a cylindrical mirror, without recourse to multiple reflections. As shown in Fig. 13, light from an incandescent lamp is concentrated on the galvanometer mirror by a condensing lens, which at the same time functions as a target to be imaged on the scale. (An opaque coating is applied to this lens, leaving a narrow clear slit with a centrally located, fine etched line for projection as a reading index.) From the galvanometer mirror the beam passes through a lens, a clear glass plate, is reflected by a convex cylindrical mirror, and forms an image of the target on the scale. The cylindrical mirror greatly increases the angular motion of the reflected ray for a given angular motion of the galvanometer mirror. As applied in the Leeds and Northrup Model E galvanometer this results in a six-fold increase in the deflection without any increase in the length of the light path. Thus, although the galvanometer length is approximately 30 cm, the deflection of the primary image on the scale is equivalent to that of an instrument having a pointer length of 300 cm. A small secondary image is obtained, as indicated, in Fig. 13, by reflection from the surface of the clear glass plate. The motion of this image on the scale is about one-tenth that of the primary image. This has the advantage of indicating the direction of the galvanometer deflection when the primary image travels beyond the scale limit. As in other portable instruments, a taut-suspension galvanometer is used. The suspensions

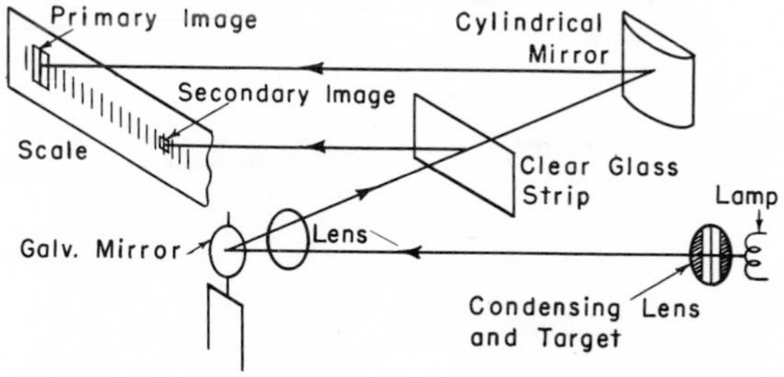

FIG. 13. Optical system of Leeds and Northrup Model E galvanometer.

are surrounded by spiral wire loops which hold drops of oil to damp oscillations resulting from shock or from the common types of vibration.

Galvanometer Shunts

In many cases it is necessary to reduce the sensitivity of a galvanometer in order that the deflection remain on scale. This is particularly true in preliminary balancing operations[18] in a bridge, potentiometer, or other network where the potential difference in the galvanometer branch may be relatively high. Here it may be necessary to protect the galvanometer against the mechanical or heating effect of currents too large to be safely carried, as well as to keep deflections to a readable value.

The simplest procedure would be to use either a high resistance in series with the galvanometer to limit the current produced by the available emf, or a shunt across the terminals of the galvanometer to by-pass most of the current. In most instances neither of these procedures alone is entirely desirable since damping will be seriously affected. A high resistance will usually reduce the damping to a low value so that the

[18] See Chapter 8 on ballistic galvanometers for discussion of the use of overdamping in preliminary balancing operations.

galvanometer will be seriously underdamped. On the other hand the low-resistance shunt will heavily overdamp the instrument so that its motion will be sluggish. In either case the time required to attain the final deflection value will be excessive. As a general rule some combination of series and parallel resistances is preferable which will give the desired reduction in sensitivity and at the same time preserve proper damping characteristics.[19]

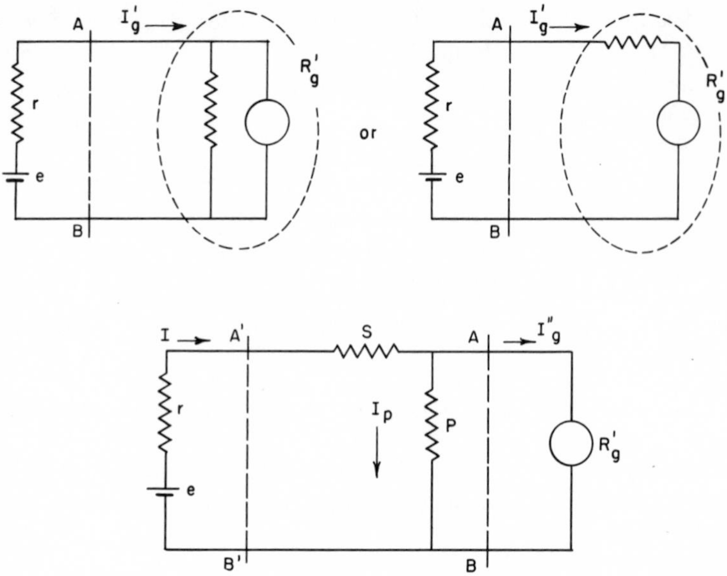

FIG. 14.

If the resistance of the network, viewed from the galvanometer terminals, is too high to give the desired damping, a shunt resistance must be introduced across the terminals of the galvanometer to adjust the damping to its proper value; or if the network resistance is too low a series resistance must be added. This preliminary adjustment having been made, we will consider the combination of series and parallel resistances needed to reduce the sensitivity by the desired factor while retaining the desired damping. In Fig. 14 we will assume a galvanometer resistance R_g' which will include the necessary shunt or series resistance at the galvanometer terminals to operate with the network resistance r and give the required damping. Our demand that the damping be unaffected requires that the combination of resistances introduced between AB and $A'B'$ be such

[19] F. Wenner, *J. Opt. Soc. Amer.*, **11,** 495 (1925).

that the total resistance to the left of AB will remain equal to r. Thus we have

$$\frac{(r+S)P}{r+S+P} = r \tag{1}$$

We will assume further that the resistances S and P used in the combination be such that the galvanometer sensitivity is reduced by a factor n, i.e. $I_g'' = I_g'/n$. Now

$$I_g' = \frac{e}{R_g' + r} \quad \text{and} \quad I_g'' = \frac{e}{(R_g' + r)n} \tag{2}$$

The total current $I = I_p + I_g''$, and $I_p/I_g'' = R_g'/P$, so that

$$I = I_g''\left(1 + \frac{R_g'}{P}\right) = I_g''\frac{(R_g' + P)}{P} \tag{3}$$

But

$$I = \frac{e}{r + S + \dfrac{R_g'P}{R_g' + P}} = \frac{e(R_g' + P)}{(r+S)(R_g' + P) + R_g'P} \tag{4}$$

Hence, from (2), (3), and (4),

$$(r+S)(R_g' + P) + R_g'P = Pn(R_g' + r)$$

or

$$\begin{aligned}(r+S)R_g' &= Pn(R_g' + r) - R_g'P - (r+S)P \\ &= P[(R_g' + r)(n-1) - S]\end{aligned} \tag{5}$$

From (1) we have

$$P = \frac{(r+S)r}{S} \tag{6}$$

Combining (5) and (6),

$$(r+S)R_g' = \frac{(r+S)r}{S}[(R_g' + r)(n-1) - S]$$

from which

$$S(R_g' + r) = r(R_g' + r)(n-1)$$

or

$$S = (n-1)r \tag{7}$$

From (6) and (7) we have

$$P = \frac{r[r + (n-1)r]}{(n-1)r} = \frac{nr}{n-1} \tag{8}$$

A series of values of S and P can be computed from (7) and (8) such that, by the use of a suitable selector switch, any desired sensitivity-reduction factor n may be made available in turn for use with a particular circuit resistance r.

If the circuit resistance is very high, as for example in a circuit used for the measurement of insulation resistance, the Ayrton-Mather universal shunt, Fig. 15, may be used to advantage. If the line current is I, then

$$\frac{I_g}{I} = \frac{\rho}{(\rho + R_g)n}$$

and $n(R_g + \rho)/\rho$ is the multiplying factor of the shunt, i.e. the factor by which the galvanometer current must be multiplied to obtain the line current. A number of taps are usually provided such that n assumes values which are powers of 10, and sensitivity can be reduced by factors of 10, 100, 1000, etc. If the resistance ρ is chosen to produce the desired damping in the galvanometer, and if the circuit resistance is very high compared to the shunt resistance, then the damping will remain constant for all values of n. It is apparent that such a shunt cannot be used with a low-resistance circuit without seriously changing galvanometer damping for small values of n.

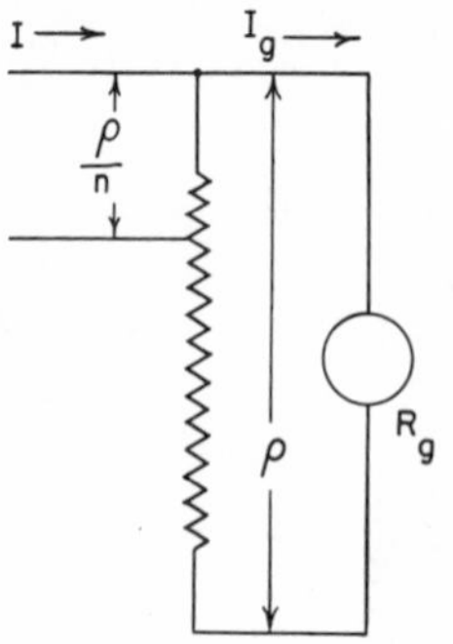

FIG. 15.

The Sensitive Galvanometer as a Detector

When current or voltage is measured by a deflection method and the expected galvanometer deflection is substantial, suitable measuring techniques are quite straightforward and should be obvious in the light of the discussion up to this point. In many cases, however, a galvanometer is used to detect *unbalance* in a bridge or potentiometer circuit. Frequently the galvanometer must operate under conditions in which its sensitivity is a limiting factor that determines the precision with which a balance can be made, or the amount of unbalance which can be detected. In such a case it is important to employ a measuring technique that will make the best possible use of the available galvanometer.

Operating Procedure. When a sensitive galvanometer is used to detect the approach to balance in a bridge or a potentiometer, its deflection is constantly changing. The changing deflection is caused in part by the balancing procedure itself, usually a series of adjustments of the circuit, from which a changing *voltage of unbalance* appears across the galvanometer· Another part of the continuous change in galvanometer deflection arises from various disturbing factors such as mechanical vibrations, changes in the local magnetic field, leakage currents, electrostatic effects, thermal emf's, Brownian movements, and related effects (in the case of a very sensitive galvanometer). In addition one must contend with failure of the moving system to return to a fixed zero because of elastic hysteresis in the suspension, or magnetic hysteresis in impurities in the moving system, or other imperfections.

If the measurements require the full sensitivity of the galvanometer, the changes in deflection which result from the various disturbing factors may well be as large as or larger than the deflections which arise from the permissible lack of balance. As far as possible, therefore, the balancing procedure should be such that the observer is able to differentiate between the changes in deflection which result from a lack of balance and those which result from the disturbing factors. This may be done by making the deflections of *unbalance* follow a definite time schedule without disturbing the random time distribution of the changes in deflection caused by the disturbing factors. In bridge balances the time pattern of the unbalance deflection may be made regular by keeping the galvanometer branch of the circuit closed while opening and closing (or reversing) the battery connections at regularly spaced time intervals. A better procedure, applicable to potentiometers as well as bridges, is to make a series of reversals of the connections to the galvanometer at uniform time intervals. This accentuates the difference between deflections resulting from lack of balance and those resulting from disturbing influences, by *doubling* the amplitude of the former *without changing the amplitude of the latter.*[20] Furthermore this procedure eliminates errors[21] which would result from a steady (or slowly changing) thermal emf and from moderate elastic or magnetic hysteresis.

Limits in the Detection of Unbalance. In discussing the conditions under which a particular galvanometer may be used to detect a specified unbalance, or the smallest discernible unbalance which a given galvanometer can detect in a particular bridge or potentiometer network, it should be emphasized that neither the *current* nor the *voltage sensitivity* alone is a sufficient specification of the behavior of the galvanometer. The circuit in which the galvanometer is expected to operate must be considered as well. We cannot completely solve the problem unless we consider the energy available from the circuit, at the galvanometer terminals, for producing deflection.

Assuming a suitable operating procedure (such as that outlined in the preceding section), we will define E as the change in voltage which would appear at the galvanometer terminals of the network (associated with each reversal) for the specified unbalance, providing the galvanometer were

[20] Under some circumstances this procedure may require making an inductive (or capacitive) balance as well as a resistance balance. Usually this presents no serious difficulty.

[21] F. Wenner, *NBS J. Research*, **22**, 425 (1939).

removed from the circuit and the galvanometer branch were open. We will define I as the current in the galvanometer branch resulting from the presence of the voltage E, if the galvanometer were replaced by a conductor of negligible resistance. We will say that the resistance of the network as seen from the galvanometer terminals is $\bar{R}$, and the time between reversals is T. Then the maximum energy which can be made available at the galvanometer terminals during the time T, under any circumstances, is

$$\frac{EIT}{4} = \frac{I^2\bar{R}T}{4} = \frac{E^2T}{4\bar{R}}$$

The energy stored in the suspensions of the galvanometer is $\frac{1}{2}U\theta^2$, where U is the torsional constant of the suspension and θ is the deflection attained in time T. If θ is the smallest perceptible change in the deflection (or any specified change in deflection), and if we know the value of U for the galvanometer, we can determine the suitability of the galvanometer for the required work since we can write

$$\frac{1}{2}\,U\theta^2 = \frac{\psi I^2\bar{R}T}{4} = \frac{\psi EIT}{4} = \frac{\psi E^2T}{4\bar{R}}$$

where ψ is the efficiency of the galvanometer in converting electrical to mechanical energy. Unfortunately the torsion constant is not usually known to us from the manufacturer's data supplied with the galvanometer, but an approximation may be made if we know the dimensions and material of the suspension. In case such an approximation is made it must be remembered that the units in which the various factors are expressed must be in a consistent system. This matter will be discussed a little later. Also, for purposes of the approximation, if T is set equal to T_0, the free period of the galvanometer, and $\bar{R}$ is such that the relative damping of the galvanometer is about 0.8, we may assume $\psi = 0.7$ and obtain a fairly good estimate of the suitability of the galvanometer for the specified task. Although the other intrinsic constants of the galvanometer are implied in the above expression and in the assumptions just made, it is necessary to state these constants explicitly if we are to specify the characteristics of a galvanometer which will be suitable, or to modify a design to attain a required set of characteristics. We will therefore examine in detail the relations which connect the intrinsic (design) constants of a galvanometer and its performance characteristics, using as a starting point the relation just established.

Galvanometer Design Constants

Our problem is three-fold: (1) we must state the relations between design constants and operating characteristics; (2) we must establish a procedure by which the design constants of a given galvanometer may be determined; and (3) we must express the relations between design (structural) constants and performance in such a way that we can determine what structural constants are required to realize a specified set of performance characteristics.

We have from the relation stated in the preceding section[22]

$$U = \frac{\psi I^2 \bar{R} T}{2\theta^2}$$

If we define $c = T_0/T$, and recall that $T_0 = 2\pi \sqrt{P/U}$, where P is the moment of inertia, we have

$$P = \frac{\psi c^2 T^3 I^2 \bar{R}}{8\pi^2 \theta^2}$$

If we recall that K represents the damping constant of the galvanometer on open circuit, and that γ_0 is the relative damping on open circuit, we have $K = 2\gamma_0 \sqrt{PU}$. We will define $d = \bar{R}/(\bar{R} + R_g)$, so that

$$\frac{dG^2}{R} = 2\gamma \sqrt{PU} - K$$

where γ is the relative damping of the galvanometer with the external resistance $\bar{R}$.

We can now state the motor constant of the galvanometer in terms of the specified performance, from the relation

$$G^2 = \frac{\psi(\gamma - \gamma_0) c T^2 I^2 \bar{R}^2}{2\pi d \cdot \theta^2}$$

From the fundamental differential equation of motion for the galvanometer, we may write an expression for G, on the assumption (already made above) that the time T is sufficient so that, practically, the deflection θ has reached its final value; thus

$$G = \frac{U\theta \bar{R}}{dE}$$

If we substitute our present value of U in this equation and square, we have

$$G^2 = \frac{\psi^2 I^2 \bar{R}^2 T^2}{4d^2\theta^2}$$

and by equating the two expressions for G^2, we arrive at an expression

[22] The following discussion is based on unpublished notes by Dr. F. Wenner and constitutes a generalization of his treatment of this same problem for the critically damped galvanometer [see *NBS Bull.*, **13**, 213 (1916)].

for the efficiency[23] in terms of the requirements set up in this and the preceding section,

$$\psi = \frac{2cd(\gamma - \gamma_0)}{\pi}$$

If we substitute this value of ψ into our previous expressions for U, P, and G, we have

$$U = \frac{1}{\pi\theta^2}(\gamma - \gamma_0)cdI^2\bar{R}T$$

$$P = \frac{1}{4\pi^3\theta^2}(\gamma - \gamma_0)c^3dI^2\bar{R}T^3$$

$$G = \frac{1}{\pi\theta}(\gamma - \gamma_0)cI\bar{R}T$$

Also, since $K = 2\gamma_0\sqrt{PU}$, we may say that

$$K = \frac{\gamma_0}{\pi^2\theta^2}(\gamma - \gamma_0)c^2dI^2\bar{R}T^2$$

By differentiating $\gamma_0(\gamma - \gamma_0)$ with respect to γ_0 it will be seen that K has the maximum value which is possible for it to attain under the specified conditions when $\gamma_0 = \gamma/2$, so that we may say

$$K \leqslant \frac{\gamma^2}{4\pi^2\theta^2}c^2dI^2\bar{R}T^2 \leqslant \frac{\gamma^2}{4\pi^2\theta^2}dI^2\bar{R}T_0^{\,2}$$

since $cT = T_0$. Also

$$\gamma_0 = \frac{\gamma}{2} \pm \sqrt{\frac{\gamma^2}{4} - \frac{\pi^2K\theta^2}{c^2dT^2I^2\bar{R}}}$$

i.e. there are two values of open-circuit damping which will satisfy the requirements we have set up. In other words, having specified c, d, γ, $\bar{R}$, T, K, and I/θ, there is still a choice of two sets of values for U, P, and G, either of which may be used to realize the same performance characteristics.

[23] The reader will note that the present expression for efficiency differs somewhat from the one previously developed on p. 60, i.e.

$$\psi = \text{eff} \cdot \frac{\bar{R}}{\bar{R} + R_g}$$

This difference arises from the fact that, for convenience in stating our present problem, we have redefined the efficiency in terms of the energy which would be available from the external circuit independently of the galvanometer, i.e. open-circuit voltage and short-circuit current. Since our definition of efficiency is arbitrary to the extent that we may choose the circuit conditions under which we will consider the behavior of the galvanometer as an electric motor, it is hoped that this change in definition will not disturb the reader unduly.

The above expressions of the relationships between performance characteristics and structural (design) constants may be used *to measure the structural constants* of a galvanometer, or *to determine the structural constants needed* in a galvanometer designed to realize a specific set of performance characteristics. However, they are not in a particularly useful form, and the units in which the various quantities are expressed must be reconciled in order to make their application to a practical problem possible.

If current is expressed in microamperes, emf in microvolts, resistance in ohms, deflection in millimeters on a scale 1 meter distant from the galvanometer mirror,[24] and other quantities in cgs electromagnetic units, we will use our symbols qualified with a prime before the letter. To express our equations in these hybrid units we should note that

$$I \text{ emu of current} = 10^{7}\ 'I\ \mu\text{a}$$
$$E \text{ emu of emf} = 10^{-2}\ 'E\ \mu\text{v}$$
$$\bar{R} \text{ emu of resistance} = 10^{-9}\ '\bar{R} \text{ ohms}$$
$$\theta \text{ radians of } \measuredangle = 2000\ '\theta \text{ mm/meter}$$

Then when we express the performance characteristics in terms of the structural constants we have

$$\frac{'I}{'\theta} = \frac{'U}{5000\, d\, 'G}$$

$$\frac{'E}{'\theta} = \frac{'G\, 'U}{400{,}000\left(\gamma\sqrt{'P\, 'U} - \dfrac{'K}{2}\right)}$$

$$'\bar{R} = \frac{d\, 'G^2}{2 \times 10^9\left(\gamma\sqrt{'P\, 'U} - \dfrac{'K}{2}\right)}$$

$$'T = \frac{6.28}{c}\sqrt{\frac{'P}{'U}}$$

and

$$\frac{'I\, 'E\, 'T}{4\, '\theta^2} = \frac{'I^2\, '\bar{R}\, 'T}{4\, '\theta^2} = \frac{'E^2\, 'T}{4\, '\bar{R}\, '\theta} = \frac{'P^{1/2}\, 'U^{3/2}}{127 \times 10^7\, cd\left(\gamma\sqrt{'P\, 'U} - \dfrac{'K}{2}\right)}$$

[24] It should be noted that the angular displacement between a fixed target and its reflected image on a scale is double the angular motion of the galvanometer mirror.

Measurement of the five structural constants of a galvanometer may be made by measuring the equivalent of five independent performance characteristics. Experimentally, the measurements which are usually convenient for this purpose are:

(1) $'T_x$, the period on open circuit.

(2) γ_0, the relative damping on open circuit.

(3) $'\bar{R}_1$, the external circuit resistance needed to give a relative damping γ_1; or γ_1, the relative damping corresponding to $'\bar{R}_1$.

(4) $'I_1$, the current which would appear in a shunt of negligible resistance placed across the galvanometer, while an emf $'E_1$ is acting in the circuit.

(5) $'R_g$, the resistance of the galvanometer, and from it d, the ratio $'\bar{R}_1/('\bar{R}_1 + 'R_g)$.

(6) $'\theta_1$, the final deflection when the external circuit resistance is $'\bar{R}_1$ and the emf acting on the circuit is $'E_1$. (Obviously, these measurements are not all independent.)

In terms of these measured performance characteristics, the structural constants may be written thus:

$$'P = 0.32(\gamma_1 - \gamma_0)(1 - \gamma_0^2)^{3/2} d\,'\bar{R}_1\,'T_x^3 \left(\frac{'I_1}{'\theta_1}\right)^2$$

$$'K = 4\gamma_0(\gamma_1 - \gamma_0)(1 - \gamma_0^2) d\,'\bar{R}_1\,'T_x^2 \left(\frac{'I_1}{'\theta_1}\right)^2$$

$$'U = 12.7(\gamma_1 - \gamma_0)(1 - \gamma_0^2)^{1/2} d\,'\bar{R}_1\,'T_x \left(\frac{'I_1}{'\theta_1}\right)^2$$

$$'G = 64{,}000(\gamma_1 - \gamma_0)(1 - \gamma_0^2)^{1/2}\,'\bar{R}_1\,'T_x \left(\frac{'I_1}{'\theta_1}\right)$$

$'R_g$, the remaining structural constant, will already have been measured.

In designing a galvanometer for detecting unbalance in a precise bridge or potentiometer, values of γ, T_0, $\bar{R}$, and I/θ may be specified from the condition of use. This leaves the galvanometer resistance R_g, and the open-circuit damping K at our disposal. We may begin by selecting a value for R_g, as low as experience indicates may be realized in a galvanometer having the required performance characteristics. This gives us a value for d which may be introduced into the expression

$$'K \leqslant \gamma^2 d\,'\bar{R}\,'T_0^2 \left(\frac{'I}{'\theta}\right)^2$$

In some cases $'K$ is deliberately made large by means of a frame or a short-circuited turn to improve the damping of a galvanometer which is expected to be used in circuits whose resistances will not be closely adjusted to a value to give correct performance. However, since open-circuit damping absorbs from the measuring circuit energy which is dissipated as heat, without producing deflection, it is obvious that it lowers the efficiency of the design. In designing a sensitive galvanometer it would be a serious mistake, therefore, to use an open-circuit damping which is larger than is necessary. Let us say that $'K \leqslant \frac{1}{2}\,'K$ maximum. It can be shown that in this case it is possible to make the relative damping on open circuit $\gamma_0 \leqslant 0.15\gamma$ (from the equation above relating γ, γ_0, and K).

With these values of d and γ_0, based on what experience indicates to be good practice, and with the specified values of $'\bar{R}$, $'T_0$, and $'I/'\theta$, we can write our remaining structural constants as

$$'P = 0.32(\gamma - \gamma_0)d\,'R\,'T_0^3 \left(\frac{'I}{'\theta}\right)^2$$

$$'U = 12.7(\gamma - \gamma_0)d\,'R\,'T_0 \left(\frac{'I}{'\theta}\right)^2$$

$$'G = 64{,}000(\gamma - \gamma_0)\,'R\,'T_0 \left(\frac{'I}{'\theta}\right)$$

CHAPTER 4

INDICATING INSTRUMENTS

Most of the types of indicating instruments which will be discussed in this book have certain features in common that can appropriately be considered at this time. The proper functioning of an instrument, the accuracy with which it is capable of measuring a desired electrical quantity or relation, its initial cost, and the care that must be taken in handling and using it are closely related to design features which are common to most types of instruments; and the final quality and usefulness of an instrument depend very largely on the skill and experience of the maker in meeting certain general requirements.

For convenience, simplicity, and compactness in electrical and mechanical design the motion of the indicating system of an electrical instrument is made one of rotation, and in general we may consider that the mechanical systems with which we will deal will have only one degree of freedom—that of rotation about an axis whose space orientation is fixed. Whatever the means used to produce deflection (usually electrostatic or electromagnetic forces), the torque resulting from the action of the deflecting force on the moving system must be opposed by a countertorque (usually from the action of a spring) which is a function of the displacement of the system. Under the action of these opposing torques the instrument takes up a definite equilibrium position such that they are equal, and from some indication of the balance position (usually a pointer and scale arrangement), the magnitude of the quantity evoking the deflecting torque is determined. In addition there must be some means by which the energy of motion is absorbed, so that the system will come to rest in its equilibrium position. It is also necessary that the system turn freely. The presence of mechanical friction is an unavoidable consequence of mounting the moving system in bearings; but, if there is excessive friction either in the bearings or elsewhere in the moving system, an appreciable "frictional" countertorque will be present to oppose the motion in either direction. The indication will therefore be uncertain by an amount which depends on the relative magnitudes of the friction and the stiffness of the spring, as we shall see presently. Since frictional forces are difficult to control closely and since their action results in uncertainty in the deflection, they cannot be used to assist in the proper functioning of the instrument. Almost without exception the instrument maker tries to keep their magnitude so low that they will not seriously interfere with the action of the controllable forces deliberately incorporated into the instrument design.

Thus there are several features which are common to most indicating instruments: (1) a restoring mechanism to oppose and balance the deflecting torque; (2) a damping mechanism to absorb the energy of motion; (3) an indication mechanism by which the balance position between deflecting and restoring torques is shown and by means of which the measured quantity is evaluated; and (4) a bearing mechanism, preferably as nearly frictionless as possible, so that the moving system of the instrument may take up equilibrium positions with certainty and without interference. Other features, such as the means by which deflecting torque is evoked and the electrical quantity which is evaluated from the scale reading, serve to differentiate one type of instrument from another. We shall now examine these several features.

Springs

Instrument springs must meet a number of requirements. (1) They must be stressed well below their elastic limit at the maximum deflection of the instrument, in order that no change in deflection (or zero shift) will result from inelastic yield.[1] (2) Where the springs are used to lead current into the moving system, their cross-sectional area must be sufficient to carry the current without a temperature rise which would affect their torque constant.[2] (3) The spring material must be non-magnetic in most types of instruments. A number of alloys have been used as spring

[1] The amount of shift that can be tolerated in the zero position when the instrument is removed from the circuit after having been deflected to its full-scale position for a considerable time (say 30 minutes) will depend on the rated accuracy of the instrument. For a laboratory instrument of the highest grade (carrying an accuracy guarantee of 0.1%) such zero shift should be imperceptible; a shift in the zero position of as much as the width of the knife-edge pointer is too high. For a switchboard instrument whose guaranteed accuracy is 2% a zero shift of 0.1 to 0.2% of full-scale deflection would be negligible. Since the making of good springs requires a high order of skill and knowledge on the part of the manufacturer, a significant test of instrument quality is the ability of the spring to return the instrument pointer to its zero position *immediately* after a prolonged full-scale deflection.

[2] In effect this limits the maximum current that can be used in the moving coils of instruments to a fraction of an ampere (usually 25 ma or less).

material, but for most applications phosphor-bronze is the most suitable,[3] except in instruments of low resistance (such as millivoltmeters) where the resistance of the springs is of considerable importance. In this application special bronze alloys of relatively low resistance may be used with some sacrifice in their mechanical quality.

Flat spiral control springs are used in almost all deflecting instruments.[4] The space required for these springs is less than for other types. One end of the spring is anchored to a stationary abutment, and the other end is attached to the moving system. If the spring is properly designed the torque developed is very closely proportional to the angular deflection of the free end, and there is no component of force in the direction of the spring axis. For a flat spiral spring the torque developed by deflection is

$$T = 83 \times \frac{Ewt^3}{l} \cdot \beta \text{ gm-cm}$$

where E is the Young's modulus of the spring material in kilograms per square centimeter; w, t, and l are respectively the width, thickness, and length of the spring strip, all in centimeters; and β is the angular deflection in radians. The maximum fiber stress developed in the spring by this applied torque is

$$\bar{S} = \frac{0.006T}{wt^2} \text{ kg/cm}^2$$

Combining these formulas, we have

$$\frac{l}{t} = \frac{E}{\bar{S}} \cdot \frac{\beta}{2}$$

as the ratio of length to thickness of the spring strip. For phosphor-bronze (the most commonly used spring material) the maximum allowable fiber stress $\bar{S}$ may be taken as 300 kg/cm², and $E = 12 \times 10^5$ kg/cm². From this,

$$\frac{l}{t} = \frac{12 \times 10^5}{3 \times 10^2} \times \frac{\beta}{2} = 2000\ \beta$$

and if $\beta = \pi/2$, $l/t \approx 3000$. If inelastic yield is to be avoided, the ratio of length to thickness of the spring strip must not be much less than this value. Some designers use a ratio as low as 2100 (for a maximum deflection of 90°) for portable instruments. For switchboard instruments,

[3] Beryllium-copper has many exceptionally good properties as a spring material but has not been widely adopted in instrument applications, primarily because it soft-solders with difficulty, and special techniques are required for its use.

[4] In cases where the spring is required to support a portion of the weight of the moving system, a helical spring or a combined helix and spiral is sometimes used (see p. 134, Chapter 5).

whose indications are of lower precision, a ratio as low as 1000 (for a 90° deflection) is sometimes used.[5] The ratio of spring length to thickness being fixed by the maximum fiber stress, the conductance (for springs of a given stiffness) increases as the ratio of width to thickness w/t increases. Hence the spring section should be wide and thin. This ratio w/t may be as high as 30/1, and is usually greater than 10/1. Both resistance and stiffness of a spring are to some extent functions of temperature. For the usual spring alloys the temperature coefficient of resistance will be in the neighborhood of 0.2%/°C, while the temperature coefficient of stiffness will be about 0.04%/°C, the resistance increasing and the stiffness decreasing with increasing temperature.

Balance

Since the temperature coefficient of stiffness of the spring will generally result in a temperature coefficient in the indication of the instrument, and since the inelastic yield in the spring results in displacement in the zero position of the moving system, it might appear advantageous to substitute gravity control for spring control in instruments. Certainly a gravity control for the moving system would be free from the effects mentioned. However, it would have a defect which would be far more serious in many instrument applications. The control would be sensitive to the space orientation of the moving element, and the constancy of the instrument calibration would depend on the precision with which a particular orientation could be maintained or reproduced. Since it is advantageous that the indications of an instrument be independent of level, it is usual to balance the moving system statically so that its center of gravity is brought as nearly as possible into coincidence with the axis of rotation, to eliminate the possibility of any gravity control. This is accomplished by means of adjustable weights attached to arms on the moving system as shown in Fig. 1. There are generally three arms, and adjustments are made by changing the positions of self-locking nuts threaded on the arms. The use of shellac or solder to fix the location of a balance weight, or the use of solder as a means of weight adjustment, represents very poor practice.

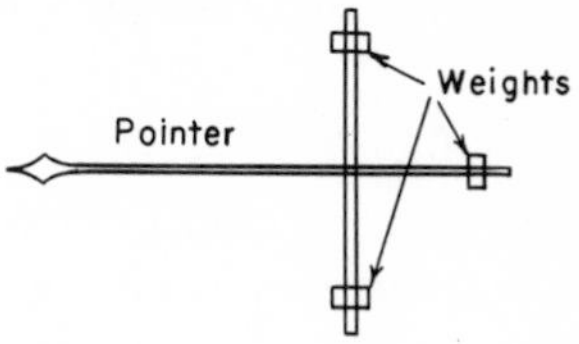

FIG. 1.

[5] For details concerning these spring formulas, and for further information on spring characteristics, see Keinath, *Die Technik elektrischer Messgeräte*, 3rd edition, vol. 1, p. 16, Springer, 1928; Drysdale and Jolley, *Electrical Measuring Instruments*, vol. 1, p. 45, Benn, 1924; Edgcumbe and Ockenden, *Industrial Electrical Measuring Instruments*, p. 50, Pitman, 1933.

A test for the static balance of a portable instrument can be performed by setting the instrument on a turntable whose plane is inclined at 10° to the horizontal. The turntable, carrying the instrument, is then rotated through 360°, and the maximum excursion of the pointer from the zero mark of the scale is noted. In a well-balanced instrument this should be less than 10 minutes of arc.[6] It is of course impossible to bring the center of gravity of the moving system into exact coincidence with its axis of rotation, but for most instruments the balance may be made good enough that the effects of any residual gravity control are negligible. Laboratory standard instruments of the highest grade (0.1% accuracy class) are frequently equipped with leveling screws and should be carefully leveled before being used. Such instruments usually have a bubble level mounted in the case to indicate the reference plane in which they were calibrated. By returning the instrument to the same plane the control forces resulting from any residual unbalance of the moving system act in precisely the same way that they did when the scale was marked.

Bearings

In order to reduce friction to a low value hardened steel pivots rotating in polished jewel cups are used.[7] Most portable instruments are operated with the scale in a horizontal position and with the axis of the moving system vertical. The entire weight of the system is on the lower bearing, and the upper jewel serves merely as a guide bearing to hold it in alignment. An appreciable part of the friction, however, is in the upper bearing. Where both the operating torque and weight of the moving system are small, a "unipivot" construction is sometimes used. In this construction the moving system is supported by a single pivot-jewel bearing. The bearing is above the center of gravity of the moving system which is therefore stable. A pivot with very small radius of curvature (with a light-weight moving system) results in a low value of friction. This construction is suitable for torque values down to 10 mg-cm for 90° deflection.[8] For still lower torque values, bearing friction becomes excessive and the moving system is supported by strip suspensions.

It has been shown experimentally that frictional torque is, for jewel

[6] In the American Standard C39.1 for Electrical Instruments (American Standards Association) and also in the Armed Forces Specification JAN-I6, a balance adjustment is required such that the pointer deflection shall be less than 1% of full-scale value when the instrument is tilted through 60° in any direction from its normal use position.

[7] Steel pivots in bronze bearings have sometimes been employed in the cheapest instruments but cannot be considered satisfactory in laboratory instruments.

[8] In some instances part of the weight of the moving system is supported by a spring. See Chapter 5.

bearings, proportional to the area of contact between the pivot and jewel. The pivot is ground to a cone, and its tip is rounded to a hemispherical surface of small area. The jewel is ground to a cone of somewhat larger angle, and its bottom is also rounded. Pivot angles are generally held to about 60°[9] but may amount to 100°. Pivot radii will be found to lie between 0.0005 in. and 0.002 in. The radius of the hemispherical bottom of the jewel cup may be as much as four times that of the pivot. As a result the weight of the moving system may be carried on a bearing surface whose diameter is at most a few mils. The pivots of many modern instruments are loaded very nearly to the yield point of the steel, and the end of the pivot actually distorts slightly to fit the jewel bearing as the yield point is passed. Mechanical shock or severe vibration will, of course, further distort the pivot and increase the friction as the contact area is increased.

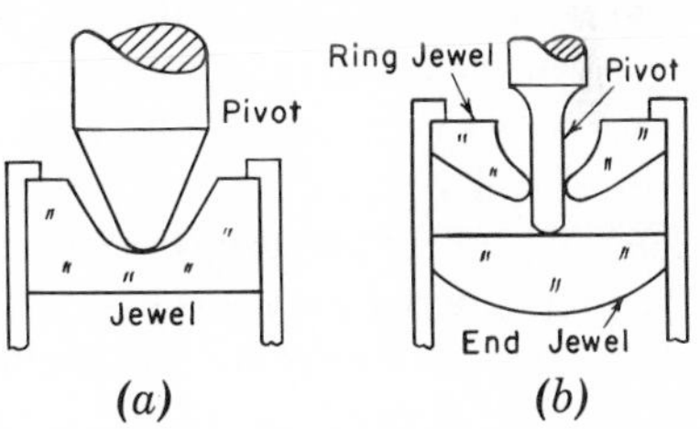

FIG. 2.

Conditions of shock or vibration should be avoided in portable instruments; where such conditions are encountered or expected, it is well to place the instruments on felt pads to absorb vibration and to deaden shock. For instruments which must withstand severe vibration, pivots and jewels may be shaped to larger radii than is standard, i.e. larger bearing area. Although the use of a large bearing area permits higher shock loading without injury to the bearing surfaces, it also results in greater friction than is associated with a small bearing area. Because of the adverse effect of increased friction on over-all instrument performance, the bearing area is generally held to a low value unless expected shock or vibration conditions require an increase. The usual type of instrument bearing is shown schematically in Fig. 2(*a*), the rounded end of the pivot being carried in the rounded bottom of a conical cup in a stationary jewel. Such a bearing is generally operated without lubrication and, when properly constructed, probably has a lower and more constant value of friction than any other known type. In some constructions the jewel is backed by a light spring to absorb a portion of the impact under shock conditions. An alternative bearing construction [Fig. 2(*b*)] makes use of a ring stone and an end stone. Although such a construction is standard as a low-friction bearing in watches and other fine mechanisms in which accurate alignment must be maintained between gears or other elements of a linkage, the friction is considerably higher than in the cup

[9] This is the total included angle and not the angle from the axis.

bearing, and this type of bearing finds very little application in electrical instruments except where alignment requirements are critical. Ring-stone bearings which support weight or end thrust are sometimes used in the mechanism of recording instruments, and have occasionally been employed in switchboard instruments designed for marine applications in which vibration conditions are exceptionally severe.

Not only must the contact area of the bearing be small, but the pivot and jewel must be highly polished and free from abrasive points or edges. Carbon steel[10] is generally used as pivot material, and it must be heat-treated at a temperature sufficiently high (900°C) to dissolve all the cementite (small aggregates of iron carbide containing about 7% of carbon), which is very hard and which acts as a grinding agent on the jewel as well as reduces the strength of the steel. The pivot turns in a cup of polished sapphire. Both natural and synthetic sapphire (corundum) have been extensively used. Synthetic sapphire is generally a better bearing material since it is much freer from flaws, inclusions, and twinning than is the natural stone, and manufacturing techniques are now perfected to such an extent that it is relatively abundant and inexpensive. During World War II, when European sources of instrument jewels were cut off and before synthetic sapphire production was sufficiently developed in this country, molded vee-jewels made from a special hard glass were developed as a substitute for use in small instruments. They are suitable for light-weight moving systems, and in such applications they have certain advantages over the best sapphire jewels. Since they are hot-molded, the surface is fire-polished and is smoother than can be attained by the mechanical lapping process used to polish the surface of sapphire. The shape of the cone (or vee) and its rounded bottom can be held to much closer tolerances in the molded unit than is possible by the mechanical grinding used to make sapphire cup-jewels. Also the glass jewel can be produced more cheaply. Actually, in a small instrument where bearing load and shock can be kept well within the strength of the material, the glass vee-jewel has less friction and shows less wear than the sapphire.

Torque-Weight Ratio. No matter how well the pivot and jewel faces are shaped and polished, some friction remains and may be expected to increase above its initial value as a result of the hazards to which the instrument is subjected in use. Frictional torque may be expressed as a function of the weight W of the moving system, the coefficient of friction f of the bearing materials, and the effective bearing radius r as $\mathscr{T}_f = K \cdot fWr$. But since the pivot material is elastic it will tend to flatten

[10] Pivots of other materials, for example noble-metal pivots of an alloy of osmium and iridium, are used in some instances.

with increasing load, so that r is itself a function[11] of W, generally $r \propto \sqrt[3]{W}$. Then we may write

$$\mathcal{T} = K' \cdot f \cdot W^{4/3}$$

For a hardened steel pivot against synthetic sapphire, it was found experimentally that $\mathcal{T}_f = 0.02W^{4/3}$ dyne-cm, and that the frictional torque was closely proportional to $W^{4/3}$ over a weight range between 7 and 136 gm.

The effect of frictional torque on the performance of an instrument depends on its magnitude relative to the control torque exerted by the springs. Obviously, if the frictional torque is comparable to a considerable fraction of the deflecting torque acting on the moving system, the equilibrium position of the moving system will depend on frictional torque to an appreciable extent for any particular combination of couples.

[11] Using the formula of Hertz [*Miscellaneous Papers* (authorized English translation), pp. 146–183, Macmillan, 1896] for a force acting along the line of centers of two elastic spheres, Keinath (*ibid.*, p. 71) arrives at the following formulas:

(1) The radius of the contact circle (bearing radius) is

$$r = \sqrt[3]{0.68W\left(\frac{\dfrac{1}{E_p} + \dfrac{1}{E_j}}{\dfrac{1}{r_p} - \dfrac{1}{r_j}}\right)}$$

(2) The specific loading of the bearing surface is

$$\sigma = \sqrt[3]{0.235W\left(\frac{\dfrac{1}{r_p} - \dfrac{1}{r_j}}{\dfrac{1}{E_p} + \dfrac{1}{E_j}}\right)^2} \text{ kg/cm}^2$$

where W is the weight of the system in kilograms, E is the modulus of elasticity (2×10^6 for steel and 5×10^6 for sapphire), and r_p, r_j are the radii in centimeters of the pivot and jewel surfaces respectively. Stott has shown [*Collected Research Papers of the NPL*, **24**, pp. 1–55 (1938)] that, when the axis of the moving system is vertical and operating within the elastic limits of the materials, the frictional torque in gram-millimeters is

$$\mathcal{T} = \pi\mu \cdot \left(\frac{3W}{16}\right)^{4/3} \left(\frac{\theta_p + \theta_j}{\dfrac{1}{r_p} - \dfrac{1}{r_j}}\right)^{1/3} = W^{4/3} \times \text{constant}$$

where

$$\theta = \frac{4G + 3B}{G(G + 3B)}$$

G and B being the shear and bulk moduli respectively in kilograms per square millimeter. [Stott estimates that $(\theta_p + \theta_j) = 0.16 \times 10^{-3}$ for steel against sapphire], μ is the coefficient of static friction between pivot and jewel, and r is in millimeters. When the

The deflection attained will depend on the direction from which the equilibrium position is approached and will be uncertain. On the other hand, if the frictional torque is very small compared with the deflecting torque, its effect on deflection will be negligible. Thus the ratio of frictional torque to deflecting torque is a measure of the reliability of the instrument indications and of the inherent quality of the design. Now the friction depends on the condition of the bearing as well as on its materials and may be expected to increase rather than diminish with use, but in any event it is a function of the weight of the moving system. Although a statement of frictional torque might perhaps be made for an instrument as it leaves the maker's hands, such a statement might not be significant after a period of use. However, the weight of the moving system and its ratio to the full-scale deflecting torque of the instrument continue to be significant, and this ratio serves as an index of the ability of the instrument to function properly, not only initially but during its useful life, since it indicates the ability of the deflecting and control torques to overcome such friction as may reasonably be anticipated. The *torque-weight ratio* of an instrument is therefore a useful criterion of the mechanical performance to be expected from the instrument and the care which must be taken in handling and operating it. It serves as a design "figure of merit" in comparing instruments of different types and is used to determine whether the available torque is sufficient to insure proper operation. On the basis of theoretical considerations the ratio $\mathcal{T}/W^{4/3}$

---

static loading is such that permanent deformation results, Stott has shown that the frictional torque may be written as $\mathcal{T} = W^{3/2} \times$ constant. For a moving system with a horizontal axis Nylander [*G.E. Rev.*, **49**, No. 7, 12 (1946)] has developed the following formulas for frictional torque:

(1) When the end clearance P_r (in millimeters) is such that the pivot is in contact with the spherical surface at the base of the jewel recess,

$$\mathcal{T} = \mu W r_p \cos\left[\tan^{-1}\frac{\mu}{\cos\left(\sin^{-1}\left\{1 - \frac{P_r}{r_j - r_p}\right\}\right)}\right]$$

(2) When the end clearance P_c is such that the pivot is in contact with the conica surface of the jewel recess,

$$\mathcal{T} = \mu W r_p \cos\left[\tan^{-1}\frac{\mu}{\cos\frac{\lambda}{2}}\right]$$

where λ is the total angle of the jewel cone. In Nylander's formulas, W is in grams, r in millimeters, and $\mathcal{T}$ in gram-millimeters. See also:

Stott, *J. IEE*, **69**, 751 (1931) and **70**, 359 (1932).
Szabo, *J. Sci. Inst.*, **26**, 301 (1949).

might perhaps be a better index of performance, and it should be pointed out that $\mathcal{T}/W^{3/2}$ is also frequently used by designers.[12]

Bearing Clearance. A clearance (end play) of 0.002 in. to 0.004 in. must be allowed in instrument bearings for thermal expansion, and the jewels must be restrained from loosening or turning by a lock nut or set screw, since the bearing clearance must be maintained within rather close limits. (An end play of more than 0.004 in. is excessive.) Because of this bearing clearance there results an uncertainty in pointer position in instruments having a vertical axis, such as the usual laboratory instrument. The reason for this is shown in Fig. 3. If the lower pivot point is considered fixed in position, the axis of the moving system is free to tilt from the vertical by an amount which depends on the relative radii of curvature of the upper jewel and pivot, and on the bearing clearance. This axis tilt (sometimes called pivot roll) affects the pointer position by an amount which is a function of the height of the pointer above the lower bearing. The uncertainty of pointer position relative to the instrument scale is decreased by decreasing the radius of curvature of the upper jewel. It may amount to 0.1% of the scale length when the bearing clearance is adjusted to a safe value.[13]

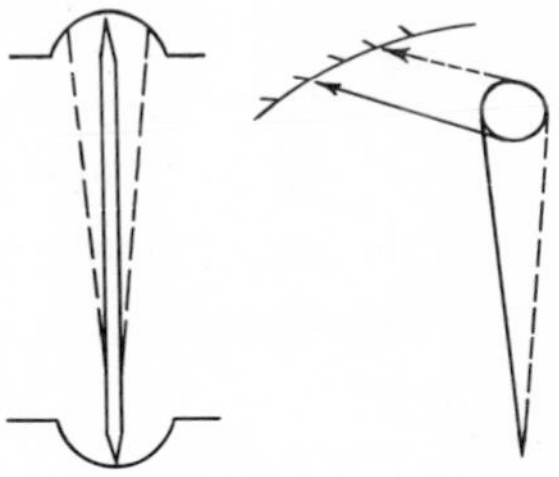

FIG. 3.

[12] An examination of data on instruments by three leading manufacturers shows the following results:

Type of Instrument	$\mathcal{T}/W$			$\mathcal{T}/W^{4/3}$			$\mathcal{T}/W^{3/2}$		
	Max	Min	Avg	Max	Min	Avg	Max	Min	Avg
Permanent magnet, moving coil (8 instruments)	0.25	0.064	0.14	0.199	0.058	0.113	0.182	0.054	0.102
Electrodynamic (10 instruments)	0.094	0.032	0.066	0.074	0.016	0.044	0.066	0.011	0.036
Moving iron (4 instruments)	0.11	0.046	0.080	0.073	0.035	0.058	0.067	0.030	0.050

These various types of instruments will be described later. (See Chapters 5, 10, and 11.) In all cases $\mathcal{T}$ is full-scale torque measured in gram-centimeters, and W is the weight of the moving system in grams.

[13] The uncertainty of pointer position would be eliminated if the pointer and scale were in the horizontal plane which contains the pivot point on which the moving system

Scales and Pointers

Instrument scales and pointers may be considered together in two classes: (1) those intended for reading quickly and (in the case of switchboard instruments) at a distance; and (2) those intended for accurate, close reading. In both classes of instruments the pointer motion is usually limited by buffers or stops to a little more than the length of the scale. These stops are constructed as very light springs (insulated from the pointer by ceramic sleeves) since if they are too rigid the pointer may be bent when it strikes them sharply on a sudden overload or reversal of the operating current.

Switchboard and Panel Instruments. In this class, conspicuousness of pointer position, legibility of scale markings, and contrast with background are essential. Pointers are usually broad, or carry a broad target at their end, and are finished to give good contrast against the scale which is their background. This does not imply excessive weight in the pointer system. The pointer may be formed from light sheet aluminum and ribbed for strength and rigidity, or a ribbed arrowhead pointer formed from aluminum foil may be rigidly mounted at the end of a trussed frame of light aluminum tubing. The scale is generally printed on the enameled surface of a metal plate, or on paper or cardboard firmly cemented to a metal backing plate. Scale markings are usually rather broad, and, for ease in reading, the scale is generally subdivided into 2, 5, or 10 parts between major scale divisions. Other marking schemes have been used, but it has been found that markings involving quantities other than 1, 2, and 5, together with their decimal multiples or submultiples, make scale reading and interpolation more laborious and much more liable to reading errors.

The enamel or paper on which the scale is printed must have a dull matte finish to avoid highlights and reflections, and the glass window through which the scale is read is, in switchboard instruments, sometimes specially treated to avoid glare. In small panel-type instruments the scale markings and the pointer may be coated with self-luminous radioactive paint or with a fluorescent material (to be illuminated with ultraviolet light) for use where readings must be made in the dark. Aircraft instruments are an example of this type of marking. Switchboard instruments are sometimes arranged for scale illumination by a lamp

---

rests. However, such a construction is generally convenient only in unipivot instruments, and is seldom used in conventional types of instruments. Hartmann and Braun has used this construction in portable instruments, which they designate as "Kippfehlerfrei." They have been described by Palm, *Elektrische Messgeräte*, 3rd edition, pp. 71 and 73, Springer, 1948.

mounted inside the instrument case. Small clearance between pointer and scale (0.05 to 0.1 in.) is necessary to minimize the parallax errors which result from reading the scale at various angles. Parallax can be completely eliminated in switchboard instruments by mounting the scale on a raised platform so that it is in the same plane as the tip of the pointer. The scale calibration is usually such that switchboard instruments fall in the 1% class, while small instruments of panel types are generally in accuracy classes not better than 2%. Such calibrations are adequate since in most applications of panel and switchboard instruments precise readings are not required.

Portable Instruments. Since portable instruments are almost always read from a short distance, the pointer and scale need not have the boldness and contrast required for switchboard instruments. Portable instruments having a calibration better than 1% are characterized by a knife-edge pointer moving over a scale marked with fine lines, usually not appreciably wider than the knife edge itself. The knife edge may be formed by flattening the end of a light aluminum tube which forms the body of the pointer, or it may be a thin flat strip carried in the end of the pointer, or a fine wire stretched in a rigid frame. Parallax in reading is avoided by the use of a mirror strip mounted in an opening in the scale beneath the pointer, so that when the pointer and its mirrored image are brought into coincidence the observer's eye is in the correct position to read the deflection.

Division lines are laid out individually for each instrument, in contrast to the scales of switchboard or panel instruments, which are usually preprinted. This procedure is necessary because of the higher accuracy expected in the indications of portable instruments. Alternative procedures for locating the principal (cardinal) points of the scale are (1) the calibration points are read from a dummy scale, marked in degrees of angle, and then transferred to the real scale; or (2) a blank scale plate is mounted in the instrument and the cardinal points are located by pin-pricking or otherwise marking the pointer position for the required values of the quantity indicated. The scale plate is then removed from the instrument and the scale is inked in. In either case the scale must be subdivided between the calibrated cardinal points, and various procedures are used by different manufacturers for this operation. In some instances the subdivision is done mechanically in a dividing engine. It is possible by suitable gear or cam arrangements to allow for non-linearity of the scale between the calibrated points. In other instances a skilled operator subdivides the scale free-hand. While such subdivision, when undertaken by a skilled person, may be adequate for instruments in the $\frac{3}{4}$% accuracy class, the markings are necessarily less accurately located than can be done by mechanical means; and frequently the irregularities in spacing of the division marks on such hand-divided scales can be noticed from a casual inspection.

Interpolated Readings. The presence of irregularities in the subdivision of instrument scales makes the usual interpolation procedure of questionable value for applying corrections to the instrument readings. A user will frequently check the calibration at cardinal points and apply corrections by linear interpolation throughout the interval between the cardinal points. It will be apparent that such an interpolation will result in errors in the measured values unless the subdivisions in the interval are properly located. If the instrument is of a type in which the scale is linear, the divisions should be equally spaced. For other types of scales, proper account must be taken of the instrument scale law in the subdivision, in order that corrections may be applied by interpolation from corrections which are measured at the cardinal points. If precise values are required from the indications of an instrument, it is generally necessary to examine the scale for irregularities in its subdivision which would invalidate interpolated corrections; and, if such irregularities are present, to check the instrument calibration not only at the cardinal points but also at each marked scale division which will be used. Such an elaborate check of the calibration is not usually necessary, of course, unless one wishes to use the instrument to an accuracy better than is implied by the maker's guarantee, by applying corrections to its indications. But if the subdivision of an instrument scale is of high quality it is frequently possible to apply corrections found by linear interpolation from measured corrections at the cardinal points, to obtain from an instrument in the $\frac{1}{2}\%$ or even in the $\frac{3}{4}\%$ class[14] values which are reliable to 0.2%. Instruments which are rated in the $\frac{1}{4}\%$ or 0.1% accuracy class must have scales which are of very high quality throughout.

Damping

In the absence of damping the moving system of an instrument would oscillate in simple harmonic motion about the position at which the deflecting and restoring torques are equal. The function of damping is to absorb energy from the oscillating system and to bring it to rest promptly in its equilibrium position so that its indication may be observed. We have already seen[15] that the promptness with which the moving system comes to rest is a function of its relative damping, and that this time is a minimum when the system is somewhat underdamped. For the galvanometer it was seen that in practical operation the damping is largely

[14] See p. 122.

[15] See Chapter 3.

conservative; i.e. most of the energy of the moving system is returned to the circuit by generator action and only a minor portion is dissipated by air friction as open-circuit damping. The situation is quite different for most indicating instruments. Here the damping is largely dissipative and usually depends only to a negligible extent on circuit conditions. This is a consequence of the characteristics of the instrument and the constants of the operating circuits, and is, indeed, very desirable. If the instrument is to be generally useful the time required for the moving system to come to rest should not be dependent on the constants of the circuit in which it is connected. The damping of some types of very sensitive microammeters does depend on the external circuit, and its resistance must be approximately adjusted to a particular value for proper operation. However, this is not a desideratum but must be tolerated as a necessary consequence of the fact that the low energy level at which the instrument operates does not permit a large dissipative damping. In most types of indicating instruments the energy level of operation permits the full use of dissipative damping with the resulting advantage that response time is independent of external circuit conditions.

Three types of dissipative damping are available for bringing the moving system of an instrument to rest: (1) *solid friction* whose torque is a function of load but is independent of velocity; (2) *fluid damping*, which is proportional to velocity;[16] and (3) *eddy-current damping*, which is also proportional to velocity.[17] Solid friction is always unavoidably present in the instrument bearings, and always plays some part (usually quite small) in bringing the system to rest. Either fluid damping or eddy-current damping is generally incorporated into the instrument design and is used to absorb and dissipate the energy of motion of the system.

Friction. If the equation of motion of a damped harmonic oscillator[18] is rewritten to include the effect of frictional torque, we have

$$P\frac{d^2\theta}{dt^2} + A\frac{d\theta}{dt} + U\theta \pm F = 0$$

where P is the moment of inertia of the system, A is the damping constant proportional to velocity (fluid or electromagnetic damping or a combination of the two), U is the control constant of the spring, and F is the frictional torque. The $\pm$ sign is necessary since the frictional torque always acts in such a direction as to oppose the motion. For simplicity

[16] At high velocities the torque of fluid damping is proportional to the square of the velocity, but in most instrument applications the velocity is low enough that, to a sufficiently good approximation, the torque may be assumed to be proportional to the first power of velocity.

[17] This is true at all velocities, provided no temperature change is involved.

[18] See Chapter 3.

we will consider that no external forces act; i.e. that the moving system is returning to its zero rest position after the removal of a deflecting torque. The "steady-state" solution to this equation can be immediately written from its similarity to the galvanometer equation

$$\theta = \pm \frac{F}{U} = \pm \zeta$$

defining an angle ζ at which the system will rest in equilibrium between the control torque and the frictional torque.

The motion of the system can be deduced to a sufficient approximation for our purposes without completely solving the equation. It will be noted that the rest position under the action of solid friction differs from the rest position without friction by ζ, the angle of repose at which frictional torque balances spring torque since, when both the acceleration and velocity are zero, we have $U\theta = F$, or $\theta = F/U = \zeta$. Now, if we were to consider a system in which the only damping torque were that resulting from pivot friction, our equation of motion would be

$$P\frac{d^2\theta}{dt^2} + U\theta \pm F = 0$$

or

$$\frac{d^2\theta}{dt^2} = \frac{-U\theta \pm F}{P} = \frac{-U}{P}(\theta \pm \zeta)$$

The acceleration is proportional, not to the displacement (θ) but to the difference between the displacement angle and the angle of repose ($\theta \pm \zeta$), the sign of ζ being taken so that at any instant the frictional torque opposes the motion. Such a system would oscillate in a succession of simple harmonic excursions of diminishing amplitude, whose reference zero is shifted for each excursion by an amount ζ in the direction from which it last traveled. Thus, if we start with a deflection θ, its excess over ζ is $(\theta - \zeta)$, and the system will swing to an equal deflection $-(\theta - \zeta)$ on the other side of the apparent zero $+\zeta$, so that the negative maximum is $(-\theta + 2\zeta)$. On the next swing in the positive direction the apparent zero is $-\zeta$, a zero shift of 2ζ, and the amplitude will be $(\theta - 2\zeta)$, so that the new maximum will be $(\theta - 4\zeta)$. Thus for every complete oscillation the amplitude decreases by a constant amount 4ζ; i.e. the amplitude of the deflection decreases in an arithmetic progression. This is shown in Fig. 4(*a*). As we have seen previously in our analysis of the galvanometer equation,[19] the effect of fluid or electromagnetic damping is to decrease the deflection by a constant ratio, i.e.

$$\frac{\theta_1}{\theta_2} = \frac{\theta_2}{\theta_3} = \ldots = \delta$$

[19] See p. 54, Chapter 3.

as shown in Fig. 4(*b*). The combined effects of frictional and damping torques are superposed in the actual motion to bring the system to rest more quickly as shown in Fig. 4(*c*).[20] These relations have been considered by Drysdale and Jolley,[21] who state that in the presence of both pivot friction and damping the relation between successive maximum excursions of the pointer is

$$\theta_{n+1} = \alpha\theta_n - (\alpha + 1)\zeta$$

where $\alpha = 1/\delta$. In Fig. 5, deflection is plotted against time for a damped harmonic oscillator with and without pivot friction, for three values of

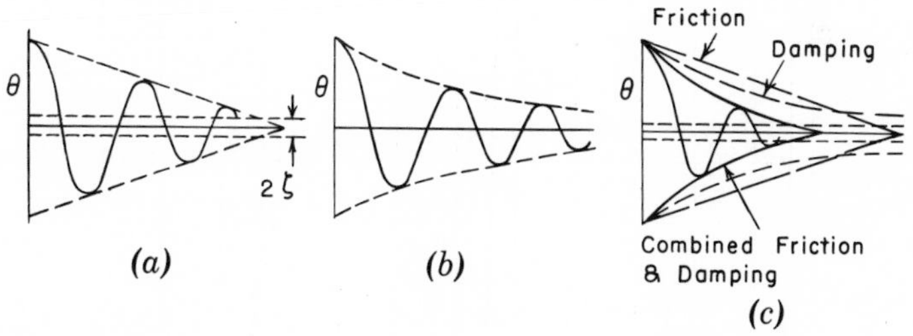

FIG. 4.

damping corresponding to $\delta = 2.5$, 5, and 10. It is assumed that the pivot friction corresponds to an angle of repose ζ which is 1% of the initial deflections.[22] It will be seen that the system comes to rest somewhat sooner in the presence of friction than would be the case if friction were absent, but that the effect is really quite small even if the friction angle amounts to as much as 1% of the deflection (a comparatively large value of friction). The fact that the equilibrium position of the pointer is indefinite by the amount of the angle of repose and depends on the way in which the rest position is approached is usually far more significant to the user than is the decrease in the response time of the system as a result of friction. Since the angle of repose has a constant value for a given combination of spring and bearing, it will be apparent that the effect of friction in bringing the system to rest is relatively greater for small than for large changes in deflection.

[20] For the purpose of illustration, the relative effect of friction has been greatly exaggerated over what would be found in an actual instrument.

[21] Drysdale and Jolley, *op. cit.*, vol. 1, p. 90.

[22] In portable instruments the angle of repose is rarely more than a few tenths of a degree, and is 0.1° or less in high-grade instruments. If, in the example of Fig. 5, the angle of repose is 0.2°, the initial deflection plotted would correspond to a 20° arc, or about $\frac{1}{5}$ of full-scale deflection in a typical instrument.

Fluid Damping. The only type of fluid damping employed in modern instruments[23] is air damping, and, since free-air damping is relatively inefficient, a closed damping system is generally used. This generally consists of a light aluminum vane (or pair of vanes) moving with small clearance in a closed sector-shaped box.[24] The air enclosed in the box is compressed ahead of the moving vane and flows back over its edge

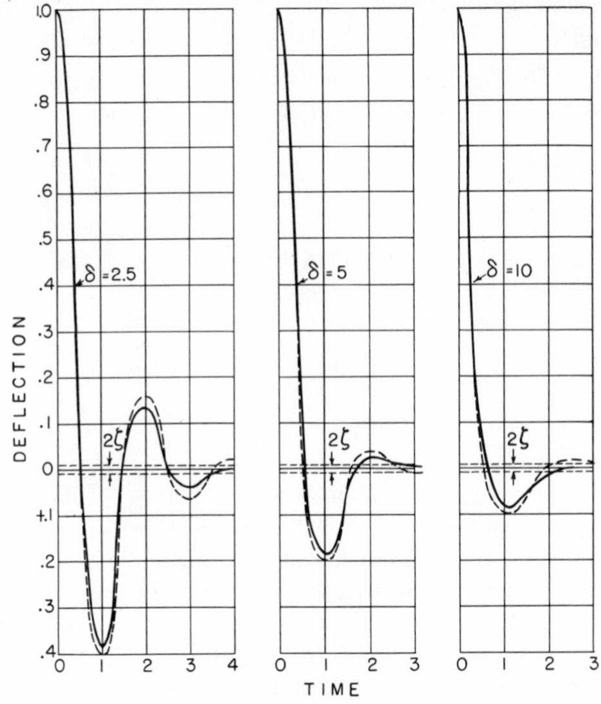

FIG. 5.

into the space behind it to equalize the pressure. In this process energy is extracted from the moving system and converted to heat, so that the system is brought to rest. Drysdale and Jolley[25] have stated and experimentally verified the following approximate formula for air damping with plane vanes in a sector box:

$$A = \left(\frac{0.345}{d} + 0.235\right) ba^2 \text{ dyne-cm/radian/sec}$$

where b is the width and a the length (in centimeters) of the rectangular

[23] Except for the galvanometer oscillograph in which oil damping is used. See Chapter 14 on wave-form and frequency measurements.

[24] See Chapter 10.

[25] Drysdale and Jolley, *op. cit.*, vol. 1, p. 99.

vane, and d is the clearance in millimeters between the edge of the vane and the sector box. This formula is for double vanes, one on either side of the axis of the moving system. For a single vane having the same dimensions the damping constant would be half as large. If the edges of the vane are folded back into the form of a tray, so that a longer path is provided for the air returning to the low-pressure side of the vane, the damping constant is increased by about 30%. This latter construction has the added advantage that it materially increases the stiffness and mechanical strength of the vane without adding much to the weight or inertia of the system.

Magnetic Damping. In a permanent-magnet, moving-coil instrument, whose moving system operates in a strong magnetic field, electromagnetic damping is accomplished by using a short-circuited turn on the moving coil. This is usually a light aluminum frame (or coil former) on which the coil is wound. By properly choosing the width and thickness of this coil frame, the damping can be brought to a suitable value. In addition the aluminum frame greatly increases the mechanical strength and dimensional stability of the moving system.[26] The damping effect of such a frame is easily computed. Considering it as a single-turn coil moving with an angular velocity ω in a radial field, the current induced in it is

$$i = \frac{aB}{10^8 R}\,\omega$$

where a is the area of the coil in square centimeters, and B is the flux density in gausses in the air gap of the magnet. The torque developed by the reaction between the magnetic field and the current is

$$\mathcal{T} = \frac{i}{10} \cdot ldB = \frac{iaB}{10}$$

where l is the length and d the diameter of the frame. If the frame has width w centimeters and thickness t centimeters, and is made of a material having a resistivity of ρ microhm-centimeters, its resistance is

$$R = \frac{2(l + d)\rho}{10^6 wt} \text{ ohms}$$

Then we have finally, as the damping constant,

$$A = \frac{wta^2B^2}{2\rho(l + d)} \times 10^{-3} \text{ dyne-cm/radian/sec}$$

[26] In cases where the damping effect of such a frame is not desired, it is frequently used because of mechanical considerations, but is slotted so that it does not form a closed circuit.

In other types of instruments, damping is accomplished by a light aluminum disc or sector moving in the air gap between the poles of a permanent magnet. Eddy currents set up in the disc by its motion in the field dissipate the energy of the system and bring it to rest. The arrangement is shown schematically in Fig. 6. If B is the flux density (assumed uniform) in the air gap of the magnet and u is the linear velocity of the element of the disc under the magnet pole, an emf of magnitude $V = (cBu/10^8)$ volt is induced in the disc. This produces a belt of current of width b under the pole.[27] If the disc thickness is t and its resistivity is ρ microhm-cm, the resistance of the section beneath the pole is $\dfrac{c\rho}{bt \times 10^6}$ ohm. We will assume that the total effective resistance of the eddy-current paths is K times as great as the section under the pole. Then the current is

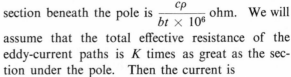

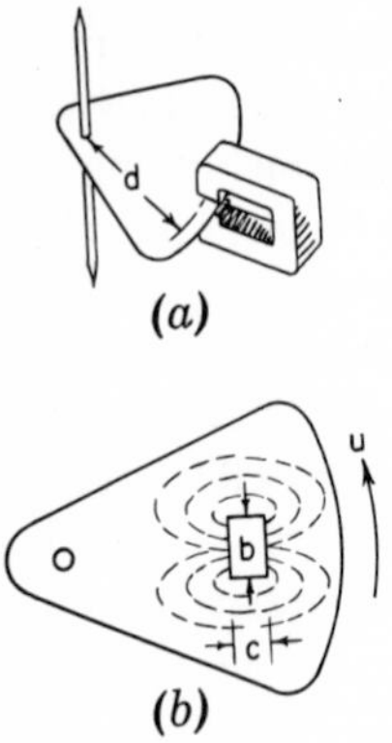

FIG. 6.

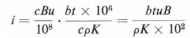

$$i = \frac{cBu}{10^8} \cdot \frac{bt \times 10^6}{c\rho K} = \frac{btuB}{\rho K \times 10^2}$$

The force of the reaction between the current and field is

$$F = \frac{cBi}{10} = \frac{cbtuB^2}{\rho K \times 10^3} = \frac{tu\Phi^2}{\rho Ka \times 10^3}$$

where $a = bc$ = area of the pole face, and $\Phi = Ba$ is the total flux in the air gap. Now the moment arm of this force is the distance (d) from the axis of the disc to the magnet pole face, the linear velocity $u = d\omega$, and the torque $\mathscr{T} = dF$. Then[28]

$$A = \frac{\mathscr{T}}{\omega} = \frac{\Phi^2 d^2 t}{\rho Ka \times 10^3} \text{ dyne-cm/radian/sec}$$

As defined above, K is the ratio of the total resistance of the eddy-current paths to the resistance of the portion directly under the pole face. K may be expected to increase rapidly as the magnet is moved toward the edge of the disc, since the return flow paths are restricted to a small volume of the disc. Experimentally[29] it has been found that the factor K has a

[27] It will be realized that this is only approximately true since it represents an idealized flux distribution. However, the factor K, to be introduced into the expression to obtain total resistance, will also permit the use of the stated approximation.

[28] Φ is in maxwells, ρ in microhm-centimeters, and all mechanical dimensions are in centimeters in this formula.

[29] Drysdale and Jolley, *op. cit.*, vol. 1, p. 107. See also Edgcumbe and Ockenden, *op. cit.*, p. 67.

moderately low value (approximately 6) when the magnet pole is well away from the edge of the disc but rises rapidly as the edge is approached ($K > 30$ at the disc edge). It must be expected, then, that the damping constant will first increase with d^2 as the magnet is moved from the axis toward the edge of the disc, go through a maximum, and then decrease rapidly near the disc edge as K becomes very large. Actually, the torque maximum occurs, for a given angular velocity, when d is approximately 80% of the disc radius.

Damping Factor. The damping of an instrument is frequently expressed in terms of its damping factor,[30] which we have already defined as the ratio of successive pointer excursions ($\delta = \theta_1/\theta_2$). This factor is usually most conveniently determined by taking the ratio of the final steady deflection to the initial overshoot when the instrument is suddenly deflected from its zero position to some convenient scale point. Both the overshoot and the final deflection should be expressed in terms of angular measure if the scale is not uniform. Not only are these excursions (θ_1 from zero to the equilibrium deflected position, and θ_2 from the equilibrium position to the first maximum) more easily determined than any subsequent excursion of the pointer as it comes to rest, but since they are larger they can be measured with less uncertainty and therefore will yield a more accurate value of damping factor. The damping factor, together with the period of the instrument, determines its *response time*, the time which is required after an abrupt change in the measured quantity until the pointer has come to apparent rest in its new equilibrium position. Response time is of considerable importance to the user of an instrument since it is a measure of the time of waiting before a reading of the indication can be made. Its significance is emphasized if a fluctuating quantity must be observed, for, unless the response time is less than the interval between changes of the quantity, observation of the changes will be difficult or even impossible.[31]

Operating Torque

The means by which an electrical stimulus is converted into a mechanical force, in order that the moving system may deflect, differs widely in various types and designs of instruments. The means of operation of various instrument types will be examined in detail later, but it is

[30] The relation between damping factor and relative damping may be obtained from Fig. 7, p. 63, Chapter 3.

[31] A bridge method for electrically determining the mechanical parameters (period, damping coefficient, moment of inertia, and restoring torque gradient) of permanent-magnet moving-coil instruments has been described by R. W. Gilbert of the Weston Electrical Instrument Corporation. See *Trans. AIEE,* **67**, 411 (1948).

appropriate at this point to call attention to a fundamental principle which governs the operation of all deflecting instruments. It can be shown from dynamical considerations that, for a mechanical system such as that in an indicating instrument (having one degree of freedom—rotation about an axis), *the torque which produces the rotation is proportional to the rate of change with angular displacement of the potential energy of the system.* Since the work done on a conservative[32] system is equal to the gain in the energy of the system, we can say that force × displacement equals gain in energy or, in our particular system, torque × angular displacement equals gain in energy. Now the system is at rest at the beginning and end of the displacement so that only the change in the potential energy need be considered. We are concerned here only with equilibrium conditions. Thus we may say that $\mathscr{T}\theta = W_\theta - W_0$, where $\mathscr{T}$ is torque, θ is angular displacement, W is the potential energy stored in the electric or magnetic arrangement which produces deflection. If we differentiate this expression with respect to θ, we have the expression $\mathscr{T} = dW/d\theta$, which can be used to determine the law of response of any deflecting instrument for which we can set up an expression for the potential energy of the system and differentiate it with respect to θ.[33] For example, in the permanent-magnet, moving-coil instrument (including the d'Arsonval galvanometer) the potential energy of the system is $W = Ni$, where N is the number of flux linkages of the coil with the field and i is the current in the coil. The deflecting torque is then $\mathscr{T} = dW/d\theta = i(dN/d\theta)$. If N is in maxwell-turns and i in abamperes, the torque will be in dyne-centimeters. If the field in the air gap of the instrument is uniform (radial) in the region in which the coil moves, then $dN/d\theta =$ constant. Since the deflecting torque is proportional to the current it is to be expected in these circumstances that the angular deflection will be proportional to the current and the instrument will have a uniform scale. Other examples[34] of the application of this principle will be considered later as the various types of instruments are discussed.

Errors

As related to deflection instruments, errors may be divided into two classes: (1) errors of indication, and (2) errors of observation.

Errors of Indication. In addition to errors that result from incorrect

[32] Although it is true that the system which we are considering is not completely conservative because of the presence and effect of friction, this may be ignored in the present argument since friction is so small as to be practically negligible in a well-constructed instrument.

[33] See Drysdale, *J. Sci. Inst.*, **9**, 209 (1932).

[34] See Chapter 10.

placement of the scale marks in calibration and from inelastic yield of the instrument springs (zero drift), errors in indications may result from pivot friction, from incorrect zero setting, or from various external influences (such as temperature, magnetic fields, frequency, and wave form). Failure of the pointer to come to rest at the proper position as a result of friction can usually be counteracted by *gently* tapping the instrument with a finger. Vigorous tapping will defeat this purpose and may even injure the bearing.

Almost all modern instruments are equipped with a zero adjuster so that the pointer may be correctly set on the zero of the scale.[35] Generally this consists of a crank arm which engages a fork on the upper spring abutment, allowing the equilibrium position of the pointer to be moved through several degrees. This adjustment is accessible from the outside of the instrument case and should have sufficient friction to prevent it from loosening and changing position. The linkage should be such that the external member can be rotated through 360° without damage to the mechanism. The instrument should be gently tapped while the zero adjustment is being made, in order that the effect of pivot friction may be eliminated.

Corrections can be applied for the effect of temperature influence if the temperature coefficient of indication is known. Allowance can be made for the effects of other influences in certain cases, while in others the influence itself must be minimized or the condition giving rise to it avoided to ensure freedom from errors. No general discussion of these considerations is practicable at this point, but they will be examined for particular types of instruments later.

Observational Errors. Apart from misreading the scale, observational errors may be either parallax errors or errors of estimation. Parallax errors arise when the observer's line of sight is not the same as that used in the calibration. If the line of sight during calibration was perpendicular to the plane of the scale, then the parallax error for a line of sight departing from the normal by an angle α will be $e = d \tan \alpha$, where d is the perpendicular distance from the pointer to the scale (d and e are expressed in the same units here). For precise indicating instruments the usual device employed to eliminate parallax errors is a mirror in the plane of the scale,[36] coincidence of the pointer and its reflected image being used to establish the correct line of sight. This method of avoiding parallax assumes a single line of sight, so that observations should be made with one eye. This may result in fatigue or eyestrain in a long series of observations,

[35] It will be obvious that the effect of a bent pointer cannot be compensated by zero adjustment if the instrument scale is not uniform. For a complete discussion of this point see Brooks, *Trans. AIEE*, **39**, part 1, pp. 503–508 (1920).

[36] See p. 107.

and in such circumstances a projection camera or some other optical device which will convert binocular vision to single-line vision is helpful.

An observer normally estimates pointer position to the nearest tenth of a scale division. However, it must be realized that such estimation may be in error, and that its accuracy will depend on width of scale lines and pointer, distance between scale lines, the individual observer's unconscious bias, and the particular tenth which is being estimated.

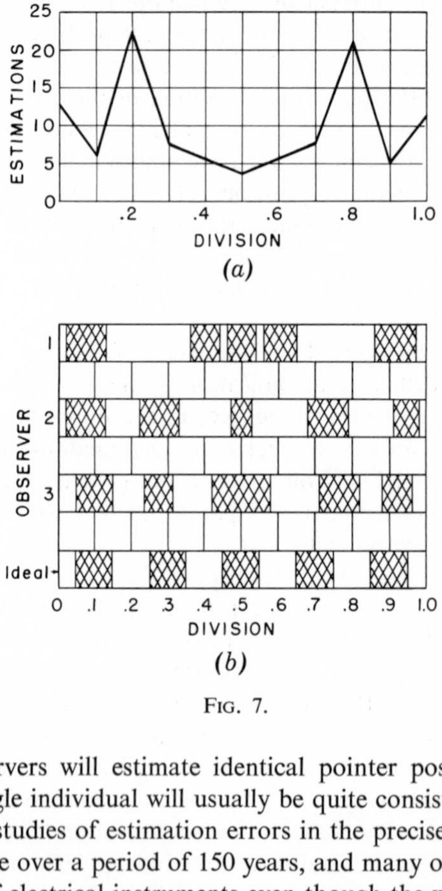

FIG. 7.

Different observers will estimate identical pointer positions differently, although a single individual will usually be quite consistent in his estimations. Many studies of estimation errors in the precise reading of scales have been made over a period of 150 years, and many of the results apply to the scales of electrical instruments even though the work refers largely to other types of uniformly divided scales on which the position of an index mark is estimated to tenths of the marked divisions.

A very comprehensive and systematic study of the effects of various factors on estimation errors was made by Bäckström,[37] and some of the

[37] Bäckström, *Zeits. für Instrumentenk.*, **50,** 561, 609, 665 (1930) and **52,** 105, 260 (1932).

significant results of his work on uniform scales will be summarized here. For a series of observations in which the index (pointer) position was uniformly distributed over the interval between division marks (appearing once at each 0.01 division in a series of 100 readings), he found that (1) the several tenths were estimated with different frequencies; (2) these frequencies remained constant for individual observers from one set of observations to another over a period of as much as 6 years; (3) the estimations were symmetrical about the midpoint of the division. A typical set of results is shown in Fig. 7(*a*). The general shape of the curve remained the same although its details differed considerably from one observer to another. These differences in the patterns of individual

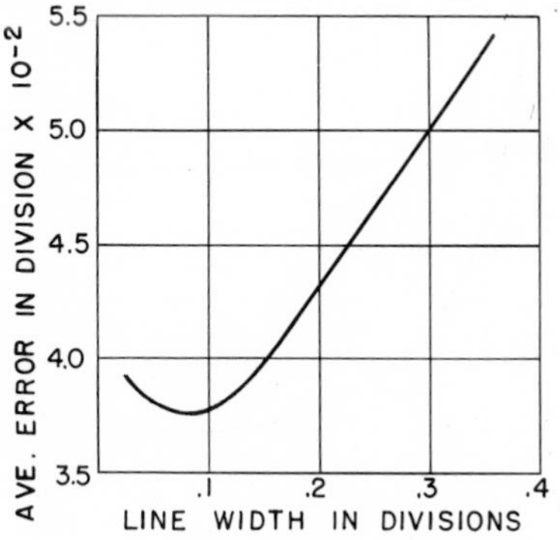

FIG. 8.

observers are shown in Fig. 7(*b*), in which the actual pointer position is shown, for each estimation in 100, for 3 observers. If the pointer position were correctly estimated all the blocks would be of equal width and centered on the indicated tenth division, as shown for the ideal observer. While the subjective division of the scale into tenths is different for each of the observers, it is in each instance symmetrical about the midpoint of the division. The results shown are typical of a large group of observers.

Bäckström also studied the influence of the thickness of scale lines on decimal estimation. His results are shown graphically in Fig. 8, for scales whose divisions were 2 mm wide, and whose lines had the width indicated in the figure. The width of the index line whose position was estimated was the same in each case as the width of the scale lines. The curve represents the average error of estimation of 6 skilled observers. Significant deviations were found for individual observers, just as in the previous series of observations. It may be noted that the minimum error of estimation occured when the line width was 0.1 of the division width[38]

[38] About this line width is used on the scales of high-grade portable instruments.

but was not critical, as is apparent from the flatness of the curve in this region.

Another series of tests showed the influence of the size of scale divisions on the accuracy of estimation. The results of these tests are shown in Fig. 9, as average errors for a group of observers. The average error of estimation decreased with increasing division width, and the results indicate that errors of estimation are significantly reduced by increasing the division width to about 2 mm, but that there is very little gain from further increase.[39]

It may be concluded from these data that, although an individual observer will make estimations of tenths of a division in much the same

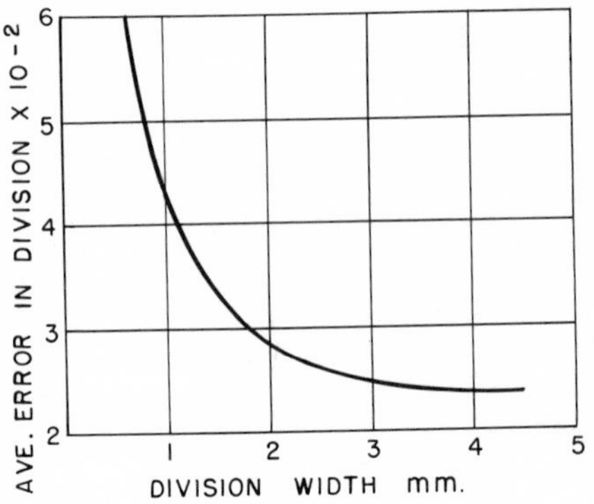

FIG. 9.

manner over long periods of time, the estimations of any particular observer cannot generally be depended on to be *accurate* to the nearest tenth of a division, except at the division marks themselves and at the midpoint of the division. It may also be concluded that different observers subjectively subdivide a scale interval differently; and that in general, even for practiced observers, observations by several individuals would be necessary to ensure that an estimation of pointer position was correct within a tenth division.

Instrument Specification

In the purchase of instruments, the user frequently has some choice between competing makes, and may desire either to secure the best

[39] It may be inferred from this that the use of a magnifying glass as a reading aid would be expected to improve reading accuracy up to a division width of about 2 mm, provided the field of the magnifier were flat and free from distortion, but that it would not be of significant assistance in reading more open scales. This conclusion is also in line with the writer's experience.

possible performance within a certain price range or to obtain an instrument which will satisfy certain minimum performance requirements at the lowest possible cost. In either case it is desirable to use a performance specification to ensure that the instrument purchased will adequately meet his needs. While the requirements of purchasers will vary widely, depending on the purpose for which the instrument will be used, consideration should be given to a number of factors which describe the instrument's appearance, its performance under operating conditions, and its ability to withstand the various hazards to which one may reasonably expect it to be subjected. These factors include such items as the appearance and workmanship of the case, mounting dimensions and interchangeability (if a panel or switchboard instrument), length of the scale, rated accuracy of indications, response time and damping of the moving system, effects of various influences (such as temperature, external field, and position), power consumption, ability to withstand shock or vibration, and effect of humidity on operation.

The writing of such specifications demands skill and judgment, and a considerable amount of technical knowledge about instruments as well as about the requirements of the particular application involved. Fortunately much of the information needed for specifications is available in the current revision of American Standard C39.1 for Electrical Indicating Instruments.[40] Representatives of leading manufacturers, users, and testing laboratories were included in the group who wrote this standard, and it represents their agreement on necessary and desirable features which manufacturers can incorporate in their products. Instrument users should acquaint themselves with this standard, which forms a suitable basis for writing purchase specifications. It is feasible in many instances to state the special requirements for a particular instrument which is to be purchased, and to require that "in addition the instrument shall comply with the applicable requirements of American Standard C39.1." It is not practicable, of course, to make tests for compliance with all requirements of this standard on each instrument purchased, nor was this intended by the writers of the standard. Some of the requirements are such that compliance tests would impair the usefulness of the individual instrument tested, e.g. vibration and shock tests; some would be too elaborate or expensive to make on each individual instrument, e.g. temperature-influence tests. Tests of this nature should be considered as type tests which need be performed only on a representative sample of an instrument type or model. Other tests, which are both simple and nondestructive, can readily be made by the purchaser, e.g. accuracy, loss, and

[40] Published by the American Standards Association, 70 East 45th Street, New York 17, N.Y.

balance tests, and will give a general indication of instrument quality. The extent to which a particular purchaser can or should check instruments for compliance with all features of a comprehensive specification will depend on the volume and importance of his purchases as well as his test facilities. In many instances the purchaser must rely on the established reputation for integrity of the manufacturer; the buyer's ability to discount the claims of overly enthusiastic sales engineers and writers of advertising copy will largely depend on his own knowledge of instruments and their expected limitations.

It is sometimes desirable that a portable instrument, in addition to complying with the over-all requirements of a particular accuracy class (for example, in the $\frac{1}{2}\%$ class, that no scale point be in error by more than $\frac{1}{2}\%$ of the full-scale value of the instrument), shall have scale subdivision of sufficiently high quality that linear interpolations may be applied from corrections obtained at cardinal points of the scale, in order to obtain results whose accuracy is somewhat better than that guaranteed for the accuracy class. In such a case a specification of scale subdivision which has been found useful is as follows: "The scale shall be accurately divided so that, after experimental corrections have been determined for cardinal points and after corresponding corrections have been applied to the subdivisions by linear interpolation, the difference between the experimental value and the interpolated value at any given subdivision shall not exceed 0.2% of full-scale value."[41]

[41] Where a scale of very high quality is required, 0.1% should be specified in place of 0.2%.

CHAPTER 5

DIRECT-CURRENT AMMETERS AND VOLTMETERS

Operating Principle

Permanent-magnet, moving-coil ammeters and voltmeters, universally used in d-c measurements, were first constructed as practical laboratory instruments by Edward Weston in 1888. Although the basic operating principle of all d-c instruments is the same as that of the d'Arsonval galvanometer,[1] there are some important differences which contribute greatly to their portability, permanence of calibration, and convenience in use. (1) The suspension, used in the galvanometer,[2] is replaced by hardened steel pivots which turn in jewel cup bearings. The restoring torque (arising from the elastic properties of the suspension strip in the case of the galvanometer) is supplied by spiral or helical springs which also conduct the operating current to and from the moving coil. (2) The mirror and optical system usually associated with the galvanometer are replaced by a pointer attached to the moving system, the deflection being indicated by the position of the pointer relative to a fixed scale, calibrated for reading the quantity measured, in amperes, volts, or some decimal multiple of them (micro, milli, kilo), or some derived quantity such as speed, temperature, resistance. Their operation, as is the case for all types of indicating instruments, is subject to the equations of motion already discussed for the galvanometer.

[1] Permanent-magnet, moving-coil instruments are sometimes referred to as d'Arsonval type instruments. This usage is deprecated.

[2] Some types of very sensitive pivoted instruments are called galvanometers by their manufacturers and are referred to as such by some writers. Although this classification (on the basis of sensitivity) can be justified, it seems preferable to this writer to distinguish between sensitive instruments on the basis of mechanical friction. We shall call galvanometers only those sensitive instruments whose moving systems are supported by suspensions so that their motions are free from the mechanical friction which is always present in the bearings of pivoted instruments.

The deflecting torque of permanent-magnet, moving-coil instruments results from the interaction of the current in the winding of the moving coil, and the field in the air gap of the permanent magnet. This torque is $\mathcal{T}_1 = BINlb$, where Nlb is area-turns in the moving coil, B is the field in the air gap, and I is the current through the moving coil. Control (restoring) torque is usually supplied by spiral springs (in some cases helical springs are used) and is $\mathcal{T}_2 = U\theta$, directly proportional to the angular deflection (θ) of the coil from its neutral position, the proportionality factor being the stiffness (U) of the springs. At equilibrium these two torques are equal and $\theta = I(BNlb/U)$; so that, if B has the same value at any position around the air gap, the angular deflection is directly proportional to the current in the moving coil. Actually the field is almost never completely uniform around the air gap. The field may be expected to fall off in strength toward the ends of the air gap as a result of the fringing effect, shown in Fig. 1. In addition inhomogeneities in the magnet pole pieces or core will result in small local irregularities of the field.[3] These departures from uniformity are usually small so that we are accustomed to think of the scale of a d-c instrument as being uniform. However, they are sufficient that precision instruments must be individually calibrated and their scales drawn after the instrument is assembled. On the other hand, when high accuracy is not required, as in switchboard or panel instruments, scales may be printed in advance of assembly, thus reducing the cost of the instrument. The departure of the scale from uniformity as a result of fringing may sometimes be detected by close examination, the scale being more open in its central portion than near its ends.

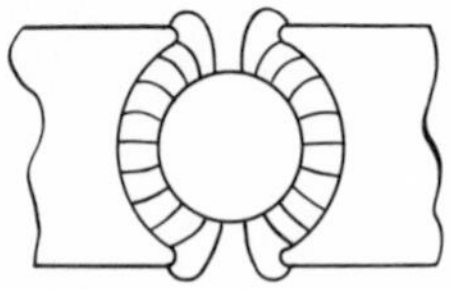

FIG. 1.

Damping torque is supplied in most d-c instruments by electromagnetic forces set up in the coil and the circuit to which it is connected, and in a metal frame or former on which the coil is wound. This frame acts as a short-circuited turn, and the magnitude of the damping torque is a function of the resistance of the damping frame. Damping is controlled in design by the proper choice of the thickness, width, and material of this frame. Aluminum, brass, and copper have all been used for the construction of damping frames. In some instruments, such as very sensitive microammeters, where the required air-gap field is so strong that a metal coil frame would provide too much damping, the coil is made self-supporting and the metal winding frame is eliminated, or, if a frame is used, it is cut so that it does not form a complete turn. In such instances

[3] Since the coil width subtends a considerable arc (usually 15° or more), local field irregularities will tend to be averaged out.

a resistor is usually connected across the coil to provide the necessary damping by absorbing energy from the moving system in the closed loop formed by the moving coil and the resistance across it, as a result of the back emf generated by the coil moving in the air-gap field.[4] Generally the resistance of this shunt is several times that of the coil itself. In addition to the electromagnetic damping provided by the metal winding form (or by the shunt circuit) there is always some bearing friction present which opposes coil motion and assists in bringing the coil to rest. Except in certain special applications, it is usually desirable that the sum of the damping torques from friction and from electromagnetic action be *less* than would be required for critical damping. Thus the moving system of a d-c instrument is usually moderately underdamped, the relative damping being not less than 0.2 to 0.3 for small instruments and not less than 0.45 for portable and switchboard instruments.[5] It is therefore to be expected that, after the current in a d-c instrument is suddenly changed, the pointer will overshoot its new equilibrium position by a moderate amount, coming to rest after one or more oscillations.

Power Requirements of D-C Instruments

Both ammeters and voltmeters are, in principle, current-measuring devices since their operation depends on the current in the moving coil. The ampere-turns in the moving coil at full-scale deflection will generally range between 0.1 and 1.5 ampere-turns, depending on the instrument size, the operating torque requirements, and the strength of the field in the air gap. In microammeters and low-range milliammeters up to perhaps 20 ma, the entire current to be measured is sent through the moving coil. An exception to this rule is the use of a high-resistance shunt to provide damping in sensitive microammeters that do not have a metal coil form. Since the instrument springs serve as current leads to the moving coil, their current-carrying capacity limits the current which can be used in the moving coil; i.e. the current which they will carry without appreciable temperature rise as a result of I^2R heating is the effective limit of coil current. For higher current ranges (usually above 20 ma) the moving element is shunted to by-pass current around the coil

[4] Some makers have used frameless coils over which are wound a few turns to form a closed damping circuit. This increases the value of the external resistance needed for critical damping; by proper choice of wire size and number of turns in the damping winding, the same basic coil may be made to meet various "CDRX" requirements.

[5] These values of relative damping correspond to damping factors of 2, 2.5, and 5 respectively, where damping factor is defined as the ratio of deviations of the pointer in consecutive swings from its equilibrium position. (See the current American Standard for Electrical Indicating Instruments, ASA C39, published by the American Standards Association, New York City.)

and springs. Voltmeters of all ranges use a moving coil together with sufficient series resistance to limit the instrument current to the desired value.

The essential difference in design between ammeters and voltmeters arises from considerations of the effect of the instrument on the circuits in which it will be used. When an ammeter is inserted in a circuit [Fig. 2(*a*)] to measure current it introduces additional resistance and to some extent reduces the current which would have flowed in its absence. It is therefore desirable to keep the resistance, and hence the voltage drop, of an ammeter low for minimum effect on the circuit. By a similar argument [Fig. 2(*b*)] it may be seen that the current drawn by a voltmeter should be kept small and that its resistance should be high. The same conclusions are reached if one considers the power consumption in the instrument. An ammeter is used to measure current. Its power consumption may be written as I^2R. Therefore R must be kept small to limit power consumption except in low-range instruments where I is small. On the other hand a voltmeter is used to measure voltage. Its power consumption may be written as E^2/R, and R must be large to limit power requirements.

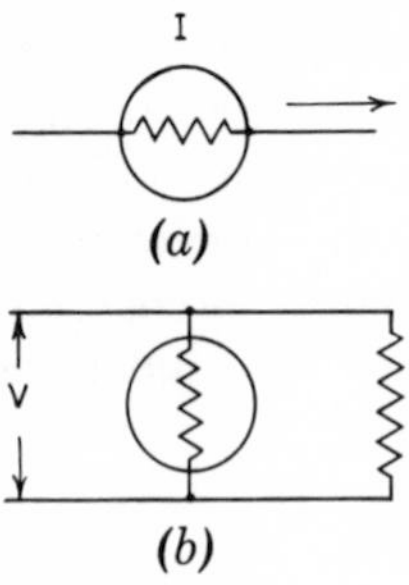

FIG. 2.

In present American practice most d-c ammeters are designed to have a voltage drop of 50 mv at full scale. In older designs, and for special applications, the voltage drop may range upward to 200 mv. Most d-c voltmeters (except in special applications) are designed for a full-scale current of 20, 10, 5, or 1 ma. There is a considerable tendency to standardize on the lower (1 ma) value.[6] In some special types of d-c voltmeters, full-scale current may be as low as 10 or even 5 μa. However, such instruments are delicate and are not used for general laboratory work. Thus, excluding low-range current-measuring instruments, most d-c ammeters are actually 50-mv millivoltmeters operated with a suitable shunt; while voltmeters are low-range milliammeters (or even microammeters) operated with a suitable series resistance.[7]

[6] Instead of stating the full-scale operating current, manufacturers often give equivalent information by listing the "ohms per volt" of a voltmeter. Thus if the full-scale current is 1 ma the voltmeter is stated to have a resistance of 1000 ohms per volt. A 10-volt instrument of this type would have a resistance of 10,000 ohms, and a 100-volt voltmeter a resistance of 100,000 ohms.

[7] The American Standard for Electrical Indicating Instruments (ASA C39.1—1949) specifies the "loss" of instruments. The term *current loss* applies to voltage circuits, and in a voltage-measuring instrument is the *current* required for full-scale deflection. *Voltage loss* applies to current circuits, and in a current-measuring instrument is the *voltage* between terminals at full-scale deflection.

In the case of d-c ammeters or voltmeters the power requirements of the instrument together with its auxiliary shunt or series resistance can be calculated very simply. For a 10-amp instrument consisting of a 50-mv millivoltmeter and shunt, the power loss at full scale will be $0.05 \times 10 = 0.5$ watt. For a 100-volt voltmeter having a 1000-ohm/volt movement, the full-scale power loss will be $100 \times 0.001 = 0.1$ watt. These losses should not be confused with those of the deflecting element itself, which may be very much less. For example, the resistance of a 50-mv instrument may be 5 ohms, of which 1 ohm is in the coil and 4 ohms are in a series resistance.[8] The power loss in this circuit at full-scale current is 0.0005 watt, of which only 20% (0.0001 watt) is in the coil itself. In the example above, of the 100-volt voltmeter having a total power loss of 0.1 watt, most of this loss is in the series resistor, there being less than 0.003 watt dissipated in the coil itself at full-scale current. It should be pointed out that this power requirement represents the heat loss (I^2R) in the instrument coil, resulting from the current I in the resistance of the winding. Although this power must be supplied continuously to maintain the deflection at a fixed value, the energy stored in the springs of the deflected instrument may be much smaller. If the deflecting torque of the instrument is 300 dyne-cm/radian (a reasonable value for a portable instrument) and the angular displacement at full scale is 100°, the energy stored in the springs at full-scale deflection ($\frac{1}{2}U\theta^2$) is 450 ergs or 0.000045 watt-sec. If we consider the instrument as an electric motor whose useful work is stored as potential energy in the springs, and if we assume that deflection is attained in 2 sec, the average rate of conversion is about 0.00002 watt. Of course this represents a rather low efficiency (i.e. only a few percent of the electrical energy available at the instrument coil is converted into mechanical work during the motion of the deflecting system), but low motor efficiency must be expected since the instrument damping is principally accomplished by dissipating energy in the damping winding, only a small fraction being returned to the circuit as conservative damping by the action of the back emf generated in the moving coil itself.[9] This is a necessary consequence of the usual requirement that the response of the instrument be practically independent of the characteristics of the circuit in which it operates. For very sensitive microammeters this is not true; much less energy is available to deflect the moving system of the instrument in a reasonable time, and the damping is made conservative to a much greater extent than in a high-torque instrument. It will be found, therefore, that for such instruments the damping is dependent on

[8] The use of series resistance for the temperature compensation of millivoltmeters will be discussed below.

[9] See discussion of efficiency and its relation to damping in Chapter 3.

circuit conditions to a considerable extent; and the resistance of the circuit in which the instrument will be used must be considered. For this reason many manufacturers list the external critical damping resistance of low-range microammeters together with their internal resistance.

Instrument Magnets

Special alloy steels are used in instrument-magnet construction. Tungsten steel has been popular since the early days of electrical instruments. Cobalt-chrome steels, because of their higher coercivity, have sometimes been employed where economy of weight and space is important. In recent years Alnico magnets have been used to an increasing extent in instrument applications. Ideally, an instrument magnet should have in its air gap high magnetic flux density,[10] which does not change with time or temperature. The design of instrument magnets involves considerations of weight and economy of space, expense of materials and manufacturing procedures, and permanence of magnetization both as regards aging and the hazards of demagnetization encountered in service conditions, as well as the field strength desired in the air gap. In most cases, the field strength may be expected to be between 500 and 2500 lines per sq cm in a gap 1.5 to 2.5 mm long, depending on the size and type of instrument. The use of laminated magnet structures, particularly in some miniature instruments, is dictated by considerations of convenience in manufacture. Such structures may be inferior to solid steel forgings or castings but can be turned out as punchings from sheet material and are sometimes employed in cheap mass-produced instruments.

Some of the important factors which must be considered in the design of permanent magnets for instrument use are discussed in another chapter,[11] together with the factors which influence their stability. It is there shown that, for efficient design, the cross section of the magnet may be large and its length small for materials of high coercivity and low remanence; whereas the length of the magnet should be large and its cross section small if the material has low coercivity and high remanence. Thus the magnetic properties of a material determine the best shape of magnet made from it. Long, thin magnets of horseshoe shape are characteristic of tungsten and chromium steels because of their high remanence and low coercivity. Developments in the field of magnet materials have been in the direction of increased coercivity combined usually with reduced remanence. Hence magnets made from the newer materials are generally shorter and of greater cross section. Also, since the

[10] In practice, the flux density must be limited to such values that magnetic impurities in the coil will not cause trouble.

[11] See Chapter 9.

dispersion-hardening alloys such as Alnico are generally very hard and brittle so that they cannot be machined except by grinding, instrument magnets made from them must be of simple shape.

A typical instrument-magnet structure [Fig. 3(*a*)] consists of a horseshoe-shaped magnet of forged and hardened tungsten steel with accurately

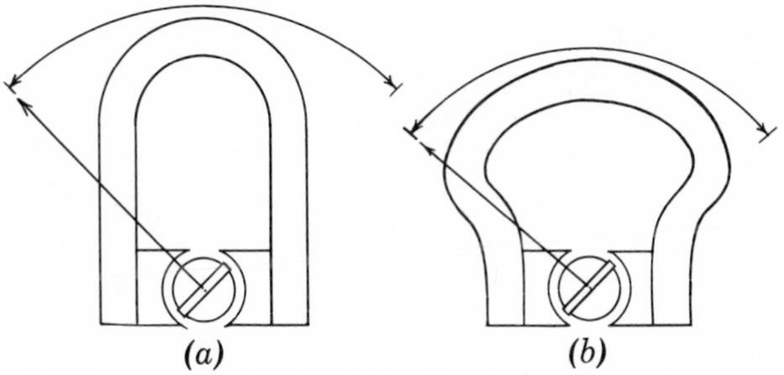

FIG. 3.

machined soft-iron pole pieces bolted to the inner faces of the magnet. A soft-iron cylinder fixed between the pole pieces completes the magnetic circuit and provides a uniform air gap in which the moving coil of the instrument turns. A variation of this horseshoe shape [Fig. 3(*b*)] makes

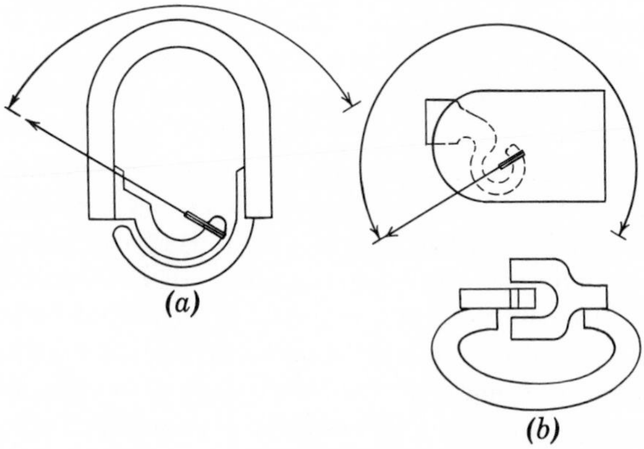

FIG. 4.

more efficient use of the available space under the scale of the instrument and thus permits a longer scale in the same size of instrument.

By using hook-shaped pole pieces (Fig. 4) and a single air gap operating on only one side of the moving coil, further scale expansion is possible. The form of Fig. 4(*a*) permits the construction of a uniform scale over about 120° of arc in contrast to the 90 to 100° scale of Fig. 3(*b*). The scale can be expanded to 250 to 300° of arc by magnets and pole pieces of special shapes. Figure 4(*b*) indicates how this is accomplished in one line of instruments, using a low-coercivity magnet. Such expanded scales do not offer any advantages over the normal type of scale, for portable instruments in which accuracy of reading is of primary importance, since a very long scale imposes severe design requirements on the instrument springs in order that they operate properly over an angular deflection of 300°. However, the expanded scale is of advantage in some switchboard applications where accuracy of indication is not of primary importance

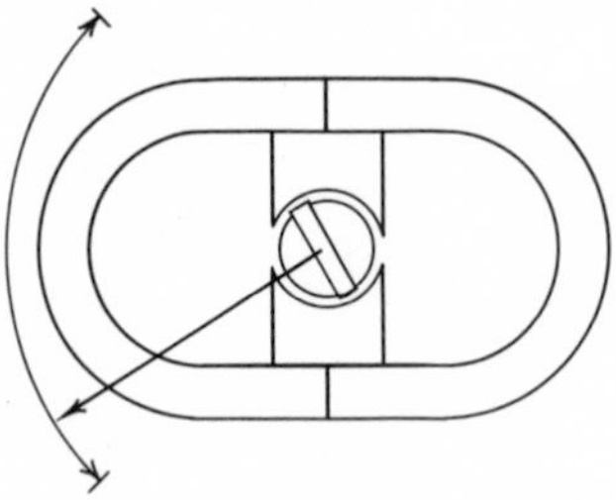

FIG. 5.

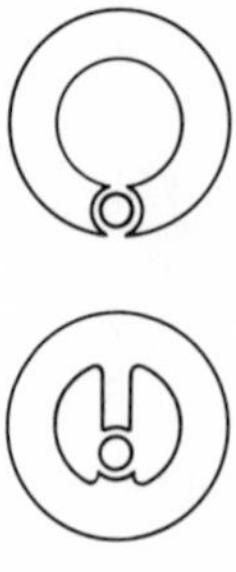

FIG. 6.

but where space is at a premium and instrument indications must be read at a distance.

Double magnets (Fig. 5) are sometimes used where a particularly strong field is needed, as well as in the large laboratory standard type of instrument.

The use of cobalt steel, having a higher coercivity than tungsten steel, permits the design of shorter, thicker magnets such as those shown in Fig. 6. Since a high cobalt content (up to 35%) is required for best performance, and since this steel is considerably more expensive than tungsten or chromium steels, it is generally employed only where economy of space or reduction in weight is important. A tungsten steel magnet can be replaced by a much lighter one of cobalt steel. In some cases cast magnets result in important manufacturing savings, and cobalt steel is sometimes used for this purpose. It will be noted that in the designs sketched in Fig. 6 soft-iron pole pieces have been eliminated. Because of the greater cross-sectional area of the magnet required with this material it is possible to utilize the ends of the magnet as the outer sides of the air gap.

Figure 7 illustrates one type of magnet construction in which Alnico is used. It will be noted that the magnet itself is very short and thick, and that the only machining required on it is to grind the ends flat and parallel to receive the soft-iron pole pieces. Another magnet design (Fig. 8) utilizing the special properties of Alnico is the concentric structure used by General Electric. Two sector-shaped Alnico magnets, having ground cylindrical faces, are placed inside a soft-steel ring and the assembly is die-cast together. The moving element and the soft-iron core are

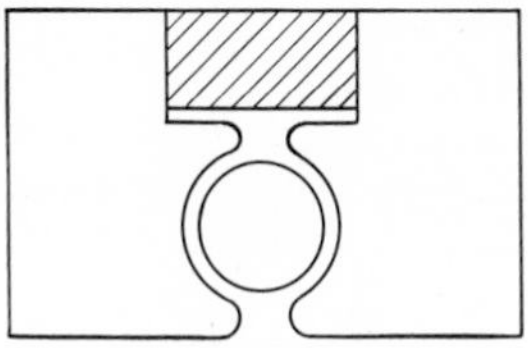

FIG. 7.

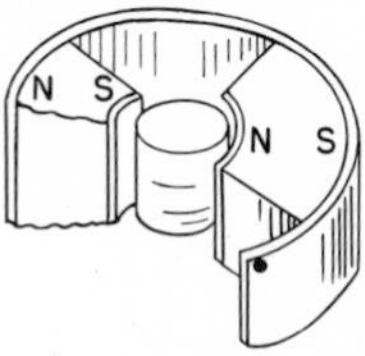

FIG. 8.

mounted in a separate die-cast frame which fits between the inner Alnico pole faces. The soft-steel ring, surrounding the Alnico magnets, serves two purposes: (1) it completes the magnetic circuit, and (2) it shields the element against stray magnetic fields. Alnico is also used in the magnet structure of General Electric's long-scale switchboard instruments as shown in Fig. 9. The pole shoe and armature are of soft iron, and the outer ring, forming the return magnetic circuit, is a laminated steel shell. The Alnico is magnetized radially. Alnico is used in a somewhat different structure in the Westinghouse long-scale instrument (Fig. 10). The Alnico ring is magnetized vertically, and the magnetic circuit is completed by the inner and outer soft-steel pole pieces which are brazed to the Alnico. The magnetic shunt which bypasses flux around the air gap is used to adjust the strength of the air-gap field. By means of a screw, accessible from the front of the instrument, the position of the shunt and therefore the magnitude of its shunting action, can be adjusted after the instrument is completely assembled. In this way the pointer is brought to coincidence with the end mark on the preprinted scale for full-scale current.

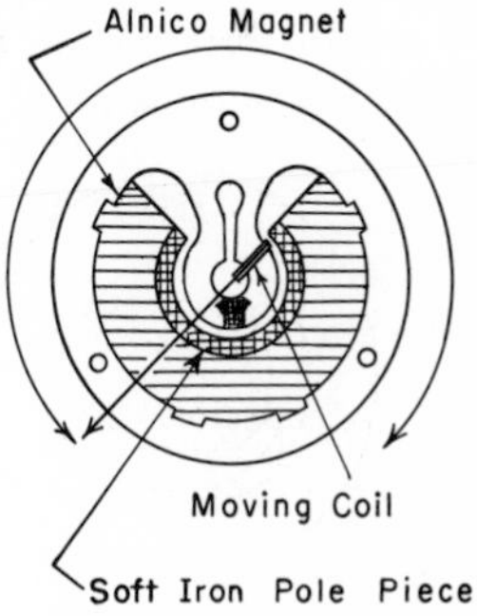

FIG. 9.

Figure 11 shows the magnetic circuit used in the Weston[12] Model 931 instruments, and designated by the manufacturer as a "core magnet." In this construction, made feasible by the magnetic properties of Alnico V, the usual magnet structure is completely inverted. The central armature, with its Alnico V magnet and soft-steel pole pieces, provides the magnetomotive force to produce flux in the air gap; and the magnetic

[12] Miller, *Weston Engineering Notes*, **4**, 1 (1949).

circuit is completed by the outer soft-steel ring which provides a return path for the flux. The ends of the Alnico magnet are flat and parallel. The sides of the magnet bulge, and the additional material in the central section in effect supplies the leakage flux to the sides of the system. This magnet shape, together with the tapered tips at the ends of the pole pieces,

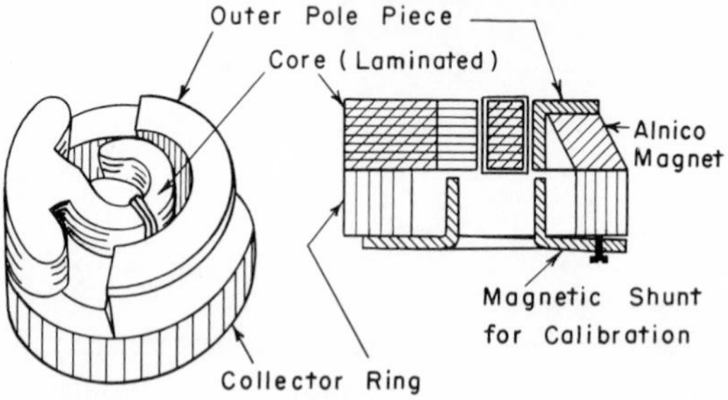

FIG. 10.

provides a radial field in the air gap and ensures scale uniformity over a deflection angle of 125°. The design is self-shielded against external magnetic fields to a remarkable extent. The presence of an external 50-gauss field results in an indication error of less than 1% of full-scale value and does not produce any significant permanent change in the strength of the air-gap field.

As an example of the economy of space and weight which can be achieved with Alnico, Fig. 12 shows an instrument designed for panel

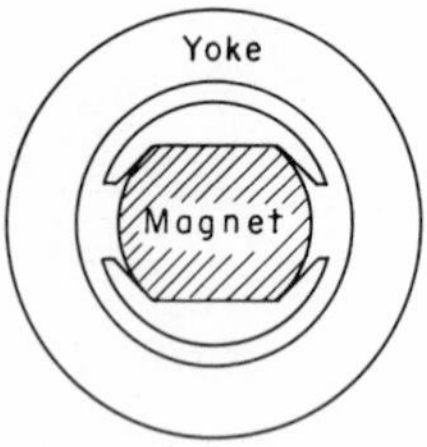

FIG. 11. Core magnet. (Courtesy of the Weston Electrical Instrument Corporation.)

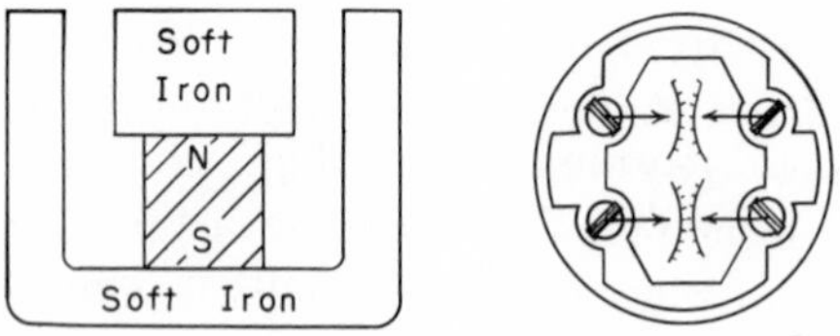

FIG. 12.

mounting in aircraft. A single sintered Alnico magnet provides the air-gap flux of four moving-coil instruments.[13] The permanent magnet is very short and of large cross section. A soft-iron plate, laid on one pole

[13] Difficulties are encountered in making independent full-scale adjustments to the separate indicating systems of such multiple-element instruments, and they are not generally manufactured.

of the magnet, is used for one pole piece. The soft-iron case of the instrument forms the other pole piece and completes the magnetic circuit.

In some instruments, a magnetic shunt is used to adjust the deflection obtained from rated current and to bring the pointer to coincidence with a scale mark for a particular value of current. This may consist of a soft-iron strip or wedge (Fig. 13; see also Fig. 10) placed at the edge of the air gap in order to by-pass a portion of the flux. If this magnetic shunt is made adjustable in position, the air-gap field can be changed over a limited range and the calibration of the instrument adjusted.

The air gaps in the magnet structures discussed above are all sections of right circular cylinders. Although this simplifies construction it is not theoretically the best arrangement possible. An arrangement having a circular coil which moves in an air gap that is a portion of a spherical shell yields a higher torque for a given coil weight than the conventional rectangular coil in a cylindrical air gap.[14] However, this requires that the pole pieces have hollow spherical faces and that the central armature be a concentric sphere. Aside from difficulties of construction, this arrangement has the disadvantage that air-gap clearances cannot be seen after assembly. This arrangement is sometimes used in very sensitive instruments for which a good torque/weight ratio cannot be obtained by conventional means.

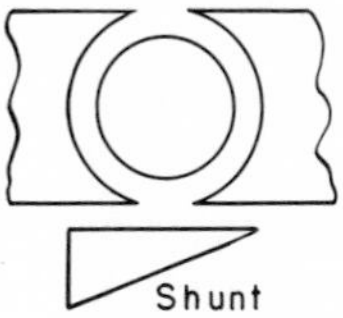

FIG. 13.

Semi-suspended, High-Sensitivity Instruments

Where extreme sensitivity is required in a d-c instrument, some manufacturers not only make use of circular coils in spherical air gaps,[15] but also utilize some system of semi-suspension in order to reduce bearing friction. The semi-suspension system used by the Sensitive Research Instrument Company is shown in Fig. 14. An internal pivot, mounted on a shaft which extends downward from the top of the moving coil, rests in a jewel bearing which is backed by a light spring. Restoring torque is supplied by a flat strip suspension similar to that used in galvanometers. The upper end of the suspension is fastened to a leaf spring, and the weight of the moving system is thus shared between the jewel bearing and the suspension, and the bearing friction is thereby lessened. The moving

[14] Keinath, *Die Technik electrischer Messgeräte*, 3rd edition, vol. 1, p. 163. See also Figs. 14 and 15.

[15] The use of a circular coil, with a spherical core and pole-faces having a cylindrical bore is sometimes adopted to avoid manufacturing difficulties arising from the use of hollow spherical pole faces.

system may be lifted off the jewel by the coil clamp shown so that the pivot will not be injured by shock when the instrument is being moved. Since the pivot and the jewel bearing are not in contact when the coil is clamped, and are thus protected from the hazards of shock which would be encountered in handling an instrument with the usual external jewel and pivot bearings, the pivot point can have a smaller radius and its area of contact with the jewel face be less than would be necessary in the orthodox mounting. As the bearing friction is, to some extent, a function of the area of contact between the pivot and jewel, a coil clamp which

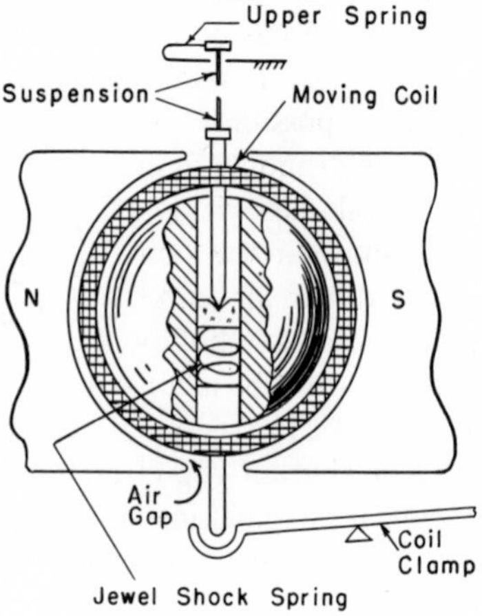

FIG. 14.

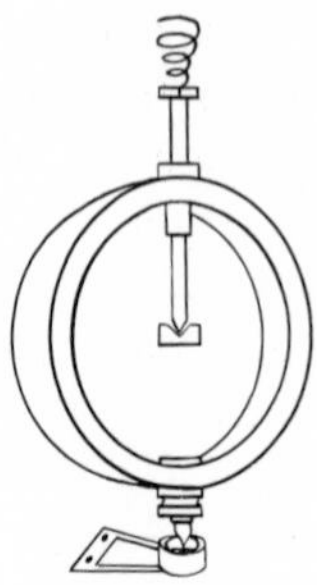

FIG. 15.

permits a reduction in contact area results in a further reduction of friction.

A comparable type of suspension is used in a line of very sensitive Rawson instruments. In this design two jewel bearings share the load as shown in Fig. 15. The upper jewel is spring-cushioned, and the lower jewel is mounted on a very weak leaf spring. Restoring torque is provided by a helical spring which carries a portion of the weight of the moving system and reduces the loading on the bearings. In this way sharp-pointed pivots can be used and the bearing area reduced to a very small value with a consequent reduction of friction as in the previous case. In this design also the moving system must be lifted off the jewels and clamped during transportation to prevent injury to the pivots from shock. Instruments with full-scale deflections for a current of 0.5 μa or less can be constructed in this way. It may be noted that this design permits the construction of voltmeters having a resistance of 2 megohms per volt.

External Field Effects

Unidirectional magnetic fields such as those produced by conductors carrying direct currents, by permanent magnets, or by d-c electromagnets may produce errors in the indications of permanent-magnet moving-coil instruments by their influences on the field in the air gap of the instrument. The presence of a 5-gauss field may change the indication of an unshielded instrument by as much as 2 or 3%. Even unmagnetized iron in the neighborhood, for example a steel table top on which the instrument is placed or a steel panel in which the instrument is mounted, may affect the working field of the instrument by shunting flux around the air gap, and thus introduce errors in its indications. Where instruments are to be mounted in a steel panel, the scale calibration should be made with the instrument similarly mounted in a steel panel of the same thickness, since otherwise errors in indication may amount to several per cent.

Magnetic shielding, which amounts to surrounding the operating system of the instrument, including the magnet, with a soft-iron enclosure, will reduce both the effect of stray fields and the shunting effect of neighboring magnetic material to a very considerable extent. The effectiveness of a magnetic shield will depend on its thickness and the degree to which it encloses the magnetic circuit of the instrument as well as the magnetic properties of the shield material. In well-designed, shielded instruments the effect of an external field of 5 gausses may be less than $\frac{1}{2}$% of full-scale deflection.

Whether an instrument is shielded or not, certain precautions should be observed in using it. Heavy-current shunts and their current leads should not be close to the instrument, and, where possible, large loops in a current circuit should be avoided by keeping current leads (of a pair) close together. It is frequently necessary to use two or more instruments together for a measurement job. The fields of such instruments may interact and produce errors if they are too close together. If possible, a distance of at least 18 in. should be maintained between unshielded instruments. If space is so limited that they must be placed close together, they should be so arranged that the neutral zones of their magnets are nearest each other and their poles are as far apart as possible. The effect of an unshielded portable instrument, with various spacings and arrangements, has been studied by Brooks,[16] and his findings are summarized in Fig. 16. With unshielded instruments, side by side and as close together as possible, the error of indication amounted to 0.8%; in the worst case, with the pole pieces adjacent, the error was 2%. As the instruments were separated the error decreased, becoming negligible for spacings 20 in. or more between instrument coil centers. When one of the

[16] Brooks, *Trans. AIEE*, **39**, 495 (1920).

instruments was shielded the effect on it was considerably less, becoming negligible if the separation between coil centers was as much as 8 in. Although Brooks did not measure the effect of one well-shielded instrument on another, it is obvious that the effect would be less than that in any of the combinations which he studied. In a number of combinations of modern, well-shielded instruments, the observed effect has been found to be less than 0.05% at the closest possible spacing. It is sometimes possible, when instruments must be used in the presence of stray fields,

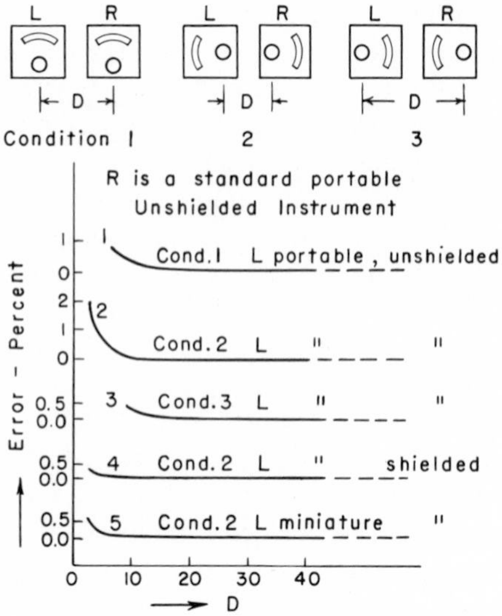

FIG. 16.

to reduce or eliminate the error by taking the mean of two readings, the instrument being turned through 180° about the axis of rotation of the moving element for the second reading. The effect of an alternating magnetic field on a permanent-magnet moving-coil instrument is negligible unless the field is great enough to reduce permanently the strength of the magnet.

Temperature Effects

Milliammeters. In a permanent-magnet, moving-coil type of instrument a 1°C increase of temperature reduces the strength of the instrument springs by about 0.04% and reduces the flux density in the air gap of the magnet by about 0.02%.[17] The weakening of the springs tends to increase the deflection for a given current in the instrument coil, whereas the

[17] This temperature coefficient for magnets is an average of the values found by Brooks for six instruments of three makes. Individual values of the coefficient ranged from 0.01 to 0.03% (see Brooks, *op. cit.*).

weakening of the magnet tends to decrease it. The net effect, on the average, is to increase the deflection for constant current by about 0.02%/°C. This value represents approximately the temperature coefficient of microammeters and of low-range milliammeters, in which the total current to be measured is passed through the instrument coil. The situation is quite different, however, for voltmeters, and for current-measuring instruments in which the moving coil is shunted by a resistor, either for the adjustment of damping as in the case of some low-range microammeters, or for increasing the current range by by-passing a considerable portion of the current around the moving coil as in the millivoltmeter-shunt combination used as an ammeter.

Voltmeters. The moving coil of a permanent-magnet, moving-coil instrument is usually wound with copper (or sometimes aluminum) wire, and its resistance increases by about 0.4%/°C rise in temperature. If the voltage to be measured were applied directly across the moving coil, the indication of the instrument for constant voltage would decrease by $0.40 - 0.02 = 0.38\%$ per degree rise in temperature, since the coil current would decrease by 0.40% while the deflection per unit current would increase by 0.02%. This temperature coefficient (0.38%) may be reduced to a negligible amount or entirely eliminated in voltmeters by using resistance wire having a negligible temperature coefficient in the series resistor of the voltmeter. Thus, if the series circuit comprising the moving coil and series resistor were made up of manganin (or constantan) and copper in the ratio of 19 to 1, the over-all temperature coefficient of resistance of the combination would be 0.02%/°C. In this case the decrease of current (0.02%/°C) would exactly equal the increase in deflection per unit current (0.02%/°C), and the net temperature coefficient of voltage would be zero. The voltmeter would be completely compensated for temperature. In a particular series of portable instruments in which the voltmeters are deflected to full scale by 1 ma (1000 ohms/volt), the 1-ma milliammeter has a resistance of approximately 90 ohms. If this same moving coil were used in the voltmeters of the series, complete temperature compensation could be secured for any voltage range $\geq (90 \times 20)/1000 = 1.8$ volts. For lower ranges and for millivoltmeters using the same moving coil, only partial compensation could be secured by this method. If the ratio of manganin to copper is greater than 19 to 1, the voltmeter will be overcompensated. However, it should be noted that in such a case the temperature coefficient of the instrument will be quite small ($< 0.02\%$/°C). The situation is less favorable in low-range, undercompensated instruments, since the temperature coefficient of voltage may range upward to a maximum of 0.38%/°C.

Millivoltmeters and Ammeters. Undercompensation is to be expected in those millivoltmeters which depend on series resistance alone. Hence a fairly large temperature coefficient may generally be expected in ammeters, which consist of a millivoltmeter and shunt combination. If, as is usually the case, the combination is designed to have full-scale deflection for a 50-mv drop in the shunt, a series "swamping" resistance 19 times the coil resistance would leave only 2.5 mv across the coil at full-scale deflection and would require undesirably delicate construction in the moving system. Usually a compromise is made in designing inexpensive portable ammeters and those for switchboard use. A manganin "swamping" resistance of 1 to 5 times the coil resistance results in a temperature coefficient between 0.2 and 0.05%/°C, and permits the use of a moving system having an acceptable torque/weight ratio. In the highest grades of ammeters (where the additional expense can be justified) complete temperature compensation can be accomplished by a suitable combination of series and parallel resistances. Two such systems of millivoltmeter compensation, which have been used commercially, will be described below.

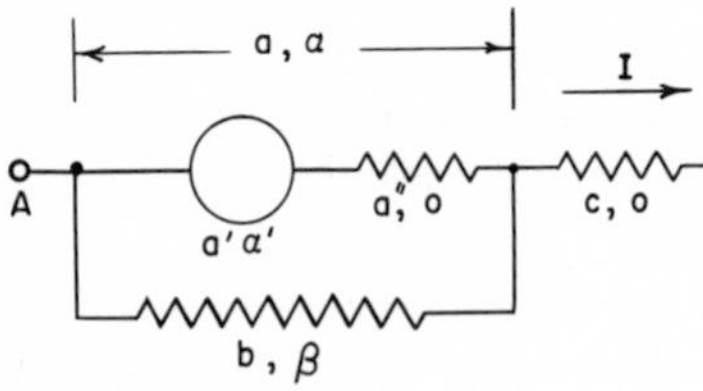

FIG. 17.

THE SWINBURNE METHOD.[18] This method of millivoltmeter compensation has been exhaustively treated by Brooks.[19] It consists of the circuit shown in Fig. 17. Here the coil a', having a temperature coefficient of resistance α', is in series with a "swamping" resistance a'', having a temperature coefficient zero. The over-all temperature coefficient, α, of the combination is thus lower than the coefficient, α', of the coil alone. In parallel with this combination is a resistance b, having a high temperature coefficient β. Now, since $\beta > \alpha$, a larger fraction of the total current I will flow through branch a as the temperature rises, reducing the effective temperature coefficient to a still lower value. In other words, the effect on the coil current of the shunt, b, is equivalent to that of a larger "swamping" resistance than a''. The compensation is completed with a second "swamping" resistance c, having zero temperature coefficient, in series with the combination a in parallel with b. By using this circuit, complete temperature compensation can be attained for a voltage drop across the coil[20] of $\frac{1}{5}$ the voltage drop between A and B. If we

[18] Swinburne, *Electrician* (*London*), **19**, 405 (1887).

[19] Brooks, *NBS J. Research*, **17**, 497 (1936).

[20] This value of $\frac{1}{5}$ should be contrasted with the fraction of the terminal voltage available at the coil ($\frac{1}{20}$) if the complete compensation were made by the simple series method.

neglect the coefficients of springs and magnets, then the compensation is approximately complete if $c/b = \alpha/(\beta - \alpha)$. It should be noted that, of the resistance materials having negligible temperature coefficient of resistance, only those, such as manganin, whose thermoelectric power against copper is very small should be used in millivoltmeter circuits. If a material such as constantan, having a high thermoelectric power against copper, were used, then a difference of temperature between circuit branch points would produce a thermal emf and result in a deflection of the instrument. This deflection may be either in the same direction or in the opposite direction to the deflection resulting from the voltage drop across the shunt and hence may result in either a positive or a negative error.

THE CAMPBELL[21] METHOD. This method of millivoltmeter compensation is somewhat more complicated, but has the advantage that it makes a

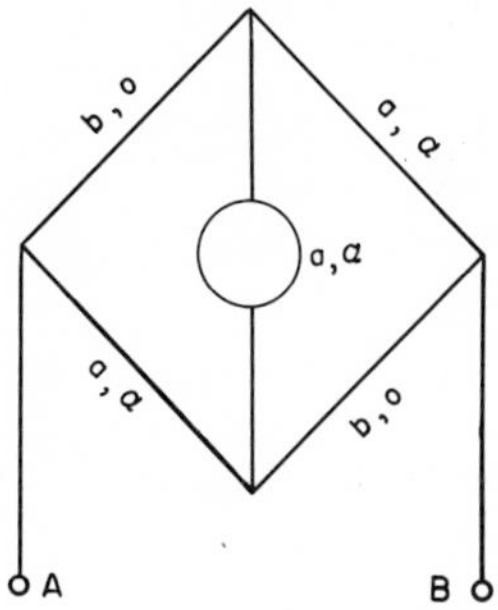

FIG. 18.

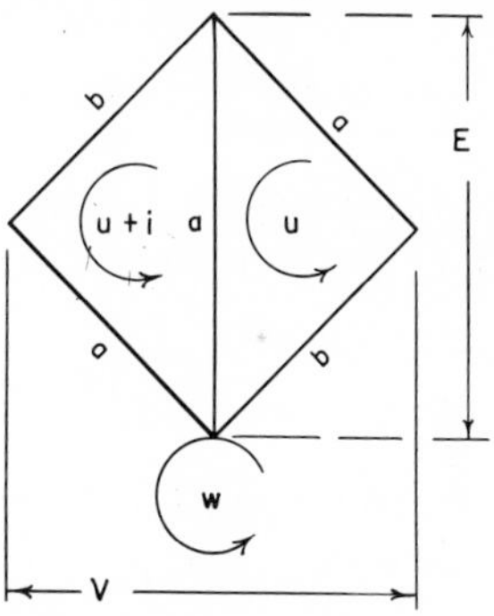

FIG. 19.

larger fraction of the terminal voltage available at the coil. It consists of a four-arm bridge with the moving coil of the millivoltmeter across one diagonal and the instrument terminals (or the current shunt) across the other diagonal as shown in Fig. 18. Two of the bridge arms (a, α) are, in the simplified case, equal to the moving coil in resistance and have the same temperature coefficient. The other two arms (b, o) are of manganin, having a negligible temperature coefficient. We will examine the conditions for which the current in the moving coil is independent of temperature. Referring to Fig. 19 and using Maxwell's mesh currents,[22] we have

$$(a + b)w - (a + b)u - ai = V$$
$$-aw + (a + b)u + (2a + b)i = 0$$
$$-bw + (a + b)u - ai = 0$$

[21] A. Campbell, *J. IEE (London)*, **35**, 197 (1905).
[22] See discussion in Chapter 15.

From which we may write

$$\frac{i}{V} = \frac{\begin{vmatrix} a+b & -1 & 1 \\ -a & 1 & 0 \\ -b & 1 & 0 \end{vmatrix}}{\begin{vmatrix} a+b & -1 & -a \\ -a & 1 & (2a+b) \\ -b & 1 & -a \end{vmatrix}}$$

$$= \frac{b-a}{-a(a+b) + b(2a+b) + a^2 - ab - (2a+b)(a+b) + a^2}$$

$$= \frac{a-b}{a(a+3b)}$$

Now, if $di/dT = 0$, we have

$$a(a+3b)\frac{da}{dT} - (a-b)\left[(a+3b)\frac{da}{dT} + a\frac{da}{dT}\right] = 0$$

since we have assumed that db/dT, the temperature coefficient of b, is zero. From this we may write that

$$\frac{da}{dT}(a-3b)(a+b) = 0$$

Whence $a = 3b$ for $db/dT = 0$, independent of the value of da/dT. Also for this condition

$$\frac{E}{V} = \frac{ia}{V} = \frac{a-b}{a+3b} = \frac{1}{3}$$

If the bridge is constructed having manganin resistors in the b-arms, each $\frac{1}{3}$ of the resistance of the moving coil, then the current in the moving coil (for a constant voltage between the terminals A and B) is independent of temperature. Such an arrangement used with a shunt as an ammeter will have a very low temperature coefficient and will have a voltage drop across the moving coil equal to $\frac{1}{3}$ of the voltage drop across the current-carrying shunt.

GENERAL CONSIDERATIONS. It should be noted that the above discussion has been greatly simplified by the assumption that constant current is desired in the moving coil and that there are no other requirements. The practical compensation of millivoltmeters by either the Swinburne or the Campbell method is considerably more complicated than would be indicated by the simplified analysis above. The temperature coefficient of resistance of the springs has been assumed equal to that of the coil. Actually this coefficient is usually somewhat lower, and this fact would have to be taken into account. Furthermore, a complete analysis would have to consider the temperature coefficients of strength of the magnet and springs. For a particular moving-coil mechanism the compensation would have to be based on the particular current required to give full-scale deflection at a stated temperature and to take account of the exact voltage available at the shunt terminals. Instrument damping resulting from the compensating circuit would also have to be considered. If external shunts were used, the lead resistance between millivoltmeter and shunt and the possible effect of their temperature coefficients would have to be analyzed. For multirange instruments or for voltammeters the analysis would be even more complex. In view of these considerations it will be apparent that these systems of complete temperature compensation can be justified only in the case of the highest grade of instruments. For the usual grade of portable ammeters and for switchboard ammeters, an appreciable temperature coefficient must be expected. A statement of temperature coefficient is often available from the data supplied by the maker with an instrument so that allowance may be made for it where necessary.

The suggestion is occasionally made that it should be possible to secure temperature compensation in a shunted instrument by constructing the shunt of material having the same temperature coefficient as the moving coil. This would not be practical in an instrument having separate external shunts since it might well be that, in use, a temperature difference would be present between the shunt and the millivoltmeter, resulting in a temperature error. In an instrument with an internal shunt, compensation by such a method would be possible only if the circuits were so arranged that the shunt temperature was always equal to the coil temperature and would limit such shunts to low current values for which the power dissipation would not be excessive.[23] A further argument against attempting temperature compensation in ammeters by this method would be the bulk that would be necessary in a copper shunt to secure the needed voltage drop with adequate heat dissipation and current-carrying capacity.

Multirange Instruments

Voltmeters. Since a voltmeter consists of a milliammeter with sufficient added series resistance to absorb the IR drop from the highest voltage to be measured, a multirange voltmeter may be made up with a resistor appropriate to the highest range desired, with tap points appropriate to

[23] The power which can be dissipated continuously within an instrument without undue temperature rise will depend on the size of the instrument as well as other structural factors. For the usual types of portable instruments, one may say that the power dissipation should be limited to 5 to 7 watts or less.

the various lower ranges brought out to binding posts as in Fig. 20(*a*), or to a rotary selector switch as in Fig. 20(*b*). If the full-scale values of voltage in the various ranges differ by a factor of 2 or 10, the same scale may be used for both ranges with multiple labeling of the cardinal points as shown in Fig. 20(*c*). For some other common combinations of ranges, double scales, separately labeled, would have to be drawn. This would be the case, for example, if the full-scale values of two ranges were in the ratio 1/3 (e.g. 50 and 150), the former being conveniently subdivided into 50 parts, while the latter is more conveniently subdivided into 150 parts.

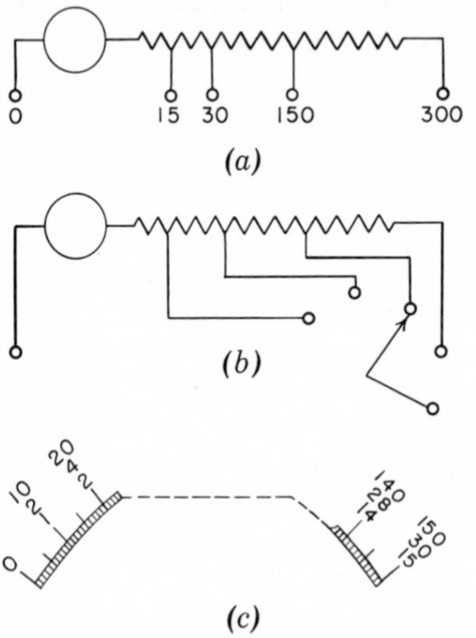

FIG. 20.

Ammeters. The combination of a millivoltmeter and shunt employed as an ammeter is readily adaptable to multirange construction either by separate, interchangeable, single-range shunts[24] or multirange shunts. A method of operation with multirange shunts is illustrated in Fig. 21. The shunt is selected (i.e. the current passes through one or more shunt sections, depending on the position of the selector switch) to provide the necessary voltage drop for the millivoltmeter. The swamping resistance in series with the moving coil may be nearly constant, assuming the shunt resistance to be low compared to the swamping resistance. Of course, the switch contact must be constructed to carry the entire current being measured, but the development of resistance at this point will not affect the accuracy of indication of the combination.

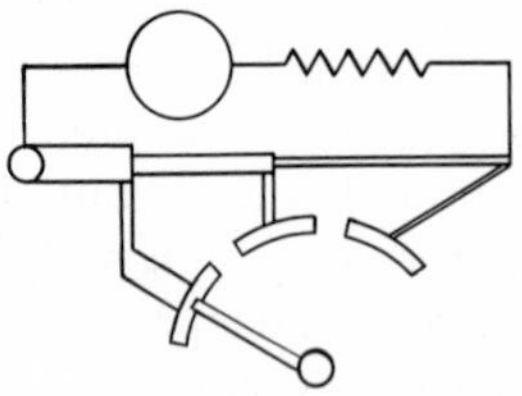

FIG. 21.

[24] It should be noted that, where external shunts are used with a millivoltmeter to measure current, the leads connecting the shunt to the instrument terminals may have a resistance that is a significant fraction of the low resistance of the instrument itself, and that may therefore affect the instrument accuracy. In such cases the leads used with the millivoltmeter-shunt combination should have the same resistance as those with which the combination was calibrated. Frequently the maker provides a pair of leads for a particular instrument, which should be kept and used with it. If this is not feasible, the leads used should be made up to have an equivalent resistance.

Voltammeters. Combination voltammeters are possible, making use of a single indicating element with shunt resistances for current measurements and with series resistances for voltage measurements. Such combination multirange instruments are quite commonly made up as test sets (frequently with added "ohmmeter" ranges) but are not common in precision classes of instruments. Two arrangements used in voltammeters are shown in Fig. 22. An arrangement is shown in (*a*) in which

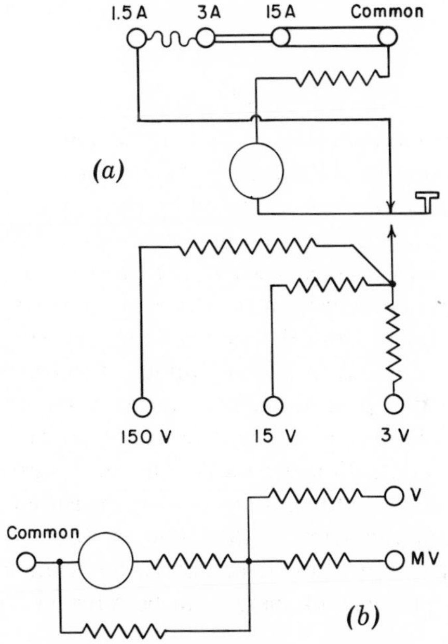

FIG. 22.

the instrument is alternatively connected as a millivoltmeter-shunt combination to measure current, or with series resistance to measure voltage. Range selection is available at the binding posts, and use as an ammeter or voltmeter is controlled by the key which is depressed in order to read volts. Figure 22(*b*) shows an arrangement as a Swinburne-compensated millivoltmeter to be used with shunts, or as a voltmeter. In some instances a voltmeter and a separate ammeter are built into a single case. This arrangement has the advantage that readings of current and voltage may be made simultaneously. Furthermore, each instrument can be designed around a single set of operating requirements in which no compromise is needed between characteristics suitable for ammeters and those suitable for voltmeters.

CHAPTER 6

POTENTIOMETERS

Definition. A potentiometer[1] is an instrument for measuring an unknown emf or potential difference by balancing it, wholly or in part, by a known potential difference produced by the flow of a known current in a network of circuits of known characteristics.[2] Potentiometers are extensively used in measurements where the precision required is higher than can be obtained by deflection instruments, or where it is important that no current be drawn from the source under measurement, or where this current must be limited to a small value. Electromotive forces are measured directly with a potentiometer in terms of the emf of a standard cell. By using, in addition, a standard resistor (shunt), current can also be measured. From potentiometer measurements of current and voltage, power can be calculated and, if time is also measured, energy can be calculated. The potentiometer is thus one of the most fundamental instruments of electrical measurements and is the means by which values of current, voltage, power, and energy can be referred back to the basic electrical units.

Poggendorff's Compensation Methods. The potentiometer principle was first described by Poggendorff[3] in 1841 as a "compensation" method for measuring the emf of a primary cell without drawing appreciable current from it. All potentiometers make use of one or both of the compensation methods described by Poggendorff. In his first method (developed in the course of a study of polarizable cells) a constant (non-polarizing) cell E caused a current to flow through a wire of resistance R (see Fig. 1) and produced a potential difference $ER/(R + r)$ between its ends, where E was the emf and r the internal resistance of the constant

[1] It should be noted that a three-terminal resistor used as a potential divider is *not* a potentiometer. Such a device is often incorrectly called a potentiometer by radio technicians, but it will be obvious that it does not have the characteristics of a measuring instrument. This usage is deprecated.

[2] Definition by H. B. Brooks.

[3] Poggendorff, *Ann. Phys. u. Chemie*, **54** (1841).

cell. The emf, E', of the unknown cell was opposed to this difference of potential through a galvanometer G, and the value of R was varied or additional resistance was placed in series with the constant cell until the galvanometer current was reduced to zero. At balance $E' = ER/(R + r)$, E, R, and r being known. This compensation method (by which the

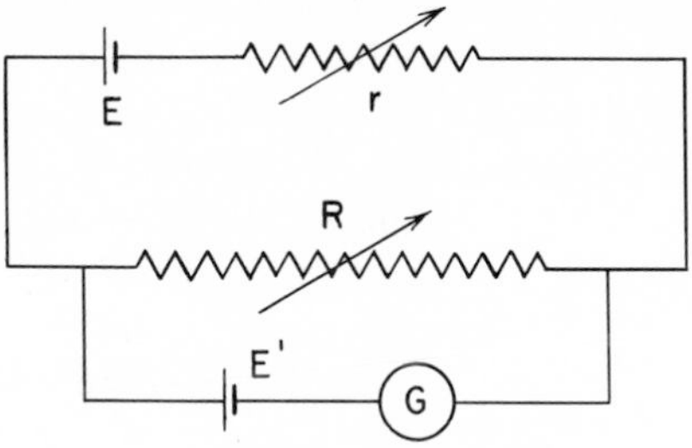

FIG. 1.

emf of the cell E' under investigation was "compensated" or opposed by the potential drop in R so that no current was drawn from it) forms the basis of all *constant-current* potentiometers.

To avoid the necessity for repeated determinations of E and r, where the measurements lasted for several hours, Poggendorff devised a second method which differed from the first method in that a tangent galvanometer A was used to measure the current I supplied by the non-polarizing cell (see Fig. 2). In this case, at balance, $E' = IR$; and a knowledge of

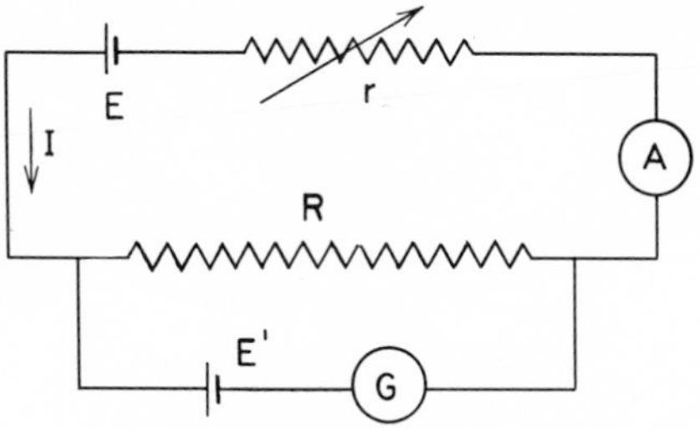

FIG. 2.

E and r was not necessary. Poggendorff's second method forms the basis of *constant-resistance* potentiometers.

THE CONSTANT-CURRENT POTENTIOMETER

Operating Principle. The constant-current potentiometer (Poggendorff's Method I) is used to measure the emf e connected (see Fig. 3), together with a galvanometer G, across a section of the resistance R which carries the fixed current I flowing in circuit A. The section a–b, across which e is connected, is varied until the galvanometer indicates that no current is flowing in circuit B. For this balance condition $e = IR_{ab}$. In the simplest potentiometer of this type, R is a slide wire having uniform resistance per unit length, with a linear scale mounted beside it as indicated in the figure. In order that e may be measured without computation the current is set to the value needed to make the potentiometer direct reading, by the following procedure. With a primary cell of known emf (sc) connected in circuit B, the sliders a–b are set to read the voltage E_{sc} from the scale (say $a - b' = 1.019$ in the figure for the particular standard cell used). The current in the main circuit A is then varied by means of the rheostat until the galvanometer is balanced. Then, without changing the current I, e is substituted for sc and the potentiometer is balanced by varying the position of slider b. At balance the emf of e may be read directly from the slide-wire scale. If the slide wire is uniform and the current I is unchanged between the balances, we have

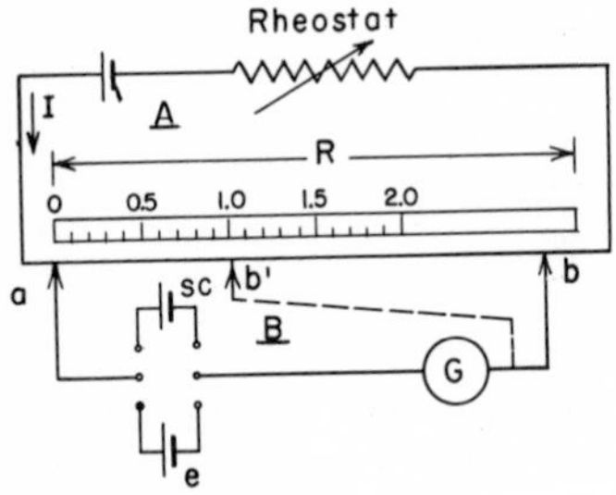

FIG. 3.

$$\frac{E_e}{E_{sc}} = \frac{\text{reading }(ab)}{\text{reading }(ab')}, \quad \text{or} \quad E_e = E_{sc} \times \frac{\text{reading }(ab)}{\text{reading }(ab')}$$

But

$$\frac{E_{sc}}{\text{reading }(ab')} = 1$$

since this reading was set to the numerical value of E_{sc}. Hence

$$E_e = \text{reading }(ab)$$

It will be noted that: (1) the value of the calibration current, I, need not be known but *must* be constant; (2) only the ratio of resistances is used; their actual values in ohms are not needed for the measurement. Most general-purpose potentiometers are an elaboration of this simple slide-wire, *constant-current* potentiometer.

It will be evident from the discussion above, and throughout the discussion of potentiometers which follows, that we must assume the availability of a precisely known reference standard of voltage, since the potentiometer is actually a device for comparing emf's. In laboratory work the unsaturated Weston cadmium cell, having an emf of approximately 1.019 volts, is used as a working standard. Its characteristics and the precautions needed for its proper use will be discussed in a later section on the standard cell. It will be sufficient here to call attention to the fact that such cells do *not* all have quite the same voltage. The range of voltage encountered, while small, is not negligible (1.0183 to 1.0195 volts) and must be allowed for in potentiometer construction and use.

Development. The modern, general-purpose potentiometer incorporates a number of important special features which should be examined in some detail, and it will be helpful to review the historical development of the potentiometer, since it happens that these features were separately introduced during a period of more than half a century.[4]

The first instrument using Poggendorff's Method I and incorporating a continuously variable slide wire with a graduated scale was described by DuBois-Reymond[5] in 1862. He called this instrument a compensator. His first "compensator" was a straight two-meter slide wire of brass. He also described an instrument of more refined construction in which a platinum wire was laid in a helical groove in a cylinder of insulating material. His contact (*b* of Fig. 3) was a platinum roller. Means were provided for fine adjustment of the roller position, and a lens was used to provide an accurate scale reading.

In 1868, Latimer Clark[6] described an instrument having a very long slide wire wound spirally on a drum. Clark employed separate cells for supplying the slide-wire current and for a standard of emf, and added a rheostat (rheo. of Fig. 3) by which the current could be adjusted until the potential difference across the full length of the slide wire was equal to the emf (open-circuit voltage) of the cell which he used as a reference standard. The platinum slide wire was wound in a screw thread of 100 turns cut in a hard-rubber cylinder. A 100-division scale on the edge of the cylinder made it possible to read the slider position directly to 1/10,000 of the total length of the wire. Clark devised a standard cell having an emf of 1.457 volts at 15.5°C for use as a reference standard, and originated the name "potentiometer" for his apparatus. His slider position was read in turns and fractions of a turn of the drum so that he measured emf's, not directly in volts, but as a decimal fraction of the emf of his standard cell. Clark stated that he had used this method since 1859, and his work may possibly antedate that of DuBois-Reymond.

In 1882 Fleming[7] made Clark's method *direct reading in volts*, by

[4] The writer is indebted to Dr. H. B. Brooks for the historical material included in this survey. A very complete history of the potentiometer will be found in Dr. Brooks' report to the International Congress of Electricity, Paris, 1932 (Section 2, *Report* 14).

[5] DuBois-Reymond, *Abh. Akad. Wiss. Berlin*, p. 107, 1862.

[6] Clark, *Elementary Treatise on Electrical Measurements*, p. 106, 1868.

[7] Fleming, 50 *Years of Electricity*, p. 272, 1921.

balancing the reference cell against a suitable fraction of the slide wire so that the value of potential difference per scale division on the slide wire would equal an exact *decimal* fraction of a volt. With a reference cell having an emf of 1.434 volts and a slide wire of 2000 divisions, the "standard-cell balance" was made with the slider set at 1434 divisions. Thus the potentiometer at balance would read emf's directly in volts over a 2-volt range with each slide-wire division corresponding to 0.001 volt.

In 1893 Crompton[8] constructed a potentiometer in which high precision could be obtained without the use of a long slide wire by adding 14 extension coils, each equal in resistance to the whole of the slide wire (see

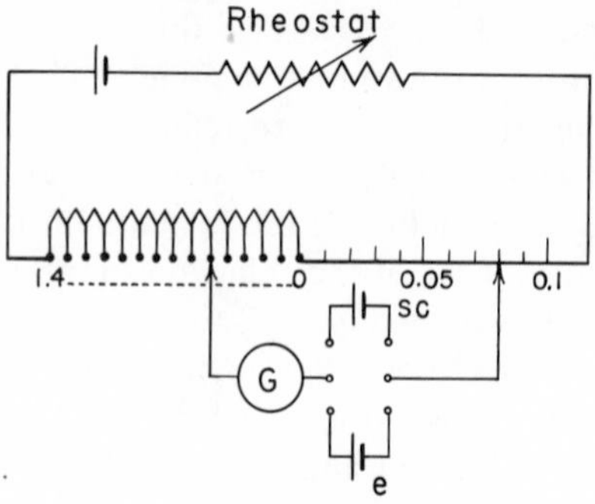

FIG. 4.

Fig. 4). A dial switch having 15 contact points and a relatively short (60-cm) slide wire were thus made the equivalent of a slide wire 15 times as long. This improvement greatly facilitated the operation of the potentiometer, making it possible for an observer to obtain a balance condition more easily and quickly by means of the coarse (dial) adjustment and the fine (slide-wire) adjustment. This arrangement has been adopted and modified in many modern potentiometers. Crompton's potentiometer was designed for a current of 10 ma. The slide wire and each of the fixed sections were 10 ohms (a total of 150 ohms), and the instrument was direct reading from zero to 1.5 volts.

The direct-reading potentiometers described above required that the sliders and dials of the instrument be set to read the voltage of the reference cell when the calibrating current was set or checked. The first attempt to eliminate this troublesome feature was described by Raps[9] in 1895. In his potentiometer, coils of 102, 1020, and 10,200 ohms were provided,

[8] Crompton, *Electrician*, **31**, 32 (1893).
[9] Raps, *Zeits. für Instrumentenk.*, **15**, 215 (1895).

through which the calibration current flowed. By means of a switch the standard-cell emf (assumed to be 1.020 volts) could be balanced around any of these resistors to establish the calibrating current at 0.01, 0.001, or 0.0001 amp as desired. It will be noted that this device also provided 3 ranges for the potentiometer.

Another type of range-changing device was described by Franke[10] in 1897. In a potentiometer similar to that of Crompton, he introduced a shunt coil having a resistance one-ninth of the combined resistance of the slide wire and group of fixed coils. This shunt was not in the circuit during the adjustment of the calibrating current but could be inserted by

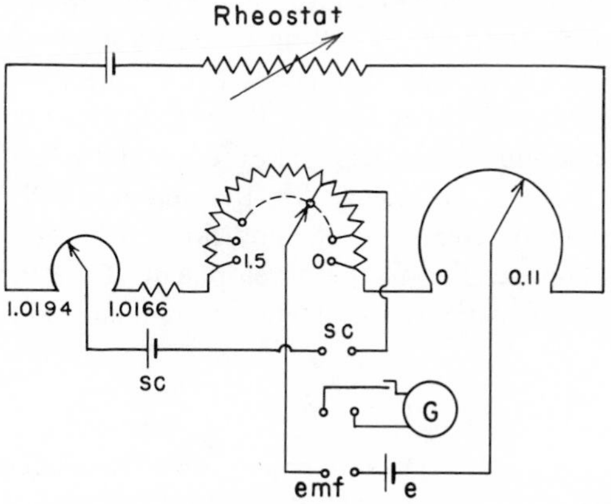

FIG. 5.

means of a plug after the standard-cell balance was made, reducing the range of the potentiometer to one-tenth of its former value.

The method for making a quick standard-cell check, first used by Raps, was modified and improved in a potentiometer described by the Leeds and Northrup Company[11] in 1906. Ten of the coils in the main dial constitute nearly all the resistance across which the standard cell is connected in setting the calibrating current. A further refinement was made by providing a means of adjusting the standard-cell balancing resistance to suit the value of the particular standard cell used. As shown in Fig. 5 the standard cell is connected across a section of the main dial and a small auxiliary slide wire. The fixed resistance in this circuit corresponds to a potential difference of 1.0166 volts, and the auxiliary slide wire covers a range of 0.0028 volt and has a scale marked from 1.0166 to 1.0194. This range is sufficient to cover the variation in voltage

[10] Franke, *Elektrot. Zeits.*, **18**, 318 (1897).

[11] U.S. Patent 819,355 (1906).

of all standard cells which are suitable for use in potentiometer work.[12] A similar arrangement has been incorporated into all modern potentiometers of the *constant-current* type since it permits the operator to check the standard-cell balance at any time during the course of a measurement without disturbing the potentiometer setting. In operation the auxiliary slide wire (standard-cell dial) is set to read the emf of the particular standard cell which is connected to the potentiometer. The selector switch is set in the standard-cell position, and the "rheostat" is adjusted until no current flows in the galvanometer. This fixes the calibration current at its proper value. The selector switch is then set in its emf position and e may be measured. The constancy of the calibration current can be quickly checked at any time by setting the selector switch back on "sc" and checking the standard-cell balance. The frequency with which such checks must be made is dependent on the stability and constancy of the supply battery and must be determined experimentally, but it can be done so easily that there is no excuse for the standard-cell balance to be incorrect when any measurement of importance is being made.

The contributions leading to the development of the modern, general-purpose constant-current[13] potentiometer are summarized in the following table:

Worker	*Date*	*Contribution*
Poggendorff	1841	Basic principle; two methods incorporating it.
DuBois-Reymond	1862	Continuously variable slide wire.
Clark	1868	Separate reference cell for calibration.
Fleming	1882	Direct-reading scale in volts.
Crompton	1893	Separate circuit elements for coarse and fine adjustment of balance.
Raps	1895	Circuit element for quick check of standard-cell balance.
Franke	1897	Shunt element for range changing.
Leeds and Northrup	1906	Standard-cell dial.

General-Purpose Potentiometers

Leeds and Northrup Type K Potentiometers. Two models of these potentiometers have been produced. The earlier Type K-1 potentiometer was designed to incorporate most of the desirable features known to the art at the time, and is still used in laboratory work to some extent today,

[12] Many of the potentiometers constructed in recent years were planned in anticipation of the change in the value of the volt which was effective January 1, 1948. In these instruments the standard-cell dial was extended to 1.0200 volts to include all the newly assigned voltage values for standard cells.

[13] Constant-resistance potentiometers will be discussed in a later section.

nearly 50 years later. As shown schematically in Fig. 6, it has a range shunt, a standard-cell dial, a fine-adjustment slide-wire element, and a coarse-adjustment step dial. When the shunt is in use, the current in the main dial and slide wire is reduced to 0.1 of its normal value and a series resistor is inserted in the battery circuit to keep the current from the supply battery unchanged. Range selection is controlled by a plug

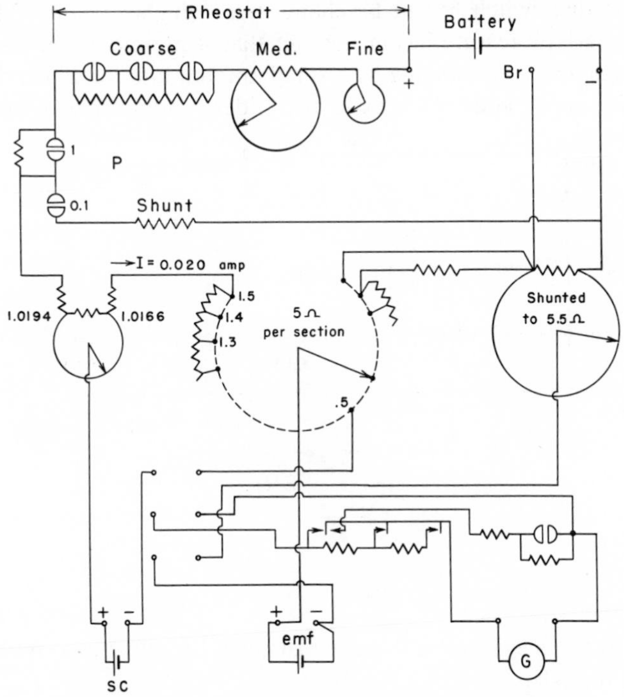

FIG. 6. Leeds and Northrup Type K–1 potentiometer.

at *P*. It will be seen that with *P* in the 0.1 position, the contact resistance between the plug and studs forms a part of the shunt resistance. This contact resistance is negligibly small if the contacts are clean and well fitted but could be sufficient to cause an error if the contacts were allowed to become dirty. Such a plug should always be inserted with a turning motion to secure the lowest possible contact resistance. No provision is made for checking the standard cell balance on the 0.1 range. The plug must be returned to the 1 range to check this balance.

The normal ranges of the instrument are 1.61 and 0.161 volts. An upward range extension to 16 volts is possible by the following device. If the 2-volt supply battery normally used is replaced by a 20-volt battery and if the calibration current (standard-cell balance) is set with the range plug in the 0.1 position, the range plug may then be set in the 1 position and the normal current and range of the potentiometer are multiplied by 10 so that voltages up to 16 volts are measured.

The slide wire is helically wound on a drum which may be operated through 11 complete turns. Ten turns on the slide wire correspond to 1 dial step, so that a 10% overlap is available in voltage measurement before the dial switch has to be changed to a higher value. The value of this "overlap" feature lies in the fact that it permits the measurement of a voltage which is changing by a small amount and for which the slider is near its upper end. Otherwise the slider would have to be moved

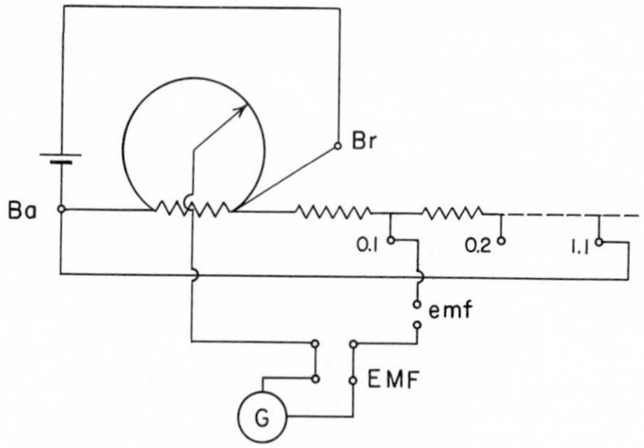

FIG. 7.

through 10 turns every time it passed through the value corresponding to the main dial step.

The studs in the main dial are accessible for checking the accuracy of the potentiometer. If plugs carrying flexible leads are inserted in holes provided in these studs, the resistance of each section can be measured in turn in a Wheatstone bridge. It is important to note that the bridge used in these measurements should have sufficient sensitivity to detect inequalities of 0.01% in the resistors. The dial steps are 5 ohms each and should be equal to within 0.01%. The slide wire can be checked for uniformity, using the connections shown in Fig. 7. The *Ba* – binding post is connected to the 1.1 stud, placing the first 11 steps of the dial in parallel with the slide wire. A battery is connected between the *Ba* – and the *Br* posts. With the emf binding posts shorted and the selector switch in the emf position, a Wheatstone bridge is formed from the potentiometer elements themselves, which may be balanced by rotating the slide-wire drum. If the dial switch is set on successive points from

0.1 to 1.0 the slide wire may be checked at 10 equally spaced points corresponding to complete revolutions of the drum.

A simple one-point operating test can be made on this potentiometer, or on any general-purpose null potentiometer having a range of more than 1 volt. The potentiometer dials are first set to read the value of emf indicated by the standard-cell dial. After the standard-cell balance has been made by adjusting the operating current, the standard cell used in this balance is shifted from the standard-cell terminals to the emf terminals of the potentiometer. A balance should be indicated on this circuit also. If a different setting of the potentiometer dials is required for balance, the potentiometer error at this point is equal to the change in dial setting. Such a test will furnish a quick check on the accuracy of adjustment of the potentiometer. Strictly speaking, it applies only to the single point that is checked, but by inference the quality of adjustment found for this point (usually not too far from the midpoint of the range) may reasonably be expected to be representative of the general performance of the instrument.

Leeds and Northrup Type K-2 Potentiometer. This model (1930) has the same basic design as the earlier one but incorporates a number of

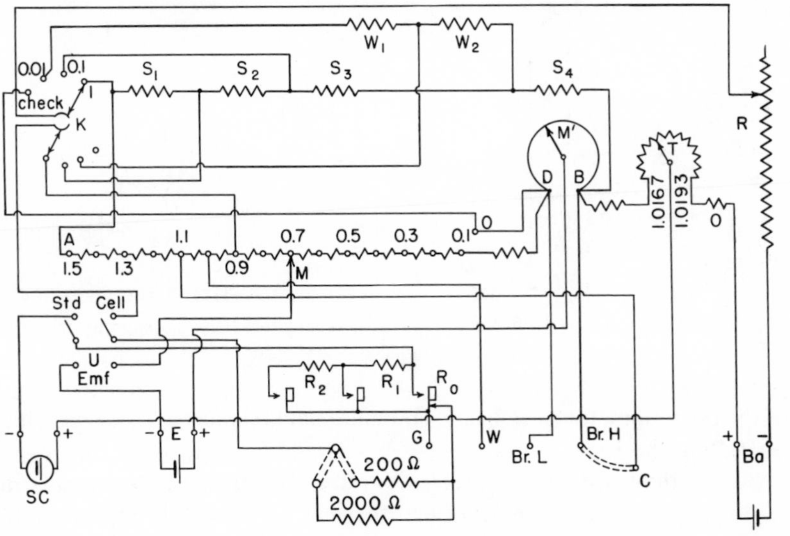

FIG. 8. Leeds and Northrup Type K–2 potentiometer.

improvements. The circuits are rearranged (Fig. 8) in such a way that one of the range-changing switch-contact resistances is in the galvanometer circuit and therefore does not affect the calibration. The other switch contact is in the supply circuit, rather than in the shunt circuit, and its effect on the calibration is negligibly small. There are 3 ranges, 1, 0.1, and 0.01, and a standard-cell check is possible on any range. These features can best be seen in the simplified schematic diagrams of Fig. 9. (*a*), (*b*), and (*c*) show the active circuits for the 1, 0.1, and 0.01 ranges respectively; and (*d*) shows the over-all schematic diagram and the switching arrangement. Provisions are made for checking the accuracy

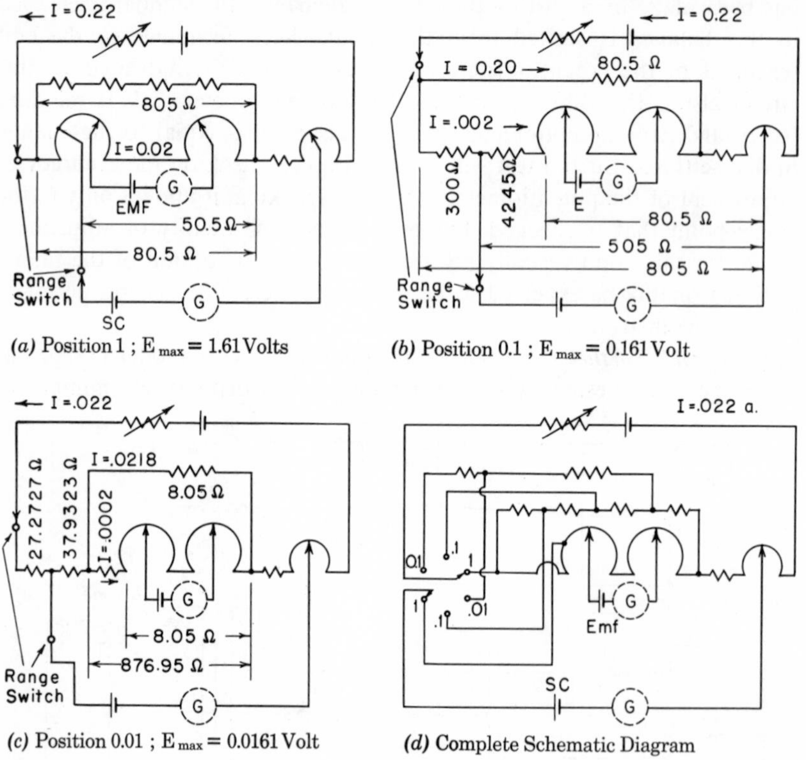

(*a*) Position 1 ; E_{max} = 1.61 Volts

(*b*) Position 0.1 ; E_{max} = 0.161 Volt

(*c*) Position 0.01 ; E_{max} = 0.0161 Volt

(*d*) Complete Schematic Diagram

FIG. 9.

of the potentiometer by resistance measurements similar to those described for testing the K-1.

In both these instruments precautions must be observed when measuring low voltages, because of transient thermal emf's which appear in the measuring circuit as a result of manipulating the dial and slide wire to secure balance. The motion of the switch blades on the contact studs of the dial and of the contactor along the slide wire generates heat from friction. If the motion is rapid an emf of several microvolts may be generated. In the dial switch this is not important since only the preliminary balance requires motion of the dial, and the transient emf disappears rather quickly. Thermal emf's generated in this way may be somewhat more troublesome in the slide-wire balance, but again are not serious since they die away in a few seconds and therefore do not affect the final balance. However, the operator should use caution in approaching the final balance when a very low voltage is being measured and should move the slider rather slowly to keep thermal emf's to a low value.

It should be observed that parasitic thermal emf's of the order of a microvolt or more are usually continuously present and must be expected in any potentiometer unless proper precautions are strictly observed in the design. The nature of these precautions, which will be discussed later in some detail, is such as to add greatly to the cost of the potentiometer. In the K-2 and other general-purpose potentiometers, the source of such parasitics may reside in the binding posts, in switches, in the galvanometer key, and in connections or soldered joints between portions of the circuit, even where the junction is copper-to-copper. They may be expected, in fact, wherever heat may flow to or from the potentiometer circuit. For this reason no potentiometer, except those that have been specifically designed to be thermo-free, can be used to measure emf's reliably to better than a few microvolts, although if the parasitic emf's present are changing slowly, differences or changes in emf may be measured over a short time interval to a somewhat better precision than the emf itself.

Rubicon Type-B Potentiometer. This general-purpose instrument covers the same range as the Leeds and Northrup Type K-2. The

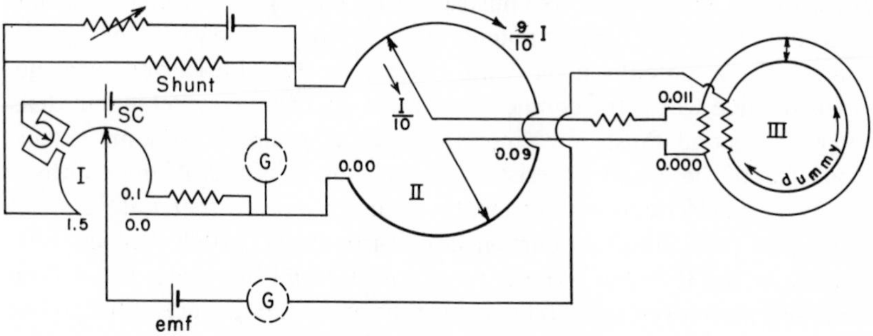

FIG. 10. Rubicon Type B potentiometer.

essential differences in design are (1) 2 dials and a 1-turn slide wire in place of the 1 dial and 11-turn slide wire used in the L & N potentiometer; and (2) a circuit arrangement to reduce the effect of thermal emf's set up by manipulation of the slide wire. This arrangement of a coarse, intermediate, and fine control is at least as rapid and convenient as the coarse and fine control (11-turn slide wire) of L & N. The circuit is shown schematically in Fig. 10. The range-changing circuits are not shown but are similar to those already described. Dial I is for the coarse balancing adjustment and is of the construction already described. Dials II and III are of special design. It will be seen from the figure that the contact points of dial II contribute to the resistance of the potentiometer circuit and could introduce an error into the reading if contact resistances were high. In order to reduce the effect of these contact resistances to a negligible value the circuit is arranged so that the contacts and switch carry only $\frac{1}{10}$ of the potentiometer current. Hence the effect of contact resistance is reduced to $\frac{1}{10}$ of the value it would have as a series element of the circuit. The arrangement of dial III (the slide wire) is such that the thermal emf's generated at the two sliding contacts act in opposite directions on the measuring circuit and will tend to neutralize each other. A key of special construction, designed to reduce thermal emf's, is used in the galvanometer branch, and in some instances binding posts in the measuring circuit are of copper. As a result of these precautions less than 1 μv of parasitic thermal emf is present in the measuring circuit under normal conditions of use. It will be noted that the inner circle of dial III represents a "dummy" slide wire which is in the galvanometer branch of the circuit together with the slide-wire contactors. The resistances of the circuit elements can be checked if the instrument is removed from its case and low-resistance clamps are attached to the stud ends.

Feussner Potentiometer. Feussner[14] was the first worker to design a potentiometer having more than two circuit elements. His work led to the series of potentiometers constructed by Otto Wolff in Germany and to a later Feussner type of potentiometer built by Eppley in the United States. In a potentiometer with more than two measuring elements (dials or slide wires) the contact resistances involved in switching all dials after the second must enter into the measuring circuit to some extent. The effect of these contact resistances can be made negligible in two ways: (1) by parallel circuit arrangements of such a nature that only a small portion of the calibration current flows through the switch contacts (this is done in the Rubicon Type B potentiometer and in others that will be described presently); and (2) by making the over-all resistance of the potentiometer so high that the resistance of switch contacts will be negligible in comparison (this has been done in the Feussner potentiometers of Wolff and Eppley). Since low-resistance elements are inherently more stable than high-resistance elements,[15] the use of high-resistance elements calls for a very high grade of workmanship in making the coils (in order that they be stable) and in the switch construction (in order that contact resistances be low and constant).

[14] Feussner, *Zeits. für Instrumentenk.*, **10,** 113 (1890).

[15] See discussion in Chapter 7.

Figure 11 is a schematic diagram of the Feussner potentiometer. It will be noted that the switch contacts for 2 dials (the 1000-ohm and 100-ohm elements) are in the galvanometer circuit and therefore do not enter into the measurement. However, the switch contacts of the 3 lower double dials (the 10-, 1-, and 0.1-ohm elements) are in series with the supply battery and contribute to the resistance of the measuring circuit. It is these latter switches that must be of very high quality. When clean and in good operating condition their resistance is of the order of 0.0001 ohm per contact. The Wolff form of this potentiometer has 12 such contacts, 4 in each of 3 dials. Eppley has reduced the number of contacts

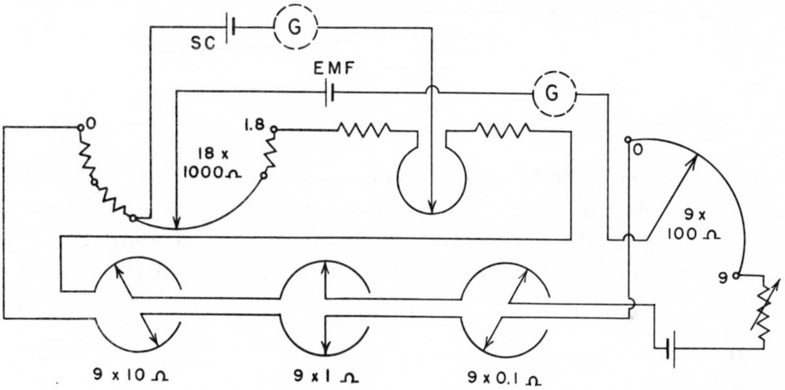

FIG. 11. Feussner potentiometer.

from 12 to 6 by using low-resistance flexible soldered leads to replace the inner contact points of the Wolff dials. The standard current in this potentiometer is 0.0001 amp and the range is 2 volts. Measurements can be made to 5 significant figures or to 10 μv. It will be noted that there is no slide wire in this instrument, all circuit elements being constructed of resistance coils having fixed values. The switches in the double dials are mechanically coupled so that the two halves operate together. Resistance is switched into the lower half dial as it is cut out of the upper half by the movement of the switch. In this way the total circuit resistance is kept constant.

Kelvin-Varley slide. In this circuit arrangement, used in some potentiometers and shown in Fig. 12, two coils of one element (dial I) are shunted by an entire element (dial II) having a resistance equal to the combined resistance of the two shunted steps. Two sliders on dial I are mechanically linked so that they move together, keeping the total shunted resistance constant regardless of switch position. Thus the current is divided equally between the elements, and the voltage drop on element II is equal to the voltage drop on one unshunted coil of element I. Because of the division of current between the elements the effect of contact resistance in the switch points is somewhat reduced.

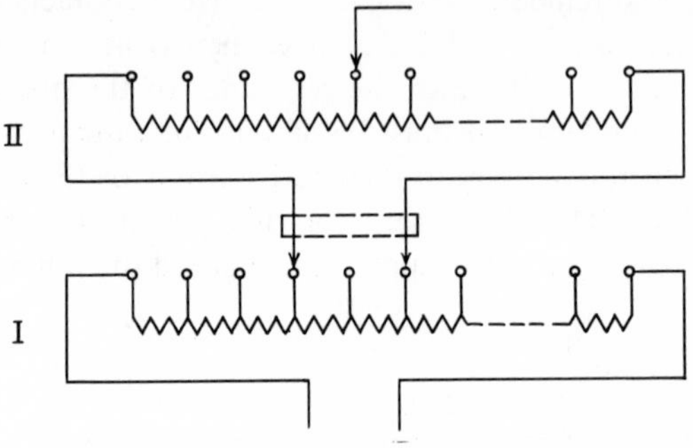

FIG. 12.

Tinsley Vernier potentiometer. This potentiometer, shown schematically in Fig. 13, makes use of the Kelvin-Varley slide principle between the coarse and intermediate dials. It should be noted that only the switch contacts in dial I affect the measuring circuit, the contacts in dials II

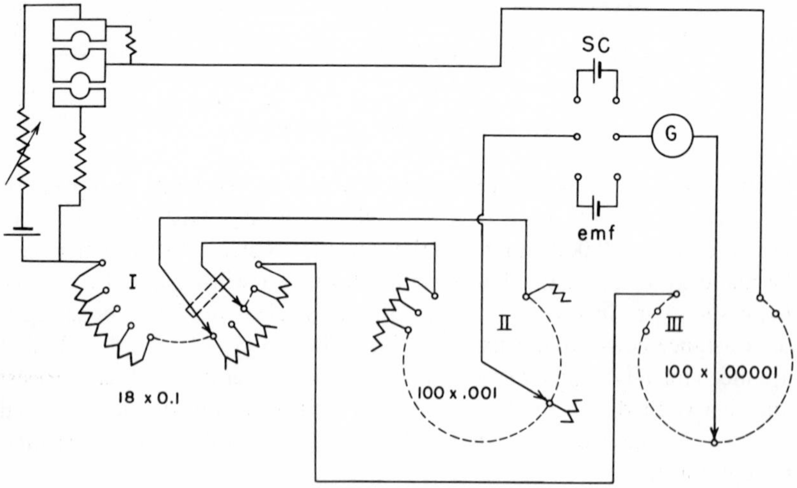

FIG. 13. Tinsley Vernier potentiometer.

and III being in the galvanometer circuit. This potentiometer also incorporates a range-changing shunt. It has a normal range of 1.9 volts in 10-μv steps, and a shunted range of 0.19 volt in 1-μv steps. An unusual feature is the subdivision of the intermediate and fine dials into 100 steps each.

Bonn Potentiometer.[16] Made by Rubicon as a five-dial precision potentiometer, this is an interesting adaptation of two types of circuit elements. It will be seen from the simplified circuit diagram of Fig. 14 that dials II through V employ modified Feussner compensated elements. Also these elements constitute a modification of the Kelvin-Varley slide principle. Actually the circuit arrangement may be considered an extension of the principle first applied in the Rubicon Type B potentiometer described above. The use of the successive parallel elements

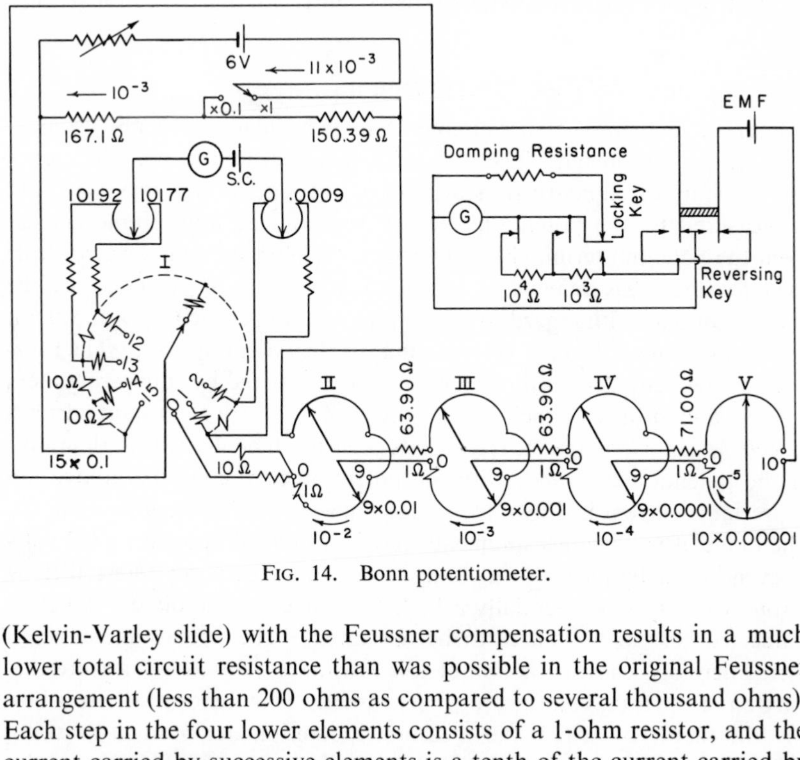

FIG. 14. Bonn potentiometer.

(Kelvin-Varley slide) with the Feussner compensation results in a much lower total circuit resistance than was possible in the original Feussner arrangement (less than 200 ohms as compared to several thousand ohms). Each step in the four lower elements consists of a 1-ohm resistor, and the current carried by successive elements is a tenth of the current carried by the preceding element. The switch in element I carries no current at balance, and its contact resistance does not introduce any error into measurements. The switch in element II carries 10^{-3} amp when the high range of the potentiometer is in use, and 10^{-4} amp on the low range. If we assume a total contact resistance of 0.002 ohm in this switch with a variation of $\pm$ 10%, there will be a fixed error of 2 μv on the high range and 0.2 μv on the low range with a random error of $\pm$ 0.2 μv and $\pm$ 0.02 μv on the two ranges respectively. The error introduced by

[16] This potentiometer was designed by N. E. Bonn of the Rubicon Company.

similar contact resistances in the switches for the lower elements will be less by factors of 10, 100, and 1000 and hence will be entirely negligible. The thermal emf's introduced into measurements by the dial switches are estimated to be less than 1 μv. In this connection the fact that the switch in element V is not directly in the galvanometer circuit is of considerable advantage. The final key in the galvanometer circuit and the galvanometer reversing key have gold contacts and are designed to minimize thermal emf's. The reversing key is of the same type as is used in the Rubicon microvolt potentiometer but is not enclosed in a thermal shield.

Current and Voltage Measurements

Current and voltage measurements may be made with any general-purpose potentiometer. The current to be measured is sent through a known shunt or standard resistor, and the voltage drop across the shunt is measured by the potentiometer without drawing appreciable current from the potential terminals of the shunt. The shunt (standard resistor) used for the measurement of any particular value of current must be chosen not only with regard to the current-carrying capacity[17] of the shunt but also with regard to the voltage range of the potentiometer. The four-terminal resistances of two resistors may be compared by connecting them in series and measuring their voltage drops in turn with a constant current.

Volt Boxes. Voltage measurements offer no difficulty within the range of the potentiometer, and, with the potentiometers described above, no appreciable current is drawn from the voltage source under measurement. The range of voltage measurements may be extended upward to 750 volts or even higher by means of a voltage-ratio box, commonly referred to as a *volt box*. This is essentially a high-resistance voltage divider which is connected across the source to be measured. The potentiometer, connected across a known fraction of this resistance, is used to measure this fraction of the total voltage drop. The multiplying factor of the volt box (i.e. the factor by which the measured potentiometer voltage must be multiplied to obtain the total voltage across the box) is the ratio of the total resistance to the resistance of the section connected across the potentiometer. Such volt boxes usually have a number of ranges. Multirange volt boxes are of one of the two types shown in Fig. 15. In (*a*) the total resistance is varied to change the range while the resistance connected across the potentiometer remains constant. In (*b*) the total resistance is constant while the resistance across the potentiometer is changed by means of a rotary selector switch to change ranges. In either case care must be exercised that the proper range is selected for use, since otherwise

[17] For a discussion of standard resistors see Chapter 7.

the resistor in Type (*a*) may be injured by excessive current, and for either type there is danger of injury to the potentiometer from excessive voltage if too low a range is selected. Experience indicates that Type (*a*), and the use of separate binding posts for the various ranges, is somewhat safer than Type (*b*), and the use of a rotary switch for range selection.

It should be emphasized that the combination of a potentiometer and volt box is not a *null* instrument. Current is supplied to the volt box from the source being measured. For this reason a high resistance

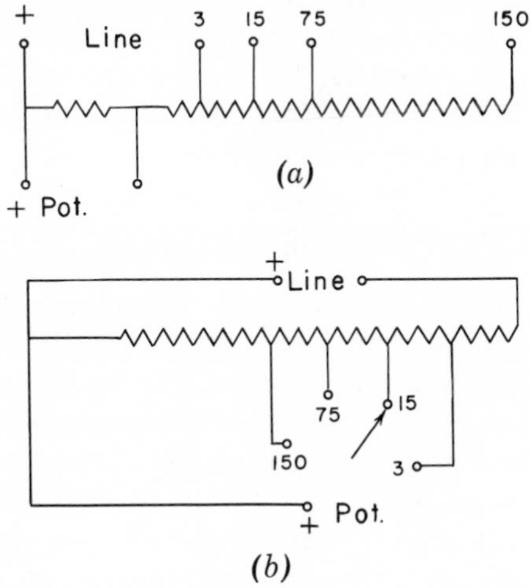

FIG. 15.

(large value of ohms per volt) is desirable. Also a high-resistance volt box consumes less power and therefore has less self-heating than a low-resistance unit for the same voltage. If the section of the volt box connected across the potentiometer were constructed of wire of the same size and material as the remainder of the resistance and were so situated that in use it would always have the same temperature as the remainder of the resistance, the effect on measurements of self-heating would be unimportant. However, in practice this ideal cannot be attained, and it is therefore important in precise work that the ratio of the volt box be known for the operating voltage. The change of ratio resulting from self-heating is generally small in well-designed volt boxes, usually not more than 0.01 or 0.02%, and is not fully developed until the resistance elements have had time to reach equilibrium temperature, perhaps an hour or more after connection to the circuit.[18]

[18] Silsbee and Gross, Testing and Performance of Volt Boxes, *NBS J. Research*, **27**, 269 (1941).

A practical limit is set to the resistance of a volt box by a number of considerations: (1) high-resistance elements are expensive to make and adjust; (2) they are inherently less stable than low resistances; (3) for a given insulation resistance the shunting effect of leakage currents is greater for high than for low resistances; (4) if the volt box contributes a large resistance to the measuring circuit the sensitivity of the measurement may be reduced. Within the limits set by these considerations the resistance of a volt box should be as high as feasible.

By the use of a volt box and suitable standard resistors very precise measurements of direct voltages and currents can be made on any of the general-purpose potentiometers described above. Such measurements furnish a means of checking the calibration of voltmeters and ammeters as well as a basis for power and energy measurements.

SPECIAL-PURPOSE POTENTIOMETERS

The Brooks Deflection Potentiometer. In any of the general-purpose potentiometers described above, the galvanometer serves as a *null* instrument to detect any departure from balance in the circuit, and only secondarily to estimate the magnitude of a departure from balance. Where circuit conditions are unsteady so that the voltage under measurement varies, it is often difficult or even impossible to attain a balance. In any case the adjustments required for an exact balance are time-consuming and tedious, a decided disadvantage for measurements of moderate precision. These were some of the considerations that led to the development of the Brooks deflection potentiometer.[19] This instrument was specifically designed for measurements in an accuracy class intermediate between the highest grade of deflection instruments and the precision, null potentiometers. It is therefore completely adapted to the calibration and testing of deflection instruments and finds its chief use in instrument and meter laboratories. In the deflection potentiometer the adjustment of a single dial gives an approximate balance, and the greater portion of the voltage is read from this dial setting. The residual unbalance is read from the deflection of a sensitive millivoltmeter which replaces the galvanometer of the null potentiometer. Thus balances can be rapidly made and small variations in voltage are readily followed. The essential difference between the circuits of a null potentiometer and those of a deflection potentiometer is that the latter has supplementary resistance coils which maintain a constant resistance in the galvanometer branch of the circuit for all positions of the potentiometer dial as well as for all values of volt-box ratio and of shunts used in voltage and current measurements.

[19] Brooks, *Bull. Bur. Standards*, **2**, 225 (1906); **4**, 275 (1908); **8**, 395 and 419 (1912).

We shall analyze the circuit requirements of the Brooks deflection potentiometer by making use of *Thévenin's theorem*.[20] This theorem, generally applicable to networks, states that the current in any branch of a network is equal to that which would flow in the branch if an emf, equal to the potential difference which would appear at the break if the branch were opened, were inserted in the branch and all other sources of emf were removed from the network. The analysis is made in three steps: (1) the voltage at the break, E_a, is computed; (2) the resistance of the network, R_a, as seen from the break is computed; (3) the current in

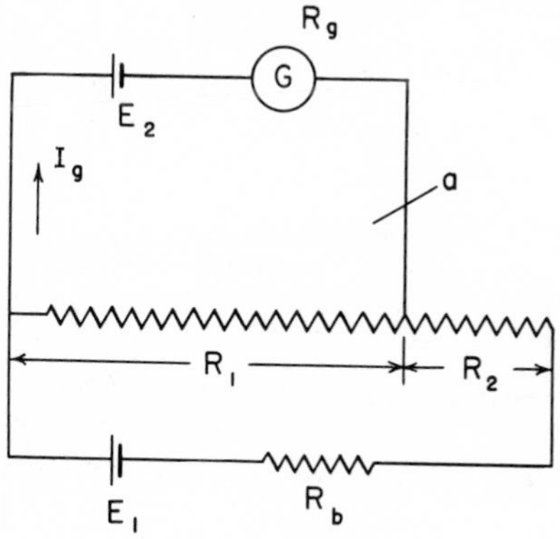

FIG. 16.

the branch is then E_a/R_a. To illustrate the method we will first take as an example the simple circuit of Fig. 16, which is similar to that of the Brooks potentiometer. The transverse line (*a*) in the figure indicates the point at which the theoretical cut or break is made in the circuit.

$$E_a = \frac{R_1E_1}{R_1 + R_2 + R_b} - E_2$$

$$R_a = R_g + \frac{R_1(R_2 + R_b)}{R_1 + R_2 + R_b}$$

$$I_g = \frac{E_a}{R_a} = \frac{\dfrac{R_1E_1}{R_1 + R_2 + R_b} - E_2}{R_g + \dfrac{R_1(R_2 + R_b)}{R_1 + R_2 + R_b}}$$

[20] Thévenin, *Compt. rendus*, **97**, 159 (1883). See also Wenner, *Sci. Papers Bur. Standards*, **21**, 191 (1926).

The schematic circuit of the Brooks deflection potentiometer is shown in Fig. 17 for the case in which it is connected directly to a source of potential V having negligible resistance.[21] Here

$$E_a = V - \frac{Er_1}{r_1 + r_2 + R_b}$$

and

$$R_a = R_g + r_3 + \frac{r_1(r_2 + R_b)}{r_1 + r_2 + R_b}$$

Then

$$I_g = \frac{V - \dfrac{Er_1}{r_1 + r_2 + R_b}}{R_g + r_3 + \dfrac{r_1(r_2 + R_b)}{r_1 + r_2 + R_b}}$$

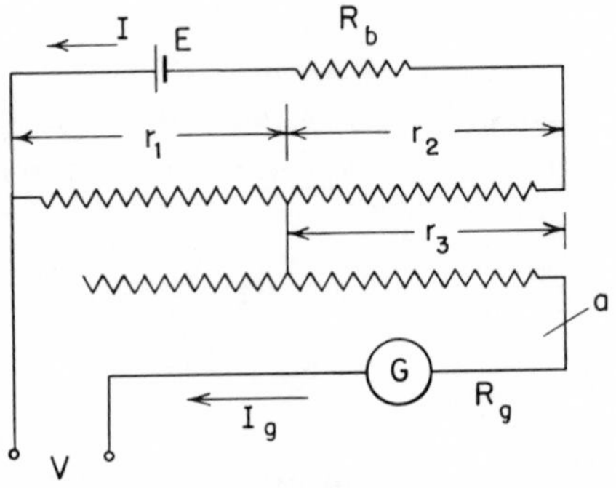

FIG. 17.

There are two possibilities: (1) if the balance is exact, so that $I_g = 0$, then

$$V = \frac{Er_1}{r_1 + r_2 + R_b} = Ir_1$$

where I is the potentiometer calibrating current supplied by E and set to its correct value by a standard-cell balance in which R_b is varied; (2) if the balance is not exact, V being the part which is balanced by the dial setting corresponding to r_1, and ΔV the unbalanced part which must be read from the deflection, θ, of the millivoltmeter, then

$$I_g = \frac{V + \Delta V - \dfrac{Er_1}{r_1 + r_2 + R_b}}{R_g + r_3 + \dfrac{r_1(r_2 + R_b)}{r_1 + r_2 + R_b}} = \frac{\Delta V}{R_g + r_3 + \dfrac{r_1(r_2 + R_b)}{r_1 + r_2 + R_b}}$$

[21] In these schematic diagrams the standard cell circuit for checking the potentiometer current is omitted for simplicity.

and $V + \Delta V = Ir_1 + K\theta$. The reading is in two parts, the balanced voltage V being read from the dial setting and the unbalanced voltage ΔV being read from the scale of the deflecting instrument. Now, in order to satisfy the condition $\Delta V = K\theta$ (i.e. for the deflection to be proportional to ΔV), I_g must also be proportional to ΔV, since we will assume a uniform scale for the deflecting instrument ($I_g \propto \theta$). This condition is completely met when

$$R_g + r_3 + \frac{r_1(r_2 + R_b)}{r_1 + r_2 + R_b} = \text{constant}$$

If r_3 (the supplementary resistance in the galvanometer branch) could be fixed for each dial position so that it just compensated for the change in $r_1(r_2 + R_b)/(r_1 + r_2 + R_b)$, then $I_g/\Delta V$ would be the same for any dial setting. Actually this cannot be done precisely since the term which is to be compensated contains R_b, which will vary with the state of charge of the supply battery, becoming less as the battery is discharged. (As E becomes less, R_b must be decreased to keep I constant.) Fortunately it is unnecessary that the condition of "constant resistance" be completely satisfied. The deflecting element of the potentiometer (a pointer and scale instrument) has 30 divisions on either side of its zero position and can be read to 0.1 division. It therefore follows that the voltage calibration of the instrument scale will not be affected by an *observable* amount if the change in R_b affects the total resistance

$$R = R_g + r_3 + \frac{r_1(r_2 + R_b)}{r_1 + r_2 + R_b}$$

by less than a part in 300 or $\frac{1}{3}\%$. This condition can easily be met. For example in Brooks Model 7 deflection potentiometer

$$R_g = 7.4 \text{ ohms}$$

$$R_b = \begin{matrix} 136.4 \text{ ohms minimum} \\ 162.0 \text{ ohms maximum} \end{matrix}$$

	Dial at zero	*Dial at* 150
$r_1 =$	0	6 ohms
$r_2 =$	6 ohms	0
$r_3 =$	5.77 ohms	0

At zero setting the variation of R_b has no influence on R, while it makes the maximum difference at a setting of 150 (the maximum dial setting). At dial setting zero, $R = 13.17$ ohms. At dial setting 150, $R = 13.15$ ohms for the minimum value of R_b, and $R = 13.18$ ohms for the maximum value of R_b, a total change of 0.03 ohm in 13.15 ohms, or 0.23%, well within the required limit. The range of this potentiometer (Model 7) is from 0 to 150 mv on the dial in steps of 5 mv and 0 to 3 mv on the galvanometer. The galvanometer has a scale with 30 divisions on each side of the center zero, so that its marked divisions represent 0.1 mv. Readings may be estimated to 0.1 scale division or 0.01 mv, a part in 15,000 of full-range voltage. Full-scale current of the galvanometer is 0.4 ma, so that the current drawn from the source under measurement ranges between this value and zero. It should be noted that the emf (open-circuit voltage) of a source is measured with this potentiometer only if the galvanometer reading is zero. If any current flows in the galvanometer, the voltage measured is the voltage which appears across the terminals of the potentiometer under the condition of measurement. The relation of this voltage to the emf of the source can be stated only if one knows the internal resistance of the source.

VOLTAGE MEASUREMENTS. By using a special volt box the range of this instrument may be extended to larger voltages. Applying an argument

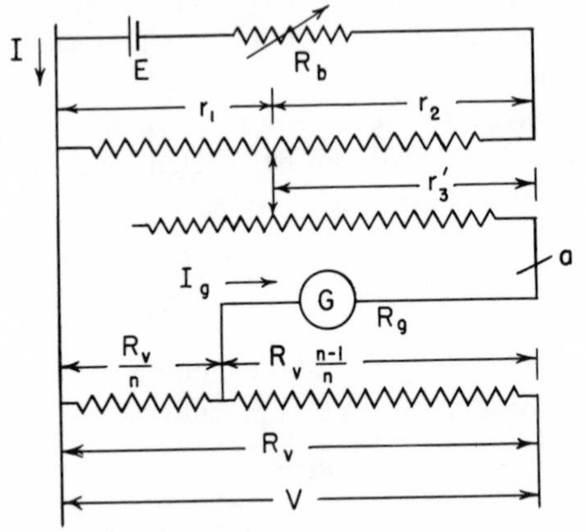

FIG. 18.

similar to the analysis above to the circuit of Fig. 18, we have

$$V_a = \frac{V}{n} - \frac{Er_1}{r_1 + r_2 + R_b}$$

and

$$R_a = R_g + r_3' + \frac{R_v(n-1)}{n^2} + \frac{r_1(r_2 + R_b)}{r_1 + r_2 + R_b}$$

As before, at balance, $I_g = 0$, and $V/n = Ir_1$ so that $V = nIr_1$. If the potentiometer is not balanced so that we have $V + \Delta V$, then

$$I_g = \frac{\dfrac{\Delta V}{n}}{R_g + r_3' + R_v \dfrac{n-1}{n^2} + \dfrac{r_1(r_2 + R_b)}{r_1 + r_2 + R_b}}$$

and

$$V + \Delta V = nIr_1 + nI_g \left[R_g + r_3' + R_v \frac{n-1}{n^2} + \frac{r_1(r_2 + R_b)}{r_1 + r_2 + R_b} \right]$$

As before, the coefficient of nI_g must be constant in order that I_g be proportional to ΔV. It follows that as n is varied in the volt box (i.e. as the range is changed) resistance must be changed in the galvanometer circuit. A special design of volt box is used for this purpose, with the necessary compensating resistance inserted in the lead to the potentiometer as shown in Fig. 19. These resistances are of such values that, whatever range is connected to the potentiometer, the total resistance of the circuit is constant as seen from a break in the galvanometer branch, with the supply battery terminals and the input terminals of the volt box shorted.

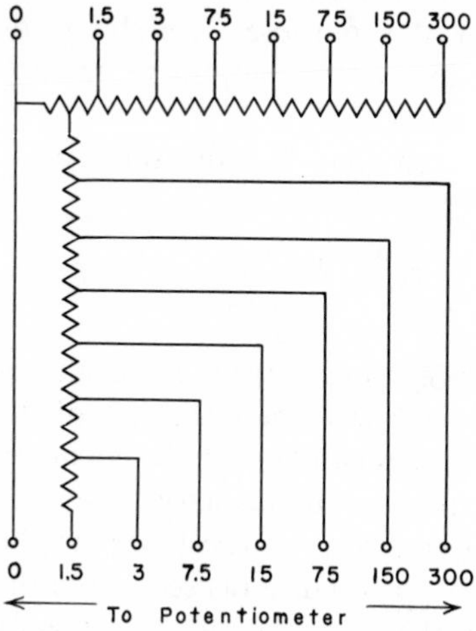

FIG. 19.

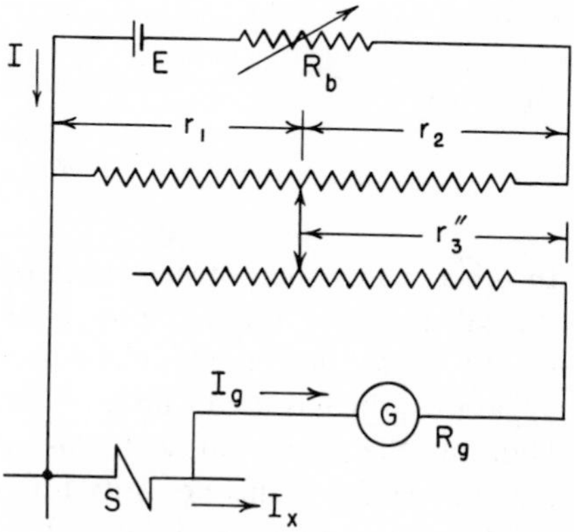

FIG. 20.

CURRENT MEASUREMENTS. A similar situation exists (Fig. 20) when a shunt (S) is used to measure current. Here

$$V_a = SI_x - \frac{Er_1}{r_1 + r_2 + R_b} = SI_x - Ir_1$$

and

$$R_a = R_g + r_3'' + S + \frac{r_1(r_2 + R_b)}{r_1 + r_2 + R_b}$$

If the shunt current is $I_x + \Delta I_x$,

$$I_g = \frac{S\Delta I_x}{R_g + r_3'' + S + \dfrac{r_1(r_2 + R_b)}{r_1 + r_2 + R_b}}$$

and

$$I_x + \Delta I_x = \frac{r_1 I}{S} + \frac{I_g}{S}\left[R_g + r_3'' + S + \frac{r_1(r_2 + R_b)}{r_1 + r_2 + R_b}\right]$$

The sum of the resistances of the galvanometer branch, the shunt, and the shunt leads must be constant. An adjustable resistor is included in the "shunt" circuit of the potentiometer for this purpose. As shunts of higher resistance are used with the potentiometer this adjustable resistor must be decreased by a corresponding amount.

GENERAL CONSIDERATIONS. It will be seen that, for the three cases discussed,

$$r_3 = r_3' + R_v \frac{n-1}{n^2} = r_3'' + S$$

In other words the potentiometer resistance, as seen from a "break" in the galvanometer branch, must have a fixed resistance regardless of the use to which the potentiometer is put and regardless of the auxiliary apparatus which is used with it. The arrangement of auxiliary resistances built into the potentiometer to ensure this constancy of resistance may be seen in Fig. 21. This necessity for constant resistance (as seen from the galvanometer) requires the use of a special volt box designed expressly for this potentiometer, and also limits the maximum resistance of any current-measuring shunt to a value not greater than the total resistance provided for shunt compensation (6 ohms in the Model 7 potentiometer). It should be noted that neither of these limitations exists for *null*-type potentiometers. For instrument calibration and checking (for which the Brooks potentiometer was expressly designed) these limitations do not seriously restrict the range of usefulness of the potentiometer. However, it should be recognized that, if the instrument is to serve as a general-purpose potentiometer, the operator should be aware of its limitations and use it *only* in those applications for which the "constant-resistance" requirement will not be violated.

Potentiometers for Small Emf's

In the measurement of emf's or voltage drops which range downward from a few millivolts to a few microvolts, special precautions must be taken to eliminate or compensate parasitic emf's in the circuit (including the circuit of the galvanometer that is used as a null detector). Potentiometers designed for the measurement of small voltages are usually low-resistance instruments, and the circuits must also be designed to minimize the effect of contact resistances in the measuring circuit. A number of

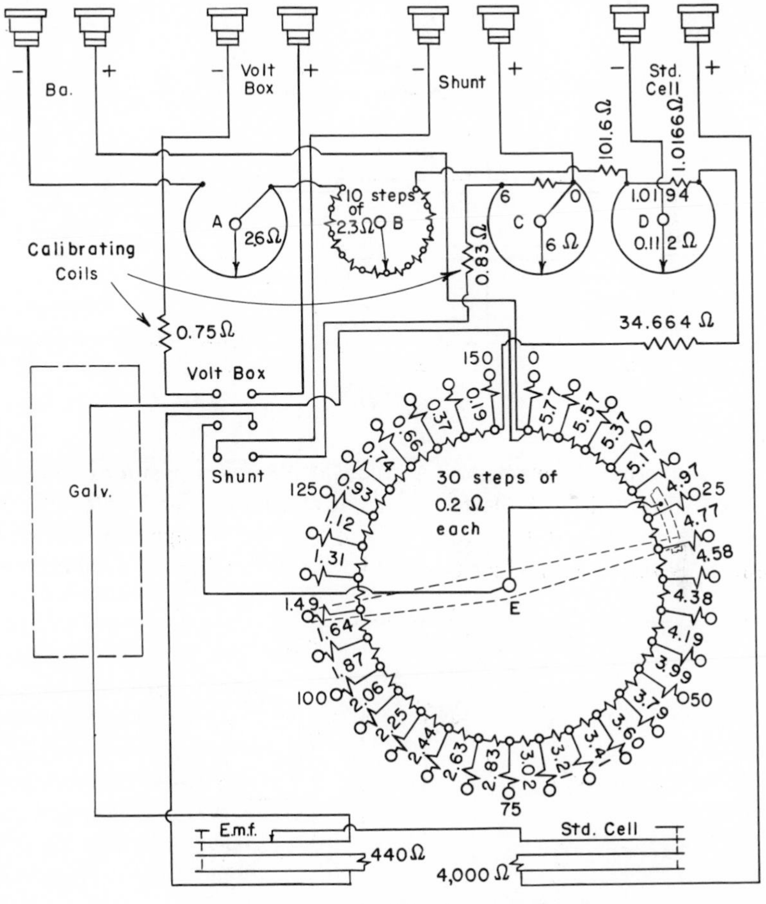

FIG. 21. The Brooks deflection potentiometer.

special circuits and circuit elements have been devised for these low-range potentiometers, used principally in thermocouple applications.

HAUSRATH ELEMENT. The split-circuit element of Hausrath[22] represented an attempt to eliminate parasitic emf's resulting from sliding contacts by removing them to an auxiliary circuit. This element is shown schematically in Fig. 22. The numbers 1.0, 0.9, etc., represent conductances from

[22] Hausrath, *Ann. der Phys.*, **322**, 735 (1905).

the points U and O in the two branches to the contact blocks K and K' respectively. For any position of the mechanically linked sliders the total resistance from U to O is 1.0 ohm so that the total drop of potential through the element is a constant, independent of slider position, for any

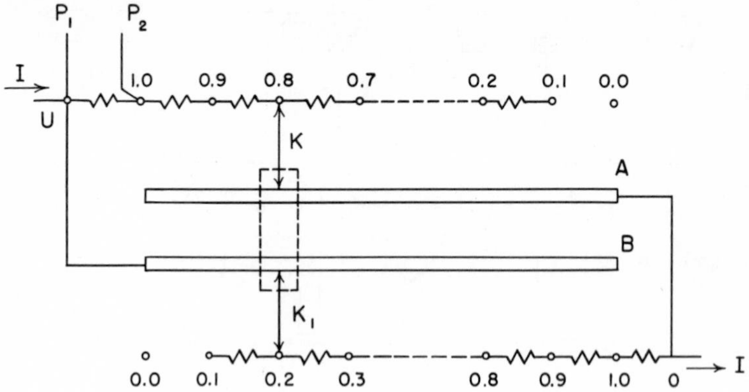

FIG. 22.

current I entering the element. As the slider K takes positions 1.0, 0.9, 0.8, etc., the fraction of the total current carried by the 1-ohm resistor between P_1 and P_2 is I, $0.9I$, $0.8I$, etc., so that the voltage drop between P_1 and P_2 is varied with slider position without changing the total current

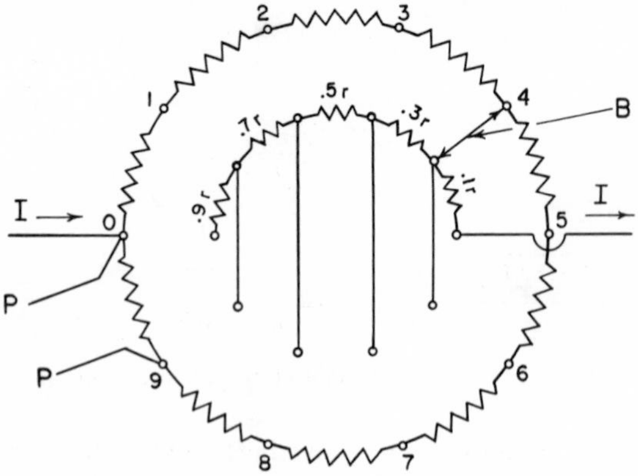

FIG. 23.

in the element. Parasitic emf's between P_1 and P_2 would be small since the sliding contacts are in the auxiliary circuit. It should be noted, however, that variations of contact resistance at the sliders will introduce an error into the measurement.

DIESSELHORST ELEMENT. The split-circuit element of Diesselhorst[23] avoids the defects of the Hausrath element and accomplishes the same result with fewer coils (15 instead of 20). Ten equal coils are connected between contact studs in the outer circle of Fig. 23. Five supplementary coils are connected to the inner circle as shown to maintain a constant resistance in the element. As the contactor B is placed in positions 0, 1, 2, · · ·, the current between studs 0 and 9 takes on the values 0, $0.1I$, $0.2I$, · · ·, so that the potential drop P_1–P_2 increases in 10 equal steps. It should be noted that the division of current between the parallel circuits which comprise the outer ring is independent of the resistance of the switch contacts. The constancy of the current I is dependent on this contact resistance, but if I is held constant, the voltage drop P_1–P_2 is correct.[24]

WAIDNER-WOLFF ELEMENT. White[25] suggested the use of the Waidner-Wolff[26] element, previously employed in resistance apparatus, as a poten-

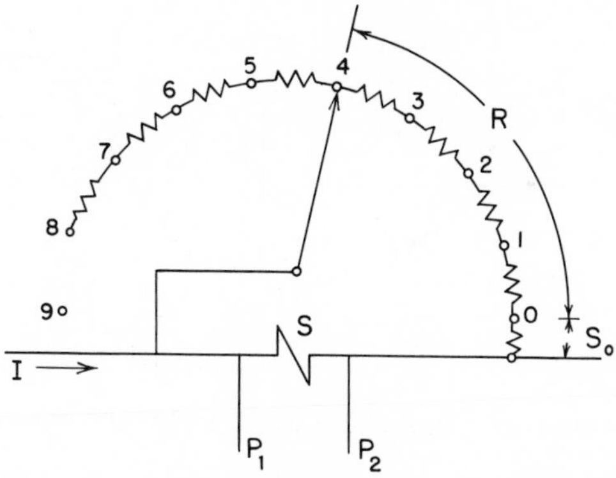

FIG. 24.

tiometer element. This element, shown in Fig. 24, consists of a fixed resistance S shunted by a relatively high resistance, adjustable from a minimum value S_0 to infinity. These shunt coils are of such values that the resultant total resistance of the circuit is changed by equal small steps (e.g. 0.001 ohm) as the switch position is changed. The potential drop

[23] Diesselhorst, *Zeits. für Instrumentenk.*, **28,** 1 (1908).

[24] In an informal communication to the author, Dr. H. B. Brooks has pointed out the interesting fact that ". . . the Diesselhorst element is simply an Ayrton-Mather universal galvanometer shunt used to pass an adjustable fraction of an incoming *constant* current; whereas Ayrton-Mather used the same device to pass a substantially constant current from an arriving current which could vary over a wide range."

[25] White, *Zeits. für Instrumentenk.*, **27,** 210 (1907).

[26] Waidner, *Phys. Rev.*, **19,** 57 (1904).

P_1–P_2 therefore changes by uniform small steps if the current I is constant. This arrangement makes the effect of contact resistance at the switch small since it is in series with a very large resistance. At the same time the effect of thermal emf's in the switch is made negligible. If an emf e is present in the circuit it circulates a current through the closed loop S–S_0–R. The parasitic emf which appears in the measuring circuit at S is then $eS/(S + S_0 + R)$. Since S_0 and R are purposely made large compared to S, the effect of the parasitic emf on the measuring circuit is negligibly small.

Diesselhorst Difference Potentiometer. Using results of work by Hausrath, Diesselhorst, and White, Diesselhorst[27] designed a constant-

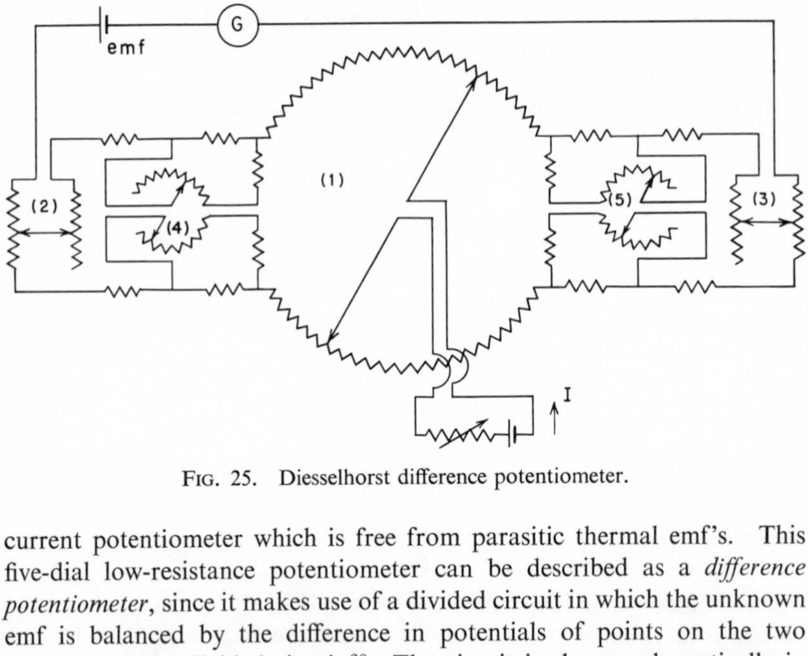

FIG. 25. Diesselhorst difference potentiometer.

current potentiometer which is free from parasitic thermal emf's. This five-dial low-resistance potentiometer can be described as a *difference potentiometer*, since it makes use of a divided circuit in which the unknown emf is balanced by the difference in potentials of points on the two branches of the divided circuit.[28] The circuit is shown schematically in Fig. 25, with the standard-cell balancing circuit omitted for simplicity. The resistances are such that the left-hand branch containing dials 2 and 4 carries 10 times the current of the right-hand branch containing dials 3 and 5. The position of the branch points is controlled by dial 1. Contacts 1 and 1′ are in series with the supply battery (2 volts), and any parasitic emf at this point simply adds to the supply voltage. Since such

[27] Diesselhorst, *op. cit.*

[28] A three-element difference potentiometer had previously been described by Hausrath, *Ann. der Phys.*, **322,** 740 (1905).

parasitic emf's (a few microvolts at most) are negligible in comparison with the supply voltage, the effect on the potentiometer current is not appreciable. Thermal emf's present at switches 2 and 3 are neutralized by the divided circuit. They cause the flow of currents in the two branches which result in compensating potential drops. Only the small difference in these voltage drops affects the measurement. This amounts at most to around 1% of the thermal emf present at 2 or 3. Thermal emf's at switches 4 and 5 are absorbed in the parallel resistance of the Waidner-Wolff elements so that only about 1% of them appears in the measuring circuit.

Wenner Difference Potentiometer. One of the disadvantages of the Waidner-Wolff element is the large number of resistance coils which must

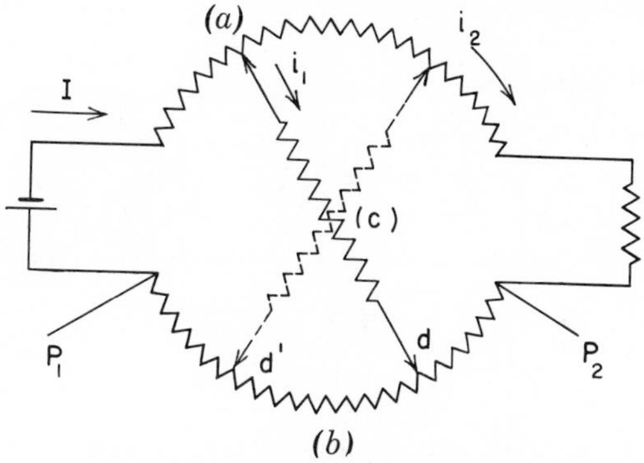

FIG. 26.

be adjusted to odd values. A circuit element devised by Wenner[29] avoids this difficulty. This element is shown schematically in Fig. 26. The upper and lower dials (*a*) and (*b*) are identical and consist of 10 equal steps each. The resistance (*c*) between the contact points on the switch is fixed in value. Hence the resistance of the element as seen from the battery is constant. As the switch is moved from *d* to *d'* the current in that part of *b* between *d* and *d'* changes by an amount i_1 carried by *c*, while the current is unchanged in the remaining parts of *b*. The change in potential drop between P_1 and P_2 is then the product of i_1 and the resistance from *d* to *d'*. Since the resistance of each of the 10 steps is equal it will be seen that the potential difference from P_1 to P_2 changes with dial position in 10 equal steps. Because of the divided circuit the effects of thermal emf's at the switch contacts are compensated as in the previous case, and the residual that appears in the measuring circuit amounts to 1% or less of the parasitic. Since the resistance *c* is high

[29] Wenner, *Phys. Rev.*, **31**, 94 (1910).

compared to a and b the effect of the switch-contact resistances in series with c is negligible.

A difference potentiometer of the Wenner type made by Leeds and Northrup is shown schematically in Fig. 27. The current divides in dial I, one branch including dials II and IV and the other branch including III and V. The unknown emf is compensated by the difference in potential drops in the branches to the right and left of the contacts of dial I. Compensating resistances are used in dial IV to keep the total resistance of the potentiometer constant. The total resistance of dial V is low enough that its variation does not cause a detectable error, and similar compensation is not needed here. In operation the current in the left branch is

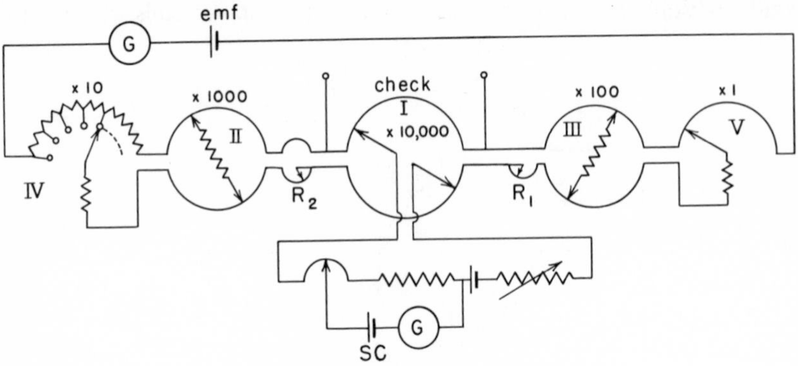

FIG. 27. Wenner difference potentiometer.

9 times the current in the right branch. To establish the correctness of this current division, dial switch I is set on its 1 position and a galvanometer is connected to the terminals marked "check." A slide-wire resistance R_1 is adjusted to bring the galvanometer to zero, setting the currents in their proper ratio. With all the dials set at their zero position and the emf terminals shorted, any voltage present in the measuring circuit is the result of inequality of voltages in the main branches and of any parasitic emf that may be present. With a galvanometer connected in the emf circuit under these conditions resistance R_2 is varied, introducing a small adjustable voltage drop into the measuring circuit to balance the inequalities or parasitic emf's present. The standard-cell balance, to set the potentiometer current to its correct value, is made in the auxiliary circuit as shown in the figure. A range-changing device, not shown in the figure, reduces the current in the measuring circuit by a factor of $\frac{1}{10}$ without changing the battery current. Measurements on the high range, between 0 and 0.1 volt, are made to $\pm 0.01\% + 0.5\ \mu v$; on the low range, from 0 to 0.01 volt, the limiting error is $\pm 0.01\% + 0.1\ \mu v$. The

lowest dial is calibrated to read to 1 μv on the high range and 0.1 μv on the low range.

White Combination Potentiometer. The difference potentiometers described above have resistances which must be closely adjusted to special "odd" values. Furthermore very few laboratories possess the necessary facilities for checking them. This disadvantage is avoided in the White[30]

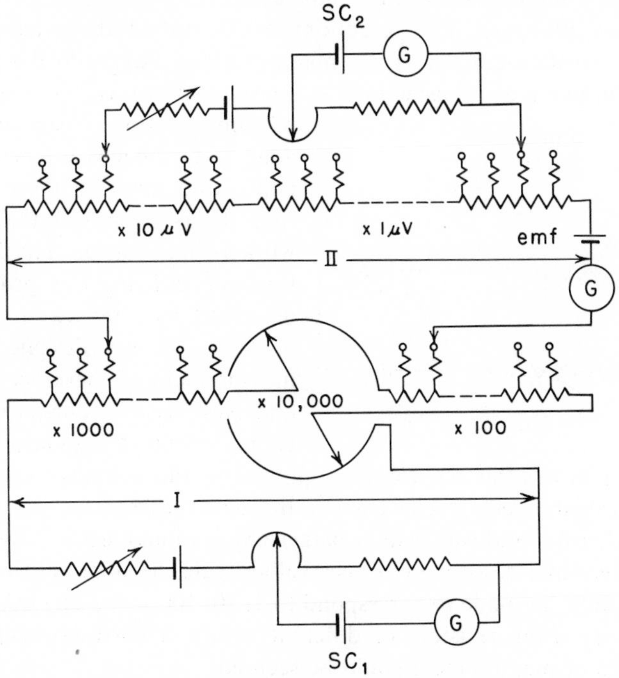

FIG. 28. White combination potentiometer.

combination potentiometer. In this arrangement the unknown emf is measured as the sum of the readings of two potentiometers, one of high and the other of low range. The Eppley Laboratory's version of this potentiometer is shown schematically in Fig. 28. Potentiometer I measures to 0.1 volt in 100-μv steps; Potentiometer II measures to 110 μv in 1-μv steps. Each potentiometer has its own supply battery and standard cell checking circuit, the standard cell and galvanometer being switched from one circuit to the other by a selector switch. The current in circuit I is 0.001 amp, and in circuit II is 0.0001 amp. Parasitic emf's resulting from switching in circuit I are in the measuring circuit but should not affect the balance, since they will die out before the final

[30] White, *Zeits. für Instrumentenk.*, **34,** 71, 107, 142 (1914).

balance is made in circuit II. Parasitic emf's resulting from switching in circuit II are in series with the supply battery and do not affect the balance. If high-grade switches are used, contact resistance will be of negligible effect since both circuits have high resistances in series with the contact points. Only copper and manganin are used in the electrical circuits to minimize thermal emf's, and the entire potentiometer is immersed in oil to ensure a uniform operating temperature.

Lindeck Element. The potentiometers described above have all been of the "constant-current" type, making use of Poggendorff's *first* compensation method. Poggendorff's "constant-resistance" (*second*) method of compensation is particularly well adapted to the measurement of smali emf's, and deserves more attention than it has received in the past from workers in this field. The first potentiometer utilizing this principle was described by Lindeck and Rothe[31] in 1899. It was designed for the measurement of thermocouple emf's and made use of a four-terminal manganin resistance standard (Fig. 29). The drop across this resistor was opposed to the unknown emf in series with a galvanometer. The current through the resistor was adjustable with a rheostat and was read at balance by a milliammeter. By choosing a four-terminal resistor of proper value, scale divisions on the milliammeter could be made to correspond to 1, 10, 100 μv or any other desired value. By using resistors of different values, a corresponding number of ranges of measurement could be secured.

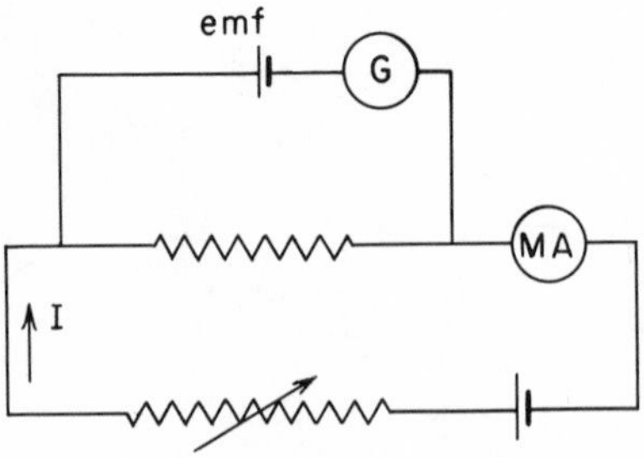

FIG. 29.

Although the percentage accuracy of this instrument is not high, being limited to the accuracy with which the scale of the milliammeter can be read, it has some decided advantages over constant-current potentiometers in the low-voltage range. The circuit which must be protected against parasitic emf's is relatively simple, consisting of the shunt, galvanometer, and galvanometer key, and contains no sliding contact or adjustable element. It can therefore be easily isolated within a thermal shielding enclosure to ensure a closely uniform temperature. Range changing can be accomplished by means of a selector switch[32] to change the standard resistor, and a number of ranges can be easily made available. Balance is secured by a single resistance adjustment, and readings can be made quickly to two- or three-place accuracy. The value of a changing emf

[31] Lindeck, *Zeits. für Instrumentenk.*, **19,** 249 (1899); **20,** 285 (1900).

[32] If this switch is in the milliammeter circuit it need not be thermally shielded.

can be measured at a particular instant by adjusting the rheostat to maintain balance continuously, and ceasing to adjust the rheostat at the critical moment. The milliammeter can then be read at leisure. The arrangement can be made compact and readily portable. Possible disadvantages of the arrangement are its low accuracy compared with other types of null potentiometers and the necessity for occasional calibration of the milliammeter with another potentiometer and standard resistance. Since the shunts used in these potentiometer elements are of low resistance, their permanency should be comparable to that of other standard resistors, and, since their resistances need be known only to the reading accuracy (0.1%), such shunts should not be a source of trouble or inaccuracy in the instrument. A potentiometer of this type, having 6 ranges with full-scale voltages from 40 μv to 2 mv, has been described by Brooks and Spinks.[33] This instrument is shown schematically in Fig. 30, and the portion of the circuit which is sensitive to the presence of parasitic emf's is indicated by the dotted line enclosure. It should be noted that the shunt selector switch and the reversing switch are in series with the supply battery and need no thermal protection.

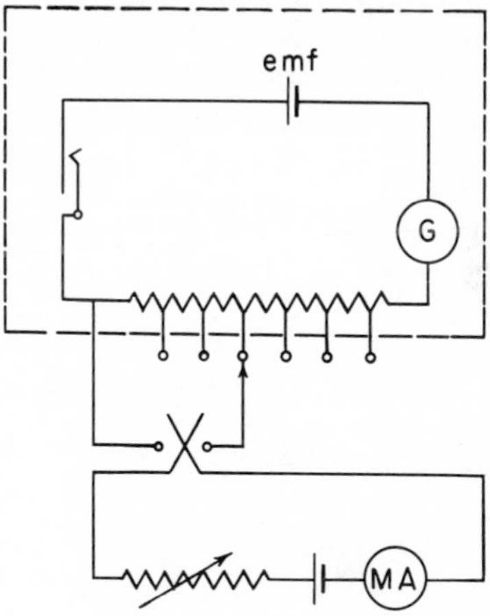

FIG. 30.

A modification of the Lindeck element, shown in Fig. 31, can be used to measure small emf's to a precision higher than can be attained by a deflecting instrument. Two known four-terminal resistors, R_1 and R_2, are connected in series and carry the same current. The unknown emf, E, is opposed by the voltage drop across R_1, and the current, I, at balance is measured with any general-purpose null potentiometer from the voltage drop across R_2. The emf, E, is equal to the ratio R_1/R_2 multiplied by the reading of the potentiometer at balance. The resistances of R_1 and R_2 can usually be chosen so that the potentiometer may be operated at a convenient value within its range. Thus it is possible to measure a rather small emf quite precisely with a high-range potentiometer by properly

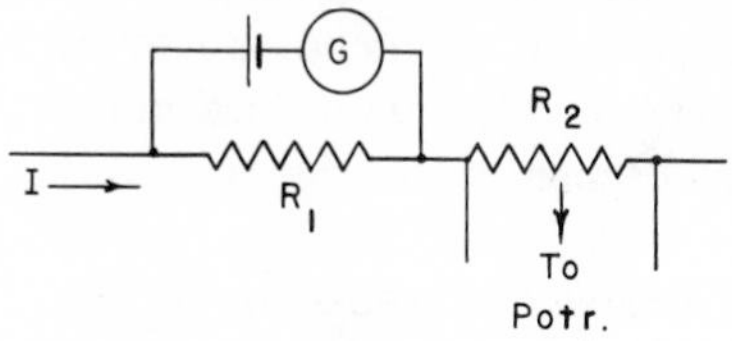

FIG. 31.

[33] Brooks and Spinks, *NBS J. Research*, **9**, 781 (1932).

selecting the ratio R_1/R_2. It will be realized that any thermal emf present in the Lindeck element of the combination will appear undiminished in the final result, so that precisely the same precautions must be taken to avoid parasitic emf's as are necessary in any other low-range potentiometer.

Brooks Standard-Cell Comparator. This is a low-emf, combination potentiometer incorporating both "constant-current" and "constant-resistance" elements. Specifically designed for measuring the difference in emf's of standard calls to 1 μv, the instrument (shown schematically in Fig. 32) has a "constant-current" element in which the balancing potential

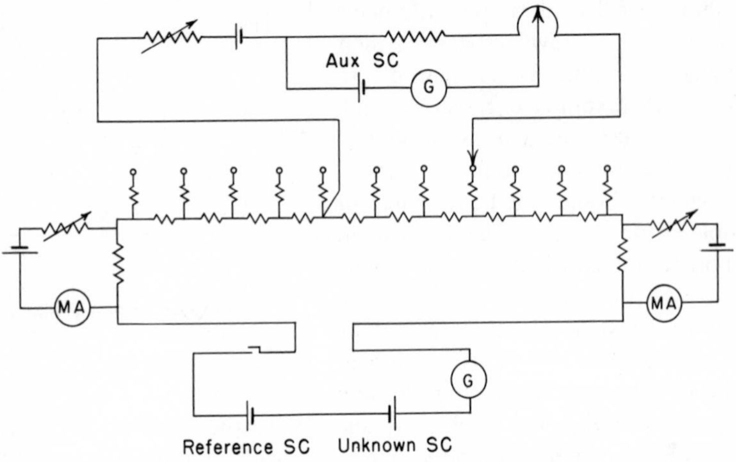

FIG. 32. Brooks standard-cell comparator.

drop may be changed by 100-μv steps, and two (Lindeck) "constant-resistance" elements each covering a range of 100 μv. The milliammeters in these latter elements have 100 scale divisions and are marked to read directly in microvolts. These milliammeters have magnetic shunts by means of which they may be adjusted so that for full-scale deflection the potential difference in their associated four-terminal resistors is precisely 100 μv.

By means of an ingenious dial and switch arrangement shown in Fig. 33, the potentiometer is made direct reading. A reference scale is engraved on the panel which carries the contact studs of the constant-current element. A second scale (the *X*-scale) is engraved on the slider which carries the contact brush and moves with it. An opaque screen covers both scales except for a single number on each scale which can be read through the windows (*W–R* and *W–X*) cut in the screen. In operation the screen is moved until the first 4 digits in the emf of a *known* reference cell are exposed in the *R*-window. The next two significant digits of the reference cell are set on the milliammeter of the left-hand Lindeck element (Fig. 32) by adjusting its current. The potentiometer is then balanced by adjusting the dial switch and the current in the right-hand Lindeck element. At balance the first 4 digits in the emf of the unknown cell are read in the X-window and the next 2 from the right-hand milliammeter. The potentiometer thus measures the difference in emf of two standard cells and is used to read directly the emf of one in terms of the other to 6 significant figures. Its total range is approximately 4 mv, and its balance is adjusted to 1 μv.[34] Parasitic thermal emf's in the measuring circuit[35] are avoided by extreme care in construction. The resistors comprising the main dial and the Lindeck elements are enclosed within an aluminum box which serves as a thermal shield. The circuit is of manganin and copper, and the galvanometer key in the measuring circuit is of a special design which is free from thermals to about 0.02 μv. The sliding contact in the dial switch is in series with the supply battery, and a thermal emf at this point does not affect the measuring circuit.

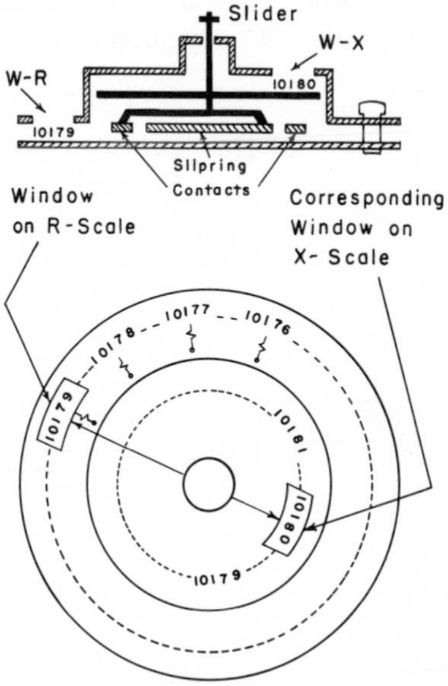

Fig. 33.

Rubicon Microvolt Potentiometer. This follows the fundamental design of the Brooks comparator described above in combining a constant-current and a constant-resistance element to measure low emf's. The residual thermal emf's have been reduced below 0.01 μv in this potentiometer by (1) eliminating sliding contacts from the measuring circuit; (2) arranging the measuring circuit so that only 2 junctions (manganin to copper) are present and locating these in close proximity to each other in order that their temperature may be the same; (3) using heavy cast-aluminum thermal shields to enclose the thermally vulnerable resistors, keys, and contacts; (4) using a thermo-free key. Range-changing shunts are incorporated, and ranges from 0.1 volt full scale to 100 μv full scale are covered in 3 double-range instruments. Ninety-nine per cent of the range is covered by 2

[34] Actually, differences in emf can be estimated to tenths of a microvolt by interpolation between marked divisions on the milliammeter scale.

[35] Brooks, *NBS J. Research*, **11**, 211 (1933).

decade dials and 1% by the Lindeck element whose milliammeter has 120 divisions marked from − 10 to + 110 (microvolts or submultiples of a microvolt). A 10% overlap of the smallest dial division is thus provided.

The wiring of a three-range potentiometer of this type is shown schematically in Fig. 34. Range changing in the "constant-current" section is accomplished by a combination of series and parallel resistances which maintain the current delivered by the supply battery at a fixed value while the fraction in the measuring circuit is reduced by a factor of 10 or 100. The range shunt in the "constant-resistance" (Lindeck) section

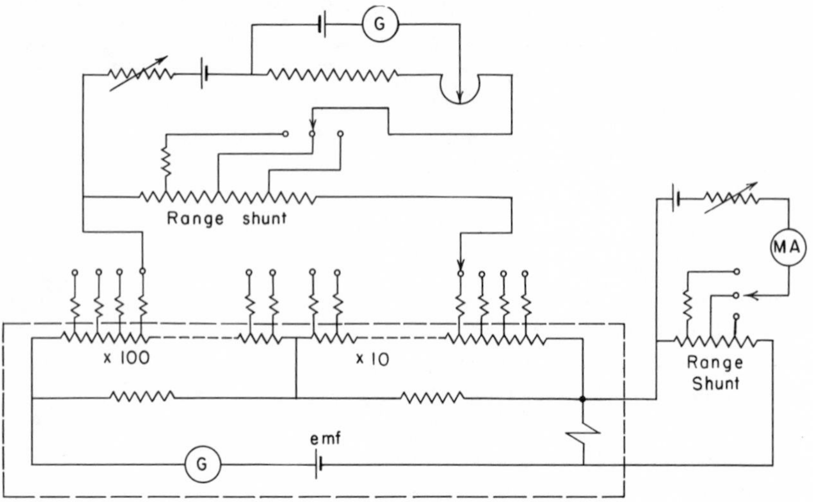

FIG. 34. Rubicon microvolt potentiometer.

of the potentiometer by-passes milliammeter current around the Lindeck shunt. The part of the circuit which is sensitive to the presence of thermal emf's is shown in the figure as the area within the dashed lines.

Brooks Thermo-free Galvanometer Key. Wherever very low voltages are to be measured special efforts must be made to avoid introducing extraneous thermal emf's into the measuring circuit and to reduce the parasitic emf present to a value below the limit of detection. To accomplish this result, one must use in the measuring circuit only metals or alloys which are very close to copper in thermoelectric power, and must thermally shield the measuring circuit, particularly at junction points, which are especially susceptible to thermals. Various devices for minimizing thermal emf's within the potentiometer have been discussed above. Galvanometers having high voltage sensitivity, used with low-voltage potentiometers, frequently have all-copper circuits including the suspensions and binding posts, and are sometimes enclosed within thermal shields so that their temperature may remain uniform and change only slowly. Another point at which troublesome thermal emf's may appear is the galvanometer key. Some of the ordinary types of keys are quite bad in this respect. If key springs are constructed of materials chosen solely with regard to suitable mechanical properties, it may well happen that they are such as to develop considerable thermal emf in an electric circuit. Since the galvanometer key is manipulated continuously during the balancing procedure it receives considerable heat from the observer's hand. In some designs an appreciable part of this heat flows into the switch mechanism and produces a temperature rise at the junction point, giving rise to thermals. Other, more obscure causes also contribute to the production of thermal emf's in the key.

The design of a thermo-free galvanometer key requires that attention be given to a number of important points. The elements necessary to such a design have been stated by Brooks.[36] (1) For key springs and contact points materials should be chosen which are very close to copper in their thermoelectric properties. (2) The design should be thermoelectrically astatic with respect to heat flow; i.e. all junctions of dissimilar metals should be so arranged in adjacent pairs that heat flow in any direction will set up equal thermal emf's of opposite sign in the key circuit. (3) The key should be enclosed in a shield which tends to maintain all parts of the key at a uniform temperature despite heat radiation and conduction to and from the shield.

In a thermo-free key which Brooks designed the key springs were of hard-rolled copper with United States coin gold[37] for contact points. The thermal shield was of 30-mil ($\frac{3}{4}$-mm) sheet aluminum. The thermally astatic arrangement used is shown in Fig. 35. Two springs of hard-rolled copper separated by a thin sheet of mica are clamped at one end between Bakelite blocks and carry gold contact discs at their free ends. Above these contact buttons is a half-cylindrical gold contact piece soldered to the lower surface of a copper block secured to a flat phosphor-bronze spring by thermally insulating Bakelite blocks. The plunger through which the bronze spring carrying the contact bar is depressed is Bakelite to retard heat flow from the observer's hand.[38] Heat entering the bronze strip will be impeded from flowing into the active circuit by the Bakelite insulation at either end of the bronze strip. It should be noted that, because of the symmetrical construction of the active circuit and because the copper contact strips are in thermal contact through the thin sheet

[36] Brooks and Spinks, *op. cit.*, p. 790 (1932).

[37] United States coin gold, an alloy of 90% gold, 10% copper, has a thermal emf against copper of 2.2 μv/°C at room temperature.

[38] See Brooks and Spinks, *op. cit.*

of mica, the switch is thermally astatic to both lateral and vertical heat flow.

Reduction or Elimination of Very Small Thermal Emf's. When it is desired to reduce the effect of thermal emf's to very small values, say 0.001 or 0.002 μv, precautions beyond those described above are necessary. These requirements, together with suitable procedures for meeting them, will be discussed in terms of a special Lindeck type of potentiometer[39] designed to measure 10 μv to 0.1%.[40]

(*a*) THERMAL SHIELD. An ideal thermal shield would be a cavity within a block of metal of high conductivity, having no openings to the outside

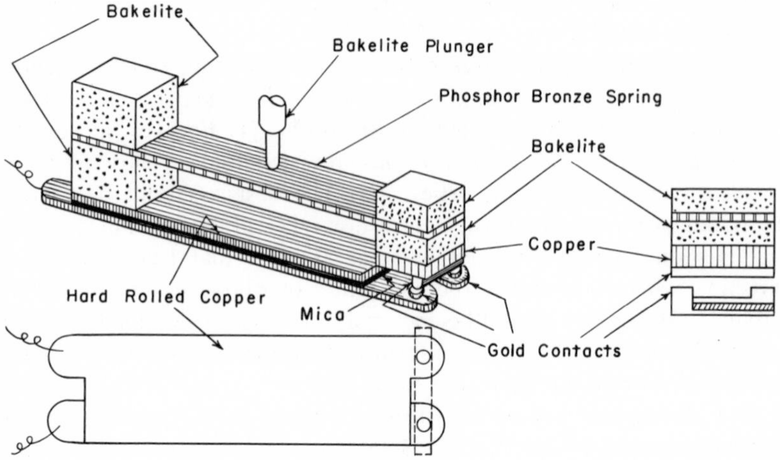

FIG. 35.

and thermally isolated from its surroundings. This is unattainable since both the measuring circuit and means for manipulating the galvanometer key must go through the walls of the enclosure. The nearest approach to such a shield is a symmetrically divided enclosure. Because of symmetry the two halves have equal thermal capacity, and, when the joint is such that there is good thermal contact between the halves, the possibility of unequal temperature distribution along the enclosure walls is greatly reduced. The thermal shield used by Teele and Schuhmann was an aluminum casting with $\frac{3}{8}$-in. walls. Machinibility of the casting was improved by the use of 15% of zinc in the alloy, without serious loss of heat conductivity. This shield was enclosed in a box of balsa wood 2 in. thick to minimize heat transfer to and from the surroundings.

[39] Teele and Schuhmann, *NBS J. Research*, **22**, 431 (1939).

[40] In Teele and Schuhmann's potentiometer tests indicated that no uncompensated extraneous emfs were present which amounted to as much as 0.002 μv.

(*b*) GALVANOMETER KEY. The reversing key used in the galvanometer circuit of the Teele and Schuhmann potentiometer was of a design somewhat different from that of Brooks. The springs were of cold-rolled copper with silver contact points.[41] In order to minimize temperature differences at the silver-copper junctions in the measuring circuit the fixed ends of the springs were clamped between massive copper blocks and insulated with thin mica strips. The copper blocks were connected mechanically and thermally to the thermal shield. In addition to these precautions the spring and contact pairs were arranged to be thermoelectrically astatic.

(*c*) SHUNT TERMINALS AND LEADS. The Lindeck-element shunt, a four-terminal resistor, was U-shaped with its open end clamped (with mica insulation) between copper blocks which were bolted to the thermal shield. The potential leads were bent toward each other and brought as close together as possible while still avoiding the danger of short circuit. Thus all four of the terminal leads were brought close together and were in the same thermal environment.

(*d*) THERMAL TIE-DOWN. The principle of "thermal tie-down"[42] was used to avoid temperature differences arising from heat flow along the wires. Wires entering the shielded enclosure passed through a copper block fastened to the outside of the shield. Polyethylene phthalate resin, used as an electrical insulator, has good thermal conductivity, and about 95% of the heat conducted along the wire flowed to the thermal shield at this point so that only 5% entered the enclosure via the wire. Just inside the enclosure each wire was coiled into a small helix. The path along the helix offered added resistance to heat flow along the wire and thus increased the effectiveness of heat transfer at the "tie-down" between the block and the thermal shield. Beyond the helix the wires were again clamped (with mica insulation) between copper blocks and the shield with a heat transfer again about 95% complete. One more set of coils and blocks was used before the wires were led to the various terminals. The heat transfer resulting from the three "tie-downs" was quite complete, and it was estimated that less than 1 part in 10^4 of the heat flowing along the wire was not diverted to the shield.

(*e*) KEY-ACTUATING MECHANISM. To minimize heat transfer from the operator's hand to the reversing switch used as a galvanometer key, the switch was actuated by linen threads operated by the hard-rubber key lever. These threads were interrupted by metal links where they entered the shielded enclosure. These links served to transfer to the shield any heat which was flowing along the linen thread. In addition the thermal

[41] The thermoelectric power of a silver-copper junction is about 0.5 μv/°C.

[42] Osborne, Stimson, and Fiock, *NBS J. Research*, **5**, 425 (1930).

shield was insulated from heat from the observer's hand by a balsa-wood barrier.

(*f*) PARASITIC EMF'S IN THE GALVANOMETER CIRCUIT. It is not practical to keep the galvanometer and its leads at a uniform temperature. It must be expected that with ordinary galvanometer construction emf's of $\pm 1\ \mu$v will be present in the galvanometer circuit even under favorable circumstances, while with an "all-copper" galvanometer and the utmost precautions these will be reduced to $\pm 0.1\ \mu$v. Such an emf adds to or subtracts from the emf being measured, and it must be compensated or its effect must be eliminated from the measurement. The effect of these and other extraneous emf's in the galvanometer circuit, and in fact any action in the galvanometer which produces a change in deflection, such as gradual shift of the galvanometer zero from mechanical causes, or deflection resulting from a difference of potential between the galvanometer case and coil, may be automatically eliminated from the measurement by the reversal procedure[43] described below.

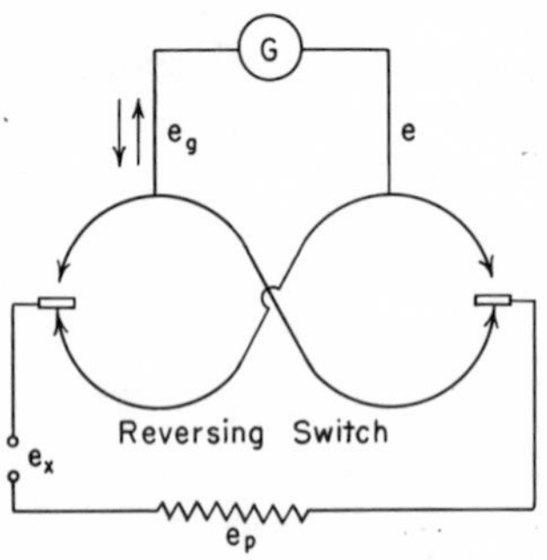

FIG. 36.

Let Fig. 36 represent the portion of the circuit in which an extraneous emf would affect the measurement if it were not taken into account. The "unbalanced" voltage e_g is the difference between the unknown emf e_x and the balancing potentiometer voltage e_p. This voltage difference, e_g, enters the galvanometer branch of the circuit through the reversing switch and is reversed in direction when the key is operated. It therefore produces a *change* in deflection on reversal which is *double* the deflection it causes in one direction. On the other hand the parasitic emf, *e*, in the galvanometer branch of the circuit is not reversed when the key is operated and so, if it has not itself changed, produces *no change* of deflection on reversal. Thus the effect of the reversal, with change in deflection as the criterion of unbalance, not only eliminates the effect of constant parasitic emf's in the galvanometer branch of the circuit but also *doubles* the sensitivity of the galvanometer to the voltage difference to be detected. Suitable balancing procedure requires operation of the reversing key at regular intervals timed approximately to the swing of the galvanometer, and simultaneous adjustment of the potentiometer balance until there is *no change* in deflection upon operation of the reversing key. If a drift is present in the equilibrium position of the galvanometer moving system, or if the parasitic emf's tending to produce deflection are changing, their

[43] F. Wenner, *NBS J. Research*, **22**, 425 (1939).

effects may still be minimized by the above procedure, using *minimum change* of deflection on reversal as the criterion of balance.

STANDARDS OF EMF

The Weston cadmium cell.[44] This cell, which is universally used as a reference standard of electromotive force, was described by Edward Weston[45] in a patent application in 1891. It is a primary cell employing mercury as a positive electrode and cadmium in a mercury amalgam as a negative electrode, with cadmium sulfate as electrolyte, and mercurous

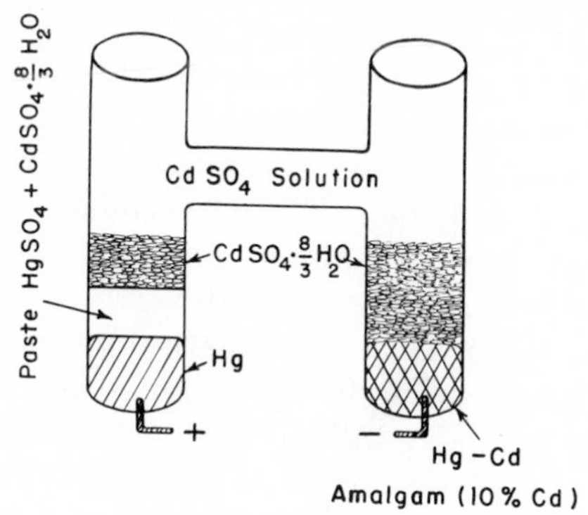

FIG. 37.

sulfate as a depolarizer. In addition to its constancy, permanence, and reproducibility the Weston cell has a very low temperature coefficient of emf. These features are just those required in a cell which is to be used as a reference standard, and it has entirely superseded the earlier Daniell cell[46] (1836) and the Clark cell[47] (1872), formerly used for this purpose. The Weston normal cell, shown in Fig. 37, has a saturated solution of $CdSO_4$ in the presence of an excess of $CdSO_4 \cdot \frac{8}{3}H_2O$ crystals to maintain the solution at saturation for all temperatures within its working range. When properly made from suitably purified materials, cells may be constructed to have the same emf to within a few microvolts, and such cells may be expected to maintain a nearly constant emf over long periods of time. A group of cells of this type, maintained at constant temperature

[44] Much of the material in this section is based on a paper of the same title by Vinal, Craig, and Brickwedde, *Trans. Electrochem. Soc.*, **68,** 139 (1935).

[45] U.S. Patent 494,827 (April 4, 1893).

[46] *Phil. Mag.*, III, **8,** 433 (1836).

[47] *Trans. Roy. Soc.*, **164** (1874).

at the National Bureau of Standards, is the primary standard of emf for the United States. Some of the cells in the group forming the primary standard were prepared in 1906 and have been in use for more than 40 years. The temperature coefficient of the normal cell (about 40 μv/°C) is the difference between the rather large temperature coefficients of the positive limb (about $+ 310$ μv/°C) and of the negative limb (about $- 350$ μv/°C). It is therefore essential that the cell be maintained at a constant temperature and that the temperature of the + and − limbs be closely the same. The primary group at the NBS is maintained at about 28°C in an oil bath in which the temperature is held constant within ± 0.006°C.

Materials of the highest purity are essential to the construction of satisfactory standard cells. The basic materials—mercury, cadmium, sulfuric acid, and water—are all purified by distillation, starting with the purest materials available. Cadmium sulfate is preferably prepared from cadmium metal and acid, the cadmium being dissolved in nitric acid, crystallized several times as a nitrate, precipitated as cadmium sulfate with redistilled sulfuric acid, and purified by repeated recrystallization as the sulfate.[48] Mercurous sulfate is prepared electrolytically in a darkened room. The cadmium amalgam (10% cadmium) is prepared either electrolytically or by heating the two metals together.

Saturated cells may be made either as "neutral" or as "acid" cells. The Weston *normal* cell is a neutral cell employing a saturated solution of cadmium sulfate in water. Acid cells employ a similar solution to which some sulfuric acid is added. The emf of acid cells is lower than that of the normal cell (1.018636 volt at 20°C) by an amount which depends on the concentration of the acid. This difference in emf is given by the formula $d = -(0.00060N + 0.00005N^2)$, where N is the normality of the sulfuric acid. There is evidence that acid cells are more constant with time than neutral cells, but opinions differ as to the relative merit of the two types. The temperature correction of the Weston normal cell is given by the formula

$$E_t = E_{20} - 0.0000406(t - 20) - 0.00000095(t - 20)^2 + 0.00000001(t - 20)^3$$

The Unsaturated Cadmium Cell. This is the form of standard cell used almost universally in America in laboratory work. As the name implies

[48] The preparation of $CdSO_4 \cdot \frac{8}{3}(H_2O)$, which is the form used in standard cells, should be carried out at a temperature below 43.4°C. At temperatures above this value the monohydrate $CdSO_4 \cdot H_2O$ is fotmed and persists as a metastable crystal at lower temperatures. Presence of the monohydrate affects the emf of the cell and is believed to contribute to the hysteresis effect which will be described later. Vinal and Brickwedde, *NBS J. Research*, **26,** 455 (1941).

the electrolyte is unsaturated at ordinary temperatures, and therefore the cell contains no crystalline cadmium sulfate. It becomes saturated (for the concentration used) at a temperature of about 4°C. The unsaturated Weston cell has the advantage that its emf has a much lower temperature coefficient than that of the saturated type; this emf is given by the relation $E_t \approx E_{20} - 0.000005(t - 20)$. This low temperature coefficient results from the fact that the rather high temperature coefficients of the two limbs are much more nearly equal than in the saturated Weston cell. As usually constructed, the unsaturated cell also has the advantage of greater portability, the electrode material and mercurous sulfate being held firmly in place by porous plugs. It is neither as permanent nor as reproducible as the saturated cell, but these disadvantages are outweighed by the advantages of portability and low temperature coefficient in most laboratory work. The unsaturated cell also may be obtained in either the "neutral" or the "acid" type.

Characteristics of Unsaturated Standard Cells

Permanence. Data on about 600 cells tested repeatedly at the National Bureau of Standards show that about 5% increase in emf with time, the average change being 28 μv per year. The remaining 95% decrease in emf, the average change being 85 μv per year. Of the group which decreases, nearly half change by more than 50 μv per year, and one-fourth change by more than 100 μv per year. From this it follows that a standard cell should be checked at least once a year by comparison with a suitably maintained saturated cell if its value is to be known within 0.01%. Also the expected life will range from 7 to 14 years if its emf is 1.0190 volts when new; it is to be discarded when it reaches an emf of 1.0183 volts.[49] Actually other characteristics, such as fluctuation of emf, excessive hysteresis, or high internal resistance, may set a limit to its useful life before its voltage has decreased below the limiting value. This decrease in emf with age depends largely upon conditions within the cell itself but may be accelerated by misuse or abuse.

Temperature Coefficient. Since the temperature coefficient is negligible over the ordinary range of room temperatures as a result of the balance of large coefficients of opposite sign in the two limbs, it is very important that all parts of the cell be at the same temperature when in use. Unequal heating of the limbs might result from its use near a rheostat or other source of heat, from handling, from exposure to sunlight or other source of radiant heat, or from being located in a draft of warm or cool air, or near a cold wall. This effect is considerably reduced by enclosing the cell

[49] The NBS will not certify a cell whose emf is less than 1.0183 volts.

within a copper container[50] or in a copper-lined case, but sources of heat or cold should be avoided in the neighborhood of a standard cell. A difference of 2.7°C between the cell limbs results in a change of about 1 mv (0.1%) in emf.

Hysteresis. When the temperature of a cell is suddenly changed, its emf changes. When the normal temperature is again established, there is a delay in the attainment of the corresponding emf. This hysteresis may extend over hours or even days. The emf of the cell returns only slowly to its normal value. A rise in temperature is usually accompanied by a temporary decrease in emf which is, however, usually much less than the change accompanying a decrease in temperature. This effect is usually much greater in old cells than in new ones and may amount to 0.02 or 0.03% for a temperature change of 5°C. A group of 16 cells studied by Vinal[51] recovered their emf to within 30 μv (on the average) in 1 day. However, 1 cell of the group was still 260 μv away from its normal value after 24 hours. This effect is greater for a more rapid temperature change, and may be considerably decreased by placing the cell in a box with good thermal insulation in order to decrease the rate of temperature change at the cell.[52] However, in cases where large, sustained room temperature changes occur, the only means of eliminating hysteresis errors is to keep the cell in a container whose temperature can be thermostatically controlled. Where this is not feasible it is advisable, for work where high accuracy is required, to use cells whose hysteresis has been measured and found to be small. For work where the utmost accuracy is required, it is best to use a saturated cell which is kept at a constant, closely regulated temperature.

Internal Resistance. In unsaturated cells this may be expected to be between 80 and 500 ohms, depending on cell construction. Abnormally high internal resistance may occur in old cells and is sometimes the result of the formation of a gas bubble over the amalgam, constricting the current path to a much smaller cross section than normal. High internal resistance may result in loss of voltage sensitivity in the galvanometer circuit in which the cell is used. Where it is necessary to know the internal resistance of a cell,[53] it can be obtained to a sufficient accuracy by the following procedure. After the emf, *E*, of the cell is carefully measured, a 1-megohm resistance is temporarily connected across its terminals and

[50] The walls of this copper enclosure should be not less than $\frac{1}{16}$ in. thick.

[51] Vinal, Craig, and Brickwedde, *op. cit.*

[52] Park found that for a cell showing a large hysteresis effect the change in emf could be decreased by 50 % by using a 3-in. layer of loosely packed mineral wool as thermal insulation. *NBS J. Research*, **10**, 89 (1933).

[53] A low-resistance cell is essential for use with a deflection potentiometer.

the terminal voltage E' is measured as quickly as possible. The internal resistance is then

$$R = \frac{E - E'}{E} \times 10^6 \text{ ohms}$$

Effect of Current. Even though small, this is important if the flow is continued. A microampere through the cell for several minutes can produce a measurable difference in emf. Standard cells ordinarily recover their emf in a short time after the current ceases, providing the drain was small and not continued unduly. A cell discharged for 3 min at 20 μa recovered its original emf to within 10 μv in an hour, but when discharged at 100 μa for 3 min required 24 hours to recover. A cell which was short-circuited for 30 min was low by nearly 1 mv after 24 hours, and had recuperated to within 75 μv of its original value after 5 weeks. Currents in excess of 100 μa should *never* be drawn from the cell,[54] and a cell which has been short-circuited is of questionable value. A standard cell is ordinarily used only in a potentiometer circuit in which a null balance is desired. It should be protected by a key which is operated so that the galvanometer circuit is closed for as short a time as possible, and, in preliminary balancing, it should be further protected against excessive current by an adequate series resistance in the galvanometer circuit. Ordinarily the insulation of the case, between the standard-cell terminals, is 10,000 megohms or more, but if the conditions of use are such that moisture may condense on the case, this insulation resistance may decrease to such an extent that the resultant leakage current will affect the emf of the cell.

Precautions in the Use of Standard Cells

With careful and intelligent use, the unsaturated cadmium cell is a thoroughly reliable laboratory standard of emf. This requires that certain precautions be observed as a matter of ordinary laboratory routine.

(1) Cells which are in general laboratory service should be frequently checked against each other. It is advisable to have three or more cells available in the laboratory, of which one or more are reserved solely for such checks and are not subject to the hazards of routine operation. Such cells should be sent to a standardizing laboratory[55] once a year for certification. It should be noted that shipment will expose the cell to abnormal temperature and handling conditions, and that its emf value

[54] Current through the cell in the reverse (charging) direction has a more serious effect on the emf than a corresponding current drain, according to Vinal, Craig, and Brickwedde (*op. cit.*).

[55] In addition to the standard cell laboratory at the National Bureau of Standards, facilities for such checking are maintained by the manufacturers of standard cells.

may not be normal and dependable for some days after its return to the laboratory. A recovery period of a week should always be allowed for a reference cell after it has been shipped, handled roughly, or exposed to large changes in temperature.

(2) Conditions of use which expose the cell to large or sudden changes of temperature, or to temperature differences between the cell limbs, should be avoided. The effects of temperature changes can be greatly reduced by keeping the cell in a copper or aluminum container which is provided in addition with thermal insulation.

(3) Current drain from the cell should be kept to a minimum by protective resistances in standard-cell circuits and by proper manipulation of keys. Laboratory conditions which would result in the condensation of moisture on the cell case should be avoided.

(4) The unsaturated cell is not a reliable standard of emf at temperatures either below 4°C or above 40°C, and exposure to such extreme temperatures should be avoided if possible. If such exposure occurs the emf of the cell should be carefully checked after a suitable time has been allowed for recovery.

(5) Abnormally low sensitivity of the galvanometer in a standard cell balance may indicate that the resistance of the cell is too high. This may be checked by a measurement of cell resistance. In some cases, where the high resistance results from the presence of a gas bubble at the electrode, the bubble may be dislodged and the cell restored by gentle tapping and tilting. Where the high resistance persists the cell must, of course, be discarded.

(6) The emf of an unsaturated cell may be expected to decrease gradually with time. When the emf has fallen to a value of 1.0183 the cell should be discarded as it is no longer a reliable standard of emf.

ELECTROCHEMICAL MEASUREMENTS[56]

It may be said in general that any chemical reaction involving an exchange of electric charges has associated with it a characteristic electromotive force. A familiar example is the differences of potential that exist between electrodes in a primary battery. If current is allowed to flow between the electrodes, heat is developed. A portion of the chemical energy which is released in the reaction appears as heat, and the equilibrium potential difference is not fully developed between the electrode and

[56] For explanation of the theoretical considerations involved in this section, as well as for a more complete discussion of the phenomena involved, the student should refer to a modern text on physical chemistry, e.g. Daniels, *Outlines of Physical Chemistry*, 8th edition, John Wiley, 1948.

the solution in which it is immersed. The internal resistance of the battery is a complicating factor since when current is drawn from it some portion of the available voltage is absorbed as a drop of potential in the solution itself. An additional complicating factor in many reactions is the counter emf which appears as a result of polarization when current flows. If one wishes to measure the equilibrium potential associated with a chemical system *no appreciable current can be drawn.* The null potentiometer is the ideal precision method by which such potentials may be measured since at balance no significant current is drawn from the source under measurement.

The potential of an electrode in equilibrium with a solution cannot be directly measured. However, the potential difference which exists between such an electrode and another (reference) electrode which is maintained under standard conditions can be measured with a potentiometer, and, if we assign a value to the potential of the reference electrode, we obtain a numerical value of potential which can be associated with the test electrode in equilibrium with its surroundings. Such a system is completely arbitrary, and we could, if we wished, assign the value of *zero potential* to any particular combination of electrode and solution. It has been found convenient to assign the value *zero* to the equilibrium potential of a particular hydrogen, hydrogen-ion system.

The Normal Hydrogen Electrode. This electrode, which is used as the basic reference electrode and to which reaction potentials are usually referred, consists of a strip of platinum (covered with platinum black to give a large area for absorption) which is partly immersed in pure hydrogen at atmospheric pressure and partly immersed in an aqueous solution of hydrogen ions that contains 1 gram-ion in 1000 grams of water. The electrode is usually so arranged that the hydrogen bubbles up around it and the electrode is bathed alternately with hydrogen and with the solution.

Such a normal hydrogen electrode forms a *half-cell* and may be connected electrically with another half-cell, containing some other combination of electrode and solution, by means of a "salt bridge" as shown in Fig. 38. The salt bridge consists of a tube filled with a suitable conducting solution and has its open ends in contact with the solutions in the two half-cells.[57] The difference in potential E, which appears between the normal hydrogen electrode (I) and a platinum electrode immersed in solution (II), represents the equilibrium potential of system II on the basis that the normal hydrogen electrode is at zero potential. Measurements

[57] Strictly speaking, there are often small *liquid-junction potential* differences in the system, associated with the salt bridge, which are, however, frequently neglected in measurements. In precise work these liquid-junction emf's must be taken into account.

of such potentials are of great value in thermodynamical calculations. Measurements of this type are much used for determining the end points of reactions,[58] and for determining or controlling the acidity or alkalinity of solutions. The latter is of great importance in many industrial processes.

The Normal Calomel Electrode. Actually, while the normal hydrogen electrode serves as a primary reference standard, it is not a system which lends itself readily to general use in measurements, since it is inconvenient to set up and since many solutes interfere with its proper operation. A

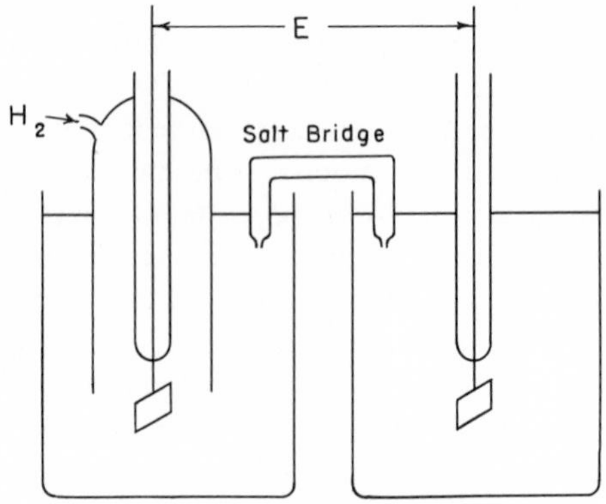

FIG. 38.

number of secondary reference electrodes have been devised for routine measurements. One of these is the *normal calomel electrode*, which consists of pure mercury in contact with a paste of mercury and mercurous chloride (calomel). A normal solution of potassium chloride saturated with mercurous chloride is kept over the electrode and may be used as a salt bridge to make electrical contact through a loosely fitted ground-glass joint with another half-cell as shown in Fig. 39.[59]

If the normal calomel electrode is set up for measurement against the *normal* hydrogen electrode, its potential is found to be + 0.2801 volt at 25°C. It is still more positive with respect to a hydrogen electrode in a solution having a hydrogen-ion concentration which is less than normal.

[58] In potentiometric titration, the potential of the reacting system changes very rapidly as the end point is reached. (See Fig. 40.) In applications of this kind one is interested in the point at which the potential is changing most rapidly but not at all in the value of the potential itself. For this purpose the voltage measurement need not be precise, and usually a very simple measuring arrangement is sufficient.

[59] Sometimes a beaker of potassium chloride solution is inserted between the calomel half-cell and the system under measurement in order to minimize the diffusion of mercurous ions into the solution.

The pH Scale. Hydrogen-ion concentrations are commonly expressed in terms of *p*H, using a logarithmic scale, rather than directly in terms of the effective concentration of hydrogen ions. The relation between *p*H and hydrogen-ion concentration, C_{H^+}, is expressed by the formula

$$pH = \log \frac{1}{C_{H^+}}, \quad \text{or} \quad C_{H^+} = 10^{-pH}$$

The emf of a normal calomel electrode measured against a hydrogen electrode (Fig. 39), using hydrogen at atmospheric pressure, in a solution

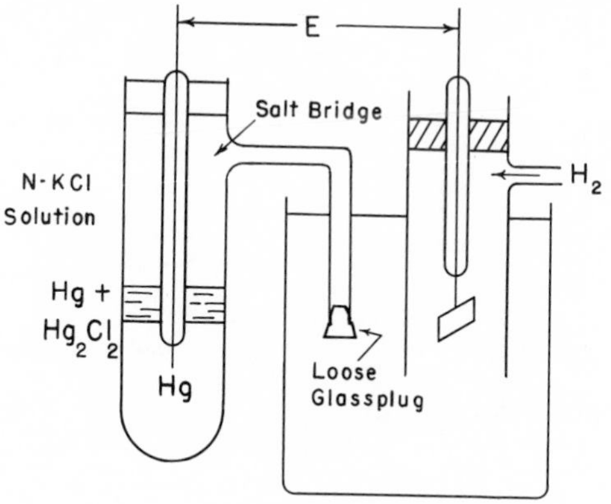

FIG. 39.

whose effective hydrogen-ion concentration is C_{H^+}, is given by the formula

$$E = 0.0591 \log_{10} \frac{1}{C_{H^+}} + 0.2801$$

The *p*H of the solution may be found with the formula

$$pH = \frac{E - 0.2801}{0.0591}$$

Relations between emf as measured with a normal calomel electrode, hydrogen-ion concentration, and *p*H are shown in Fig. 40. The change in emf as a hydrochloric acid solution is neutralized by sodium hydroxide is also shown in the figure. It should be noted that, when the solution is at a concentration considerably different from the neutral point, the addition of a small amount of OH^- ions does not greatly change the *p*H or the voltage; but as the neutral point is approached a very small addition of OH^- ions produces an enormous change in *p*H and an abrupt change in potential. The shapes of such curves will vary widely, depending on the concentration and strength of the titrated solution.

The Glass Electrode. As has been previously mentioned, although the hydrogen electrode is the primary reference standard for the measurement of hydrogen-ion activities, it is not convenient to set up and use. Furthermore it is frequently not suitable because of the effects on it of gases, oxidizing or reducing agents, organic materials, colloidal suspensions,

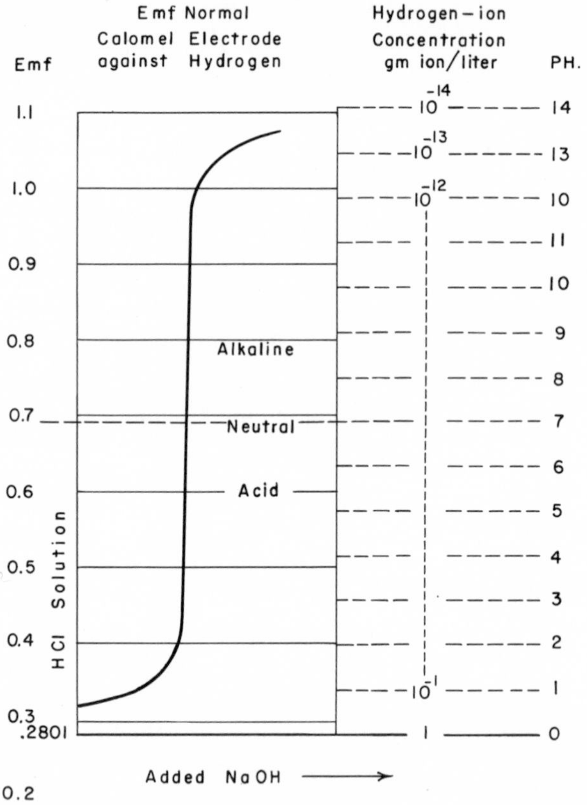

FIG. 40.

etc. The *glass electrode*[60] has largely replaced the hydrogen electrode for routine laboratory and industrial applications. It has been shown that potential differences which are a function of hydrogen-ion activity are obtained between two electrodes when the solutions in contact with the individual electrodes are separated by a thin glass membrane, usually in the form of a bulb enclosing one electrode. For example such a cell could be made up in the following way: calomel electrode—solution of

[60] For a detailed discussion of the theory and use of the glass electrode, the reader may refer to Dole, *The Glass Electrode*, John Wiley, 1941.

known *p*H—glass membrane—solution of unknown *p*H—calomel electrode. The voltage obtained from such a cell would be a logarithmic function of the difference in hydrogen-ion activities of the two solutions.

The resistance of the glass membrane is of course very high, and the current that can be drawn from the cell without a significant voltage drop across this resistance is correspondingly low. Now the potential difference corresponding to one *p*H unit at room temperature is approximately 60 mv, and it is desirable to keep the voltage drop across the glass membrane to a value that will not be significant in terms of *p*H. If this voltage drop is limited to 0.6 mv, corresponding to 0.01 *p*H unit, and the membrane resistance is 50 megohms, the maximum current that can be taken from the cell is approximately 10^{-11} amp. For currents of this magnitude the usual type of d-c galvanometer cannot be used as a detector of unbalance in the measuring potentiometer. However, suitable vacuum-tube amplifier circuits are available for this purpose, and *p*H meters are built which incorporate the necessary amplifier detector together with an appropriate potentiometer.

In addition to the ohmic voltage drop which results from the current, a small emf, known as the "asymmetry potential" (AP), appears across the glass membrane. This asymmetry potential appears to be associated with properties of the glass itself, or, more specifically, with differences in properties between the inner and outer surfaces of the glass bulb which forms the membrane,[61] and is altered temporarily by exposure of the glass surface to strongly alkaline or acid solutions. This makes it necessary to calibrate the *p*H meter against a buffer solution of known *p*H, whose value is reasonably close to that of the unknown. Such calibrations must be made occasionally as a part of the routine of *p*H measurement. An emf to compensate the asymmetry potential is introduced into the potentiometer circuit at the time of calibration by means of an adjustable resistance. An additional slide wire for temperature compensation of the *p*H meter is included in the potentiometer circuit.

*p*H *Meters.* Figure 41 shows a typical circuit arrangement for a portable *p*H meter. In Fig. 41(*a*) the vacuum-tube detector circuit[62] is shown schematically. The grid bias of the detector tube is initially set to its proper value by adjusting R_1 with the input terminals shorted by

[61] In the course of the glass-blowing procedures used in forming a bulb, the surface layer of glass which will become the outer face of the membrane is exposed to the hot gases of the torch; whereas deeper layers, which will form the inner face, are protected. It is therefore to be expected that the inner and outer faces of the bulb will be somewhat differently constituted. Hamilton and Hubbard, *NBS J. Research*, **27**, 27 (1941); Bräuer, *Zeits. für Elektrochem.*, **47**, 638 (1941).

[62] For an explanation of the operation of such circuits the reader may refer to the section on vacuum-tube voltmeters in Chapter 10.

means of switch S. This ensures that the input current to the detector grid (drawn from the measurement cell) will be at a suitably low level when the potentiometer is balanced. Figure 41(*b*) shows the circuit arrangement for the standard-cell balance of the potentiometer. This balance is made by adjusting R_2, with the temperature-compensating dial

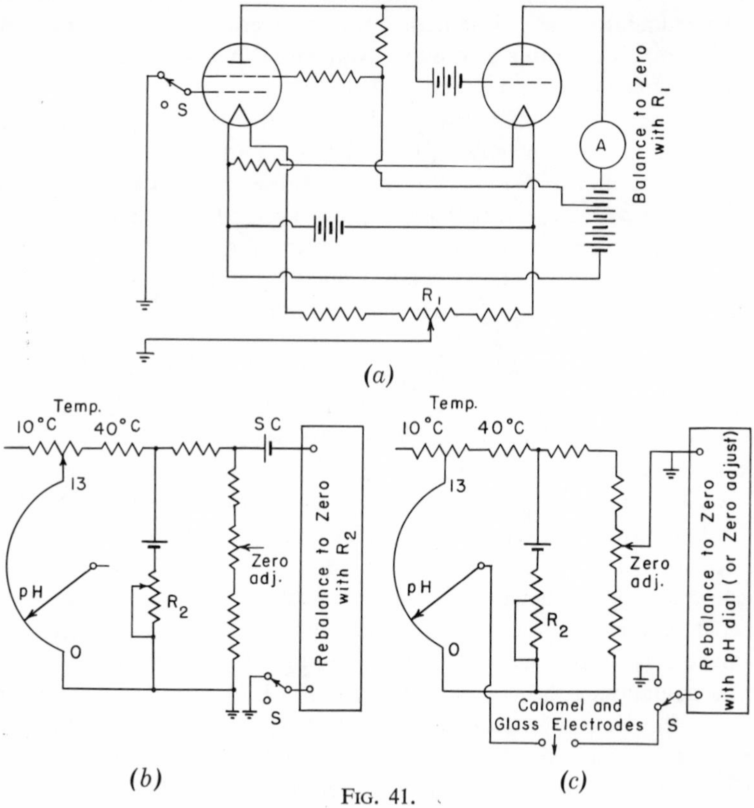

FIG. 41.

set to the operating temperature. Figure 41(*c*) shows the circuit arrangement for calibration or operation of the *p*H meter. With the electrode system immersed in a buffer solution of known *p*H, the *p*H dial of the potentiometer is set to read this value and the potentiometer is balanced by means of the resistance marked "zero adj." The instrument is now ready for use, and, with the electrode system in the unknown solution, balance is restored by adjustment of the *p*H dial. At balance this dial indicates directly the *p*H of the solution.

In commercial instruments both the glass electrode and the calomel reference electrode are permanently filled and sealed when constructed, and a liquid junction to the calomel reference electrode is established by means of an inert fiber or wick extended through the glass wall of the calomel-electrode container. The behavior of different types of glass used as electrode membranes varies to some extent, particularly in extremely alkaline solutions, and the glass electrode is not entirely satisfactory for *p*H measurements above about 10. A particular type of sodium-calcium silicate glass (Corning No. 015) is quite generally used for electrode work. The addition of lanthanum and certain other metals[63] to the glass (covered by Leeds and Northrup patents) has been found to improve the performance of the glass electrode at the alkaline end of the scale.

As in all measurements in which extremely minute currents are utilized, care must be taken to ensure adequate insulation and proper shielding of the measuring circuit. Insulation troubles are likely to be serious at high humidities because of the comparatively low-resistance moisture films which form on insulating surfaces. High insulation resistance[64] from other circuit elements is particularly important for the lead from the glass electrode to the grid of the detector tube. Furthermore this lead must be well shielded, and the shield should be integral with that of the amplifier enclosure. In some instances a desiccant is kept in the enclosure which houses the vacuum-tube circuit.

ALTERNATING-CURRENT POTENTIOMETERS

Since the potentiometer network is such that two voltages can be compared, it is to be expected that the potentiometer principle would be applied to a-c measurements as well as to d-c measurements. A number of a-c potentiometers have been devised, and some of them have proven quite useful in engineering measurements. All such devices have one limitation in common. While the *ratio* of two voltages may be determined with a high degree of precision, the accuracy with which the *value in volts* can be stated is limited by the accuracy to which the reference voltage is known, or the accuracy with which a reference current can be set up. There being *no a-c equivalent of the standard cell*, the absolute accuracy with which an alternating voltage can be measured in an a-c potentiometer cannot be comparable with the corresponding type of d-c measurement. It is, of course, possible in some types of very refined measurements to determine an alternating voltage to perhaps 0.01% by making use of a suitable transfer procedure for comparing the alternating voltage with a

[63] Perley, *Anal. Chem.*, **21** (3), 394 (1949).

[64] Polyethylene, or a polystyrene-base insulating material such as Amphenol-912, has good insulation characteristics at relatively high humidities.

known direct voltage. However, in commercial a-c potentiometers this is not done. Usually the standard current or voltage is established in terms of the reading of a deflecting instrument which fixes the limit of accuracy of voltage determinations.

The practical field of usefulness of a-c potentiometers is in engineering measurements in which an accuracy of 0.5 to 1% is adequate, and in cases where the potentiometer method may be more convenient or simpler than other types of voltage determination. The potentiometer method is indispensable when one is concerned with accurate measurements of the ratio of two voltages but when one does not need to know accurately the precise magnitude of either of them. A third type of measurement in which a-c potentiometers are used is that in which a voltage must be resolved into quadrature components. The a-c potentiometer has achieved excellent results in magnetic testing and in the precise determination of ratio and phase angle of instrument transformers.

In addition to the fundamental accuracy limitation of a-c potentiometers there are three important factors which must be considered. (1) A necessary requirement for balance is the *instantaneous* equality at all times of the voltages being compared. This requires a *phase* balance as well as a *magnitude* balance, and assumes that the frequencies of the two voltages are *exactly* the same. (2) In the presence of harmonics in one or both of the voltages being compared, the balance point may not be the same if a tuned detector (responding to only one frequency) is used, as if a detector is employed which responds to a wide range of frequencies. Also an *average* indicating detector may not show the same balance point as an *rms* indicating detector. It is even possible that a null balance cannot be achieved, the detector indicating only a minimum, i.e. an approach to balance condition which cannot be made exact. (3) Extraneous emf's picked up from stray fields or by coupling between portions of the circuit must be eliminated, compensated, or measured since they may add vectorially to the measured voltage.

If voltages are to be read directly from the dial settings of an a-c potentiometer, the potentiometer current must be set to a "standard" value, just as in the case of a d-c potentiometer. This is usually done with an electrodynamic[65] milliammeter which can be so constructed that its response to alternating current is the same as its d-c response. Such an instrument can be calibrated on direct current and then brought to the same setting on alternating current. Alternatively a thermocouple[66] instrument or a thermoelement and d-c potentiometer arrangement may be used to set the potentiometer current.

[65] See discussion of electrodynamic instruments in Chapter 10.
[66] See Chapter 10.

Two types of a-c potentiometers have been developed which differ basically in the method by which *phase balance* is achieved. In the *polar* potentiometer, an unknown voltage is balanced by means of a single voltage which is continuously variable in both magnitude and phase. In the *coordinate* potentiometer, balance is obtained in terms of two voltages which are in quadrature (i.e. have a phase difference of 90 electrical degrees). Each of these voltages can be varied in magnitude, and a means is usually provided by which the quadrature phase relation may be adjusted or checked. At balance the unknown voltage may be stated in terms of two mutually perpendicular components.

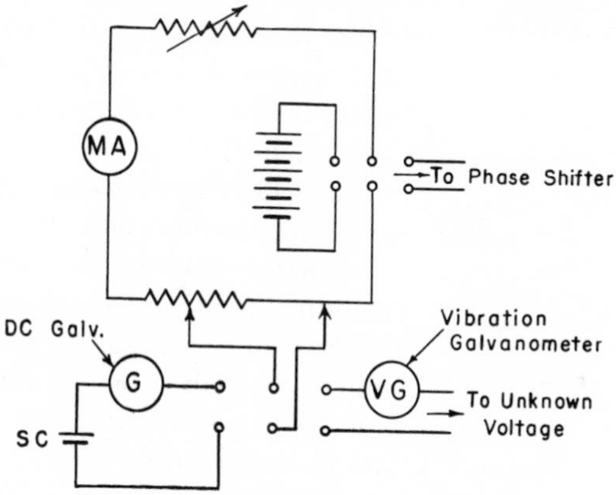

FIG. 42. Drysdale potentiometer.

Drysdale's Potentiometer. The first direct-reading, polar potentiometer was developed by Drysdale[67] in 1908 and has been used extensively up to the present time. The arrangement of this potentiometer is shown schematically in Fig. 42. In Drysdale's arrangement, the operating current (50 ma) is set on an electrodynamic instrument which is calibrated on direct current against a standard cell by the following procedure. With the potentiometer supplied from a d-c source, the dials are set to read the standard-cell voltage. A balance is made against the standard cell by varying the potentiometer current. The indication of the milliammeter is noted, and, when the circuit is operated on alternating current, the milliammeter is brought to the same setting by adjusting the value of the alternating current. The precision to which the milliammeter setting can be repeated fixes the limit of accuracy of the potentiometer to 0.1 or 0.2% in determination of the magnitude of a voltage. Under very favorable circumstances, the phase-angle setting of a balance may be good

[67] Drysdale, *Phil. Mag.*, (6), **17**, 402 (1909).

to perhaps 0.1 or 0.2 degree, but under most conditions 0.5 degree more nearly represents the accuracy with which the phase angle can be determined at balance. A three-phase supply and a phase-shifting transformer are better in this respect than a phase-splitting circuit since the latter is more sensitive to small changes in frequency. If the detector of balance is sensitive only to the frequency coinciding with the fundamental of the unknown and reference voltages, only equality of the fundamental is indicated at balance. If the unknown voltage has harmonics which do not coincide in phase and relative magnitude with those of the reference voltage, the rms values of these voltages may not be equal at the indicated balance. If the detector responds to a range of frequencies, an exact balance may not be possible if the harmonic contents of the unknown and reference voltages are not identical.

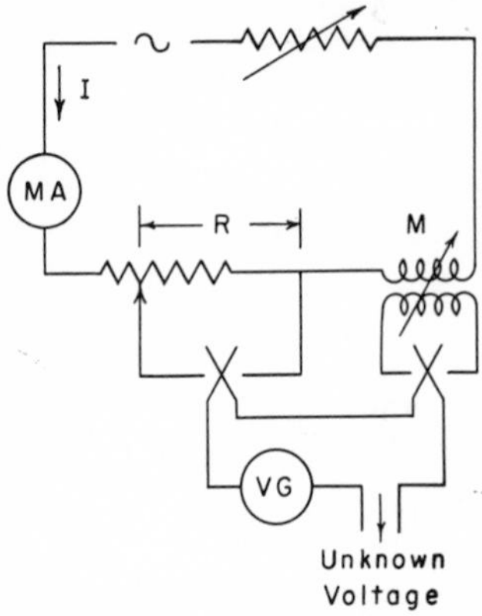

FIG. 43. Larsen potentiometer.

Larsen's Potentiometer. The first *coordinate* potentiometer was described by Larsen[68] in 1910 and is shown schematically in Fig. 43. The reference voltage is divided into quadrature components RI and ωMI, each of which can be independently varied in magnitude. A reversing switch in the output of each component of the reference voltage makes it possible to balance an unknown voltage in any quadrant. At low frequencies either I or M must be large in order that the range of the ωMI component of the reference voltage be adequate. The frequency must be accurately known, and only at one frequency can this element of the potentiometer be made direct reading in volts.

Campbell-Larsen Potentiometer. This coordinate potentiometer is Campbell's[69] modification of the above circuit, and is shown schematically in Fig. 44. I' being set to its standard value on the milliammeter, the scale of the resistance element of this potentiometer is made direct reading in volts. If S is the resistance of the shunted portion of the upper element as indicated in the figure, and if R is the total resistance of the circuit mesh, then $I'/I = S/R$. By varying the value of S with frequency, while holding I' constant, the current I in the primary of the mutual inductor can be set to such a value that the induced secondary voltage ωMI can be made direct reading in volts from the scale of the mutual inductor for any selected frequency.

[68] Larsen, *Elektrot. Zeits.*, **31,** 1039 (1910).
[69] Campbell, *Proc. Roy. Soc.*, **41,** 94 (1928).

Pedersen's[70] *Potentiometer.* This coordinate potentiometer makes use of the parallel circuit arrangement shown in Fig. 45. If one branch of the circuit consists of inductance L and resistance R in series, while the other branch consists of capacitance C and resistance R in series, the combination is non-reactive at any frequency if $R = \sqrt{L/C}$; and the currents in the two branches are in quadrature at any frequency. Hence the potential drop on one resistance element will be in quadrature with the potential drop in the other resistance element over the entire frequency range for which the above relation holds. If it is desired to have different resistances R_1 and R_2 in the two branches, the relation which must be satisfied is $R_1R_2 = L/C$. A voltage of the same frequency as the potentiometer current may thus be balanced against the quadrature voltages tapped off from the resistance elements. By using center-zero slide wires a voltage in any quadrant may be balanced. This potentiometer has no provision for standardizing the slide-wire currents in terms of the volt, and must be considered simply a comparison instrument. For example, it may be used to measure the two components

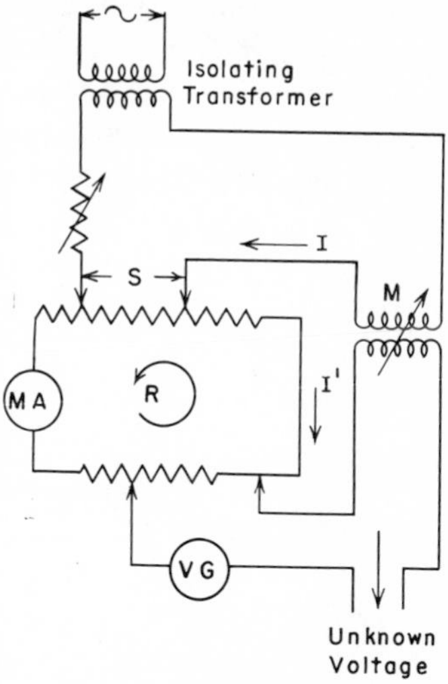

FIG. 44. Campbell-Larsen potentiometer.

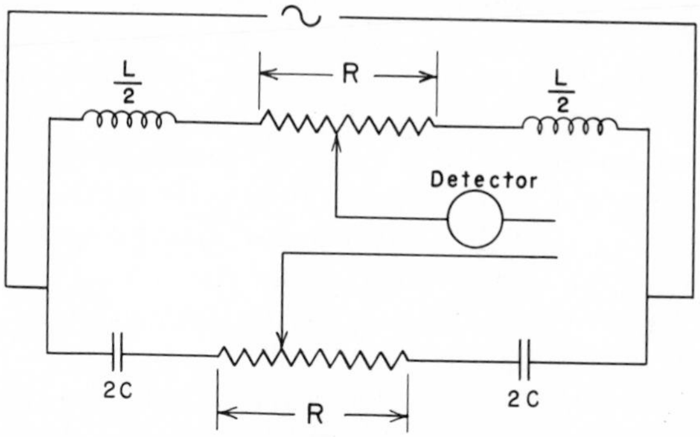

FIG. 45. Pedersen potentiometer.

of impedance drop on each of two impedances in series. If the resistance and reactance of one are known, the other may be computed. It is intended specifically for impedance measurements at audio and higher

[70] Pedersen, *Electrician*, **83**, 523 (1919).

frequencies (up to 100 kc) and is not well adapted to the measurement of voltages at power frequencies.

Gall's[71] *Potentiometer*. This coordinate potentiometer is a combination of two similar potentiometers, one of which carries a current substantially in phase with the supply voltage and the other a current in quadrature with this in-phase current. As in other coordinate potentiometers, the unknown voltage is balanced by the vector sum of the voltages tapped off from the two elements. Reversing switches permit a voltage

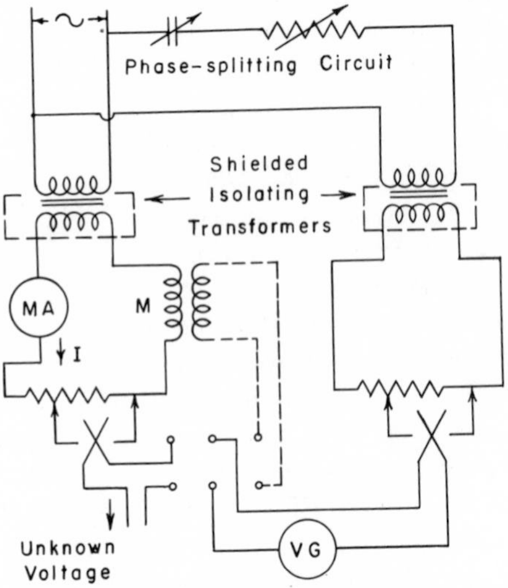

FIG. 46. Gall potentiometer.

in any quadrant to be balanced. This potentiometer is shown schematically in Fig. 46. The current of the in-phase element is set to the standard value (50 ma) by means of a sensitive, torsion-head electrodynamic instrument which is stated to be free from error up to 2000 cps. The magnitude and phase of the current in the second element are adjusted with the aid of the mutual inductor shown in the figure. With the secondary of this inductor connected across the quadrature element of the potentiometer, its dials are set to read a value of voltage ωMI equal to the secondary voltage of the inductor for the particular frequency used. The element is then brought to balance by adjusting the phase-splitting circuit. Since the accuracy of this adjustment is dependent on the accuracy with which the frequency is known, a second electrodynamic instrument is sometimes used in the circuit of the quadrature element to

[71] Gall, *Electrician*, **90,** 360 (1923). Also see Gall, *Direct and Alternating Current Measurements*, Chapman and Hall, 1938.

set the magnitude of its current correctly if the frequency is not known with sufficient accuracy.

The current of the "in-phase" element is only approximately in phase with the supply voltage, since the circuit contains inductive elements—the electrodynamic instrument and the primary of the mutual inductor. Furthermore, although these circuit elements are nominally astatic, they cannot be entirely so and must be so located that they neither appreciably affect nor are affected by other parts of the equipment.

CHAPTER 7

RESISTORS AND RESISTANCE MEASUREMENTS

In the discussion which follows we shall confine our attention to resistors and resistance devices which are used in measurements and in measuring circuits, and shall leave out of consideration resistors whose primary function is to regulate or control the current in a circuit or to absorb energy. Thus the discussion of resistance devices will be primarily limited to those which are used for establishing a ratio, for measurement of other resistances by comparison or by substitution, and for measurement of current. In all such devices it is desirable that the resistance (1) be permanent in value; (2) have a low temperature coefficient of resistance; (3) be resistant to oxidation, corrosion, and moisture; and (4) have a reasonably small bulk. This latter requirement necessitates the use of material of high specific resistance. In addition it is often necessary or desirable that the material have a very low thermoelectric power against copper.

Resistance Alloys

There is no metal or alloy available which meets all the above requirements perfectly. The pure metals may have some of the needed properties but in general have a rather high temperature coefficient of resistance. For example, platinum is quite stable in resistance, but its temperature coefficient is around 0.36% per °C. There are a number of alloys which have a low temperature coefficient and can be used in resistance apparatus. Those most frequently used are manganin, constantan, and Nichrome.

Manganin.[1] This alloy of copper, manganese, and nickel most nearly

[1] A patent on low-temperature-coefficient alloys was issued to Weston in 1889. Alloys of the general characteristics of manganin were covered by this patent, but the correct proportions were worked out by Feussner, Lindeck, and others at the Physikalisch-Technische Reichsanstalt.

meets the requirements for a material suitable for precision resistors. It has a high specific resistance (about 25 times that of copper) and a very low thermoelectric power against copper (2 or 3 μv/°C). When properly annealed and protected its resistance is quite permanent. However, resistance to corrosion or oxidation must be obtained by use of a suitable protective coating, especially in wire of the smaller sizes. For completely effective protection it must be sealed in an airtight container.

The characteristic variation of resistance of manganin with temperature is shown in Fig. 1. It will be seen that the resistance changes by perhaps

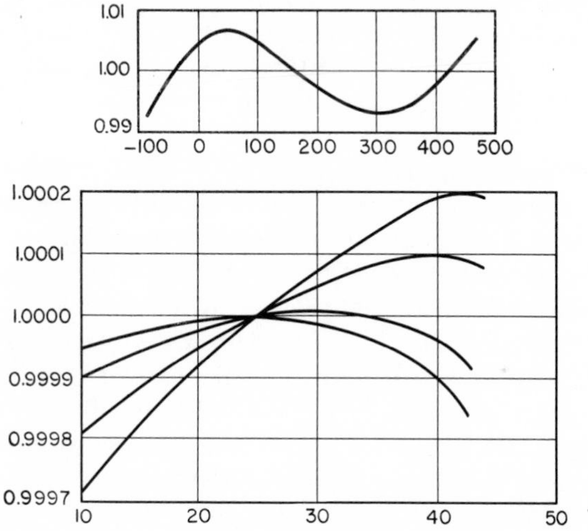

FIG. 1.

$1\frac{1}{2}\%$ between a maximum near room temperature and a minimum at about 350°C. The maximum of resistance generally occurs between 20°C and 50°C, its position being influenced by composition,[2] heat-treating, and cold-working in a way that is neither completely understood nor closely predictable. Over a considerable interval on either side of the maximum, the temperature-resistance curve can be accurately represented by a quadratic equation of the form

$$R_t = R_{25}[1 + \alpha(t - 25) + \beta(t - 25)^2]$$

where R_t is the resistance at t°C and R_{25} is the resistance at 25°C. The coefficient α is the slope of the curve at 25°C and, for manganin of proper quality for resistance standards, generally has a value less than 10×10^{-6}.

[2] A composition of 84% copper, 12% manganese, and 4% nickel may be considered representative of manganin suitable for most purposes.

The value of β generally lies between -0.3×10^{-6} and -0.8×10^{-6}. Over a range of temperature of several degrees in the neighborhood of the maximum, the variation of resistance is very small. If the manganin is selected so that its maximum falls within the expected range of operating temperature, its variation will be a minimum and may be expected to be negligible except in cases where extreme accuracy is required. Thus, if 25°-maximum manganin is used in laboratory resistors which will be operated at a power low enough to make self-heating negligible, the total variation of resistance between 20° and 30°C may be expected to amount to not more than 10 to 20 parts in a million. On the other hand, where operating power is high, as in ammeter shunts, so that a temperature rise of 15°C or more above room temperature is to be expected, 40°-maximum manganin would show a smaller variation of resistance in its operating range.

In the use of manganin, special care must be taken in soldering joints. A soft-soldered manganin-copper joint is not dependable and should never be used for connection to manganin wire or thin, narrow strip material. The manganin should be silver-soldered to copper wire or strips which may in turn be soft-soldered to terminal lugs. Only for heavy strip material, where the heat needed for silver-soldering is excessive, is soft-soldering advisable. In such cases the contact area in the manganin-copper joints should be large, and it is advisable to use slotted copper block terminals into which the manganin strips are fitted, in order to afford maximum mechanical support to the joint.

Constantans. All the members of this group of copper-nickel alloys containing 40 to 60% nickel with a small amount of manganese to improve their mechanical properties have very similar electrical properties. Under various trade names, they are sold for use as thermocouple materials and have thermoelectric powers against copper of about 40 μv/°C. The temperature-resistance curve of constantan is quite similar to that of manganin (see Fig. 1) with a maximum around room temperature and a minimum around 500°C. The difference between the maximum and minimum resistance is somewhat less than that of manganin, and the curvature in the neighborhood of the maximum is also less. Consequently, the change in resistance at room temperature is somewhat less than is the case with manganin. Constantan has a specific resistance at ordinary temperatures of about 25 times that of copper (about the same as manganin), is corrosion-resistant, inexpensive, and easy to work, and soft-solders to copper without difficulty. In cases where its high thermoelectric power against copper is not a disadvantage, there is much to recommend it. For example, it is frequently used in precision resistors designed for a-c operation, and it also finds application in voltmeter multipliers where the thermal emf generated at the copper-constantan junctions is negligibly small compared to the voltage being measured.

Nickel-Chromium Alloys. These alloys, of which Nichrome is representative, have a somewhat higher temperature coefficient of resistance than the manganin and constantan alloys, and cannot be used in precision resistors. Nichrome has a very high specific resistance (about 50 times that of copper) and resists corrosion well at elevated temperatures. It is often used in the rougher class of resistors, where minimum bulk is required, or where the element operates at an elevated temperature. The addition of small amounts of copper and aluminum considerably reduces the temperature coefficients of nickel-chromium alloys.

Therlo. Among other resistance materials are copper-manganese-aluminum alloys known as Therlo. These alloys have been investigated by Thomas,[3] who found that the best composition of Therlo is 85% copper, 9.5% manganese, and 5.5% aluminum. This alloy has about the same resistivity as manganin, its change in resistance with temperature is somewhat less than that of manganin, and its time stability is equal to that of manganin. Its thermoelectric power against copper is about 10% that of manganin and can be reduced still further by adding a very small percentage of iron. Thomas states that manganin and Therlo may be used interchangeably in most applications.

Gold-Chromium Alloy.[4] This alloy, containing about 2% of chromium, has a resistivity about 80% that of manganin. By heat-treating it at moderately low temperatures its temperature coefficient can be made small enough that it does not change in resistance by as much as one part in a million in the interval 20° to 30°C. However, its thermoelectric power against copper amounts to 7 to 8 μv/°C at room temperature, and the temperature coefficient of resistance must be adjusted for individual coils by suitable heat treatment, so that it will probably be found useful only in special applications.

Special Resistance Materials

Carbon, either alone or in combination with other materials, and thin metallic films of various kinds are employed in making a class of resistors which are much used in radio and other communication circuits. Since resistors of these types are sometimes used in measuring circuits and as instrument components, they will also be considered here. The commonest form of mass-produced resistors is the *composition* resistor, in which the conducting material, graphite or some other form of carbon, is mixed with fillers that serve as diluents, and combined with some type

[3] Thomas, *NBS J. Research,* **16,** 149 (1936).

[4] Developed by Thomas, *NBS J. Research,* **13,** 681 (1934).

of binder, usually organic. Two general types of composition resistors are the *solid-body*, which is molded or extruded, and the *filament*[5] type, in which the resistance material is baked on a glass or ceramic rod and sealed in a ceramic or Bakelite tube. The chief advantages of composition resistors are their compactness (resulting from the high resistivity of the material used) and their cheapness (since they are easily made by mass-production methods). The electrical properties of such resistors[6] differ markedly from those of wire-wound resistors that make use of any of the resistance alloys. (1) The resistance usually decreases with increasing voltage. The magnitude of this effect varies with composition, dimensions, and value of the resistor, being greater for physically smaller resistors and for those of higher resistance. The change of resistance (exclusive of heating effect) ranges from a few tenths of a per cent to several per cent between low and rated voltage. (2) At high frequencies the resistance decreases with increasing frequency, both because of the shunting effect of capacitance between conducting particles in the resistance element and because of dielectric losses in the filler, binder, and housing. The effect increases with increasing diameter of the element but is not usually important at frequencies in the power and audio ranges. At these low frequencies the resistors can be considered as practically pure resistance elements. (3) Increasing humidity generally results in an increase in the value of resistance. The humidity effect, which may amount to several per cent, can be decreased by various moisture-resistant coatings but can be eliminated only by hermetic sealing. (4) Composition resistors may be expected to have a considerably higher temperature coefficient of resistance than do wire-wound resistors. The temperature coefficient of pure carbon is about $-0.04\%/^\circ C$ and is nearly constant over the usual range of laboratory operation. However, the curve of resistance against temperature for composition resistors is usually parabolic in shape. The minimum may occur at a temperature as low as 10° to 15°C but may occur at much higher temperatures. (5) Composition and film-type resistors generally have a defect referred to by communication engineers as *noise*. There is some "noise" present, of course, in all conductors as a result of thermal agitation of the electrons which serve as carriers of electric current. This is known as "Johnson noise"[7] and corresponds to a very low level of current fluctuation in the usual type of conductor. A second

[5] The so-called "metallized-filament" resistors are usually of this type.

[6] For an extensive discussion of the properties of carbon resistors see Blackburn, *Components Handbook*, pp. 33, 97, of Vol. 17, MIT Radiation Laboratory Series, McGraw-Hill, 1949. See also Coursey, *Proc. IEE*, **96**, part III, p. 169 (1949). This paper has a bibliography of 187 references.

[7] Johnson, *Phys. Rev.*, **32**, 97 (1928).

type of noise, peculiar to composition and film-type resistors, is present when direct current flows, and results from random changes in the resistance of the unit. It is proportional to the direct voltage impressed on the unit and may be expressed in microvolts per volt. At low frequencies it is much more important than Johnson noise, and may range upward of 3 μv/volt in acceptable resistors of small sizes.

The power rating of composition resistors is established in terms of an acceptable change in resistance rather than in terms of a definite temperature rise. This rating is usually for a change in resistance of 10% after 500 hours of a $1\frac{1}{2}$-hour-on, $\frac{1}{2}$-hour-off duty cycle at an ambient temperature of 40°C.[8] If the unit is required to operate at a higher ambient temperature, its power rating must be reduced. For example, at a 70°C ambient temperature the power rating is cut about in half. The voltage rating of low-resistance units is fixed by the power rating; for high-resistance units, by the dielectric strength of the materials and the allowable voltage gradient.

Composition resistors of the usual type are notoriously unstable in resistance values. If they are used only at a low power level, the change in resistance results principally from the effect of humidity on the unit. If operated near the rated load, the changes in resistance result primarily from the deterioration or decomposition of the organic binder used in the construction.

Much better stability is found in a special film type of resistor known as a pyrolitic or "cracked-carbon" resistor. Such resistors are formed by depositing crystalline carbon at a high temperature on a ceramic rod by "cracking" an appropriate hydrocarbon. In one process for making pyrolitic film resistors,[9] carbon is deposited from methane gas in a nitrogen atmosphere from which water vapor and oxygen are carefully excluded. No binder is used, and the carbon deposit consists of a hard gray crystalline form from which graphite and carbon black are completely absent. After the deposit is formed the resistor is adjusted to its required value by cutting a helical groove around the cylinder with a diamond-impregnated copper wheel. This removes part of the deposit and leaves a helical conductor of suitable length and width for the desired resistance. After terminals are applied by crimping or some other suitable process, the surface of the resistor is lacquered (a glyptal or silicone type of varnish may be used) to provide insulation, moisture resistance, and mechanical protection. For 1-watt resistors of this type a temperature coefficient of $-0.02\%/°C$ was found for 10,000-ohm resistors, and $-0.04\%/°C$ for

[8] Complete performance specifications will be found in the Armed Services Specification JAN–R–11, Fixed Composition Resistors.

[9] Holmes, *J. IEE*, **94**, part III–A, p. 912 (1947).

5-megohm resistors. These resistors changed by 0.2 to 0.8% after 12 months of service, and by 0.3 to 1.5% after 22 months. When the resistor was sealed in glass in an atmosphere of hydrogen or helium the power rating was considerably increased. For example, the change in resistance of a sealed $\frac{1}{4}$-watt unit was less than 1% after 120 hours at 2 watts. The shelf stability of the latter units was 0.1% over an 8-month period, and they were unaffected by humidity. Noise levels (a function of film thickness) were considerably lower than in composition resistors, ranging from 0.05 μv/volt on a 100-ohm resistor to 2 μv/volt on a 10-megohm resistor. The voltage coefficient was low and inversely proportional to resistance, ranging from 10 parts per million/volt for a 10-megohm resistor to 40 ppm/volt for a 10,000-ohm unit.

Similar deposited-carbon resistors, which are hermetically sealed in a helium or nitrogen atmosphere and which have remarkable stability characteristics, have been developed by the Bell Telephone Laboratories. BTL 2-watt resistors of this type change by 2.5% in resistance between no-load and rated load, and show a permanent change of resistance amounting to only 0.01% after 1000 hours at rated load, and a change of less than 0.01% after a year of shelf storage. Their noise level at rated load (excluding Johnson noise) is less than $\frac{1}{4}$ μv/volt at rated load.

Metal-film resistors, formed by evaporating metal on a ceramic tube, have also been made in resistances up to 10 megohms, with high stability and a lower voltage coefficient than deposited-carbon resistors. The temperature coefficient of resistance can be controlled by adjusting the composition of the metal mixture in the film. Platinum, rhodium, palladium, and silver are used in various combinations.

RESISTORS

Resistance Coils. In constructing resistance coils, it is desirable that the winding be in a single layer in order to obtain maximum heat dissipation. It should be protected from air and moisture, and, if the resistance is to be used in a-c work, it should be non-inductively wound. The winding form should also be unaffected by air or moisture and, for a-c applications, is preferably non-metallic. For high-quality resistors which are to be used in d-c work only, the winding form is usually a metal tube, preferably of brass, since this has about the same coefficient of expansion as most resistance alloys. Metal coil forms are also of advantage in dissipating heat, particularly if they are vertical tubes with both ends open for free air circulation. If cotton or silk insulation is used on the resistance wire, the fibers of the insulation will contract or expand with changing humidity and may set up strains in the resistance wire which result in a variation of resistance with humidity. This effect is more pronounced when wire of small cross section is used and may amount to a difference between summer (high-humidity) and winter (low-humidity) values of resistance of as much as 400 ppm in high-resistance coils (1000 ohms or higher). Usually resistance coils which are exposed to air are protected by shellac, varnish, or wax which will slow down action of the humidity effect but cannot be expected to prevent it. In the course of a few hours or days (depending on the nature of the protective coating) sufficient moisture is transferred through the protective coating to affect the resistance. Dike[10] (of the Leeds and Northrup Company) has developed an insulation consisting of a mixture of cotton and silk fibers which largely eliminates the effect. This is possible since one type of fiber (cotton) lengthens, while the other (silk) contracts with increasing humidity. Hence a mixture of cotton and silk fibers in suitable proportions is unaffected by humidity. This material is known as Esco and is much used on precision resistors for resistance boxes.[11] The effect of humidity can also be avoided by sealing the resistor into an airtight container so that moisture cannot penetrate. This is done with the highest grade of precision resistors. Formerly such standards were sealed in a double-walled container, the resistor being in the annular space between the coil form and the outer wall of the container, and immersed in a light mineral oil which filled the space and improved heat transfer from the standard. It has been found that such oil eventually becomes acid and changes the value of the resistance by corrosion, so that this practice is no longer followed. The annular space between the coil form and the outer container is sealed as before but is left dry. Coils used in resistance boxes were often coated with paraffin wax in former times. This practice has also been generally abandoned because it was found that the paraffin deteriorated after a number of years and affected the value of the resistor. Ceresin wax is used to some extent at present, as are certain waxes of vegetable origin such as carnauba wax. Although these waxes are not entirely impervious to moisture, they do greatly decrease the rate at which the coil resistance responds to humidity changes.

In order to ensure permanence in resistance coils, they must be aged or "annealed" at an elevated temperature in order to remove, as much as possible, the strains in the wire resulting from the winding process, since the resistivity of the material is affected by the presence of strains. The temperature at which coils can be aged must be kept below a value at

[10] Dike, *Rev. Sci. Inst.*, **7**, 278 (1936).

[11] Recent experiments indicate that the humidity effect may also be quite small where nylon insulation is used.

which the silk or cotton insulation is affected. Aging is often carried out by holding the coil at 150°C during a 48-hour interval. As a result of this baking process, the value of the resistance may decrease permanently by as much as 1 or 2%. This aging does greatly improve the stability of a resistance coil but does not completely eliminate further drift in its value. Annealing is far from complete at the baking temperature (150°C) so that considerable strain remains in the wire. In use the operating temperature of the resistor must be kept low lest the value of resistance be permanently changed by further annealing. Safe operating currents for precision resistors depend on construction and on the rate at which heat can be dissipated. Such information is often supplied by the maker. If this figure is not available it may be roughly estimated from the exposed surface of the resistor. We may say that if a coil is mounted well away from other coils, so that air can freely circulate around it, it may usually be expected to dissipate continuously 0.002 watt/sq cm of exposed surface/°C rise in temperature above the ambient. If the coil is mounted in a confined space or is situated so that air circulation is restricted, its dissipation may be reduced to half this value. If we compute the power dissipated on this basis for a 15°C rise in temperature we shall have a reasonably safe value of operating current in most instances. Precision standards of resistance are often constructed so that they may be used in an oil bath in order to dissipate more heat. Such resistors may be operated in oil with a power dissipation of up to 10 watts for several hours, although for very precise work power should be limited to 1 watt. If it is suspected that a precision resistor has been overloaded its resistance should be checked without delay and it should be rechecked at intervals until it again assumes a steady value. As a result of overload the resistance of the unit may drift for weeks or even months.

Standard Resistors

These are used to establish the values of other resistors, and for reference purposes in the calibration of resistance apparatus. They should be resistors of the highest quality, whose resistance is closely adjusted to some convenient nominal value and is accurately known, and whose stability is assured by proper construction and care. With proper precautions in their design and treatment it is to be expected that they may be reliably used over extended periods of time with only occasional comparison checks against other standards of equal or better quality. Since the stability of resistors depends on the residual strains in the resistance material and on the action which proceeds at its surface (i.e. oxidation or corrosion) such resistors should be as completely annealed as possible and should be sealed away from contact with the air or with other oxidizing agents. In a design developed by Thomas[12] for precision resistance standards, bare manganin wire is used. This wire is wound on a mandrel with a suitable spacer and annealed at 550°C in an inert atmosphere. It is then slipped on a silk-insulated, metal coil form without stressing it, fixed in place, and sealed in a dry double-walled container. After the wire of the resistor has reached equilibrium with the small amount of air which is sealed in with it between the double walls of the container, no further significant drift in resistance occurs unless the seal develops a leak and there is an exchange of air between the container and the outside. Probably the most stable resistors that have ever been made are a group of 1-ohm manganin resistors of this type, sealed in double-walled air-filled containers, now being used at the National Bureau of Standards to maintain the unit of resistance. Some of these 1-ohm standards have not changed by as much as 1 ppm over a period of several years.[13]

The stability of commercially available standard resistors may be summarized in terms of an analysis made at the National Bureau of Standards as a result of periodic tests on 600 standards whose values ranged from 10^{-4} to 10^4 ohms.[14] "The average yearly change, without regard to sign, was found to be 8 ppm. Of the total only 2% averaged greater than 60 ppm, and for nearly 90% of all standards tested the annual change was 10 ppm or less. · · · The average yearly change was about − 0.3 ppm for sealed and about + 5 ppm for unsealed standards. That is to say, sealed standards about as often decrease as increase in resistance with time, whereas the change in unsealed resistors is predominately upward."

Time Constants of Resistors

If resistors are to be used in alternating-current measurements, impedance as well as resistance must be considered. In the case of a resistance coil, it is often convenient to express its impedance in terms of its resistance and its time constant τ, where $\omega\tau = \tan \phi$ and where ϕ is the angle by which the current through the coil lags behind the voltage impressed on it at a frequency $f = \omega/2\pi$. The time constant of an impedor may also be defined as the time required for the current to reach $1/\varepsilon$ of its final value when a fixed voltage is suddenly applied. The value of τ is usually stated in seconds or microseconds and, for a well-designed resistor, may be less than 10^{-8} sec.

[12] Thomas, *NBS J. Research*, **5**, 295 (1930); **36**, 107 (1946).

[13] See discussion of resistance standards in Chapter 2, p. 32.

[14] Thomas, *NBS Circ.* 470, Precision Resistors and Their Measurement.

All resistors have inductance because of the area enclosed within the winding loop. They also have capacitance between different parts of the wire which forms the winding. For inductance in the absence of capacitance $\tau = L/R$, and for capacitance in the absence of inductance $\tau = CR$ (if we assume that the entire capacitance effectively shunts the entire resistance). In general, since both effects are present,

$$\tau = \frac{L - CR^2}{R} = \frac{L_r}{R}$$

In this expression it is convenient to designate the residual as an "equivalent" inductance L_r, and to assign it a positive value for $L > CR^2$, or a negative value for $L < CR^2$. One would then speak of the "equivalent" inductance $\pm L_r$, in describing the residual of a resistance coil.

Bifilar Winding. In the construction of precision resistors an attempt is always made to keep coil residuals small. The most widely used non-inductive winding is the *bifilar* winding in which the wire is doubled and wound from the point of doubling. In this way the directions of the current in adjacent turns are respectively clockwise and counterclockwise and their magnetic fields will tend to cancel each other. There is always, however, a residual inductance which results from the flux in the area enclosed within the thin loop formed by the doubled wire. Obviously this area cannot be zero since the centers of the wires cannot coincide. The residual capacitance of a bifilar winding is necessarily high; and, since at the ends of the coil the full voltage drop in the coil is applied between adjacent turns, the capacitive residual rises rapidly as the length of the winding is increased. It will be apparent that at some point the inductive and capacitive effects will be equal and as a result of their mutual cancellation the residual inductance L_r will be zero. Actually, most bifilar windings having a resistance of 10 ohms or less have a positive (inductive) residual, whereas for coils of 100 ohms or more the residual is negative (i.e. the capacitive effect predominates). In constructing precision resistors of 100 ohms or more, for a-c operation, other types of windings are frequently used to reduce the effective capacitance.

A number of factors influence the behavior of resistance coils on alternating current: (1) the inductance of the winding; (2) the distributed capacitance of the winding; (3) the capacitance between the coil and its surroundings; (4) the insulation between turns of the coil; (5) the skin effect in the wire.

For low values of resistance, in which the cross section of the conductors must be large, bifilar strips are used with the conductors separated by thin sheets of mica. In this way the residual loop formed by the conductor encloses much less area than would be the case if wire of round cross section were used. The skin effect is also less for strip material since the conductor is of thinner cross section. In high-resistance coils, where the bifilar loop is long, so that the capacitance is large and the average potential difference between adjacent wires is high, a considerable gain results from subdivision of the winding into a number of bifilar sections connected in series. It will be apparent that, if a bifilar winding is divided into two sections connected in series, the capacitance of each section is approximately half as great since each of the loops is half as long. Furthermore the average potential difference across each section is half as great as with a single loop so that the capacitance current is $\frac{1}{4}$ as great. Thus the effect of the capacitance is $\frac{1}{4}$ as great in a two-section bifilar winding as in a similar resistor consisting of a single bifilar loop. Similarly, if the resistor be divided into n bifilar sections, the capacitance effect is reduced to a value approximately $1/n^2$ as large as if the same wire were arranged in a single loop. The winding should be on an insulating tube (such as porcelain) since a metal winding form would increase the capacitance between sections. In contrast to this, the time constant of a low-resistance bifilar coil may be decreased by connecting in parallel a number of bifilar sections of higher resistance, wound on a common metal tube. By this method, Wagner[15] decreased the time constant of a 10-ohm coil by a factor of 5 (to 1.6×10^{-8} sec), using five bifilar sections in parallel in place of a single bifilar winding.

Chaperon Winding. A modification of the bifilar winding was described by Chaperon.[16] In this arrangement a coil is wound in an even number of layers with the winding direction reversed at the end of each layer. Thus there are as many clockwise as counterclockwise turns in the coil and the inductance is small, while the voltage remains low between neighboring turns, resulting in a lower capacitive residual than would be the case for a bifilar winding. This winding lends itself readily to subdivision, and Wagner[17] has constructed a six-section, 1000-ohm coil on an insulating tube with a time constant of about 10^{-8} sec. This winding has the same disadvantages as other multilayer windings in that its ability to dissipate heat is low.

Card-Wound Resistors. An alternative to bifilar winding for high resistances is a single-layer inductive winding on a thin card of mica or other insulating material. The capacitive residual of such a winding is much less than for a bifilar winding since adjacent turns have only a very small difference in potential. This winding was introduced by Rowland

[15] Wagner, *Elektrot. Zeits.*, **34**, 613, 649 (1913).
[16] Chaperon, *Comptes rend.*, **108**, 799 (1899).
[17] Wagner, *op. cit.*

in 1899 and is much used in instrument multipliers.[18] It is also employed to some extent in precision resistors. The time constant of such resistance cards may be expected to be between 10^{-6} and 10^{-7} sec. A variation of this type of winding consists in a two-layer winding on a thin card, the outer layer being wound in the reverse sense to the inner layer, and the two layers being connected in parallel.

Woven-Wire Resistors. Another type of resistor with low residuals is the woven-wire arrangement originally described by Duddell and Mather[19] and later improved by Leeds and Northrup. This winding is analogous to a ribbon in which the warp is silk or cotton thread and the filler is the resistance wire. In such an arrangement residual inductive loops are very small and neighboring conductors have a very small potential difference. The completed ribbon may be wrapped as a single layer around a porcelain cylinder and fixed in place with lashings of silk thread. Woven resistors of the Leeds and Northrup type have time constants ranging from 1.4×10^{-8} sec (capacitive) for a 20,000-ohm unit to 0.4×10^{-8} sec (inductive) for a 100-ohm unit.

Curtis Winding. A winding described by Curtis[20] is quite effective in reducing the residuals of high-resistance coils but is tedious and expensive

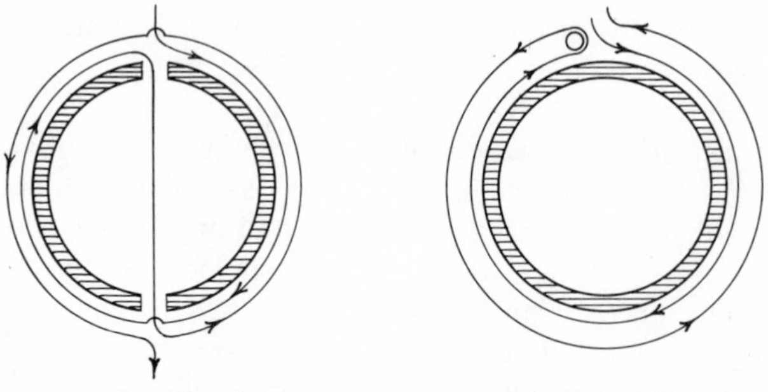

Curtis Winding
(*a*)

Wenner Winding
(*b*)

FIG. 2.

to wind and results in poor stability. This winding makes use of a slotted porcelain tube with the resistance wire passed through the slot and reversed in direction at the end of each turn as shown in Fig. 2(*a*). A 10,000-ohm coil wound in this way has been found to have a time constant

[18] Card-wound resistors operating at high voltage may have corona at the edges and show a tendency to failure at such points if fine wire is used. This situation may be greatly improved by building up a layer of solid insulation over the wire at the edges of the cards.

[19] British Patent No. 5171 (1901).

[20] Curtis and Grover, *Bull. Bur. Standards*, **8**, 495 (1913).

of 10^{-8} sec. A winding scheme which is quite effective and is simpler to carry out where coils having low residuals must be wound by hand is that devised by Wenner. A glass or porcelain tube may serve as a winding form, and a heavy cord, anchored at one end of the tube, is used for reversing the winding direction as shown in Fig. 2(*b*). The loose end of the cord is anchored down along the tube by the successive turns as they are looped around it and reversed.

Resistors Having Computable Residuals. In the forms of coils discussed above, the aim in general was to reduce the time constant by separately reducing the inductive and capacitive residuals to small values. It is also possible to construct coils whose time constants are very small, by

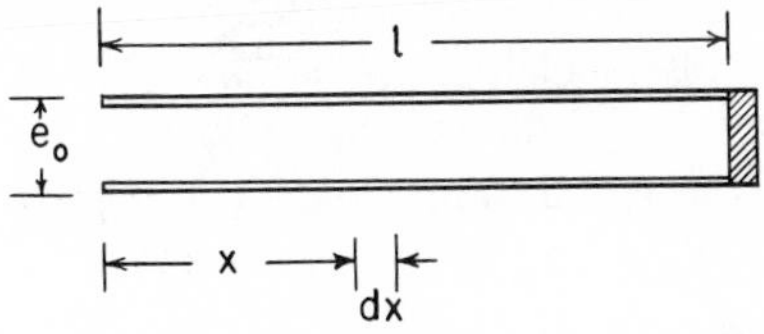

FIG. 3.

arranging the winding so that the inductive and capacitive effects approximately balance each other. One of the early applications of the compensation principle was that of Brown,[21] who mounted a pair of parallel wires on a board at such a separation that their inductive and capacitive effects were balanced. Although this construction is not used in commercial coils, we will examine it in some detail since it illustrates the general application of the principle of compensation. It is of special importance since it can be utilized for the construction of parallel-wire resistance standards having computable residuals, for use in the determination of the time constants of resistors by a-c bridge methods.[22]

In our previous approximation ($L_r = L - CR^2$), it was assumed that the "effective" capacitance shunted the entire resistance and that the "effective" inductance was in series with it. Actually, for a resistor consisting of a parallel-wire loop, inductance, capacitance, and resistance are distributed uniformly along the loop, which may be considered to be the equivalent of a transmission line open at one end and short-circuited at the other.

In the loop of Fig. 3, let

ρ = resistance per unit length of the loop
γ = capacitance per unit length of the loop
λ = inductance per unit length of the loop

[21] Brown, *Phys. Rev.*, **29**, 369–391 (1909).
[22] See Chapter 15.

These characteristic parameters will be assumed to be distributed uniformly along the parallel wire loop so that:

$$R = l\rho = \text{total resistance of the loop}$$
$$C = l\gamma = \text{total capacitance of the loop}$$
$$L = l\lambda = \text{total inductance of the loop}$$

The equilibrium equations[23] for the loop are obtained by writing the elementary voltage drop at an element equal to the current times the elemental impedance:

$$de = (\rho + j\omega\lambda)i\, dx$$

and the current leaving the line over an element dx is the voltage times the shunt admittance of the element $di = j\omega\gamma e\, dx$. Then

$$\frac{de}{dx} = (\rho + j\omega\lambda)i \quad \text{and} \quad \frac{di}{dx} = j\omega\gamma e$$

Eliminating i, we have

$$\frac{d^2e}{dx^2} = (\rho + j\omega\lambda)\frac{di}{dx} = j\omega\gamma(\rho + j\omega\lambda)e = a^2e$$

where $a = \sqrt{j\omega\gamma(\rho + j\omega\lambda)}$. The solution of this equation may be written as

$$e = C_1 \sinh ax + C_2 \cosh ax$$

and the boundary conditions are

$$\begin{cases} e = e_0, & \text{at } x = 0 \quad (1) \\ e = 0, & \text{at } x = l \quad (2) \end{cases}$$

From condition (2)

$$0 = C_1 \sinh al + C_2 \cosh al, \quad \text{or} \quad C_2 = -C_1 \tanh al$$

whence

$$e = C_1(\sinh ax - \cosh ax \tanh al)$$

From condition (1)

$$e_0 = -C_1 \tanh al$$

and we have

$$e = \frac{-e_0}{\tanh al}(\sinh ax - \cosh ax \tanh al) = e_0\left(\cosh ax - \frac{\sinh ax}{\tanh al}\right)$$

Now

$$i = \frac{1}{\rho + j\omega\lambda}\cdot\frac{de}{dx} = \frac{e_0 a}{\rho + j\omega\lambda}\left(\sinh ax - \frac{\cosh ax}{\tanh al}\right)$$

[23] See Kerchner and Corcoran, *A-C Circuits*, p. 342, John Wiley, 1938.

and at $x = 0$,

$$i = i_0 = \frac{e_0 a}{\rho + j\omega\lambda}\left(\frac{1}{\tanh al}\right) = \frac{e_0 a}{(\rho + j\omega\lambda)\tanh al}$$

The impedance operator

$$Z = \frac{e_0}{i_0} = \frac{(\rho + j\omega\lambda)}{a}\tanh al$$

Now

$$\tanh al = al - \frac{a^3 l^3}{3} + \frac{2a^5 l^5}{15} - \frac{17a^7 l^7}{315} + \cdots$$

So that

$$Z = \sqrt{\frac{\rho + j\omega\lambda}{j\omega\gamma}}\left[l\sqrt{j\omega\gamma(\rho + j\omega\lambda)} - \frac{l^3(j\omega\gamma\{\rho + j\omega\lambda\})^{3/2}}{3} + \frac{2l^5}{15}(j\omega\gamma\{\rho + j\omega\lambda\})^{5/2}\cdots\right]$$

$$= l(\rho + j\omega\lambda) - \frac{l^3}{3}(\rho + j\omega\lambda)^2 j\omega\gamma + \frac{2}{15}l^5(\rho + j\omega\lambda)^3(j\omega\gamma)^2\cdots$$

$$= (R + j\omega L)\left[1 - \tfrac{1}{3}(R + j\omega L)(j\omega C) + \tfrac{2}{15}(R + j\omega L)^2(j\omega C)^2\cdots\right]$$

$$\approx R + j\omega\left(L - \frac{CR^2}{3}\right)$$

since L and C are small compared to R, and all powers above the first have been dropped in this approximation. It should be noted that the

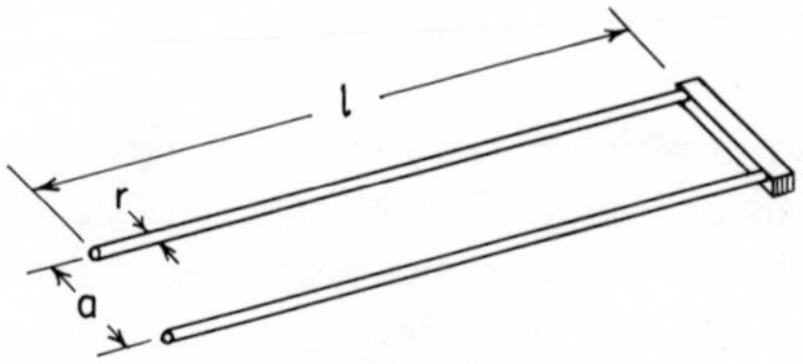

FIG. 4.

approximation is good in the low-frequency range but breaks down with increasing frequency.

Our new approximation[24] for the effective residual of a bifilar loop is, then,

$$L_r = L - \frac{CR^2}{3}$$

[24] It should be noted that in our previous approximation, $L_r = L - C'R^2$, we assumed that an "equivalent" capacitance was shunted across the entire resistance unit. It therefore appears that $C' = C/3$.

For such a loop (Fig. 4) it may be shown[25] that

$$L = 4l\left(\log_\varepsilon \frac{a}{r} + \frac{1}{4} - \frac{a}{l}\right) \times 10^{-9} \text{ henry}$$

and

$$C = \frac{l}{3.6 \log_\varepsilon \dfrac{a-r}{r}} \text{ micromicrofarad}$$

Four-Terminal Resistors

Any resistor may be considered to be a network, simple or complicated, depending on whether there is a simple current path through it, or a multiplicity of ways in which current can flow between its terminals. In a low-resistance resistor, made of sheet material, the current distribution is determined both by the physical construction of the shunt and frequently by the way in which the current is introduced at the terminals. Ideally, the terminal blocks of a low-resistance standard should be massive, of high conductivity, and so designed that the current is distributed uniformly throughout the volume of the resistance material which makes up the resistor. Even if this condition is met, the total two-terminal resistance (see Fig. 5) E_{FG}/I_{AB} between external points F, G is indefinite to the extent of both the resistance external to the resistor terminals A and B, i.e.

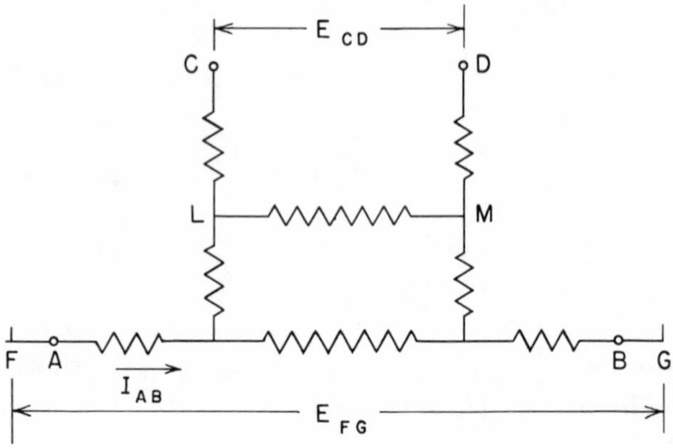

FIG. 5.

[25] For discussions of resistors having computable residuals see Wagner, *Elektrot. Zeits.*, **34**, 613 (1913) and **36**, 606 (1915); Curtis and Grover, *Bull. Bur. Standards*, **8**, 467, 495 (1913); Astbury, *J. IEE*, **76**, 389 (1935).

A method for the absolute determination of the time constants of resistors has been described by Köhler and Koops, *Philips Research Reports*, **2**, 454 (1947).

$R_{FA} + R_{BG}$, and in addition the contact resistance at A and B, where the resistor is connected to the measuring circuit. Unless great care is taken these effects may amount to 0.001 ohm or more. Although this much resistance would be negligible for most purposes if the resistance between A and B were 100 ohms, it would amount to 10% of the total if the resistance from A to B were 0.01 ohm. Thus, for low resistances, the usual two-terminal resistance is uncertain by a significant amount. The resistance can be precisely defined only as a *four-terminal resistance*, where two additional (potential) terminals are provided (C, D). This four-terminal resistance is defined as $R = E_{CD}/I_{AB}$, the ratio of the voltage at the potential terminals to the current entering and leaving the resistor at the current terminals. The reciprocal theorem states that an equivalent resistance is defined if the potential terminals (C, D) are used as current terminals, and the current terminals (A, B) are used as potential terminals, i.e.[26] $E_{CD}/I_{AB} = E_{AB}/I_{CD}$. Actually, other resistances can be defined by using different pairs of terminals for current and potential. The resistance defined above is the one which is usually of practical importance, and is known as the "direct" four-terminal resistance. The others are the "cross" resistance, $E_{AC}/I_{DB} = E_{DB}/I_{AC}$, and the "diagonal" resistance, $E_{CB}/I_{AD} = E_{AD}/I_{CB}$, which are usually significant only in the design of a precision resistor. Wenner[27] has stated certain conditions which must be met by a precision resistor in order that its resistance be definite: (1) the current must always enter and leave the resistor in such a way that there is the same or an equivalent distribution of current density between the particular equipotential surfaces used to define the resistance; (2) the potential drop must always be taken between the same or equivalent equipotential surfaces. In addition, referring to Fig. 6 in which the four terminals are shown schematically by the heavy lines 1–2–3–4, the following potential ratios must be less than the expected uncertainty in the measurement of the value of resistance: (1) the potential difference between any two points on terminal 2 to the potential difference between terminals 2 and 3, with 1 and 4 used as current terminals; (2) the potential difference between any two points on terminal 3 to the potential difference between terminals 2 and 3, with 1 and 4 used as current terminals; (3) the potential difference between any two points on terminal 1 to the potential difference between terminals 1 and 4, with

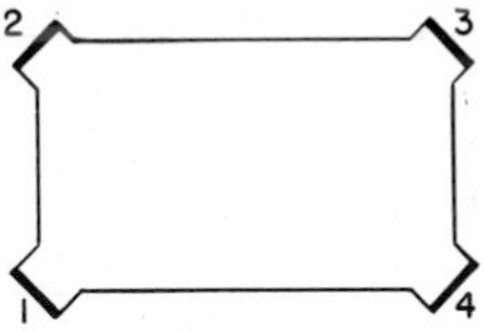

FIG. 6.

[26] If these relations are to be exact, each of the terminals must be considered as a geometrical point.

[27] Wenner, *NBS J. Research*, **25**, 259 (1940).

2 and 3 used as current terminals; (4) the potential difference between any two points on terminal 4 to the potential difference between terminals 1 and 4, with 2 and 3 used as current terminals. In standard resistors designed for precision work these conditions are usually satisfied to a degree permitting resistance measurement to a part in a million. The conditions are not nearly so closely met in resistors designed to carry heavy currents. Here the resistance may depend on the manner in which the current leads are connected to the current terminals to the extent of 0.01% or more and in exceptional cases to the extent of 1%. It is therefore important in measuring the resistance of heavy current shunts that the current leads be connected to the current terminals during the measurement in as nearly as possible the same manner that they will be connected in use.

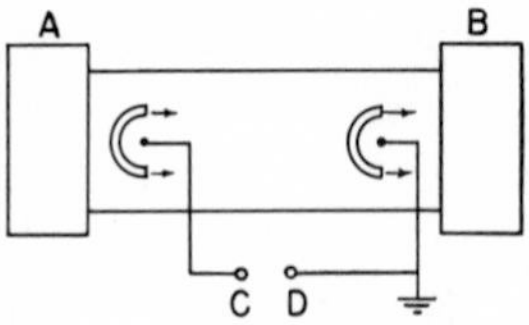

FIG. 7.

In addition to their function in precisely defining values of low resistances, four-terminal methods can often be used to analyze or measure the significant portion of a circuit between inaccessible branch points of permanently connected conductors. As we shall see later, four-terminal techniques make it possible to define a resistance independently of the resistances *CL* and *DM* of Fig. 5.

Where the resistor comprises a single sheet of manganin, the potential terminals may be attached to the sheet material itself by silver-soldered wires. The adjustment of the resistor to a precise value is possible in such cases by making semicircular cuts in the resistance sheet around the junction points of the potential terminals as shown in Fig. 7. The resistance can be decreased by extending the ends of the cut around the left-hand terminal, or increased by extending the ends of the cut around the right-hand terminal as shown by the arrows. Thus a continuous adjustment is provided for changing the resistance to either a higher or a lower value. If the resistor is made up of a number of sheets of material connected in parallel through massive copper terminal blocks as shown in Fig. 8, the potential terminals, *C* and *D*, are usually located on the terminal blocks themselves but well away from the current terminals, *A* and *B*, in order that any local irregularities in current distribution (resulting from the manner in which the resistor is connected to the circuit busses) may affect the potential distribution at *C* and *D* by as little as possible. In some cases the terminal blocks are designed to minimize the effect of variations in the current pattern caused by the method of connection of the terminal to the circuit busses. Figure 8(*b*) shows one such design. The copper terminal block is slotted to its full depth between the outer end where it bolts to the circuit busses and the inner face where it joins to the resistor strips. In this way the current is all forced through the outer portion of the terminal block, and the flow pattern between the slot and the inner face should be very nearly independent of the location and the manner of attachment of the circuit

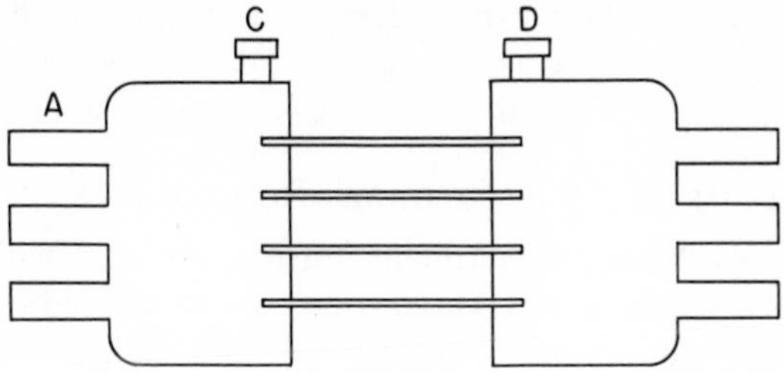

(a)

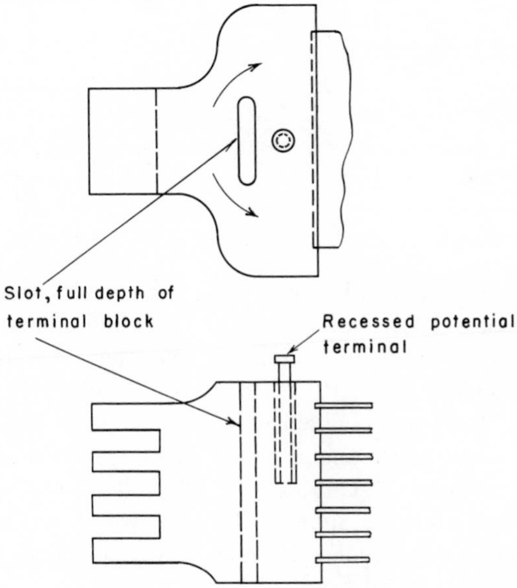

(b)

FIG. 8.

busses. A further gain is made by recessing the point of attachment of the potential terminal to a depth midway of the terminal block. In this way the junction between the potential circuit and the current circuit of the shunt will be at an equipotential surface which changes its location much less with changes in current distribution in the terminal block than is the case at the upper surface. For this type of shunt the resistance may be increased by filing the edges of the resistor sheets to remove material. The resistance can be decreased only by paralleling the resistor with a suitable high-resistance element connected between the terminal blocks. Such multiple leaf shunts are usually necessary only if heavy currents must be carried and considerable heat must be dissipated, and in such applications it is usually unnecessary that the resistance be adjusted as accurately to a definite value as is the case for precision resistors.

Time Constants of Four-Terminal Resistors

In many applications four-terminal resistors are used with alternating current. It is essential that resistors which are to be used in a-c applications be as nearly non-inductive as possible, since if the resistance is small

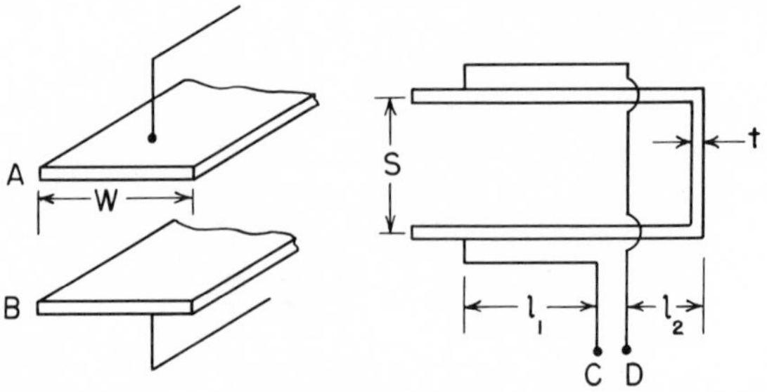

FIG. 9.

the inductance which can be tolerated is very small. For example, if the phase angle of a 0.001-ohm shunt is to be 1 milliradian (about 3 min of angle) at 60 cycles, its time constant must be 2.7×10^{-6} sec and its residual inductance 2.7×10^{-9} henry (or 2.7 abhenrys), an exceedingly small value. Such small inductances can be attained only by very careful design, but, since phase angles of the order indicated are significant in certain measurements,[28] considerable effort has been expended in the design of non-inductive shunts. Designs which reduce the effective inductance of four-terminal resistors to very small values have been made by Campbell[29] and by Silsbee.[30]

Strip Resistors. It is evident from Fig. 9 that flux produced by current through the strip of resistance material between the current terminals, *A* and *B*, will link with the potential circuit between the potential terminals, *C* and *D*. A change in this flux gives rise to an induced voltage in the potential circuit, and hence the number of flux linkages in the potential

[28] For example, the use of current shunts in the measurement of power at very low power factors, and the measurement of the phase angles of current transformers.

[29] Campbell, *Electrician*, **61**, 1000 (1908).

[30] Silsbee, *Bull. Bur. Standards*, **13**, 375 (1916–17); *NBS J. Research*, **4**, 73 (1930).

circuit for unit current in the current circuit is a measure of the effective four-terminal inductance of the resistor. If this induced voltage can be brought to zero the effective inductance will be zero. This can be done very nearly for certain types of resistor by properly locating the potential leads with respect to the current circuit. We will consider that the current circuit of Fig. 9 is formed by bending a uniform strip of resistance material into a narrow U. The leads from the potential terminals will be brought back along the strip and very close to it, to their point of attachment to the current circuit, and will be located midway between the edges of the strip. If we assume that the current is distributed uniformly throughout the cross section of the strip (i.e. neglect skin effect, proximity effect, and non-uniformity of the material) it can be shown that the effective inductance of the shunt is

$$L = \frac{4\pi}{W}\left[-\frac{l_1 t}{3} + l_2\left(S - \frac{t}{3}\right)\right]$$

If the potential leads are carried along the middle of the strip to the base of the U (so that $l_2 = 0$) the inductance will be negative and will have the value

$$L = \frac{-4\pi l t}{3W}$$

If the leads are brought to terminals very close to the current terminals (so that $l_1 = 0$) the inductance will be positive and have a value

$$L = \frac{4\pi l}{W}\left(S - \frac{t}{3}\right)$$

If the potential terminals are so located that

$$\frac{l_1}{l_2} = \frac{S - t/3}{t/3} = \frac{3S}{t} - 1$$

then the inductance will be zero. Under these conditions the self-inductance is balanced against the mutual inductance so that the resistor is effectively non-inductive. When the potential leads are brought to the base of the U the mutual inductance is too large. Physically, this is a more convenient construction to use. It will be apparent, however, that the mutual-inductance term can be decreased by displacing the potential lead from the middle of the strip toward its edge so that the flux linkages between the current circuit and the potential circuit are decreased. Actually, when the potential leads are located at a distance from the edge equal to 0.2 of the strip width and are brought together at the base of the U, the resistor is very nearly non-inductive. This construction has been used by Silsbee in 0.0025- and 0.001-ohm, air-cooled, strip shunts built at the National Bureau of Standards for current transformer testing. In the lower-resistance shunt (0.001 ohm) having a current rating of 500 amp, two sets of potential leads are used. They are symmetrically located near the upper and lower edges of the resistor strip in order to minimize the effect of stray fields.

Tubular Resistors. For a-c resistors used at currents above 500 amp, Silsbee has constructed tubular oil-cooled shunts in which the resistance element is a thin-walled manganin tube and the return current lead is an internal coaxial copper tube. The shunts are immersed in oil, and additional cooling is obtained by circulating oil through the annular space between the coaxial cylinders. Such a structure has no external field provided the current distribution is uniform in the cylinders. Four sets of potential leads are used, spaced at 90° intervals around the manganin cylinder in order to reduce the effect of stray fields. Since it is impossible to locate the points of attachment of these leads precisely in the same equipotential surfaces at the ends of the cylinder, a resistance of a few tenths of an ohm is inserted in each set of potential leads to reduce the circulating currents which result from their connection in parallel. The potential difference at the binding posts is therefore an average value. Discrepancies of about 0.4 min at 60 cycles have been observed between the values of phase angle computed for shunts of this construction and values arrived at as a result of experimental intercomparisons. This uncertainty in phase angle is believed to result from inhomogeneities in the manganin tubes which give rise to a non-uniform current distribution. Such inhomogeneities, where present, cannot be taken into account in the design of non-inductive shunts and must be expected to give rise to a small residual effective inductance.

Skin Effect. The assumption was made above that the skin effect in the a-c shunts described is negligible; i.e. that the current distribution for alternating current is the same as for direct current throughout the thickness of the sheet of resistance material. As the frequency is increased this is no longer true. The current density decreases in the interior of the sheet and increases toward its surface. The material is less efficiently used, and the effective resistance increases with frequency. The increase in resistance with frequency is a function of the resistivity of the material and the geometry of the conductor arrangement. Silsbee (*op. cit.*) has given formulas from which this change in resistance can be computed for certain arrangements. For the case of two thin, wide strips which are close together

$$\frac{R_{ac}}{R_{dc}} = 1 + \frac{a^4}{45t^4} - \frac{a^8}{4725t^8} + \cdots$$

where t is the thickness of the strips and $a^2 = 8\pi^2 f/10^9\rho$, f being the frequency in cycles per second and ρ the resistivity in ohm-centimeters.

If the strips are far apart, so that they do not affect each other, the current density is higher near the edges of the strip, and

$$\frac{R_{ac}}{R_{dc}} = 1 + 0.0087432b^4 - 0.000384b^8 + 0.000019b^{12} \cdots$$

where $b = a^2tw/\pi$, w being the strip width. No formulas are available for intermediate spacings. For a thin-walled tube with the return conductor at a distance

$$\frac{R_{ac}}{R_{dc}} = 1 + \frac{a^4t^4}{45}$$

and for coaxial thin-walled tubes

$$\frac{R_{ac}}{R_{dc}} = \frac{\rho\left(1 + \frac{a^4t_1^{\,4}}{45}\right)}{\pi(r_1^{\,2} - r_2^{\,2})} + \frac{\rho\left(1 + \frac{a^4t_2^{\,4}}{45}\right)}{2\pi\left(r_3t_2 - \frac{t_2^{\,2}}{2}\right)}$$

where r_1, r_2, t_1 are the outer and inner radii and wall thickness respectively of the outer tube, and r_3, t_2 are the outer radius and wall thickness of the inner tube.

Surge Resistors. Recently Park[31] has designed a tubular shunt for use in the measurement of surge currents. Since such measurements involve

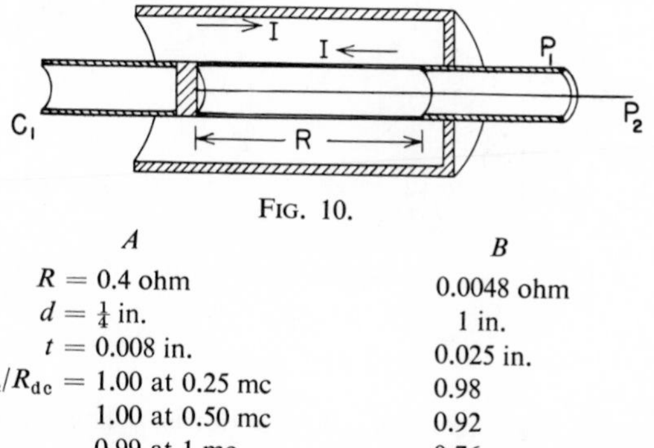

FIG. 10.

	A	*B*
$R =$	0.4 ohm	0.0048 ohm
$d =$	$\frac{1}{4}$ in.	1 in.
$t =$	0.008 in.	0.025 in.
$Z_{ac}/R_{dc} =$	1.00 at 0.25 mc	0.98
	1.00 at 0.50 mc	0.92
	0.99 at 1 mc	0.76

frequencies up to perhaps 10^6 cycles, the requirement regarding the time constant is much more severe than in a four-terminal resistor designed for measurements at power frequencies. However, because the current pulse is of very short duration, the energy which must be dissipated as heat is not large and the cooling of the resistor is not a problem as it is in the case of shunts designed for continuous operation. In fact, since the current surge releases energy in the shunt during a time so short that no

[31] Park, *NBS J. Research*, **39**, 191 (1947).

heat can be effectively dissipated, it is necessary only to ensure that the total volume of resistance material and its heat capacity are sufficient that the temperature rise, computed from considerations of heat capacity and total energy release, will not be excessive. The structure of the shunt is shown schematically in Fig. 10, together with data on two such shunts

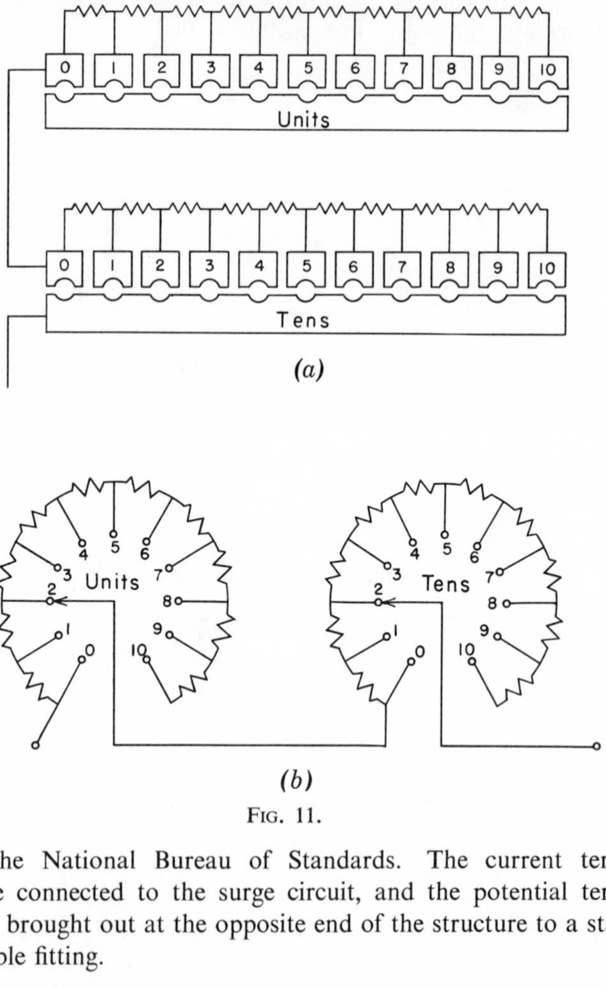

FIG. 11.

built at the National Bureau of Standards. The current terminals (c_1, c_2) are connected to the surge circuit, and the potential terminals (p_1, p_2) are brought out at the opposite end of the structure to a standard coaxial cable fitting.

Resistance Boxes

Most resistance boxes are so arranged that the total resistance inserted in the circuit can be varied by small equal steps from the smallest unit to the maximum resistance of the box. This is usually accomplished by arranging the coils in a series of decades. For example, there may be ten 1-ohm coils for the unit decade, ten 10-ohm coils for the ten decade, etc. Individual coils are inserted in the circuit either by means of plug and stud connectors or by dial switches as shown in Fig. 11. In many cases decades run from 1 to 9 instead of 1 to 10. This has the advantage that one less coil is used in each group, while the decade feature is preserved in that the resistance can still be varied throughout the range of the box in steps equal to the smallest unit present. However, in this case

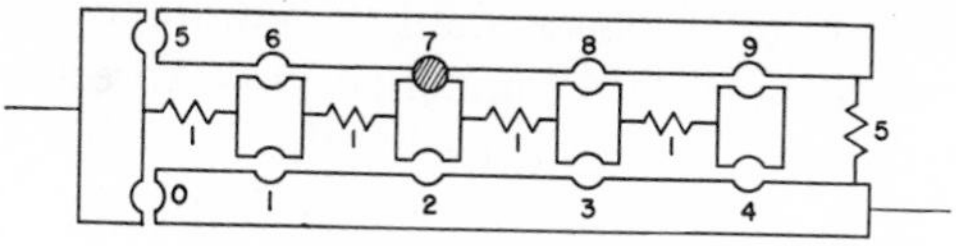

Feussner Decade
(7 Units in Circuit)

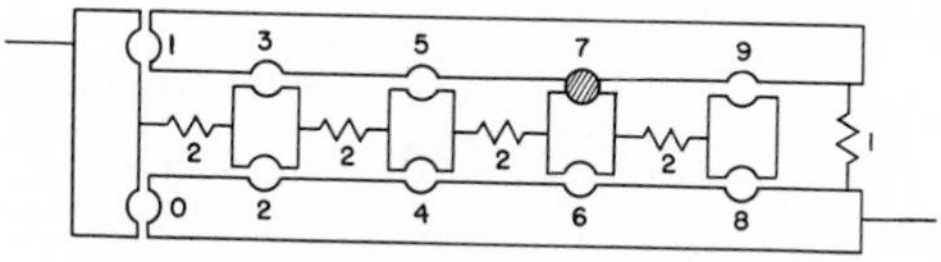

Smith Decade
(7 Units in Circuit)

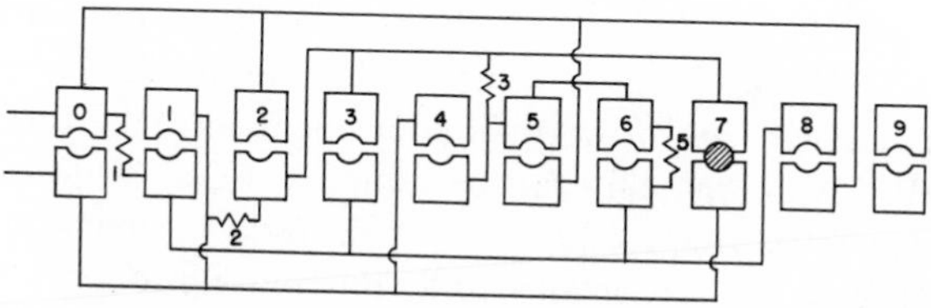

Northrup Decade
(7 Units in Circuit)

FIG. 12.

it is no longer possible to intercompare the resistances in the box by a simple substitution method (i.e. in the arrangement shown in the figure an internal check is possible by comparing all ten of the unit coils in series, with each of the resistors in the 10 decade, etc.).

The decade principle is used almost universally at the present time in resistance boxes, since it permits resistances to be inserted in the circuit conveniently and with only one set of switches or plug contacts per decade. However, in the arrangement shown in Fig. 11, a large number of coils must be made and adjusted. Several arrangements have been devised which reduce the number of coils required in a decade. Some of these are shown in Fig. 12. It will be noted that in all these arrangements a single plug contact is used in inserting any resistance from 0 to 9 units into the circuit. An arrangement devised by Behr[32] is used by the Leeds and Northrup Company in some of its resistance boxes. This arrangement is shown in Fig. 13. Six coils are used in a decade, each coil having a value of 2 decade units. One coil is stationary and is connected between two brushes to the next decade. The remaining five coils are arranged in series on the rotor as shown. In the position shown, the current does not go through any coil. This is the zero position of the decade. In the next position of the rotor in a counterclockwise direction the first coil on the rotor is connected in parallel with the fixed coil and the resulting resistance is 1 unit. In the next rotor position the fixed coil is shorted and the first rotor coil is in the circuit alone, the resistance being 2 units. In the third position the first rotor coil is in series with the parallel combination of the fixed coil and the second rotor coil, the total resistance being 3 units, etc. With suitable shield arrangements the time constants of this decade are quite low for all dial settings.

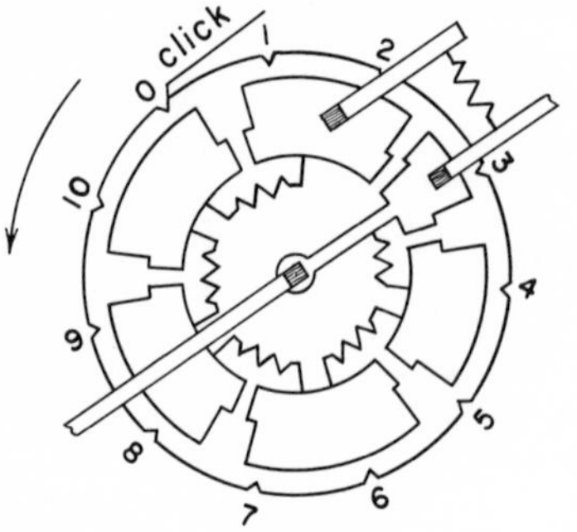

FIG. 13.

In many types of resistance measurements it is desirable to set up fixed ratios of resistances, and it is often convenient to make this ratio some power of 10. Although this can be done by a dial switch, a plug and stud arrangement is frequently used, particularly in precision apparatus. In order to keep contact resistance to a minimum it is desirable to arrange the coils and studs so that only one plug is needed for connecting each arm of the ratio. Two such arrangements are shown in Fig. 14. One of these, designed by Schöne,[33] is much used in precision apparatus. The resistors are connected between a common bar, C, and the various stud blocks. One plug is inserted between bar A and some particular stud block, another between bar B and another of the stud blocks to form a ratio. This arrangement has the advantage on a unity ratio that the resistance coils can be interchanged between the ratio arms, by transferring the plugs to the opposite ends of the stud blocks that are in use. This not only permits a check to be made of the equality of the resistors, but also in some types of measurement permits the reduction or elimination of certain measurement errors.

Of the two types of switching arrangements in common use, the older

[32] Behr and Tarpley, *Proc. IRE*, **20**, 1101 (1932).

[33] Schöne, *Zeits. für Instrumentenk.*, **18**, 133 (1898).

is the plug and stud arrangement, in which a tapered plug is inserted into a reamed hole between two massive stud blocks, either to complete the circuit or to by-pass unwanted resistance coils by short-circuiting them. The taper is important. If the taper is too steep, the plug tends to loosen, increasing the contact resistance. If the taper is too shallow, the plug tends to bind or to distort the remaining holes. Where brass plugs and studs are used a taper in the neighborhood of 1 in 12 on the diameter is considered good. In order to ensure good contact the plug should be very well fitted to the reamed hole. This arrangement is difficult to keep

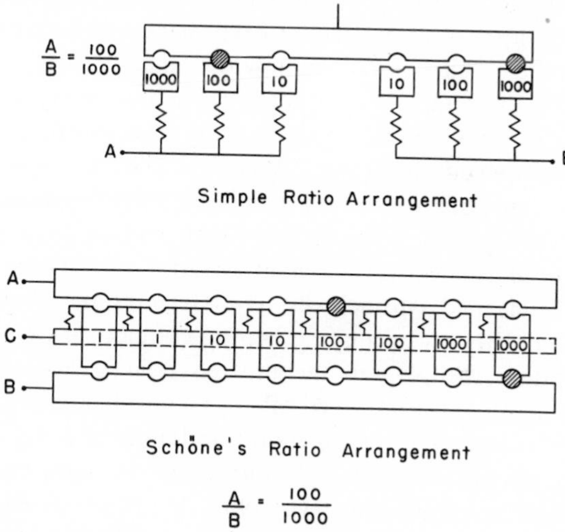

FIG. 14.

clean and in good working order, and thus requires more attention than a well-built rotary switch. Plugs may be mislaid or lost. Plug positions must be noted in order to evaluate the resistance used. However, a clean, well-fitted plug has a resistance which is both lower[34] and more definite than that between the brush and stud of a rotary switch. Hence the plug-stud switching arrangement is still used to a considerable extent in precision resistance apparatus, particularly in the ratio arms of bridges. The switching arrangement most common in decade resistance boxes at the present time is the rotary switch having brushes which bear on contact studs. Generally these brushes are subdivided into a number of thin leaves which provide individual parallel contacts on the stud and thus decrease the contact resistance. In some instances, where the contact resistance must be low and constant, the switch leaves and studs are made

[34] The resistance of a plug-stud contact may be as low as 0.00005 ohm under favorable conditions.

of silver or a silver alloy in place of the usual phosphor-bronze brushes and brass studs. Alternatively, brass studs are sometimes used with silver-alloy brush leaves. Silver plating is not a satisfactory substitute for either of these constructions. Manipulation of a rotary switch is simpler than the operation of a plug and stud arrangement. The switch may be enclosed for shielding, to keep the contact surfaces clean or to protect the operator at high voltages. Usually a detent or click arrangement is built into the switch to ensure that the brush centers itself on the contact stud. Frequently the rotary switch incorporates a disc which carries numbers to indicate the switch position, the number of the active switch position appearing opposite a fixed mark on the mounting panel, or being exposed to view in the window of a mask.

In cleaning plugs and studs, an abrasive such as emery which tends to bed itself in the metal should never be used since it will continue to cut and will eventually ruin the fitting. Vienna lime or a similar soft abrasive is suitable for removing oxide film from the contact surface. It is much better to clean exposed metal surfaces with canvas or a similar hard-finished cloth moistened with a light, neutral oil. Often a plug-stud contact can be cleaned satisfactorily by moistening the plug surface with a drop of oil and then working the mating contact surfaces against each other by rotating the plug in the tapered hole. Dirt and oxide film loosened in this way may be wiped off with a clean, soft cloth. The plug and stud, when clean, will stay in condition longer and will have a lower, more definite contact resistance if lubricated. A light, neutral mineral oil may be used as a lubricant. The plug should be seated with a slight twisting motion to ensure minimum resistance. The brush-stud contacts of precision rotary switches operate with a rather high contact pressure (up to 5 or 6 lb in some cases), and a solid lubricant may be used to advantage. Here also a neutral lubricant is advisable, and white Vaseline has been found effective. Only a thin coating should be applied; any excess may be removed by wiping. The brushes should be examined to make sure that all the leaves bear independently on the contact studs. Boxes should be kept covered when not in use to reduce the accumulation of dust and laboratory dirt. There is another very important reason for keeping laboratory apparatus with hard-rubber (ebonite) panels or insulation covered when not in use. Sulfuric acid is formed at the surface of hard rubber which is exposed to light. This acid absorbs moisture from the air and forms a conducting film over the surface of the insulation, increasing surface leakage and eventually ruining the insulation.

Time Constants of Resistance Boxes

If a group of resistance coils is to be used together in a resistance box, we must consider not only the time constants of the individual coils but also the capacitance between units, to the case, and to ground. Such effects may be much larger than the residuals of the coils themselves so that the time constant of a decade of resistors may be several times that of the individual coils. Coil arrangements and clearances within the box, the method of mounting the coil units, and shielding and switch arrangements all play a part.

In a case examined by Gall[35] the effect of grouping is shown to be very large. One-thousand-ohm coils, having effective residuals of − 10 microhenrys (μh) each, were mounted in a decade, and the group residuals were measured for each switch position with the results shown in the accompanying table. It will be noted that the total effective residual for the

Switch position	0	1	2	3	4	5	6	7	8	9	10
ΣR, ohms	0	1000	2000	3000	4000	5000	6000	7000	8000	9000	10,000
Effective inductance, μh	+ 1	− 10	− 50	− 110	− 240	− 370	− 500	− 700	− 880	− 1100	− 1250
Time constant, μsec	—	0.010	0.025	0.037	0.060	0.074	0.083	0.100	0.110	0.122	0.125

decade is 125 times that for a single coil and that the time constant (and hence the phase angle for a fixed value of frequency) increases by a factor of 12.5 when the whole decade is used. This illustrates the effect of intercapacitance between units and of capacitance to ground. Gall has designed a resistance box (made by Tinsley) in which this effect is compensated by adjusting the residual of each coil in accordance with its position in the decade. Each coil is made sufficiently inductive to neutralize the accumulated capacitance in the part of the decade that is in use. In this design each decade is separately shielded to eliminate the influence on it of switch positions in other decades of the box.

For low resistances it is essential that lead inductance from the coils to the control switches or studs be kept low since the residuals are themselves inductive. Similarly it is desirable to arrange high-resistance coils to reduce their intercapacitance and lead capacitance to as low a value as possible. Part of the effective residual in a decade results from the capacitance to the surroundings of the coils which are not in use but which are joined in series with the active coils, i.e. are "floating" on the decade. Where possible it is frequently helpful to connect the box so that the "floated" coils are as near to ground (or case) potential as possible.

An arrangement by Behr[36] (Leeds and Northrup Company) eliminates floating coils and the effect of intercoil capacitance by constructing a

[35] Gall, *J. Sci. Inst.*, **5**, 222 (1928).
[36] Behr, *Proc. IRE*, **20**, 1101 (1932).

decade so that only one coil is connected in the circuit at a time. Ten coils, having values from 1 to 10 units, are mounted on a rotor as shown in Fig. 15. The switch blades are fixed in position and the coils are moved under them in turn by a handle which extends from the rotor through the top of the box. Thus only one coil of the decade is connected and active at one time, and the active coil is always in the same position relative to active elements of other decades and to ground or the case. Each dial setting therefore has a time constant associated with the residuals of only a single coil. In a box using this arrangement with woven-wire

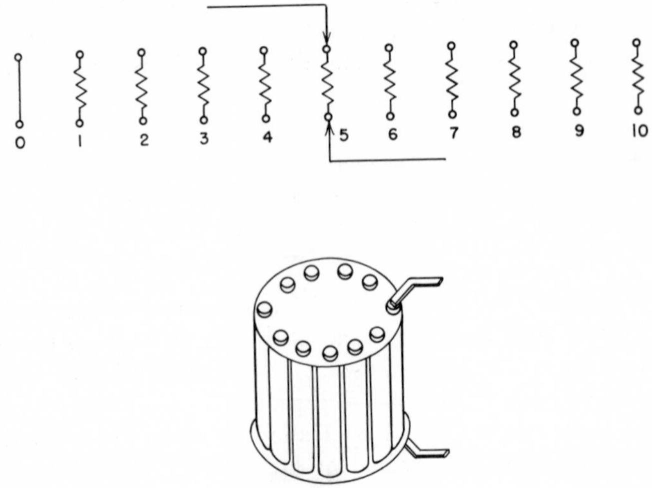

FIG. 15.

coil construction, the time constant of the 1000-ohm decade was found to be about 1.5×10^{-8} sec.

Shielded Resistors

Although high-resistance coils which have very small time constants can be wound, the effective phase angles of such units will depend on their surroundings. Furthermore, when a number of such units are connected in series, the capacitance between sections may be important as well as the capacitance to ground or to neighboring objects. Because of the effects of these distributed capacitances the current will vary from point to point along the resistor, and the potential drop along a particular section will not necessarily be exactly proportional to the resistance of the section. In order to make the effect of such distributed capacitance definite the resistor (or resistor sections) may be enclosed within metal shields which are maintained at fixed potentials with respect to the resistors which they enclose. We shall see that, for certain values of relative shield potentials, the effect of distributed capacitance on voltage distribution is also decreased.

We will first consider a shielded resistor with one end at ground potential as shown in Fig. 16.

Let $\rho =$ resistance per unit length
$K =$ capacitance per unit length to shield
$S =$ shield potential
$\omega = 2\pi f$, where f is frequency

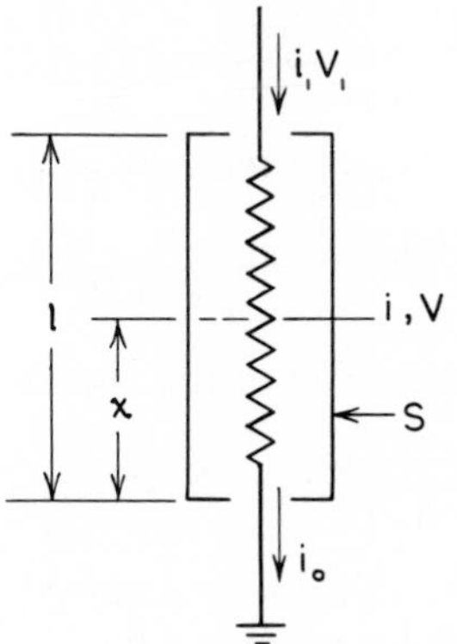

FIG. 16.

The voltage drop along an element, dx, is $dv = i\rho\, dx$, and the capacitance current leaving the resistor in the same element is

$$di = j\omega(V - S)K\, dx$$

so that

$$\frac{dV}{dx} = i\rho, \quad \text{and} \quad \frac{di}{dx} = j\omega K(V - S)$$

from which

$$\frac{d^2V}{dx^2} = j\omega K\rho(V - S) = \alpha^2(V - S)$$

where $\alpha^2 = j\omega K\rho$. The solution of this equation is

$$V = A \cosh \alpha x + B \sinh \alpha x + S$$

subject to the conditions

$$\begin{cases} V = 0 & \text{when } x = 0 \\ V = V_1 & \text{when } x = l \end{cases}$$

From the first condition we have

$$0 = A + S \quad \text{or} \quad A = - S$$

From the second condition we have

$$V_1 = -S\cosh\alpha l + B\sinh\alpha l + S$$

and

$$B = \frac{-S(1-\cosh\alpha l) + V_1}{\sinh\alpha l}$$

Then

$$V = \frac{V_1 - S(1-\cosh\alpha l)}{\sinh\alpha l}\sinh\alpha x - S\cosh\alpha x + S$$

and consequently

$$i = \frac{\alpha}{\rho}\left[\frac{V_1 - S(1-\cosh\alpha l)}{\sinh\alpha l}\cosh\alpha x - S\sinh\alpha x\right]$$

The current at the grounded end of the resistor ($x = 0$) is

$$i_0 = \frac{\alpha}{\rho}\left[\frac{V_1 - S(1-\cosh\alpha l)}{\sinh\alpha l}\right] = \frac{\alpha}{\rho\sinh\alpha l}(V - S + S\cosh\alpha l)$$

The current at the high-voltage end of the resistor ($x = l$) is

$$i_1 = \frac{\alpha}{\rho\sinh\alpha l}[(V_1 - S)\cosh\alpha l + S]$$

Now, if we assume that the shield is maintained at a potential between V_1 and 0, and in phase with V_1, we may write

$$S = \eta V_1, \quad \eta \text{ being a real quantity less than unity}$$

In this case

$$i_0 = \frac{\alpha}{\rho\sinh\alpha l}[(1-\eta) + \eta\cosh\alpha l]V_1$$

and

$$i_1 = \frac{\alpha}{\rho\sinh\alpha l}[(1-\eta)\cosh\alpha l + \eta]V_1$$

At low frequencies, where αl is small, we may write

$$\sinh\alpha l = \alpha l + \frac{\alpha^3 l^3}{3!} + \frac{\alpha^5 l^5}{5!}\cdots \approx \alpha l\left(1 + \frac{\alpha^2 l^2}{6} + \frac{\alpha^4 l^4}{120}\right)$$

$$\cosh\alpha l = 1 + \frac{\alpha^2 l^2}{2!} + \frac{\alpha^4 l^4}{4!}\cdots \approx 1 + \frac{\alpha^2 l^2}{2} + \frac{\alpha^4 l^4}{24}$$

so that

$$\frac{\alpha\cosh\alpha l}{\sinh\alpha l} \approx \frac{1}{l}\left[\frac{1 + \dfrac{\alpha^2 l^2}{2} + \dfrac{\alpha^4 l^4}{24}}{1 + \dfrac{\alpha^2 l^2}{6} + \dfrac{\alpha^4 l^4}{120}}\right] \approx \frac{1}{l}\left[1 + \frac{\alpha^2 l^2}{3} - \frac{\alpha^4 l^4}{45}\right]$$

Then we may say approximately (at low frequencies)

$$i_0 = \frac{\alpha}{\rho}\left[\frac{1-\eta}{\sinh \alpha l} + \eta\,\frac{\cosh \alpha l}{\sinh \alpha l}\right] V_1$$

$$\approx \frac{1}{\rho l}\left[\frac{1-\eta}{\left(1+\dfrac{\alpha^2 l^2}{6}+\dfrac{\alpha^4 l^4}{120}\right)} + \eta\left(1+\frac{\alpha^2 l^2}{3}-\frac{\alpha^4 l^4}{45}\right)\right] V_1$$

$$\approx \frac{1}{\rho l}\left[(1-\eta)\left(1-\frac{\alpha^2 l^2}{6}+\frac{7\alpha^4 l^4}{360}\right) + \eta\left(1+\frac{\alpha^2 l^2}{3}-\frac{\alpha^4 l^4}{45}\right)\right] V_1$$

$$\approx \frac{1}{\rho l}\left[1+(3\eta-1)\frac{\alpha^2 l^2}{6}-(15\eta-7)\frac{\alpha^4 l^4}{360}\right] V_1$$

$$\approx \frac{1}{R}\left[1+(3\eta-1)\cdot j\,\frac{\omega CR}{6}+(15\eta-7)\frac{\omega^2 C^2 R^2}{360}\right] V_1,$$

since
$$\begin{cases} \alpha^2 = j\omega K\rho \\ \rho l = R \\ Kl = C \end{cases}$$

Also

$$i_1 = \frac{\alpha}{\rho}\left[\frac{(1-\eta)\cosh \alpha l}{\sinh \alpha l} + \frac{\eta}{\sinh \alpha l}\right] V_1$$

$$\approx \frac{1}{\rho l}\left[(1-\eta)\left(1+\frac{\alpha^2 l^2}{3}-\frac{\alpha^4 l^4}{45}\right) + \eta\left(1-\frac{\alpha^2 l^2}{6}+\frac{7\alpha^4 l^4}{360}\right)\right] V_1$$

$$\approx \frac{1}{\rho l}\left[1-(3\eta-2)\frac{\alpha^2 l^2}{6}+(15\eta-8)\frac{\alpha^4 l^4}{360}\right] V_1$$

$$\approx \frac{1}{R}\left[1-(3\eta-2)\cdot j\,\frac{\omega CR}{6}-(15\eta-8)\frac{\omega^2 C^2 R^2}{360}\right] V_1$$

A number of cases are of interest. If the shield is maintained at ground potential ($\eta = 0$),

$$i_0 \approx \frac{V_1}{R}\left(1 - j\frac{\omega CR}{6} - \frac{7}{360}\,\omega^2 C^2 R^2\right), \quad \text{and} \quad i_1 = \frac{V_1}{R}\left(1 + j\frac{\omega CR}{3} + \frac{\omega^2 C^2 R^2}{45}\right)$$

The current leaving the grounded end of the resistor is slightly less than would be computed by neglecting the effect of distributed capacitance, and lags the applied voltage by an angle which is (to a very good approximation) $\omega CR/6$. The current at the high-voltage end of the resistor is slightly greater than would be found in the absence of distributed capacitance and leads the applied voltage by an angle $\omega CR/3$, approximately. If we say $i = V_1/R$, then the magnitude of the current at the ground end is

$$i_0 \approx i\left(1 - \frac{\omega^2C^2R^2}{180}\right)$$

and, at the high-voltage end, the current is

$$i_1 \approx i\,(1 + \tfrac{7}{90}\,\omega^2C^2R^2)$$

The magnitude of the current is very little different from what it would be in the absence of distributed capacitance, but its angular displacement may be significant in some measurements.

If the shield is maintained at a potential $V_1/3$, ($\eta = \frac{1}{3}$), the current at the ground end of the resistor is

$$i_0 \approx i\left(1 - \frac{\omega^2C^2R^2}{180}\right)$$

and is in phase with the applied voltage. The current at the high-voltage end of the resistor leads the voltage by an angle $\omega CR/6$, and its magnitude is

$$i_1 \approx i\left(1 + \frac{\omega^2C^2R^2}{60}\right)$$

If the shield potential is $V_1/2$, ($\eta = \frac{1}{2}$), the current at the ground end of the resistor leads the applied voltage by an angle $\omega CR/12$, and its magnitude is

$$i_0 = i\left(1 + \frac{7}{1440}\,\omega^2C^2R^2\right)$$

The current at the high-voltage end of the resistor also leads by the same angle and has the same magnitude as the current at the ground end.

The above analysis assumes that the time constant of the resistor itself is zero. Let us consider a resistor having a residual inductance L, and a self-capacitance which may be represented by a lumped capacitance C' shunting the entire resistor as shown in Fig. 17. The admittance of the combination may be written as

$$\frac{1}{Z} = \frac{1}{R + j\omega L} + j\omega C' = \frac{R - j\omega L}{R^2 + \omega^2L^2} + j\omega C'$$

$$= \frac{R + j\omega R\left[C'R - \dfrac{L}{R}(1 - \omega^2LC')\right]}{R^2 + \omega^2L^2}$$

Since, in any practical case C' and L are small, we may (at low frequencies) neglect $\omega^2 LC'$ in comparison with unity, and $\omega^2 L^2$ in comparison with R^2, and we have

$$\frac{1}{Z} \approx \frac{1}{R}\left[1 + j\omega\left(C'R - \frac{L}{R}\right)\right]$$

The phase angle resulting from the residuals of the resistor is $\omega\left(C'R - \frac{L}{R}\right)$, which must be added to the phase angle resulting from

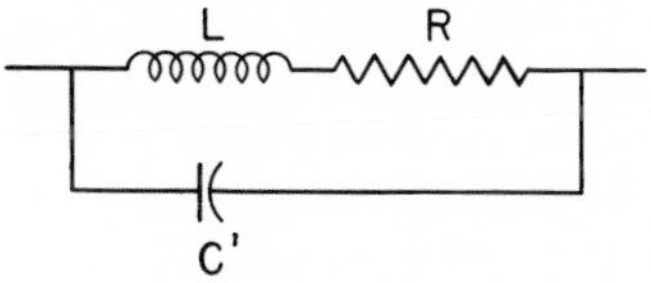

FIG. 17.

the presence of the shield at a potential ηV. Then if the shield is at ground potential

$$i_0 = \frac{V_1}{R}\left[1 + j\omega\left(C'R - \frac{L}{R}\right)\right]\left(1 - j\frac{\omega CR}{6}\right)$$

The angle between the impressed voltage and the current at the grounded end of the resistor is $\omega\left[\left(C'R - \frac{L}{R}\right) - \frac{CR}{6}\right]$.

It will be seen that, for a large resistor whose residual is predominantly capacitive, the current at the ground end may lead or lag the impressed voltage, depending on whether the contribution from the residual or from the shield capacitance is the greater. If the shield is at the midpotential the phase angle is $\omega\left[\frac{CR}{12} + \left(C'R - \frac{L}{R}\right)\right]$ and the current leads the voltage. In this case the current may be brought into phase with the voltage by adding inductance to the resistor. If series inductance were added to an amount $L_1 = \left(\frac{C}{12} + C'\right) R^2 - L$, the phase angle would be zero.

Shielded Resistors in Series

Distributed capacitance from a resistor to its shield would have no effect on the potential distribution along the resistor if the shield potential were at each point equal to the potential of the resistor at the same point. This would require that the shield be very finely divided and that its potential be graded just as finely. This is not practical except in special cases,[37] so that in general large shielded resistors are composed of a number of sections in series, each section being enclosed within a separate shield which is maintained at an appropriate potential. Such a system comprising *m* units is shown in Fig. 18. We will assume that the voltages across the various sections are $V_1, V_2, \cdots, V_m$ and that the shields are maintained at fractions $\eta_1, \eta_2, \cdots, \eta_m$ of these voltages. From the

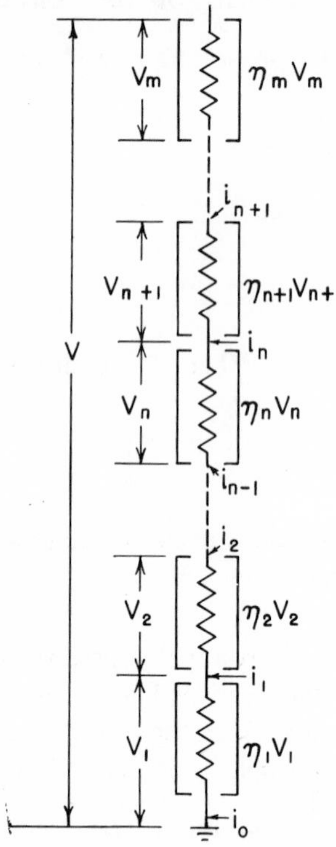

FIG. 18.

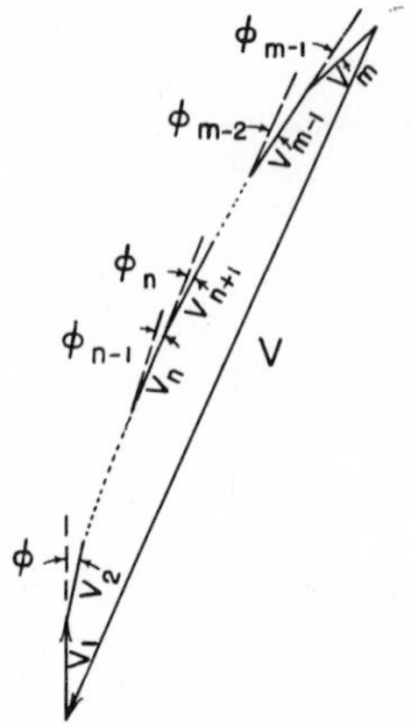

FIG. 19.

previous analysis we may write for the current at the lower end of the *n*th section

$$i_{n-1} = \frac{V_n}{R_n}\left[1 + \frac{j\omega C_n R_n}{6}(3\eta_n - 1)\right]$$

At the upper end of the *n*th section the current is

$$i_n = \frac{V_n}{R_n}\left[1 - \frac{j\omega C_n R_n}{6}(3\eta_n - 2)\right]$$

[37] De la Gorce, *Compt. rend.*, **191**, 1297 (1930); Berberich, *Trans. AIEE*, **52**, 521 (1933); Jimbo and Sakimura, *Researches Electrotech. Lab. Tokyo*, No. 353 (1934).

But this is also the current at the lower end of the $(n + 1)$th section:

$$i_n = \frac{V_{n+1}}{R_{n+1}} \left[1 + j\omega \frac{C_{n+1}R_{n+1}}{6} (3\eta_{n+1} - 1)\right]$$

Now, if we assume that the resistances of all sections are equal ($R_n = R_{n+1}$) and that each section has the same capacitance to its shield ($C_n = C_{n+1}$), we may write

$$V_n \left[1 - j\frac{\omega CR}{6} (3\eta_n - 2)\right] = V_{n+1} \left[1 + j\frac{\omega CR}{6} (3\eta_{n+1} - 1)\right]$$

or

$$V_{n+1} = V_n \frac{\left[1 - \dfrac{j\omega CR}{6} (3\eta_n - 2)\right]}{\left[1 + \dfrac{j\omega CR}{6} (3\eta_{n+1} - 1)\right]} \approx V_n \left[1 - \frac{j\omega CR}{2} (\eta_n + \eta_{n+1} - 1)\right]$$

$$\approx V_n(1 - j\phi_n)$$

where

$$\phi_n = \frac{\omega CR}{2} (\eta_n + \eta_{n+1} - 1)$$

We will assume that all the voltages are equal in magnitude ($V_1 = \cdots = V_m$) and that the phase angles are very small, so that $\cos \phi = 1$, and $\sin \phi = \phi$. The voltages of the sections may be added vectorially to make up V, as is shown schematically in Fig. 19. The components of V, resolved along V_1 and perpendicular to V_1, are

$$mV_1, \quad \text{and} \quad V_1\phi_1 + V_1(\phi_1 + \phi_2) + V_1(\phi_1 + \phi_2 + \phi_3) + \cdots + V_m(\phi_1 + \phi_2 \cdots + \phi_{m-1})$$

$$= V_1[\phi_1(m - 1) + \phi_2(m - 2) + \cdots + \phi_{m-1}]$$

Then

$$V \approx m(1 - j\phi)V_1$$

where

$$\phi = \frac{1}{m} [\phi_1(m - 1) + \phi_2(m - 2) + \cdots + \phi_{m-1}]$$

The current at the ground end of the first unit is

$$i_0 = \frac{V_1}{R} \left[1 + j\frac{\omega CR}{6} (3\eta_1 - 1)\right] = \frac{1}{mR} \left[1 + j\frac{\omega CR}{6} (3\eta_1 - 1)\right] \frac{V}{1 - j\phi}$$

$$\approx \frac{V}{mR} \left[1 + j\left\{\frac{\omega CR}{6} (3\eta_1 - 1) + \phi\right\}\right]$$

Now

$$\phi = \frac{1}{m}\,[\phi_1(m-1) + \phi_2(m-2) + \cdots + 2\phi_{m-2} + \phi_{m-1}]$$

$$= \frac{1}{m}\cdot\frac{\omega CR}{2}\,[(\eta_1+\eta_2-1)(m-1) + (\eta_2+\eta_3-1)(m-2) + \cdots + 2(\eta_{m-2}+\eta_{m-1}-1) + (\eta_{m-1}+\eta_m-1)]$$

$$= \frac{1}{m}\cdot\frac{\omega CR}{2}\left[\eta_1(m-1) + \eta_2(2m-3) + \eta_3(2m-5) + \cdots + 3\eta_{m-1} + \eta_m - \frac{m(m-1)}{2}\right]$$

So that

$$i_0 \approx \frac{V}{mR}\left[1 + \frac{j\omega CR}{2}\left\{\eta_1 - \frac{1}{3} + \frac{\eta_1(m-1)+\eta_2(2m-3)+\eta_3(2m-5)+\cdots+3\eta_{m-1}+\eta_m-\dfrac{m(m-1)}{2}}{m}\right\}\right]$$

$$\approx \frac{V}{mR}\left[1 + \frac{j\omega CR}{2}\left\{\eta_1\left(2-\frac{1}{m}\right) + \eta_2\left(2-\frac{3}{m}\right) + \eta_3\left(2-\frac{5}{m}\right) + \cdots + \frac{3}{m}\,\eta_{m-1} + \eta_m\cdot\frac{1}{m} + \frac{1}{6} - \frac{m}{2}\right\}\right]$$

If $\eta_1 = \eta_m$ and $\eta_2 = \eta_3 = \cdots = \eta_{m-1}$, then

$$i_0 \approx \frac{V}{mR}\left[1 + \frac{j\omega CR}{2}\left\{2\eta_1 + \eta_2\left[2(m-2) - \sum_{a=1}^{a=m-2}\frac{2m-(2a+1)}{m}\right] + \frac{1}{6} - \frac{m}{2}\right\}\right]$$

$$\approx \frac{V}{mR}\left[1 + \frac{j\omega CR}{2}\left\{2\eta_1 + (m-2)\eta_2 + \frac{1}{6} - \frac{m}{2}\right\}\right]$$

Now if

$$2\eta_1 + (m-2)\eta_2 + \frac{1}{6} - \frac{m}{2} = 0$$

the current at the grounded end of the resistor (i_0) would be in phase with the applied voltage (V). This would require that

$$\eta_1 = m\left(\frac{1}{4} - \frac{\eta_2}{2}\right) - \frac{1}{12} + \eta_2$$

and if this is to be true independently of m, we must have

$$\frac{1}{4}-\frac{\eta_2}{2}=0 \quad \text{or} \quad \eta_2=\frac{1}{2} \quad \text{and} \quad \eta_1=\eta_2-\frac{1}{12}=\frac{5}{12}$$

Thus, if the shields of the end units are maintained at a potential $\frac{5}{12}$ of that across the resistors and all the other shields are at the midpoint potential of their resistor, the current at the ground end of the resistor will be in phase with the impressed voltage. Such zero-phase-angle resistors have been constructed by Orlich[38] and Kouwenhoven.[39] This system is inconvenient to use if the number of shielded units in the resistor is to be varied, since in that case it is necessary to rearrange the shield connections. This disadvantage does not exist if all the shields are at the midpoint potentials. Such a system was described by Silsbee,[40] and has been extensively applied in the construction of high-voltage shielded resistors. In this case the phase angle is positive and amounts to $\omega CR/12$. In the National Bureau of Standards shielded resistor, designed for operation at 30 kv, the shielded units are 20,000 ohms each and are made up of card-wound resistors immersed in oil and enclosed in a brass box. The shield potentials are maintained by connecting each shield to the midpoint of a similar 20,000-ohm card-wound resistor in air, as shown in Fig. 20. The total resistance is 520,000 ohms, but any number of the shielded units may be connected in series to make up a smaller total resistance.

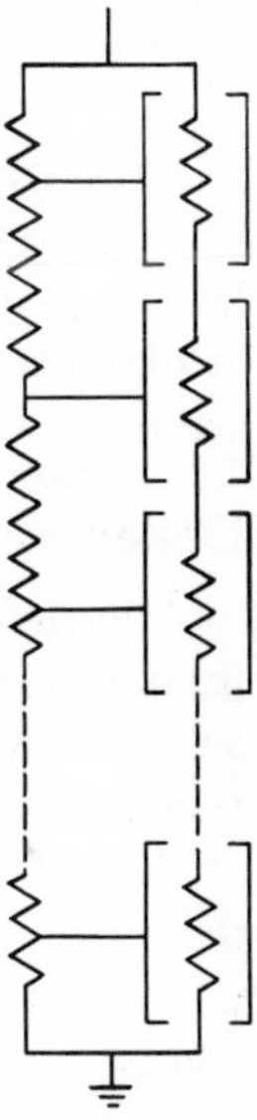

FIG. 20.

It is important that the shields be maintained fairly close to the midpoint potentials. If the shield potentials are all offset from the midpoint by δ per cent,

$$\eta=\frac{1}{2}\left(1+\frac{\delta}{100}\right)$$

and the phase angle becomes

$$\frac{\omega RC}{12}\left\{1+3m\frac{\delta}{100}\right\}$$

so that the departure of the phase angle from its minimum value is $(\omega RC/12)\times(3m\delta/100)$, a change of $3m\delta$ per cent. The change in phase angle will be smaller if the shield potentials are offset in a random fashion by small amounts. Such effects can, however, be stated quantitatively

[38] Orlich and Schultze, *Arch. für Elektrot.*, **1,** 1, 88, 232 (1913).

[39] Kouwenhoven, *Arbeit. Elektrot. Inst. Karlsruhe*, **3,** 1 (1913).

[40] Silsbee, *Bull. Bur. Standards*, **20,** 489 (1926).

only in terms of the individual values of ϕ. A larger phase angle is produced by the non-uniform potential distribution in the unshielded auxiliary resistor resulting from distributed capacitance to ground. This effect could be corrected by suitably shielding the auxiliary resistor as well as the working resistor, but such an arrangement would be very expensive to build and maintain.[41]

RESISTANCE MEASUREMENTS

Although the precise measurement of resistance involves the use of a bridge, potentiometer, or some other network in which the resistor can be compared with another whose value is known,[42] direct methods are available and are often more convenient where the accuracy requirements are not too severe.

Deflection Methods

Ammeter-Voltmeter Method. The simultaneous measurement, by deflection methods, of current through a resistor, and of the potential drop across it, yields a moderately accurate value over a very wide range of resistances. The attainable accuracy depends primarily on the accuracy of the deflecting instruments used to measure the current and voltage, if the ranges of the available instruments are such that fairly large deflections are obtained, and if proper allowance is made for the effect of the instruments. It will be seen from Fig. 21 that there are two ways in which the ammeter and voltmeter can be connected for the measurement, and that, in either case, the resistance of one of the instruments will affect the measurement to some extent. If the voltmeter is connected directly across the resistor [Fig. 21(a)] the current measured by the ammeter includes both the current through the resistor and that taken by the voltmeter. In this case the resistance is given by the formula

$$R = \frac{E}{I\left(1 - \dfrac{E}{IR_V}\right)}$$

where E is the voltage indicated by the voltmeter, R_V is the resistance of the voltmeter, and I is the current indicated by the ammeter. If the ammeter is connected so that it indicates only the current through the

[41] A 132-kv shielded resistor, whose shield potentials are maintained by taps on special autotransformers, has been built by the General Electric Company. Its 60-cycle phase angle is approximately 4 min. Weller, *J. AIEE*, **48,** 312 (1929).

[42] It should be recalled that in nearly all physical measurements the precision with which two similar magnitudes can be compared is much greater than the precision with which either can be directly determined.

resistor [Fig. 21(*b*)], the voltmeter indicates the voltage drop across the ammeter as well as that across the resistor. In this case the resistance is given by the formula

$$R = \frac{E}{I} - R_A$$

where R_A is the resistance of the ammeter. Although this method can generally be considered to yield values of resistance which are good to a few per cent, with high-grade instruments the method is capable of accuracy to within 0.1 or 0.2%, provided the instrument ranges are such that large deflections are obtained.

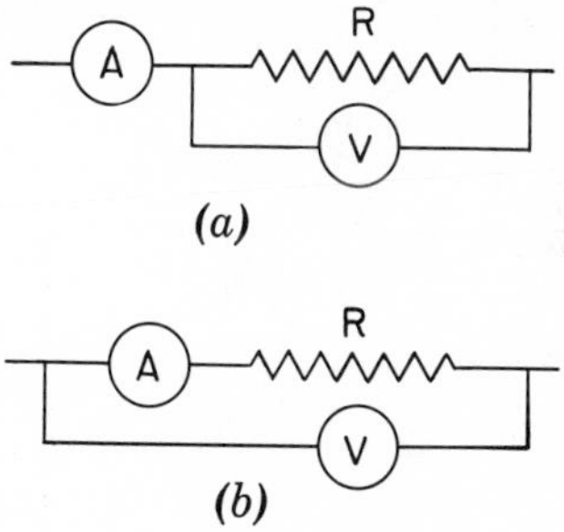

FIG. 21.

Ohmmeters. These moderate-accuracy instruments (usually a few per cent) are designed for indicating by their deflection the resistance of a circuit connected across their terminals. They are available in a wide range of resistance values, from microhmmeters indicating a microhm for the smallest scale division to megohmmeters reading to 50,000 megohms. The simplest of these instruments consists of a milliammeter connected as shown in Fig. 22(*a*) to measure the current through the unknown resistor *X*. The milliammeter is usually adjusted to full-scale

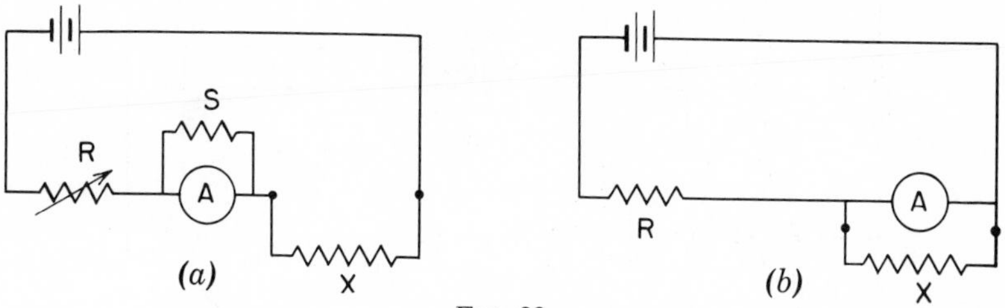

FIG. 22.

reading with its *X*-terminals short-circuited, by means of a variable resistor *R*. The scale is marked to read directly the value of the resistance inserted at *X*. A shunt *S* may be incorporated to change the range of the ohmmeter. Simple instruments of this sort, based on a milliammeter movement, can be used up to a megohm or more. An alternative method of connection [Fig. 22(*b*)] places the unknown resistor *X* in parallel with the milliammeter. This method of connection is applicable to the measurement of low resistances. In this case the current in the milliammeter, and its deflection, decrease with decreasing resistance of the unknown.

CROSSED-COIL OHMMETERS. Another type of ohmmeter depends on the ratio of currents through two moving coils for its indication. The principle of operation of the ratio or "crossed-coil" ohmmeter may be seen from Fig. 23. Two separate moving coils, fixed on a single shaft, are arranged so that their torques oppose. One of these, *V*, is connected with a series resistor across the supply so that its torque is proportional to the voltage impressed on the unknown resistance *X*. The other coil, *C*, carries the current through the unknown. No springs are used, so that the moving system takes up a position which is a function of the quotient of the voltage by the current, since we can consider that the instrument is basically a milliammeter whose control torque is proportional to voltage. The scale can therefore be marked directly in ohms, and the indication is independent of the value of the applied voltage.

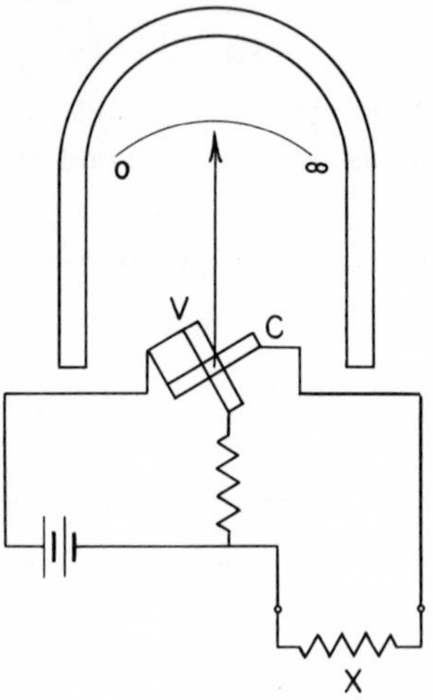

FIG. 23.

Although ratio-type ohmmeters can be designed so that their ranges cover low or high resistances, the principle is particularly well adapted to application in portable insulation testers, and forms the basis of the well-

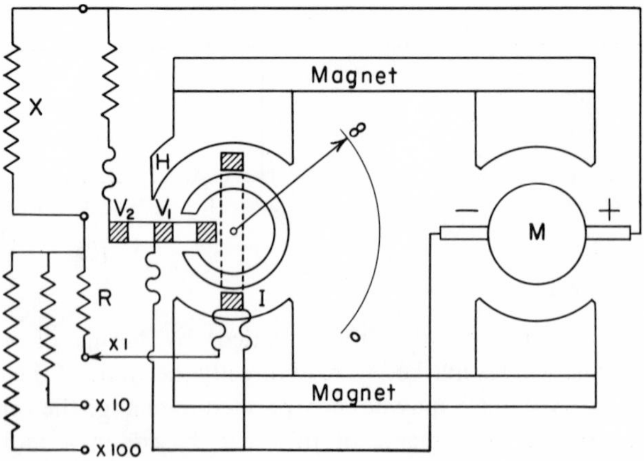

FIG. 24.

known line of "Meggers" designed by Evershed and built in this country by James G. Biddle. The essential parts of the Megger are shown in Fig. 24. The current coil *I* is similar to that of the usual moving-coil instrument. The voltage coil V_1 threads over the annular core. Since it is in a weak field when the instrument pointer is at the infinity position, it exerts very little torque. The torque which it exerts increases as it moves into a stronger field and reaches a maximum where it is under the pole face and the pointer is at the zero end of the resistance scale. To modify further the torque in the voltage circuit, a second voltage coil V_2 is used. This also is in a field which increases rapidly as the pointer position moves toward the zero end of the scale and V_2 moves toward and finally threads around the extension H of the pole piece. The combined action of the voltage coils V_1 and V_2 can be considered as though the coils constituted a spring of variable stiffness, being very stiff near the zero end of the scale where the current is large in the current coil, and very weak near the infinity end of the scale where the current through the unknown resistor X is small. In effect this compresses the low-resistance portion of the scale and opens up the high-resistance end. The effective range of the instrument is controlled by the resistance R in series with the current coil. The test voltage (usually 500, 1000, or 2500 volts) is generated by the magneto M, which in many portable models is driven by means of a hand-operated crank. In some models a centrifugal clutch which slips at a predetermined shaft speed is incorporated in the magneto-drive mechanism. This permits a constant voltage to be applied to the insulation under test. This voltage provides a test of the strength of low-voltage insulation as well as a measure of its resistance, since it is sufficient to cause breakdown at faults. Such breakdowns are indicated by the sudden motion of the pointer off scale at the zero end. Since the same magnet system supplies the fields for both the instrument and the magneto, and since the voltage and current coils move in a common field, the instrument indications are independent of the magnet strength.[43]

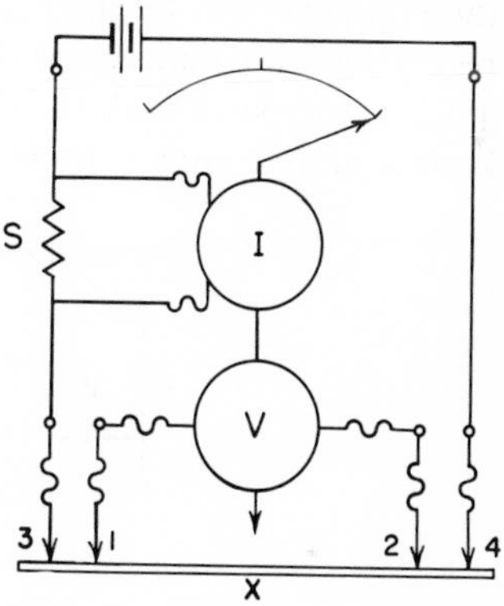

FIG. 25.

The same principle may be used in the measurement of low resistance. The Evershed Ducter ohmmeter is shown schematically in Fig. 25. Here the current coil I is connected across a shunt which carries the current through the unknown X, and the voltage coil V carries a current proportional to the voltage drop between the potential terminals 1 and 2. The instrument deflection indicates the four-terminal resistance between

[43] See Brooks, *Electrical World*, **85**, 973 (1925) for accuracy tests on Meggers.

the potential points 1 and 2 for current between the current terminals 3 and 4. The shunt S may be changed to obtain different ranges of resistance.

DIRECT-CURRENT VACUUM-TUBE VOLTMETERS.[44] These instruments can be adapted to use as ohmmeters over a wide range of resistance. The operation of such a voltmeter as an ohmmeter depends on the fact that the resistance of the measuring circuit of the instrument is very high (perhaps many megohms), the current required for operation of the deflecting element being supplied by an auxiliary source of voltage. Thus, the voltmeter can be used to compare the voltage drop across a known resistance with that across the unknown. For ohmmeter ranges which are low compared with the effective input resistance of the voltmeter, the known and unknown resistances can be connected in series to form a

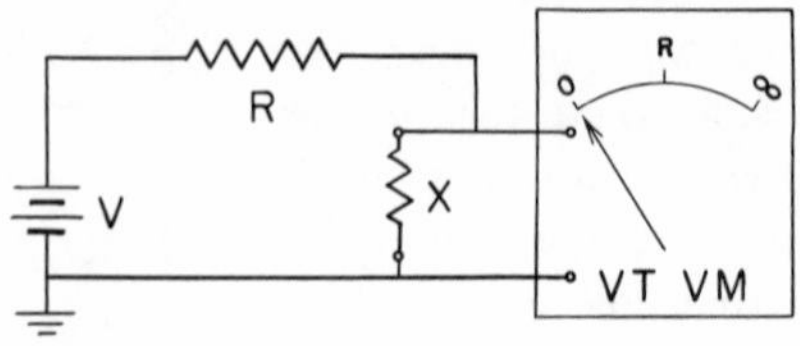

FIG. 26.

voltage divider. This connection is shown in Fig. 26. The scale may be made direct-reading in ohms by the following procedure: Initially, with the X-terminal open, the voltmeter sensitivity is adjusted to read full scale, i.e. to read the supply voltage V. Then, for any value of X, the voltage divides between R and X in proportion to their resistances. The voltmeter indication will be full scale when $X = \infty$, half-scale when $X = R$, and zero when $X = 0$. For a particular value of R, and with a value of V for which full-scale sensitivity is within the adjustment range of the voltmeter, the scale may be marked to read the resistance X directly in ohms. Such a scale will, of course, be open at its zero end and compressed at its high end. Its useful range may be as much as 10 to 20 times the value of the reference resistance. Multirange ohmmeters may be constructed by the use of a number of values of R, controlled by a selector switch. If these reference resistors are 10, 100, 1000 ohms respectively, for example, the midpoint of the corresponding ohmmeter ranges will be 10, 100, and 1000 ohms, and a single marked scale can be used with multiplying factors $x1$, $x10$, and $x100$. For the measurement of resistances which are high compared with the input resistance of the voltmeter, the input resistance of the voltmeter can itself serve as the

[44] See Chapter 10.

reference resistance, as shown in Fig. 27. If the supply voltage, across the unknown resistor X and the voltmeter of resistance R in series, is E volts and the reading of the voltmeter is V volts, the resistance X is given by the formula

$$X = R\left[\frac{E - V}{V}\right]$$

When $X \gg R$, we have approximately

$$X = R\frac{E}{V}$$

In this way the range of resistance measurements can be extended upwards to very high values, 10^4 or 10^5 megohms, by using a large supply voltage.

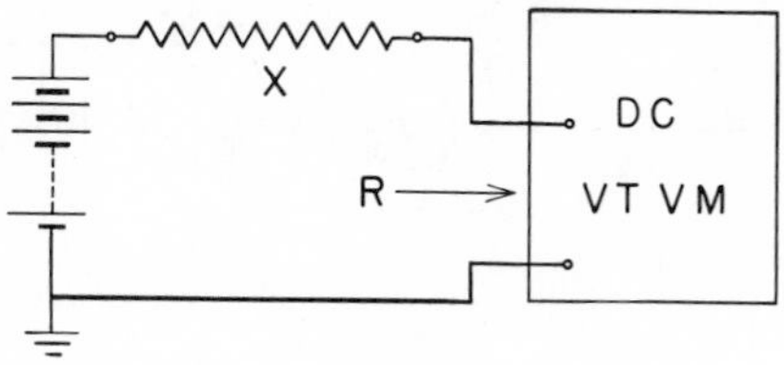

FIG. 27.

For example, if the input resistance R of the voltmeter is 10 megohms, E is 500 volts, and V is 0.5 volt, $X = 10^4$ megohms. In the measurement of very high resistances it is usually necessary to provide shielding[45] in order to avoid errors resulting from leakage currents over imperfect insulation.

A circuit operating on vacuum-tube voltmeter principles and designed for the measurement of extremely high resistances, up to 10^{17} ohms, has been described by Rose[46] and is shown schematically in Fig. 28. An electrometer tube (FP–54), designed especially for a very low grid current and a very high input resistance,[47] was used together with a very high reference resistance R which was determined stepwise in terms of lower resistances in the same circuit.

Direct-Current Voltmeter. A permanent-magnet moving-coil voltmeter of high resistance may be used for the approximate measurement of moderately high resistances. If the voltmeter reads a voltage V_1 when connected directly across the d-c supply, and a voltage V_2 when the

[45] See discussion of shielding below.

[46] Rose, *Rev. Sci. Inst.*, **2**, 810 (1931).

[47] See discussion of electrometer tube and of slide-back voltmeters in Chapter 10.

unknown resistance X is connected in series with it, the value of X is given by the formula

$$X = R_V \frac{(V_1 - V_2)}{V_2}$$

where R_V is the resistance of the voltmeter. This method will serve for the rough determination of resistances from a few hundred ohms to a megohm or more. If this method is used to measure a resistor which is grounded at one end, the grounded side of the d-c supply voltage must be connected to the ground terminal of the resistor.

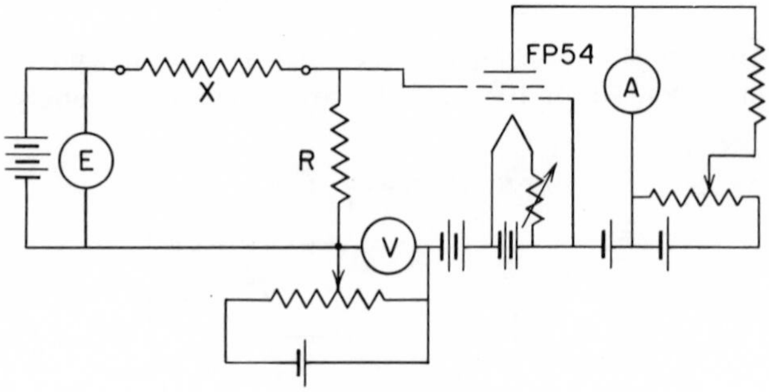

FIG. 28.

Galvanometer Method for Measuring High Resistance. A sensitive galvanometer can be used to measure the resistance of high resistors or of insulation up to 10^{10} ohms or more by a deflection method, deflections being compared when the galvanometer is carrying the current through a known resistor, and through the unknown in turn, at the same applied voltage. The essential features of the method are shown schematically in Fig. 29, together with the precautions that must be taken against errors resulting from leakage paths in parallel with the resistance being measured. The galvanometer should have a high current sensitivity, and it will be assumed that its deflection is proportional to its current, or that the relation connecting its current and deflection is known. If the resistance X is very high it may be necessary to use a rather high supply voltage (perhaps up to 500 volts) in order to obtain suitable deflections.

The unknown resistance X is shown equipped with a guard ring around the measuring electrode. This guard ring, maintained at a potential approximately equal to that of the measuring electrode, C, intercepts the current which flows across the surface of the test specimen from the high-voltage electrode and by-passes it around the galvanometer so that it is not part of the measured current. The remainder of the guard circuit, shown as a dotted line, is a metal enclosure or plate interposed between the measuring circuit and its surroundings. It is shown connected to the terminal of the supply battery which goes directly to the galvanometer and is therefore maintained at the same potential as the galvanometer. The entire measuring circuit within the guarded area must be adequately insulated from the guard so that there will be no appreciable leakage current between it and the measuring circuit. Since the point A is at the guard potential its insulation need be only moderate. Leakage at B affects the multiplying factor of the galvanometer shunt, since it acts as

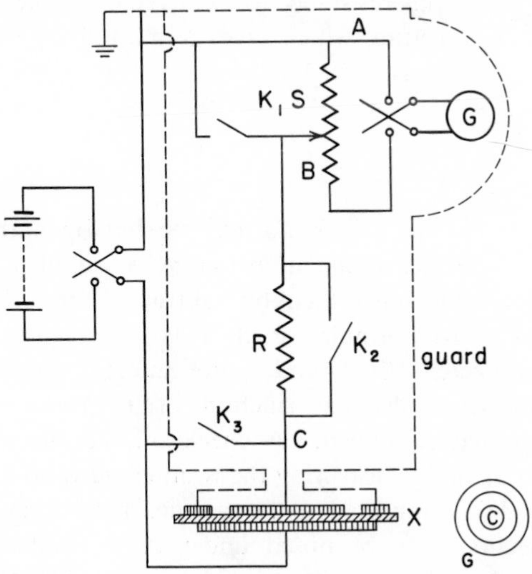

FIG. 29.

a parallel current path. However, for any reasonable value of shunt resistance the insulation at B need not be greater than, say, 10 megohms. Leakage at C acts as a shunt on the calibrating resistance R, and the insulation between measuring circuit and guard should be at least 100 times as great as the calibrating resistance R if 1% accuracy is to be realized in the measurement. If the guard circuit is to be grounded as shown in Fig. 29, the supply battery should be well enough insulated from ground that its leakage is not excessive. An Ayrton universal shunt[48] is shown connected to the galvanometer to control the magnitudes of the deflections by known factors.

In operation the test voltage is applied to the specimen X. (If the capacitance of X is large, the switch K_1 should be closed when the circuit is energized in order to protect the galvanometer from the initial charging current.) When K_1 is opened the galvanometer deflection d_1 times the

[48] See Chapter 3.

shunt multiplying factor f_1 represents the measured current through X. The switch K_2 may be closed when the reading is taken so that the calibrating resistance R is not included in the measurement. However, in preliminary adjustments the switch K_2 should be left open, as the resistance R affords some protection to the galvanometer against excessive current in case the insulation of X fails. To calibrate the galvanometer, the switch K_2 is opened and K_3 is closed, so that the calibrating resistor replaces X in the circuit. The galvanometer deflection is adjusted for this resistance to a convenient value d_2 with a shunt setting which gives a multiplying factor f_2. The resistance X is then

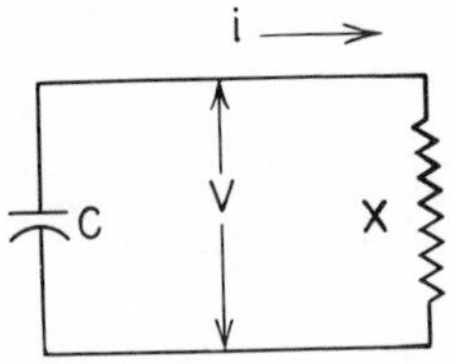

FIG. 30.

$$X = R \cdot \frac{d_1 f_1}{d_2 f_2}$$

The switch K_2 may be left open throughout the measurement so that R is included in the circuit at all times. Its value must then be subtracted from the value of X computed by the above formula, or, if X is much greater than R, its effect may be neglected. If f_1 and f_2 are integral powers of 10, and R is a megohm or a decimal fraction of 1 megohm, the computations are somewhat simplified. A check on the effectiveness of the shielding may be made by measuring the residual galvanometer deflection with the lead to X disconnected at the guarded measuring electrode. A *momentary* deflection may be noted under these conditions when the circuit is energized as the capacitance of the guarded system is charged. A sustained deflection indicates improper shielding or faulty insulation in the shielded circuit.

Resistance by Loss of Charge. In the deflection method just described, a limit is reached when the insulation resistance is so high that the galvanometer deflections are no longer adequate. Since the upper limit of current sensitivity in the d-c galvanometer is of the order of 10^{-9} amp/mm, and since it is usually unsafe or inconvenient to work with batteries above about 500 volts, the practical limit of the method is reached with resistances of 10^{11} to 10^{12} ohms. For higher values of resistance the rate at which charge is lost from a capacitor through the unknown resistance may be used as a convenient measure of its value. This method of resistance measurement may be seen from the following considerations. In Fig. 30, let C be a known capacitance and X be the unknown resistance. The current at any time is

$$i = \frac{-dQ}{dt} = -C\frac{dV}{dt}$$

But by Ohm's law $i = V/X$, where V is the potential difference between the terminals of the capacitor, and hence impressed across the resistor X. Then

$$\frac{V}{X} = -C\frac{dV}{dt} \quad \text{or} \quad \frac{V}{X} + C\frac{dV}{dt} = 0$$

The solution of this equation is

$$V = V_0\varepsilon^{-t/CX}$$

where V_0 is the initial voltage to which the capacitor was charged. Then

$$X = \frac{t}{C \log_\varepsilon \dfrac{V_0}{V}}$$

t being the time of discharge in seconds. If C were a perfect capacitor, X would be only the external resistance connected across its terminals. In general, however, a leakage resistance is associated with the capacitor which would act as a current path in parallel with any external resistor. Hence the leakage resistance of the capacitor would have to be determined separately as a correction factor. As a matter of fact, this method is most useful as applied to the determination of the leakage resistance of imperfect capacitors. A number of methods have been used to measure the relation between voltage[49] and time. A convenient method of measuring the change in voltage with time is to use an electrostatic voltmeter[50] or (for higher sensitivity) a quadrant electrometer.[50] The insulation resistance of the voltmeter must be considered a parallel leakage path, and, if the capacitance of the voltmeter is an appreciable fraction of that of the circuit, allowance must be made for it and for its change with deflection.

A modification[51] of the loss-of-charge method is shown in Fig. 31. This is a null method in which the deflection of the detector (a quadrant electrometer)[52] is maintained at zero by balancing the rate at which charge would accumulate on its quadrants, as a result of the current in the unknown resistor X, by a current produced by continuously varying the capacitance C of a capacitor across which a constant voltage is impressed. The current i_r to the ungrounded quadrant of the electrometer is the resultant of the current, i_x, through the test resistance X, the charging current i_c of the capacitance C, and the leakage current i_y to

[49] See Laws, *Electrical Measurements*, p. 201, McGraw-Hill, 1938, for description of the use of a ballistic galvanometer for this measurement.

[50] See Chapter 10.

[51] Higgs, *J. Sci. Inst.*, **10**, 169 (1933).

[52] See electrometer, Chapter 10.

ground across the insulation of the ungrounded quadrant, the low-voltage electrode of C, and the shielded lead to X. We have then $i_r = i_x - i_y - i_c$. Now, if v is the potential of the ungrounded quadrant, this expression may be written as

$$i_r = \frac{V_1 - v}{X} - \frac{v}{Y} - (V_2 - v)\frac{\Delta C}{\Delta t}$$

where $\Delta C/\Delta t$ is the time rate of change of the capacitance C. Initially the switch S is closed, bringing both quadrants of the electrometer to ground potential and establishing the electrometer deflection corresponding to this condition. When S is opened, C is increased at a rate which is

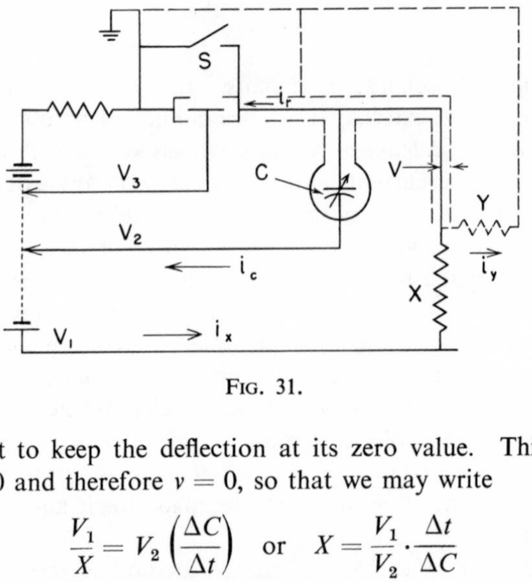

FIG. 31.

just sufficient to keep the deflection at its zero value. This procedure makes $i_r = 0$ and therefore $v = 0$, so that we may write

$$\frac{V_1}{X} = V_2\left(\frac{\Delta C}{\Delta t}\right) \quad \text{or} \quad X = \frac{V_1}{V_2}\cdot\frac{\Delta t}{\Delta C}$$

It is difficult in practice to keep the electrometer deflection at its null position by changing C at precisely the correct rate. The observer is much more likely to allow the electrometer deflection to move slightly upscale and then to return it to zero by a change in the rate of varying C, since it is only by a change in the deflection that the observer is informed that the rate at which he is changing C is incorrect. Let us suppose that, instead of maintaining the insulated quadrant at zero potential, it is maintained at a small positive potential v, but that the average value of its charging current is zero ($i_r = 0$) during the experiment. In this case we would have approximately

$$\left(\frac{V_1}{X} - \frac{v}{Y}\right) - V_2\left(\frac{\Delta C}{\Delta t}\right) = 0$$

If the error in the value of X which would result from neglecting the term v/Y is δ, we may write

$$\frac{V_1}{X} - \frac{v}{Y} = \frac{V_1}{X}(1 - \delta) \quad \text{or} \quad \delta = \frac{v}{V_1} \cdot \frac{X}{Y}$$

Expressed in per cent, this error would be $\eta = 100 \dfrac{v}{V_1} \cdot \dfrac{X}{Y}$. It will be seen that this error is dependent on the relative values of X and Y. It is therefore important to hold the deflection to zero (i.e. $v = 0$) very closely only if the resistance under test is comparable in magnitude to the insulation resistance of the ungrounded electrometer quadrant. This method

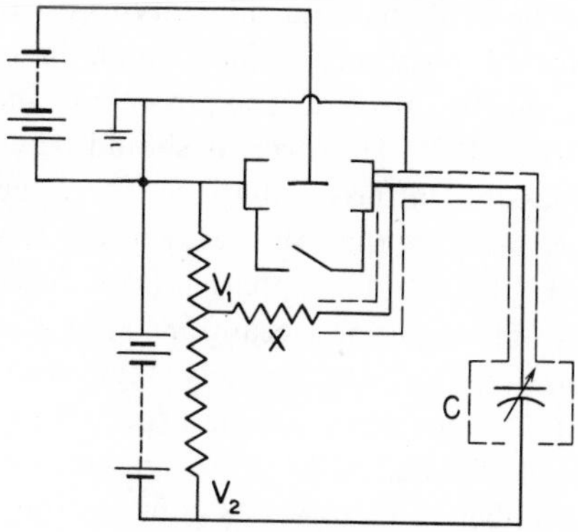

FIG. 32.

is capable of considerable precision for the measurement of high resistances, since the ratio V_1/V_2 and the change in capacitance ΔC of a calibrated air capacitor can be precisely determined. It should be noted that the determination of X does not depend on a precise voltage calibration of the electrometer.

A modification of the above method for measuring high resistances, by Dr. A. H. Scott of the National Bureau of Standards,[53] has proved to be very useful in the measurement of extremely high resistances which can be subjected to only a small voltage. In Scott's modification, shown in Fig. 32, a low voltage V_1 is impressed on the unknown X, and a shielded precision air capacitor C maintains the insulated quadrant of the electrometer at zero potential. The balance equation is the same as in the previous case, $X = \dfrac{V_1}{V_2}\left(\dfrac{\Delta t}{\Delta C}\right)$. The ratio V_1/V_2 can be precisely determined from the ratio of resistances in the voltage divider. The sensitivity

[53] Informally communicated.

of the method may be changed by altering the potential of the electrometer needle, or by connecting additional capacitance C' in parallel with the quadrants of the electrometer.

Comparison Methods

The comparison methods which will be discussed below are generally considered precision methods of measurement, and they involve the determination of resistances in terms of other resistances presumed to be known. With ordinary precautions the ratio of two resistances can be determined far more precisely than it is possible to measure a single resistance directly by any of the deflection methods described above. Such comparisons can be made without difficulty to 0.1 or 0.01% over a moderately wide range of resistance values; and, in cases where the utmost in refinements can be justified, it is possible to measure the ratio of resistances to a part in 10^7. However, it should be emphasized that, despite the precision possible in the comparison, the value of a resistance so measured *is no more accurate* than the value of the resistance in terms of which it is measured. It should be apparent from the earlier discussion of resistance coils that unless special precautions are taken the resistances of coils cannot be considered to be completely stable, and that no resistor which is exposed to the atmosphere can be expected to retain its value over an extended period of time. The actual amount by which its value varies depends on a number of factors: its construction; the conditions under which it is kept and used; and the value of the resistance itself, high resistances being less stable than low resistances. It may be stated in general that the measurement of a resistance to within 0.01% is very nearly impossible unless the resistance is determined either in terms of a sealed standard[54] which has a low drift with time or in terms of a resistor whose value has been very recently determined by comparison with such a standard. It should be remarked that the situation is much better with respect to the ratio of resistances, provided certain requirements are met. Two resistors having the same construction and approximately the same value, made from the same melt of alloy, and having the same history of laboratory use, may be expected generally to drift in about the same way with time, so that their ratio of resistances will probably be much more nearly constant with time than their individual values. Hence resistance apparatus which is designed to establish or maintain only a ratio of resistances can be expected to retain their ratio value considerably better

[54] See discussion above of standard resistors. In particular a group of Thomas-type resistance standards, which form a portion of the primary resistance standard of the United States, appear to have held their values to within 1 part in 10^6 over a 15-year period.

than individual resistors can maintain their constancy. Thus the calibration of a potentiometer, of a volt box, or of the ratio arms of a bridge generally remains usable over a longer period of time than the calibration of a decade resistance box.

The Potentiometer Method. This method of comparing four-terminal resistances is capable of high accuracy if a good potentiometer is used. If a standard resistor S is connected in series with the unknown X, as shown in Fig. 33, so that the current is the same in both resistors, the

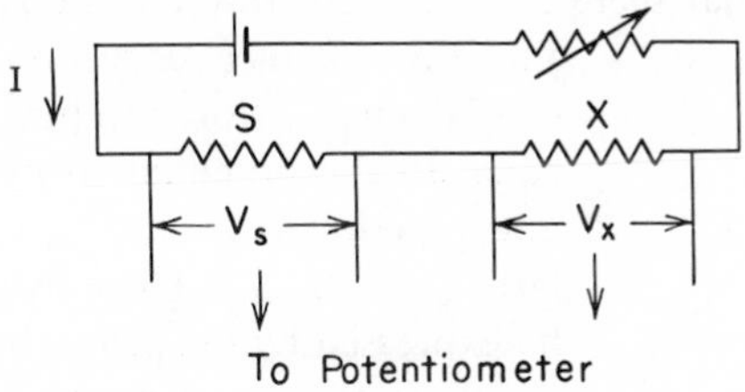

FIG. 33.

ratio of their voltage drops (as determined with a potentiometer) is the same as the ratio of their resistances. Hence

$$X = S\frac{V_x}{V_s}$$

where V_x is the balance reading of the potentiometer when connected to X, and V_s is the reading when connected to S. It is essential that the current I, through the resistors, and the potentiometer current be constant throughout the measurement. That I is constant may be verified by repeated measurements of the voltage drops, with S and X alternately connected to the potentiometer.

The potentiometer method of measuring resistance has an advantage over ordinary bridge methods in that the unknown resistance may be determined directly in terms of a suitable standard resistor rather than in terms of the resistance coils of a bridge arm. However, the potentiometer method is more difficult to use than a bridge method since it requires that two currents be held constant, whereas the balance of a bridge is independent of the current in its arms, except for heating effects. The potentiometer method is particularly well adapted to measurement of the four-terminal resistances of portions of networks, where connection to the unknown resistance can be made only through other resistors. Any resistance included in the potential leads of a four-terminal resistor does not affect the null balance of a potentiometer connected to it, except in so far as the sensitivity of balance may be reduced, or the damping of the galvanometer affected by the extra resistance in the galvanometer circuit.

The Wheatstone Bridge. This is one of the most widely used comparison methods for the measurement of resistance. The network shown in Fig. 34 was first described by Christie in 1833. However, it did not become widely known until Wheatstone called attention to Christie's work in 1843, and Wheatstone's name has been associated with the network in its subsequent general use. In applying this network to the comparison of resistances, one or more of the four resistors (A, B, X, S) is varied in value until no potential difference exists between the junction points 2 and 4, so that there is no current through the galvanometer G.

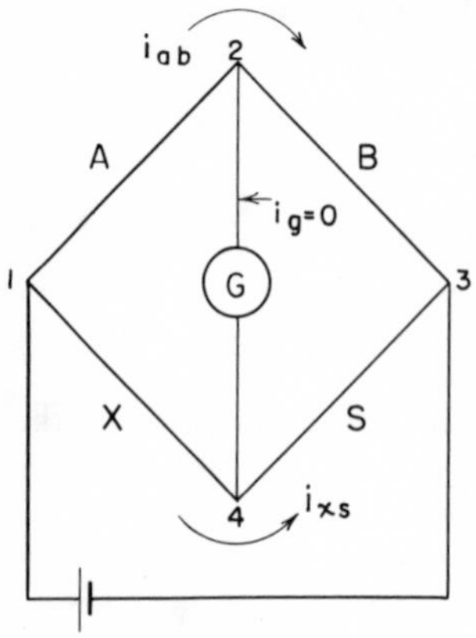

FIG. 34.

For this balance condition, the potential drop from junction 1 to junction 2 must be equal to the potential drop from junction 1 to junction 4, so that $i_{ab}A = i_{xs}X$. Similarly $i_{ab}B = i_{xs}S$. These two equalities may be expressed by the proportion $A/B = X/S$, which is the usual equation of balance of the Wheatstone bridge. Since this relation can equally well be expressed by $A/X = B/S$, it will be seen that, if the position of the battery and the galvanometer is interchanged and the bridge resistances are adjusted until no current flows in the galvanometer, the balance equation is the same as before, $A/B = X/S$. Thus we can connect the supply battery in either diagonal of the network and the galvanometer in the remaining diagonal without affecting the relation at balance between the resistances of the bridge arms.

Although, so far as the balance condition is concerned, it is immaterial into which bridge diagonal the galvanometer is connected, it may be advantageous in some cases to use a particular one of the alternative possibilities. Kotter[55] has stated a criterion by which it may be established which of the alternative connections gives the greater sensitivity in balancing the bridge: "Calculate the resistance of the bridge between each pair of opposite branch points with the battery and galvanometer circuits open. Compute the ratio or reciprocal ratio (whichever is less than unity) of these bridge resistances to the external resistance required for the particular damping at which it is desired to operate the galvanometer. Connect the galvanometer to the pair of branch points for which this ratio is nearer unity." The assumptions are made that: (1) the galvanometer will be used with a particular constant damping; (2) the

[55] Kotter, *NBS J. Research*, **40**, 401 (1948). Kotter's criterion is proved in this paper.

limitation on maximum power is the same for each bridge arm; and (3) sufficient voltage is applied to dissipate this limiting power in one bridge arm and no greater amount in any other arm. Whether the power rating of any bridge arm is exceeded for a particular connection and supply voltage must be determined by appropriate calculation. Indeed, the power dissipation in the resistors forming the bridge should always be examined for a new arrangement, since this may become the criterion for deciding the appropriate galvanometer connection, rather than the criterion of maximum sensitivity.

(*a*) SENSITIVITY. It is frequently desirable to know the galvanometer response to be expected in a bridge which is slightly unbalanced, so that a current flows in the galvanometer branch of the network. This may be used either for (1) selecting a galvanometer with which a given unbalance may be observed in a specified bridge arrangement; (2) determining the minimum unbalance which can be observed in the specified bridge with a given galvanometer; or (3) determining the deflection to be expected for a given unbalance. We will analyze the slightly unbalanced Wheatstone bridge, making use of Thévenin's[56] theorem and assuming that the resistance of the circuit in which the galvanometer operates is that which is required to damp it properly. Assuming that the bridge of Fig. 35(*a*) (p. 261) is balanced when the branch resistances are A, B, X, S, so that $A/B = X/S$, and that the unbalanced resistance is ΔX in the X-arm, we require the emf e which would appear in the galvanometer branch (across the cut) if this branch were opened. We will assume that the voltage impressed between terminals 1 and 3 is E. (If the battery branch of the network has negligible resistance this will be the battery voltage.) With the galvanometer branch open, the voltage drop between points 1 and 2 is

$$E_{12} = \frac{EA}{A + B}$$

Similarly

$$E_{14} = \frac{E(X + \Delta X)}{X + \Delta X + S}$$

Then the voltage difference between points 2 and 4 (across the cut) is

$$e = E_{14} - E_{12} = E\left(\frac{X + \Delta X}{X + \Delta X + S} - \frac{A}{A + B}\right)$$

and since

$$\frac{A}{A + B} = \frac{X}{X + S}$$

[56] See explanation of Thévenin's theorem in Chapter 6.

we have

$$e = \frac{EX}{X+S}\left(\frac{1+\dfrac{\Delta X}{X}}{1+\dfrac{\Delta X}{X+S}} - 1\right)$$

$$\approx \frac{EX}{X+S}\left[\left(1+\frac{\Delta X}{X}\right)\left(1-\frac{\Delta X}{X+S}+\frac{(\Delta X)^2}{(X+S)^2}\cdots\right)-1\right]$$

or

$$e \approx \frac{ES\,\Delta X}{(X+S)^2}$$

if the bridge is near balance, so that second- and higher-order terms in the power expansion may be neglected.

We will let $dX = \Delta X/X$ represent the proportional unbalance of the bridge, so that we may write

$$e = \frac{EXS\,dX}{(X+S)^2}$$

We will also let D be the voltage sensitivity of the galvanometer (i.e. its change in deflection in scale units per unit change in emf in the galvanometer circuit when the total resistance V, seen from the galvanometer terminals, is that required for the specified damping). The resistance W of the bridge, as seen from the galvanometer junction points 2–4, may be written, by inspection from the equivalent circuit diagram of Fig. 35(b), as

$$W = \frac{AB}{A+B} + \frac{XS}{X+S}$$

Case I. We will assume that $W < V$, so that a resistance U must be placed in series with the galvanometer in order that the total circuit resistance (seen from the galvanometer terminals) be $W + U = V$, as is required for the specified damping. Under these conditions the change in deflection of the galvanometer produced by the emf e (i.e. by the bridge unbalance) may be written as

$$d\theta = \frac{DEXS\,dX}{(X+S)^2}$$

If we represent the combined galvanometer-bridge sensitivity by $M = d\theta/dX$, we may write

$$M = \frac{DEXS}{(X+S)^2}$$

or, since

$$\frac{XS}{(X+S)^2} = \frac{AB}{(A+B)^2}$$

we may also write

$$M = \frac{DEAB}{(A+B)^2}$$

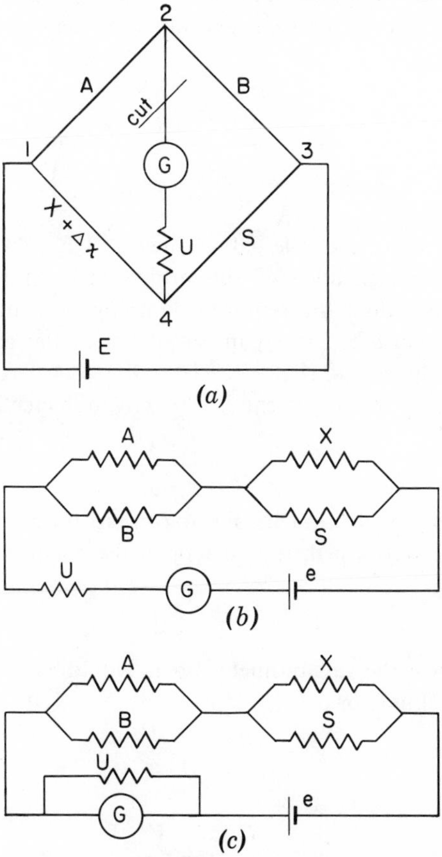

FIG. 35.

In many cases, particularly where the limit of sensitivity is approached, it is advantageous to observe the change in deflection produced by a reversal[57] of the emf of unbalance, thus doubling the effective sensitivity

[57] This reversal may be obtained by reversing either the battery or the galvanometer connections to the bridge.

of the bridge-galvanometer combination. Here the sensitivity has been defined by Wenner[58] as

$$N = \frac{2DEXS}{(X + S)^2} = \frac{2DEAB}{(A + B)^2}$$

It should be noted that, if the current in the galvanometer branch of the network is required under the conditions stated above, it can easily be obtained by dividing the emf of unbalance which appears in the galvanometer branch by the total resistance of the circuit as seen at the galvanometer, thus:

$$I_g = \frac{e}{V + G} = \frac{\dfrac{ES\,\Delta X}{(S + X)^2}}{\left(G + U + \dfrac{AB}{A + B} + \dfrac{XS}{X + S}\right)}$$

where G is the resistance of the galvanometer.

Case II. If the resistance of the bridge between the galvanometer terminals is greater than the required damping resistance (i.e. $W > V$), the resistance U must be placed in parallel with the galvanometer [see Fig. 35(*c*)] and adjusted so that $UW/(U + W) = V$. As before, the emf of unbalance which would appear in the galvanometer branch would be

$$e = \frac{EXS\,dX}{(X + S)^2}$$

if both the galvanometer and its shunt U were open circuited. If only the galvanometer were open, the current in the shunt would be

$$i_u = \frac{e}{U + W}$$

while the emf across the galvanometer break would be equal to the voltage drop across the shunt, or

$$e' = Ui_u = \frac{eU}{U + W}$$

But

$$\frac{U}{U + W} = \frac{V}{W}$$

so that

$$\frac{e'}{e} = \frac{V}{W}$$

i.e. the emf available for deflecting the galvanometer is reduced in the ratio V/W by connecting the shunt across its terminals. Consequently

[58] Wenner, *NBS J. Research*, **25**, 229 (1940).

the combined bridge-galvanometer sensitivity is reduced by the same factor, so that under these conditions

$$M = \frac{DEXS}{(X + S)^2} \cdot \frac{V}{W} = \frac{DEAB}{(A + B)^2} \cdot \frac{V}{W}$$

and the corresponding sensitivity for a reversal of voltage is

$$N = \frac{2DEXS}{(X + S)^2} \cdot \frac{V}{W} = \frac{2DEAB}{(A + B)^2} \cdot \frac{V}{W}$$

It should be noted that although the above sensitivity equations are derived as first-order approximations they are, for the purpose of computing sensitivity, very nearly exact since, under the conditions in which they will normally be used, the second- and higher-order terms which have been neglected are vanishingly small.

The above sensitivities are stated without reference to the current-carrying capacity of the resistors which make up the bridge arms. We should therefore define a *permissible sensitivity* in terms of the maximum voltage which may be used without raising the temperature of any of the bridge elements sufficiently to change its resistance by more than an amount which is permissible or which corresponds to the final precision desired in the measurement. If we know the power which may be dissipated in each of the resistors, we may then state the maximum voltage which can be impressed on it. An examination will show for any particular bridge arrangement which branch will arrive at its maximum permissible voltage first with increasing bridge voltage. The corresponding value of bridge voltage E_m is then the maximum which can be used, and the permissible sensitivity may be expressed in terms of it. However, the expression may be somewhat simplified in any particular case. For example, we will suppose that for a particular arrangement the X-arm is the one which limits the bridge voltage and that the maximum voltage which may be impressed on it is E_x. Then

$$E_m = E_x \frac{(X + S)}{X}$$

When this value of E_m is substituted into our sensitivity equations we have

$$M = \frac{DE_x \cdot S}{(X + S)} \cdot \frac{V}{W} \quad \text{and} \quad N = \frac{2DE_x \cdot S}{(X + S)} \cdot \frac{V}{W}$$

Similar expressions can be written for any of the branches which may limit the power dissipation in the bridge. It should be noted that in the above formulas the case was illustrated in which the galvanometer was shunted. If the circuit resistance is adjusted with a resistance in series with the galvanometer, the factor V/W must be considered unity for our purposes.

In connection with the Kelvin bridge, which will be discussed later,[59] the question of sensitivity may also arise. This bridge circuit, shown in Fig. 36(*a*), can be transformed into an equivalent Wheatstone network [Fig. 36(*b*)] by Kennelly's[60] Δ–Y transformation; i.e. by considering the

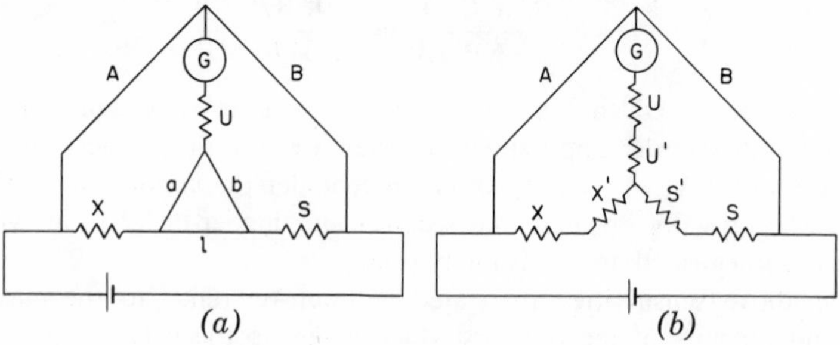

FIG. 36.

resistors *a*, *b*, *l*, which form a Δ in Fig. 36(*a*), as replaced by the equivalent Y-connected elements X', S', U', in accordance with the relations

$$X' = \frac{la}{(l + a + b)}; \quad S' = \frac{lb}{(l + a + b)}; \quad U' = \frac{ab}{(l + a + b)}$$

and the sensitivity equations may be immediately written in terms of those which have been developed above for the Wheatstone bridge by substituting $(X + X')$ for X, and $(S + S')$ for S.

(*b*) GENERAL-PURPOSE WHEATSTONE BRIDGES. These are frequently made so that any one of several resistors can be selected for use in the ratio arms A and B. In the best grade of commercial instruments, resistance coils are inserted in the ratio arms by means of plugs. Since the contact resistance in the plug adds to the resistance in the arm, and since any variation in the contact resistance contributes to uncertainty in the ratio, it is desirable that these resistances be large. However, high resistances are affected by humidity to a greater extent than low resistances and are less stable, so that they are accurately known for a shorter time after calibration. It is therefore advisable to use intermediate values of resistance, 10 and 100 ohms, wherever possible in the ratio arms, although 1-ohm and 1000-ohm coils are often provided in order that the bridge may be used to measure a greater range of values of resistance. The resistor to be measured is connected in the X-arm by means of binding

[59] See p. 282.

[60] Kennelly, *Electrical World*, **34**, 282 (1899).

posts, and the remaining arm, S, is an adjustable resistance which can be continuously varied by means of decade switches over a wide range. The same conditions govern the choice of resistance here that control the selection of resistances in the ratio arms, with the additional consideration that there will be several contact resistances in series in this arm from the decade switches. Since the combined effects of these contacts cannot be expected, in general, to be definite to better than about 0.01 ohm, steps of less than 0.1 ohm in the adjustable resistance are not usually provided, but somewhat closer estimations of the balance point may be made by interpolation from galvanometer deflections at successive switch positions. Measurements to 0.1 % can be made, without applying corrections to the readings, with many moderately priced bridges. If measurements are required to 0.01 %, a number of precautions must be observed. The bridge must be calibrated so that corrections may be applied to the settings of the various arms, and the bridge must be maintained within a few degrees of the temperature of calibration. Because of the change in value of resistance coils with humidity it may be necessary to make frequent calibrations of the bridge or to maintain it in constant-humidity surroundings. In the latter case the constancy of the bridge may be checked occasionally at selected points by measuring the resistance of standard resistors. Where possible, ratio coils below 10 ohms should be avoided because of the possibility of error from contact resistances. Also it is well not to use in either the ratio or the adjustable arms resistances much in excess of 1000 ohms, since high resistances are inherently less stable than low. It follows that for precision measurements (to 0.01 %) the Wheatstone bridge is best adapted to measurements of resistance in the range between 10 and 10^4 ohms.

It will often occur that spurious or parasitic emf's, such as those resulting from thermoelectric effects, will be present in the measuring circuit and must be taken into account since such emf's may be so located that they affect the galvanometer in the same fashion as an emf of unbalance in the bridge. A simple method of procedure which is usually effective in eliminating parasitic emf's of constant magnitude from consideration in the balance is operation from a *false zero*. If the battery key is left open and the galvanometer key is closed, the galvanometer will take up an equilibrium position under the action of the parasitic emf's alone with the emf of unbalance absent. If the bridge balance is adjusted so that, with the battery key closed, the galvanometer is brought to this same deflection (or false zero), the effect of any constant parasitic emf is eliminated from the balance. Where it is possible, a better procedure is to reverse the battery connections to the bridge through a quick-acting reversing switch or key and to adjust the balance until no change in galvanometer deflection can be observed on reversal. By this means the response to the emf of unbalance is doubled since it is applied to the galvanometer first in one direction and then the other by the successive reversals, whereas the effect of the constant parasitic emf is unchanged by the reversal. The sensitivity of the bridge is therefore effectively doubled. Of greater importance is the fact that any parasitic emf's which are present in the bridge as a result of current in its various branches are more effectively eliminated than by the "false zero" procedure described above. It should be noted that balance by battery reversal may not be convenient if an uncompensated inductance is present in one of the bridge arms.

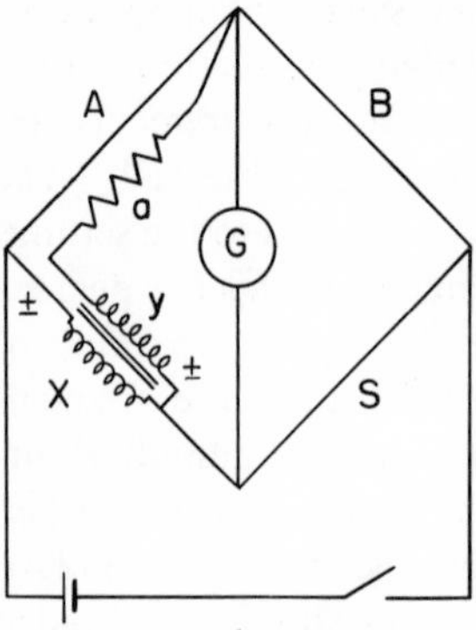

FIG. 37.

(*c*) INDUCTIVE RESISTANCES.[61] When the resistor measured has sufficient inductance that its time constant, L/R, is comparable with the response time of the galvanometer, the transient emf set up on closing the battery switch may be very annoying. The induced emf on opening the current circuit may be equally inconvenient. The galvanometer key may, of course, be left open until the initial transient has died away and may be reopened before the battery connection is opened, but it may well be that the observer cannot afford this loss of time, e.g. if a rapidly changing resistance of a machine winding is being measured during a heating run. When the inductive effect is not large it is often possible to compensate it by using an adjustable mutual inductor whose primary is placed in series with the supply battery and whose secondary is in the galvanometer branch of the bridge. It is of interest to note in this connection that, where an inductive coupling exists between the bridge and a fluctuating field from some external source, the inductive effects may sometimes be compensated by connecting a small inductor in the galvanometer branch of the circuit and so orienting it with respect to the external field that the emf induced in it neutralizes that resulting from the coupling between the bridge circuit and the field. When measuring the resistance of a transformer winding, compensation may be secured by the compensating circuit shown in Fig. 37, if an idle winding is available on the transformer. If the resistance (a) in the compensating circuit is adjusted to satisfy the relation $a = AN_y/N_x$, where N_y and N_x are the number of turns in y and x respectively, the emf induced by the changing flux in the transformer

[61] Some of the remarks made in this paragraph apply generally to the measurement of inductive resistors, whether or not the Wheatstone bridge method is used.

core (common to x and y) will not affect the galvanometer. The adjustment of S or B to secure bridge balance can then proceed without waiting for the current to become constant. The presence of the compensating circuit may reduce the sensitivity of the galvanometer somewhat, or may affect the damping, but will not affect the value of the final resistance balance even if a is not adjusted for perfect compensation.

(*d*) THE SLIDE-WIRE BRIDGE. A very simple and moderately accurate form of Wheatstone bridge can be made up by using a slide wire for the ratio arms. The slide wire may consist of a uniform wire stretched beside a linear scale (e.g. a meter scale divided into millimeters) or wound on a graduated drum. Such an arrangement is shown schematically in Fig.

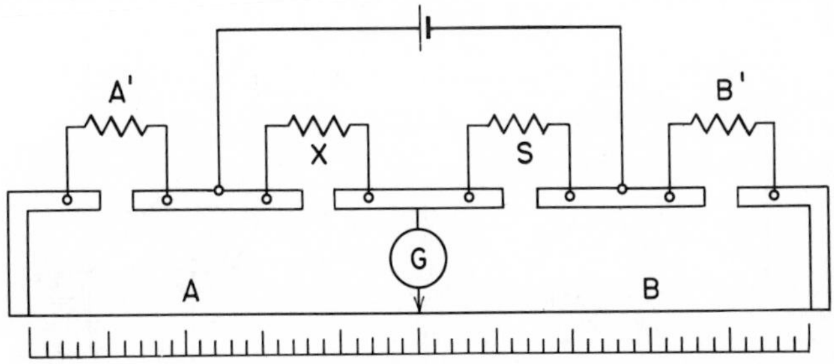

FIG. 38.

38. It is intended that the connectors between the various bridge arms be of low resistance (e.g. copper straps). In the simple slide-wire bridge the resistors A' and B' are replaced by links of very low resistance. In this case (if we suppose that the slide wire has N equal divisions and the balance position of the slider is A divisions from the left end) we have

$$X = S\frac{A}{N-A}$$

The accuracy of balance is greatest with the slider near the center of the slide wire (i.e. with X nearly equal to S) and may be improved in this case by taking the mean of two values of X, with X and S interchanged between the readings. The scale of the slide wire may be made more open by using extension coils at A' and B'; and, by proper choice of values for the extension coils, the total range of the slide wire may be made some definite small percentage of the ratio. In this way a convenient limit bridge may be made up for sorting resistors which are required to be equal within a specified tolerance. Resistors A' and B' are equal and are of such a value that a convenient portion of the slide wire represents the limits of the tolerance in per cent or proportional parts. With a resistor of the correct value inserted in S the resistors to be sorted can be placed in succession in the *X*-arm and their departure from equality with *S* measured by the slider reading at balance.

(*e*) THE MEGOHM BRIDGE. Use of the Wheatstone network has been extended to the measurement of insulation resistance and of other very high values of resistance by replacing the galvanometer by a suitable vacuum-tube voltmeter. If the voltage of unbalance is impressed between the grid and filament of a triode in a suitable circuit,[62] a sensitive detector

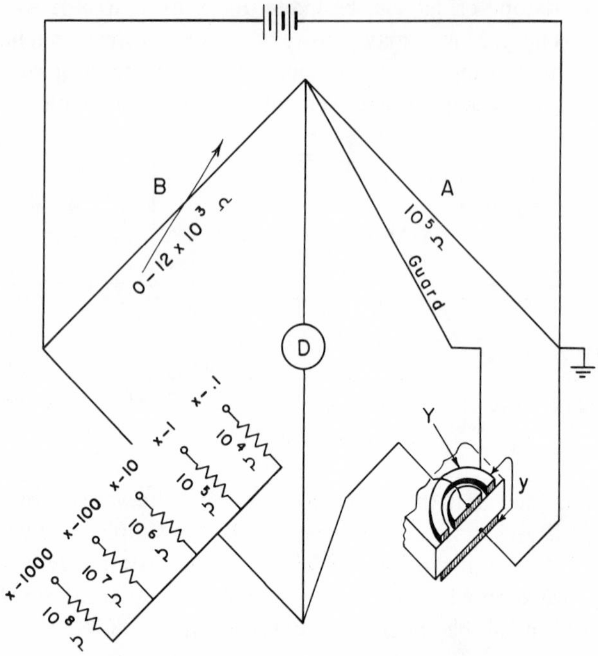

FIG. 39. General Radio megohm bridge.

is formed in which the voltage of unbalance of the bridge is used to produce a deflection in a microammeter supplied by a separate source of power; i.e. the unbalance voltage is in a control circuit and no appreciable power is drawn from the bridge. In such bridges care must be taken to guard the high-resistance arm so that surface leakage across insulation will not affect the balance point. Such a shielding connection for the measurement of insulation resistance is shown in Fig. 39. It will be seen that the guarded electrode *X* is in the measuring circuit but that the guard ring *Y* is maintained at an equal potential by connection to the opposite end of the detector diagonal of the bridge. Leakage current *y* across the surface of the insulation is thus by-passed around the detector and does

[62] See Chapter 10 for discussion of such circuits.

not appreciably affect the measurement. The leakage resistance does, of course, shunt the arm A of the bridge but is usually so high as not to affect it appreciably. The circuit shown in the figure is that of the General Radio Megohm bridge. A circuit arrangement (omitted from the diagram for simplification) is also available for charging the capacitance of the unknown resistor; and the ground, shown connected to one side of the unknown, may be alternatively connected to the guard (i.e. the junction of A and B). Resistors A and B and the three lower values of the third arm (10^4, 10^5, 10^6 ohms) are wire wound. The two higher values (10^7, 10^8 ohms) are not wire wound and are less stable than the lower values. They may be occasionally connected in place of the unknown and checked against the wire-wound megohm. In these checks, balance is obtained in the usual way, using the adjustable arm B, and the values of these resistances are read directly from the dial setting of B. The lower arms may be checked by using a calibrated megohm box connected in place of the unknown. Bridge voltages are 90 and 500 volts respectively in two models of this bridge, and the upper limit of measurement is about 10^{12} ohms.

(*f*) LOOP TESTS. Special Wheatstone bridge circuits serve for the location of ground or short-circuit faults in telephone cables. The Murray and the Varley test loops are used to locate the position of such faults and will serve to illustrate the procedures in fault location. The Murray test loop, shown in Fig. 40, consists of a good line connected (by means of a low-resistance jumper) to the faulty line at the end remote from the operator. A and B are the ratio arms of the bridge and may consist of step-resistors or a slide wire. In either the ground test (*a*) or the short-circuit test (*b*) the fault is located in the battery branch of the bridge circuit so that its resistance does not enter into the measurement. Of course, if the resistance to ground or the resistance between faulty lines is large, it may reduce the sensitivity of the test. The bridge is balanced by adjustment of the ratio A/B until the galvanometer indicates zero deflection. At balance

$$\frac{A}{B} = \frac{R}{X} \quad \text{or} \quad \frac{A+B}{B} = \frac{R+X}{X}$$

Then

$$\frac{B}{A+B} = \frac{X}{R+X} = \frac{X}{2r}$$

where r is the resistance of a single good line. If the resistance of the line is known from its length, cross section, and temperature, the distance of the fault from the operator's position may be determined from r and the measured value of X, the resistance of the line between the operator and the fault. The Varley loop test differs from that of Murray in that provision is made for measuring the total loop resistance, with the faulty line included in the loop. The bridge arrangement is shown in Fig. 41. In this loop test the ratio arms A and B are fixed, and the bridge is balanced by adjustment of a resistor Y which is in series with the lower-resistance

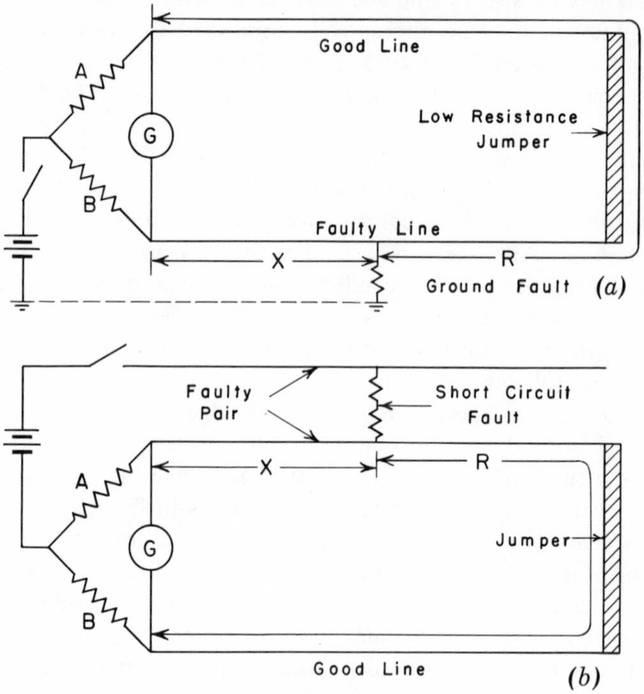

FIG. 40.

section of the loop. With the selector switch in position n for either the ground test or the short-circuit test, we have

$$\frac{A}{B} = \frac{R}{X + Y} \quad \text{or} \quad \frac{A + B}{B} = \frac{R + X + Y}{X + Y}$$

Then

$$X + Y = \frac{B(R + X + Y)}{A + B}$$

or

$$X = \frac{B(R + X + Y) - Y(A + B)}{A + B} = \frac{B(R + X) - AY}{A + B}$$

Now A, B, Y are known, and $(R + X)$ may be measured by rebalancing the bridge with the selector switch on position m. For this connection the balance condition is $A/B = (X + R)/Y'$, where Y' is the resistance of the adjustable arm at the new balance. The measured value of the loop resistance $(R + X)$, together with the computed resistance X to the fault, is then used to determine the distance to the fault.

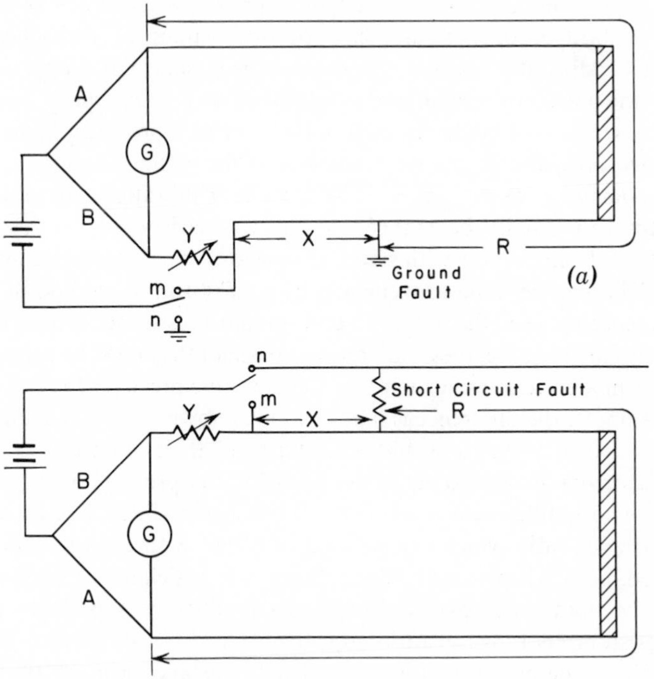

FIG. 41.

(*g*) SUBSTITUTION METHOD. This is necessary for bridge measurements of the highest precision. In using this procedure the unknown resistor, and a known standard resistor having approximately the same resistance, are measured in turn. If these resistances are not very different, the ratio arms of the bridge need not be disturbed and only a small change need be made in the adjustable arm. In consequence, the exact values of the ratio arms and of the undisturbed portion of the adjustable arm need not be known. Only the change in the adjustable arm is of significance in determining the difference between the known and unknown resistance. Thus, if the two resistors differ in value by 0.1% and if this difference is determined to 1%, the unknown is determined in terms of the standard to within 10 parts in a million. Contact resistances must, of course, be sufficiently constant that the bridge settings can be repeated to the desired precision. In order that the bridge may be used in this way without calibration it is essential that the standard and unknown be nearly equal. Since standard resistors are usually available only in a limited number of values (generally decimal multiples or submultiples of an ohm) the substitution method is not applicable for general resistance measurements. Of course the method can be used to improve the accuracy of an uncalibrated bridge for measurements of odd values of resistance if a calibrated, adjustable decade resistance box is set to the approximate value of the unknown resistor and substituted for it. Obviously, however, the unknown cannot be determined in this way to a precision higher than the known precision of the reference box at the setting used.

Direct-Reading Ratio Set.[63] The precise calibration of resistance apparatus can usually be reduced to the comparison of the resistance elements of the apparatus with standard resistors having the same nominal value. This can be done conveniently by a substitution method in which the difference between the unknown and standard resistance is determined. If, as is usually the case, these differences are small they need be determined with only moderate accuracy in order to determine precisely the unknown. If, for example, the difference is 0.01% and is known to 1%, the unknown is determined to 1 part in a million in terms of the standard.

The direct-reading ratio set is designed for the precise comparison of resistors whose differences are small. It consists essentially of an adjustable resistance ratio which can be used, together with the resistors to be compared, as a Wheatstone bridge. Since it is anticipated that the ratio set will be used only to measure the small differences between nearly equal resistors, its range of ratio adjustment need not be great. The set which will be described consists of a fixed resistance arm of 100 ohms and an adjustable arm whose resistance may be varied by 0.001-ohm steps from a minimum of 99.445 ohms to a maximum of 100.555 ohms in three decades. With all dials at their midposition the variable arm has a resistance of 100 ohms, and changes from this value represent 0.1, 0.01, and 0.001% for the three dials respectively. Thus the range of ratio adjustment extends from $\frac{1}{2}$% below to $\frac{1}{2}$% above unity. The direct-reading ratio set, together with a suitable selection of standard resistors, can be used as a Wheatstone bridge which will meet most laboratory needs for very precise resistance measurements.

(*a*) CONSTRUCTION. Before discussing the application of the direct-reading ratio set to measurement problems we will discuss its construction. It will be evident that the ratio adjustment cannot be made simply by

[63] The following discussion is largely taken from Precision Resistors and Their Measurement, *NBS Circular* 470, by Thomas; from unpublished notes of Dr. Thomas; and from instructions written by Leeds and Northrup for operation of a "ratio box."

inserting or removing resistance in series with a fixed resistance, since the variation of resistance at the various dial-switch contacts in the circuit might well be the equivalent of several steps on the smallest dial. The effect of switch-contact resistance is therefore made negligible by using Waidner-Wolff[64] elements. The Waidner-Wolff element consists of an adjustable high resistance in parallel with a low resistance, the switch-contact resistance being introduced into the high-resistance arm. The effect of the variable resistance on the parallel combination may be seen from the following considerations. If R_1 and R_2 are the two resistances and R_0 the resistance of the parallel combination, then

$$R_0 = \frac{R_1 R_2}{R_1 + R_2}$$

Now, if R_1 is varied by an amount ΔR, the change in the parallel resistance is

$$\Delta R_0 = \frac{(R_1 + \Delta R)R_2}{R_1 + \Delta R + R_2} - \frac{R_1 R_2}{R_1 + R_2} = \Delta R \frac{R_2^{\,2}}{(R_1 + \Delta R + R_2)(R_1 + R_2)}$$

$$\approx \Delta R \frac{R_2^{\,2}}{(R_1 + R_2)^2}$$

if ΔR is small compared to R_1 and R_2. The effect of the variation is less by a factor $\left(\frac{R_2}{R_1 + R_2}\right)^2$ than it would be in series with an equivalent single resistance having the value R_0.

The dials of the ratio set are made up of fixed 60-ohm resistors in parallel with a shunt of about 300 ohms whose value can be varied by means of a dial switch. The variation of resistance at the switch contacts may be expected to be less than 0.001 ohm if the switch is of good construction and is kept clean and properly lubricated with Vaseline or a high-grade light oil.[65] The variation in switch-contact resistance should therefore result in an uncertainty of not more than $0.001 \times \frac{1}{36}$ ohm or 3 parts in 10^7 of the total resistance (100 ohms) of the ratio arm and is entirely negligible. The construction of the dials for the adjustable ratio arm is shown schematically in Fig. 42. With the dials set at 5, the parallel combinations consist of 60 ohms shunted by 300 ohms, so that the combined resistance is 50 ohms. The two Waidner-Wolff elements are connected in series to form the adjustable arm of the ratio set, and, as may be verified from the figure, a change of one step on the 0.1% dial changes the resistance by 0.1 ohm. One-step changes on the other dials amount to 0.01 and 0.001 ohm respectively.

[64] See also Chapter 6.
[65] See p. 232 of this chapter.

In using the ratio set for comparing resistors it is often possible to adjust the balance accurately to 1 step on the smallest dial and even, with a good galvanometer, to interpolate to a tenth of the smallest dial step from the galvanometer deflections observed for the two dial settings which bracket the balance point. Thus it is possible to estimate the balance to within 1 or 2 parts in a million (ppm). The question therefore arises whether the ratio box can be constructed so that it may be relied on to as high an accuracy as it can be read. In measurements requiring

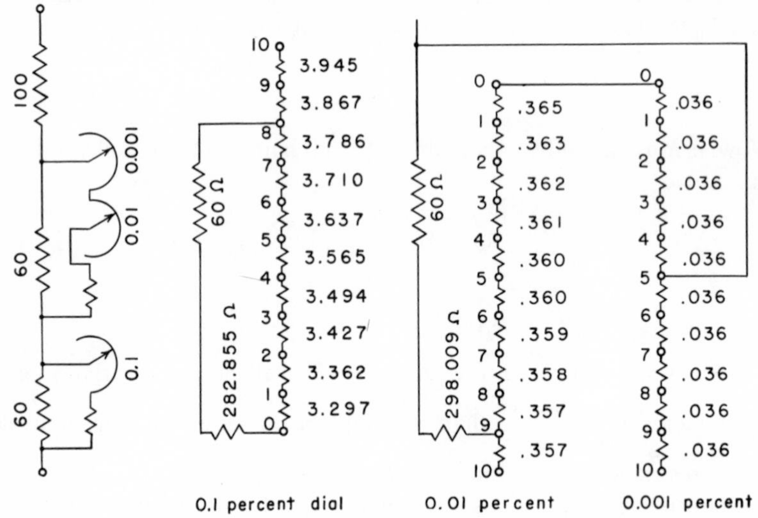

FIG. 42.

the highest accuracy a substitution method is used, so that actually our interest is in small differences of ratios rather than in the ratios themselves, and these differences can be accurately adjusted and maintained. The 0.001% dial changes the ratio by steps of 10 ppm by changing a shunt resistance in steps of 0.036 ohm. An error of 10% in the value of one of these steps would cause an error of only 1 ppm in the ratio. Similarly an error of 1 ppm in the ratio would result from a 1% maladjustment of a 0.01% dial, or from a 0.1% maladjustment of a 0.1% dial step. Obviously then it is easily possible to construct these coils so that their lack of adjustment will not cause errors greater than a few parts in 10^7. The accuracy of adjustment required for the 60-ohm coils depends on the difference in ratios which must be measured. If the 60-ohm coils are not to cause an error of more than 1 ppm when the maximum difference in ratios must be read, their adjustment must be to about 60 ppm (i.e. within about 0.004 ohm). The error produced by a given maladjustment will be less for smaller differences. It is, of course, desirable that the larger-resistance coils be constructed in an identical manner from a single lot of wire, so that the ratios may be unaffected by changes of temperature during the course of a measurement and so that the drift with time of the individual resistors will be as nearly as possible the same. Such a uniform drift would be expected to produce a minimum effect on measured differences in ratio.

(*b*) COMPARISON OF TWO-TERMINAL RESISTORS. The simplest type of measurement which can be made with the direct-reading ratio set is the *comparison by substitution of two-terminal resistors* having the same

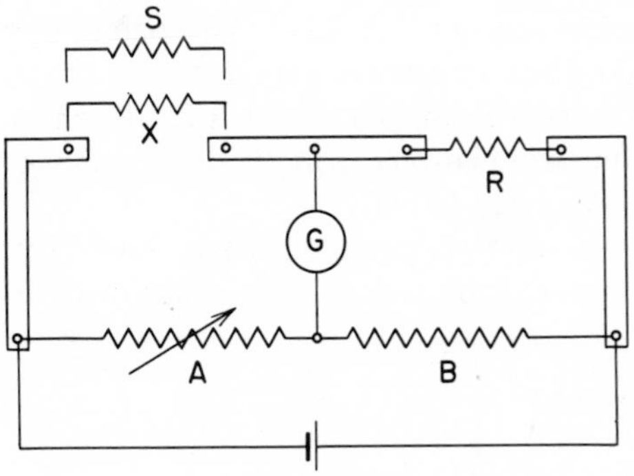

FIG. 43.

nominal value. For such a measurement a Wheatstone bridge is made up as shown in Fig. 43. The resistor R has the same nominal value as the resistors X and S which are to be compared, but need not be accurately known. The bridge is balanced with the resistor X in place, and the percentage dials of the ratio set are read. A second balance is made with the resistor S substituted for X, and the percentage dials are again read. The percentage difference between S and X is then the difference of the dial readings. Which resistance is higher must be determined by whether the dial reading is increased or decreased when the second balance is made. Alternatively X and S could be compared by using them together to form the two arms of the Wheatstone bridge (instead of X and R as shown in Fig. 43). After balance is obtained by adjusting the ratio set the resistors are interchanged and the bridge is rebalanced. The percentage difference between X and S is then half the difference in the dial readings for the two balances. If the ratio set is of good construction and a suitable galvanometer is used, such comparisons of standard resistors should be possible to 1 or 2 ppm, provided they do not differ by more than 0.1%. Connections to the bridge should, of course, be made by placing the amalgamated resistor terminals in mercury cups, since the resistance of such contacts will be constant to within a few microhms.[66] Mercury contacts are both more stable and of lower resistance than binding-post connections. Also, in operating the substitution method with two-terminal resistors, the use of mercury cups with a permanent copper strap or bar structure for intermediate connections enables the substitution to be made without disturbing any portion of the remaining bridge circuit except at the mercury cups themselves. The fixed bridge connections do not enter into the measurement which involves only differences. Hence the only points of uncertainty are variations in the mercury-contact resistances themselves before and after the substitution. In the comparison of resistances of less than 10 ohms, the variations in the mercury-contact resistances may result in an appreciable error. For this reason standard resistors smaller than 10 ohms are now almost always of the four-terminal type. Methods of comparing four-terminal resistors will be discussed later.

(*c*) COMPARISONS OF TWO-TERMINAL WITH FOUR-TERMINAL RESISTORS. These comparisons can be conveniently made with the direct-reading

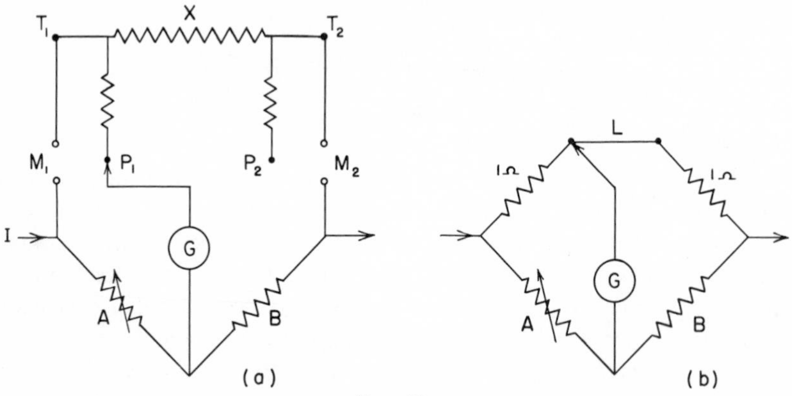

FIG. 44.

ratio set. In many types of electrical apparatus it is difficult or impossible to make connections to some elements except through comparatively large connecting resistances. However, it is frequently possible to make potential connections to the ends of the element and to measure it as a four-terminal resistor. In doing so, it is often convenient to make the measurement in terms of a two-terminal standard resistor. In Fig. 44(*a*),

[66] Actually, an amalgamated flat on the copper bus structure moistened with mercury will be found to have as low a resistance as a mercury-cup contact and to be much easier to keep clean.

X is the four-terminal resistor to be measured, with current terminals T_1, T_2 and potential terminals P_1, P_2. The potential terminals may contain considerable resistance, since in the measurement this will be in the galvanometer branch of the bridge. M_1 and M_2 are mercury cups into which a two-terminal standard resistor or a short-circuiting link may be placed. A–B is the ratio set. Starting with the galvanometer at P_1, a standard resistor nominally equal to X is placed in the gap M_1, and M_2 is shorted by the link. After this balance is taken, the galvanometer is shifted to P_2, the standard is placed in M_2, and M_1 is shorted. The percentage difference between the unknown and standard is half the difference between the two balance readings. Unless the resistance is large a correction must be applied for the resistance of the short-circuiting link. Its resistance should be subtracted from that of the standard, and we may consider that a standard of this reduced value is being interchanged with a link of zero resistance. To measure the resistance of the link we may make up a bridge as shown in Fig. 44(*b*), the link (L) being between two 1-ohm resistors. Balances are taken with the galvanometer connected first at one end of the link and then the other. Half the difference between these readings is the resistance of the link in per cent of the 1-ohm resistors. If the link resistance is large it may be necessary to use larger resistances in place of the 1-ohm coils. This procedure is very convenient for measuring small resistances such as links, connectors, switch contacts, etc. It is not a precision method but is usually sufficiently accurate for the measurement of small resistances such as those mentioned, which are to be used in series with much larger resistances.

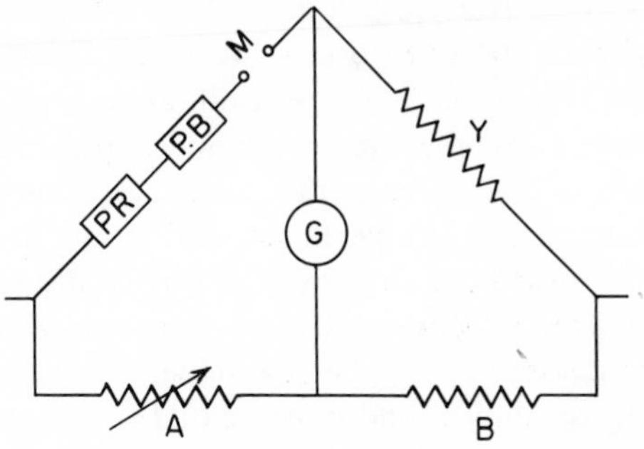

FIG. 45.

(*d*) TESTS OF RESISTANCE BOXES. A substitution method for the decades of resistance boxes is shown in Fig. 45, using a standard of the same nominal value as the decade steps. *PR* is the resistance box to be calibrated, and *PB* is another box having a decade with the same steps as the decade to be measured. *M* is a pair of mercury cups in which is placed a standard resistor having a resistance of the same value as the decade steps. Y is a resistor having a value approximately equal to 10 decade steps. If we assume that a 10-ohm-per-step decade is to be calibrated, the resistor at M is a 10-ohm standard and Y is 100 ohms. The latter need not be accurately known. The reading of the rheostat under calibration is set at zero, the auxiliary rheostat PB is set at 90 ohms, and the 10-ohm standard is inserted at M, making the total nominal resistance of the arm equal to that of the Y-arm (100 ohms). The bridge having been balanced by means of the ratio set, the standard is replaced by a short-circuiting link at M, the dial of PR is set to 10 ohms, and a new balance is taken. In effect the decade resistance unit has been substituted for the 10-ohm standard, and the difference in the balance readings of the ratio set is a measure of the difference in resistance of the dial step and the standard in *percentage of the* 100-*ohm arm*, Y. Since a 10-ohm step is measured in a 100-ohm arm, the accuracy is reduced by a factor of 10; i.e. in order to obtain this resistance to 0.01% the ratio-set balances must be determined to 0.001%. The above procedure is continued for successive steps on the decade of PR. For the second step PR is left at its 10-ohm setting, PB is set at 80 ohms, and the standard is inserted at M, keeping the arm at a nominal 100 ohms. The dial of PR is next set to read 20 ohms, and the link is substituted for the standard at M. In this way the second decade step is substituted for the 10-ohm standard. The procedure is continued, the steps of PR being successively substituted for the standard resistor. It should be noted that the steps in the auxiliary box PB are also being replaced by the standard resistor as PR is increased and PB is decreased in reading. Thus data are obtained for calibration of both PR and PB in terms of the standard resistor, and the two precision rheostats may be calibrated simultaneously. The resistance determined by the above method represents the resistance exactly as the box will be used; the particular contacts and internal connectors which are active at a particular dial setting in actual operation are included in the measuring circuit. The only additional measurement required is the resistance between the box terminals with its dials set at zero. This "zero resistance" can be determined by the method described for measuring link resistances and must be added, for any setting, to the sum of the step resistances.

(*e*) RATIOS OTHER THAN 1:1. All the foregoing discussion has assumed that the resistors to be compared have the same nominal value, so that the 100:100 ratio of the set is appropriate. However, it is often convenient to use the set at other ratios to compare resistors which are not equal in value. Referring to Fig. 46, the ratio can be changed by adding resistance in series with the fixed arm B. The ratio $A/(B + R)$ is then adjustable in the same percentage steps as the 1:1 ratio. In order to use the ratio set in this way, we must determine its reading for a precisely known ratio. For simple whole-number ratios this may be done conveniently in the following manner. Suppose, for example, we wish to realize a ratio of 1:4. We may take five nearly equal resistors, and place one of them in the X-arm and the other four in series in the S-arm. This gives a ratio which is approximately 1:4. However, if each of the five resistors is placed in turn in the X-arm, with the remaining four resistors in the S-arm, the average of the five ratios will be very accurately 1:4. The general theorem of which this is a special case will now be

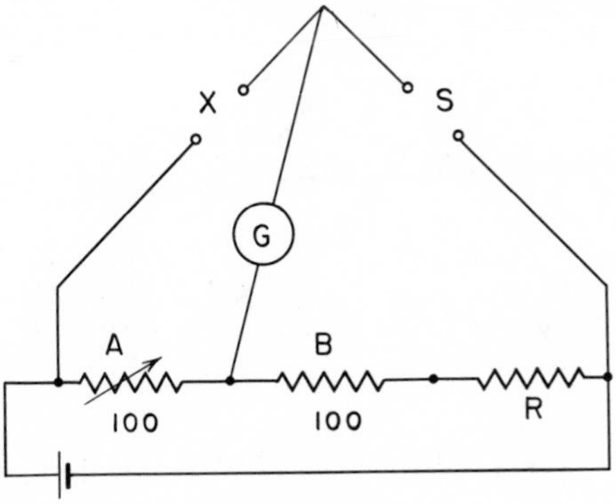

FIG. 46.

proved. Assume that we have $(n + 1)$ resistors which are nearly equal, and that the average value of all the resistors is A. The values of the individual resistors may be written as

$$R_1 = A + a_1; \quad R_2 = A + a_2; \quad \cdots; \quad R_{n+1} = A + a_{n+1}$$

Since A is the average resistance, we have

$$a_1 + a_2 + \cdots + a_{n+1} = 0, \quad \text{and} \quad a_2 + a_3 + \cdots + a_{n+1} = -a_1$$

The ratio with resistor 1 in the X-arm and all the others in S may be written

$$\frac{A + a_1}{nA + a_2 + a_3 + \cdots + a_{n+1}} = \frac{A + a_1}{nA - a_1} = \gamma_1$$

We may write

$$\gamma_1 = \frac{\dfrac{1}{n}\left(1 + \dfrac{a_1}{A}\right)}{\left(1 - \dfrac{a_1}{nA}\right)} = \frac{1}{n}\left(1 + \frac{a_1}{A}\right)\left[1 + \frac{a_1}{nA} - \left(\frac{a_1}{nA}\right)^2 + \left(\frac{a_1}{nA}\right)^3 + \cdots\right]$$

$$= \frac{1}{n}\left(1 + \frac{n+1}{n}K_1 + \frac{n-1}{n^2}K_1^2 - \frac{n-1}{n^3}K_1^3 + \cdots\right)$$

where $K_1 = a_1/A$. Similarly the other ratios may be written as

$$\gamma_2 = \frac{1}{n}\left(1 + \frac{n+1}{n}K_2 + \frac{n-1}{n^2}K_2{}^2 - \frac{n-1}{n^3}K_2{}^3 + \cdots\right)$$

....

$$\gamma_{n+1} = \frac{1}{n}\left(1 + \frac{n+1}{n}K_{n+1} + \frac{n-1}{n^2}K^2{}_{n+1} - \frac{n-1}{n^3}K^3{}_{n+1} + \cdots\right)$$

The average of all the ratios is

$$\sum_1^{n+1} \frac{\gamma_r}{n+1} = \frac{1}{n}\left[1 + \frac{1}{n}\sum_1^{n+1} K_r + \frac{n-1}{n^2(n+1)}\sum_1^{n+1} K_r{}^2 - \frac{n-1}{n^3(n+1)}\sum_1^{n+1} K_r{}^3 + \cdots\right]$$

$$= \frac{1}{n}\left[1 + \frac{(n-1)}{n^2(n+1)}\sum_1^{n+1} K_r{}^2 - \frac{(n-1)}{n^3(n+1)}\sum_1^{n+1} K_r{}^3 + \cdots\right]$$

since

$$\sum_1^{n+1} K_r = \frac{a_1 + a_2 + \cdots + a_{n+1}}{A} = 0 \quad \text{by definition}$$

It may be seen from inspection that, if the resistors do not differ by more than 0.1% (i.e. $K_r \leqslant 0.001$), the average of the $(n+1)$ ratios will be $1:n$ to better than 1 ppm.

Referring again to Fig. 46, the ratio set may be used in the example cited (1:4) to measure a 25-ohm resistor in terms of a 100-ohm standard by placing the 25-ohm resistor in the X-arm and the standard in the S-arm. If A is the balance reading for this condition, and A_0 the setting of the ratio set as determined above for an exact 1:4 ratio, we have as the true ratio of the resistors

$$\frac{X+x}{S+s} = \frac{X}{S}(1 + A - A_0)$$

Here X and S represent the nominal values of the resistors (in our case 25 and 100 since the nominal ratio of the ratio set is 1:4), and x and s are their departures in ohms from their nominal values. Then

$$\frac{X}{S}\cdot\frac{1+\dfrac{x}{X}}{1+\dfrac{s}{S}} = \frac{X}{S}(1 + A - A_0) \quad \text{or} \quad \frac{1+C_x}{1+C_s} = 1 + A - A_0$$

where C_x and C_s are the proportional corrections to the resistors. Since C_x and C_s are small compared with unity we have

$$1 + C_x - C_s = 1 + A - A_0, \quad \text{or, finally,} \quad C_x = A - A_0 + C_s$$

In this determination, and in the preceding determination of the reading of the ratio set for the exact integral ratio (e.g. 1:4), it was assumed that either the lead resistances in the X- and S-arms were negligible, or that their resistances were in the ratio $X:S$. The latter condition can be set with sufficient accuracy by shorting X and S and balancing the resulting bridge by adjusting the lengths of the lead wires.

(*f*) HIGH RESISTANCES. These may be measured with the ratio set by making use of a theorem similar to that discussed in the preceding section: *The proportional correction to a group of nominally equal resistors is the same when they are connected in parallel as when they are connected in series.* For example, the ten 100,000-ohm sections of a megohm box may be connected in parallel and measured against a 10,000-ohm standard. If the parallel group is high by 0.01% their series resistance (1 megohm) will also be high by 0.01%. This theorem may be proved as follows. Let A be the average resistance of the members of the group, so that $R_1 = A + a_1$; $R_2 = A + a_2$; $\cdots$. The series resistance of the group

$$S = A\left(1 + \frac{a_1}{A} + 1 + \frac{a_2}{A} + \cdots\right)$$
$$= nA$$

since by definition $a_1 + a_2 + \cdots + a_n = 0$. When the resistors are connected in parallel, we have

$$\frac{1}{P} = \frac{1}{A + a_1} + \frac{1}{A + a_2} + \cdots = \frac{1}{A}\left(\frac{1}{1 + \dfrac{a_1}{A}} + \frac{1}{1 + \dfrac{a_2}{A}} + \cdots\right)$$

$$\approx \frac{1}{A}\left[1 - \frac{a_1}{A} + \left(\frac{a_1}{A}\right)^2 + 1 - \frac{a_2}{A} + \left(\frac{a_2}{A}\right)^2 + \cdots\right]$$

$$\approx \frac{n}{A}\left(1 + \frac{1}{nA^2}\sum_1^n a_r^2\right)$$

and

$$\frac{S}{P} \approx n^2\left(1 + \frac{1}{nA^2}\sum_1^n a_r^2\right)$$

If, for example, the individual resistors do not differ from their mean value by more than 0.1%, the ratio of their series to their parallel resistance will be n^2 to within a part per million. If we say that the nominal resistance of the individual resistors is N, then the total series resistance may be written

$$S = nN + b_s = nN\left(1 + \frac{b_s}{nN}\right) = nN(1 + C_s)$$

where b_s is the departure in ohms of the total from the nominal value, and C_s is the departure in proportional parts. Similarly the parallel resistance may be written

$$P = \frac{N}{n} + b_p = \frac{N}{n}(1 + C_p)$$

where b_p and C_p are the departures in ohms and in proportional parts from the nominal value of the parallel resistance. The ratio of series to parallel resistance then is

$$\frac{S}{P} = n^2\left(\frac{1 + C_s}{1 + C_p}\right) \approx n^2(1 + C_s - C_p)$$

Now, since we have shown that $S/P \approx n^2$, it must follow that $C_s - C_p = 0$; i.e. the proportional correction is the same with the resistors connected in series or in parallel. It should be noted that we have also established a method by which certain integral ratios can be set up very accurately, i.e. the ratios corresponding to the squares of integers. Commercial direct-reading ratio sets, made by the Leeds and Northrup Company, have the B-arm subdivided so that its resistance may be made 10 or 100 ohms while the resistance of the A-arm is 100 ohms. In this way a 1:10 ratio or a 1:1 ratio is available.

The methods of measurement described for the direct-reading ratio set are also suitable for any ratio set having small, definite steps.[67] For example, a slide wire with extension resistances at each end could be employed, or a ratio set could be made up by shunting a 2500-ohm decade box by a resistance of 105 ohms and using this combination as the adjustable arm, a change of 0.1 ohm in the high resistance changing the 100 ohms by about 1 part per million. Such an adjustable 100-ohm resistor, together with a fixed 100-ohm resistor, can serve as a ratio set. Of course the changes in the resistance of the adjustable arm are not directly proportional to the change in the high-resistance branch but may be readily calculated.

The Kelvin Double Bridge. It is difficult to attach copper lead wires to

[67] For particulars of a universal ratio set and its use in checking the calibration of potentiometers, see J. L. Thomas, Precision Resistors and Their Measurement, *NBS Circ.* 470 (1948).

a resistor by means of binding posts or other clamping devices without introducing contact resistances of the order of 0.0001 ohm or more. For a resistance of 1 ohm the contact resistance would amount to 0.01 %, but for a 0.001-ohm resistance would be 10 %. Standard resistors of low values are therefore usually of the four-terminal type[68] and are measured in such a way that their points of attachment to the circuit and their lead resistances do not enter the measurement. The Wheatstone bridge is, of course, not convenient for such measurements, and another type of network was devised by Lord Kelvin for the comparison of four-terminal

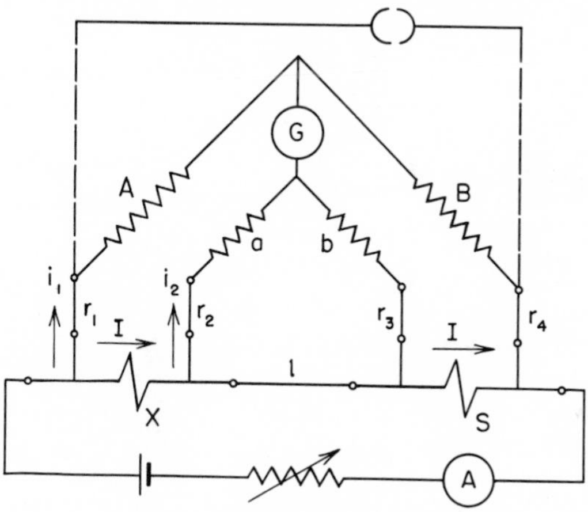

FIG. 47.

resistances. The Kelvin double bridge is shown schematically in Fig. 47. By using this bridge together with the procedure described below (or its equivalent), the resistances of the leads between the potential terminals of the resistor and the bridge are eliminated from the measurement, and the four-terminal resistance of the unknown, X, is determined in terms of the four-terminal resistance of the standard, S, and the ratio arms, A and B.

(a) EQUATION OF BALANCE. Let A, B, a, b be the *total* resistance in the designated bridge arms, including the lead and contact resistance between the bridge arm and the potential junction point on the resistor. We shall designate the resistance between the galvanometer junction point and the bridge binding post as A', B', a', b'. Then

$$A = A' + r_1; \quad a = a' + r_2; \quad b = b' + r_3; \quad B = B' + r_4$$

At balance (no current in the galvanometer branch), the voltage drop

[68] See p. 220.

across A is equal to the sum of the voltage drops across X and a. Then $i_1A = IX + i_2a$. Similarly $i_1B = IS + i_2b$. Also

$$(I - i_2)l = i_2(a + b)$$

so that

$$Il = i_2(a + b + l) \quad \text{or} \quad i_2 = I\frac{l}{a + b + l}$$

If this value of i_2 is substituted, we have

$$i_1A = I\left(X + \frac{al}{a + b + l}\right)$$

and

$$i_1B = I\left(S + \frac{bl}{a + b + l}\right)$$

From these equations we have

$$\frac{A}{B} = \frac{X + \dfrac{al}{a + b + l}}{S + \dfrac{bl}{a + b + l}} \quad \text{or} \quad BX = AS + \frac{Abl}{a + b + l} - \frac{Bal}{a + b + l}$$

so that

$$X = S \cdot \frac{A}{B} + \frac{bl}{a + b + l}\left(\frac{A}{B} - \frac{a}{b}\right)$$

If the values were such that $A/B = a/b$, we would have the simple relation $X = S(A/B)$. A method must therefore be devised by which as nearly as possible we may make $A/B = a/b$ when the bridge is balanced. Also we see that l must be kept small so that the residual $(A/B - a/b)$ will have as little effect as possible. As regards the resistors which make up the inner and outer ratio arms of the bridge, the two ratios A'/B' and a'/b' can be kept closely equal for all settings by mechanically coupling the dial switches used in adjusting for balance, so that the inner and outer ratios are adjusted together and any change in one is automatically made in the other; or, if the inner and outer ratio elements have independent controls, we can follow each adjustment of the outer ratio by duplicating the adjustment on the inner ratio. However, since the resistances of the arms will range from perhaps 50 ohms to a few hundred or a few thousand ohms, the resistances of the leads r_1, r_2, r_3, r_4 up to the permanent junction points on the four-terminal resistors must be considered in evaluating the true bridge ratios. There is no hope of reducing their contributions to the ratios to a negligible value, since their resistances may amount to as much as 0.1 ohm, which would be 0.2% of the total resistance of a 50-ohm arm. It is therefore necessary that the resistances of these potential leads be adjusted to such values that their presence will not alter the ratio from that obtained from the bridge settings.

We will now consider the lead resistances which were included in the balance equation derived above. We have

$$\frac{A}{B} = \frac{A' + r_1}{B' + r_4} = \frac{\dfrac{A'}{B'} + \dfrac{r_1}{B'}}{1 + \dfrac{r_4}{B'}} = \frac{A'}{B'}\left(\frac{1 + \dfrac{r_1}{A'}}{1 + \dfrac{r_4}{B'}}\right)$$

$$\approx \frac{A'}{B'}\left[\left(1 + \frac{r_1}{A'}\right)\left(1 - \frac{r_4}{B'}\right)\right] \approx \frac{A'}{B'}\left(1 + \frac{r_1}{A'} - \frac{r_4}{B'}\right), \quad \text{if } \frac{r_1}{A'} \text{ and } \frac{r_4}{B'}$$

are sufficiently small that second- and higher-order terms in the power expansions may be neglected. This approximation is justified in practical

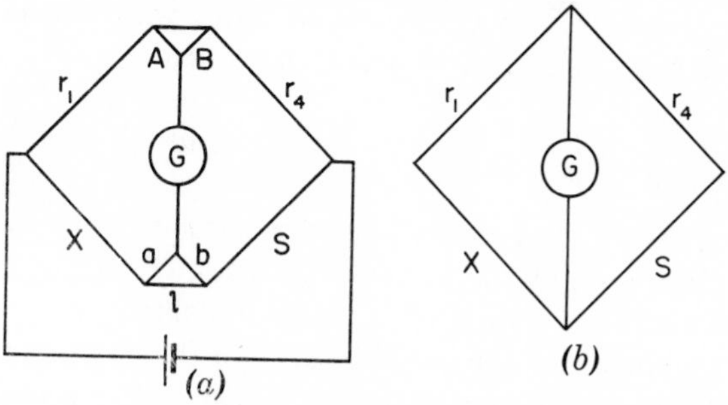

FIG. 48.

cases, since we may expect that A and B will be 50 ohms or more while r_1 and r_4 will be 0.1 ohm or less. In the extreme case the error resulting from the approximation is only a few parts in a million. From the above expression it appears that A/B may be made equal to A'/B' by making $r_1/A' = r_4/B'$, or what is equivalent, $A'/B' = r_1/r_4$. To do this the main ratio arms A', B' are short-circuited by inserting the shorting plug, as shown in Fig. 48. The resulting network is practically the equivalent of a Wheatstone bridge as may be seen from Fig. 48(*a*). In this arrangement the outer ends of the outer ratio arms A, B are brought to the same potential by the shorting plug in the auxiliary arm, and the inner ratio arms a, b are short-circuited by the much lower resistance of l, so that effectively the bridge is that shown in Fig. 48(*b*). This bridge is balanced by adjusting r_1 or r_4. In many cases this adjustment is made by changing the length of one or the other of the lead resistances. Some Kelvin bridges are equipped with an adjustable rheostat of low resistance in series with one of the leads for making this adjustment without manipulating the lead itself. At balance $X/S = r_1/r_4$, and in the previous balance of the double bridge we had very nearly $X/S = A/B$. Then to a fair approximation we have for the new balance condition $r_1/r_4 \approx A/B \approx A'/B'$, which is the relation needed to make $A/B = A'/B'$.

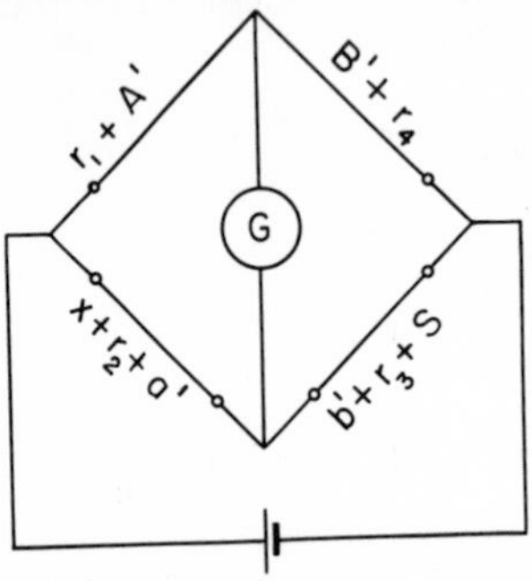

FIG. 49.

As the next step in adjusting the bridge, we will remove the link l and the shorting plug, and we have the simple Wheatstone bridge of Fig. 49. To a first approximation we have $A'/B' \approx r_1/r_4 \approx X/S \approx a'/b'$, and the bridge will be balanced if r_2/r_3 is adjusted to this same ratio. This adjustment is made by varying the length of r_2 or r_3, or by adjusting a low-resistance rheostat in series with one of them. If these balances were all correct we would have finally

$$\frac{A}{B} = \frac{A'}{B'} = \frac{a}{b} = \frac{a'}{b'} = \frac{r_1}{r_4} = \frac{r_2}{r_3} = \frac{X}{S} \quad \text{and} \quad X = S\frac{A'}{B'}$$

where A' and B' are the corrected balance settings of the ratio arms of the bridge. We have, by the auxiliary balances, eliminated the effect of the lead resistances r_1, r_2, r_3, r_4 from the main balance.

It should be noted that the initial balance of the outer and inner ratio arms will be somewhat affected by the changes made in the lead resistances which are in series with them. The bridge will therefore not be exactly in balance after the auxiliary balances (lead adjustments) are made, so that as a final step the bridge must be rebalanced.

(*b*) BALANCING PROCEDURE. The experimental steps necessary to the comparison of four-terminal resistances in a Kelvin bridge are the following:

1. With the bridge arranged as in Fig. 47, a balance is obtained by adjusting the resistances of the ratio arms. (This balance is preliminary and need only be approximate.) If the adjustments of the inner and outer ratios are not mechanically coupled, the observer must make sure that the two ratios are the same. Now we have $A/B \approx a/b \approx X/S$.

2. With the outer ratio arms short-circuited, as shown in Fig. 48, the bridge is rebalanced by adjusting the resistance of one or both of the outer potential leads r_1, r_4 between the four-terminal resistors and the bridge ratio arms. This balance gives us approximately $r_1/r_4 \approx A'/B'$.

3. With the short circuit removed from the outer ratio arms and with the link l removed from between X and S, the bridge (see Fig. 49) is

rebalanced by adjusting the resistance of one or both of the inner potential leads r_2, r_3 to the four-terminal resistors. This balance gives us approximately $r_2/r_3 \approx A'/B'$ and improves our approximation to $A/B \approx a/b$.

4. With the link l connecting the current terminals of X and S replaced and the bridge returned to the original arrangement of Fig. 47, a new balance is made by adjusting the ratio arms. Under most circumstances this balance will be sufficient for the final determination of the four-terminal resistor X. However, if a considerable change has to be made in the ratio-arm settings, it follows that the contribution of the lead resistance to the original balance values was large. In this case it is necessary to repeat steps 2, 3, and 4 in order to arrive at a second, closer approximation to the desired balance relation $X/S = A'/B'$. In fact, for precise values,

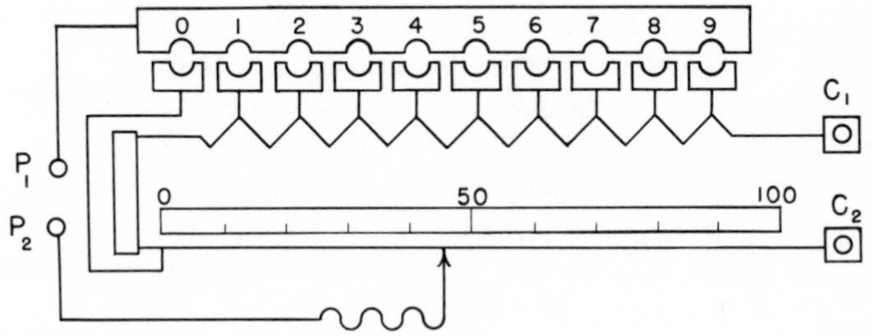

FIG. 50.

the steps should be repeated cyclicly until no significant readjustment has to be made on step 4 after the auxiliary balances, steps 2 and 3.[69] It may be noted that when this procedure is followed the inner ratio arms a, b need not be calibrated. The outer arms A, B, in terms of which X and S are compared, must of course be accurately known.

It should be pointed out that alternative procedures are sometimes used, depending on the bridge construction. For example, in steps 1 and 4, the comparison four-terminal resistor, S, may be adjustable either in steps or by shifting the position of one of its potential terminals along a low-resistance slider. In this case fixed ratio arms may be used and the balance adjustment made by varying S. Such an adjustable four-terminal resistance standard is shown in Fig. 50.

The Kelvin bridge may be used for the precision comparison of four-terminal resistance standards, for determining the four-terminal resistance of shunts, and for measuring the conductance of wires and cables. Where high precision is required a substitution procedure similar to that described above for the Wheatstone bridge should be used. If the standard and

[69] Wenner and Weibel, *Bull. Bur. Standards*, **11**, 65 (1914); see also Wenner, *Bull. Bur. Standards*, **8**, 580 (1912).

the unknown have the same nominal value, and are measured in turn in the *X*-arm, the adjustable arms of the bridge are changed very little between the comparison balances and the other bridge arms not at all. Hence, only a small difference is measured, and the actual resistance values of the bridge arms do not have to be precisely known in order that the precision of the comparison be high. When the four-terminal resistance of a heavy-current shunt is to be measured, care should be taken that the current distribution at the current terminals shall as nearly as possible duplicate the current distribution encountered in service, since in the majority of such shunts, except of the precision-resistance type,[70] the current terminals are rather massive copper blocks which are equipped with slots or flats to which the current-carrying cables or bus bars are bolted. In many such designs no special precautions are taken to ensure that the current distribution in the body of the shunt is uniform and independent of the location and manner of attachment of the current leads. Shunts in which the potential leads are connected directly to the face of the copper terminal block by means of screws or binding posts, which form the potential terminals, are particularly sensitive to the distribution of the current, since the location of the equipotential surfaces in the terminal blocks may depend to an important extent on the location and manner of attachment of the current leads.

(*c*) CONDUCTANCE MEASUREMENT. The measurement of conductance of a sample of wire or cable is often an important preliminary to the purchase of a quantity of a particular lot of conductors. Frequently a condition of the sale contract is based on the conductivity of the conductor material or on the conductance of the wire or cable per unit length. For a single wire the problem is quite simple. The resistance of a known length of the conductor is measured as a four-terminal resistor by comparison with a resistance standard or with a standard wire sample of known size and conductivity. The conductance or conductivity of the unknown can then be computed in terms of its measured dimensions. To prepare a sample for such a test, a straight length of the wire, some inches more than the length whose four-terminal resistance is to be measured, is used. For small wire the ends may be clamped to binding posts to form current terminals; for larger wires it may be more convenient to solder the ends to current lugs of suitable capacity which may be connected to the circuit by binding posts or an equivalent clamping arrangement. The potential terminals may be probes which are pressed against the wire at the measured distance apart, or may be wires wrapped around the conductor and soldered to it at the proper spacing. Care must be taken that the potential terminals are well away from the current terminals so that the current

[70] See discussion, p. 222, of four-terminal resistors.

distribution in the conductor is uniform between the potential terminals. As a matter of convenience, the assembly of binding posts for the current terminals and the probe and clamp arrangement used for the potential terminals may be mounted on a board of suitable length. If the conductor is stranded, the measurement of its resistance is somewhat more difficult. In this case it is almost essential that the ends of the conductor be soldered into a terminal lug,[71] well away from the position of the potential terminals in order to ensure uniform current distribution throughout the strands of the conductor at the potential terminal. The use of a probe to make the potential contact is not entirely effective since the probe can make contact with only one strand of the conductor. A more representative value is obtained if a fine wire is wound tightly around the bundle of conductors at the designated point and brought away as a potential lead. If the individual strands of the conductor are tinned, the potential terminal so made may be soldered to the bundle of conductors. Since the conductivity is usually specified in terms of an accepted standard value at 20°C, a temperature correction must be applied if the sample departs from this temperature. Also care must be taken that the current density used in the resistance determination is not high enough to cause heating in the wire.

(*d*) THE HOOPES CONDUCTIVITY BRIDGE. This modification of the Kelvin bridge is designed for the rapid determination of the conductivity

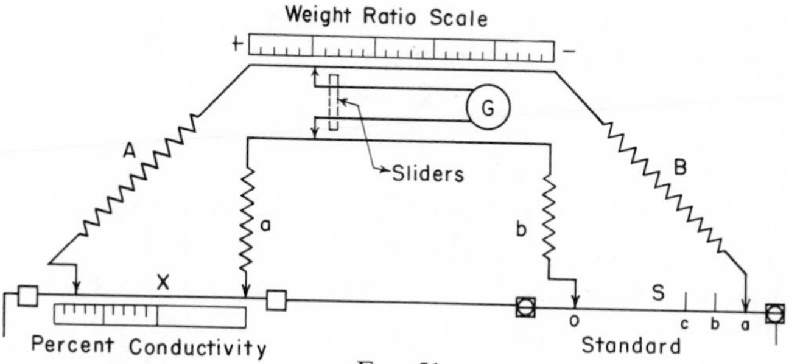

FIG. 51.

of wire samples and is useful where a large number of such determinations must be made. It is convenient to manipulate, is direct reading in terms of a standard, does not require temperature corrections, and is sufficiently precise for the routine testing of wire samples (perhaps 0.1%). It is shown schematically in Fig. 51. The standard *S* and the unknown *X*

[71] In the case of a stranded aluminum conductor for which the usual soldering techniques are not effective, the bundle of conductors must be clamped together in some sort of suitable terminal clamp to which connection may be made.

are of the same metal, and if they are at the same temperature, no correction is needed. The sliders on the weight-ratio scale are rigidly connected together so that the ratios A/B and a/b remain equal when the slider positions are changed. The sample is cut precisely to a fixed length and weighed. The weight-ratio scale is provided to correct for irregularities or variations in weight of the samples. The sliders on the weight-ratio scale are set at a mark representing the excess or defect in weight of the sample, referred to a sample of correct size. The bridge is then balanced by adjusting the position of the slider x, and the conductivity of the sample is read from the percentage scale beside the sample. The standard sample S has tap points a, b, c corresponding to the resistances of standard lengths of three consecutive wire sizes. Standard samples covering the various sizes to be tested must be available and should be kept with the bridge so that they will be at the temperature of the remainder of the test apparatus. The bridge may be enclosed in a metal box and immersed in light oil in order to keep its temperature uniform.

Temperature Measurements by Resistance Methods. The temperature coefficient of most metals is positive and, for pure metals, is usually about 0.4%/°C. The temperature coefficient used as standard for annealed copper decreases from 0.00427 at 0°C to 0.00352 at 50°C and at 20°C is taken as 0.00393. In the testing of electrical apparatus, the average temperature rise of copper windings may be determined from their change in resistance. The winding resistance is measured before and at the conclusion of a heating run by whatever method is convenient, and, for approximate values of temperature rise, the assumption may be made that the increase in resistance is 0.4%/°C.

Resistance thermometers, made up as calibrated coils of wire, are much employed for temperature measurements. For the precise determination of temperatures, platinum resistance thermometers are widely used. If temperatures are to be measured over an extended range, the variation of resistance may be expressed as the initial terms of a power series. For example, the temperature resistance curve for a coil of very pure platinum wire of the type used in resistance thermometers is represented over an extended range of temperature by the equation

$$R_t = R_0(1 + 0.003985t - 0.000000586t^2)$$

R_0 being the resistance at 0°C, and R_t the resistance at t°C.[72] The coil of wire used as a thermometer may be at a considerable distance from the measuring apparatus (a Wheatstone bridge, for example), and allowance must be made for the resistance of the leads between the thermometer coil and the bridge. For ordinary temperature measurements, this may

[72] Stimson, *NBS J. Research*, **42**, 209 (1949).

be done quite simply by using a dummy loop made up to match the actual leads as nearly as possible and carried with them as a twisted set, so that the temperature of the dummy loop will be at all points the same as that of the leads themselves. A Wheatstone bridge having a 1:1 ratio is suitable for the resistance measurement, and the dummy loop may be inserted in the arm adjacent to the thermometer as shown in Fig. 52. In some cases a slide wire is used which may be calibrated directly in degrees, the temperature being read from the slider position at balance.

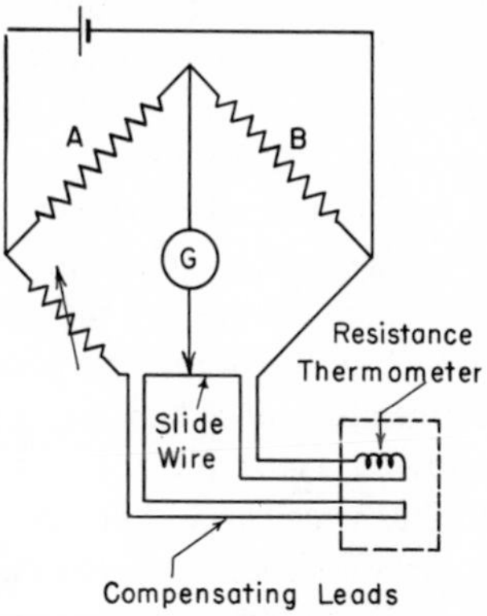

FIG. 52.

The Mueller Bridge.[73] This is used in conjunction with a four-terminal platinum resistance thermometer for measurements of the highest precision. It is a special modification of the Wheatstone bridge and is intended for the accurate measurement of four-terminal resistances up to 110 ohms. The arrangement of the bridge is shown schematically

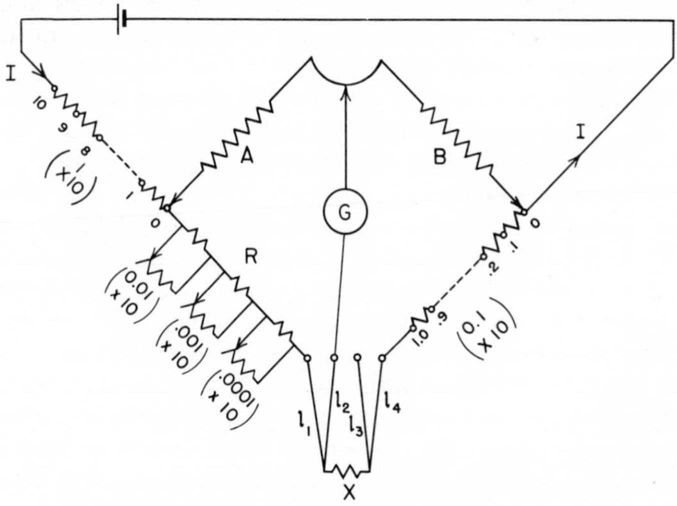

FIG. 53.

in Fig. 53, but with the special switching arrangements referred to below omitted for simplicity. The bridge is always used with the ratio arms *A*, *B* equal. The ratio is adjusted to unity by means of a small slide

[73] *Bull. Bur. Standards*, **13**, 547 (1916).

wire inserted at the junction of the *A*-, *B*-arms, and the equality of the *A*-, *B*-arms is tested by interchanging them in the bridge, while holding the *R*- and *X*-arms fixed. The slide-wire adjustment is correct and the ratio is unity if no change in bridge balance results from the interchange of the ratio arms. *X* is the resistance thermometer or other four-terminal resistor to be measured.

In the connection shown, arms *R* and *X* would be equal at balance only if leads l_1 and l_4 are equal. Instead of adjusting l_1 and l_4 to exact equality, their connections are interchanged and a second bridge balance is taken with l_4 in the adjustable arm *R* and l_1 in the *X*-arm. (The galvanometer connection must be switched to l_3 for this balance in order that the unknown remain in the *X*-arm.) The average of the two balances is equal to that which would be obtained if l_1 and l_4 were equal. The interchange is accomplished by a special switch with amalgamated mercury contacts, and the uncertainty in resistance in the switch amounts to only a few microhms. Since the smallest step in the adjustable arm is 100 microhms, the resistance uncertainty introduced in the mercury switch is negligible. As indicated in the figure the three lower dials of the adjustable arm (0.01-, 0.001-, and 0.0001-ohm steps) are of the Waidner-Wolff type in order to eliminate trouble from switch contacts and from thermal emf's at these points. The minimum resistance in the adjustable arm is 1.6 ohms. However, since the bridge has a 1:1 ratio, an equal resistance can be set into the *X*-arm to compensate it, and the value of *X* determined by making two balances, one with *X* in the bridge arm and one with *X* shorted out by means of a plug arrangement not shown in Fig. 53. The difference in readings of the adjustable arm between these two balances gives the value of *X*. The larger adjustable decades (0.1 ohm and greater) are not of the Waidner-Wolff type since this would result in a rather large resistance when the dials are set to zero. The switch-contact resistance of the 1-ohm dial is made a part of the ratio arm *A*, and the contact resistance of the 0.1 dial is in ratio arm *B* as shown in the figure. Since the ratio arms are 1000 ohms each, the resistance of the direct contacts can be tolerated. (An uncertainty of 0.001 ohm in this resistance would amount to only 1 ppm.) The 0.1-ohm decade is actually in the *X*-arm, but, since a 1:1 bridge ratio is used, the effect of reducing *X* by 0.1 ohm is exactly the same as if *R* were increased by 0.1 ohm. The 10-ohm-per-step decade, not shown in the Fig. 53, is the only one whose contact resistance is directly in the adjustable arm *R*. A special type of switch with amalgamated contacts is used for this dial, and its uncertainty of resistance (a few microhms) may be neglected in comparison with the smallest step (100 microhms) in the arm. Mueller bridges which are available commercially have the galvanometer and battery interchanged from the positions assumed in the above discussion. This does not, however, in any way affect the validity of our argument. The arrangements used for interchanging l_1 and l_4 in the bridge arms and for short-circuiting X are shown in Fig. 54.

The Mueller bridge may be calibrated in a fairly simple manner with apparatus which is available in most laboratories. Since this bridge is always used with a 1:1 ratio, and since this ratio is accurately established by the interchange of the ratio arms, there remains only the adjustable

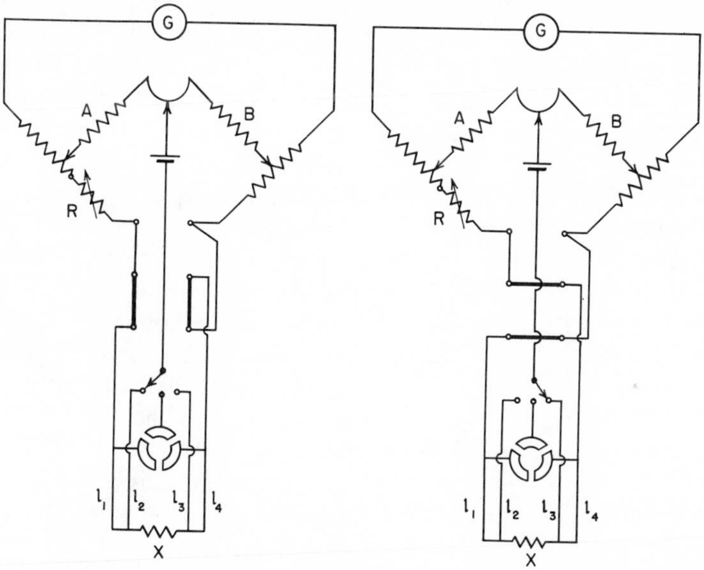

FIG. 54.

arm to be calibrated, and usually only relative values of resistance are needed, since in operation temperatures are determined by the ratios of resistance of the X-arm. In measuring relative values only, standard resistors are not required, and a Mueller bridge may be calibrated for temperature measurements with a decade box having 0.1-ohm minimum steps and a 0.1- or 1.0-ohm resistor in parallel with a fairly high-resistance slide wire. The circuit arrangement is shown in Fig. 55. The calibrating procedure involves the determination of each step on each decade of the adjustable arm in terms of the average of the steps in the lowest decade.

With the ratio arms accurately adjusted to equality, the lowest decade is set to zero and the bridge is balanced by adjusting X. (During the intercomparison of the steps in this decade the other dials of R are set and left at any convenient value.) The galvanometer deflection is now read when the lowest dial reading is changed 1 step (from 0 to 1). Leaving the dial on 1, the bridge is again balanced by adjusting *X*, and the galvanometer deflection is determined for the shift of the lowest *R*-dial from 1 to 2. This procedure is continued until the value of each step is measured in terms of galvanometer deflections. These steps should all be equal within 0.1 dial step unless the decade is defective. Each of the steps of the second decade should be equal to 10 steps on the lowest decade. To determine this, the second decade is set to zero and the lowest to 10. After the bridge is balanced by adjustment of *X*, the lower dial is turned back to zero and the second dial is set to 1. Any change in the galvanometer deflection from the previous balance represents an inequality between the total of the lowest decade and the first step of the second. The magnitude of this inequality may be evaluated from the galvanometer deflection in terms of the steps of the lowest dial by noting the galvanometer deflection corresponding to 1 unit on the lowest dial. To measure the second step on the second dial it is left at 1, the low dial is again set at 10, and the bridge is balanced with *X*. The low dial is now set to zero, the second dial to 2, and any resulting deflection is again evaluated in terms of 1 step on the low dial. This procedure is continued until each step of the second decade has been compared with the 10 steps of the lowest decade. The values of the steps of the third decade are similarly evaluated in terms of the 10 steps of the second decade. This process is continued until all the dials have been calibrated in terms of the next lower decade and finally the resistance of each step of each decade may be stated in terms of the unit of the lowest decade. These values of resistance, measured in "dial units" rather than in ohms, may be used for temperature measurements with any resistance thermometer, provided the resistance thermometer is standardized in terms of "dial units" by measurements at known temperatures (i.e. the ice point, the boiling point of water, the boiling point of sulfur, etc.).

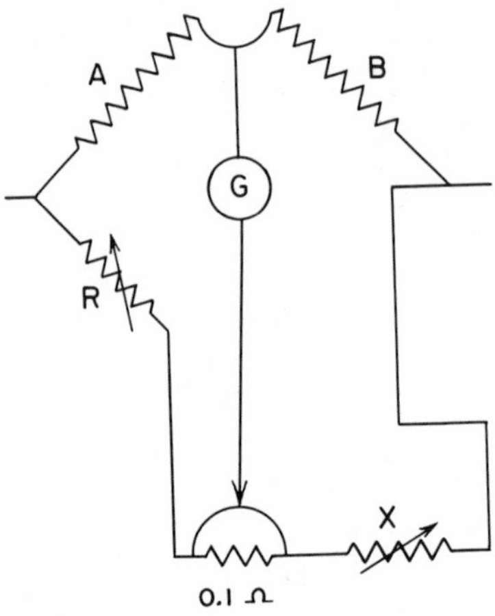

FIG. 55.

In order to convert the above calibration into ohms (so that the bridge may serve for the general measurement of four-terminal resistors) it is necessary only to measure the resistance of a standard four-terminal resistor in the X-arm of the bridge. The ratio of the known resistance of the standard in ohms to its resistance determined in "dial units" may then be used as a multiplying factor to convert any reading of the R-arm of the bridge to ohms. By a similar procedure the adjustable arm of a Wheatstone bridge may be calibrated in terms of steps of its lowest decade, and then in ohms by comparison with a standard resistor.

Measurement of the Resistance of Electrolytes. This measurement presents special problems and cannot usually be accomplished by d-c methods, since the chemical action and emf's of polarization produced by the current through the electrolyte interfere with the measurement. Generally an a-c supply is used for this purpose, and the measurement becomes an impedance measurement rather than a resistance measurement. A four-arm bridge may be made up with the electrolyte in a suitable container (i.e. a conductivity cell made up to specified dimensions and with platinum electrodes) comprising one arm. As shown in Fig. 56, the adjacent arm is a known resistance R of the same order of magnitude as the resistance X of the cell of electrolyte. The ratio arms A, B could, for example, be formed from a slide wire. The source may be some type of audio-oscillator, and the detector may be a telephone receiver. Balance is indicated by minimum sound in the receiver. However, because of the capacitance usually associated with an electrolyte in contact with the electrodes of the cell, this minimum of sound may not be zero unless a similar capacitance is included in the R-arm. At balance the usual Wheatstone bridge relation holds, and $X = R \cdot A/B$. If a is the cross-sectional area of the cell and l is the length, the resistivity K of the electrolyte may be written as $K = X(a/l)$. It should be noted that the temperature coefficient of resistance of most electrolytic solutions is quite high, so that the measured resistance (or resistivity) must be associated with the temperature at which the observation was made.

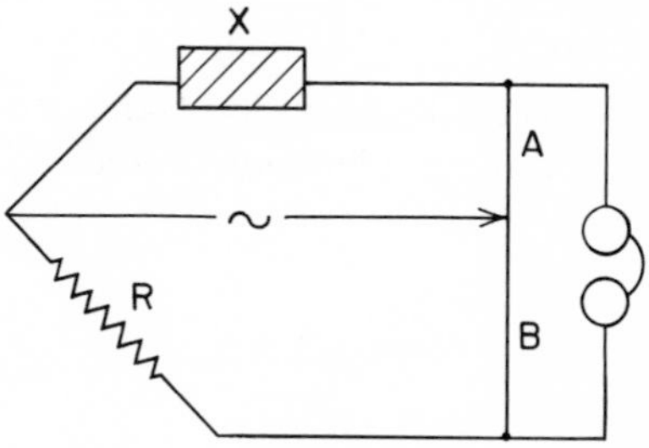

FIG. 56.

Ground Resistance

Insulation Resistance to Ground. The line-to-ground resistance of a power circuit is sometimes of interest. Where this resistance is not too high (less than 1 or 2 megohms) and the supply is direct current, a voltmeter method may be used. Three voltmeter readings are taken as indicated in Fig. 57: the supply voltage E of the power circuit, and the voltage V_1, V_2 from each line to the ground. (The ground in question may be a system of water pipes, gas pipes, etc.) When the voltmeter is

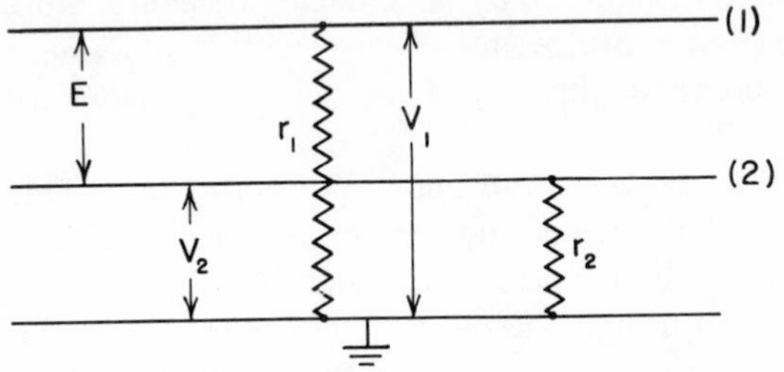

FIG. 57.

connected between line 1 and ground, its resistance R is in parallel with r_1 and the combination in series with r_2. The current is

$$i_1 = \frac{E}{r_2 + \dfrac{r_1 R}{r_1 + R}}$$

and the voltage V_1 read on the voltmeter is

$$V_1 = E - i_1 r_2$$

Then

$$V_1 = i_1 \frac{r_1 R}{r_1 + R}, \quad \text{and} \quad \frac{E - V_1}{V_1} = \frac{r_2(r_1 + R)}{r_1 R}, \quad \text{or} \quad \frac{E}{V_1} = \frac{r_1 r_2 + R(r_1 + r_2)}{r_1 R}$$

Similarly, when the voltmeter is connected between ground and line 2, the current

$$i_2 = \frac{E}{r_1 + \dfrac{r_2 R}{r_2 + R}}$$

and the voltage is $V_2 = E - i_2 r_1$, so that

$$\frac{E}{V_2} = \frac{r_1 r_2 + R(r_1 + r_2)}{r_2 R}$$

We can therefore write

$$\frac{V_1}{V_2} = \frac{r_1}{r_2}, \quad \text{or} \quad r_2 = r_1 \cdot \frac{V_2}{V_1}$$

This value of r_2 may be substituted in our expression for E/V_1, and we have

$$\frac{E}{V_1} = \frac{r_1 \cdot r_1 \dfrac{V_2}{V_1} + r_1 R + R \cdot r_1 \dfrac{V_2}{V_1}}{r_1 R} = \frac{r_1 V_2 + R(V_1 + V_2)}{R V_1}$$

Then

$$r_1 = R\,\frac{E - (V_1 + V_2)}{V_2}$$

Similarly

$$r_2 = R\,\frac{E - (V_1 + V_2)}{V_1}$$

Measurement of Ground Resistance.[74] Since the conduction of electricity in the soil is electrolytic, the measurement of ground resistance is subject to the effects of chemical action and of polarization. It is therefore necessary that alternating current (or periodically reversed direct current) be used in such measurements. The effects of electrode capacitance are usually negligible, however. The distribution of current in the neighborhood of a ground electrode is such that, if the soil is of uniform resistivity, the equipotentials are roughly hemispherical surfaces centered on the electrode. Most of the voltage drop occurs close to the electrode. With the assumption of uniform resistivity it has been calculated that, in the case of an electrode formed by driving a metal rod into the ground, approximately 90% of the resistance is localized within a hemisphere whose radius is twice the depth of the electrode, and that 99% is localized within a radius of 20 times the electrode depth. For plates buried at a considerable depth, 90% of the resistance is localized within a radius of 6 or 7 times the greatest dimension of the plate. In measuring ground resistances, auxiliary potential electrodes should be located outside the equipotential surface, which includes 90% of the resistance of the ground under measurement. Another complication may arise in ground-resistance measurements from the presence of stray currents in the earth or in the electrode under measurement. Their effects may be minimized by using a frequency not present in the stray current.

If a *reference ground* is available whose resistance *is known to be low*,[75] one may measure the combined resistance of the reference ground and the test ground in series, by means of a voltmeter-ammeter method or a Wheatstone bridge, and (neglecting the resistance of the reference ground)

[74] The following discussion is based on the AIEE Master Test Code for Resistance Measurements, AIEE, No. 550, Sept., 1947.

[75] Such a ground might be an extensive system of water pipes at some distance from the electrode under test, or a number of driven grounds separated rather widely from each other and from the test electrode and connected in parallel.

assign the entire resistance to the ground under test. An a-c supply should be used for the measurement, and if the supply is itself grounded an insulating transformer is needed to isolate the measuring circuit. Errors resulting from the presence of stray currents at the measurement frequency may be reduced by taking the mean of measurements made with the connections between the secondary terminals of the isolating transformer and the measuring circuit reversed. If no reference ground is available it is necessary to provide two grounds in addition to the one

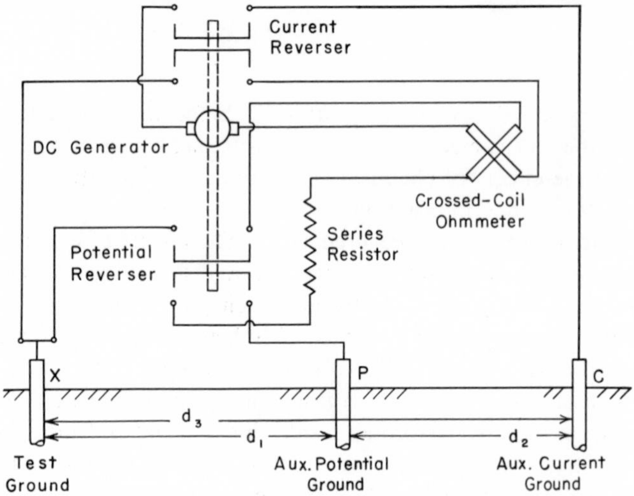

FIG. 58.

under test, one to conduct the measuring current and one to serve as a basis for separating the resistance of the ground under test from that of the auxiliary current-carrying ground. If the two auxiliary grounds are of approximately the same resistance as the ground under test and are sufficiently far removed that the regions of their localized resistances do not overlap, total resistances may be measured successively between pairs of electrodes and the resistance of the test ground can be computed. If these combined resistances of the ground pairs are designated as R_{AB}, R_{AC}, and R_{BC}, the resistance of the test ground R_A is given by the expression $R_A = (R_{AB} + R_{AC} - R_{BC})/2$. If the auxiliary grounds are of considerably higher resistance than the test ground, it may be seen that the expression $R_{AB} + R_{AC} = 2R_A + (R_B + R_C)$ will not differ greatly from $R_{BC} = R_B + R_C$. In this case our expression for R_A becomes the difference between nearly equal quantities, and errors in the individual resistance determinations will be greatly magnified in the final result.

A common method of ground-resistance measurement, making use of a ratio-type ohmmeter, is shown in Fig. 58. Current from the d-c generator, periodically reversed by the "current reverser," flows in the ground between the test electrode and the auxiliary current electrode. The potential drop between the test electrode and the auxiliary potential electrode is rectified by the "potential reverser" operated synchronously with the "current reverser." Since the coils of the ohmmeter carry respectively a current proportional to the voltage PX and the current through X the ohmmeter scale may be marked directly in terms of the

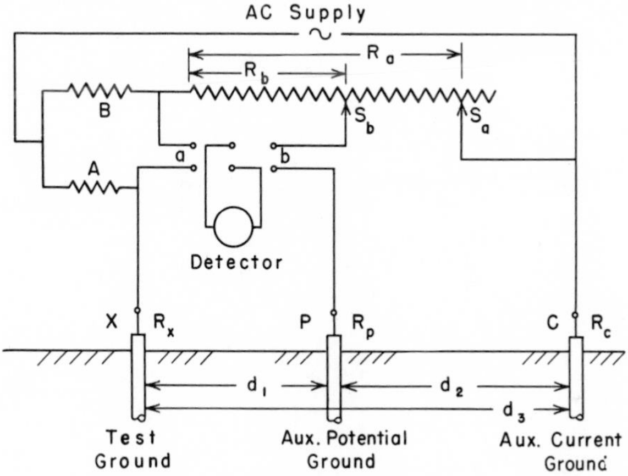

FIG. 59.

resistance of X. It is essential that the resistance of auxiliary potential electrode R_p be negligible compared with that of the series resistor. A high resistance R_c at the auxiliary current electrode reduces the sensitivity of the ohmmeter and the definiteness of its indication. The distances d_1, d_2, and d_3 must be great enough that the localized resistances of the electrodes do not overlap. Usually 50 ft is a reasonable separation.

A bridge method for measuring ground resistance is shown in Fig. 59. Current from an a-c source flows in two parallel circuits. The lower circuit includes the resistor A, the test ground X, and the auxiliary current ground C. The upper circuit includes the fixed resistor B and the adjustable resistor with two slider contacts S_a and S_b. With the detector in position a, slider S_a is adjusted until the detector indicates balance. The currents in the two branches are then inversely proportional to the resistances A and B. With the detector in position b, slider S_b is adjusted until balance is again indicated. The potential drop between grounds S and P is then equal to the drop in the resistance R_b between the detector and the slider S_b. The resistance of the test ground is then $R_x = R_b(A/B)$, and the scale over which S_b moves may be calibrated to read R_x directly in ohms. Resistance at P (R_p) limits the sensitivity of the bridge, and resistance at C (R_c) limits the range of resistances which may be measured. Spacings of the electrodes d_1, d_2, d_3 are subject to the same conditions as for the ohmmeter method above. The a-c source may be a battery-operated buzzer and the detector a telephone receiver. The buzzer tone can usually be recognized and balanced out even in the presence of considerable background noise caused by stray currents.

CHAPTER 8

BALLISTIC GALVANOMETERS

In ballistic measurements our interest is confined to the response of the galvanometer to a transient current or voltage of short duration.[1] A single, short-time impulse is given the moving system of the galvanometer, and the deflection is read at its extreme value, on the first swing. From this maximum deflection the magnitude of the impulse may be determined. Although any d'Arsonval galvanometer may be used ballistically, we shall see that certain characteristics make one galvanometer more suitable for ballistic measurements than another. Also, it will appear from the analysis that the optimum operating conditions for ballistic measurements differ greatly, depending on the type of measurement involved, although in any case the ballistic impulse results from the short-time flow of current through the moving coil of the instrument. Under proper conditions the ballistic deflection of the instrument will be a measure of $\int i\,dt = Q$. In such measurements we may be directly concerned with the quantity of electricity, $Q = \int i\,dt$, which produces the deflection, as, for example, in capacitance measurements in which a capacitor is discharged through the galvanometer circuit. In this case we are interested in the *coulomb sensitivity* of the galvanometer. In inductance measurements (generally d-c magnetic measurements are in this category) we are concerned with $\int e\,dt$ and are interested in the *emf-time* (or flux-linkage) *sensitivity* of the instrument. It is true that in general $Q = \int (e/R)\,dt$, where R is the circuit resistance in which the galvanometer operates, so that we could, if we wished, consider the coulomb sensitivity of the galvanometer in this case also. However, we shall see that consideration of the emf-time sensitivity leads more readily to an expression of the operating conditions which are favorable to the measurement.

We will consider first the question of *coulomb sensitivity* in ballistic

[1] This may be contrasted to our previous study of galvanometer response under conditions in which the current or voltage in the circuit remained at a fixed value for a long enough time that the deflection reached and remained at its steady-state value.

measurements and later will derive the factors which control the measurement of $\int e\,dt$.

QUANTITY MEASUREMENTS

In quantity measurements, it is desirable that the total time during which the current flows to produce $Q = \int i\,dt$ be short compared to the galvanometer period, since it is only under this condition that the galvanometer accurately integrates the current. This requires that the time constant of the measuring circuit (CR or L/R) be small compared to the period of the galvanometer. In capacitance measurements, usually no trouble is encountered in keeping the time constant of the circuit small, but in inductance measurements this is often difficult or impossible since such circuits may be characterized by large inductance associated with small resistance, or our measurement may be such that the flux linkages are changing comparatively slowly in the circuit under test. It is therefore desirable for proper integration of $\int i\,dt$ that the galvanometer period be long.

We have previously seen[2] that the free period of a galvanometer is $T_0 = 2\pi\sqrt{P/U}$, where P is the moment of inertia of the moving system and U is the elastic constant of the suspension. If, then, P is very large or U is small, the free period will be long and the time interval during which the instrument will effectively integrate current will be relatively long. Both these devices are used in ballistic galvanometers. However, it is generally preferable to obtain a long period by large inertia rather than by the use of a small restoring moment, since the decrease of U is limited by zero instability, as we have already seen from the discussion of the d-c galvanometer.[3]

Instantaneous Discharge

We will assume that the quantity to be measured $\left(Q = \int_0^{t'} i\,dt\right)$ passes through the galvanometer coil in a time so short compared to the galvanometer period that no appreciable motion takes place during the impulse interval $(0 - t')$. For all practical purposes the impulse is instantaneous, and there is no subsequent motor torque Gi tending to deflect the

[2] See Chapter 3.

[3] We will see later how in "flux-meter" operation heavy overdamping can be used to increase the effective ballistic interval. In this case zero instability is of minor importance, and it is better to increase the period by a decrease in U rather than to increase P.

galvanometer, during the entire time it is in motion. The equation stating the forces acting on the galvanometer during its motion is[4] then

$$P\frac{d^2\theta}{dt^2} + \left(K + \frac{G^2}{R}\right)\frac{d\theta}{dt} + U\theta = 0$$

or, if for convenience we combine the air-damping and electromagnetic-damping terms, we have

$$P\frac{d^2\theta}{dt^2} + A\frac{d\theta}{dt} + U\theta = 0$$

In this case we have the galvanometer coil moving only under the action of the couples inherent in its construction and in the circuit in which it operates, without the action of any outside driving force after the initial impulse. These couples may be recalled as:

1. Inertial, $P\dfrac{d^2\theta}{dt^2}$ (moment of inertia $\times$ angular acceleration);
2. Air damping, $K\dfrac{d\theta}{dt}$, and electromagnetic damping, $\dfrac{G^2}{R}\dfrac{d\theta}{dt}$;
3. Elastic, $U\theta$ (suspension constant $\times$ angular displacement).

The solution of this equation is

$$\theta = C_1\varepsilon^{m_1t} + C_2\varepsilon^{m_2t}$$

where C_1, C_2 are constants to be determined from our initial (boundary) conditions, and m_1, m_2 are the roots,

$$m = \frac{-A \pm \sqrt{A^2 - 4PU}}{2P}$$

of the equation

$$Pm^2 + Am + U = 0$$

It should be noted that only the transient term of our previous expression is present in the equation of ballistic motion of the galvanometer.

The Underdamped Galvanometer. If the damping is less than critical, m_1 and m_2 are conjugate complex quantities and the equation of motion can be put into the form

$$\theta = \varepsilon^{-At/2P}\, C \sin\left(\frac{\sqrt{4PU - A^2}}{2P}\, t + \alpha\right)$$

where C and α are now the constants of integration which must be determined from the initial conditions. As in the discussion on d-c

[4] See Chapter 3.

galvanometers we will define the relative damping, $\gamma = A/A_c$, and recall that

$$\frac{A_c}{2P} = \sqrt{\frac{U}{P}} = \frac{2\pi}{T_0}$$

where T_0 is the free (undamped) period of the galvanometer. When these substitutions are made, we have

$$\theta = C\varepsilon^{-2\pi\gamma t/T_0} \sin\left(\frac{2\pi t}{T_0}\sqrt{1-\gamma^2} + \alpha\right)$$

We will assume that the motion of the galvanometer starts from the equilibrium position (i.e. $\theta = 0$ when $t = 0$), but to obtain the second initial condition we must examine more closely what happens during the impulse. During this interval the turning moment is the motor couple Gi tending to produce deflection. Then throughout the duration of the impulse the equation of motion is

$$P\frac{d^2\theta}{dt^2} + A\frac{d\theta}{dt} + U\theta = Gi$$

and on integration over the impulse period we have

$$P\frac{d\theta}{dt}\bigg|_0^{t'} + A\theta\bigg|_0^{t'} + U\int_0^{t'}\theta\,dt = G\int_0^{t'} i\,dt = GQ$$

Now, if the impulse time is so short that no appreciable motion has taken place, the terms in A and U are zero since $\theta = 0$, and the equation becomes

$$P\frac{d\theta}{dt} = GQ \quad \text{at} \quad t = 0$$

for an *instantaneous* displacement of electricity producing the impulse. The angular momentum acquired by the moving system is equal to the impulse GQ. Now

$$P = \frac{T_0^{\,2}}{4\pi^2}U$$

and

$\dfrac{G}{U} = \left(\dfrac{\theta_F}{I_g}\right)$ = *current sensitivity* of the galvanometer in the steady-state condition, acting under the influence of a *constant* current[5] I_g

Then

$$\frac{G}{P} = \left(\frac{\theta_F}{I_g}\right)\cdot\frac{4\pi^2}{T_0^2}$$

[5] See Chapter 3.

and we have as initial conditions

$$\begin{cases} (1)\ \theta = 0 \\ (2)\ \dfrac{d\theta}{dt} = Q\left(\dfrac{\theta_F}{I_g}\right)\cdot\dfrac{4\pi^2}{T_0^{\,2}}\bigg|_{t=0} \end{cases}$$

From condition (1) we have $0 = C \sin \alpha$, from which $\alpha = 0$.

From condition (2) we have

$$\frac{d\theta}{dt} = Q\left(\frac{\theta_F}{I_g}\right)\cdot\frac{4\pi^2}{T_0^{\,2}} = C\cdot\sqrt{1-\gamma^2}\cdot\frac{2\pi}{T_0}$$

or

$$C = Q\left(\frac{\theta_F}{I_g}\right)\cdot\frac{2\pi}{T_0}\cdot\frac{1}{\sqrt{1-\gamma^2}}$$

We have then for the equation of ballistic motion of the underdamped galvanometer, following an *instantaneous* impulse,

$$\theta = Q\left(\frac{\theta_F}{I_g}\right)\cdot\frac{2\pi}{T_0}\,\frac{1}{\sqrt{1-\gamma^2}}\,\varepsilon^{-2\pi\gamma t/T_0}\sin\left(\frac{2\pi t}{T_0}\sqrt{1-\gamma^2}\right)$$

The maximum deflection θ_1 on the first swing of the galvanometer is used as a measure of the quantity Q which produced the ballistic impulse. This deflection occurs at a time t_1 when $d\theta/dt = 0$. If we apply this condition we have

$$\gamma\cdot\sin\left(\frac{2\pi t_1}{T_0}\sqrt{1-\gamma^2}\right) = \sqrt{1-\gamma^2}\cdot\cos\left(\frac{2\pi t_1}{T_0}\sqrt{1-\gamma^2}\right)$$

or

$$\tan\left(\frac{2\pi t_1}{T_0}\sqrt{1-\gamma^2}\right) = \frac{\sqrt{1-\gamma^2}}{\gamma}$$

which may be written as

$$\frac{2\pi t_1}{T_0}\sqrt{1-\gamma^2} = \tan^{-1}\frac{\sqrt{1-\gamma^2}}{\gamma}$$

The time to first maximum is then

$$t_1 = \frac{T_0}{2\pi}\cdot\frac{1}{\sqrt{1-\gamma^2}}\tan^{-1}\frac{\sqrt{1-\gamma^2}}{\gamma}$$

When this time is substituted in the equation of motion we obtain for the first maximum deflection

$$\theta_1 = Q\cdot\left(\frac{\theta_F}{I_g}\right)\cdot\frac{2\pi}{T_0}\cdot\frac{1}{\sqrt{1-\gamma^2}}\,\varepsilon^{\frac{-\gamma}{\sqrt{1-\gamma^2}}\tan^{-1}\frac{\sqrt{1-\gamma^2}}{\gamma}}\sin\left(\tan^{-1}\frac{\sqrt{1-\gamma^2}}{\gamma}\right)$$

$$= Q\cdot\left(\frac{\theta_F}{I_g}\right)\cdot\frac{2\pi}{T_0}\,\varepsilon^{-\frac{\gamma}{\sqrt{1-\gamma^2}}\tan^{-1}\frac{\sqrt{1-\gamma^2}}{\gamma}}$$

since

$$\sin\left(\tan^{-1}\frac{\sqrt{1-\gamma^2}}{\gamma}\right) = \sqrt{1-\gamma^2}$$

The coulomb (or ballistic) sensitivity[6] of the galvanometer is then

$$\frac{\theta_1}{Q} = \left(\frac{\theta_F}{I_g}\right)\cdot\frac{2\pi}{T_0}\,\varepsilon^{\frac{-\gamma}{\sqrt{1-\gamma^2}}\tan^{-1}\frac{\sqrt{1-\gamma^2}}{\gamma}}$$

in terms of its current sensitivity, free period, and relative damping. It should be noted that the ballistic sensitivity of a galvanometer, unlike its current sensitivity, is a function of the damping, and that the time to first maximum deflection for a ballistic impulse decreases with increasing damping, whereas the time to first maximum increases with damping for a constant current through the galvanometer coil.

If the damping is so small that $\sqrt{1-\gamma^2} \approx 1$, we have

$$\frac{\theta_1}{Q} = \left(\frac{\theta_F}{I_g}\right)\cdot\frac{2\pi}{T_0}\,\varepsilon^{-\pi\gamma/2}$$

and at zero damping

$$\frac{\theta_1}{Q} = \left(\frac{\theta_F}{I_g}\right)\cdot\frac{2\pi}{T_0}$$

From this relation we may see that the undamped *coulomb sensitivity* of a galvanometer is $2\pi/T_0$ times its current sensitivity.

Ballistic sensitivity is frequently stated in terms of the logarithmic decrement λ, where $\lambda = \log(\theta_1/\theta_2)$ defines the decrement as the natural logarithm of the ratio of successive extreme deflections. It has been shown[7] that

$$\lambda = \frac{\pi\gamma}{\sqrt{1-\gamma^2}}$$

and for small damping we may write

$$\frac{\theta_1}{Q} = \left(\frac{\theta_F}{I_g}\right)\cdot\frac{2\pi}{T_0}\,\varepsilon^{-\lambda/2}$$

If λ is small

$$\varepsilon^{-\lambda/2} = 1 - \frac{\lambda}{2} + \frac{1}{2!}\left(\frac{\lambda}{2}\right)^2\cdots \approx 1 - \frac{\lambda}{2}$$

[6] Here, as elsewhere, sensitivity is defined as the response to unit stimulus.

[7] See Chapter 3.

so that the ballistic sensitivity for small damping may be written as

$$\frac{\theta_1}{Q} \approx \left(\frac{\theta_F}{I_g}\right) \cdot \frac{2\pi}{T_0}\left(1 - \frac{\lambda}{2}\right)$$

in terms of current sensitivity, free period and logarithmic decrement.

The Critically Damped Galvanometer. At critical damping the equation of ballistic motion becomes

$$\theta = \varepsilon^{mt}(C_1 + C_2 t)$$

where

$$m = \frac{-A_c}{2P} = \frac{-2\pi}{T_0}$$

For an *instantaneous* impulse our initial conditions are the same as before:

$$\begin{cases} (1)\ \theta = 0 \\ (2)\ \dfrac{d\theta}{dt} = Q\left(\dfrac{\theta_F}{I_g}\right) \cdot \dfrac{4\pi^2}{T_0^2} \end{cases}\Bigg|_{t=0}$$

From condition (1), $C_1 = 0$.
From condition (2),

$$C_2 = Q\left(\frac{\theta_F}{I_g}\right) \cdot \frac{4\pi^2}{T_0^2}$$

so that our equation of motion becomes

$$\theta = Q\left(\frac{\theta_F}{I_g}\right) \cdot \frac{4\pi^2 t}{T_0^2}\, \varepsilon^{-2\pi t/T_0}$$

The maximum deflection θ_1 occurs when $d\theta/dt = 0$, at a time $t_1 = T_0/2\pi$, and is

$$\theta_1 = Q\left(\frac{\theta_F}{I_g}\right) \cdot \frac{2\pi}{T_0}\, \varepsilon^{-1}$$

On comparing these results with those obtained for the undamped galvanometer, we see that for a given quantity of electricity Q, *instantaneously* displaced through the galvanometer coil, the ballistic deflection of the critically damped galvanometer is $1/\varepsilon$ or 37% of the undamped deflection; and that the time to maximum deflection is $2/\pi$ or 64% of the time to first maximum of the undamped galvanometer.

The Overdamped Galvanometer. For damping greater than critical ($\gamma > 1$) the equation of ballistic motion following an *instantaneous* impulse is

$$\theta = C_1\varepsilon^{m_1 t} + C_2\varepsilon^{m_2 t}$$

where

$$m_1 = \frac{2\pi}{T_0}(-\gamma + \sqrt{\gamma^2 - 1}) \quad \text{and} \quad m_2 = \frac{2\pi}{T_0}(-\gamma - \sqrt{\gamma^2 - 1})$$

with the same initial conditions as before.

From condition (1) we have $0 = C_1 + C_2$.

From condition (2)

$$Q\left(\frac{\theta_F}{I_g}\right) \cdot \frac{4\pi^2}{T_0^2} = (m_1 - m_2)C_1 = 2C_1\sqrt{\gamma^2 - 1} \cdot \frac{2\pi}{T_0}$$

whence

$$C_1 = -C_2 = Q\left(\frac{\theta_F}{I_g}\right) \cdot \frac{2\pi}{T_0} \cdot \frac{1}{2\sqrt{\gamma^2 - 1}}$$

The equation of motion becomes

$$\theta = Q\left(\frac{\theta_F}{I_g}\right) \cdot \frac{2\pi}{T_0} \cdot \frac{1}{2\sqrt{\gamma^2 - 1}}\left(\varepsilon^{\frac{2\pi t}{T_0}(-\gamma + \sqrt{\gamma^2 - 1})} - \varepsilon^{\frac{2\pi t}{T_0}(-\gamma - \sqrt{\gamma^2 - 1})}\right)$$

$$= Q\left(\frac{\theta_F}{I_g}\right) \cdot \frac{2\pi}{T_0} \cdot \frac{1}{2\sqrt{\gamma^2 - 1}}\,\varepsilon^{\frac{-2\pi\gamma t}{T_0}}\left(\varepsilon^{\frac{2\pi t}{T_0}\sqrt{\gamma^2 - 1}} - \varepsilon^{\frac{-2\pi t}{T_0}\sqrt{\gamma^2 - 1}}\right)$$

$$= Q\left(\frac{\theta_F}{I_g}\right) \cdot \frac{2\pi}{T_0} \cdot \frac{1}{\sqrt{\gamma^2 - 1}}\,\varepsilon^{\frac{-2\pi\gamma t}{T_0}} \sinh\left(\frac{2\pi t}{T_0}\sqrt{\gamma^2 - 1}\right)$$

For the time t_1 to maximum deflection (when $d\theta/dt = 0$) we have

$$\gamma \sinh\left(\frac{2\pi t_1}{T_0}\sqrt{\gamma^2 - 1}\right) = \sqrt{\gamma^2 - 1} \cosh\left(\frac{2\pi t_1}{T_0}\sqrt{\gamma^2 - 1}\right)$$

whence

$$\tanh\left(\frac{2\pi t_1}{T_0}\sqrt{\gamma^2 - 1}\right) = \frac{\sqrt{\gamma^2 - 1}}{\gamma}$$

or

$$\frac{2\pi t_1}{T_0}\sqrt{\gamma^2 - 1} = \tanh^{-1}\frac{\sqrt{\gamma^2 - 1}}{\gamma}$$

and

$$t_1 = \frac{T_0}{2\pi} \cdot \frac{1}{\sqrt{\gamma^2 - 1}} \tanh^{-1}\frac{\sqrt{\gamma^2 - 1}}{\gamma}$$

Then the maximum deflection is

$$\theta_1 = Q \cdot \left(\frac{\theta_F}{I_g}\right) \cdot \frac{2\pi}{T_0} \cdot \frac{1}{\sqrt{\gamma^2 - 1}}\,\varepsilon^{-\frac{\gamma}{\sqrt{\gamma^2 - 1}}\tanh^{-1}\frac{\sqrt{\gamma^2 - 1}}{\gamma}} \sinh\left(\tanh^{-1}\frac{\sqrt{\gamma^2 - 1}}{\gamma}\right)$$

Now

$$\tanh^{-1}\frac{\sqrt{\gamma^2-1}}{\gamma} = \frac{1}{2}\log_\varepsilon\frac{\gamma+\sqrt{\gamma^2-1}}{\gamma-\sqrt{\gamma^2-1}} = u$$

and

$$\sinh u = \frac{1}{2}(\varepsilon^u - \varepsilon^{-u}) = \frac{1}{2}\left(\varepsilon^{\log\sqrt{\frac{\gamma+\sqrt{\gamma^2-1}}{\gamma-\sqrt{\gamma^2-1}}}} - \varepsilon^{-\log\sqrt{\frac{\gamma+\sqrt{\gamma^2-1}}{\gamma-\sqrt{\gamma^2-1}}}}\right)$$

$$= \frac{1}{2}\left(\sqrt{\frac{\gamma+\sqrt{\gamma^2-1}}{\gamma-\sqrt{\gamma^2-1}}} - \sqrt{\frac{\gamma-\sqrt{\gamma^2-1}}{\gamma+\sqrt{\gamma^2-1}}}\right)$$

$$= \frac{1}{2}\left(\frac{\gamma+\sqrt{\gamma^2-1}-\gamma+\sqrt{\gamma^2-1}}{\gamma^2-(\gamma^2-1)}\right) = \sqrt{\gamma^2-1}$$

Then

$$\theta_1 = Q\left(\frac{\theta_F}{I_g}\right)\cdot\frac{2\pi}{T_0}\,\varepsilon^{-\frac{\gamma}{\sqrt{\gamma^2-1}}\tanh^{-1}\frac{\sqrt{\gamma^2-1}}{\gamma}}$$

It will be seen later that the case in which γ is very large is of considerable importance. Here our expression can be reduced to a simpler form. If $\gamma \gg 1$, we have approximately

$$\varepsilon^{-\frac{\gamma}{\sqrt{\gamma^2-1}}\tanh^{-1}\frac{\sqrt{\gamma^2-1}}{\gamma}} = \varepsilon^{-\log_\varepsilon\sqrt{\frac{\gamma+\sqrt{\gamma^2-1}}{\gamma-\sqrt{\gamma^2-1}}}} = \sqrt{\frac{\gamma-\sqrt{\gamma^2-1}}{\gamma+\sqrt{\gamma^2-1}}}$$

$$= \sqrt{\frac{1-\sqrt{1-\frac{1}{\gamma^2}}}{1+\sqrt{1-\frac{1}{\gamma^2}}}} \approx \sqrt{\frac{1-\left(1-\frac{1}{2\gamma^2}\right)}{1+\left(1-\frac{1}{2\gamma^2}\right)}}$$

$$\approx \sqrt{\frac{1}{4\gamma^2}} = \frac{1}{2\gamma}$$

So that

$$\theta_1 \approx Q\left(\frac{\theta_F}{I_g}\right)\cdot\frac{2\pi}{T_0}\cdot\frac{1}{2\gamma}, \quad \text{and} \quad t_1 \approx \frac{T_0}{2\pi}\frac{\log_\varepsilon(4\gamma^2-1)}{2\gamma} \quad \text{for } \gamma \gg 1$$

Summary. The formulas for coulomb sensitivity may now be summarized for the condition that the quantity Q, which gives rise to the ballistic impulse, is displaced through the galvanometer *instantaneously*. We will compare the deflection θ_1 in each case with the deflection at zero damping, and the time to maximum deflection t_1 with the corresponding time for the undamped galvanometer, designating the undamped deflection and time by the subscripts 0, 1.

γ		θ_1	t_1
$\gamma = 0$	(undamped)	$\theta_1 = Q \cdot \frac{2\pi}{T_0} \cdot \left(\frac{\theta_F}{I_g}\right) = {}_0\theta_1$	$t_1 = \frac{T_0}{4} = {}_0t_1$
$\gamma \ll 1$	(under-damped)	$\theta_1 \approx {}_0\theta_1 \cdot \varepsilon^{-\pi\gamma/2}$	$t_1 \approx {}_0t_1 \cdot \frac{2}{\pi} \cdot \tan^{-1}\frac{1}{\gamma}$
$\gamma < 1$	(under-damped)	$\theta_1 = {}_0\theta_1 \cdot \varepsilon^{-\frac{\gamma}{\sqrt{1-\gamma^2}} \tan^{-1}\left(\frac{\sqrt{1-\gamma^2}}{\gamma}\right)}$	$t_1 = {}_0t_1 \cdot \frac{2}{\pi} \cdot \frac{\tan^{-1}\left(\frac{\sqrt{1-\gamma^2}}{\gamma}\right)}{\sqrt{1-\gamma^2}}$
$\gamma = 1$	(critically damped)	$\theta_1 = {}_0\theta_1 \cdot \varepsilon^{-1}$	$t_1 = {}_0t_1 \cdot \frac{2}{\pi}$
$\gamma > 1$	(over-damped)	$\theta_1 = {}_0\theta_1 \cdot \varepsilon^{-\frac{\gamma}{\sqrt{\gamma^2-1}} \tanh^{-1}\left(\frac{\sqrt{\gamma^2-1}}{\gamma}\right)}$	$t_1 = {}_0t_1 \cdot \frac{2}{\pi} \cdot \frac{\tanh^{-1}\left(\frac{\sqrt{\gamma^2-1}}{\gamma}\right)}{\sqrt{\gamma^2-1}}$
$\gamma \gg 1$	(over-damped)	$\theta_1 \approx {}_0\theta_1 \cdot \frac{1}{2\gamma} \underset{(\gamma \to \infty)}{\to} 0$	$t_1 \approx {}_0t_1 \cdot \frac{2}{\pi} \cdot \frac{\log_\varepsilon 4\gamma^2}{2\gamma} \underset{(\gamma \to \infty)}{\to} 0$

The ballistic behavior of the d-c galvanometer with varying damping may be seen from Figs. 1 to 3. From Fig. 1 it will be seen that the reading time t_1 (time to maximum deflection) decreases continuously as γ

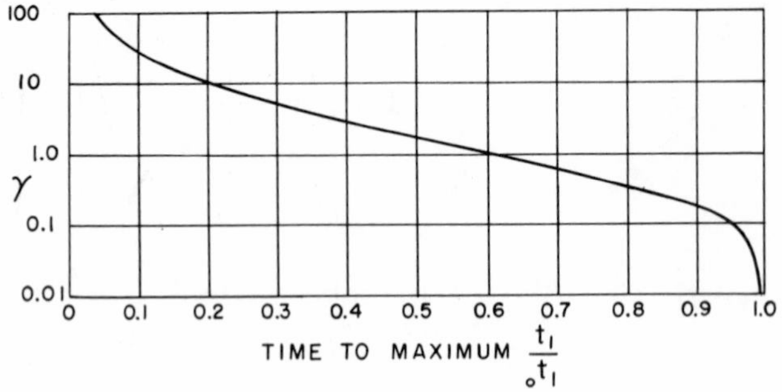

FIG. 1.

is increased, so that, if this is an important factor in a measurement, it will be profitable to work with fairly large damping. On the other hand, if the maximum *coulomb sensitivity* is desired, the damping should be reduced to the minimum value possible with the circuit conditions encountered, as may be seen from Fig. 2. It will also be noted from Fig. 3 that in either extreme case the return of the galvanometer to rest at zero deflection is slower than for intermediate values of damping near the critical value. There is, near critical damping, little to choose in convenience over a considerable range of damping. The final return to rest

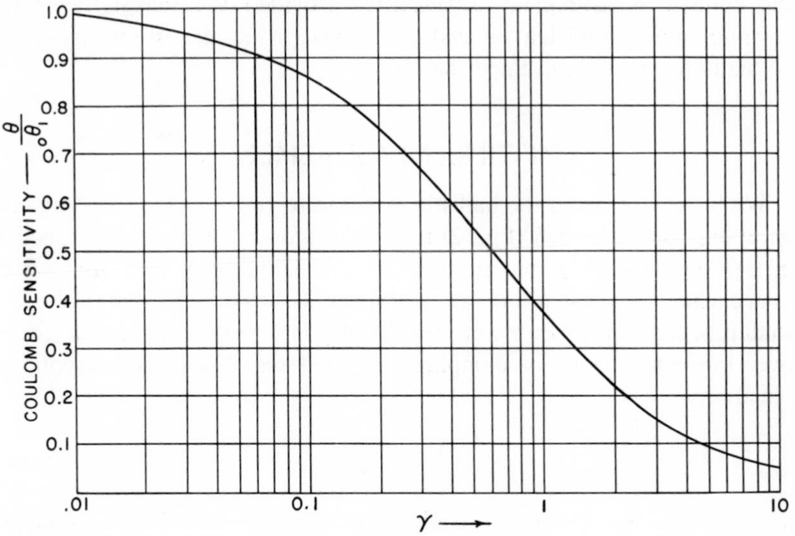

FIG. 2.

within less than 2% of the maximum deflection takes about the same time at $\gamma = 0.8$ and $\gamma = 1$, but a slight overshoot past zero followed by return to zero is often desirable, as it informs the observer that the coil is moving

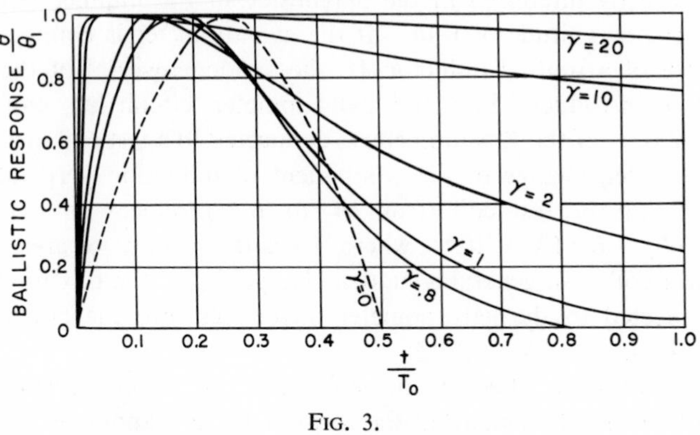

FIG. 3.

freely without obstruction or sticking. It is therefore convenient in many cases to adjust the damping to slightly less than critical (say, $\gamma = 0.8$). The return to rest is then accomplished in the minimum time possible without manipulation on the part of the observer (see p. 335), who has in addition the assurance that there is no sticking of the moving system. This may be said to constitute the optimum use condition for the ballistic measurement of *quantity*, provided the sensitivity of the galvanometer is sufficient so that the necessary sacrifice in sensitivity can be made to secure convenient damping.

EMF-TIME MEASUREMENTS

We have considered the ballistic response to $\int i\,dt = Q$ for any possible damping and have seen (Fig. 2) that the *coulomb sensitivity* is a function of damping which is maximum when the damping is zero, and which approaches zero when the galvanometer is heavily overdamped. We shall now derive the expressions for the response to $\int e\,dt$ in a closed circuit over the entire range of damping and shall see that the corresponding sensitivity

$$_{\gamma}S_{\phi N} = \frac{_{\gamma}\theta_1}{\int e\,dt}$$

is zero when $\gamma = 0$ and approaches a maximum when the galvanometer is heavily overdamped.

Actually from a practical viewpoint the *flux-linkage* sensitivity of a galvanometer and its specification are far more useful and important than the corresponding statements of *coulomb sensitivity* already derived. In most of the ballistic measurements which are made in the laboratory we are directly interested in the magnitude of the impulse $\int e\,dt$, rather than in the magnitude of $\int i\,dt$. If the galvanometer is connected to the secondary of a mutual inductor M, the sudden reversal of the primary current I introduces into the galvanometer circuit an emf impulse $\int e\,dt = 2MI$. If the galvanometer is connected to a test coil in a magnetic field, a sudden change of the component of induction perpendicular to the plane of the test coil (from B_1 to B_2) produces an emf impulse $\int e\,dt = (B_1 - B_2)AN \times 10^{-8}$, where AN is the product of area and turns in the test coil. In general a sudden change $\Delta\phi$ of the flux linking a test coil connected to the galvanometer introduces into the circuit an emf impulse $\int e\,dt = \Delta\phi N \times 10^{-8}$.

In evaluating the effect of an emf impulse $\int e\,dt$ on the galvanometer we will first modify somewhat the form of the galvanometer equation of motion. In its most general terms this equation is

$$P\frac{d^2\theta}{dt^2} + \left(K + \frac{G^2}{R}\right)\frac{d\theta}{dt} + U\theta = \frac{Ge}{R}$$

where e is the instantaneous value of the emf acting in the circuit. If we recall that $U/P = 4\pi^2/T_0^2 = \omega_0^2$, that $K = 2\gamma_0\sqrt{PU}$, and that $K + (G^2/R) = 2\gamma\sqrt{PU}$, we may write

$$\frac{d^2\theta}{dt^2} + 2\gamma\omega_0 \frac{d\theta}{dt} + \omega_0^2\theta = \frac{2\omega_0(\gamma - \gamma_0)}{G} e$$

Instantaneous Impulse

If the galvanometer starts from its equilibrium position ($\theta = 0$, at $t = 0$), and the impulse is of such short duration that the displacement during the impulse interval has no effect on the subsequent motion of the galvanometer, the galvanometer equation may be integrated over the impulse interval to

$$\left.\frac{d\theta}{dt}\right|_0^{t'} + \left. 2\gamma\omega_0\theta\right|_0^{t'} + \omega_0^2\int_0^{t'} \theta\, dt = \frac{2\omega_0(\gamma - \gamma_0)}{G}\int_0^{t'} e\, dt$$

As before the terms in θ and $\int\theta\, dt$ are substantially zero during the impulse period, and we have

$$\frac{d\theta}{dt} = \frac{2\omega_0(\gamma - \gamma_0)}{G}\int_0^{t'} e\, dt$$

(at $t = 0$ for an *instantaneous* emf impulse). The initial (boundary) conditions just set up are analogous to those established in the previous discussion of the *coulomb sensitivity*, and, as before, the subsequent motion is described by setting the right-hand side of the equation of motion equal to zero. Thus we must solve the equation

$$\frac{d^2\theta}{dt^2} + 2\gamma\omega_0 \frac{d\theta}{dt} + \omega_0^2\theta = 0$$

subject to the initial conditions

$$\begin{cases} (1)\ \theta = 0 \\ (2)\ \dfrac{d\theta}{dt} = \left.\dfrac{2\omega_0(\gamma - \gamma_0)}{G}\displaystyle\int_0^{t'} e\, dt\right|_{t=0} \end{cases}$$

The Underdamped Galvanometer. For the underdamped case ($\gamma < 1$), the roots of the auxiliary equation are

$$\begin{Bmatrix} m_1 = -\ \omega_0(\gamma + j\sqrt{1 - \gamma^2}) \\ m_2 = -\ \omega_0(\gamma - j\sqrt{1 - \gamma^2}) \end{Bmatrix}$$

and the solution may be expressed as

$$\theta = C_1\varepsilon^{m_1t} + C_2\varepsilon^{m_2t} = C\varepsilon^{-\ \omega_0\gamma t}\sin(\omega_0 t\sqrt{1 - \gamma^2} + \alpha)$$

where C and α are the constants of integration.

From boundary condition (1) we have $\alpha = 0$.
From boundary condition (2) we have

$$C = \frac{2(\gamma - \gamma_0)}{G\sqrt{1-\gamma^2}} \int_0^{t'} e\, dt$$

The equation describing the ballistic response of an *underdamped* galvanometer to an instantaneous emf impulse, $\int e\, dt$, is then

$$\theta = \frac{2(\gamma - \gamma_0)\int e\, dt}{G\sqrt{1-\gamma^2}} \cdot \varepsilon^{-\omega_0 \gamma t} \sin(\omega_0 t\sqrt{1-\gamma^2})$$

Recalling that $\omega_0 = 2\pi/T_0$, we have

$$\theta = \frac{2(\gamma - \gamma_0)\int e\, dt}{G\sqrt{1-\gamma^2}} \varepsilon^{-2\pi\gamma t/T_0} \sin\left(\frac{2\pi t}{T_0}\sqrt{1-\gamma^2}\right)$$

The time to maximum deflection has previously been found to be

$$t_1 = \frac{T_0}{2\pi\sqrt{1-\gamma^2}} \tan^{-1}\frac{\sqrt{1-\gamma^2}}{\gamma}$$

so that the maximum deflection is

$$\theta_1 = \frac{2(\gamma - \gamma_0)}{G} \int e\, dt \cdot \varepsilon^{-\frac{\gamma}{\sqrt{1-\gamma^2}} \tan^{-1}\frac{\sqrt{1-\gamma^2}}{\gamma}}$$

The emf-time (or flux-linkage) sensitivity of the underdamped galvanometer may now be written as

$$(\gamma < 1) \qquad {}_{\gamma}S_{\phi N} = \frac{\theta_1}{\int e\, dt} = \frac{2(\gamma - \gamma_0)}{G} \varepsilon^{-\frac{\gamma}{\sqrt{1-\gamma^2}} \tan^{-1}\frac{\sqrt{1-\gamma^2}}{\gamma}}$$

The Critically Damped Galvanometer. For the critically damped galvanometer ($\gamma = 1$) the solution of the equation of motion is

$$\theta = \varepsilon^{-\omega_0 t}(C_1 + C_2 t)$$

From boundary condition (1) we have $C_1 = 0$.
From boundary condition (2) we have

$$C_2 = \frac{2\omega_0(1 - \gamma_0)\int e\, dt}{G}$$

so that

$$\theta = \frac{2\omega_0(1 - \gamma_0)\int e\, dt}{G} t\varepsilon^{-\omega_0 t}$$

describes the ballistic response of the *critically damped* galvanometer to an emf impulse. For maximum deflection

$$t_1 = \frac{1}{\omega_0} = \frac{T_0}{2\pi} \quad \text{and} \quad \theta_1 = \frac{2(1-\gamma_0)\int e\,dt}{G}\,\varepsilon^{-1}$$

The emf-time sensitivity of the critically damped galvanometer is

$$(\gamma = 1) \qquad {}_1S_{\phi N} = \frac{\theta_1}{\int e\,dt} = \frac{2(1-\gamma_0)}{G}\,\varepsilon^{-1}$$

The Overdamped Galvanometer. For damping greater than critical $(\gamma > 1)$ the equation of motion is

$$\theta = C_1\varepsilon^{m_1t} + C_2\varepsilon^{m_2t}$$

where

$$\begin{cases} m_1 = -\,\omega_0(\gamma + \sqrt{\gamma^2 - 1}) \\ m_2 = -\,\omega_0(\gamma - \sqrt{\gamma^2 - 1}) \end{cases}$$

From boundary condition (1) we have $C_1 + C_2 = 0$.
From boundary condition (2) we have

$$(m_1 - m_2)C_1 = -\,2\omega_0\sqrt{\gamma^2 - 1}\,C_1 = \frac{2\omega_0(\gamma - \gamma_0)\int e\,dt}{G}$$

so that

$$C_1 = -\,C_2 = \frac{(\gamma - \gamma_0)\int e\,dt}{-\sqrt{\gamma^2 - 1}\cdot G}$$

and

$$\theta = \frac{(\gamma - \gamma_0)\int e\,dt}{-\,G\sqrt{\gamma^2 - 1}}\,\varepsilon^{-\,\omega_0\gamma t}[\varepsilon^{-\,\omega_0\sqrt{\gamma^2-1}\,t} - \varepsilon^{\omega_0\sqrt{\gamma^2-1}\,t}]$$

But

$$\varepsilon^{-\,\omega_0\sqrt{\gamma^2-1}\,t} - \varepsilon^{\omega_0\sqrt{\gamma^2-1}\,t} = -\,2\sinh\,(\omega_0\sqrt{\gamma^2 - 1}\;t)$$

and the ballistic response of the *overdamped* galvanometer to an instantaneous emf impulse is described by the equation

$$\theta = \frac{2(\gamma - \gamma_0)\int e\,dt}{G\sqrt{\gamma^2 - 1}}\,\varepsilon^{-\,\omega_0\gamma t}\sinh\,(\omega_0 t\sqrt{\gamma^2 - 1})$$

$$= \frac{2(\gamma - \gamma_0)\int e\,dt}{G\sqrt{\gamma^2 - 1}}\,\varepsilon^{-\,2\pi\gamma t/T_0}\sinh\left(\frac{2\pi t}{T_0}\sqrt{\gamma^2 - 1}\right)$$

For maximum deflection

$$t_1 = \frac{1}{\omega_0\sqrt{\gamma^2 - 1}} \tanh^{-1} \frac{\sqrt{\gamma^2 - 1}}{\gamma}$$

and

$$\theta_1 = \frac{2(\gamma - \gamma_0)\int e\, dt}{G}\, \varepsilon^{-\frac{\gamma}{\sqrt{\gamma^2 - 1}} \tanh^{-1} \frac{\sqrt{\gamma^2 - 1}}{\gamma}}$$

The emf-time sensitivity of the *overdamped* galvanometer is

$$(\gamma > 1) \qquad {}_\gamma S_{\phi N} = \frac{\theta_1}{\int e\, dt} = \frac{2(\gamma - \gamma_0)}{G}\, \varepsilon^{-\frac{\gamma}{\sqrt{\gamma^2 - 1}} \tanh^{-1} \frac{\sqrt{\gamma^2 - 1}}{\gamma}}$$

If the damping is very large the sensitivity may be expressed approximately as

$$(\gamma \gg 1) \qquad {}_\gamma S_{\phi N} \approx \frac{2(\gamma - \gamma_0)}{G} \cdot \frac{1}{2\gamma} \underset{(\gamma \to \infty)}{\to} \frac{1}{G}$$

Summary. The formulas for flux-linkage (emf-time) sensitivity as a function of damping may be summarized as follows (for an instantaneous $\int e\, dt$ impulse), using the characteristic equation

$${}_\gamma S_{\phi N} = \frac{\theta_1}{\int e\, dt} = \frac{(\gamma - \gamma_0)}{G} M$$

$$1 > \gamma > \gamma_0 \qquad M = 2\varepsilon^{-\frac{\gamma}{\sqrt{1 - \gamma^2}} \tan^{-1} \frac{\sqrt{1 - \gamma^2}}{\gamma}} \qquad t_1 = \frac{T_0}{2\pi\sqrt{1 - \gamma^2}} \tan^{-1} \frac{\sqrt{1 - \gamma^2}}{\gamma}$$

$$\gamma = 1 \qquad M = 2\varepsilon^{-1} \qquad t_1 = \frac{T_0}{2\pi}$$

$$\gamma > 1 \qquad M = 2\varepsilon^{\frac{-\gamma}{\sqrt{\gamma^2 - 1}} \tanh^{-1} \frac{\sqrt{\gamma^2 - 1}}{\gamma}} \qquad t_1 = \frac{T_0}{2\pi\sqrt{\gamma^2 - 1}} \tanh^{-1} \frac{\sqrt{\gamma^2 - 1}}{\gamma}$$

$$\gamma \gg 1 \qquad M \approx \frac{1}{\gamma} \qquad t_1 \approx \frac{T_0}{2\pi} \frac{\log_\varepsilon 4\gamma^2}{2\gamma}$$

In the above equations the flux-linkage sensitivity is expressed in terms of damping and of the motor constant, G, of the galvanometer. The latter is a design constant and is not usually known to us from catalog information. Hence, if we are to compute the flux-linkage sensitivity of a galvanometer in order to determine its suitability for a particular measurement job, it will be well to express the sensitivity in terms of working constants whose values are readily available. We have that

$$Q = \int i\, dt = \frac{1}{R} \int e\, dt$$

R being the total resistance of the circuit (including that of the galvanometer itself). For any particular value of damping γ we have then

$$\frac{\theta_1}{\int i\,dt} = \frac{\theta_1}{\dfrac{1}{R}\int e\,dt}$$

so that

$${}_\gamma S_{\phi N} = \frac{{}_\gamma S_q}{R}$$

but, from our previous discussion of galvanometers,[8] we have that

$$R = R_c \frac{1-\gamma_0}{\gamma-\gamma_0}$$

where R_c is the circuit resistance at critical damping. Then

$${}_\gamma S_{\phi N} = \frac{{}_\gamma S_q}{R_c\left(\dfrac{1-\gamma_0}{\gamma-\gamma_0}\right)} = \frac{{}_\gamma S_q\,(\gamma-\gamma_0)}{R_c\,(1-\gamma_0)} = \left(\frac{\theta_F}{I_g}\right)\cdot\frac{2\pi}{T_0}\cdot\frac{1}{R_c}\cdot\frac{\gamma-\gamma_0}{1-\gamma_0}\cdot\frac{M}{2}$$

For the case which is of greatest interest ($\gamma \gg 1$) we have

$${}_\gamma S_{\phi N} = \left(\frac{\theta_F}{I_g}\right)\cdot\frac{2\pi}{T_0}\cdot\frac{1}{R_c}\cdot\frac{\gamma-\gamma_0}{1-\gamma_0}\cdot\frac{1}{2\gamma} \rightarrow \left(\frac{\theta_F}{I_g}\right)\cdot\frac{2\pi}{T_0}\cdot\frac{1}{2R_c}\cdot\frac{1}{1-\gamma_0}$$

giving us the limiting value of flux-linkage sensitivity in terms of current sensitivity, free period, critical damping resistance, and open-circuit damping. The flux-linkage sensitivity is of course zero when $\gamma = \gamma_0$ (i.e. on open circuit) and increases with increasing γ to the limiting value just stated as γ becomes very large.[9] This may be seen from Table 1, in which values of M and of the ratio ${}_\gamma S_{\phi N}/{}_\infty S_{\phi N}$ have been computed.

The manner in which flux-linkage sensitivity varies with damping is shown in Fig. 4.

It appears from the above discussion that, if $\int e\,dt$ is to be measured ballistically, the greatest sensitivity is attained by using the galvanometer in a circuit in which it is heavily overdamped. It is important to note, however, that this sensitivity is not fully utilized if the damping is obtained

[8] See p. 62.

[9] It should be noted that γ does not become infinite on short circuit since we still have left the resistance of the galvanometer coil as the minimum circuit resistance attainable. In practice γ cannot usually attain a value of more than 50, and its maximum value is much less than this in many cases.

TABLE 1

FLUX-LINKAGE SENSITIVITY AS A FUNCTION OF DAMPING

γ	M	$\frac{_{\gamma}S_{\phi N}}{_{\infty}S_{\phi N}}$ For $\gamma_0 = 0$	For $\gamma_0 = 0.1$
0.1	1.726	0.1726	0.000
0.2	1.512	0.3024	0.1512
0.5	1.092	0.546	0.437
0.7	0.918	0.643	0.551
0.8	0.848	0.678	0.594
0.9	0.788	0.709	0.630
1.0	0.736	0.736	0.662
1.5	0.550	0.825	0.770
2	0.437	0.874	0.830
3	0.308	0.924	0.893
4	0.237	0.948	0.924
5	0.193	0.965	0.946
10	0.099	0.990	0.980
20	0.0498	0.996	0.991
30	0.03324	0.997	0.994
40	0.02496	0.998	0.996
50	0.0200	1.000	0.998
100	0.0100	1.000	0.999

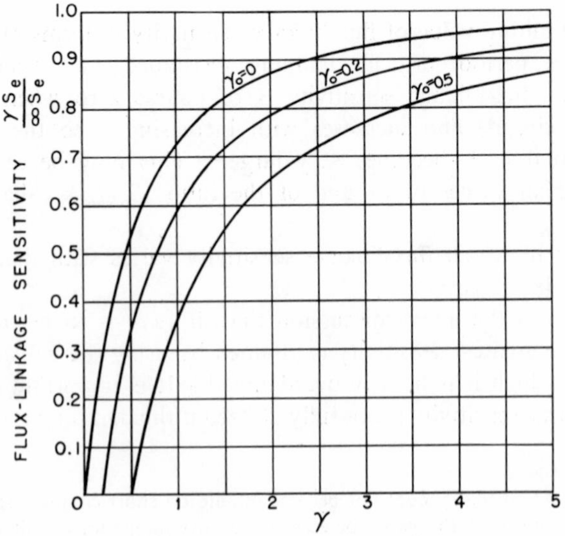

FIG. 4.

by shunting the galvanometer with a low resistance at its terminals so that current is by-passed around the galvanometer coil. It is usually possible to attain heavy overdamping without the use of shunts, since the usual type of ballistic galvanometer has a long period and consequently a high critical damping resistance, whereas the resistance of a search coil or of the secondary of a mutual inductor is low compared to the resistance required for critical damping. There are other important reasons for operating a ballistic galvanometer heavily overdamped, as we shall see from the discussion below. But, since shunts are used frequently to adjust the "working" sensitivity of a galvanometer to an $\int e\,dt$ impulse in its circuit, we shall first discuss the effect of such a shunt in the case of

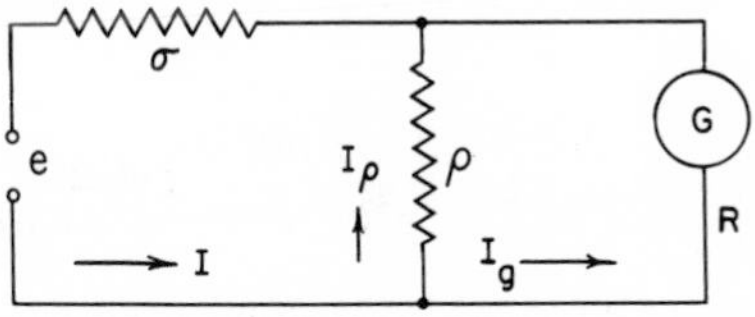

FIG. 5.

the heavily overdamped ballistic galvanometer. The result will be directly applicable to fluxmeters.

The Shunted Galvanometer. In the circuit shown in Fig. 5 we will consider separately the effects of the emf e responsible for the ballistic impulse, and of the counter emf generated by the motion of the galvanometer coil. The current which would flow if there were no counter emf is

$$I = \frac{e}{\sigma + \dfrac{\rho R}{\rho + R}} = \frac{e(\rho + R)}{\sigma\rho + \sigma R + \rho R}$$

and

$$\frac{I_\rho}{I_g} = \frac{R}{\rho}$$

so that

$$I = I_g\left(\frac{\rho + R}{\rho}\right)$$

The current through the galvanometer coil if e only were acting is

$$I_g = \frac{e\rho}{\sigma\rho + \sigma R + \rho R}$$

As viewed from the galvanometer terminals the circuit resistance is

$\sigma\rho/(\sigma + \rho)$, so that the current through the galvanometer coil resulting from its generator action only would be

$$I_g' = \frac{-G\dfrac{d\theta}{dt}}{R + \dfrac{\sigma\rho}{\sigma + \rho}} = \frac{-G(\sigma + \rho)\dfrac{d\theta}{dt}}{\sigma\rho + \sigma R + \rho R}$$

Let $I_g + I_g' = i$ be the galvanometer current resulting from the combined action of the external and the counter emf. The equation of motion

$$P\frac{d^2\theta}{dt^2} + K\frac{d\theta}{dt} + U\theta = Gi$$

can be written as

$$P\frac{d^2\theta}{dt^2} + \left[K + \frac{G^2(\sigma + \rho)}{\sigma\rho + \sigma R + \rho R}\right]\frac{d\theta}{dt} + U\theta = \frac{G\rho e}{\sigma\rho + \sigma R + \rho R}$$

Now for $\gamma \gg 1$ we have the maximum deflection

$$\theta_1 = Q \cdot \frac{2\pi}{T_0}\left(\frac{\theta_F}{I_g}\right)\frac{1}{2\gamma} = \frac{QB}{2\gamma}$$

and for our case in the presence of the shunt

$${}_\rho\theta_1 = \frac{Q_\rho B}{2\gamma_\rho}$$

where

$$Q_\rho = \frac{\rho\int e\,dt}{\sigma\rho + \sigma R + \rho R}$$

For the same series resistance, but without the shunt ($\rho = \infty$), we could write

$${}_\sigma\theta_1 = \frac{Q_\sigma B}{2\gamma_\sigma}$$

where

$$Q_\sigma = \frac{\int e\,dt}{R + \sigma}$$

Now

$$\gamma_\rho = \frac{A}{A_c} = \frac{K}{A_c} + \frac{G^2(\sigma + \rho)}{A_c(\sigma\rho + \sigma R + \rho R)}$$

But $K/A_c = \gamma_0$, which can be neglected if γ_ρ is very large, so that

$$\gamma_\rho \approx \frac{G^2}{A_c} \cdot \frac{(\sigma + \rho)}{(\sigma\rho + \sigma R + \rho R)}$$

Similarly

$$\gamma_\sigma = \frac{G^2}{A_c} \cdot \frac{1}{(\sigma + R)}$$

Then

$$\frac{\gamma_\rho}{\gamma_\sigma} = \frac{(\sigma + \rho)(\sigma + R)}{(\sigma\rho + \sigma R + \rho R)}$$

We may now write the ratio of the two deflections

$$\frac{{}_\rho\theta_1}{{}_\sigma\theta_1} = \frac{B\rho\int e\,dt}{(\sigma\rho + \sigma R + \rho R)2\gamma_\rho} \bigg/ \frac{B\int e\,dt}{(\sigma + R)2\gamma_\sigma}$$

$$= \frac{\rho(\sigma + R)}{(\sigma\rho + \sigma R + \rho R)} \cdot \frac{\gamma_\sigma}{\gamma_\rho} = \frac{\rho}{\sigma + \rho}$$

For a given $\int e\,dt$ the ballistic deflection is decreased by the presence of a shunt across the galvanometer terminals in the ratio of the shunt resistance to the sum of the shunt and external series resistance. It should be noted that the resistance of the galvanometer (or fluxmeter) does not enter into this expression.

Prolonged Impulse

In the previous discussion we have considered only those cases in which the impulse was instantaneous or was completed so quickly that no appreciable deflection took place during the impulse interval. These assumptions were implied both in the equation of motion and in the boundary conditions. Where these assumptions are not valid the galvanometer deflection does not *exactly* represent the integral of the impulse, on the basis of the elementary theory developed above. However, it may be noted that this failure to integrate prolonged impulses correctly does not generally give rise to large errors in most practical cases, and that by a proper choice of galvanometer period and relative damping the error of integration may be made negligible for most measurements.

In order to examine the ballistic response to a prolonged impulse we will start with the general equation of motion

$$P\frac{d^2\theta}{dt^2} + A\frac{d\theta}{dt} + U\theta = \frac{Ge}{R}$$

where $e = f(t)$. The solution of this equation is

$$\theta = C_1\varepsilon^{m_1t} + C_2\varepsilon^{m_2t} + \frac{G}{PR(m_1 - m_2)}(\varepsilon^{m_1t}\int\varepsilon^{-m_1t}e\,dt - \varepsilon^{m_2t}\int\varepsilon^{-m_2t}e\,dt)$$

If we assume that the galvanometer is at rest in its equilibrium position when $e = f(t)$ is first applied, we have

$$\left\{\begin{array}{l}(1)\quad \theta = 0 \\[2ex] (2)\ \dfrac{d\theta}{dt} = 0\end{array}\right|_{t=0}$$

from which

$$\begin{cases} 0 = C_1 + C_2 + \dfrac{G}{PR(m_1 - m_2)}\left(\displaystyle\int_{t=0} \varepsilon^{-m_1t}e\,dt - \int_{t=0} \varepsilon^{-m_2t}e\,dt\right) \\[2ex] 0 = m_1C_1 + m_2C_2 + \dfrac{G}{PR(m_1 - m_2)}\left(m_1\displaystyle\int_{t=0} \varepsilon^{-m_1t}e\,dt - m_2\int_{t=0} \varepsilon^{-m_2t}e\,dt\right)\end{cases}$$

Then

$$C_1 = \frac{-G}{PR(m_1 - m_2)}\int_{t=0} \varepsilon^{-m_1t}e\,dt$$

and

$$C_2 = \frac{G}{PR(m_1 - m_2)}\int_{t=0} \varepsilon^{-m_2t}e\,dt$$

For any subsequent time t we have

$$\theta = \frac{G}{PR(m_1 - m_2)}\left[-\varepsilon^{m_1t}\int_{t=0} e\varepsilon^{-m_1t}\,dt + \varepsilon^{m_2t}\int_{t=0} \varepsilon^{-m_2t}e\,dt \right.$$
$$\left. + \varepsilon^{m_1t}\int_{t=t} \varepsilon^{-m_1t}e\,dt - \varepsilon^{m_2t}\int_{t=t} \varepsilon^{-m_2t}e\,dt\right]$$

$$= \frac{G}{PR(m_1 - m_2)}\left[\varepsilon^{m_1t}\int_0^t \varepsilon^{-m_1t}e\,dt - \varepsilon^{m_2t}\int_0^t \varepsilon^{-m_2t}e\,dt\right]$$

This expression cannot be evaluated by analytic methods unless e can be expressed as an analytical function of t. Since in practice this is not usually possible, we must convert it into a form suitable for graphical evaluation. We will assume that e becomes and remains effectively zero after a time t'. In this case the integrals in the above expression are fixed in value if taken for a time $t \geqslant t'$.

The Underdamped Galvanometer. For the underdamped galvanometer

$$\begin{Bmatrix} m_1 = -a + jb \\ m_2 = -a - jb \end{Bmatrix}$$

where[10]

$$\begin{cases} a = \dfrac{A}{2P} = \dfrac{2\pi\gamma}{T_0} \\ b = \sqrt{\dfrac{U}{P} - \dfrac{A^2}{4P^2}} = \dfrac{2\pi}{T_0}\sqrt{1-\gamma^2} \end{cases}$$

and

$$\theta = \frac{G\varepsilon^{-at}}{bPR}\left(\sin bt\int_0^t \varepsilon^{at} e \cos bt\, dt - \cos bt \int_0^t \varepsilon^{at} e \sin bt\, dt\right)$$

If we define

$$A = \frac{\int_0^{t'} e\varepsilon^{at}\cos bt\, dt}{\int_0^{t'} e\, dt} = \frac{\int_0^{t'} e\varepsilon^{2\pi\gamma t/T_0}\cos\left(\dfrac{2\pi t}{T_0}\sqrt{1-\gamma^2}\right) dt}{\int_0^{t'} e\, dt}$$

and

$$B = \frac{\int_0^{t'} e\varepsilon^{at}\sin bt\, dt}{\int_0^{t'} e\, dt} = \frac{\int_0^{t'} e\varepsilon^{2\pi\gamma t/T_0}\sin\left(\dfrac{2\pi t}{T_0}\sqrt{1-\gamma^2}\right) dt}{\int_0^{t'} e\, dt}$$

we may write

$$\theta = \frac{G\varepsilon^{-at}}{PRb}(A\sin bt - B\cos bt)\int_0^{t'} e\, dt$$

for all values of $t \geqslant t'$.

For a maximum deflection $d\theta/dt_1 = 0$, and

$$(aA - bB)\sin bt_1 = (aB + bA)\cos bt_1$$

or

$$t_1 = \frac{T_0}{2\pi\sqrt{1-\gamma^2}}\tan^{-1}\frac{\gamma B + \sqrt{1-\gamma^2}A}{\gamma A - \sqrt{1-\gamma^2}B}$$

Then the maximum deflection is

$$\theta_1 = \frac{\int_0^{t'} e\, dt}{R}\cdot\left(\frac{\theta_F}{I_g}\right)\cdot\frac{2\pi}{T_0}\cdot\sqrt{A^2+B^2}\,\varepsilon^{-\frac{\gamma}{\sqrt{1-\gamma^2}}\cdot\tan^{-1}\frac{\gamma B + \sqrt{1-\gamma^2}A}{\gamma A - \sqrt{1-\gamma^2}B}}$$

[10] See development in Chapter 3 for further details.

provided $t_1 \geqslant t'$, since

$$\sin\left(\tan^{-1}\frac{\gamma B + \sqrt{1-\gamma^2}A}{\gamma A - \sqrt{1-\gamma^2}B}\right) = \frac{\gamma B + \sqrt{1-\gamma^2}A}{\sqrt{A^2+B^2}}$$

and

$$\cos\left(\tan^{-1}\frac{\gamma B + \sqrt{1-\gamma^2}A}{\gamma A - \sqrt{1-\gamma^2}B}\right) = \frac{\gamma A - \sqrt{1-\gamma^2}B}{\sqrt{A^2+B^2}}$$

If the impulse were instantaneous ($t' \to 0$), we would have $A = 1$ and $B = 0$. We could then write

$$\theta_1' = \frac{\int_0^{t'} e\,dt}{R} \cdot \left(\frac{\theta_F}{I_g}\right) \cdot \frac{2\pi}{T_0}\, \varepsilon^{-\frac{\gamma}{\sqrt{1-\gamma^2}} \cdot \tan^{-1}\frac{\sqrt{1-\gamma^2}}{\gamma}}$$

as we have already seen for the *instantaneous* case. Note that $\dfrac{\int_0^{t'} e\,dt}{R} = Q$. The ratio of the maximum deflection for the "prolonged" discharge to that for an "instantaneous" discharge is

$$\frac{\theta_1}{\theta_1'} = \frac{\varepsilon^{-\frac{\gamma}{\sqrt{1-\gamma^2}} \cdot \tan^{-1}\left(\frac{\gamma B + \sqrt{1-\gamma^2}A}{\gamma A - \sqrt{1-\gamma^2}B}\right)}}{\varepsilon^{-\frac{\gamma}{\sqrt{1-\gamma^2}} \cdot \tan^{-1}\left(\frac{\sqrt{1-\gamma^2}}{\gamma}\right)}} \cdot \sqrt{A^2+B^2}$$

and, if we recall that

$$\tan(x+y) = \frac{\tan x + \tan y}{1 - \tan x \tan y}$$

we may write

$$\frac{\theta_1}{\theta_1'} = \varepsilon^{-\frac{\gamma}{\sqrt{1-\gamma^2}} \cdot \tan^{-1}\frac{B}{A}} \cdot \sqrt{A^2+B^2} = \frac{\sqrt{A^2+B^2}}{\varepsilon^{\frac{\gamma}{\sqrt{1-\gamma^2}} \cdot \tan^{-1}\frac{B}{A}}}$$

This formula may be used to evaluate the error introduced into the equation for response to an "instantaneous" impulse, in cases where the impulse is "prolonged," provided the impulse interval $(0 - t')$ is not greater than the time (t_1) to maximum deflection, i.e. the error resulting from failure of the galvanometer to integrate exactly the impulse $\int_0^{t'} e\,dt$.

A and B are in a form suitable for graphical evaluation if we can represent $e = f(t)$ graphically as a function of t. If the time variation of e can be determined, either from a knowledge of the circuit or by an oscillogram, we may compute the products $e\varepsilon^{2\pi\gamma t/T_0}\cos\left(\frac{2\pi t}{T_0}\sqrt{1-\gamma^2}\right)$ and $e\varepsilon^{2\pi\gamma t/T_0}\sin\left(\frac{2\pi t}{T_0}\sqrt{1-\gamma^2}\right)$ for a series of values of t, from 0 to t' where e is effectively zero. These products together with e itself may

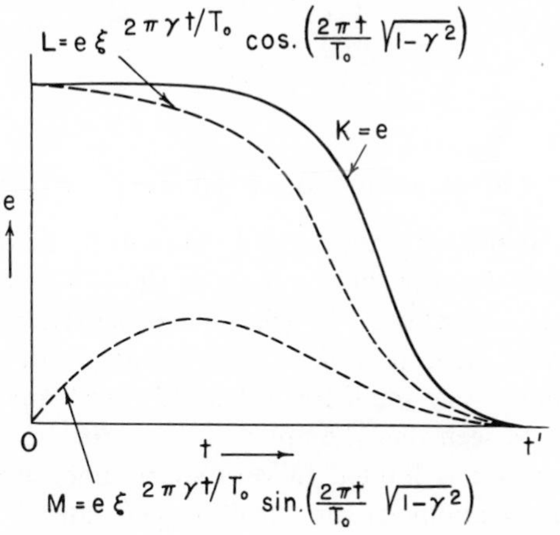

FIG. 6.

then be plotted on a graph to the same scale of ordinates, as shown in Fig. 6, and the areas under the curves measured. Then

$$A = \frac{\text{area under } L}{\text{area under } K}$$

and

$$B = \frac{\text{area under } M}{\text{area under } K}$$

Having evaluated A and B and knowing the relative damping γ, the error of integration of an *underdamped* galvanometer can be calculated for its response to a "prolonged" impulse $\int_0^{t'} e\,dt$, where $e = f(t)$.

The Overdamped Galvanometer. A similar analysis could be undertaken for the overdamped galvanometer, and we would arrive at the following result

$$\frac{\theta_1}{\theta_1'} = B^{\frac{-\gamma+\sqrt{\gamma^2-1}}{2\sqrt{\gamma^2-1}}} \cdot A^{\frac{\gamma+\sqrt{\gamma^2-1}}{2\sqrt{\gamma^2-1}}}$$

where

$$A = \frac{\int_0^{t'} e\varepsilon^{\frac{2\pi t}{T_0}(\gamma - \sqrt{\gamma^2 - 1})} dt}{\int_0^{t'} e\, dt}$$

and

$$B = \frac{\int_0^{t'} e\varepsilon^{\frac{2\pi t}{T_0}(\gamma + \sqrt{\gamma^2 - 1})} dt}{\int_0^{t'} e\, dt}$$

by which the error of integration for an impulse $\int_0^{t'} e\, dt$ could be evaluated. This is subject to precisely the same limitation as before: the analysis applies *only* if the duration of the impulse $(0 - t')$ is less than the time (t_1) to maximum deflection. It will be recalled from Fig. 1 that the time to maximum deflection decreases rapidly with increasing over-damping, becoming very small for a heavily overdamped galvanometer. It will therefore be seen that the application of this analysis to the *over-damped* galvanometer is limited to very short time impulses and, for a heavily damped galvanometer, practically degenerates to the case already studied, namely the response to an instantaneous impulse. In fluxmeter applications, where flux linkages may change rather slowly, we must examine the error which results when the duration of the impulse is greater than the time (t_1) to maximum deflection.

Galvanometer "Memory." A general graphical procedure is available for calculating the effect of a prolonged impulse on the ballistic response of a galvanometer.[11] Although the method is applicable for any condition of damping, we will illustrate its use for the heavily damped galvanometer. Under this condition the characteristic shape of the deflection-time curve is shown in Fig. 7(*a*). If an instantaneous impulse occurs at time zero, the deflection may be read at any subsequent time. At time t_1 we would read the maximum, θ_1. If the reading were delayed to t_2 the reading would be less, θ_2, and on the basis of our sensitivity formula we would underestimate the impulse by $(\theta_1 - \theta_2)/\theta_1$.

If this curve is replotted in Fig. 7(*b*) as the mirror image of the deflection curve, we have the *memory* characteristic of the galvanometer, which may be interpreted as follows. Let 0 on our time scale be the instant of reading, and the *negative* time to the left indicate time previous to the reading. Then the ordinate corresponding to the time $-t_2$ represents

[11] This procedure was suggested in an informal communication by Dr. F. Wenner and is based on what he has called the "memory" characteristic of the galvanometer.

the deflection θ_2 remaining at reading time for an instantaneous impulse which occurred at the time t_2 previous to the reading. In other words θ_2 is the "memory," which persists in the galvanometer when read, of an incident which occurred at a previous time t_2. Similarly θ_1 would be the deflection if the same impulse had occurred at $-t_1$. The ordinate of the "memory" curve for any time $-t$ can be used as a weighting function to determine the relative magnitude of the deflection which would be read after an elapsed time t. Now, if we know $e = f(t)$, the prolonged impulse resulting in a deflection, its graph can be superposed on our "memory" graph, using a positive time scale, and placing its zero of time in coincidence with the time $-t'$ of our "memory" graph, at which the impulse was initiated. This is shown in Fig. 7(*c*). If the *prolonged* impulse is considered the sum of a series of short-time contributing impulses, each of which is practically instantaneous, we can apply the above argument for each contribution. The "memory" graph furnishes a series of weighting factors by which the response (at reading time) to each component of the impulse can be determined. The ordinates of the graph $e = f(t)$ can now be multiplied by the corresponding ordinate θ/θ_1 of our weighting function, and a new curve

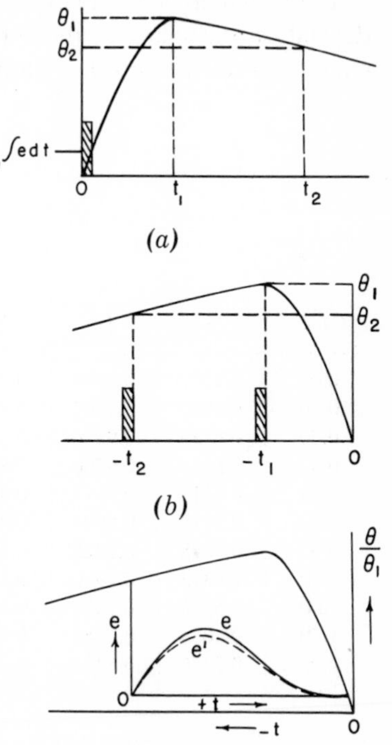

(*a*) (*b*) (*c*)
FIG. 7.

$$e' = e\frac{\theta}{\theta_1} = \phi(t, \theta)$$

can be obtained. From the relative areas under e and e' the error of integration may be found. This is

$$K = 1 - \frac{\text{area under } e'}{\text{area under } e}$$

K being the error of integration of $\int_0^{t'} e\,dt$ by the galvanometer operating at the specified damping and with the times of initiating the impulse and of reading as specified above. (area e')/(area e) is the ratio of the deflection resulting from a particular total change in flux linkages, if it occurs as specified, to the deflection which would result if $\int e\,dt$ were an instantaneous impulse.

The actual error in the evaluation of $\int e\,dt$ will, for any particular case, depend on the shape of the curve $e = f(t)$ and upon the damping in the circuit. Table 2 gives the relative deflection at various values of damping

TABLE 2

$$\frac{\theta}{\theta_1}$$

$\frac{t}{T_0}$	γ						
	5	10	20	30	40	50	100
0.05	0.9787	0.9999	0.9974	0.9973	0.9975	0.9979	0.9987
0.10	0.9920	0.9862	0.9896	0.9921	0.9936	0.9949	0.9971
0.20	0.9329	0.9556	0.9741	0.9818	0.9858	0.9885	0.9941
0.30	0.8756	0.9260	0.9590	0.9715	0.9781	0.9823	0.9909
0.40	0.8217	0.8973	0.9440	0.9614	0.9705	0.9762	0.9878
0.50	0.7712	0.8694	0.9294	0.9514	0.9629	0.9701	0.9847
0.60	0.7238	0.8425	0.9148	0.9415	0.9553	0.9650	0.9816
0.80	0.6375	0.7910	0.8865	0.9220	0.9404	0.9519	0.9755
1.00	0.5615	0.7428	0.8590	0.9029	0.9258	0.9401	0.9693
1.50	0.4088	0.6345	0.7941	0.8568	0.8901	0.9110	0.9542
2.00	0.2976	0.5421	0.7341	0.8130	0.8558	0.8829	0.9394

for times up to $2T_0$. These data were computed for galvanometer response to an instantaneous impulse and may serve to construct the "memory function" used above as a weighting function, provided the relative damping is known for the measuring circuit. The error may be evaluated approximately in some cases from Table 3. In this table are listed the times required for the deflection to decrease from its maximum value by 1, 3, and 10% after an instantaneous impulse. For example, any impulse (whatever its shape) whose duration is not greater than 3% of the free period of the galvanometer will be integrated with an error of not more than 1% by using a relative damping of 5 or more, while for an impulse of duration not exceeding 10% of the free period a relative damping of 30 or more will ensure that the integration is correct to within 1%. For an impulse of the same duration ($T_0/10$), we see that for a relative damping of 2 the error of integration cannot exceed 10%, and for a relative damping of 10 the integration error will be less than 3%. It should be noted that the use of this table permits one to evaluate only the *maximum* error which could result in integration, regardless of the shape of the voltage impulse. Actually, in almost any practical case, the error of integration will be less than this maximum value by a considerable amount since during the entire impulse period the weighting factor lies

TABLE 3

TIME TO RETURN FROM θ_{max}

γ	$\frac{t_{1.00}}{T_0}$	$\frac{t_{0.99}}{T_0}$	$\frac{t_{0.97}}{T_0}$	$\frac{t_{0.90}}{T_0}$	$\frac{t_{0.37}}{T_0}$	$\frac{t_{0.99}-t_{1.00}}{T_0}$	$\frac{t_{0.97}-t_{1.00}}{T_0}$	$\frac{t_{0.90}-t_{1.00}}{T_0}$
2	0.1210	0.1453	0.1674	0.2231	0.7557	0.0243	0.0464	0.1021
3	0.0992	0.1258	0.1525	0.2248	1.038	0.0266	0.0533	0.1256
4	0.0848	0.1125	0.1429	0.2372	1.351	0.0277	0.0581	0.1524
5	0.0745	0.1042	0.138	0.256	1.65	0.0297	0.0635	0.182
10	0.0479	0.0830	0.151	0.388	3.214	0.0351	0.103	0.340
20	0.0294	0.0971	0.227	0.704	6.35	0.0677	0.198	0.675
30	0.0217	0.1279	0.322	1.033	9.483	0.1062	0.300	1.011
40	0.0174	0.1511	0.412	1.366	12.67	0.1337	0.395	1.349
50	0.0147	0.1633	0.500	1.674	15.83	0.1486	0.485	1.659
100	0.0084	0.3216	0.973	3.358	31.66	0.3132	0.965	3.350

TABLE 4

TIME AVAILABLE FOR READING

$\frac{\Delta t}{T_0}$	γ						
	5	10	20	30	40	50	100
$\frac{\Delta t_{0.2\%}}{T_0}$	0.0205	0.0209	0.0239	0.0300	0.0318	0.0385	0.0654
$\frac{\Delta t_{1\%}}{T_0}$	0.0476	0.0551	0.0798	0.1084	0.1371	0.1689	0.3252

between unity and the value stated. Table 4 shows the time available for reading the maximum value of deflection for various values of damping. This figure is of some importance since many observers find it difficult to read the maximum value precisely when the spot is moving rapidly. It will be seen that the deflection is within 0.2% of its maximum value during a time interval of $0.032T_0$ for a relative damping of 40; i.e. if the galvanometer has a free period of 30 sec, 1 sec is available for reading the maximum to an accuracy of 0.2% for this condition.

Fluxmeter

We have now arrived at the conditions which must be met by a ballistic galvanometer in order to measure $\int e\,dt$ without appreciable error, regardless of the impulse time involved: (1) the *relative damping* must be very large (i.e. the galvanometer should be heavily overdamped); and (2) the period T_0 of the galvanometer should be long. These requirements are a qualitative description of the *fluxmeter*, which is specifically designed for the measurement of magnetic flux. Actually the fluxmeter deflection is a measure of changes in flux linkages between a magnetic field and a test coil connected to the terminals of the instrument. Such a test coil may be used in either of two conditions: (1) the test coil may be stationary in a changing magnetic field; or (2) the test coil may be moved in such a way as to alter the flux which it links in a constant field. In either case the change in flux linkages induces an emf in the fluxmeter circuit, and the instrument deflection is a measure of $\int e\,dt$. Frequently an appreciable time interval may be involved, especially if the test coil is held stationary in a field which is changing slowly. The *ideal* fluxmeter is, then, a ballistic galvanometer in which the restoring couple of the suspension is reduced to zero with the result that its period is very great, and which is heavily damped when it operates in a low-resistance circuit such as is constituted by a test coil and its connecting leads.

In commercial fluxmeters, the strip suspension characteristic of a galvanometer is sometimes replaced by a silk fiber, and the current leads to the moving coil are delicate spirals of annealed copper, silver, or gold strip. Alternatively, the suspension may be replaced by pivots and jewel bearings in which the moving coil turns. In some fluxmeters strip suspensions of gold or copper are used, but their restoring force is neutralized by a countertorque set up by a magnetic or gravitational couple in the way described for high-sensitivity galvanometers in a previous chapter. Practically it is unnecessary and is virtually impossible to eliminate the control couple completely, and the instrument will drift slowly toward its zero indication after a deflection.

Any galvanometer can be given approximately fluxmeter characteristics so that it will integrate $\int e\,dt$ with fair accuracy, but it is better to use a ballistic galvanometer for this purpose. If the regular suspension is replaced by one having the minimum possible stiffness, we will increase the free period and at the same time increase the critical damping resistance, since

$$T_0 = 2\pi\sqrt{\frac{P}{U}} \quad \text{and} \quad R_c = \frac{G^2}{2(1-\gamma_0)\sqrt{UP}}$$

Since the critical damping resistance is increased we will have increased the damping resulting from a fixed value of circuit resistance. We have already seen that the accuracy of integration of $\int e\,dt$ improves both with increasing damping and with increasing period.

We have (from p. 317)

$$_{\gamma}S_{\phi N} \approx \frac{2\pi}{T_0}\left(\frac{\theta_F}{I_g}\right)\cdot\frac{1}{2\gamma R_c}\left(\frac{\gamma-\gamma_0}{1-\gamma_0}\right) \quad \text{for } \gamma \gg 1$$

Also, in this case $\gamma \gg \gamma_0$, so that

$$\frac{\theta_1}{\int e\,dt} = \frac{2\pi}{T_0}\left(\frac{\theta_F}{I_g}\right)\frac{1}{2R_c(1-\gamma_0)}$$

Now $\theta_F/I_g = G/U$; and if we substitute, for θ_F/I_g, $2\pi/T_0$, and R_c, their values we have

$$\frac{\theta_1}{\int e\,dt} = \frac{1}{G}, \quad \text{or } G\theta_1 = \int e\,dt$$

But $\int e\,dt = N\Delta\phi$, where $N\Delta\phi$ is the total change in flux linkages in a test coil having N turns. Hence $G\theta_1 = N\Delta\phi$. The deflection of the heavily overdamped galvanometer is proportional to the change in flux linkages in the test coil connected to its terminals, and the proportionality factor is the motor constant of the galvanometer $G = Bnlb$, the product of field in the air gap times area-turns in the galvanometer coil. From this relation it is apparent that, with a given galvanometer coil, the *flux-linkage* sensitivity is inversely proportional to the field strength B in the air gap of the galvanometer, and that a galvanometer can be made more sensitive as a fluxmeter by making its field weaker, i.e. by the use of a magnetic shunt.

It will also be apparent that in the idealized fluxmeter case, with no moment of restoration and no losses in the circuit, the emf in the test coil will at all times equal the counter emf in the galvanometer coil, i.e.

$$Bnlb\,\frac{d\theta}{dt} = N\frac{d\phi}{dt} = e$$

The velocity with which the galvanometer coil moves ($d\theta/dt$) will be exactly enough so that flux-linkages change in the galvanometer coil at the same rate that they change in the test coil. The galvanometer deflection will then accurately and immediately follow any change in flux linkage in the test coil. This leads to the further conclusion that in the idealized case no current would flow in the circuit since the emf and counter emf are always equal. This explains the rather surprising conclusion that we previously reached (see p. 321) that the effect of a shunt in a fluxmeter circuit is independent of the galvanometer resistance and depends solely on the relative resistance of the shunt and the external circuit.

The flux-linkage sensitivity of a fluxmeter can be derived in a very simple and direct fashion, provided the restoring moment is negligible.[12] We will assume that the fluxmeter, having a resistance R_f and inductance L_f, is connected to a test coil of resistance R_t and inductance L_t and having N turns, as shown in Fig. 8. Let the emf induced in the test coil be e_t and the emf in the fluxmeter coil be e_f. Actually, in a practical case we will always have $e_f < e_t$, so that there will be a small current i flowing in the circuit. Now $e_t = N(d\phi/dt)$, where $d\phi/dt$ is the rate of change of flux in the test coil; and $e_f = G(d\theta/dt)$, where $d\theta/dt$ is the angular velocity of the fluxmeter coil and G is its *motor* constant.

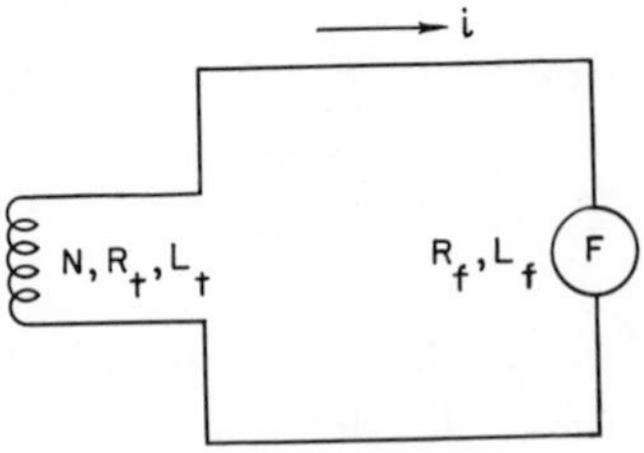

FIG. 8.

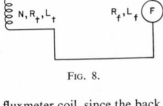

Using Kirchhoff's law to sum the voltages around the fluxmeter circuit, we have

$$e_t = e_f + (L_t + L_f)\frac{di}{dt} + (R_t + R_f)i$$

In practical applications the potential drop in the resistance $(R_t + R_f)i$ is small at all times during the motion of the fluxmeter coil, since the back emf generated in the fluxmeter approaches the value of the applied emf generated in the test coil.[13] If we assume that the resistance drop is at all times negligible compared to the other voltages in the circuit, we have as an approximation

$$N\frac{d\phi}{dt} = G\frac{d\theta}{dt} + (L_t + L_f)\frac{di}{dt}$$

This may be integrated as

$$N\int_0^t \frac{d\phi}{dt}\,dt = G\int_0^t \frac{d\theta}{dt}\,dt + (L_t + L_f)\int_0^t \frac{di}{dt}\,dt$$

which is the equivalent of

$$N\int_{\phi_1}^{\phi_2} d\phi = G\int_{\theta_1}^{\theta_2} d\theta + (L_t + L_f)\int_{i_1}^{i_2} di$$

or

$$N(\phi_2 - \phi_1) = G(\theta_2 - \theta_1) + (L_t + L_f)(i_2 - i_1)$$

[12] See Golding, *Electrical Measurements*, 3rd edition, p. 347, Pitman, 1940.

[13] The circuit resistance is usually kept as small as is feasible. If this resistance is very small compared to the critical damping resistance of the fluxmeter, it may be seen by examination of the relation previously developed for flux-linkage sensitivity that the sensitivity is affected only to a very minor extent by circuit resistance. In the absence of dissipative damping, any circuit resistance less than 0.1 of the critical damping resistance will affect the fluxmeter by less than 1%.

Now, if we assume that the period in which the flux is changing is completely contained within the period $(0 - t)$ over which the integration is carried, both the initial and final currents are zero.[14] Also we may say that $\phi_2 - \phi_1 = \Delta\phi$, the total flux change in the test coil, and that $\theta_2 - \theta_1 = \Delta\theta$, the total change in angular position of the fluxmeter coil. Then we have $N\Delta\phi = G\Delta\theta$, where $N\Delta\phi$ is the total change in flux linkages in the test coil corresponding to the deflection $\Delta\theta$. If the fluxmeter coil moves in a radial field which does not change with angular position (so that G is the same for all positions of the coil), the deflection of the fluxmeter accurately follows any change in flux in the test coil.

It should be emphasized that there is no essential difference between a properly designed fluxmeter and a heavily overdamped ballistic galvanometer. In portable commercial fluxmeters, the moving coil is frequently pivoted and generally the scale is marked so that $N\Delta\phi$ may be estimated in maxwell-turns by using a simple multiplying factor applied to the deflection. Multirange fluxmeters usually incorporate a selection of shunts with which the effective response is controlled[15] so that the factor used to obtain maxwell turns may be varied by convenient numbers. However, the parameters which control the behavior and sensitivity of a fluxmeter are precisely those which are effective in the ballistic response of a galvanometer. Any dissipative damping which might be introduced, either by friction or by the use of a damping frame or a short-circuited turn on the moving coil, would decrease the sensitivity which could be attained, since such damping absorbs energy without any useful return. Also the resistance of the circuit in which the fluxmeter operates (including the coil resistance) is subject to limitations of the same type as those imposed on the ballistic galvanometer. It is to our advantage to keep this resistance as low as possible, since not only is the sensitivity of the instrument decreased by large circuit resistance but also the ability of the fluxmeter to integrate correctly an impulse of long duration is adversely affected.

Since the heavily overdamped ballistic galvanometer of long period has the behavior characteristic of a fluxmeter, it is well suited to magnetic measurements. In fact the heavily overdamped galvanometer has several advantages over the underdamped or critically damped galvanometer for this purpose.

[14] In theory some approximation is also involved here. Practically no effect of inductance on fluxmeter calibration can be observed until the total circuit inductance becomes very large (considerably in excess of 100 henrys). No effect should be expected unless the inductance is so large that the time constant of the circuit is increased to such an extent that the ballistic impulse is prolonged beyond the ability of the fluxmeter to integrate it correctly.

[15] See above: the shunted ballistic galvanometer.

1. As we have seen from Fig. 3 and Table 1, the maximum deflection following any change in flux linkages in the test coil is attained so quickly that the galvanometer deflection may be said to be practically simultaneous with the change in flux, i.e. when $\gamma \gg 1$ then $t_1 \ll t_0$.

2. We have seen that, when unshunted, the galvanometer response to an $\int e\,dt$ impulse is greatest when the galvanometer is heavily overdamped.

3. No significant error is introduced into the measurements by any reasonable time interval required for the change in flux linkages. In practice this independence of time may be checked by changing the flux linkages in two equal steps separated by an appreciable time interval, and then repeating the same total change of flux linkages as rapidly as possible. The two resulting deflections should be equal.

4. Because of the heavy overdamping, the return of the coil to its zero position is extremely slow, so that sufficient time is available for an accurate reading of the deflection.[16] In most work this slow return to zero is not a disadvantage, since a second reversal of flux in the test coil immediately returns the instrument to its zero, ready for the next reading.

General Considerations

Ballistic Method for Preliminary Bridge Balance. Attention may be called to the advantages resulting from the ballistic operation of a heavily overdamped galvanometer[17] in the preliminary balance adjustment of a d-c bridge or similar circuit. In such preliminary adjustment the operator is primarily interested in the direction of the unbalance and is not at all interested in observing the magnitude of the galvanometer deflection until the balance adjustment is close. If the emf of unbalance is applied to the galvanometer for as short a time as possible by tapping and quickly releasing the control key, the operator has (to a good enough approximation) the conditions necessary for ballistic response. We have seen that in the heavily overdamped galvanometer the ballistic response is very rapid and thus may be much faster than the observation of a deflection resulting from response to a steady current with critical damping.

The direction of unbalance having been observed, a suitable circuit adjustment can be made immediately. This type of manipulation can be repeated with decreasing damping as the balance condition is approached, and only in the final stages (where full sensitivity is desired) need the

[16] In one National Bureau of Standards ballistic galvanometer, used as a fluxmeter, the period is about 30 sec and the critical damping resistance 35,000 ohms. It is used at a relative damping in excess of 40, so that its deflection is attained within $\frac{1}{2}$ sec of the completion of a ballistic impulse and the deflection remains within 0.2% of maximum for nearly 1 sec. It drifts back very slowly toward zero, the time constant of the drift being $6\frac{1}{3}$ min (i.e. the time to $\theta = 0.37\theta_{max}$).

[17] Informal communication from Dr. F. Wenner.

damping be decreased to less than unity and the actual "current" deflection observed. In this way balance conditions may be reached more quickly than if steady static deflections are observed at each stage of the adjustment. This would require that a low-resistance shunt be used across the galvanometer terminals to reduce sensitivity, rather than a high series resistor or a combination of shunt and series resistance designed to keep the damping constant.

Zero Return. Unless the galvanometer is used at a damping near critical, the return of the moving system to rest at its equilibrium position after a ballistic measurement is slow. If the damping is very small, the galvanometer coil will oscillate about its zero position with gradually diminishing amplitude. If the damping is very high, the coil will slowly drift back to zero after a deflection. In either the undamped or the greatly overdamped condition some device should be incorporated in the circuit for bringing the galvanometer quickly to rest at its zero position. This often consists of an auxiliary "check" circuit which can be connected across the galvanometer terminals in place of the measuring circuit. In the undamped case this can consist of a low resistance applied as a short circuit across the terminals of the galvanometer to stop its motion as it passes through the zero position [Fig. 9(*a*)]. Or a resistance R, approximately equal to the critical damping resistance, may be substituted quickly for the measuring circuit after a deflection to return the galvanometer to zero without overshoot. A coil may be included in the checking circuit [Fig. 9(*b*)], and the manipulation of a movable magnet relative to this coil may be used to supply a small emf in the "check" circuit to assist in returning the galvanometer promptly to zero. In this case the resistance of the "check" circuit should be low in order to take advantage of the fluxmeter response of the overdamped galvanometer. A variation of this technique, shown in Fig. 9(*c*), has some advantage over the coil and magnet arrangement from the point of view of ease of manipulation. A small adjustable voltage may be supplied to the "check" circuit from a dry cell, through a slide-wire rheostat. The slide-wire rheostat a–b, of very low resistance, has its midpoint connected to the check circuit. In series with it and absorbing most of the voltage of the dry cell is a very large resistance R. Connection to the check circuit is completed through the rheostat slider c. In this way a small voltage, adjustable in magnitude and direction, can be inserted in the check circuit; and the heavily overdamped galvanometer, moving under the action of this voltage, can be brought to its zero position by manipulation of the slider position.

The operation of check and zero-set devices described above has been discussed from the viewpoint that they will save time for the observer. If the galvanometer is of a high-sensitivity type, there is another reason for a device to check the motion of the coil. High sensitivity is usually attained in part by using a weak suspension, and the zero may shift as a result of inelastic yield of the suspension. It is good practice in taking a series of readings to deflect the galvanometer always in the same direction from the equilibrium position, and never to allow the galvanometer to swing much past zero in the reverse direction. This is accomplished automatically if the damping is near critical, but must be done

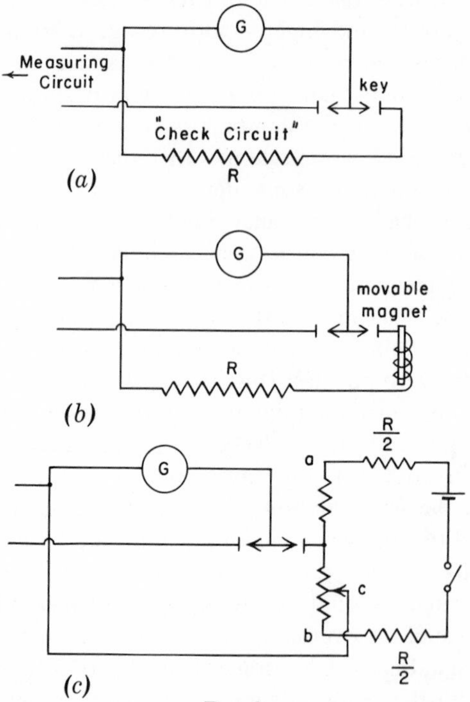

FIG. 9.

by a "check" device if the damping is small. Before taking any readings, a deflection of the galvanometer in the proper direction, as large as any deflection which is expected in the subsequent measurements, will reduce trouble from zero drift. This precaution should be taken whenever the galvanometer is to be operated after a period of idleness.

Thermal emf's may be troublesome when a very sensitive galvanometer is employed as a fluxmeter in a low-resistance circuit. The galvanometer itself should be shielded against sudden temperature changes, and the circuit should, where possible, be all copper. This should include the galvanometer suspensions and binding posts if the galvanometer is extremely sensitive, and in this case a thermal-free key should be used.

Resistors which are inserted in series or parallel to control the effective sensitivity should be of manganin, which has a low thermal emf against copper. In spite of all precautions some residual thermal emf may be present, and it is often desirable to introduce some means of thermal compensation in the measuring circuit. A combined thermal compensator and zero-setting device, shown schematically in Fig. 10, has been found very useful for fluxmeter work in the Magnetic Laboratory at the National Bureau of Standards. Two slide-wire rheostats are connected in parallel to a dry-cell through a high resistance. Their sliders are connected across a low resistance in the galvanometer circuit. One slider

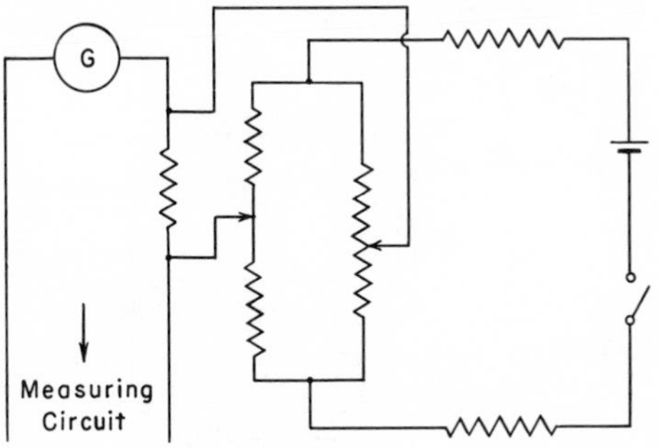

FIG. 10.

is provided with a detent at the midpoint of its travel so that it can be returned exactly to this point with certainty after an adjustment has been made. This slider is operated to insert a small voltage into the measuring circuit temporarily in order to adjust the zero setting. The second slide wire serves as a thermal compensator, and the position of the slider is adjusted until there is no drift resulting from thermal emf's when the galvanometer coil is in its zero position and the other slider is at its detent position. Both slide-wire rheostats and their sliders should be constructed of copper in order that their manipulation may not introduce additional thermal emf's into the measuring circuit.

Ballistic Galvanometer Calibration. Although the sensitivity formulas developed earlier in this chapter are useful in determining the suitability of a galvanometer for a particular ballistic measurement and the proper damping conditions to impose, it is necessary to make an experimental ballistic calibration with the circuit conditions that will be encountered in operation. In order that the damping be correct during the calibration, the actual circuit should be the same in calibration and use, since the sensitivity is a function of damping. Also, if possible, the calibration should be made with an impulse which closely approximates the characteristics of that which will be expected in the measurements. For work with capacitors, the discharge of a standard capacitor charged to a known voltage will serve for calibration, using the relation $Q = CE$. For magnetic measurements, or for inductive measurements generally, a mutual inductor may be utilized in calibrating the galvanometer. Here $\int e\,dt = 2MI_p$, since the voltage induced in the secondary of the mutual

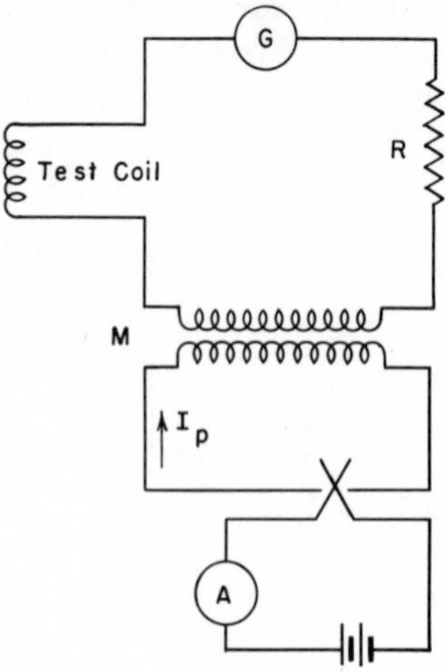

FIG. 11.

inductor (i.e. in the galvanometer circuit) is $e = M(di_p/dt)$. Then, if the current I_p is reversed as indicated in Fig. 11,

$$\int e\,dt = \int_{-I_p}^{I_p} M\,di_p = 2MI_p$$

It will be noted that the test coil to be used with the galvanometer is shown as a part of the galvanometer circuit. Hence, if the circuit is not changed after calibration so that its resistance remains at the calibration value, its damping will also be unchanged and the calibration will be for the operating condition. Of course, a *coulomb-sensitivity* calibration could be made with a mutual inductor, if desirable, since

$$Q = \int i\,dt = \int \frac{e}{R}\,dt = \frac{2MI_p}{R}$$

where R is the total resistance of the secondary circuit, including that of the galvanometer itself. If our interest is in the *flux-linkage sensitivity* of the galvanometer, this is readily obtained through the relation

$$\int e\,dt = \frac{N\Delta\phi}{10^8}$$

where $N\Delta\phi$ is the change in flux linkages in the galvanometer circuit. In this case, a test coil whose area-turns is known can be employed for the calibration, in the field of a solenoid or in some other field which is known to us. A long, single-layer solenoid is frequently used to set up a field which can be calculated.

We will consider the field of such a solenoid. For an element of a solenoid-turn [Fig. 12(*a*)], the field is $dB = i\,dl/R^2$. Now, when we

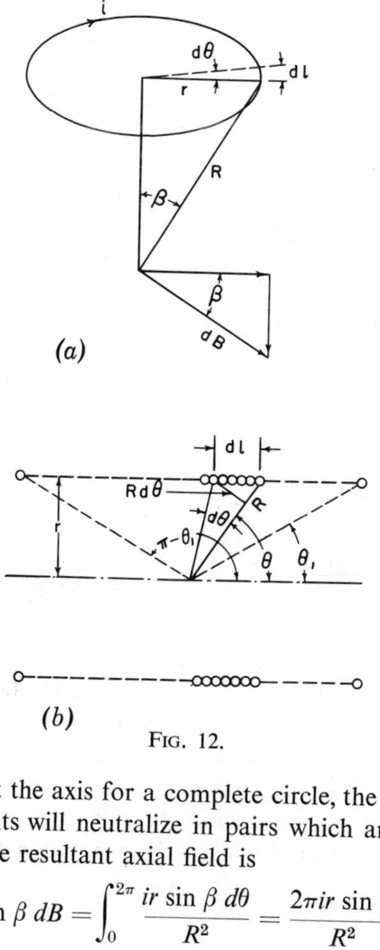

FIG. 12.

consider the field at the axis for a complete circle, the radial components from all the elements will neutralize in pairs which are at opposite ends of a diameter. The resultant axial field is

$$\sin\beta\, dB = \int_0^{2\pi} \frac{ir \sin\beta\, d\theta}{R^2} = \frac{2\pi ir \sin\beta}{R^2}$$

But $\sin\beta = r/R$. Hence, for a single turn of the solenoid, the contribution to the field at the axis is

$$dB_a = \frac{2\pi ir^2}{R^3}$$

In Fig. 12(*b*) we will assume that there are N turns per centimeter of length on the solenoid and that the solenoid radius is r. Then, for an element of length dl along the solenoid, the resultant field at the axis is

$$dB = \frac{2\pi N i r^2\, dl}{R^3}$$

But

$$R\, d\theta = dl \sin\theta \quad \text{and} \quad \sin\theta = \frac{r}{R}$$

so that

$$dB = \frac{2\pi N i r^2}{R^3} \cdot \frac{R\, d\theta}{\sin\theta} = 2\pi N i \sin\theta\, d\theta$$

At the midpoint of the solenoid, where the angle subtended by the solenoid is $(\pi - 2\theta_1)$, the field at the axis is

$$B = \int_{\theta_1}^{\pi - \theta_1} 2\pi N i \sin\theta\, d\theta$$

If the solenoid is very long compared to its radius, so that $\theta_1 \to 0$, then

$$B \approx \int_0^{\pi} 2\pi N i \sin\theta\, d\theta = 2\pi N i \cos\theta \Big|_0^{\pi} = 4\pi N i$$

and if i be stated in amperes,

$$B = \frac{4\pi N i}{10}$$

It can be shown that, under the conditions stated, the solenoid very long compared to its radius, the central field is very nearly uniform throughout the cross section of the solenoid, and the computed value, $B = 4\pi NI/10$, is, to a very good approximation, the field set up within the solenoid by a current of I amperes. It should be apparent from the development above that this field falls off in value toward the end of the solenoid, and that the test coil used to calibrate a galvanometer should be located within the central portion of the solenoid. If a test coil is available whose effective area-turns An is known, and if the current in the solenoid is reversed to obtain the change in flux linkages, then

$$\int e\, dt = \frac{8\pi N I A n}{10^9}$$

Since it is generally impossible to determine the mean diameter of the test coil with precision by mechanical measurements, it is better to obtain the value of effective area-turns by electrical methods. Such a method is discussed in Chapter 9 on magnetic measurements.

A test for the correctness of integration of the instrument can be made by the following procedure:

1. In reversing the current in the primary of the inductor, pause on open circuit for a period equal to the slowest change in ϕ expected in the measurements planned. Then close the switch to complete the reversal of current and note the *total* deflection.

2. Complete the reversal of primary current without pause and as rapidly as possible, and note the total deflection. If the fluxmeter integrates properly, the total deflection should be the same for operations 1 and 2.

No general discussion of the applications of the ballistic galvanometer to electrical measurement problems will be undertaken at this time. One of its most important engineering applications is in d-c magnetic measurements, where ballistic methods are employed almost exclusively. Formerly, ballistic galvanometers were much used in the comparison of capacitors and inductors, but these ballistic methods have been largely superseded, except in special cases, by more convenient and satisfactory a-c bridge methods.

CHAPTER 9

MAGNETS AND MAGNETIC TESTING[1]

Magnetic Units and Definitions

As we have previously seen, the numerical magnitudes of the various electrical quantities depend on the system of units in which they are defined. This is also true of the magnetic quantities, whose magnitudes may be fixed in terms of certain electrical quantities to which they are related, and in terms of which the magnetic units may be defined to form a consistent system. Although we could, if we desired, use any of the systems of electrical units to define and fix the values of consistent systems of magnetic units, we shall consider only two such systems—the cgs units, based on the cgs electromagnetic system of electrical units, and the mks units, which are derivable from the mks electrical units. Both these systems are widely used in scientific work and are the only *consistent* systems of units which appear at the present time (1951) to have a reasonable prospect of survival.

We will consider first the *magnetic circuit*, which can be defined as a closed path of magnetic flux whose direction is that of the magnetic field at every point. It will be seen that a magnetic circuit has some properties that are similar to those of an electric circuit, but that there is one respect in which the magnetic circuit differs from the usual type of electric circuit. There is nothing in the magnetic circuit which corresponds to the transport of charge in the electric circuit; and we must remember, in using any analogy, that flux and current are not exact analogs in the two types of circuit. As one moves normal to the direction of current in an electric circuit, one usually encounters an abrupt boundary between a conducting and an insulating medium beyond which the current density is found to be zero. Although various materials may have greater or lesser magnetic

[1] Much of the material of this chapter is based on Magnetic Testing, *NBS Circ.* 456, and Permanent Magnets, *NBS Circ.* 448, both by Raymond L. Sanford.

permeability, there is nothing in the magnetic circuit which corresponds to electric insulation. While the value of flux density may be abruptly changed at the boundary between a material of high and one of low permeability, magnetic flux cannot in general be considered to be completely confined within a particular volume having sharply defined boundaries.

In general, magnetization is produced by electric currents which link with a magnetic circuit. *Magnetomotive force* (mmf) is the total influence tending to produce magnetization in a magnetic circuit and is proportional to the product of the current and the number of conductor turns linking the magnetic circuit. The cgs unit of magnetomotive force is the *gilbert*, defined by the equation $\mathscr{F} = 4\pi NI/10$, where $\mathscr{F}$ is mmf in gilberts, N is conductor turns linking the magnetic circuit, and I is current in amperes. In the rationalized mks system of units,[2] the *ampere-turn* is the unit of magnetomotive force.

The effect of mmf is to induce *flux* in the magnetic circuit on which it acts. The flux has the property of inducing an emf in the conductors linked with it, whenever the linkages between the electric and magnetic circuits are changing. The unit of flux may be defined by making use of the fact that the induced emf is proportional to the time rate of change of flux linkages. The cgs unit of flux is the *maxwell*, defined by the equation $e = N(d\phi/dt) \times 10^{-8}$, where e is in volts, N is the number of turns of conductor linking the flux, ϕ is the flux in maxwells, and t is time in seconds. The mks unit of flux is the *weber*, and it may be defined as the flux which, linking an electric circuit of 1 turn, would induce an emf of 1 volt if it collapsed to zero at a uniform rate in 1 sec: i.e. $e = N(d\phi/dt)$, where e is in volts, ϕ in webers, and t in seconds. It will be noted that 1 weber = 10^8 maxwells.

The flux which is present in a magnetic circuit as the result of the action of a given mmf is determined by the *reluctance* ($\mathscr{R}$) of the circuit, in accordance with the relation $\phi = \mathscr{F}/\mathscr{R}$. This relation is sometimes cited as the analog of Ohm's law for the magnetic circuit. The unit of reluctance has no name.[3]

Magnetic induction (B) is the flux density, the flux per unit area of a section normal to the flux direction. It may be defined by the expression $\phi = \iint B\, dA$, the flux through a surface being the surface integral of the induction. The cgs unit of induction is the *gauss*, which is 1 maxwell/sq cm. The mks unit of induction is 1 weber/sq meter. Since 1 weber

[2] See discussion of rationalized units, p. 31.

[3] Before 1930 the cgs unit of reluctance was commonly called the "oersted," but this name was assigned to the cgs unit of magnetizing force at that time, leaving the unit of reluctance without a name.

$= 10^8$ maxwells, and 1 sq meter $= 10^4$ sq cm, it follows that 1 weber/sq meter $= 10^4$ gauss.

The manner in which the mmf is distributed along a magnetic circuit is determined by the reluctance of the circuit and by the distribution of the magnetizing winding. The gradient of the mmf at any point of a magnetic circuit is called the *magnetizing force*, and is defined by the relation[4] $H = d\mathscr{F}/dl$. The cgs unit of magnetizing force is the *oersted* and corresponds to an mmf gradient of 1 gilbert/cm. (For example, $H = 4\pi NI/10$ oersteds at the midpoint of a long, uniformly wound solenoid having N turns per centimeter and carrying a current of I amperes.) The rationalized mks unit of magnetizing force is the *ampere-turn* per meter and is equivalent to $4\pi \times 10^{-3}$ oersteds.

The relative *permeability* (μ) of a medium is the ratio of the induction at a point in the magnetic circuit resulting from the particular magnetizing force H acting at the point, to the induction which the same force would produce in free space. The induction in free space is $B_v = \mu_v H$, where μ_v is the permeability of free space, so that the relative permeability at a point in a magnetic circuit may be written as $\mu = B/B_v = B/\mu_v H$. In the cgs system the permeability of free space was unfortunately chosen as unity, so that in this system the induction in free space (B_v) has the same *numerical* value as the magnetizing force (H). As a result a confusing practice has grown up among a fairly large group of workers of speaking interchangeably and indiscriminately of the magnetizing force and induction in free space as though they were physically as well as numerically identical. The necessity for keeping these two physically different quantities separated is immediately apparent when their values are defined in the mks system, since here the numerical equality no longer exists. The permeability of free space is $4\pi \times 10^{-7}$ in the rationalized mks system of units, and the mks induction arising from 1 mks unit of magnetizing force is $B_v = \mu_v H = 4\pi \times 10^{-7}$; i.e. an induction in free space of 1.257×10^{-6} weber/sq meter results from a magnetizing force of 1 ampere-turn/meter.

That part of the induction which represents the excess over what would be present in free space for the same magnetizing force is called the

[4] This is not, of course, a rigorous definition of H except in those cases where $\mathscr{F}$ is an analytic function. Alternatively, one may more precisely say that *magnetizing force* is that auxiliary vector point function in a magnetic field which measures the tendency of currents (or of magnetized bodies) to produce magnetic induction at the point. The magnetizing force $\mathbf{H}_i$ at a point P, resulting from a current I in a circuit, is $\mathbf{H}_i = I \oint \frac{\mathbf{r} \times d\mathbf{s}}{r^3}$, where $\mathbf{r}$ is the vector distance from P to the element $d\mathbf{s}$ of the circuit, and the integral is taken completely around the circuit.

intrinsic induction, B_i, defined by the equation $B_i = B - B_v = B - \mu_v H$. A quantity which is sometimes used instead of intrinsic induction is the *intensity of magnetization*, J, defined in the unrationalized cgs system by the relation $4\pi J = B_i = B - \mu_v H$. The ratio of intensity of magnetization to magnetizing force is called the *magnetic susceptibility* (or volume susceptibility), $K = J/H$. It is used in describing the properties of feebly magnetic materials. If the volume susceptibility is divided by the density (ρ), the resulting value refers to unit mass, and is called the *mass susceptibility* $\chi = K/\rho$.

It will be noted that certain of the magnetic quantities defined above can be considered extensive quantities since they describe properties of a magnetic circuit. Magnetomotive force (or magnetic potential difference), flux, and reluctance are of this nature. Other quantities cannot be considered extensive since they describe properties of a particular point in the circuit. Induction, magnetizing force, and relative permeability are of this nature. The more important magnetic quantities are listed in Table 1 with their defining equations and the relative sizes of the units in the cgs and rationalized mks systems.

TABLE 1

Quantity	Symbol	cgs Unit		Name of mks Unit	To Convert a Value in cgs Units to the Corresponding Value in mks Units Multiply by
		Name	Defining Equation		
Magnetomotive force	$\mathcal{F}$	Gilbert	$\mathcal{F} = \frac{4\pi NI}{10}$	Ampere-turn	$\frac{10}{4\pi}$
Flux	ϕ	Maxwell	$e = \frac{N\,d\phi}{dt} \times 10^{-8}$	Weber	10^{-8}
Reluctance	$\mathcal{R}$	..	$\phi = \frac{\mathcal{F}}{\mathcal{R}}$	..	$\frac{10^9}{4\pi}$
Magnetizing force	H	Oersted	$H = \frac{d\mathcal{F}}{dl}$	Ampere-turn/meter	$\frac{10^3}{4\pi}$
Induction	B	Gauss	$\phi = \int\int B\,dA$	Weber/sq meter	10^{-4}
Relative permeability	μ	..	$\mu = \frac{B}{\mu_v H}$	..	..
Absolute permeability of free space	μ_v	..	..	Henry/meter	$4\pi \times 10^{-7}$

Materials may be classified with respect to their magnetic properties as ferromagnetic, paramagnetic, or diamagnetic. *Ferromagnetic* materials have a variable permeability (a function of magnetizing force) which is greater than the permeability of free space. The permeability is also a function of temperature, and for each ferromagnetic material there exists a temperature above which the material ceases to be ferromagnetic and becomes paramagnetic. This temperature is known as the *Curie point* of the material. *Paramagnetic* materials have a *constant* permeability (not a function of magnetizing force) which is somewhat greater than that of free space ($\mu > \mu_v$). *Diamagnetic* materials have a *constant* permeability which is less than that of free space ($\mu < \mu_v$).

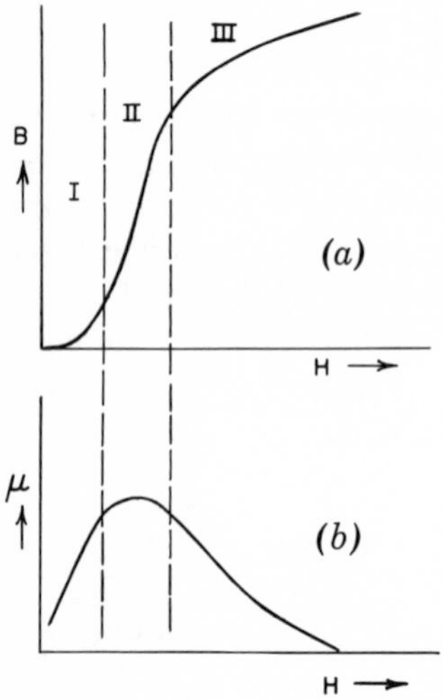

FIG. 1.

Characteristic Properties of Ferromagnetic Materials

Induction and Permeability. The magnetic properties of ferromagnetic materials are usually expressed in terms of the induction B, corresponding to specific values of magnetizing force H, or in terms of quantities derived from B and H. Figure 1 shows a magnetization curve which is typical of the relation between B and H. It should be noted that the induction is not a linear function of magnetizing force. This is a distinguishing characteristic of ferromagnetic materials. As a consequence of the fact that B is not a linear function of H, the permeability is not constant, but varies with the magnetization as shown in the figure. Three more or less distinct regions can be seen in a typical magnetization curve. In region I, at the toe of the curve [Fig. 1(*a*)], the induction increases at a low but increasing rate with magnetizing force. In region II, the rate of increase of induction with magnetizing force is much greater. In region III, at and beyond the knee of the curve, the induction rises at a continuously decreasing rate. The permeability [Fig. 1(*b*)] of the material increases continuously in region I, goes through a maximum in region II, and decreases continuously in region III. Figure 2 shows typical induction curves of a few ferromagnetic materials. Figure 3 shows permeability curves of some special-purpose alloys.

Magnetic Hysteresis. This is also a characteristic property of ferromagnetic materials. If we impress a magnetizing force on a specimen of such material and then remove it, the induction does not return to zero, but to a positive residual value B_r. To remove this residual induction, a magnetizing force ($- H_c$) in the reverse direction must be impressed on the specimen. The value of magnetizing force required to remove the residual induction is called the *coercive force*. If we continue to increase

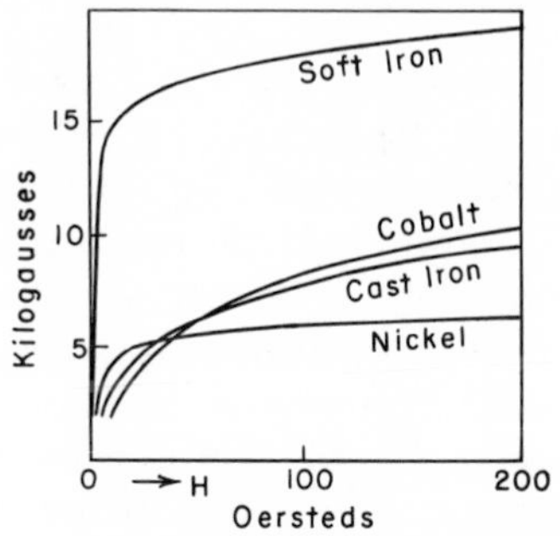

FIG. 2.

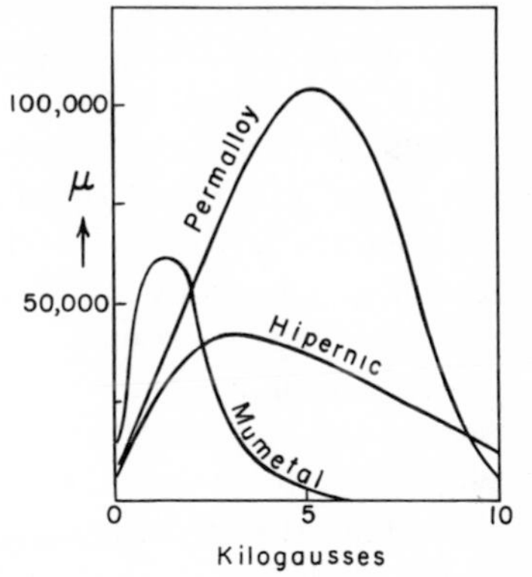

FIG. 3.

the reverse magnetizing force to a value ($- H_m$), the induction will increase to a value ($- B_m$), equal in amount and opposite in direction to the original induction (B_m). If the magnetizing force is again reduced to

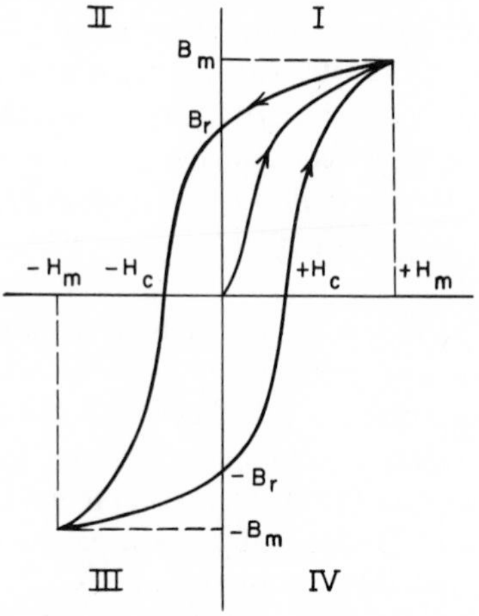

FIG. 4.

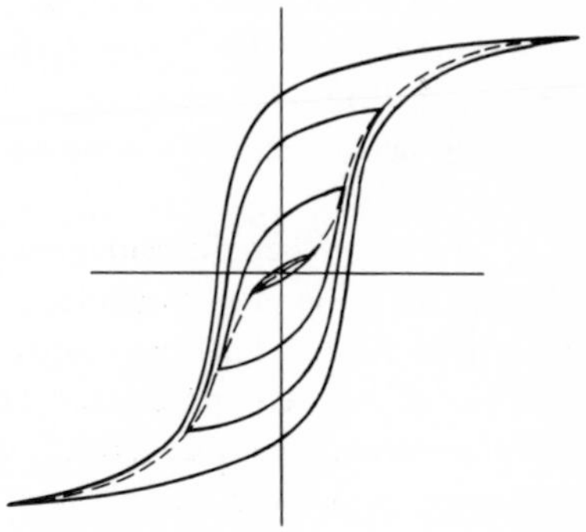

FIG. 5.

zero the induction decreases to a corresponding negative residual value ($- B_r$), and can be brought to zero only by applying the magnetizing force (H_c) in the positive direction. In other words, if H is varied cyclically between equal values in opposite directions, the values of B trace a closed loop as shown in Fig. 4. This is known as a *hysteresis loop*. The area $\int B\,dH$ enclosed by the loop for a complete cycle of values of H is a measure of the magnetic energy consumed by the specimen during the cycle and transformed into heat.

The *normal induction curve*, shown as the dashed line in Fig. 5, is the locus of the tips of a complete family of hysteresis loops, generated with the material in a "cyclic" condition.

It should be noted that, in general, the magnetic state of a specimen depends on its previous magnetic history, i.e. the magnitudes and directions of the fields to which it has already been subjected. To demagnetize a specimen we must erase the effects of its previous magnetic experiences by first impressing on it a magnetizing force sufficient to carry it well into the third stage of magnetization, and then subjecting it to a series of reversals of this magnetizing force, gradually reducing the magnitude of the magnetizing force as the cycling is continued. This process must be continued until the demagnetizing force has reached a value as small as the smallest value to be used in the subsequent magnetic testing. Demagnetization can be carried out in this way with direct current by repeatedly operating a reversing switch in the magnetizing circuit while slowly decreasing the magnitude of the magnetizing current. If a field is set up by means of alternating current in a coil surrounding the specimen, demagnetization can be accomplished by moving the specimen away from the coil which carries the current, or by leaving the specimen in place and gradually decreasing the magnitude of the alternating current to zero. In order to demagnetize the specimen completely by either procedure it is essential *to start the cycling process with a field sufficient to bring the specimen well into its third region of magnetization and then to cycle it repeatedly while gradually reducing the magnitude of the field to which it is subjected.*

Core Loss. When ferromagnetic material is subjected to alternating magnetic fields (as, for example, in a transformer) energy is expended in the form of heat. This consumption of energy is called *core loss*, and is made up of two components. The *hysteresis* component of core loss, which has already been described, depends on the magnetic characteristics of the material (i.e. the area enclosed in the hysteresis loop) at the particular maximum value of induction (B_m) present, and on the frequency of the alternating field. For values of maximum induction between 1000 and 12,000 gausses, the hysteresis component of the core loss can be represented by Steinmetz's empirical law $W_h = KfB_m^{1.6}$, where f is the frequency and K is a constant characteristic of the material. For values of B_m less than 1000 or greater than 12,000, the losses increase with some power of B_m greater than 1.6. The *eddy-current* component of core loss, arising from the eddy currents which circulate as a result of the emf's induced in the metal by the alternating magnetic field, depends not only on the flux density or induction in the material and the frequency of excitation, but also on the resistivity ρ of the material, the thickness t of the specimen, and the form factor K_f of the alternating flux. Provided that the specimen is built up of sheets thin enough so that skin effects are negligible, the eddy-current losses can be represented by the expression

$$W_e = \frac{K' K_f^2 f^2 B_m^2 t^2}{\rho}$$

where K' is a numerical constant.

PERMANENT MAGNETS

Although a detailed study of the factors involved in the design of permanent magnets is not feasible here,[5] it is well to examine some of the considerations which the designer must take into account. The actual design of instrument magnets involves considerations of weight, economy of space, expense of materials and processes, and permanence of magnetization as regards both aging and the hazards of demagnetization encountered under service conditions, as well as the field strength desired in the air gap—usually between 500 and 2500 gausses, depending on the application, in a gap 1.5 to 2.5 mm wide.

Special alloy steels are employed in magnet construction. Tungsten steel has been much used for many years. Cobalt-chrome steels, because of their higher coercivity, have advantages in some applications where economy of weight and space is important. In recent years Alnico magnets have been used to an increasing extent in instrument applications. The materials for instrument magnets are of two general types: (1) *quench-hardening* steels of high alloy content, so-called because they are hardened by rapid cooling from a high temperature by quenching in oil or water; and (2) *dispersion-hardening* alloys whose special properties are built up by various appropriate heat treatments. Steels with added tungsten, chromium, or cobalt are the most important quench-hardening magnet materials, while aluminum-nickel-iron alloys with added cobalt (Alnico) or titanium (Alnico XII) are commonly used dispersion-hardening materials.

All these materials have large hysteresis loops and are capable of retaining a relatively high degree of magnetization. This characteristic controls the properties utilized in making permanent magnets. Referring to quadrant II of Fig. 4 and assuming that the hysteresis loop is the

[5] Such a discussion is available in Permanent Magnets, *NBS Circ.* 448, by R. L. Sanford.

maximum attainable with the given material, the residual induction B_r is called the *retentivity* and the coercive force H_c is called the *coercivity*. The residual induction B_r may be considered to be a result of an inherent magnetizing force residing in the material itself, a function of its internal structure, brought into action by the previously applied external magnetizing force H_{max}. Now, if an air gap is introduced into the magnetic circuit, some of the "inherent" magnetizing force is needed to maintain the flux in the air gap, and therefore less of it is available to maintain the induction in the remainder of the magnetic circuit. Hence the induction decreases to a value B_d, as shown in Fig. 6. *The presence of the air gap partially demagnetizes the circuit.*

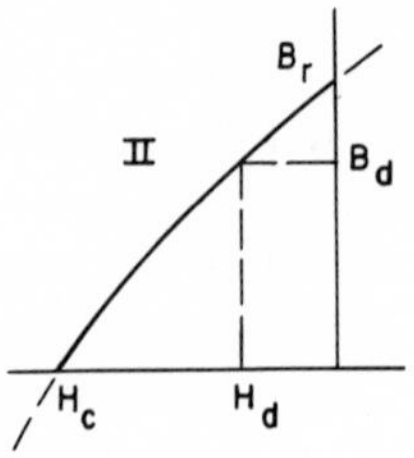

FIG. 6.

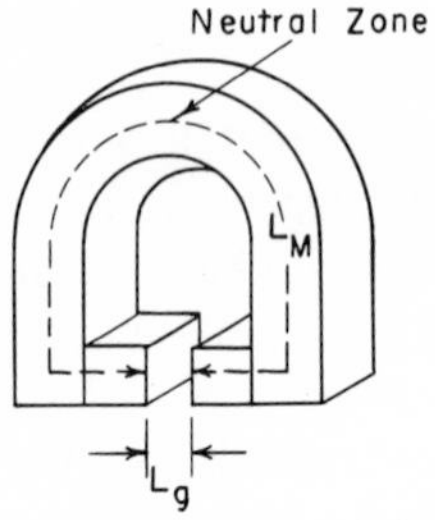

FIG. 7.

Since the sole function of an instrument magnet is to maintain flux in an air gap, we will limit our attention to this case. Suppose we have a horseshoe magnet of total length L_m, with an air gap of length L_g (Fig. 7). For the present we will make the simplifying assumption that there is no leakage flux; i.e. that all the flux present in the neutral zone of the magnet traverses its entire length and goes through the air gap. From Fig. 6 we see that a certain magnetizing force H_d corresponds to the reduced induction B_d of the partially demagnetized circuit. The effect of the gap is equivalent to a reverse magnetomotive force, $H_d \times L_m$, acting throughout the length of the magnet. The mmf required to maintain the flux in the air gap is the product of the field in the gap and its length, $H_g \times L_g$. Since these effects are the same we can write $H_d L_m = H_g L_g$. Now, since we have assumed that all the flux in the magnet traverses the air gap, we may write $B_d A_m = \mu_v H_g A_g$, where A_m and A_g are the cross-section areas of the magnet and gap respectively. From these equations

$$A_m = \frac{\mu_v H_g A_g}{B_d}, \quad \text{and} \quad L_m = \frac{H_g L_g}{H_d}$$

so that the volume of the magnet

$$V = A_m L_m = \frac{\mu_v H_g^2 A_g L_g}{H_d B_d}$$

From this relation it follows that (with no leakage) the volume of the magnet for a given field in the air gap will be a minimum if the product $H_d \cdot B_d$ is a maximum.

Energy Product. It can be shown[6] that the energy expended in carrying a magnetic circuit through a complete hysteresis loop is $(1/4\pi)\oint H \cdot dB$ ergs/cm³ per cycle, if H and B are both expressed in cgs units. Similarly, for a magnetic field in air (where no hysteresis is present and the loop of

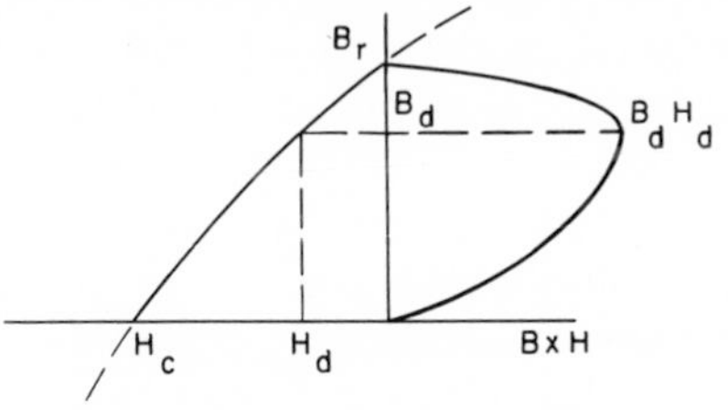

FIG. 8.

Fig. 4 reduces to a straight line), the energy stored in the field is $(1/4\pi)\int_0^{B_1} H\,dB$ ergs/cm³ when the flux density is B_1. But in air[7] we have $B = \mu_v \cdot H$, so that the energy in the air gap is

$$\frac{1}{4\pi}\int_0^{H_1} \mu_v H\,dH = \frac{\mu_v H_1^2}{8\pi} \text{ ergs/cm}^3$$

The total energy in the magnetic field of the air gap is then

$$E = \frac{\mu_v H_g^2 A_g L_g}{8\pi}$$

but, as we have previously seen, $\mu_v H_g^2 A_g L_g = V \cdot H_d B_d$, so that

$$E = \frac{V \cdot B_d H_d}{8\pi} \text{ ergs,} \quad \text{or} \quad \frac{E}{V} = \frac{B_d H_d}{8\pi} \text{ ergs}$$

per cubic centimeter of the magnet.

Since, for a uniformly magnetized magnet, the energy stored in the field of the air gap is proportional to the product $B_d \cdot H_d$, this product is called the *energy product* of the material. A typical energy-product curve is shown in Fig. 8, together with the corresponding portion of the hysteresis loop. If the ideal condition of no leakage could be realized and the magnet were magnetized with its pole pieces in place, the minimum volume

[6] Cullwick, *Fundamentals of Electromagnetism*, p. 203, Macmillan, 1939.

[7] Strictly speaking this is the relation for free space, but for practical purposes it is also true in air.

of magnetic material would be required if the magnet dimensions were chosen so that the energy product was maximum. This ideal is never realized in practice, but the maximum value of the energy product serves as a convenient index of the relative quality of various magnetic materials. Table 2 shows the energy product for a number of commercial and special magnet materials.

Leakage Flux. The principal problem in the practical design of magnets is the estimation of leakage flux, i.e. the fraction of the total flux present in the neutral zone of the magnet which does not go through the air gap. Generally this calculation cannot be made with accuracy, but may be approximated by a step-by-step process which takes account of the permeabilities and dimensions of various portions of the magnetic circuit and of the paths through air which act as "magnetic shunts" to by-pass portions of the flux around the air gap. In practical cases the leakage flux may amount to between 25 and 90% of the total flux in the neutral zone. We will define a leakage factor Λ, such that[8]

$$\Lambda = \frac{\text{flux in neutral zone}}{\text{flux in air gap}}$$

Our previous expression for magnet volume was based on the assumption that no leakage flux was present. If we take into account the leakage factor, we must write for the volume of the magnet

$$V = \frac{\Lambda \mu_v H_g^2 A_g L_g}{B_d H_d}$$

i.e. the volume of magnetic material needed to maintain a certain flux in the air gap is increased in direct proportion to the leakage factor.

Magnet Stability. Not only is it usually desirable that the field in the air gap of a magnet be high; it is even more important in the case of an instrument magnet that it be stable, since any change in the air-gap flux will change the instrument calibration. The principal influences which tend to weaken a magnet are: (1) structural changes in the magnet material, (2) mechanical shock or vibration, and (3) exposure to external magnetic fields. Since all the treatments used on magnets to improve their stability tend to weaken the air-gap field, proper allowance must be made for these losses in the design. The magnet volume therefore will have to be greater than that given by the equation of the preceding section, in order to ensure stability.

STRUCTURAL STABILIZATION. The sudden cooling of quench-hardening steels tends to suppress certain structural transformations which then

[8] For procedures suitable to the calculation of Λ reference should be made to detailed studies of this problem. For example, see *NBS Circ.* 448.

TABLE 2

MAGNETIC ALLOYS*

Type	Composition, % other than Fe	H_{max}	H_c	B_{max}	B_r	$(B_d \cdot H_d)_{max} \times 10^{-6}$	Fabrication
		oersteds		gausses			
Carbon steel	1.0 C; 0.5 Mn	300	48	14,800	8,600	0.18	Forge, machine, punch
Tungsten steel	5 W; 1 C	300	70	14,500	10,300	0.32	Forge, machine, cast
Chromium steel	3.5 Cr; 1 C	300	63	13,500	9,000	0.29	,, ,, ,,
36% Cobalt steel	36 Co; 3.5 Cr; 3 W; 0.85 C	1,000	210	15,500	9,000	0.94	Forge, machine, cast, punch
Alnico I	12 Al; 20 Ni; 5 Co	2,000	400	12,350	7,100	1.30	Cast, grind
Alnico II (cast)	10 Al; 17 Ni; 12.5 Co; 6 Cu	2,000	540	12,600	7,200	1.60	,, ,,
Alnico II (sintered)	,,	2,000	520	12,000	6,900	1.43	Sinter, grind
Alnico III	12 Al; 25 Ni	2,000	450	12,000	6,700	1.38	Cast, grind
Alnico IV	12 Al; 28 Ni; 5 Co	3,000	700	11,850	5,700	1.20	Cast, sinter, grind
Alnico V	8 Al; 14 Ni; 24 Co; 3 Cu	2,000	575	15,700	12,000	4.50	Cast, grind
Alnico VI	8 Al; 15 Ni; 24 Co; 3 Cu; 1.25 Ti	3,000	750	14,300	10,000	3.50	,, ,,
Alnico XII	6 Al; 18 Ni; 35 Co; 8 Ti	3,000	950	12,800	5,800	1.50	,, ,,
Cunife	60 Cu; 20 Ni	2,400	550	8,400	5,400	1.50	Cast, cold-roll, machine, punch
Cunico	50 Cu; 21 Ni; 29 Co	3,200	660	8,000	3,400	0.80	,,
Vectolite	30 Fe_2O_3; 44 Fe_3O_4; 26 Co_2O_3	3,000	1,000	4,800	1,600	0.60	Sinter, grind
Silmanal	86.75 Ag; 8.8 Mn; 4.45 Al	20,000	6,000	20,800	550	0.08	Cold-roll, machine, punch
Vicalloy	32–62 Co; 6–16 Va	2,000	400	..	9,400	2.40	..
77% Platinum	77 Pt; 23 Co	10,000	2,600	..	4,500	3.80	..
Pt–Fe	77 Pt; 23 Fe	..	5,500	..	500	0.06	..

* Much of the material for this table is from the General Electric *Bull.* on permanent magnets. Some material is from the Indiana Steel Products Company Permanent Magnet *Bull.* 4, and some from Permanent Magnets, *NBS Circ.* 448, by R. L. Sanford.

proceed very slowly even at room temperature. These structural changes are accompanied by changes in the magnetic properties of the material so that a magnet, magnetized immediately after hardening, will become weaker with time. The change is comparatively rapid at first but becomes slower as time goes on until finally it is negligible. The amount and rate of change, and the degree of constancy finally attained, depend on the composition and heat treatment of the alloy and the dimensions of the magnet. In some cases the total change may amount to 20% of the initial strength. The approach to a stable condition can be greatly accelerated by artificial aging (or maturing) applied either before or after magnetization. A common method of aging is to heat the magnet to 100°C and to hold it at this temperature for 10 to 12 hours. The use of 100°C is a matter of convenience. It is easy to maintain with boiling water and does not cause serious deterioration that might result from higher temperatures. Some makers subject magnets to a number of temperature cycles between 100°C and 0°C, whereas others store magnets at room temperature for a year or longer before using them. There is no substantial evidence, however, that shelf aging for a long time at room temperature results in better stability than is attained in a short time at 100°C. It is likely that the aging characteristics of permanent-magnet materials depend to a considerable extent on the original heat treatment, as well as on the stabilizing procedure. That stabilizing procedures can be made completely effective is evident from the fact that some permanent-magnet instruments have been in use as long as 40 years without any significant change from their initial calibration.

Structural instability, which is characteristic of quench-hardening steels, is very slight or completely absent in dispersion-hardening alloys. Indeed it can be said that properly treated dispersion-hardening alloys withstand all deteriorating influences much better than quench-hardening steels.

MECHANICAL STABILIZATION. In the case of quench-hardening steels, shock or vibration applied after magnetization tends to reduce the strength of the magnet. The effect of successive impacts is less, and a sufficient number of them will stabilize the magnet against further mechanical shock. The total loss depends on the type and condition of the material and may amount to between 10 and 25% of the initial strength. Either natural or accelerated aging decreases the effect of mechanical shock; but, where the highest degree of stability is required or where shock or vibration is apt to be severe in service, instrument magnets are subjected to impacts or vibration *after magnetization and aging*, in order to bring about a mechanically stable condition. The number and severity of the impacts required to produce stability depend on the nature of the material and must be empirically determined for any particular type of magnet.

MAGNETIC STABILIZATION. Structural and mechanical stabilization does not protect a magnet against the effects of external magnetic fields. If the equilibrium condition of the magnet is represented by the point P_1 on the demagnetization curve of Fig. 9 (the portion of the hysteresis loop which lies in quadrant II), and if a demagnetizing force ΔH is applied in the form of an external field, a new equilibrium P_2 is established on the demagnetization curve. If now the demagnetizing force ΔH is removed, the magnet does not return to the condition P_1 but follows a minor (interior) hysteresis loop to P_3. The induction in the magnet has been permanently decreased by an amount $(B_1 - B_3)$. The further, repeated application of any external magnetizing force less than ΔH (which is required to bring the induction back to the point P_2 on the normal demagnetization curve) will now change the induction along the minor loop, and the point P_3 will remain the equilibrium condition after the field is removed. Thus magnetic stabilization is produced by partial demagnetization. The magnet is, of course, stabilized only against the effect of fields less than ΔH. For a greater field, the induction would again drop along the normal demagnetization curve to a point (say, P_4) and then rise along a new minor loop when the field is removed. The slopes of such minor loops are, to a fair approximation, all equal to the slope of the normal demagnetization curve at its intersection with the axis ($B = B_r : H = 0$), as shown in Fig. 9,[9] and hence are substantially less than the slope of the normal demagnetization curve at P_1, P_2, or P_4.

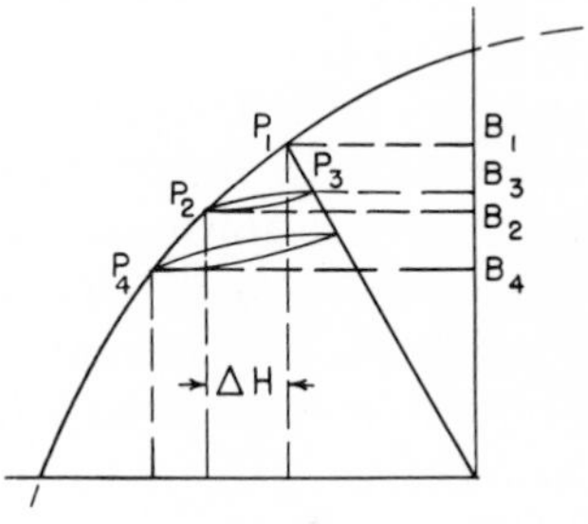

FIG. 9.

It will be seen that the presence of a demagnetizing field on an unstabilized magnet (or of a field greater than that for which the magnet was stabilized) results in a permanent loss of strength in the magnet. However, the application of such a field protects the magnet against any further permanent effect from any weaker field.

It is customary to partially demagnetize an instrument magnet after the initial magnetization in order to stabilize it against the effects of external fields. As a matter of convenience, some makers stabilize magnets at the time the completed instrument is calibrated. The instrument is designed so that initially its deflection for rated current is too high. At the time the scale is marked the instrument is subjected to a demagnetizing

[9] Underhill, Designing Stabilized Permanent Magnets, *Electronics*, **17**, 118 (1944).

field sufficient to reduce the deflection at rated current to exactly the angle which is desired for full scale. By this means full-scale deflection can be adjusted and the instrument magnet simultaneously stabilized against the effect of external fields which it is likely to encounter in service.

Magnetic stabilization can be accomplished without the application of an external field by magnetizing the magnet before putting the pole pieces in place. Referring to Fig. 9, if the equilibrium point without the pole pieces is P_2, then the addition of the pole pieces decreases the reluctance of the magnetic circuit and the induction rises along the minor loop toward P_3. The range of stability obtained in this way is determined by the relative dimensions of the magnet, the pole pieces, and the air gap.

THERMAL STABILIZATION. The strength of a magnet changes with temperature, becoming less as the temperature rises. For most magnet materials this change amounts to about 0.02%/°C. In order that the temperature coefficient shall be constant for a given magnet it is necessary to apply a thermal stabilizing treatment to the magnet after all other stabilizing is done. This consists in cycling the magnet several times between the temperature limits for which constancy is desired. If for any reason the magnet is remagnetized, the thermal stabilization must be repeated.

Magnet Shape. Returning now to the general design requirements, we can replace V by $A_m L_m$, and H_g by $A_m B_d / A_g \mu_v$, in our final design equation and write

$$\frac{H_d}{B_d} = \Lambda \frac{A_m L_g}{\mu_v A_g L_m}$$

From this equation it follows that, for a given gap length and area, the cross-section area of the magnet should be large and its length small for materials of low remanence and high coercivity, whereas the length of the magnet should be large and its cross section small if the material has high remanence and low coercivity.[10]

MAGNETIC TESTING

There are three general methods by which the magnetic properties of a material may be measured. (1) Magnetometers are used to measure values of unvarying magnetic fields or to compare the strengths of magnetic fields. Under some conditions magnetic properties of permanent-magnet materials can be deduced from magnetometer measurements. (2) Ballistic methods are usually employed in the determination of normal induction curves and in the point-by-point tracing of hysteresis loops.

[10] For a discussion of characteristic shapes of instrument magnets, see Chapter 5.

(3) Alternating-current methods are used to measure the core loss in sheet materials, the effective permeability of such materials under the action of alternating fields, and their incremental permeability under the combined action of direct and alternating fields.

Magnetometer Methods

These are the most direct and simplest methods of measuring the strength of magnetic fields. In contrast with the ballistic methods and the a-c methods to be discussed later, a magnetometer may be used to measure the actual value of an unchanging field, rather than the effect produced by a change in its magnitude. The simple magnetometer consists essentially of a pivoted or suspended magnetic needle, the suspension usually being of such a nature that it exerts very little torsional control on the needle.

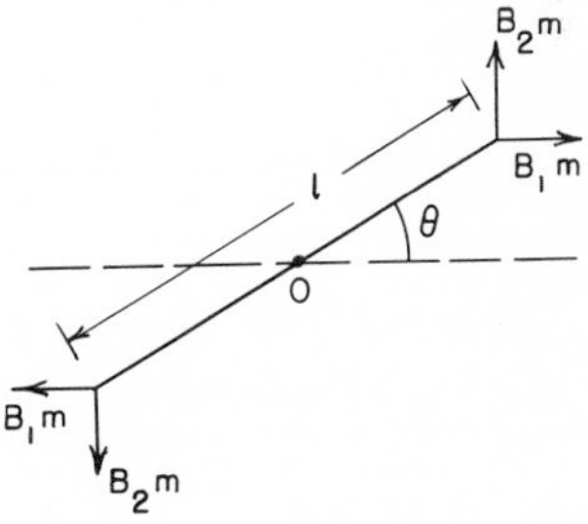

FIG. 10.

It must be realized that in any magnetic measurement in which a field is experimentally determined, either by the evaluation of a force or by changing the coupling between an electric and a magnetic circuit and evaluating the resulting voltage-time relation, it is *always* the induction B (at the point or in the region) which we measure directly. If our measurement is such that the induction B_v in free space (or in air) is evaluated, we can then compute the magnetizing force H which evoked the measured induction B_v, through the relation $B_v = \mu_v \cdot H$.

Two magnetometer methods are available by which fields may be compared, the deflection method and the oscillation method. We will assume (Fig. 10) that a magnetic needle having a magnetic moment $\mathcal{M} = ml$ (where l is length and m is pole strength) is suspended horizontally (by a torsionless filament) from its midpoint O, and is under the action of two mutually perpendicular horizontal magnetic fields, B_1 and B_2. The forces acting on each pole of the needle are B_1m and B_2m. Then two couples act on the needle:

(1) $B_1ml \sin \theta = B_1\mathcal{M} \sin \theta$ (clockwise); and
(2) $B_2ml \cos \theta = B_2\mathcal{M} \cos \theta$ (counterclockwise).

At the equilibrium position under the action of these couples we have

$$B_1\mathcal{M} \sin \theta = B_2\mathcal{M} \cos \theta, \quad \text{or} \quad B_2 = B_1 \tan \theta$$

Thus, if the strength of the field B_1 (say the horizontal component of the earth's field) is known, B_2 may be determined.

The deflection magnetometer method may be used to determine the magnetic moment of a bar magnet by the following procedure. We will suppose that the field B_2 is produced by a bar magnet, and that the magnetometer needle is located as shown in Fig. 11, in line with the axis of the magnet, which is in an east-west direction. We will say that the length of the bar magnet is A, and its pole strength m_2, so that its magnetic moment is $\mathscr{M}_2 = Am_2$. The distance between centers of the magnet and magnetometer will be C. Now the magnetizing force tending to set up a field at a point, as a result of a magnetic pole of strength m at a distance

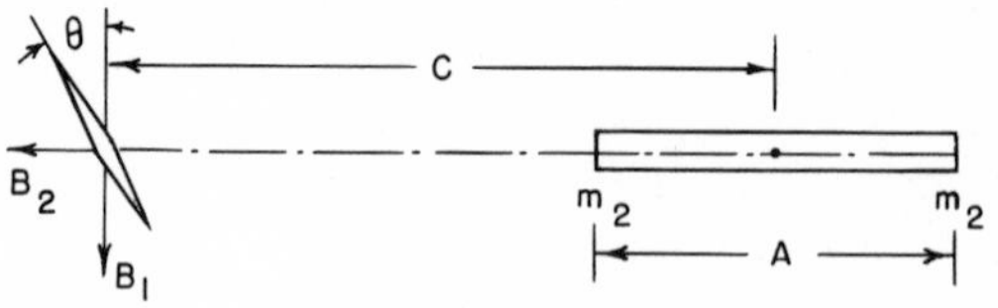

FIG. 11.

r from the point, is $H = m/r^2$. Then at the position of the magnetometer the magnetizing force from the nearer pole is

$$H_n = \frac{m_2}{\left(C - \frac{A}{2}\right)^2}$$

and from the more distant pole is

$$H_d = \frac{m_2}{\left(C + \frac{A}{2}\right)^2}$$

The resulting magnetizing force

$$H_2 = H_n - H_d = m_2\left[\frac{1}{\left(C - \frac{A}{2}\right)^2} - \frac{1}{\left(C + \frac{A}{2}\right)^2}\right]$$

$$= \frac{2m_2CA}{\left[C^2 - \frac{A^2}{4}\right]^2} = \frac{2\mathscr{M}_2C}{\left[C^2 - \frac{A^2}{4}\right]^2}$$

and if C is large compared to A, we have approximately

$$H_2 \approx \frac{2\mathscr{M}_2}{C^3}$$

The resulting induction at the point is

$$B_2 = \mu_v H_2 = \frac{2\mathscr{M}_2\mu_v}{C^3}$$

The equilibrium position of the magnetometer needle under the action of the perpendicular fields B_1 and B_2 is

$$\tan\theta = \frac{B_2}{B_1} = \frac{2\mathscr{M}_2\mu_v}{B_1C^3}$$

so that

$$\frac{\mathscr{M}_2}{B_1} = \frac{C^3\tan\theta}{2\mu_v}$$

or

$$\mathscr{M}_2 = \frac{B_1C^3\tan\theta}{2\mu_v}$$

The magnetic moment of the bar magnet is given in terms of the control field B_1 (say, the horizontal component of the earth's field) and the equilibrium position of the magnetometer needle.

It may be noted that, from the magnetic moment $\mathscr{M}_2$ of the bar magnet, we can compute the pole strength $m_2 = \mathscr{M}_2/A$, and from this value estimate the flux density in the magnet. The intensity of magnetization is

$$J = \frac{\text{pole strength} \times \mu_v}{\text{area}}$$

and, if we assume that the flux density in the magnet is uniform,[11]

$$B_i = 4\pi J = \frac{4\pi m_2\mu_v}{\text{area}} = \frac{4\pi\mathscr{M}_2\mu_v}{\text{area} \times A} = \frac{4\pi\mathscr{M}_2\mu_v}{\text{magnet volume}}$$

The magnetometer can also be used to compare the strengths of magnetic fields by measuring the period of oscillation of the magnetometer needle. If I is the moment of inertia of the needle about its axis of rotation, $\mathscr{M}$ its magnetic moment, and B_1 the strength of the field in which it swings, we can write (by analogy to the galvanometer equation) the period of the needle (in the absence of damping)

$$T_1 = 2\pi\sqrt{\frac{I}{B_1\mathscr{M}}}$$

$B_1\mathscr{M}$ being the restoration constant corresponding to the stiffness U of the galvanometer suspension. In a second field (B_2), we would have

$$T_2 = 2\pi\sqrt{\frac{I}{\mathscr{M}B_2}}$$

so that

$$\frac{T_1}{T_2} = \sqrt{\frac{B_2}{B_1}}, \quad \text{or} \quad B_2 = B_1\left(\frac{T_1}{T_2}\right)^2$$

[11] The presence of leakage flux is ignored in this approximation.

Thus we can measure the strength of a field in terms of another known field.

In the *classical magnetometer experiment*, performed at one time or another by almost every student of physics, the horizontal component of the earth's magnetic field and the magnetic moment of a bar magnet are determined by the procedures described above. The ratio

$$\frac{\mathcal{M}}{B} = \frac{C^3 \tan\theta}{2\mu_v} = K_1$$

is determined from the angular position taken by a compass needle under the combined action of the horizontal component of the earth's field and the field of the bar magnet which is set up at a considerable distance C from the compass, the magnet being placed with its axis perpendicular to the earth's field, and the compass being located on this axis. The product

$$B\mathcal{M} = \frac{4\pi^2 I}{T^2} = K_2$$

is determined from the period of oscillation of the bar magnet suspended horizontally in the earth's field, its moment of inertia I being known. From the relations $\mathcal{M}/B = K_1$, and $\mathcal{M}B = K_2$, we have[12]

$$\mathcal{M} = \sqrt{K_1K_2} \quad \text{and} \quad B = \sqrt{\frac{K_2}{K_1}}$$

[12] Carelessness in the matter of using B (in air) and H interchangeably, as though they were identities, has resulted in a great deal of needless confusion about this experiment. In some books the experiment is described as though H were being directly measured (i.e. $H\mathcal{M} = K_2$, and $\mathcal{M}/H = K_1$), whereas we can actually arrive at an experimental value of H only through computation from a measured value of B, and an assigned value of space permeability. The confusion appears to arise from a rather curious chain of reasoning: "In the cgs system B and H are numerically equal in free space, being connected by the relation $B_v = \mu_v H$, in which μ_v has been assigned unit value. Since μ_v has the value unity we will have no further need for it if we will in addition ignore any dimensional significance that it has, and say that B and H are physically identical as well as numerically equal in free space." In accepting this argument as valid one must return to a measuring system which is described in terms of three dimensional parameters; we are denied recourse to a fourth dimensional parameter which will permit discrimination between B and H. Although it is true that mechanical and electrical quantities can be described in terms of three dimensional parameters (say, length, mass, time), and although such a description may be adequate for many purposes, it must be realized that this does not constitute a complete parametric description since it leaves unresolved differences, such as that between B_v and H Three dimensional parameters are not enough to describe uniquely all the electrical quantities in terms of mechanical quantities; and, since a fourth parameter is needed

The G. E. gaussmeter is a direct-reading magnetometer of special design, which can be used to measure the field in the air gaps of instrument magnets and in various magnetic structures where access is difficult by

---

(see Chapter 2 on units), the use of only three parameters limits the resolving power of the parametric system and restricts the amount of information that can be obtained from dimensional analysis or dimensional checks.

Let us assume that B_v and H are physically different quantities and examine the validity of the dimensional relations for the equations

$$B\mathscr{M} = \frac{4\pi^2 I}{T^2}, \quad \text{and} \quad \frac{\mathscr{M}}{B} = \frac{C^3 \tan\theta}{2\mu_v}$$

Since in nature all magnetic effects result from currents [which may be in conductors whose arrangement in space we can trace, or which may exist as the oriented motion of electric charges (electrons) within the body of a magnetic material] we will base our assignments of dimensions on the idea of electric charges in motion. All the dimensional formulas which we shall need have already been developed (in the *LMTQ* system) in Chapter 1, p. 37, with the exception of the dimensions of magnetic moment and of pole strength. The dimensions of magnetic moment are most simply derived from the magnetic moment of a coil carrying current. It can be shown (Cullwick, *op. cit.*, p. 93) that a plane coil of N concentrated turns, situated in a uniform magnetic field of density B, experiences a torque whose value is $\mathscr{T} = INAB \cos\theta$, where I is the current in the coil, A its cross-sectional area, and θ the angle between the plane of the coil and the direction of the field. The torque is maximum when the plane of the coil coincides with the direction of the field, $\mathscr{T}_{\max} = INAB$, and the magnetic moment of the coil may be defined as the maximum torque which it would experience in a field of unit density, i.e. $\mathscr{M} = INA$ for the coil. The dimensions of $\mathscr{M}$ can then be written as $L^2T^{-1}Q$. Since pole strength is $m = \mathscr{M}/l$ (magnetic moment per unit length), its dimensions are $LT^{-1}Q$. Substituting the appropriate dimensions in our formula $B\mathscr{M} = 4\pi^2I/T^2$, and recalling that the dimensions of moment of inertia are L^2M, we have

$$MT^{-1}Q^{-1} \cdot L^2T^{-1}Q = L^2M \cdot T^{-2}$$

or

$$L^2MT^{-2} \equiv L^2MT^{-2}$$

i.e. the equation is dimensionally homogeneous. Similarly for the equation

$$\frac{\mathscr{M}}{B} = \frac{C^3 \tan\theta}{2\mu_v}$$

recalling that $\tan\theta$ is a dimensionless ratio, we have

$$\frac{L^2T^{-1}Q}{MT^{-1}Q^{-1}} = \frac{L^3}{LMQ^{-2}}$$

or

$$L^2M^{-1}Q^2 \equiv L^2M^{-1}Q^2$$

i.e. this equation is also dimensionally homogeneous. A dimensional check will show that it is improper to use H in place of B in these equations, since they will be found *not* to be dimensionally homogeneous.

ordinary means. As shown schematically in Fig. 12, this magnetometer has a small cylindrical Silmanal[13] magnet at the lower end of a long, thin shaft. The moving system is supported on jewel bearings, and control torque is provided by a spiral spring. The upper end of the shaft carries a pointer which moves over a 2-in. instrument dial scale calibrated to read directly in gausses. The magnet and shaft are protected by a thin-walled tube, which carries the lower pivot jewel. The moving system with its protective tube forms a probe extending from the back of the instrument. Probe diameters range from 0.052 in. to 0.090 in., and probe lengths of $1\frac{1}{4}$ in. and 5 in. are available. Ranges are from 100 gausses to 5000 gausses. In operation the probe is placed in the magnetic field and the instrument case is rotated until the pointer is at the scale zero. The pointer then indicates the direction of the field, since the probe magnet is lined up with the external field and there is no torque on the moving system. To measure the magnitude of the field, the instrument case is rotated until the upscale reading of the pointer is maximum. At this position the probe magnet is at a right angle to the field being investigated and the scale reading gives the field strength directly in gausses.

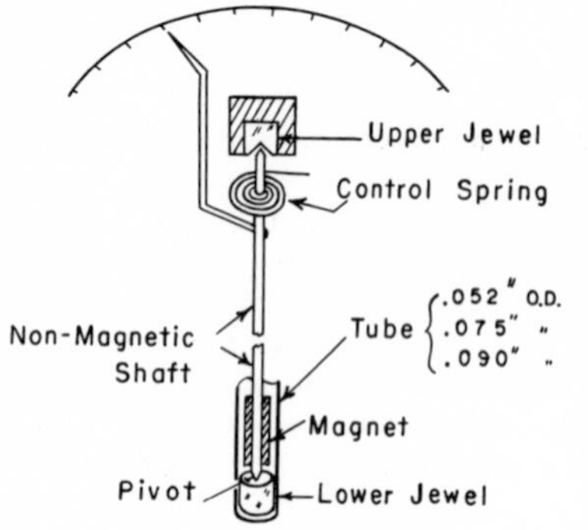

FIG. 12. General Electric gaussmeter.

Ballistic Methods

These are generally employed in the determination of normal induction curves and hysteresis loops of ferromagnetic materials. Direct current is used to provide an adjustable mmf on the magnetic circuit, and a ballistic galvanometer or fluxmeter is employed as a measuring instrument. It must be remembered that ballistic methods do not directly measure the static value of flux density in a material, corresponding to a particular value of magnetizing force, but measure instead the *changes* in flux brought about by changes in magnetizing force or by relative motion of the magnetic field and a test coil, such that the flux linkages in the test coil are changed.

General Considerations. Although the details of the manner in which the magnetic circuit is constructed may be quite different in various ballistic test methods, certain operational features are common to all. The measuring circuit consists of a test (or search) coil connected to a

[13] Silmanal is used because of its extremely high coercivity (see table on p. 353).

ballistic galvanometer. When magnetic flux linking the test coil is suddenly changed in magnitude, a momentary emf is induced in the galvanometer circuit, and the quantity of electricity which flows during the impulse or the time integral of emf, proportional to the change in flux linkages, is measured by the deflection (ballistic throw) of the galvanometer. The character of the deflection of ballistic galvanometers under various conditions of use, and the determination of $\int i\,dt$ or of $\int e\,dt$ from the ballistic deflection of a galvanometer, have already been discussed. The reader is referred to Chapter 8 on ballistic galvanometers for particulars.

Normal induction curves and hysteresis loops delineate the relations between the flux density B in a ferromagnetic material and the magnetizing force H which evokes it under certain specified conditions. The determination of flux density in the specimen of ferromagnetic material under test is usually quite straightforward. A test coil having a known number of turns N is placed around the specimen, and a predetermined change is made in H. This may be a reversal of H or some other specified change, ΔH. The corresponding change in flux linkages in the test coil, $N\Delta\phi$, induces in it an emf whose time integral $\int e\,dt$ is measured by means of a calibrated ballistic galvanometer or fluxmeter. Then, when $\Delta\phi$ has been measured, the change in induction (ΔB) is evaluated from the relation $\Delta B = \Delta\phi/A$, where A is the cross-sectional area of the specimen, on the assumption that the flux density is uniform throughout the section.[14] Evaluation of the corresponding change in magnetizing force (ΔH), which is responsible for the change in induction (ΔB) thus determined, will depend on the nature of the magnetic circuit which is being used. In some types of circuits the change in magnetizing force can be computed directly from the change in ampere-turns per unit length, at the point where ΔB is measured. In order that this may be done it is usually necessary to simulate the conditions which would exist within a section of an infinite solenoid.[15] In other types of magnetic circuits, in which the magnetizing force cannot be directly computed from ampere-turns (because of leakage flux, or the presence of counter mmf's which cannot be readily evaluated, or for other reasons), the value of H must be computed from (1) measurements of the difference in magnetic potential across the portion of the specimen under examination, or (2) measurements of induction in air close to the specimen. Both methods are used in practice, and their bases must be examined.

[14] Of course, this is merely an *average* value of ΔB throughout the section, but no value other than such an average is possible by ballistic methods.

[15] This method of evaluating H is used in measurements on "ring" specimens and in the Burrows permeameter, both of which will be discussed below.

THE MAGNETIC POTENTIOMETER. We will consider first the measurement of magnetic potential difference. It can be shown[16] that the line integral of flux density (B_v), set up in free space by a coil of N concentrated turns carrying a current I, is

$$\oint B_v\, dl = 4\pi\mu_v IN$$

around any closed path linking the coil. This is the *circuital law* of the magnetic field and forms the basis of the *magnetic potentiometer*, which can be used to determine the mmf around a closed path, or the magnetic potential difference between two points of a magnetic circuit. Suppose that we have a long solenoid, of small constant cross section (A) (of any convenient shape), having n turns per unit length, formed into a closed loop of any convenient shape, linking a current-carrying conductor having N concentrated turns, as shown in Fig. 13(a). If the component of flux density in the direction of the solenoid axis at a point P is B_{vp}, the flux linkages in an element of the solenoid δl will be $AB_{vp}n\,\delta l$. The flux linkages along the entire length of the solenoid will be $An\int B_{vp}\, dl$; and, since the solenoid forms a closed loop threading the conductor, we will have

$$An \oint B_v\, dl = An \cdot 4\pi NI\mu_v$$

from the circuital law stated above. Now, if the current in the conductor is reduced to zero so that the field is also reduced to zero, the deflection of the fluxmeter [proportional to the total change in flux linkages in the circuit (the solenoid) to which it is connected][17] will be a measure of the total mmf of the current-carrying conductor, i.e.

$$\int e\, dt = K\mu_v \cdot 4\pi NI$$

Such a solenoid of fine wire, wound uniformly on a thin strip or rod of flexible non-magnetic material of uniform cross section, and connected to a fluxmeter or ballistic galvanometer, may serve as a magnetic potentiometer. In the illustrative example it was used to measure the mmf of a coil of N concentrated turns carrying a current I. It may be shown experimentally that such a solenoid linking the coil will always produce the same deflection in its fluxmeter when the current in the coil is reduced to zero, regardless of the configuration of the solenoid, and that there is no fluxmeter deflection when the solenoid is formed into a closed loop which does not link the current-carrying coil. The magnetic potentiometer can also be used, with its ends separated, to measure the magnetic potential difference between any two points of a magnetic circuit to which

[16] Cullwick, *op. cit.*, p. 146.

[17] See p. 331, Chapter 8, on ballistic galvanometers.

its ends are applied. The return leads from the ends of the solenoid should be kept as close as possible to the surface of the strip on which it is wound, and the connections to the fluxmeter should be in the form of a twisted pair, as shown in Fig. 13(*b*), in order that the loop formed by these connecting leads will enclose the minimum possible area. It is even better to wind a magnetic potentiometer as a double-layer solenoid so that the connections to the fluxmeter may be brought out together at some convenient point on the strip. Changes in magnetic potential may be measured by changing the magnetizing current producing the field in which the potentiometer is maintained in a fixed position, or by moving one end of the strip from one point to another in the field while the other end is held in a fixed position.

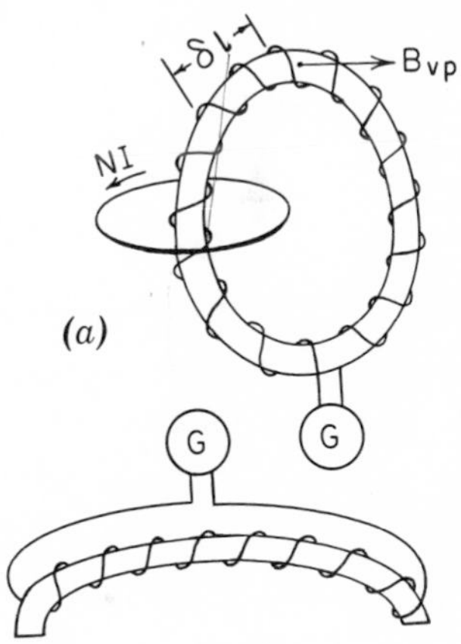

(*a*)

(*b*)

FIG. 13.

INDUCTION IN AIR. An alternative method of evaluating the magnetizing force (or its change) at some point in a magnetic circuit is based on the assumption that the tangential component of the magnetizing force at a common surface between a magnetic and a non-magnetic medium is not altered in going from one medium to the other.[18] If, then, the tangential component of induction is measured *in air* at a point adjacent to the surface of a magnetized specimen, it may be used to compute the magnetizing force which is effective in producing induction in the specimen at that point, in accordance with the formula $B_v = \mu_v H$. In some types of magnetic testing apparatus, the magnetizing force (or its change) acting on the specimen is determined in this way by measuring the induction in air adjacent to the specimen, making use of a search coil which is close to the specimen but does not surround it. Obviously, if no leakage flux is present at the point in question, such a measurement will yield the required value of H (or ΔH) precisely, and if the leakage flux is small will yield a value which is approximately correct. In some instances a series of values of induction is measured in air at intervals spaced normally to the surface of the specimen, and the values of H thus determined are extrapolated to give the magnetizing force at the surface of the specimen.

[18] This is equivalent to saying that the magnetic potential difference between two points of the magnetic circuit located on the boundary between a magnetic and a non-magnetic medium is the same whether the path between the points be taken in the magnetic or in the non-magnetic medium.

THE ELECTRICAL TEST CIRCUIT. A typical diagram of the circuits used in ballistic testing is shown in Fig. 14. Current from a storage battery or other suitable source is controlled by the rheostats R_1 and R_2 and measured by the ammeter A. C is a reversing switch, and C' a single-pole switch which may be opened to insert R_2 in the circuit, abruptly changing the value of magnetizing current without reversal. D is a selector switch, which may be closed upward to energize the mutual inductor M for calibrating the ballistic galvanometer or fluxmeter, or downward to

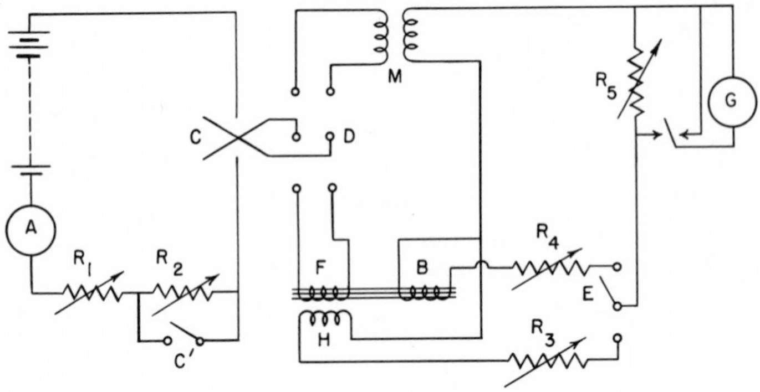

FIG. 14.

energize the magnetizing winding F surrounding the specimen under test. A second selector switch E is used to connect the test coil B (surrounding the specimen) to the galvanometer in order to measure induction, or alternatively to connect the galvanometer to the test coil H which does not surround the specimen but which is so located that it can serve to measure the magnetizing force. (In some types of apparatus, the value of the magnetizing current is used to compute the magnetizing force so that no H-coil is needed.) R_3 (or R_4) and R_5 are adjustable series and parallel resistances in the galvanometer circuit which control galvanometer sensitivity and damping. In Fig. 14 the galvanometer is shown equipped with a short-circuiting key K, for checking its swing. Alternative methods of controlling the galvanometer are discussed in Chapter 8 on the ballistic galvanometer.

GALVANOMETER CALIBRATION. It is frequently convenient to adjust the galvanometer deflection so that it is direct reading either in induction or in magnetizing force (so that, for example, 1-cm deflection corresponds to the reversal of an induction of 1000 gausses, or to the reversal of a magnetizing force of 1, 10, or 100 oersteds as may be desired). Such an adjustment can be made with the aid of the mutual inductor M, by setting proper values in R_3 (or R_4) and R_5.

The emf induced in a test coil is $e = N(d\phi/dt) \times 10^{-8}$ volts, so that $\int e\,dt = N\Delta\phi/10^8$, where N is turns in the coil and $\Delta\phi$ is the total change in the flux linking each turn. In a mutual inductor of M henrys, we have by definition $e = M(di/dt)$, so that $\int e\,dt = M\Delta I$. Since, under proper conditions, the ballistic throw of the galvanometer is proportional to $\int e\,dt$, we can say that

$$M\Delta I = \frac{N\Delta\phi}{10^8}, \quad \text{or} \quad \Delta I = \frac{N\Delta\phi}{M \times 10^8}$$

if the deflections are to be equal in the two cases.

If our test coil has area-turns $= AN$, we can, by calibration with the inductor, adjust the galvanometer circuit so that unit deflection corresponds to the reversal of an induction in air produced by a magnetizing force of H oersteds. The current which must be reversed in the primary of the inductor to produce the same value of $\int e\,dt$ as is produced by the reversal of flux in the search coil corresponding to H oersteds is $I_H = ANH/(M \times 10^8)$. If we reverse I_H in the primary of the inductor and adjust R_3 and R_5 so that we have unit deflection on the galvanometer, then the reversal of field through the test coil corresponding to H oersteds will also give unit deflection.

Similarly, if the reversal of B gausses in a test coil of N turns, wound closely around a specimen of cross section a, is to produce unit galvanometer deflection, the current in amperes which must be reversed in the primary of the mutual inductor is $I_B = aNB/(M \times 10^8)$. In this case the resistance R_4 must be adjusted.

CORRECTION FOR AIR FLUX. Since for this calibration we have assumed that the flux density B is uniform throughout the specimen, and that the effective area of the test coil is equal to the cross section a of the specimen, the observed value of induction must be corrected if the specimen is smaller in cross section than the effective area A of the test coil. Here we have

$$a \cdot NB_{\text{observed}} = a \cdot NB_{\text{true}} + (A - a) \cdot NH\mu_v$$

so that

$$B_{\text{observed}} = B_{\text{true}} + \frac{A - a}{a} H\mu_v$$

or

$$B_{\text{true}} = B_{\text{observed}} - \frac{A - a}{a} H\mu_v$$

COUPLING. In any apparatus set up for ballistic measurements one must locate the calibrating mutual inductance with respect to the remaining equipment so that the inductor will not be affected by stray fields. Leads from both the primary and the secondary of the calibrating inductor should be twisted pairs (or coaxial pairs), and in general the apparatus should be so located as to avoid any coupling which might introduce errors into the measurements.

DEMAGNETIZATION. In measuring normal induction the specimen must first be demagnetized (see p. 348). Current is then set to correspond to the lowest value of magnetizing force to be used in the test and reversed several times until successive readings of induction are in agreement. The induction is thus measured with the specimen in a cyclic condition. The value of H (the corresponding magnetizing force) may be computed from the magnetizing current or from measurements with the H-coil, depending on the test apparatus. In taking successive points on the normal induction curve the same procedure may be followed, but without further demagnetization, provided that each point taken represents a higher magnetizing force than *any* preceding one. If successive points represent decreasing values of H, the specimen must be demagnetized from each point to the succeeding one.

HYSTERESIS LOOP. In determining points on a hysteresis loop, the specimen is first demagnetized and then put into a cyclic condition at the required value of H_{max}. The switch C' is then opened, reducing the value of H without reversal, and the corresponding change in induction is measured. A series of points with various values of R_2 may be taken in this way to trace out the loop, care being taken to re-establish the cyclic condition at the tip of the loop before each reading. For points on the negative portion of the hysteresis loop, switches C and C' must be operated together, reversing the magnetizing current and reducing it simultaneously.

Bar and Solenoid. Most test methods make use of a magnetic circuit of low reluctance, of which the specimen is a part. It is, however, sometimes simpler or more convenient to employ a straight bar, magnetized in a solenoid. In this case the return circuit for the flux is in air and its reluctance is high. Also, when the bar is magnetized, the poles produced at its ends set up a counter mmf which partly demagnetizes the bar. Hence the value H of the magnetizing force which is effective in producing induction in the specimen is less than the applied magnetizing force H calculated from ampere-turns in the magnetizing solenoid. For a very long solenoid, the applied magnetizing force at the midpoint is $H' = 4\pi nI/10$ (as we have previously seen), n being turns per centimeter length, and I the current in amperes. For a relatively short solenoid whose length is l and whose mean diameter is d, we have at the midpoint approximately

$$H' = \frac{4\pi nI}{10} \cdot \frac{l}{\sqrt{l^2 + d^2}}$$

If the coil has more than one layer, a more accurate value will be obtained by calculating the contribution of each layer separately and then summing.

The value of the *applied* magnetizing force, calculated in this way, must be corrected to take into account the self-demagnetization of the specimen. This correction is proportional to the intrinsic induction in the specimen ($B_i = B - \mu_v H$, the excess over the induction which would be present in free space). The magnitude of the correction term depends on the ratio of length to diameter of the specimen, becoming less as this ratio increases. The *effective* magnetizing force H is given by the formula

$$H = H' - \frac{KB_i}{\mu_v}$$

where K is the demagnetizing factor. This factor can be calculated exactly for specimens in the form of an ellipsoid of revolution having uniform magnetic properties throughout, but such a specimen would be so difficult to prepare as to be impractical for test purposes. For long, straight bars of uniform cross section, the demagnetization factor is given approximately by the expression

$$\log_{10} K = 0.05 - 1.75 \log_{10} D$$

where D is the ratio of length to diameter of the specimen.[19]. If the cross section of the bar is rectangular instead of circular, the diameter of the circle which would have the same area may be used in the computation. K amounts to about 0.02, for $D = 10$, and 0.006 for $D = 20$.

The effective value of magnetizing force can be measured, instead of relying on the calculations outlined above, by means of a test coil wound on a thin strip of non-magnetic material and placed flat against the specimen. The value of H calculated from the measured flux density in the air at the surface of the specimen should be fully as accurate as that obtained from the calculation based on ampere-turns and demagnetization factor. This device (the ballistic determination of H by means of a test coil placed close to the specimen but not surrounding it) is used to determine the effective magnetizing force in many of the common methods of magnetic testing. The induction in the specimen is measured with the B-coil which surrounds it. If the effective area A of the test coil which surrounds the specimen is greater than that of the specimen a, a correction term $\left(\mu_v H \frac{A - a}{a}\right)$, must be subtracted from the observed value of induction.

Ring Specimens. The ballistic method which, under properly controlled conditions, has the highest accuracy is that which uses a specimen in the

[19] See Sanford, Magnetic Testing, *NBS Circ.* C456, p. 13.

form of a ring. Its principal advantage is the absence of end effects and of errors resulting from magnetic leakage. This is true, however, only if the specimen is continuous, having no joints. Magnetic inhomogeneities are always present in a joint and give rise to leakage. This is equally true of a weld, since it is not possible, even by subsequent annealing, to eliminate the effects of the weld. Hence, a bar which has been bent into a ring and has its ends welded together does not make a suitable ring specimen. The magnetizing winding on a ring specimen should be uniform, since an irregular winding would give rise to a non-uniform distribution of mmf around the magnetic circuit, causing leakage and introducing errors in the measurement. The magnetizing force is usually

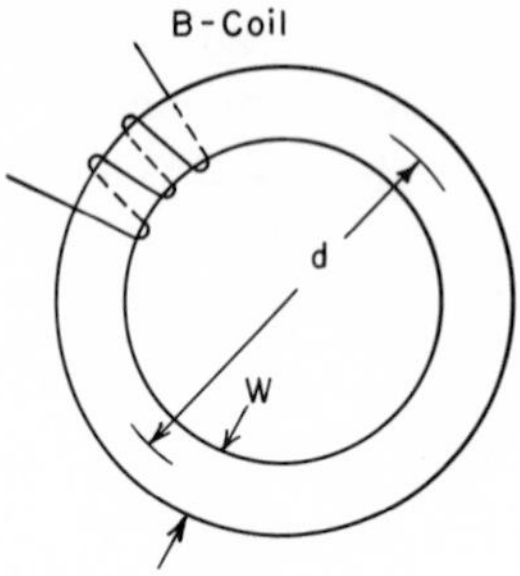

FIG. 15.

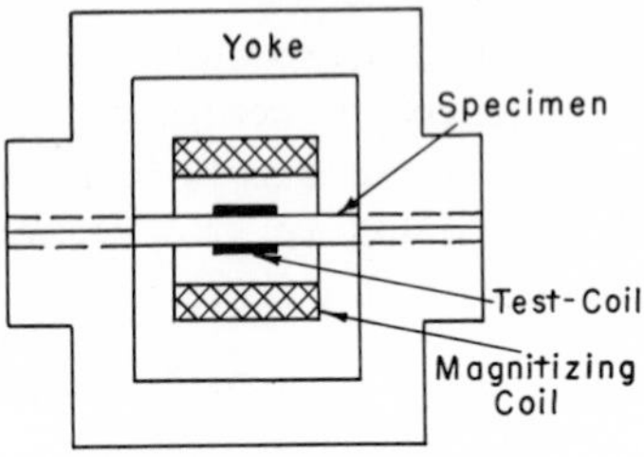

FIG. 16.

calculated in terms of the mean diameter of the ring and the ampere-turns in the magnetizing winding. However, since the inner circumference of the ring is smaller than the outer, the magnetizing force and the induction are not uniform over the cross section. The error involved depends on the ratio of the mean diameter d of the ring to the radial width w of the specimen (Fig. 15), and on the magnetic properties of the material. The average value of the magnetizing force is about 2% higher than the value calculated in terms of the mean diameter[20] if $d/w = 4$, and about 0.3% if $d/w = 10$. Generally d/w is made 10 or greater.

The use of ring specimens in magnetic testing is limited because of the labor of preparing and winding them, since this winding must be done by hand for each individual ring. Also the values of magnetizing force that can be obtained without excessive heating of the ring are limited. The principal use of ring specimens at the present time is in the testing of small quantities of material of very high permeability.

Permeameters. Most of the methods employed in magnetic testing are designed to avoid the errors or inconveniences of the simpler bar or

[20] M. G. Lloyd, Errors in Testing with Ring Specimens, *Bull. Bur. Standards*, **5**, 435 (1909).

ring tests and to combine their good features. In general, testing is done with *permeameters*, which make use of straight bar specimens but which provide a return magnetic circuit of low reluctance and thus reduce or eliminate the effect of the self-demagnetization which was described above for bars. The feature of a massive return circuit of low reluctance is common to all permeameters, but they differ in such details as the methods by which the magnetizing force acting on the specimen is determined, or in the type or degree of compensation of leakage along the specimen, or in the range of magnetizing force in which they can be used.

Many permeameters incorporate modifications of the bar and yoke arrangement first described by Hopkinson. A test coil is wound on the central part of the bar specimen. The bar is clamped between the halves of a massive yoke, whose reluctance is low compared to that of the specimen. The magnetizing winding surrounds the specimen, and the return magnetic circuit is provided by the yoke, as shown in Fig. 16.

Since the flux in the circuit is $\phi = \mathscr{F}/\mathscr{R}$, we can say

$$\phi = \frac{\dfrac{4\pi NI}{10}}{\mathscr{R}_j + \mathscr{R}_y + \dfrac{l}{A\mu}} \text{ maxwells}$$

where NI represents ampere-turns in the magnetizing winding; $\mathscr{R}_y$ and $\mathscr{R}_j$ are respectively the reluctance of the yoke and of the joints between the yoke and the specimen; l is the effective length of the specimen between the ends of the yoke, A is its cross section, and μ is its permeability for the magnetizing force H which is present. The flux density in the specimen can be written as $B = \mu H = \phi/A$, so that we may write

$$H = \frac{\phi}{A\mu} = \frac{\dfrac{4\pi NI}{10}}{\left(\mathscr{R}_j + \mathscr{R}_y + \dfrac{l}{A\mu}\right) A\mu}$$

If we let

$$\frac{A}{l} \cdot \mu(\mathscr{R}_j + \mathscr{R}_y) = K$$

then

$$H = \frac{4\pi NI}{10(K + 1)l}$$

K is made small by reducing $\mathscr{R}_y$ and $\mathscr{R}_j$; i.e. by making the yokes of large section and by fitting the specimen to the yoke so that the air gaps at the joints are as small as possible. If K is small we have approximately

$$H = \frac{4\pi NI}{10l}(1 - K)$$

The actual value of the magnetizing force is less than that computed from ampere-turns per unit length, by a factor which depends on the reluctance of the return circuit. B is measured ballistically with the test coil at the midpoint of the specimen.

BURROWS PERMEAMETER. The compensation principle is employed in the Burrows permeameter. This arrangement (Fig. 17) employs a double

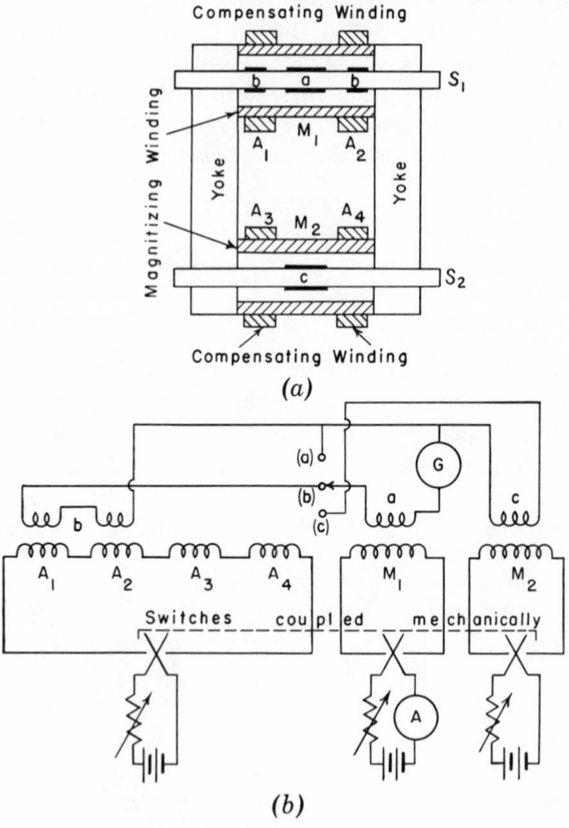

FIG. 17.

yoke on which the magnetizing windings are so arranged as to bring the entire magnetic circuit as nearly as possible to a uniform distribution of magnetic potential. If this condition could be completely realized there would be no magnetic leakage from one part of the circuit to another, and the magnetizing force could be calculated at any point in terms of the magnetizing ampere-turns per centimeter at that point. If we assume that S_1 and S_2 are specimen bars which are uniform and similar in their magnetic properties, the desired condition of uniformity can be checked in the following way. The test coils a, b, and c all have an equal number of turns and are placed as shown in Fig. 17(a): a surrounds the middle of the test specimen (S_1); b, divided into two equal parts, is located near the ends of S_1; and c is located at the middle of the auxiliary bar (S_2). The electrical connections of the test coils and of the magnetizing coils are shown in Fig. 17(b). The compensating windings A_1, A_2, A_3, A_4 are connected in series. The current in these coils and the currents in the magnetizing coils M_1 and M_2 are separately adjustable. With the selector switch in position (a), only test coil a is connected to the ballistic galvanometer; in position (b), coils a and b are connected to the galvanometer in opposition; in position (c), coils a and c are opposed across the galvanometer. The adjustments of A, M_1, and M_2 are correct when there is no deflection of the galvanometer on current reversal with the selector switch in position (b) or (c), since, with the assumed uniformity of the specimens, the flux density is then identical at each test coil. Under these conditions the reluctance of the joints and yokes is compensated, and the magnetization of the bar is equivalent to that which would exist if S_1 were infinitely long and in a solenoid of infinite length. Magnetizing force can then be computed from ampere-turns per centimeter in the magnetizing winding M_1, and the induction in the specimen can be measured with the test coil a.

It should be noted that the tests described cannot take account of the effects of any magnetic inhomogeneities in the specimen. Variations in permeability along the specimen result in magnetic leakage which cannot be compensated and thus lead to errors in the measurements. Hence the method will give dependable results only when the test specimens are known to be magnetically uniform. In addition, the necessary adjustments for compensation are tedious, and the Burrows permeameter is used chiefly to determine the properties of uniform bars which can then be utilized in the calibration of other permeameters. Magnetizing forces up to 300 oersteds are attainable with this apparatus.

FAHY SIMPLEX PERMEAMETER. This permeameter is much used for routine testing. It is simpler in both construction and operation than the Burrows permeameter, and is less sensitive to the effects of magnetic inhomogeneities in the specimen. Also it requires only a single specimen for testing. It is shown schematically in Fig. 18. The specimen is clamped across the poles of an electromagnet which carries the magnetizing winding. A uniformly wound test coil extends over the entire active portion of the specimen for measuring induction. The magnetizing force is measured by means of a second test coil wound uniformly on a non-magnetic form and mounted between the tops of two iron blocks which clamp the specimen against the pole pieces of the yoke. Actually, it measures the change in magnetic potential between its ends when the magnetizing force is changed. The function of the iron blocks is to bring the potential of the ends of the specimen to the ends of the *H*-coil, and the combination is, in effect, a magnetic potentiometer. A modification of this permeameter, developed at the National Bureau of Standards, employs a motor-driven flip coil in place of the stationary *H*-coil. The flip coil is rotated through 180° about a vertical axis in measuring magnetizing force and makes it possible to obtain more precise values of points on the hysteresis loop than can be done with a stationary *H*-coil.[21] Since the *B*-coil is wound uniformly over the entire length of the specimen it will tend to measure average values of induction and thus to "dilute" the effects of local magnetic irregularities in the specimen. Measurements can be made with this permeameter up to about 300 oersteds.

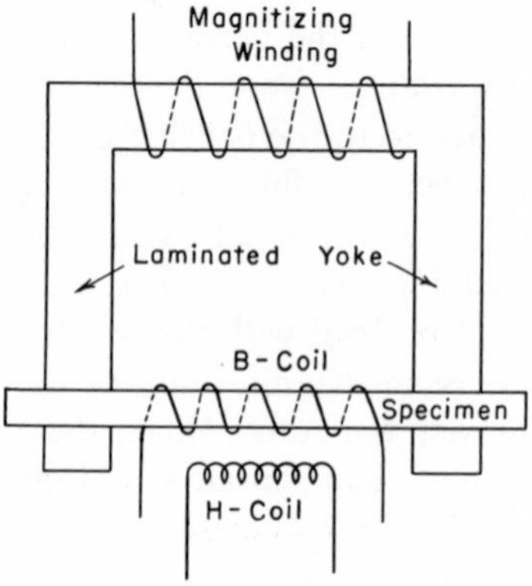

FIG. 18.

It should be noted that this type of permeameter has the same general relation to a compensated permeameter, such as the Burrows, as a working laboratory instrument has to a reference standard instrument. Under suitably controlled conditions the compensated permeameter can be used to determine the magnetic characteristics of a *selected* specimen in terms of measured induction and calculated magnetizing force, but its operation requires a technique that is too elaborate and tedious for routine testing. However, a uniform bar which has been calibrated with a compensated permeameter is suitable for checking the calibration of the *H*-coil of an uncompensated permeameter, and the permeameter thus calibrated can then be used in routine testing.

SANFORD-WINTER M-H PERMEAMETER.[22] This was designed as a medium-range permeameter (up to 300 oersteds) to be employed in place of the

[21] Galvanometer deflections with the stationary coil correspond in this case to $\Delta H = H_1 - H_2$, whereas, with the flip coil, $2H_1$ and $2H_2$ are measured directly and their difference $2\Delta H$ can be more precisely determined, particularly if ΔH corresponds to a small galvanometer deflection.

[22] Sanford and Winter, *NBS J. Research*, **45**, 17 (1950).

Burrows permeameter for the standardization of magnetic samples. It is a primary (or absolute) permeameter in the sense that its calibration is independent of reference to any other permeameter, and it has a number of decided advantages over the Burrows apparatus: it requires only one

(*a*)

(*b*)

FIG. 19. Sanford-Winter M-H permeameter.

specimen; its accuracy is certainly as good; and its operation is far less complicated and tedious. The assembled permeameter and its magnetic circuit are shown in Fig. 19. The specimen, of rectangular cross section, is surrounded by the main magnetizing coil. Symmetrical, laminated, U-shaped yokes of 16-gage silicon steel complete the magnetic circuit and carry auxiliary magnetizing coils to overcome the reluctance and compensate the leakage at the joints between the specimen and the yokes. The symmetrical construction of the yokes and good contact between yoke and specimen promote uniform flux distribution throughout the cross section of the specimen, and the auxiliary coils provide mmf of such magnitude that the longitudinal distribution of flux in the specimen is quite uniform, particularly in its middle section where B and H are determined. It is noteworthy that the construction is such that the specimen is supported without strain and is held in close contact with the yokes without clamping. (This is of importance in the testing of strain-sensitive material.)

B is measured in the usual way with a test coil surrounding the middle section of the specimen bar. An auxiliary test coil, whose area-turn value equals that of the B-coil, is located beside the B-coil but not surrounding the specimen, and is connected in series opposition to the B-coil. Thus the observed galvanometer deflections are a measure of the intrinsic induction in the specimen, and no air-flux correction is needed for bars of different cross-sectional areas. Values of magnetizing force are obtained by means of H-coils mounted in the region adjacent to the middle section of the specimen and arranged to rotate through 180°, as in the National Bureau of Standards modification of the Fahy-Simplex permeameter. Two H-coils, having equal area-turn values, are mounted one above the other on a brass turntable. When they are connected in series opposition, with their axes parallel to the specimen, and rotated through 180°, the galvanometer deflection is a measure of the gradient of the field perpendicular to the surface of the specimen. The value of the field, measured when only the H-coil nearest the specimen is used, is extrapolated to the surface of the bar by means of the observed value of the gradient. It is estimated that values of magnetizing force or induction can be determined to within 1% except at very low values of magnetizing force, where the uncertainty arising from lack of precision may amount to 0.05 oersted.

EWING'S ISTHMUS PERMEAMETER. The methods described above are suitable with magnetizing forces of at most a few hundred oersteds. For tests at higher magnetizing forces (needed to determine the properties of many alloys) special methods must be used. Most of these are *isthmus* methods, modified from that originally described by Ewing,[23] the name being derived from the shape of the magnetic circuit, in which the specimen forms a narrow isthmus between the pole pieces of a massive electromagnet (Fig. 20). In Ewing's permeameter the heavy yoke carries

[23] J. A. Ewing, *Magnetic Induction in Iron and Other Metals*, 3rd edition, p. 138. The "Electrician" Publishing Co., 1900.

the magnetizing winding. The specimen is short and is turned in a lathe to have a conical shape at each end and a central cylindrical portion [Fig. 20(*b*)]. It is situated between pole pieces which form a continuation of its conical end sections, and the assembly is mounted so that it can be rotated through 180° between the poles of the electromagnet, reversing the flux through the specimen (and thus the flux linkages in the test coils) without reversing the direction of the magnetizing current.

Because of the conical shape of the pole pieces the flux which passes through them is, in effect, constricted and forced through the cylindrical portion of the specimen, resulting in a much higher flux density because of the smaller cross section at this point. The flux density attainable in

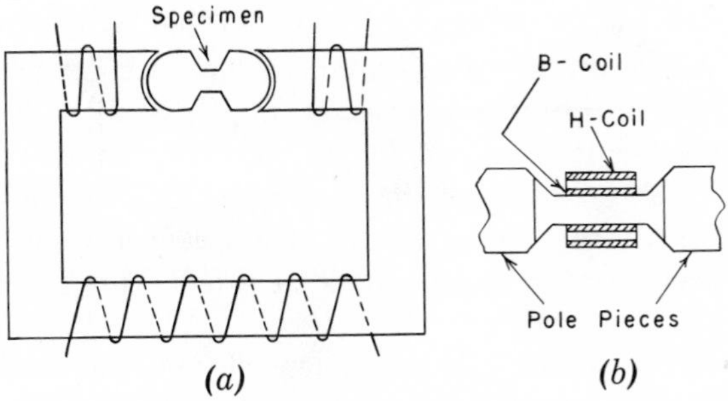

FIG. 20.

the cylindrical portion of the specimen is dependent on its cross section. Ewing reported measurements by this method at flux densities up to 45,000 gausses, and with magnetizing forces up to 24,500 oersteds. For maximum concentration of the flux in the specimen, the angle between the axis and the face of the cone should be about 60°; however, the field within the specimen is most nearly uniform if this angle is about 40°. In practice an intermediate angle is generally used.

Ewing's isthmus method must be modified for general testing since it requires the machining of specimens of a special form. Also it is not adaptable to the determination of data for hysteresis loops. The principal modifications needed to adapt the isthmus method to general testing consist in using suitable laminated material in the core of the electromagnet, so that changes in the magnetization can be made with switches and resistances in the usual way, and in making the pole pieces hollow, so that specimens can be inserted whose length is greater than the gap between poles. By proper proportioning of the magnetic circuit and distribution of the magnetizing coils, the induction can be made uniform across the specimen. Also the field in the space occupied by the H-coil can be made uniform and equal to that at the surface of the specimen.

HIGH-H PERMEAMETER OF SANFORD AND BENNETT.[24] This apparatus, developed at the National Bureau of Standards, uses a symmetrical magnetic circuit in place of the single yoke of Ewing (Fig. 21) and produces a more uniform induction throughout the cross section of the specimen. The main magnetizing coils are wound on the pole pieces, and auxiliary coils are wound on the yokes. The pole pieces are adjustable, so that the gap length can be chosen with reference to the size and properties of the specimen in order to obtain the maximum uniformity in the field immediately adjacent to the specimen. The value of this field and its gradient are determined by means of two small H-coils which can be rotated through 180° by a motor-operated linkage as in the Sanford-Winter permeameter. Induction is measured by means of a test coil wound on a thin brass form surrounding the specimen. In order to keep air-flux corrections small, the B-coil must fit the specimen closely. With this apparatus measurements can be made at magnetizing forces up to 5000 oersteds.

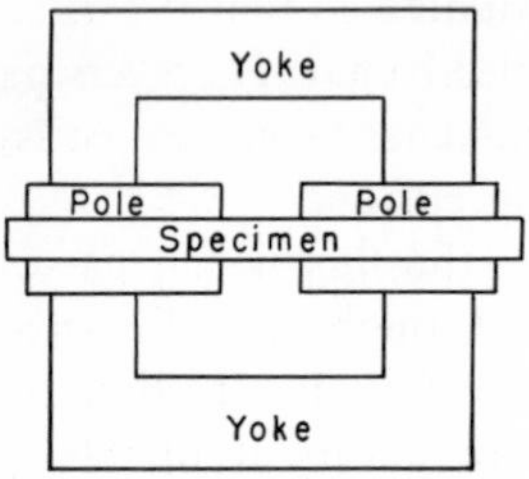

FIG. 21.

FAHY SUPER-H ADAPTER. This is designed for use with the Fahy Simplex permeameter for magnetizing forces up to 2500 oersteds. It consists of specially shaped pole pieces between which the specimen is clamped to confine the test to a short length. A magnetizing coil surrounds the pole pieces and the gap between them and is used in addition to the main magnetizing winding on the permeameter yoke. A B-coil and an H-coil are mounted in the gap between the pole pieces and function as in the Fahy-Simplex permeameter.

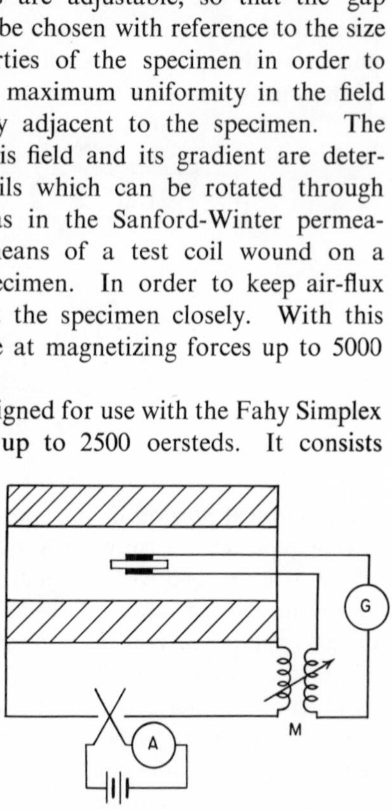

FIG. 22.

Low-Permeability Materials. Tests of materials of low permeability (only slightly greater than unity) are generally made in a straight solenoid. Since the intrinsic induction, B_i (the excess of the induction over that present in vacuum), is small, the self-demagnetization of a bar specimen is negligible. The circuit of Fig. 22 can be used for measurements of this type. Because of the

[24] Sanford and Bennett, An Apparatus for Magnetic Testing at Magnetizing Forces up to 5000 Oersteds, *NBS J. Research*, **23**, 415 (1939).

small excess of the induction over the magnetizing field, it is necessary to balance out the direct effect of the magnetizing field in order to obtain precision in the measurement of intrinsic induction. This can be done by connecting the secondary of the adjustable mutual inductor in opposition to the test coil. The primary of M is connected in series with the magnetizing coil. The search coil usually has several hundred turns in order to obtain sufficient sensitivity in the measurement. The inductor is adjusted until, with no specimen in the test coil, there is no deflection of the galvanometer when the magnetizing current is reversed. The galvanometer can then be used at its maximum sensitivity; and, when the specimen is inserted in the test coil, its deflection on reversal of the magnetizing current is a measure of the intrinsic induction. The magnetizing force can be computed from ampere-turns per centimeter in the solenoid, $H = 4\pi NI/10l$, and the induction is $B = B_i + \mu_v H$. The permeability is then

$$\mu = \frac{B_i + \mu_v H}{\mu_v H}$$

ASTM NULL METHOD. A null method of testing feebly magnetic materials has been described in the specifications of the American Society for

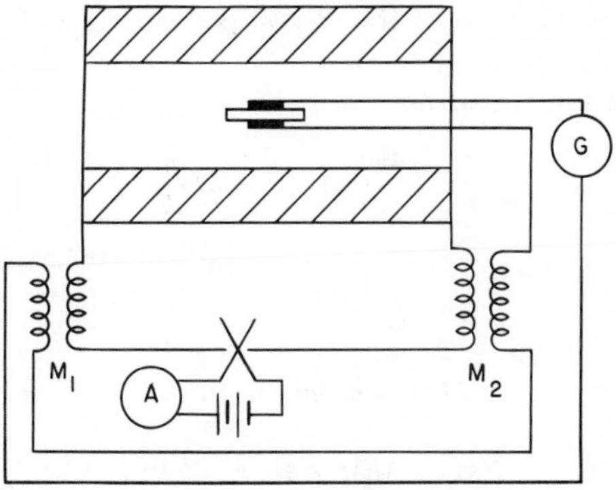

FIG. 23.

Testing Materials[25] and is shown schematically in Fig. 23. The primary windings of two adjustable mutual inductors are connected in series with the magnetizing solenoid. Their secondaries are connected in series with the search coil in such a way that both oppose it. One mutual inductor is calibrated in microhenrys. The other, which need not be calibrated, serves to compensate the test coil before the specimen is inserted. The preliminary adjustment is made with the calibrated inductor

[25] ASTM Standard A342–49.

(M_1) set to zero, by adjusting the compensating inductor (M_2) until the galvanometer in series with the test coil and the inductor secondaries shows no deflection on reversal of the magnetizing current. The specimen is then inserted, and the calibrated inductor is adjusted (leaving the setting of the compensating inductor unchanged) until the galvanometer again shows no deflection on current reversal. The permeability of the specimen is given by the equation[26]

$$\mu = 1 + \frac{M_1 \times 10^3}{4\pi N n A_s \mu_v}$$

where M_1 is the mutual inductance of M, in microhenrys; N is the total number of turns on the test coil; n is turns per centimeter length in the magnetizing solenoid; and A_s is the cross section of the specimen in square centimeters.

FAHY LOW-MU PERMEAMETER. This arrangement is also designed for testing feebly magnetic materials. Two test coils are mounted side by side in the magnetizing solenoid. One (the B-coil) serves as a specimen test coil. The other (the H-coil), having a slightly greater value of area-turns, is used to measure the induction in air at the location of the specimen, and also to compensate the induction in air in the B-coil. The effective value of area-turns of the H-coil is reduced with a shunt resistor

[26] If the cgs magnetic units are used, we have

$$H = \frac{4\pi n I}{10}, \qquad e = M\frac{di}{dt}$$

$$\int_1 e\,dt = N\Delta\phi_1 \times 10^{-8} = 2M_2 I \times 10^{-6} = \frac{2Na \cdot 4\pi n I \mu_v}{10^9}$$

so that

$$M_2 = 4\pi n N a \mu_v \times 10^{-3} \qquad (a = \text{area of test coil})$$

$$\int_2 e\,dt = N\Delta\phi_2 \times 10^{-8} = 2(M_1 + M_2)I \times 10^{-6} = 2N\left(B_i A_s + \frac{4\pi n a I \mu_v}{10}\right) \times 10^{-8}$$

and

$$B_i A_s + \frac{4\pi a n I \mu_v}{10} = \frac{(M_1 + M_2)I \times 10^{-6}}{N \times 10^{-8}}$$

$$B_i A_s = \frac{M_1 I \times 10^{-6}}{N \times 10^{-8}} + \frac{4\pi n N a \times 10^{-3} \cdot \mu_v I \times 10^{-6}}{N \times 10^{-8}} - \frac{4\pi n a I \mu_v}{10}$$

$$B_i = \frac{M_1 I \times 10^2}{A_s N}$$

$$\mu = 1 + \frac{B_i}{H\mu_v} = 1 + \frac{M_1 I \times 10^2}{AN} \cdot \frac{10}{4\pi n I \mu_v} = 1 + \frac{M_1 \times 10^3}{4\pi N n A_s \mu_v}$$

to that of the *B*-coil, and the two equal coils are opposed in the galvanometer circuit. A three-position selector switch connects the circuits as shown in Fig. 24. In position (*a*) the galvanometer is connected to the *B*- and *H*-coils in series opposition (without the specimen in the *B*-coil), and the resistor R_0 is adjusted until no galvanometer deflection results from a reversal of current in the magnetizing solenoid (not shown in Fig. 24). With this adjustment the *effective* area-turns of the *B*- and *H*-coils are equal. In position (*b*) the *H*-coil alone is connected to the galvanometer in order to measure the air induction at the location of the specimen. A resistor R_h and the secondary of a known mutual inductor M_s are included in this circuit so that the galvanometer deflection can be adjusted to indicate directly the magnetizing field in oersteds. A method for calibrating the galvanometer to be direct reading has already been discussed. In position (*c*) the *B*-coil is opposed to the *H*-coil shunted by R_0, and, with the specimen in place, the intrinsic induction (B_i) in the specimen may be read directly from the galvanometer deflection. The combination of R_b and M_s is used to calibrate the galvanometer for this reading.

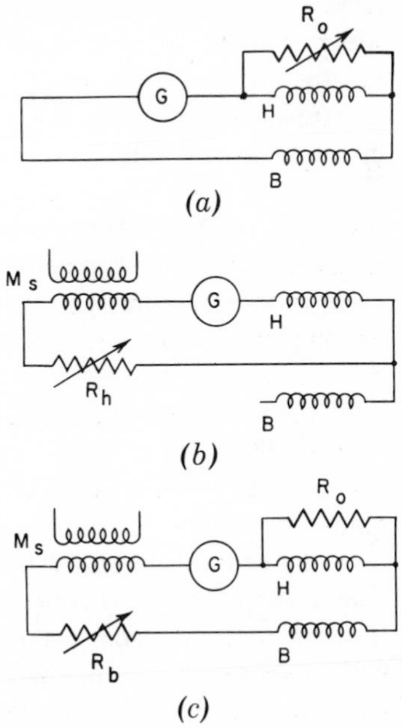

FIG. 24.

A compensation method which is similar to Fahy's consists in connecting the test and compensation coils in series opposition, together with the secondary of a small adjustable mutual inductor whose primary carries the solenoid current. The mutual inductor is adjusted so that it supplies the small difference in area-turns between the test and compensating coils.

These methods are applicable to measurements on materials having permeabilities up to 2.0, if the test coil and specimen are as specified in the 1949 ASTM Standard. They can be used equally well with specimens having somewhat higher permeabilities if the specimen dimensions are suitably modified.

Factors Affecting the Accuracy of Ballistic Testing. Magnetic testing consists in determining simultaneous values of magnetic induction and of the magnetizing force producing it. The accurate determination of the corresponding magnetizing force is usually subject to errors which arise in part from the construction of the permeameter used, and in part from inhomogeneities in the material under test. An accuracy of 1% is possible only with selected specimens and with very careful technique in testing. Specimens which are to serve as standards for the calibration or comparison of permeameters must be chosen with regard to uniformity of magnetic properties and of cross section. Metallurgical stability must also be considered. If the specimen varies in permeability along its length (or in cross section), errors are introduced into the measurements which cannot, in general, be either calculated or compensated. It is possible to have errors of 25% or more introduced into the measurements as a result of inhomogeneities. The most satisfactory method of determining the uniformity of a specimen to be used as a standard is to prepare a specimen much longer than will be finally needed and to compare the results of measurements made at intervals along its length. Steel is not magnetically stable immediately after heat treatment. Changes take place in its structure for some time and are accompanied by changes in its magnetic properties. Stability may be produced by aging, which can be accelerated by a moderate elevation of temperature. Quench-hardening steels can be satisfactorily stabilized by exposure to a temperature of 100°C for a few hours, whereas the changes may be appreciable for months (even a year or more) if the specimen is aged at room temperature.

In the calibration and use of magnetic standards and in the testing of magnetic specimens, it is necessary to avoid mechanical strain and vibration. Strain influences magnetic properties to a considerable extent, and it is therefore important that test specimens be clamped so that they are free from bending. This effect is most pronounced in the steep part of the magnetization curve. Mechanical vibration has a tendency to increase apparent permeability and to decrease hysteresis. The effect is not large generally but must be considered in accurate work.

The temperature coefficients of magnetic materials vary with the material and, for the same material, with heat treatment. Consequently, in precise work it is important that the specimen not be heated in the course of a test.

Test-Coil Calibration. The calibration of test coils is fundamentally a measurement of mutual inductance. It is usually difficult and often impossible to determine accurately the effective area-turns (AN) of a test coil from measurements of its dimensions, and an experimental determination is therefore both easier and more accurate. If the coil is placed in a long solenoid and the mutual inductance is measured between them, the area-turns will be $AN = (MI/H\mu_v) \times 10^8$ (see p. 367), where M is mutual inductance in henrys, and I is the current in amperes corresponding to the field of H oersteds (μ_v being unity in the cgs system). It is, of course, important that the axis of the test coil be aligned with the axis of the solenoid. If the angle between the axes is θ, the error resulting from lack of alignment is proportional to $(1 - \cos\theta)$ and will amount to about 0.1% for $\theta = 2.5°$.

Mutual Inductance Measurements. The measurement of inductance can be made ballistically, by comparison with a mutual inductor of known value. As shown in Fig. 25, the primaries of the mutual inductors are connected in series to a battery through a reversing switch. The secondaries are opposed, and M_1 must be the larger of the inductances. R_1 and R_2 are precision adjustable resistors used as a voltage divider. By

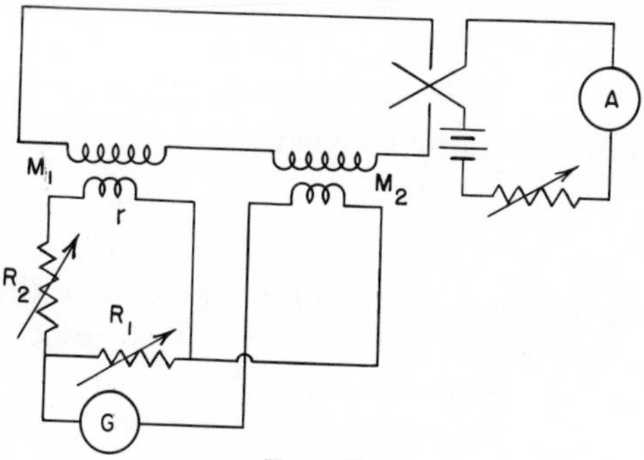

FIG. 25.

means of this voltage divider a known fraction of the voltage induced in the secondary of M_1 on reversal of the primary current is balanced against the voltage induced in the secondary of M_2. At balance

$$M_2 = M_1 \frac{R_1}{R_1 + R_2 + r}$$

where r is the resistance of the secondary of M_1. The usual precautions must be taken against stray fields. The two inductors should be some distance apart and so oriented as to avoid coupling between the primary of one and the secondary of the other. Errors caused by the capacitance between primary and secondary circuits are reduced by repeating observations after reversing the primary leads of one inductor and the secondary leads of the other, and averaging the results.

Alternating-Current Magnetic Testing

When magnetic material is placed in an alternating magnetic field it absorbs energy through hysteresis and eddy currents. The hysteresis loss per cycle could, of course, be determined from the area of a hysteresis loop obtained by d-c tests under similar conditions of magnetization.

The eddy-current loss can be measured only under a-c conditions, and it is convenient usually to measure the combined hysteresis and eddy-current losses as core loss by means of an a-c test. Very often, in acceptance tests, the core loss is specified per pound of material at a specified frequency and maximum flux density. The separation of losses into the hysteresis and eddy-current components can be accomplished, provided measurements are made at more than one frequency. Since hysteresis loss is

$$W_h = K_1 B_m^{1.6} f = A_1 f$$

and the eddy-current loss is

$$W_e = K_2 t^2 B_m^2 f^2 = A_2 f^2$$

then for a fixed value of maximum flux density we can write the total loss in the iron as

$$W_t = A_1 f + A_2 f^2$$

If we divide this expression by f we have

$$\frac{W_t}{f} = A_1 + A_2 f$$

On plotting W_t/f against f, we obtain a straight line (Fig. 26) and can obtain A_1 and A_2 from its intercept and slope respectively. For the particular value of B_m used in the determination, the separate losses can then be written for any frequency in terms of A_1 and A_2.

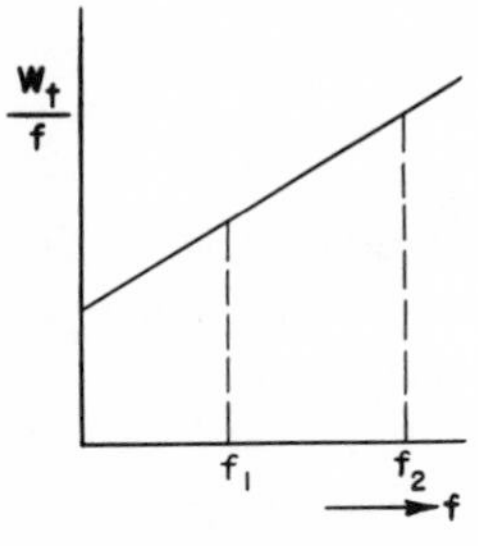

FIG. 26.

Since the eddy-current loss is also a function of form factor, we could, by holding f and B_m constant while we varied form factor, arrive at an expression which would separate the eddy-current and hysteresis losses in terms of form factor.

The Epstein Core-Loss Test. The most common method of measuring a-c loss in sheet material is by use of a wattmeter. The material is assembled as a closed magnetic circuit in the form of a square. The test square is usually assembled in accordance with ASTM specifications from strips of flat-rolled material cut to appropriate size. This assembly, together with the test frame and test coils, is known as the Epstein core-loss apparatus. The dimensions of the strips and frame, and the form of the joints at the corners of the square, depend on the type of test.

The test specimen for the 50-cm Epstein core-loss test is made up of strips 50 cm long and 3 cm wide. The standard sample amounts to 10 kg of strips, but 5 kg may be used. For the usual material, half of the strips are cut with their long dimension parallel to the direction in which the sheet material is rolled, and half at right angles to this direction. Under some conditions materials manufactured in strip form, or materials having pronounced directional magnetic properties, may be tested with all the strips cut in the same direction. The strips are grouped into four equal bundles and are assembled in the test frame to form a square with butt joints. Usually the bundles are arranged so that opposite sides of the square consist of material cut in the same direction. Corner clamps hold the strips in place. Each side of the frame carries uniformly wound coils which are connected in series to form a single magnetizing winding of 600 turns. The secondary winding (underneath the primary winding) also consists of 600 turns uniformly distributed around the sides of the

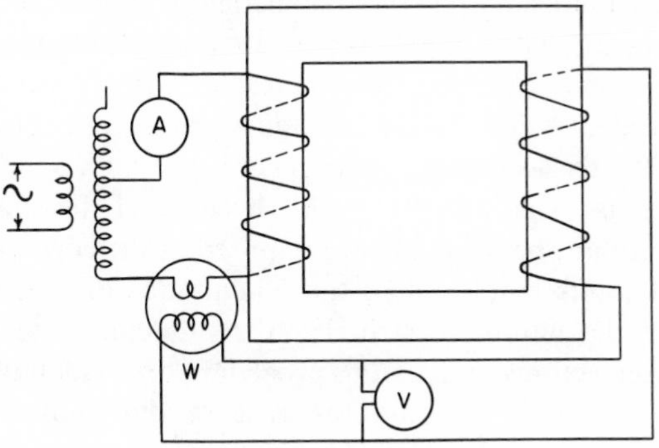

FIG. 27.

square. An emf of approximately sine-wave form is impressed on the primary winding. This circuit also contains the current coil of the wattmeter. The secondary circuit of the square supplies the voltage circuit of the wattmeter, which should be especially designed for low power-factor operation. The connections are shown in Fig. 27. The impressed voltage is adjusted, preferably by means of a suitable variable-ratio transformer, until the secondary voltage attains the value corresponding to the maximum induction chosen as test condition. The rms voltage under these conditions is

$$E = \frac{4KB_m \cdot AN_2 f}{10^8} \text{ volts}$$

where K is the form factor of the primary emf, defined as the ratio of the rms value of the emf to its half-period average value (1.11 for a sine wave); B_m is the maximum flux density in gausses; A is the cross section of the specimen in square centimeters; N_2 is the number of turns on the secondary winding; and f is the frequency in cycles per second.

The form factor can be determined by the ratio of simultaneous readings of an *average*-reading voltmeter (rectifier type) and an *rms*-reading voltmeter (for example, an electrodynamic instrument). The reading of the wattmeter includes both the loss in the specimen and the copper loss in the secondary circuit. The copper loss can be calculated and subtracted from the wattmeter reading. The net loss in the specimen divided by its weight is a measure of the quality of the specimen and is used to grade the sheet material from which the specimen is selected, or to determine its suitability for specific applications. Standard tests are specified at various values of maximum induction by the American Society for Testing Materials.

In recent years manufacturers of electrical sheet materials have so improved the uniformity of the magnetic properties of their various commercial grades that it is possible to obtain a representative sample of a given heat of steel by using 2 kg or less of strips instead of the 10 kg previously needed. The 25-*cm Epstein apparatus* is designed to test specimens of 0.5 to 2-kg mass. For general testing a sample of approximately 1-kg mass is commonly used. Because of the shorter length of the magnetic circuit, better joints are required at the corners of the square than the butt joints employed in the 50-cm square. Double lap joints are used, and the minimum strip length is 28 cm. The strip width is 3 cm. The connections and testing procedure are essentially the same as for the 50-cm Epstein test, but, because of the smaller sample cross section, the windings are increased to 700 turns each and more sensitive instruments are required. Also, allowance must be made in core-loss calculations for the material at the corners of the square. This is done by using the "active weight" of the material, calculated from the assumption that the effective length of the magnetic circuit is 94 cm (an experimentally determined value).

AIR-FLUX CORRECTION. When testing specimens whose area is small relative to the area enclosed within the secondary winding (or in tests at high magnetizing forces), where the contribution of the air flux to the secondary voltage is appreciable, it is necessary either to correct for the air flux or to compensate it. The maximum value of the magnetizing force in oersteds may be calculated from the crest value of the magnetizing current by the formula

$$H_{\max} = \frac{4\pi N I_c}{10 l'} \approx 10 I_c$$

where N turns in primary winding = 700.

I_c = crest current in amperes.

l', effective length of the magnetizing winding,[27] = 88 cm.

[27] Note that this effective length differs from the effective length of the magnetic circuit used in core-loss calculations. See S. L. Burgwin, Measurements of Core Loss and A-C Permeability with the 25-cm Epstein Frame, *Proc. ASTM*, **41**, 779 (1941).

The total flux within the secondary coil is

$$B_{max}A_s + \mu_v H_{max}(A_c - A_s) = B'_{max}A_s$$

where B_{max} is the true maximum flux density in the specimen.
B'_{max} is the apparent maximum flux density in the specimen.
A_s is the cross section of the specimen.
A_c is the cross section of the coil.

The rms voltage induced in the secondary is

$$E = \frac{4KfN_2B'_{max}A_s}{10^8} = \frac{4KfN_2[B_{max}A_s + \mu_v H_{max}(A_c - A_s)]}{10^8} \text{ volts}$$

and

$$B_{max} = B'_{max} - \mu_v H_{max}\left(\frac{A_c - A_s}{A_s}\right)$$

The compensation of the air flux is preferable to its correction by calculation. This can be done by means of a mutual inductor, if its primary is connected in series with the primary winding of the test frame and its secondary is connected in series opposition to the secondary winding of the test frame. The value of this inductor should equal the mutual inductance between the primary and secondary test coils when no specimen is in the frame. Under this condition the measured secondary voltage is proportional to the *intrinsic* induction of the specimen.

A-c permeability as well as core loss can be determined with the 25-cm Epstein square. H_{max} may be calculated as before from the crest current, and B_{max} is computed from the secondary voltage with the air flux corrected or compensated. The permeability is $\mu = B_{max}/\mu_v \text{H}_{max}$.

Bridge Methods of Testing. The methods described above are not sufficiently sensitive for testing laminated-core material at the low flux densities frequently employed in communications equipment. For such tests either an a-c bridge or an a-c potentiometer method is suitable.

A number of bridge circuits are applicable to the measurement of core loss and permeability and can be used not only where materials operate at low flux densities, but also where only a small quantity of material is available for test. The measurement is essentially in the class of inductance measurements and can be made in terms of resistance together with self- or mutual-inductance or capacitance.[28]

SELF-INDUCTANCE BRIDGE. If an adjustable resistance R_3 and an adjustable inductance L_3 (having a resistance r) are put in the arm of

[28] Reference should be made to the general discussion of a-c bridge methods for the theory of such measurements. See Chapter 15.

the bridge (Fig. 28) adjacent to the specimen (L_s, R_s), and if the remaining arms (R_1 and R_2) are pure resistances, we have at balance

$$I_1R_1 = I_2R_2$$

and

$$I_1(R_s + j\omega L_s) = I_2[(R_3 + r) + j\omega L_3]$$

ω being $2\pi \times$ frequency. From the first balance equation,

$$\frac{I_1}{I_2} = \frac{R_2}{R_1}$$

and from the second

$$I_1R_s = I_2(R_3 + r), \quad \text{and} \quad I_1L_s = I_2L_3$$

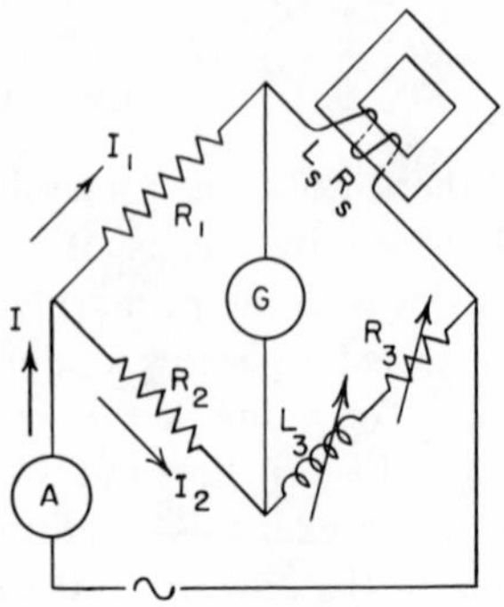

FIG. 28.

From this we have

$$R_s = (R_3 + r) \cdot \frac{R_1}{R_2}, \quad \text{and} \quad L_s = L_3 \frac{R_1}{R_2}$$

Now R_s includes the resistance of the winding on the specimen R_w, and in addition an equivalent resistance R_c corresponding to the core loss. The ohmic resistance R_w can be measured and the core loss computed. Since I_1 and I_2 are in phase, we have

$$I = I_1 + I_2, \quad \text{or} \quad I = I_1\left[1 + \frac{R_1}{R_2}\right]$$

so that

$$I_1 = I\frac{R_2}{R_1 + R_2}$$

and the iron loss in the specimen

$$P_s = I_1^2R_c = I^2\left(\frac{R_2}{R_1 + R_2}\right)^2 \cdot (R_s - R_w) \text{ watts}$$

The magnetic flux in the specimen is

$$\frac{4\pi NAI_1\mu \cdot \mu_v}{10l}$$

and the inductance (flux linkages per unit current) is

$$\frac{4\pi NA\mu I_1\mu_v}{10l} \cdot \frac{N}{I_1/10} = \frac{4\pi N^2 A\mu\mu_v}{l} \text{ cgs units}$$

The measured inductance in henrys is

$$L_s = \frac{4\pi N^2 A\mu \cdot \mu_v}{l \times 10^9}$$

so that the effective permeability is

$$\mu = \frac{l \times 10^9}{4\pi N^2 A\mu_v} \cdot L_3 \frac{R_1}{R_2}$$

CAMPBELL'S MUTUAL INDUCTANCE METHOD. Alternating-current losses can also be measured at low inductions by means of a mutual inductor.

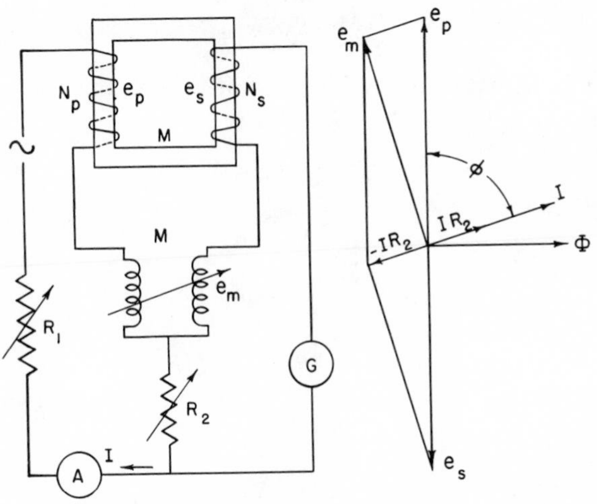

FIG. 29.

In Campbell's method[29] (Fig. 29) the specimen carries two windings of N_p and N_s turns respectively. The mutual inductor M and the resistor R_2 are adjusted for balance, as shown by the vibration galvanometer G.

[29] Campbell, *Proc. Phys. Soc.*, **22,** 214 (1910); **32,** 232 (1920). See also Golding, *Electrical Measurements*, 3rd edition, p. 385, Pitman, 1946; and Hague, *Alternating Current Bridge Methods*, 5th edition, p. 445, Pitman, 1946.

The vector diagram shows the balance condition; $\mathbf{e}_p$, $\mathbf{e}_s$, and $\mathbf{e}_m$ are the induced voltages in the primary and secondary windings of the specimen and in the secondary of the mutual inductor, respectively. The primary current (**I**) leads the flux ϕ by a small angle because of the iron loss in the specimen. At balance the vector sum of $\mathbf{e}_m$ and $\mathbf{e}_s$ balances the vector $\mathbf{IR}_2$.

Since $\mathbf{e}_m = \omega MI$, and $\mathbf{e}_s = \omega M'I$, where M' is the mutual inductance between the primary and secondary windings on the specimen, and since $|e_m| \approx |e_s|$ (see vector diagram, Fig. 29), we have $M \approx M'$.

The flux through the specimen is

$$\Phi = \frac{4\pi N_p A \mu I \cdot \mu_v}{10l} \text{ maxwells}$$

and the mutual inductance M' is the secondary flux linkages per unit current, so that

$$M' = \frac{4\pi N_p N_s A \mu \cdot \mu_v}{l \times 10^9} \text{ henrys}$$

Then we have

$$\mu \approx \frac{Ml \times 10^9}{4\pi N_p N_s A \mu_v}$$

where M is in henrys and A is the area of the specimen in square centimeters. The iron loss in the specimen is

$$P = e_p I \cos\phi$$

but

$$\cos\phi = \frac{IR_2}{e_s}$$

so that

$$P = \frac{e_p}{e_s} I^2 R_2 = \frac{N_p}{N_s} I^2 R_2$$

since

$$\frac{e_p}{e_s} = \frac{N_p}{N_s}$$

OWEN BRIDGE.[30] This bridge, in which inductance is measured in terms of resistance and capacitance, has been recommended in a modified form by the ASTM for core-loss and permeability measurements using a 25-cm Epstein square. As shown in Fig. 30, C_1 and R_2 are fixed arms. Balance is obtained by adjustment of C_4 and R_4. The bridge should be isolated from the a-c supply by a suitable variable-ratio transformer.

[30] See Chapter 15, p. 712.

The constants of the bridge arms are selected to suit the type of material and the frequency of the test. For 60-cycle tests on materials of very low loss and high permeability a 100-turn winding is used on the test frame, and R_2 is 10 ohms. For 60-cycle tests on ordinary silicon steel and similar magnetic materials, a 1000-turn test winding is used with $R_2 = 100$ ohms. $C_1 = 1\ \mu$f in either case. For incremental permeability tests direct current is supplied to a 100-turn winding through a

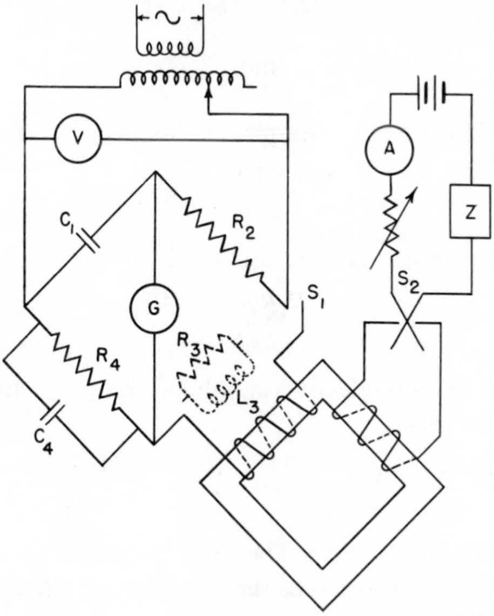

FIG. 30.

reactor Z which should have an inductance of 1 henry or more. The purpose of this reactor is to limit the a-c current in the d-c circuit to a negligible value.

The bridge balance equation is

$$Z_1Z_3 = Z_2Z_4, \quad \text{or} \quad \frac{Z_1}{Z_4} = \frac{Z_2}{Z_3}$$

Now

$$Z_1 = \frac{1}{j\omega C_1}, \quad Z_2 = R_2, \quad \frac{1}{Z_3} = \frac{1}{R_3} + \frac{1}{j\omega L_3}$$

(if the specimen is considered to be the equivalent of a pure inductance L_3, in parallel with a pure resistance R_3), and

$$\frac{1}{Z_4} = \frac{1}{R_4} + j\omega C_4$$

If these values are substituted in the balance equation, we have

$$\frac{1}{j\omega C_1}\left(\frac{1}{R_4}+j\omega C_4\right)=R_2\left(\frac{1}{R_3}+\frac{1}{j\omega L_3}\right)$$

or

$$\frac{1}{j\omega C_1 R_4}+\frac{C_4}{C_1}=\frac{R_2}{R_3}+\frac{R_2}{j\omega L_3}$$

On separating reals and imaginaries, we have

$$R_3 = R_2\frac{C_1}{C_4}, \quad \text{and} \quad L_3 = R_2R_4C_1$$

As in the previous bridge example, the inductance of the specimen is

$$L_3 = \frac{4\pi N^2 A\mu \cdot \mu_v}{l\times 10^9}\ \text{henrys}$$

so that we have, from the balance equation,

$$\mu = \frac{R_2R_4C_1 l\times 10^9}{4\pi N^2 A\mu_v}$$

If we take 94 cm as the effective length of the magnetic circuit in the Epstein square, we have

$$\mu = \frac{R_2R_4\times 10^{-6}\times 94\times 10^9}{4\pi N^2 A} = \frac{0.748R_2R_4}{N^2A}\times 10^4$$

since $\mu_v = 1$ in the cgs system. The total loss in the specimen is E_s^2/R_3, where E_s is the voltage drop across the specimen. In terms of the voltage E read on the voltmeter,

$$\left|\frac{E_s}{E}\right| = \left|\frac{E_2}{E}\right| = \frac{R_2}{\sqrt{R_2^2+\dfrac{1}{\omega^2C_1^2}}}$$

so that

$$E_s = \frac{ER_2}{\sqrt{R_2^2+\dfrac{1}{\omega^2C_1^2}}}$$

and the loss may be written

$$P = \frac{E^2R_2^2}{R_2^2+\dfrac{1}{\omega^2C_1^2}}\cdot\frac{C_4}{C_1R_2} = \frac{E^2C_4R_2}{\dfrac{\omega^2C_1^2R^2+1}{\omega^2C_1^2}\cdot C_1} = \frac{E^2\omega^2C_1C_4R_2}{1+\omega^2C_1^2R_2^2}$$

Under the conditions stated above for the test, $\omega^2C_1^2R_2^2 \ll 1$, so that, approximately,

$$P = E^2\omega^2R_2C_1C_4$$

From this must be subtracted the "copper" loss in the winding of the specimen resulting from the d-c resistance (R_{dc}) of the winding. This loss is

$$I_s^2 R_{dc} \approx \frac{E^2}{Z_4^2} R_{dc}$$

since under the test conditions the impedance in branch 4 of the bridge is very much greater than in branch 3 and therefore sets the limit of the current through the specimen. Now

$$\frac{1}{Z_4} = \frac{1}{R_4} + j\omega C_4$$

so that the "copper" loss in the winding is

$$E^2 R_{dc} \left(\frac{1}{R_4^2} + \omega^2 C_4^2 \right)$$

From this the core loss in the specimen is

$$P_s \approx E^2 \left[R_2 \omega^2 C_1 C_4 - R_{dc} \left(\frac{1}{R_4^2} + \omega^2 C_4^2 \right) \right]$$

The voltage, E, to be set on the bridge to correspond to a particular value (B_m) of maximum induction in the specimen may be derived from the following considerations:

$$E_s = \frac{4KB_m ANf}{10^8} \text{ volts rms}$$

and, if we assume sine-wave form, the form factor is $K = \pi/2\sqrt{2}$. Hence,

$$E_s = \frac{2}{\sqrt{2}} \frac{(\pi f B_m AN)}{10^8} = \frac{\omega B_m AN}{\sqrt{2} \times 10^8}$$

But

$$E = \frac{E_s \sqrt{R_2^2 + \dfrac{1}{\omega^2 C_1^2}}}{R_2} = \frac{E_s \sqrt{1 + \omega^2 C_1^2 R_2^2}}{\omega C_1 R_2} \approx \frac{E_s}{\omega C_1 R_2}$$

since $\omega^2 C_1^2 R_2^2 \ll 1$. From this we have

$$E \approx \frac{\omega B_m AN}{\omega C_1 R_2 \cdot \sqrt{2} \times 10^8}$$

and since (under the conditions specified for the ASTM test) $C_1 = 1 \times 10^{-6}$, and $N/R_2 = 10$,

$$E = 0.0707 B_m A$$

In a further modification of this bridge a series capacitor, C_s, is introduced into arm 4 as shown in Fig. 31. The value of this capacitor is chosen to balance the ohmic resistance of the test coil. It may be calculated from the relation $C_s = R_2C_1/R_{dc}$. The permeability equation developed above is unchanged, but the core loss in the specimen is now

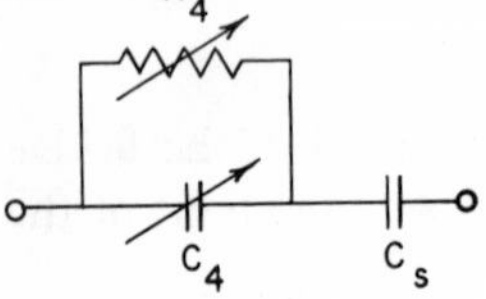

FIG. 31.

$$P_s = E^2\omega^2R_2C_1C_4$$

When incremental permeability is to be measured in this bridge (see Fig. 30) the direct current is first set to its required value with switch S_1 open, and reversed a number of times with S_2 to establish cyclic conditions in the specimen. When the test is made, S_1 is closed. The d-c magnetizing force is calculated from the equation $H = 4\pi NI/10l$; and for $N = 100$, and $l = 94$ cm, $H = 1.34I$.

Before making tests the specimen should be demagnetized. Since the permeability of most magnetic materials at low inductions drifts appreciably with time after demagnetization,[31] this should be done at least 24 hours before making the test. During the interval between demagnetization and test, the specimen should be protected from stray fields and from vibration (since vibration or mechanical shock will also change the permeability under these conditions).

Potentiometer Method. An a-c potentiometer may also be used for the determination of a-c permeability and core loss as shown in Fig. 32. The potentiometer indicates voltage in terms of two components whose phases are in quadrature. A phase-shifting device is used to adjust the phase of the potentiometer or of the magnetizing current. The d-c circuit and the procedure for applying a unidirectional magnetizing force are the same as those discussed above for the Owen bridge. The secondary winding on the specimen is connected to the potentiometer, and the

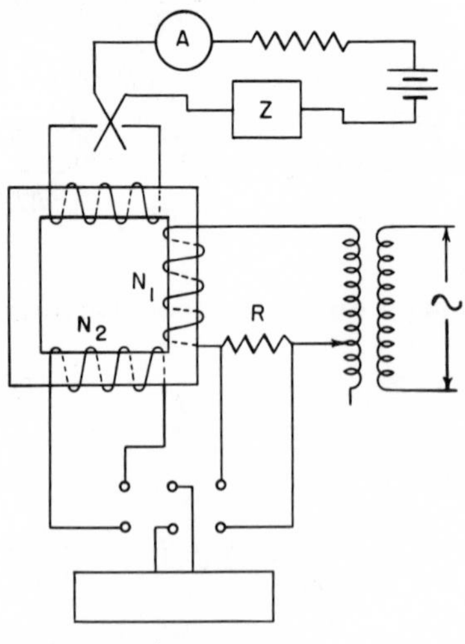

FIG. 32.

[31] R. L. Sanford, Drift of Permeability at Low Inductions after Demagnetization, *NBS J. Research*, **13**, 371 (1934); RP 714.

phase relations are adjusted so that the entire secondary voltage is read on the "in-phase" dials of the potentiometer. The voltage corresponding to a given maximum induction is calculated from the formula

$$E = \frac{\omega}{\sqrt{2}} N_2 A B \times 10^{-8} \text{ volts}$$

where E = rms secondary voltage, $\omega = 2\pi f$, N_2 = secondary turns, A = cross section of the specimen in square centimeters, and B = induction in gausses.

With the secondary voltage set at its proper value, the "in-phase" and "quadrature" components of the magnetizing current are measured by observing the drop across the non-inductive resistor R in series with the magnetizing winding. The loss component (I_p) of the magnetizing current is in phase with the secondary voltage, and the magnetizing component (I_q) is in quadrature. Permeability and core loss can be computed from the secondary voltage and the components of the magnetizing current by using the formulas

$$\mu = 52.9 \frac{B}{N_1 I_q} \quad \text{and} \quad P = \frac{N_1}{N_2} E I_p$$

since we have

$$H_{\text{max}} = \frac{4\pi N_1 I_q \cdot \sqrt{2}}{10 l} = \frac{N_1 I_q}{52.9} \quad (\text{for } l = 94 \text{ cm})$$

and the induced primary voltage is $(N_1/N_2)E$.

CHAPTER 10

ALTERNATING-CURRENT AMMETERS AND VOLTMETERS

Instrument Response Law and Scale Distribution

The motor torque of an a-c ammeter or voltmeter, acting to deflect its moving system, may be produced by electromagnetic, electrostatic, or mechanical forces, depending on the operating principle of the instrument. Since the alternating current or voltage varies cyclically, the motor torque also varies cyclically. The moving system receives a succession of impulses which generally are too rapid for it to follow individually. Hence it takes up an equilibrium position such that a balance exists between the *average* driving torque and the restoring torque from the control springs.

The relation which, for any given position of the moving system, exists between the motor torque of a deflecting instrument and the electrical quantity producing the torque determines the *law of response* of the instrument. The response law in turn determines whether the instrument indications are in terms of the *effective* (rms) values of the quantity measured or in terms of its *average* values. It also determines the "natural" scale law of the instrument. However, as we shall see, the actual distribution of the instrument scale may be very different from the natural scale distribution expected from consideration of the response law alone, either through some design feature deliberately introduced to gain an advantage in reading or through some feature which is inherent in the instrument mechanism or circuit. Hence scale distribution alone is not a completely trustworthy guide in deciding whether a specific instrument indication is in terms of *average* or *effective* values. The response law of the instrument is the only reliable criterion by which this may be decided. Depending on whether the deflecting torque is proportional to the first or the second power of the measured quantity, ammeters and voltmeters may be said to have a *first-power* law of response or a *square* law of response. If the response is proportional to the first power of the measured quantity, the instrument indications are of *average* current or voltage; for a square-law response, the indications are in terms of the effective values of the measured quantity. This will be seen from the following analysis.

RMS Indicating Instruments. If, for any given position of the moving system, the instantaneous motor torque is proportional to the square of the measured quantity and the mechanical inertia of the moving system is such that it responds only to average torque, we may write that the instantaneous torque $\mathscr{T} = Ki^2$, where i is the instantaneous current producing the torque, and K is a proportionality factor[1] which depends on the type of instrument and on the details of its design. The average torque

$$\mathscr{T}_{\text{ave}} = \frac{K}{T}\int_0^T i^2\,dt$$

in the usual case where K is not a function of time. When the moving system is in equilibrium under the action of the *average* deflecting torque and the *restoring* torque of the instrument springs, we have

$$\frac{K}{T}\int_0^T i^2\,dt = U\theta$$

where θ is the angular deflection and U is the control torque per unit angle. Now by definition

$$\frac{1}{T}\int_0^T i^2\,dt = I^2_{\text{eff}}$$

where I_{eff} is the root-mean-square or *effective* current. We can therefore write

$$I^2_{\text{eff}} = \frac{U}{K}\theta, \quad \text{or} \quad I_{\text{eff}} = f(\theta)$$

[1] In general K will be a function of angular position of the moving system, but will not be a function of time (or of the current) unless the moving system responds to the cyclic variations of torque. In this special case where, for some reason, the moving system is in resonant vibration at the frequency of the applied torque, if K is a function of position it necessarily follows that it will also be a function of time, since the moving system is being periodically displaced from its mean position. Vibration of the moving system may introduce an additional net torque whose direction and magnitude depend on the function $K = K(\theta, t)$. This torque introduces an error in the instrument indication which may be either positive or negative. The analysis of such errors can be undertaken only if $K(\theta, t)$ is known. (So far as the writer is aware this effect was first pointed out by Dr. V. E. Whitman, but his notes on the subject were never published.)

from which we see that the deflection θ is a measure of the *effective* (rms) current.[2] The instrument is then said to have a *square-law* response.

If K is not a function of angular position of the moving system, the instrument scale may be precisely marked in accordance with the square law, as shown in Fig. 1(*a*). Generally it is not practical and frequently it is not desirable that K be independent of θ. If $K = f(\theta)$ the scale no longer follows the "natural" square law exactly, as is shown in Fig. 1(*b*). It should be noted that the *response* in the latter case may still be described

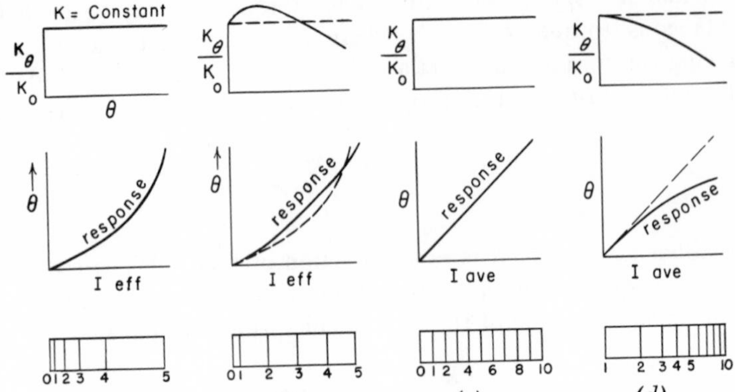

(*a*) Natural Square-Law Scale

(*b*) Modified Square-Law Scale

(*c*) Uniform Scale (First Power Law)

(*d*) Logarithmic Scale (First Power Law)

FIG. 1.

as *square law*, since, for any value of θ, K assumes a particular value K_θ so that, for this position,

$$I^2_{\text{eff}} = \frac{U\theta}{K_\theta}$$

i.e. the angular deflection is still proportional to the *square* of the effective current or voltage, but the proportionality factor changes with angle. Thus the instrument indications are in terms of *effective* current or voltage if the response is *square law*, even though the scale departs greatly from the square law.[3]

[2] The above argument applies with equal validity to current or voltage measurements since e and E_{eff} may be substituted for i and I_{eff} without altering the argument.

[3] It may be pointed out that the modification of scale distribution to gain some reading advantage, such as the expansion of some portion of the scale that is of particular interest or importance, usually is realized at the expense of sensitivity, i.e. K_θ for full-scale deflection is less than K_0 in most modifications. This can be justified, however, where the sensitivity is ample and the modification is desirable.

Average Indicating Instruments. If the motor torque tending to deflect the moving system is proportional to the first power of the measured quantity, the response follows the *first-power law*, and the scale may be expected to be uniform, as shown in Fig. 1(*c*). Here the instantaneous torque $\mathcal{T} = Ki$ and the average torque

$$\mathcal{T}_{\text{ave}} = \frac{K}{T}\int_0^T i\,dt$$

Such an instrument would not respond to an alternating quantity since for such a quantity

$$\frac{1}{T}\int_0^T i\,dt = 0$$

It would respond, however, to a direct current superposed on an alternating current, indicating the d-c quantity only. If such a system is used on *rectified* alternating current, or on *any* cyclically varying quantity whose period is so short that the moving system cannot follow the momentary changes, the response will represent the *average* value of the varying quantity since

$$\frac{1}{T}\int_0^T i\,dt = I_{\text{ave}}$$

the integral being taken over the time T required for the quantity to go through its complete pattern of values. Then we have

$$U\theta = \frac{K}{T}\int_0^T i\,dt = KI_{\text{ave}}$$

or

$$I_{\text{ave}} = K'\theta$$

The scale is uniform if K does not change with angle, but even if K does change with angle the deflection is *still* a measure of the *average* value of the quantity.

Permanent-magnet, moving-coil instruments have a *first-power* law of response and indicate the average value of the current in the moving coil. Their scales are generally uniform but may be modified in either of two ways. (1) If an intermediate element is interposed between the impressed signal (quantity to be measured) and the deflecting element, both the character of the response and the scale distribution may be affected by some characteristic of the intermediate element. (2) If the pole pieces of the instrument are modified so that the field distribution in the air gap is not uniform, the response will still follow the first-power law but the scale may be very far from uniform. As examples of the first type of modification, thermocouple ammeters have a square-law response and indicate effective values because of characteristics of the heater-thermocouple element which is introduced between line and d-c instrument; copper oxide rectifier voltmeters have a first-power law of response and indicate average values, but the scale may be distorted because of the resistance characteristic of the rectifier element; vacuum-tube voltmeters may have either square-law response or first-power-law response and may indicate effective, average, or crest values of voltage, depending on the operating characteristics of the circuit elements and of the electron tube used. As an example of the second type of modification the pole pieces of the d-c instrument may be shaped so that the scale is logarithmic, as shown in Fig. 1(*d*). Here the response follows the first-power law, and the indications are of average values unless the response is modified by circuit elements between the input terminals and the deflecting system of the instrument.

Moving-iron Instruments

The commonest ammeters and voltmeters for laboratory or switchboard use at power frequencies are moving-iron instruments. Such instruments can be constructed to measure current and voltage to the accuracy needed in most engineering work and still be produced more cheaply than any other type of a-c instrument of equal accuracy and ruggedness. The operating principle is simple. A vane or plate of "soft" iron or of high-permeability steel forms the moving element of the instrument together with the necessary pivots, spring, pointer, and damping structure. This iron vane is situated so that it may move in the field of a stationary electromagnet consisting of a coil and perhaps an iron structure, whose excitation derives from the current or voltage under measurement. When the electromagnet is excited the iron vane moves in such a way as to *increase* the flux through it. The turning couple produced by the reaction of the fields of the stationary and moving systems is then always in such a direction as to increase the inductance of the combination.

The energy stored in the magnetic field of such a system is

$$W = \frac{I^2L}{2}$$

where I is the exciting current and L is the inductance. The torque developed in the moving system is

$$\mathscr{T} = \frac{dW}{d\theta} = \frac{I^2}{2} \cdot \frac{dL}{d\theta} \text{ dyne-cm/radian}$$

if I and L are in cgs units and θ is measured in radians. The moving system turns until the motor torque is balanced by the restoring torque $U\theta$ of the instrument springs, so that in the equilibrium position

$$\theta = \frac{I^2}{2U} \cdot \frac{dL}{d\theta}$$

Hence the angular deflection is proportional to the *square* of the operating current, the instrument has a "square-law" response, and the reading is in terms of effective (rms) current or voltage. If the change of inductance with angle were uniform ($dL/d\theta$ = constant), then the scale could be laid out so that the measured quantity would be proportional to the square root of the angular deflection. In actual instruments $dL/d\theta$ is usually a function of angular position of the moving iron, and the scale is distorted from the square law in a manner dependent on the way in which inductance varies with angle. This variation can be controlled in the instrument design by the shape of the iron components of the magnetic circuit, and by their positions relative to each other and to the coil. Thus it is common practice to construct an instrument with a scale which is very nearly uniform over a considerable part of its length. Or it is possible to construct an instrument in which a small portion of the range, which is of particular importance or interest, is expanded over a large part of the scale length while the remainder of the scale is compressed into a relatively small space. It will be seen from the torque equation that the portion of the scale near zero can never be expanded or made uniform since this would require that the initial value of $dL/d\theta$ be infinite.

Attraction Instruments. Moving-iron instruments can be classified as belonging to one of three types: (1) attraction, (2) repulsion, and (3) combination. The earliest and simplest instruments were of the attraction type in which a soft-iron plunger, attached to the moving system, was drawn into the field of a solenoid (Fig. 2). It should be noted that the motor torque is in such a direction as to draw the plunger into the coil regardless of the direction of current in the solenoid. Depending on the magnitude of the current to be measured, the coil may be a few turns of very heavy conductor or many turns of fine wire, so that the total ampere-turns and the operating field of the solenoid are the same for a given displacement of the moving system regardless of the instrument range. Hence identical moving systems may be used for an entire series of instruments, from voltmeters, requiring a very small operating current, to the highest-range ammeter in the series. Thus, in a series which uses 300 ampere-turns at full scale, the highest-range ammeter could be for 300 amp (using 1 turn) while the voltmeters of the series could require 50 ma (with 6000 turns) for full-scale deflection. The fact that a single type of moving element can be used to cover this entire range is one reason that moving-iron instruments can be built at less cost than some other types. The simple solenoid-plunger type of moving-iron instrument has a scale which is very compressed at the low end and greatly expanded at the upper

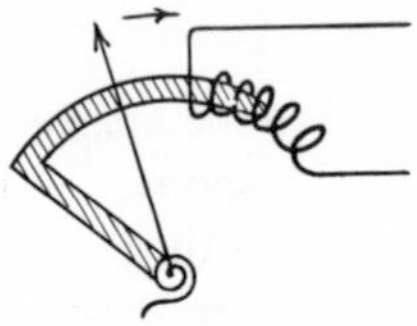

FIG. 2.

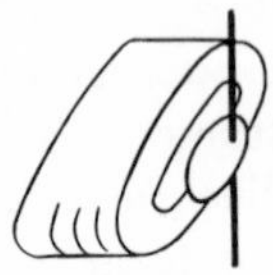

FIG. 3.

end, since the torque is quite low when the moving iron is just entering the solenoid and rises rapidly as the iron is drawn further in. However, it does permit the development of large operating torque and is still used

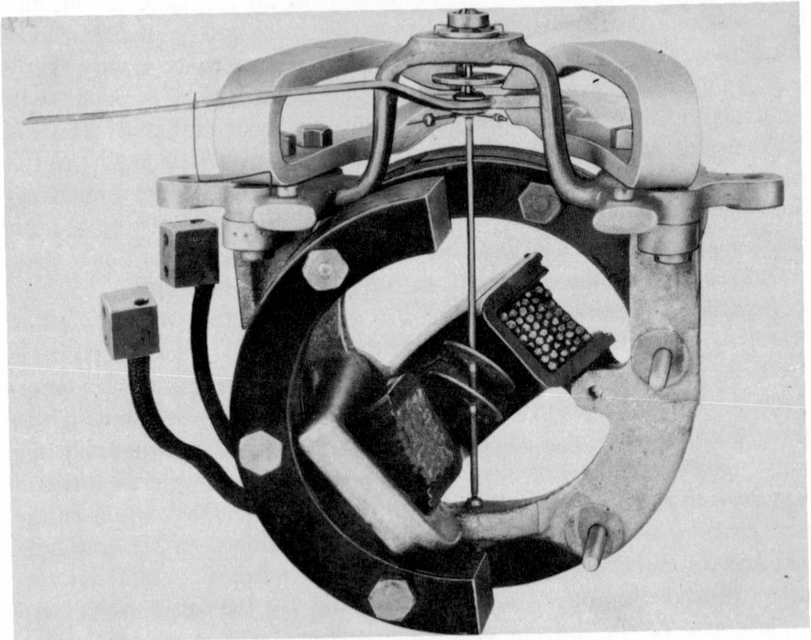

FIG. 4. Thomson inclined-coil instrument. (Courtesy of the General Electric Company.)

currently in some types of recording ammeters and voltmeters where high torque is needed.

A modification of the solenoid-plunger type of attracted iron movement is used extensively in modern instruments. In this modification the coil is flat and has a narrow slot-like opening (Fig. 3). The moving iron is a flat disc or sector which is drawn into the narrow opening of the coil. In some designs a strip of high-permeability steel is fixed in position near the coil opening to concentrate the flux through the movable vane and increase the torque available at low values of excitation. This fixed strip, together with another similar strip located just beneath the movable vane, permits the designer to control the scale distribution and results in much better performance than is possible in the simple solenoid-plunger type of system.

Another type of instrument which is usually classed with the attraction-iron types is the Thomson inclined-coil instrument, shown in Fig. 4, which utilizes the tendency of an iron strip to take up a position parallel

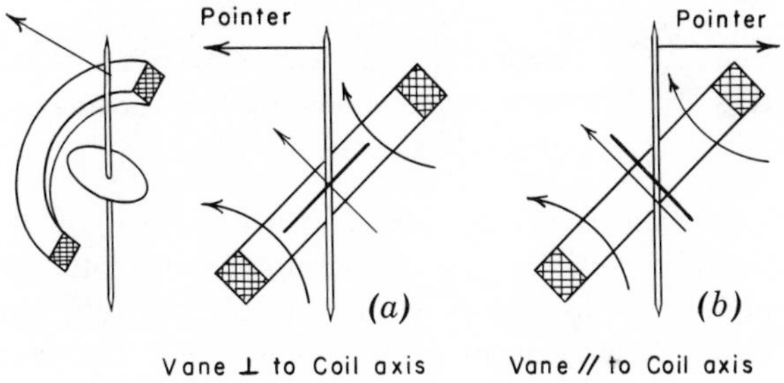

FIG. 5.

to the direction of a magnetic field. In this instrument the vane is a thin iron disc attached at an angle to the shaft of the moving element. The coil surrounds the disc, and its axis is also inclined at an angle to the direction of the shaft. It will be seen from Fig. 5 that, if the coil and vane were both set at an angle of 45° to the axis of the moving system, a total angular displacement of 180° would be necessary to move the vane from position (*a*) perpendicular to the lines of force in the coil to position (*b*) parallel to the lines of force. It should be apparent from inspection that the inductance of the combination, $dL/d\theta$, will change very little with angle for small departures from either position (*a*) or (*b*) and that $dL/d\theta$ will be much greater at intermediate positions. Hence the operating torque would be small at either extreme position, and it would be impractical to make use of the 180° of possible motion. Actually the range of motion utilized in practice is about 90°, starting about 75° away from position (*a*) and ending about 15° short of position (*b*). It is characteristic of this construction that the scale is compressed at its low end because I^2 is so small relative to the full-scale value, and somewhat compressed at its high end because here $dL/d\theta$ is decreasing rapidly. It may be seen from Fig. 6 that the scale is open and usable over more than 80% of its length. Where torque requirements are high, two vanes may be attached to the shaft so that they are parallel to each other.

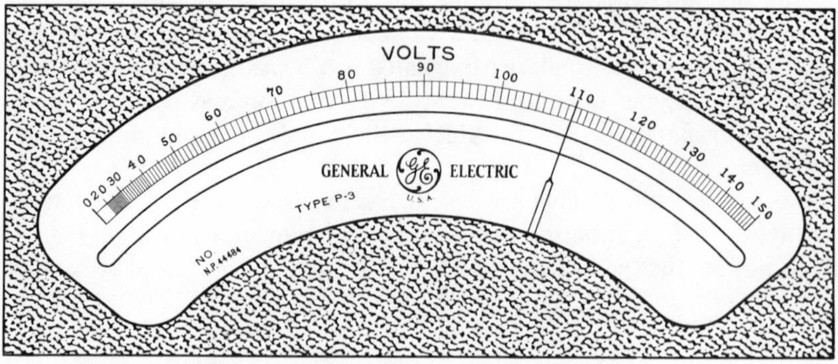

FIG. 6. Scale of Thomson inclined-coil instrument. (Courtesy of the General Electric Company.)

Repulsion Instruments. The second general class of moving-iron instruments is the repulsion type. Repulsion instruments are characterized by the presence of two vanes within the coil, one stationary and one movable. Two different designs are in common use: in one of these the vanes are radial strips of iron, and in the other are sections of coaxial cylinders.

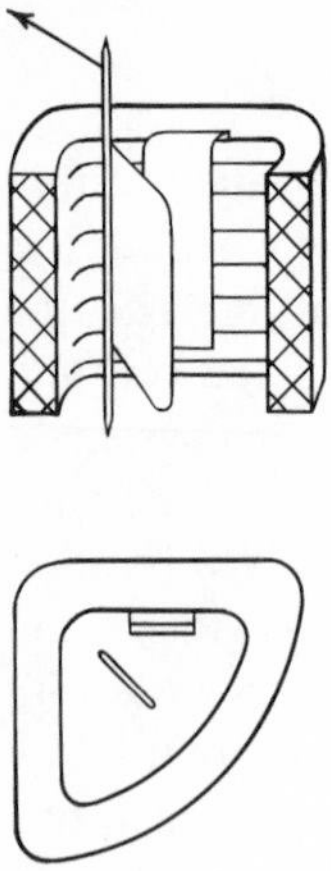

FIG. 7.

In the radial-vane form of instrument the strips are placed within the coil as shown in Fig. 7, the stationary vane being attached to the coil frame and the movable vane being attached to the shaft of the instrument. When current flows in the coil the vanes become magnets in which poles of like polarity are induced at adjacent ends of the two vanes. The mutual repulsion of these like poles tends to force the magnets apart, and the resulting operating torque rotates the moving system. The scale distribution of the instrument can be explained qualitatively in the following way. Since the induced pole strength of the magnetized vanes is proportional to the current in the coil, the force between them (proportional to the product of the pole strengths) should vary with the square of the coil current; however, as the distance between them increases, the force decreases with the square of this distance. These effects tend to neutralize each other, and, as a result, the instrument scale is very nearly uniform over most of its length as shown in Fig. 8. In terms of inductance,

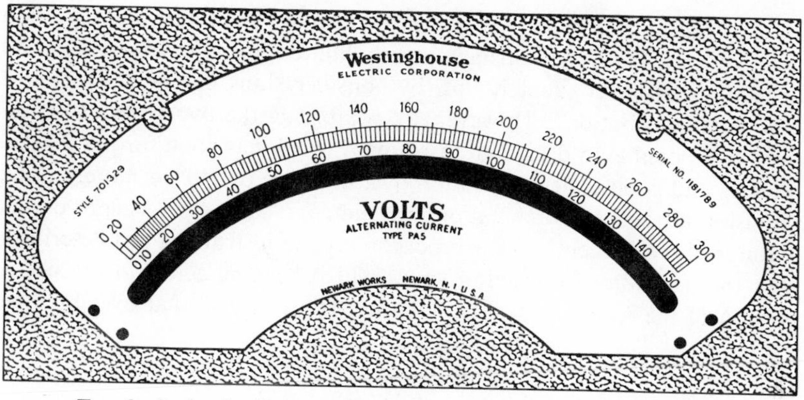

FIG. 8. Scale of radial-vane instrument. (Courtesy of Westinghouse Electric Corporation.)

when the vanes are near each other they tend to demagnetize each other because of the close proximity of like poles, and the flux concentration in each is much less than it would be if only one were present. As the distance between the vanes increases, the mutual demagnetization decreases and the flux becomes more concentrated in each vane. In consequence the inductance of the system increases as the vanes are separated, but the rate of increase with angle $dL/d\theta$ falls off as the angle increases.

The second form of repulsion-iron instrument uses fixed and moving vanes which are sections of coaxial cylinders. This design is referred to as the concentric-vane or coaxial-vane form of instrument. The stationary and moving vanes have shapes similar to those shown in the development of the cylinders in Fig. 9. An effect similar to that in the radial-vane form is obtained by tapering the fixed vane. In this case the scale distribution can be controlled by suitably shaping the fixed vane, and special scale characteristics may be secured. Also this design permits the use of short, wide vanes for which the self-demagnetization is greater, resulting in smaller reversal errors on direct current than are obtained in some other designs (see discussion below).

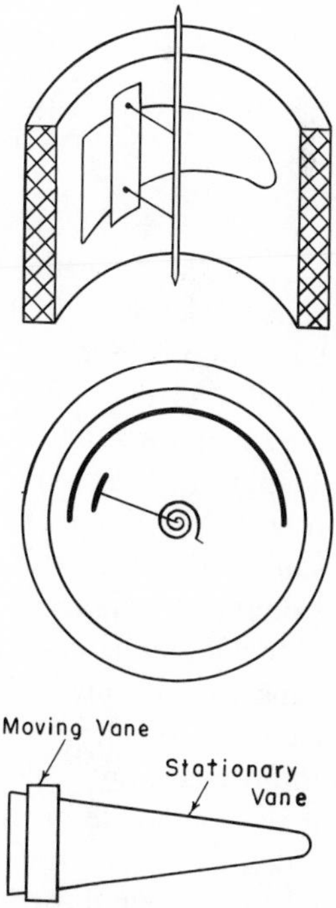

FIG. 9.

Long-Scale Combination Instruments. Both the attraction and repulsion types of moving-iron instruments are limited in practical designs to deflections of approximately 90°, by considerations of operating torque and scale distribution. However, by combining the two types of operation, it is possible to design an instrument which has good torque characteristics and good scale distribution over an angle of 240° or more. Such repulsion-attraction combination instruments have the general design features of the concentric-vane repulsion type of instrument just described, with the addition of attraction vanes which become active in the upper portion of the scale. It will be apparent from Fig. 10 that over the first

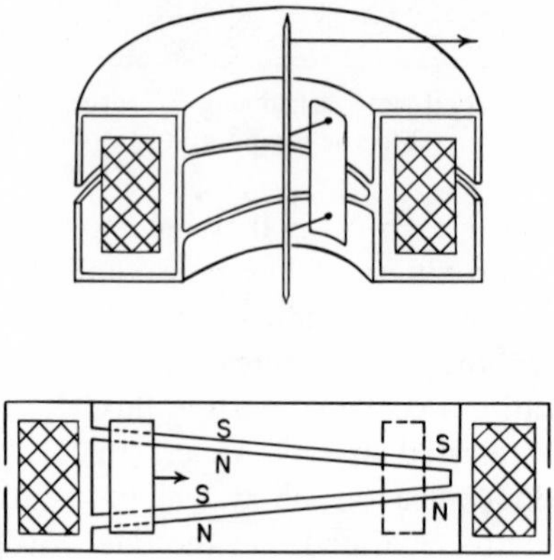

FIG. 10.

part of the scale the moving vane is repelled by the stationary middle vane, which is wide in this region. Over the lower portion of the scale the action is identical with that of the short-scale concentric-vane instrument. As the deflection increases, the outer stationary vanes exert an attractive force on the moving vane and add to the torque. By suitably shaping the vanes the scale distribution may be controlled so that it is useful over about 240°. In one type of long-scale instrument, the outer stationary vanes may be rotated through a small angle as a full-scale calibration adjustment.

In another design a steel screw near the full-scale position of the movable vane extends upward from the lower shield and acts as an attraction element. Its length can be adjusted after the instrument is assembled to provide a final calibrating adjustment. Such an adjustment is essential if the long-scale instrument, designed for switchboard use, is to be provided with a preprinted scale. In such a case the torque for full-scale current must be adjusted to give coincidence with the end mark on the printed scale. It should be noted that the chief advantage of the long-scale instrument is its compactness. It takes up less room on a switch-board than an instrument having a 90° scale of equal length and legibility. For the same length of scale there is no gain in accuracy by extending the scale over an angle of 240° instead of 90°. In fact such an instrument imposes more severe requirements on the restoring springs than a 90° instrument. However, compactness, together with the fact that for reading from a distance the long scale is the equivalent of a 90° scale in a much larger instrument, has made this a very popular type of switch-board instrument.

General Characteristics. For any particular design of instrument, the flux density in the iron at any value of deflection depends on the ampere-turns in the instrument coil. If the iron is being worked in the first stage of magnetization, a-c peak currents carry the iron into a region of higher permeability. In this case the a-c reading will be somewhat higher than the d-c reading for the same effective value of current. At high values of magnetization approaching saturation (region III of Fig. 11) the peak flux is in a lower-permeability region, and the d-c reading will be higher than the a-c reading for the same effective current. The difference in a-c and d-c indications resulting from the variable permeability of the iron will be quite small if the iron is worked at values intermediate *between* these extreme conditions (in region II). It should be noted that an error in a-c readings resulting from variable permeability may be present in the case of a highly peaked wave form. However, the wave-form error of a modern instrument with short vanes will be negligible for the third harmonic at power frequencies. For a given effective value of current the change in peak value may amount to 50% without changing the reading by more than the observational error (less than 1%) in an instrument of this type. However, a plunger-type instrument may have a wave-form error of as much as 10% in extreme cases, reading too low for a peaked wave and too high for a flat wave.

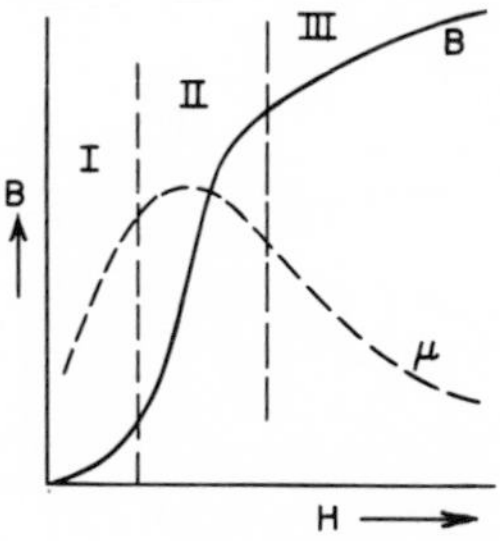

FIG. 11.

HYSTERESIS. Hysteresis in the iron will result in higher readings for decreasing than for increasing values of direct current since the flux density is higher for decreasing *I* (Fig. 12). This difference is minimized by making the iron vanes short, so that their self-demagnetization is large, and by working the iron at flux densities where hysteresis is small. Nickel-iron alloys with a very narrow hysteresis loop are used in most designs to minimize this difference. The effect may produce a difference of 2 to 3% in some types of instrument, but the difference is usually less than 0.5%. Moving-iron instruments are in general not designed for d-c measurements but can be used for this purpose with errors somewhat greater than are to be expected on alternating current. An unknown instrument may be tested for hysteresis by taking a series of readings on direct current with ascending values of current or voltage, covering the instrument range, followed by a series of readings with descending values, starting at full scale. These readings should, of course, be taken in terms of a d-c instrument or of an instrument known to be free from hysteresis. If this cannot be done, it may be possible to minimize the hysteresis effect

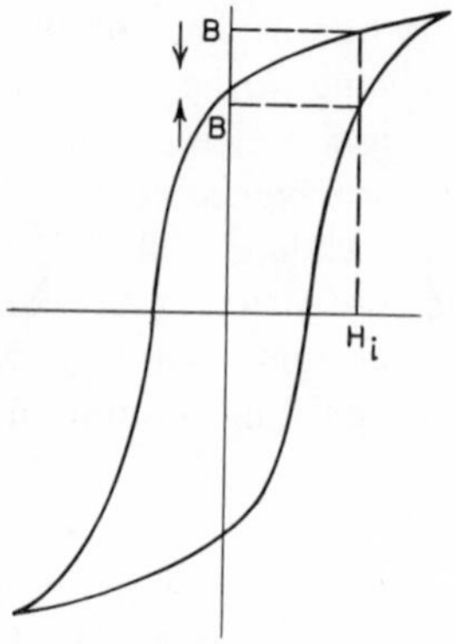

FIG. 12.

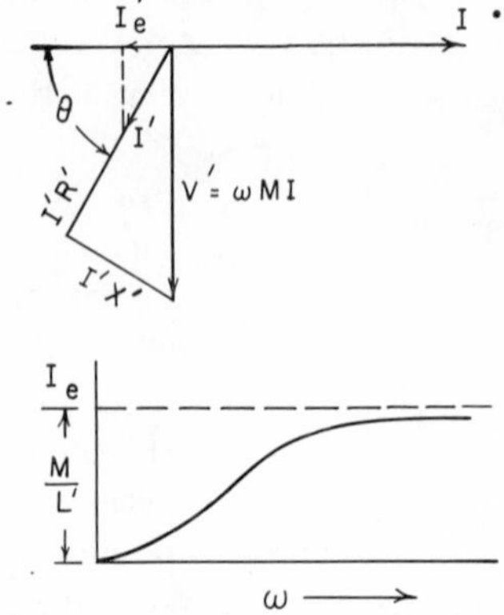

FIG. 13.

for a d-c reading by a preliminary demagnetization procedure. The instrument may be deflected to full scale on alternating current, and the excitation gradually reduced to zero by slowly decreasing the current. The mechanical zero of the instrument should be set at this time. After this, d-c readings should be reliable, providing they are taken with increasing values of excitation, but may be questionable for a low value which follows a higher reading.

EDDY CURRENTS. On alternating current, eddy currents will be set up in the vanes themselves, in any metal parts of the instrument structure, or in shields or neighboring masses of metal. The nature of the effect of eddy currents on a moving-iron instrument may be seen from the following considerations. If the mutual inductance between the field coil of the instrument and the metal object is M, a voltage $V' = \omega MI$ will be induced in it by the current I in the coil (Fig. 13). In consequence an eddy current I' will circulate, its magnitude and phase being determined by the resistance R' and inductance L' of the eddy-current circuit. A component of this induced current, $I_e' = I' \cos \theta$, will be opposed in phase to the exciting current and will set up a field opposing the field in the coil, thus reducing the torque acting on the moving system. From the vector diagram we have

$$I' = \frac{\omega MI}{\sqrt{R'^2 + X'^2}}$$

and

$$I_e' = I' \cos \theta = \frac{\omega MI}{\sqrt{R'^2 + X'^2}} \cdot \frac{X'}{\sqrt{R'^2 + X'^2}} = \frac{\omega^2 L' MI}{R'^2 + \omega^2 L'^2}$$

At low frequencies, where $R' \gg \omega L'$, I_e' is proportional to the square of the frequency. With increasing frequency, the reactance term takes control of the denominator of our expression, so that I_e' asymtotically approaches a limiting value $I_e' \rightarrow (M/L')I$. Thus at low frequencies the eddy-current error increases with the square of the frequency, but at high frequencies will tend toward a constant value. The magnitude of eddy-current errors in moving-iron instruments will vary with their design and construction but may amount to $\frac{1}{2}$ to 1% per kilocycle, in terms of current.

STRAY FIELDS. The presence of stray fields resulting from current-carrying conductors in the neighborhood of the instrument will also influence its readings. In an unshielded instrument this effect may be quite large (10 to 15% in a 5-gauss field) since the field of the instrument itself is comparatively small, 60 to 75 gausses at full scale. Both this effect and that of eddy currents are minimized in most portable and switchboard instruments by magnetic shielding of the mechanism. An iron or steel shield is used as an enclosure for the coil and moving element and should be made of high-resistivity alloy or slotted to keep down eddy currents in the shield itself. Such shielding cannot completely eliminate the effect of stray fields (without prohibitive expense), but may be expected to reduce the effect to a value ranging between a few tenths of a per cent and 2 to 3% in a 5-gauss field, depending on the design and the amount of shielding that can be economically justified. Since some types of instruments are not shielded it is well to inquire into this point in choosing an instrument for work where stray fields may be encountered, or for use near metal structures. For example, a metal table top under an unshielded instrument may seriously impair the accuracy of its indications, or the mounting of such an instrument in a steel panel may change its calibration by several per cent. Although moving-iron instruments having high current ranges can be constructed easily and are available from most manufacturers, it is much better practice to use a 5-amp instrument with a current transformer to measure large currents even if the instrument is shielded, since in this way the instrument can be kept well away from the conductors carrying heavy currents.

INDUCTANCE. In voltmeters, the self-inductance of the instrument introduces errors which set the upper limit of frequency at which it can be used without special calibration. The current in the coil of a voltmeter, for any particular voltage E across its terminals, is

$$I = \frac{E}{Z} = \frac{E}{\sqrt{R^2 + \omega^2 L^2}}$$

where R is the resistance of the coil and multiplier and L is the coil inductance. The response of the voltmeter is controlled by the current through the coil. Hence the deflection for a given impressed voltage

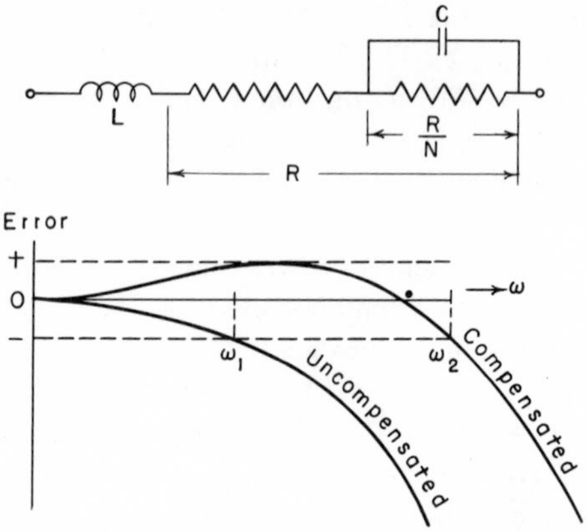

FIG. 14.

decreases with increasing frequency, and the reading for a given voltage will be less at high than at low frequency. The useful frequency range of a moving-iron voltmeter can be greatly extended[4] by compensating the inductance of the instrument coil with a capacitor connected in parallel with a portion of its series multiplier. Voltmeter frequency errors, with and without compensation, are plotted in Fig. 14. It will be seen from this figure that compensation of a voltmeter considerably extends the frequency range over which the impedance does not differ from the d-c resistance by more than the limits indicated by the dotted lines as a tolerable frequency error. By proper choice of C and N voltmeters can be compensated for frequency error over a considerable range of frequency. The extent of this range depends on the time constant L/R of the uncompensated instrument and on the error which can be tolerated at intermediate frequencies. Hence it must be individually worked out for each

[4] This statement applies equally to electrodynamic voltmeters, to be discussed below.

particular type and range of instrument. In terms of the circuit of Fig. 14 the impedance at any frequency is

$$Z_\omega = \left(\frac{N-1}{N} + \frac{N}{N^2 + \omega^2 C^2 R^2}\right) R + j\omega \left(L - \frac{CR^2}{N^2 + \omega^2 C^2 R^2}\right)$$

The effectiveness of this compensation can be illustrated by an example. If $L = 0.1$ henry and $R = 3000$ ohms, and if $N = 2$ and $C = 0.016$ μf, the compensation is exact at 2000 cycles, i.e. $Z_\omega = R$, and the maximum departure of Z from R at any lower frequency is 0.2% at 1400 cycles. Without the compensating capacitance the impedance is 4% higher than the resistance at 1400 cycles and 8% higher at 2000 cycles.[5] For a given element the uncompensated frequency error decreases with increasing range. In a particular series of instruments the frequency error was 1% at 60 cycles on the 30-volt range and reached 1% at 300 cycles on the 150-volt range. It should be noted that the uncompensated frequency error of a given instrument increases nearly with the square of the frequency. The frequency error of an uncompensated 150-volt concentric-vane voltmeter was found to be 0.6% at 100 cycles and 2.5% at 200 cycles.

General Considerations. In general the important sources of error in moving-iron instruments are of two types: (1) hysteresis errors and stray-field errors which affect both a-c[6] and d-c measurements; and (2) eddy-current and inductance errors which affect only a-c measurements and which are a function of frequency. It may be stated that for accurate work a moving-iron instrument (1) cannot be calibrated on direct current for use on alternating current; and (2) must be calibrated at a frequency *within* 10% of the range in which it is to operate. With these restrictions it should be satisfactory up to at least 1000 cycles without compensation and can be compensated for use at somewhat higher frequencies. Modern, well-designed, portable moving-iron instruments can be expected to have a d-c error of 2% or less. The initial accuracy of high-grade moving-iron instruments is stated by the makers to be $\frac{3}{4}$% for frequencies between 25 and 135 cycles, and they may be expected to be accurate to within 0.2 to 0.3% at 60 cycles if carefully calibrated. The effect of temperature changes on moving-iron ammeters arises chiefly from the temperature coefficient of the spring and may be expected to be around 0.02%/°C. For voltmeters both the temperature coefficient of the spring and the temperature coefficient of resistance of the circuit affect the

[5] For illustrations of the application of this type of compensation to actual instruments, see Whittenton and Wilkinson, *Trans. AIEE*, **65**, 761 (1946). See also Miller, *Trans. AIEE*, **70** (1951).

[6] If the instrument calibration is made on alternating current, hysteresis does not produce an a-c error.

instrument deflection. They may be balanced for a particular series resistance with the proper copper-constantan ratio and in general may be made very low, except for low-range voltmeters, by swamping the resistance of the copper coil with a large series resistance of negligible temperature coefficient.

Electrodynamic Instruments

Use. The necessity for the a-c calibration of moving-iron instruments, as well as other types of instruments which do not indicate correctly on direct current, requires the use of a *transfer* instrument which will indicate correctly on direct current and whose performance on alternating current can be accurately predicted from its circuit constants and its d-c performance. This is necessary since all measurements, and hence the calibration of all indicating instruments, must eventually be referred to standards of voltage and resistance in terms of which our electrical working units are defined and maintained. These standards are precision resistors and the Weston standard cell which can be used only in d-c measurements. To calibrate an instrument directly on alternating current in terms of our fundamental standards is impossible. In many cases it must be calibrated in two steps. First a *transfer* instrument whose difference in indication on alternating and direct current is known or negligible is calibrated on direct current by means of potentiometer circuits in terms of the standard ohm and volt. As a second step, this calibration is *transferred* to the a-c instrument on alternating current, using the conditions under which the latter operates properly. *Electrodynamic* instruments are capable of service as transfer instruments. Indeed, their principal use as ammeters and voltmeters[7] in laboratory and measurement work is for the transfer calibration of working instruments. Hence we find that electrodynamic ammeters and voltmeters are generally portable or laboratory-standard instruments of the highest attainable precision, and of course are costly to build in consequence of the care which must be taken in their construction and calibration. Although they may be employed in many types of engineering measurements, such use is not generally to be recommended where a sturdier and less expensive instrument is adequate. In fact, since their operating-power requirements are usually considerably higher than those of moving-iron instruments, they are actually not so well adapted to general laboratory and shop measurements at power frequencies.

Operating Principle. Electrodynamic instruments make use of the magnetic fields of two sets of coils, one fixed and the other movable.

[7] The adaptation of the electrodynamic principle to power measurements in the commonly used electrodynamic wattmeter will be discussed separately at a later time.

Each coil carries a current which is a function of the current or voltage to be measured, and the reaction of the fields of the fixed and movable coils supplies the operating torque to the moving system. The expression for the torque is readily derived. The energy in the magnetic field of the coils is

$$W = \frac{i_1^2 L_1}{2} + \frac{i_2^2 L_2}{2} + i_1 i_2 M$$

and

$$\frac{dW}{d\theta} = i_1 i_2 \frac{dM}{d\theta}$$

since L_1 and L_2 are not functions of θ. Then, since

$$\mathcal{T} = K \frac{dW}{d\theta}$$

we may write for the operating torque of the system

$$\mathcal{T} = K I_1 I_2 \frac{dM}{d\theta}$$

where I_1 and I_2 are respectively the currents in the fixed and movable coils, and M is the mutual inductance between fixed and movable coils. In voltmeters and ammeters each of the currents is proportional to the quantity measured, and the torque is

$$\mathcal{T} = K' I^2 \frac{dM}{d\theta}$$

The instrument therefore has a "square-law" response, and its indication is in terms of effective (rms) current or voltage.

In the usual construction, the current in the fixed coils produces a field in air at the moving coil which may amount to 60 gausses at the most (Fig. 15). Since this field is small, the flux linkages per ampere-turn in the movable coil are few (perhaps 3 to 4% of the flux linkages per ampere-turn in the permanent-magnet, moving-coil instrument). The torque is correspondingly low, and the weight of the moving system must be kept small in order that the torque/weight ratio be as high as possible. This would in itself tend to limit the magnitude of the current which can be sent through the moving coil. Another and equally important factor limiting the moving-coil current is the fact that the current is usually carried to the moving coil through the control springs. This limits the current to values which will not appreciably heat the springs. In voltmeters and low-current ammeters (up to about 0.2 amp) the fixed and moving coils are connected in series as in Fig. 16(*a*). Both sets of coils carry the entire current involved in the measurement. The currents in the fixed and moving coils are necessarily in phase, and the torque is

$$\mathscr{T} = KI^2 \frac{dM}{d\theta}$$

or in the case of a voltmeter

$$\mathscr{T} = K \frac{E^2}{Z^2} \frac{dM}{d\theta}$$

In ammeters having a larger full-scale current than 0.2 amp, the entire current cannot be carried by the moving coil. It is connected across a

FIG. 15. Shielded electrodynamic instrument. (Courtesy of Weston Electrical Instrument Corporation.)

shunt or current-carrying impedance which is in series with the fixed coils. In order that the ammeter may indicate current correctly, the currents in the fixed and moving coils must be in phase. Hence the time constant L/R of the fixed- and moving-coil branches of the circuit must be the same. An added resistance is connected in series with the moving coil, and the combination is connected in parallel with the fixed coil and shunt as shown in Fig. 16(*b*). It will be apparent from an inspection of the figure that the branch point should be at p, since if the moving coil were connected at q, across the shunt alone, the time constants of the two branches could not readily be adjusted to equality.

Characteristics. STRAY FIELDS. Since the operating field of an electrodynamic instrument is necessarily small (60 gausses at full scale), its indications are very sensitive to the presence of stray fields. Portable instruments should therefore be well shielded to minimize this effect. For example, one type of instrument has a shield made of laminated punchings (to reduce eddy-current effects), and this shield is surrounded by a drawn steel cylinder at a clearance of a few millimeters. In instruments of the laboratory-standard grade it is to be expected that the shielding will reduce the effect of a 5-gauss field to 0.2 or 0.3%. In transfer instruments of the highest grade, such as those for instrument testing at the National Bureau of Standards, where precision testing must be done over a rather wide range of frequency, no shielding is used since

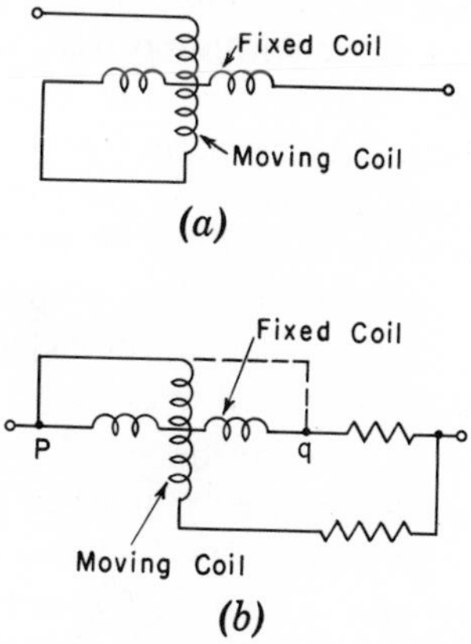

FIG. 16.

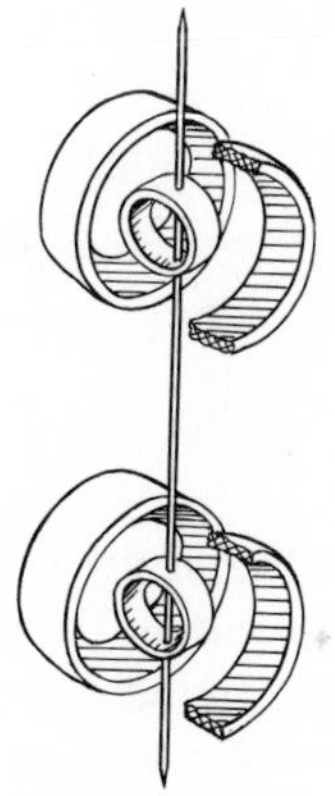

FIG. 17.

the presence of metal in the neighborhood of the coils would result in eddy-current errors. Instead, the instrument is constructed to be *astatic*. There are two sets of fixed coils, and two moving coils having the same area-turns are mounted on a common shaft as shown in Fig. 17. The connections are such that the measured current produces torques in the same direction in the two systems while a *uniform* stray field produces equal torques in opposite directions in the upper and lower systems and thus has no net effect. It should be emphasized that an astatic system indicates correctly only if the field is the same at the two moving coils since it is only in this case that the stray-field torques neutralize each other completely.

EDDY CURRENTS. The effect of eddy currents is to produce a torque as a result of coupling between the moving coil and neighboring metal objects. Hence metal in the coil supports and other structural parts is kept to the minimum possible, and such metal as is used is selected to have a high resistivity. The metal present in the coil supports, etc., and in the shield will produce a frequency error in the instrument, as we have already seen in the case of the moving-iron instrument. However, a frequency error in ammeters must be expected even in the absence of eddy currents. Here, because of the parallel branches, the coils operate in a closed circuit of comparatively low impedance, and the coupling between fixed and moving coils will produce a circulating current in this closed circuit. The frequency error of an electrodynamic ammeter is a combination of the effects resulting from circulating currents in the metal necessarily present and in the closed circuit, including the ammeter coils. It is therefore to be expected that the frequency error will be a function of scale position and will be smallest near the position of zero mutual inductance between the fixed and moving coils. In most instrument designs the position of zero mutual inductance occurs near the midpoint of the scale, and the nature of the typical frequency influence on electro-dynamic ammeters is shown in Fig. 18.

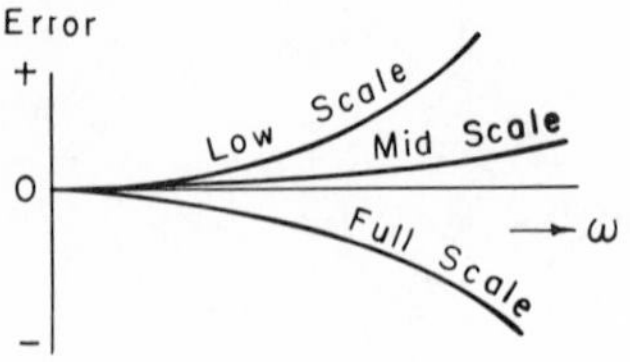

FIG. 18.

INDUCTANCE. The frequency error of an electrodynamic voltmeter is largely a result of the self-inductance of the instrument. As the frequency is increased, the impedance, $Z = \sqrt{R^2 + \omega^2 L^2}$, of the voltmeter circuit rises; and, for a given voltage impressed across the instrument terminals, the current will be less. Hence the deflection for a given voltage will decrease with increasing frequency. The self-inductance of the instrument increases with increasing deflection, being greatest at the full-scale position. Consequently the frequency error resulting from this cause will be expected to be greater at full scale than at lower deflections. In addition the eddy-current effect must be considered. This will be similar in general to the effect in an ammeter but smaller in magnitude. The eddy-current effect may also be a function of scale position, and the combined effect is that the error increases with frequency at any scale position and is to some extent dependent on position. It is generally somewhat greater in the upper than in the lower portion of the scale.

TEMPERATURE EFFECTS. In electrodynamic ammeters two sources of temperature error exist. As in other types of deflecting instruments, the springs have a temperature coefficient. In addition (see Fig. 16), both the moving- and fixed-coil circuits contain copper, together with a series resistance which may be a material having a low temperature coefficient of resistance and which therefore reduces the over-all coefficient. However, it is not generally possible to match the temperature coefficients of the two parellel circuits exactly, and hence the current division between them will be a function of temperature. This will affect the indication of the instrument for a given total current. In the electrodynamic voltmeter the situation is somewhat more favorable. Except in low-range voltmeters the temperature coefficient of the copper can be completely swamped by the series multiplier of negligible temperature coefficient, or, better, this coefficient can be balanced[8] against that of the springs, provided the entire system (coils and springs) is at the same temperature.

Since the operation of electrodynamic instruments requires considerable power, it is to be expected that the temperatures of the various parts will not remain the same after the instrument is connected to a circuit, because of the power which is dissipated in the instrument. This effect in electrodynamic ammeters and voltmeters is described as a self-heating error and will vary with the construction of the instrument and with the time that the instrument has been connected to the circuit. An hour or more is sometimes required to reach a stable condition, and self-heating errors may amount to 1% of full-scale deflection. Various expedients have been used for reducing or compensating the self-heating error. For example, the moving coil may be paralleled with a high-resistance copper shunt which is so located that it contributes extra heat to the springs (or in some cases the coils) needed to reduce the over-all error. In this way the self-heating error can be reduced to 0.1% or less.

TABLE 1

Period	1.3 sec
Resistance	
Two field coils in series	113 ohms
Moving coil plus springs	75 "
Total (including multiplier)	3300 "
Full-scale inductance	0.098 henry
Full-scale current	45 ma
Full-scale power	6.8 watts
Torque for 100° (scale angle = 86°)	140 mg-cm
Weight of moving system	1.0 gm

General Considerations. Electrodynamic instruments used as ammeters or voltmeters are generally in the high-precision class. Accuracies of $\frac{1}{4}$% of full-scale value, or better, are to be expected at power frequencies in well-designed instruments. Because of their cost and high power requirements such instruments are not generally employed in shop or laboratory measurements except where high accuracy is essential or where it is important that the indicated values be free of wave form and other

[8] Since the temperature coefficient of the springs is 0.04%/°C, the instrument whose torque is proportional to I^2 will read 0.02% high/degree for a constant value of current. If the ratio of manganin resistance to copper resistance is 19/1, the overall temperature coefficient of resistance will be 0.02%/degree and as a voltmeter compensation will be complete.

errors. By far the most important application of these instruments (apart from their use as wattmeters) is in the transfer testing of other ammeters and voltmeters which cannot be accurately calibrated on direct current for use in a-c measurements. A Weston Model 341 voltmeter, shielded and having a range of 150 volts, has approximately the characteristics given in Table 1.

Rectifier Instruments

Rectifier instruments find their principal application in measurements in high-impedance circuits at low and audio-frequencies. They are indispensable for measurements in communications circuits since, because of their very high sensitivity, the power required for their operation is small enough to be within the capabilities of the circuit.

Rectifier Elements. There are many materials and combinations of materials which show the property of rectification to some extent; i.e. whose resistance to current is less in a particular direction than if the direction of current were reversed. However, practical rectifier instruments of small size have been possible only since the copper oxide rectifier[9] cell was developed by Grondahl in 1926. The rectifier element comprises a copper disc on which a layer of cuprous oxide, Cu_2O, is formed in a furnace under carefully controlled conditions. After the formation process, the discs are annealed and quenched and the surface layer of black cupric oxide, CuO (formed in the process), is removed to expose the red cuprous oxide beneath it. An electrical contact is made to the copper oxide surface, either by covering it with graphite or with a film of gold or other metal, or by clamping a lead or other soft-metal disc against it. The discs are then assembled into a rectifier unit, together with the electrodes and a spring to apply the pressure needed for good electrical contact. These units are then sealed against moisture and other atmospheric effects. After assembly the rectifier unit is aged at an elevated temperature to ensure its later stability in use.

One possible explanation of the rectifier action, which appears to fit most of the known facts, assumes that the conducting copper and the semiconducting cuprous oxide are separated by a thin barrier layer (Fig. 19) of almost molecular dimensions which has special properties similar to those of an insulator. Let us say that this layer is thin enough that, for a

[9] Selenium rectifier cells have also been developed and used in many practical applications but are not so well adapted for instruments as copper oxide. It is true that selenium rectifiers may be operated up to about 10 volts/unit, whereas copper oxide rectifier operation is limited to about 2 volts/unit, but the lower resistance of the copper oxide units permits them to show a better over-all performance in instrument work, where they are operated at voltages well below their safe limits.

normal voltage across the cell, a very high voltage gradient (10^5 to 10^6 volts/cm) appears across the barrier. Such a field gradient at the surface of a conductor is sufficient to draw from it the free electrons which are near the surface. When the polarity is right, electrons are easily drawn from the copper, where they exist free in a plentiful supply, across the barrier into the Cu_2O, and a relatively large current results. By the usual sign convention this electron current from Cu to Cu_2O corresponds to a conventional current from Cu_2O to Cu. On the reverse polarity electrons are drawn from the Cu_2O by the barrier-layer gradient, but, since there are relatively few free electrons in the semi-conducting cuprous oxide, the current is much less. Whether this simplified picture is the true one is open to serious question, but we can say with certainty that an element made up of a conductor and a semi-conductor having a particular type of common boundary shows a resistance to the flow of current which depends on direction, the resistance being much higher when the current (conventional) is from the conductor to the semi-conductor than in the reverse direction.

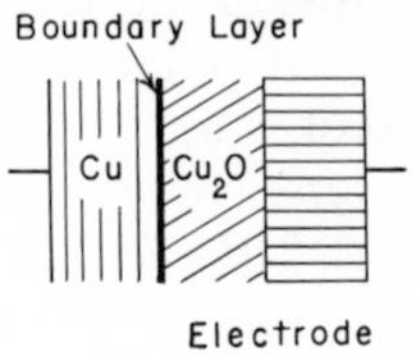

FIG. 19.

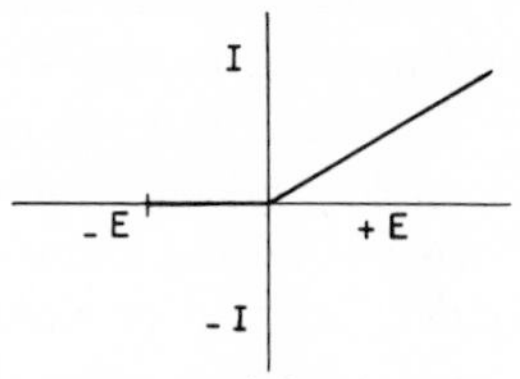

(a)

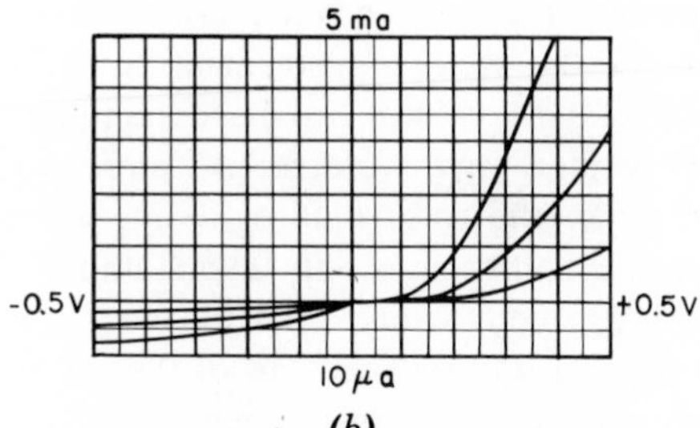

(b)

FIG. 20. (Data courtesy of Weston Electrical Instrument Corporation.)

An ideal rectifier, 100% efficient, would have a current-voltage relation such as that shown in Fig. 20(*a*), where no current flows in one direction (infinite resistance), whereas in the opposite direction the current is proportional to the voltage (constant resistance). This ideal is not realized in practice, and the characteristic current-voltage curve has no sharp discontinuity at zero potential. The actual performance differs from ideal in two respects, as may be seen from Fig. 20(*b*). The forward current is not proportional to the first power of the voltage (resistance decreases with increasing current density), and the reverse current is not zero. For a given voltage the forward current may be 25 times the reverse current, or more.

Rectifier Bridge. A single rectifier unit would pass appreciable current for only one direction of current and would act as a half-wave rectifier. This arrangement, shown in Fig. 21(*a*), would not be practical in most measurement applications, since on the reverse half-wave the resistance across the element would be very high and most of the voltage drop would appear at this point. Since the safe inverse voltage of a copper oxide rectifier element is only a few volts, it would be destroyed by the high inverse voltage. The rectifier-bridge assembly arranged as shown in Fig. 21(*b*) acts as a full-wave rectifier, passing a unidirectional current through the d-c instrument connected across its vertical diagonal for an alternating potential impressed across its horizontal diagonal. The combined resistance of the assembly is comparatively low for either direction of the applied alternating potential, and no high inverse voltage appears across an element at any time. Since the d-c instrument in the circuit is of the permanent-magnet, moving-coil type, its response follows the first-power law of deflection, and it indicates the *average* value of the current during a half-cycle.

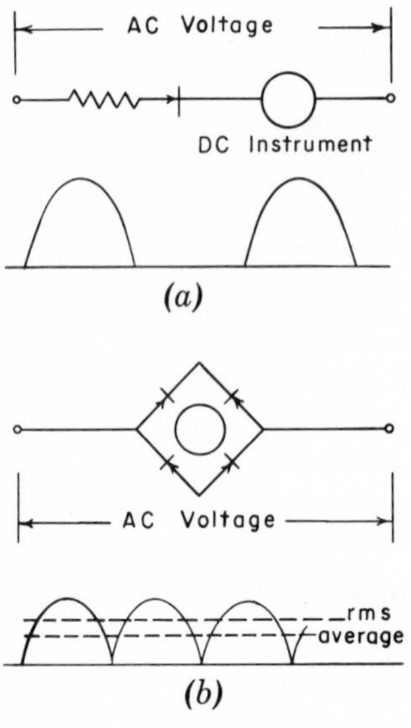

FIG. 21.

Characteristics. EFFECTS OF WAVE FORM. Usually the effective (rms) value of alternating current or voltage is required, rather than the average value, and it is customary to mark the rectifier instrument scale in terms of rms values, on the assumption that a sine-wave voltage is impressed across the rectifier. For example, when the rms value of a sine-wave current is 1 ma, the average value over a half-cycle is only 0.9 ma and the 1-ma scale marking on a rectifier instrument would coincide with the indication of the d-c moving system for a constant current of 0.9 ma in the moving coil. In laying out and marking the scale, the average values to which the moving element responds are multiplied by 1.11, the *form factor* of a sine wave. It will be apparent that the scale reading of the rectifier instrument will be in error for any type of a-c wave other than a sine wave unless the form factor happens to be 1.11. On a square or rectangular wave, the average and effective values are equal and the indications of a rectifier[10] instrument having the usual type of calibration

[10] There are other types of rectifier instruments, notably certain vacuum-tube voltmeters, which respond to crest values of voltage. The wave-form errors of such instruments depend on the ratio of crest to rms value.

will be 11% high. Its indication will, of course, also be 11% high on direct current. In the case of a complex wave the error of indication will depend on the magnitude and phase position of the harmonics. For example,[11] a 30% third harmonic in phase with the fundamental will cause the indication to be 5% high in terms of effective value, whereas the same harmonic displaced 180° in phase will result in an indication

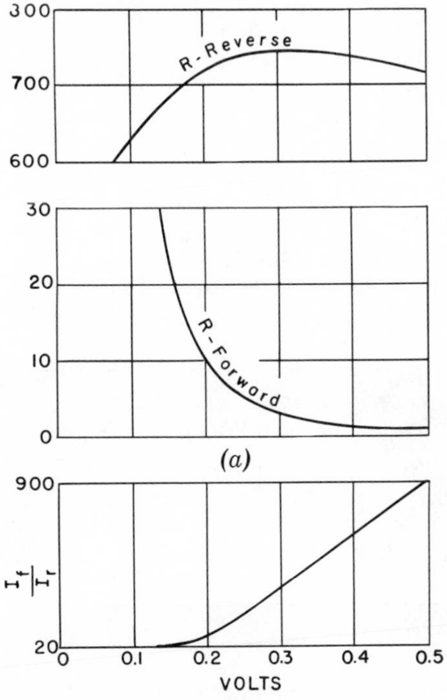

(a)

(b)

FIG. 22.

which is 14% low. Advantage may be taken of this characteristic of the copper oxide rectifier instrument to determine the form factor of a complex voltage wave.[12] Simultaneous readings may be made on a rectifier voltmeter and on a voltmeter which has an rms response (for example, a moving-iron or electrodynamic instrument). If the rectifier instrument is marked in terms of rms values for a sine wave, its scale indication must be multiplied by 0.90 to convert its reading to *average* value. The ratio of rms to average value (obtained from the two instrument readings) is the form factor of the voltage wave.

[11] Goodwin, *Instruments*, **3,** 706 (1930).

[12] Such determinations are of importance in magnetic testing.

SCALE DISTORTION. We have previously seen that both the forward and reverse resistances of a rectifier element are functions of the impressed voltage, and hence of current density in a given size of unit. For one particular element the forward resistance varies from about 30 ohms at 0.1 volt to less than 1 ohm at 0.5 volt; while the reverse resistance rises from 600 to 700 ohms in the same voltage range, as shown in Fig. 22(*a*). The rectification ratio (ratio of forward to reverse current) increases in this same range from 20/1 to 900/1, as shown in Fig. 22(*b*). In the operating range of a rectifier instrument, elements are selected of such size that the rectification ratio is at least 25/1 and is preferably 2 or 3 times this value. It will be apparent from these

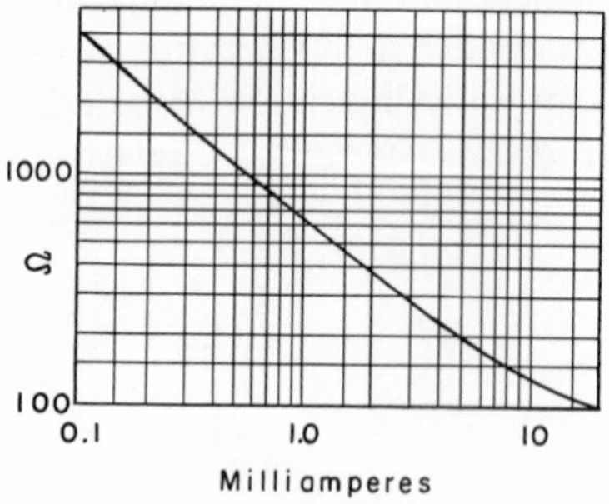

FIG. 23. (Data courtesy of Westinghouse Electric Corporation.)

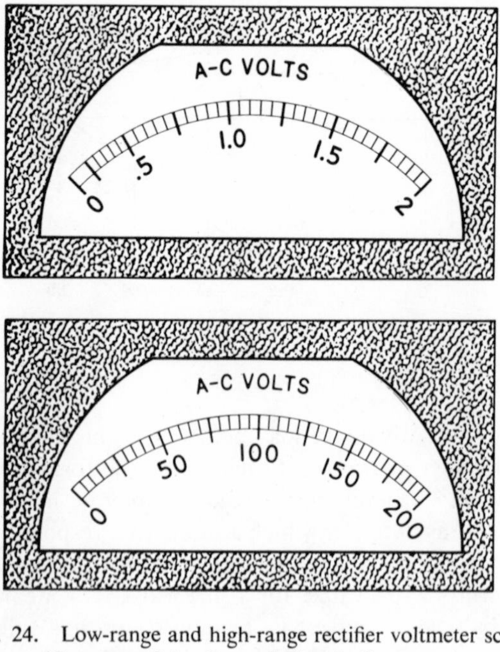

FIG. 24. Low-range and high-range rectifier voltmeter scales. (Courtesy of the General Electric Company.)

considerations that the effective resistance of a rectifier bridge will decrease as the current density in its elements increases. This is shown in Fig. 23

for a 20-ma Westinghouse unit. From this resistance variation it follows that, for a low-range voltmeter whose series resistance is not large compared with that of the rectifier bridge, the scale is compressed[13] at the low-voltage end because of the higher resistance of the rectifier elements at low current densities. For a high-range voltmeter in which the series resistance is much greater than the resistance of the rectifier units, the scale is very nearly uniform. This is shown in Fig. 24.

Another factor must be taken into account in the scale calibration of a milliammeter. It has been noted that the rectification ratio of a rectifier bridge is a function of the applied voltage and therefore of the current density in its elements. It follows from this that the ratio of the direct

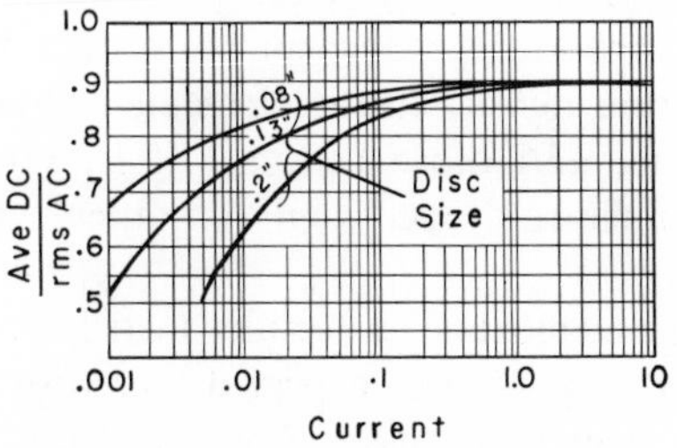

FIG. 25. (Data courtesy of Weston Electrical Instrument Corporation.)

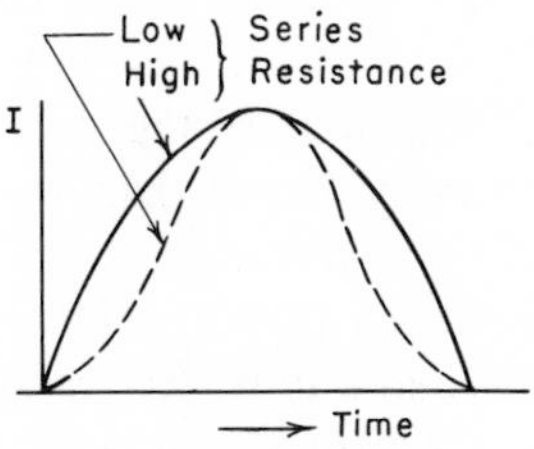

FIG. 26.

current indicated by the deflecting element to alternating current in the circuit will be a function of current density in the bridge elements. If rectification were perfect, this (average d-c/rms a-c) ratio would be 0.90 for a sine-wave current. Actually the d-c/a-c ratio is considerably less at low current densities and approaches 0.90 as a limiting value when the current density is increased. This is shown for a series of Weston elements in Fig. 25. It should be noted that a milliammeter introduces into the measuring circuit resistance which is a function of the current through the instrument. Because of the variation of resistance with current density, the presence of a rectifier milliammeter in a low-resistance circuit may distort the current wave form in the manner shown in Fig. 26. In a low-impedance circuit such an instrument should be employed with caution if current wave form is important. In most communication circuits where the use of this type of milliammeter is indicated, the circuit impedance is sufficiently high to swamp out the effect of cyclical variation of resistance in the rectifier bridge.

[13] The scale of a low-range voltmeter can be made very nearly uniform by special shaping of the pole pieces of the d-c instrument so that the field is stronger and the sensitivity higher at the low end of the scale. Thus the naturally compressed scale is expanded to equality with the remaining portion.

TEMPERATURE EFFECT. The temperature coefficients of forward and reverse resistance in a copper oxide rectifier are both negative but are not equal. The reverse resistance decreases about 3%/°C rise in temperature, while the forward resistance decreases about 1%/°C. Since the reverse resistance is in parallel with the d-c instrument its decrease will tend to by-pass current around the deflecting element. Hence for a given input current into the bridge the instrument indication will decrease as the temperature rises. This is partly counteracted by the negative coefficient of the forward resistance, which is effectively in series with the deflecting element and tends to allow more current to flow through it with rising temperature. This compensation is not complete, and the net temperature coefficient of the instrument is negative. No general quantitative statement can be made about the temperature coefficient of rectifier instruments, since this varies with current density in the element, rectification ratio, thickness of the oxide film, and other factors. It is, however, considerably larger than the temperature coefficients of other types of deflecting instruments.

FREQUENCY EFFECT. The bridge elements of a rectifier instrument may be considered imperfect capacitors. It is to be expected therefore that a frequency error would be present from this cause. Since this capacitance is effectively a shunt across the bridge, it will by-pass some of the current around the measuring element and the instrument will tend to read low as the frequency is increased. With the usual construction this effect may amount to as much as $\frac{1}{2}$%/kc. Instruments that are to be used at high frequencies are constructed with elements having a minimum plate area in order to reduce the shunt capacitance as much as possible. Obviously this requires that the element be operated at a higher current density than normal, and its overload capacity is therefore reduced. In addition to decreasing plate size, some compensation can be obtained by adding an inductively wound shunt around the bridge. By these means instruments can be built whose frequency errors do not exceed 1% at 100 kc.

CURRENT RANGE. A rectifier bridge small enough for installation in a panel instrument is limited in current-carrying capacity to about 15 ma. Rectifier instruments for current measurement are made as microammeters and milliammeters and in general have current ratings ranging from 100 μa to 15 ma. Circuits have been described for extending the current range above 15 ma, using an Ayrton shunt or a specially built current transformer. A multirange instrument employing an Ayrton shunt and having a maximum current range of 100 ma has been described by Westinghouse. The circuit diagram of this instrument is shown in Fig. 27. It will be noted that the full-scale voltage drop required by this combination varies from 5 volts for the low range to 6.25 volts for the highest range. The power required for full-scale deflection on the instrument alone is 5 milliwatts, and in the shunt the power at full scale varies from 20 mw to more than 600 mw, depending on the range in use. Current transformers[14] have been employed with rectifier instruments to a limited extent. The current transformer designed for such service would have to be of a very special type because of the low currents used with the rectifier bridge.

VOLTAGE RANGE. The extension of voltage range in rectifier instruments is relatively simple since only series multipliers are needed. For this purpose 1-, 0.5-, and 0.2-ma instruments having 1000, 2000, and 5000 ohms/volt respectively are regularly used, and voltmeters are usually self-contained up to 300 volts. For higher-voltage ranges, external multipliers simplify the problem of adequate insulation. In multirange instruments separate scales may be needed for the low-voltage ranges since, if the bridge resistance is any considerable part of the total instrument resistance, the scale is compressed at its lower end because of the greater bridge resistance at low current densities. For higher ranges, in which the series-multiplier resistance swamps out the bridge resistance, the scale is uniform and a single scale with appropriate multiplying factors can be used for the various ranges.

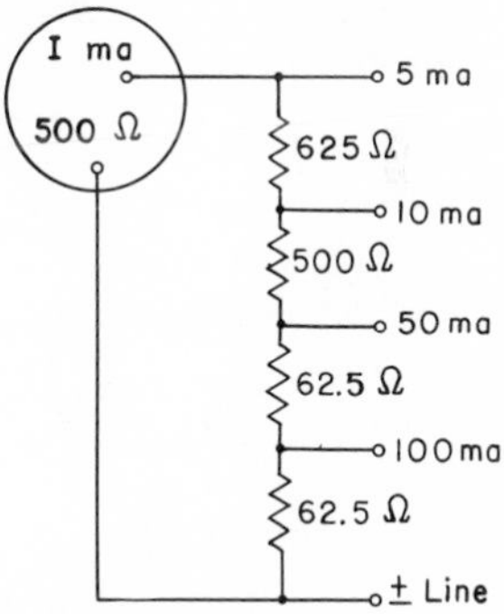

FIG. 27.

Power-Level Indicators. These instruments, generally known as db meters and in one specific case as a VU meter, are essentially rectifier voltmeters which indicate the voltage drop across a fixed load. The scale could, of course, be marked in terms of the power dissipated in the fixed load, but communications engineers have found it more convenient to state the power in terms of its departure from a chosen level of reference and to use a logarithmic scale for this purpose. The power level is expressed by stating the common (Briggs) logarithm of the ratio of the existing power to the reference value of power. The name "bel" is given to the unit in this logarithmic scale, and the name "decibel" (commonly used in communication measurements and abbreviated as db) indicates 0.1 bel. Thus 1 bel or 10 db represents a power ratio of 10/1, and 1 db corresponds to a power ratio of 1.26/1 or a voltage ratio of 1.13/1, a departure of 26% in watts or 13% in volts from the chosen level. DB meters usually have a scale marked either in terms of a reference level of 6 mw in a 500-ohm load or of 6 mw in a 600-ohm load. Since the signal

[14] Edgcumbe and Ockenden, *Industrial Electrical Instruments*, pp. 175, 491, Pitman.

measured may be greater or less than the reference value, the scale is generally marked with the reference value 0 db at the approximate center of the scale, the departure from this level being indicated by positive and negative db values. Standard scales are marked from − 10 db to + 6 db, indicating power levels of 0.6 mw and 3.9 mw respectively. On the basis of a 600-ohm load the corresponding voltages measured would be 0.60 and 3.79 volts respectively.

In 1938 a move was started to standardize on a single volume-level indicator for measuring audio-frequency power in communications circuits. In specifying this instrument a particular speed of response and sensitivity were chosen in order that the indications of all volume-level

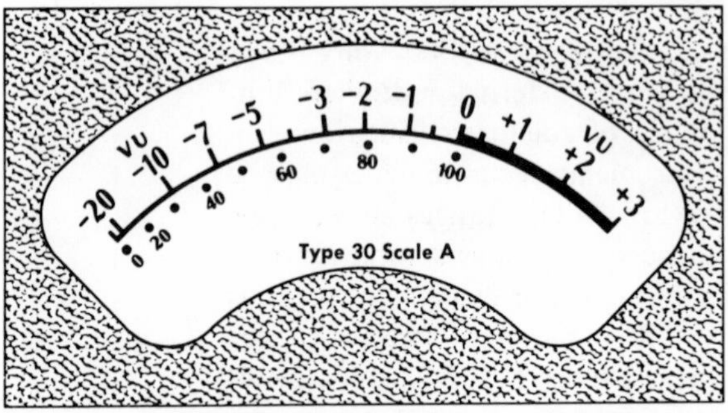

Fig. 28. Scale of VU meter. (Courtesy of Weston Electrica. Instrument Corporation.)

instruments would be comparable. The sensitivity was made high to reduce the energy taken from the line by the instrument. A new unit (VU) was defined which is numerically equal to the number of db above or below a reference level of 1 mw in 600 ohms as read on this instrument, calibrated on a sine wave.[15] As of 1945 the VU meter which has become generally accepted in the measurement of voice-frequency power has a response characteristic such that, for a suddenly applied audio-frequency signal which will give a steady deflection of 0 VU, the indication reaches 99% of its final value in 0.3 sec and the overshoot is between 1 and 1.5%.

The reference level of 1 mw in 600 ohms has proved impractical in laying out the instrument scale because of sensitivity limitations in instrument design and manufacture. Therefore the instrument is calibrated by the application of 1.228 volts rms (4 db above 1 mw in 600 ohms) to the instrument and a suitable series resistance. The corresponding deflection is marked 100% on the voltage scale and zero on the VU scale, as shown in Fig. 28. In adapting this "voltmeter" to the reading of

[15] See Chinn, Gannett, and Morris, *Proc. IRE*, **28,** 1 (1940) for a discussion of the basis on which these specifications were drawn. See also ASA Standard C16.5—1942.

audio-frequency power a particular attenuating network is used. This circuit is shown in Fig. 29. The instrument itself has a resistance of 3900 ohms. It is connected to the circuit by means of a T-pad attenuator. The circuit may be represented by 300 ohms (i.e. the combined parallel resistance of a 600-ohm line and a 600-ohm load). Between the circuit and the input side of the attenuator a resistance of 3600 ohms must be inserted. The attenuator is therefore matched to a resistance of 3900 ohms in either direction. In order that the reference level be 1 mw in 600 ohms the attenuator switch position corresponding to zero attenuation (resistor $A = 0$; resistor $B = \infty$) is marked + 4 VU. This is, of course, the minimum position on the attenuator dial, and 4 VU are added to the "true attenuation" in marking all dial settings. Thus, if for an actual

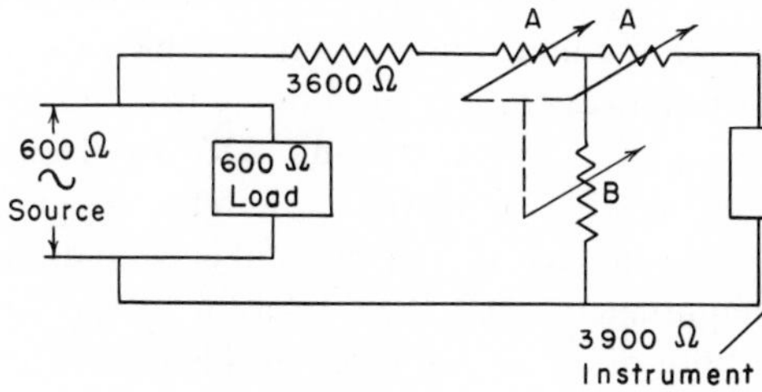

FIG. 29.

attenuation of zero the VU meter indicates 0 VU (or 100% on the voltage scale), the *true reading* (obtained by adding the instrument reading and the attenuator reading) is + 4 VU since the attenuator is marked + 4 VU at this setting. Since the power level corresponding to 0 on the instrument scale is actually 4 VU above the 1-mw level, the combination indicates correctly. In Table 2 are given the *A*- and *B*-arm resistance values corresponding to a few of the dial settings of an attenuator constructed for use with a VU meter.

TABLE 2

Attenuator Loss, DB	*Attenuator Dial Marking*, VU	*Arm A*, ohms	*Arm B*, ohms
0	+ 4	0	Open
1	+ 5	224.3	33,801
6	+ 10	1,296	5,221
10	+ 14	2,026	2,741
20	+ 24	3,191	787.8
40	+ 44	3,823	78.01

It may be noted that power loss is not generally measured in a communications circuit at voice frequencies with a *wattmeter*, but is measured by means of a *rectifier voltmeter* and with the aid of an attenuator. The instrument used as a VU meter employs a specially selected rectifier unit and has an extremely sensitive movement. Because of the large air-gap flux required, the instrument is not suitable for mounting in a steel panel unless specially calibrated for that purpose. This arrangement is used not only for monitoring voice-frequency power but also for the measurement of noise-level and other audio-frequency energy, since the characteristics of the instrument are such that the results of measurements taken in different laboratories are comparable.

General Considerations. Rectifier instruments are of greatest value in measuring current and voltage at low and audio-frequencies in high-impedance circuits. Because they utilize inherently sensitive permanent-magnet, moving-coil systems they require much less power for their operation than either moving-iron or electrodynamic instruments. Hence they can be used in communication circuits in which there is insufficient power available for the operation of moving-iron instruments. Their accuracy is moderate, in general around 5% in the audio-frequency range, but can be somewhat improved by careful design in instruments for special purposes. In such design the maker would have to consider the specific job requirements and their relation to the temperature and frequency effects, both of which are large in this type of instrument. In addition to these effects there is a wave-form error, arising from the fact that the instrument deflection is a measure of *average* value, whereas the instrument scale is usually marked in terms of *rms* values *for a sine wave*. This effect may result in a reading error of several per cent if prominent harmonics are present. Generally, however, in communications measurements we are interested in approximate values of the quantity measured, the operating temperature does not vary widely, and the wave form is sufficiently random that its summation does not introduce serious error into the instrument indications. In this type of work the rectifier instrument is quite satisfactory. Where higher accuracy is needed special instruments are required. If sufficient power is available to operate an iron-vane instrument without serious disturbance to the circuit conditions, it should be employed in precise work at power frequencies and the lower audio-frequencies. In this class of work at higher frequencies thermocouple instruments have much to recommend them.

Rectifier instruments are very rugged and will generally withstand overload conditions up to several hundred per cent without permanent damage. They are specifically designed for measurements where very little operating power is available and where moderate accuracy is acceptable. If used under these conditions and with a knowledge of their limitations, they form a most satisfactory class of instruments for measurements in the audio-frequency range.

Electrothermic Instruments

Electrothermic instruments depend for their indication on some property of a circuit element which is heated by the passage of electric current. Under proper conditions they can be used for the measurement of current without significant errors at extremely high frequencies. Their chief field of usefulness is in the measurement of *current* at frequencies above the range of moving-iron and electrodynamic instruments. At moderate frequencies they can be employed for precise *voltage* measurement, and the frequency range of voltage measurement can be extended considerably if proper precautions are taken.

There are three electrothermic effects which have been utilized for the measurement of current: (1) The linear expansion of a wire heated by the current; such instruments are called hot-wire or expansion instruments. (2) The emf developed at the junction of two dissimilar metals, the junction being heated by an auxiliary circuit which carries the current being measured; such instruments are called thermocouple instruments or, because of their usefulness at high frequencies, radio-frequency or r-f instruments. (3) The change in resistance of a circuit element which is heated by the current being measured; such instruments are called bolometers. Expansion hot-wire instruments and thermocouple instruments have been used extensively in engineering measurements. Bolometers have been employed to a limited extent in special measurement problems but have not been generally available as commercial engineering instruments.

Hot-Wire Instruments. Expansion ammeters were popular in the last decade of the nineteenth century and in the first two decades of the present century but have been largely superseded by thermocouple instruments and are not used extensively at the present time. However, their transfer characteristics are generally good up to very high frequencies, and they find some use in the determination of the differences of indication of other types of instruments on alternating and direct current and in special measurement applications.

Early hot-wire ammeters, with platinum-silver alloy wire, had a serious defect. The full-scale operating temperature was low (about 150°C), and marked changes in indication and in zero position of the pointer occurred with changes in room temperature as a result of failure to match exactly the temperature coefficient of expansion of the frame on which the hot wire was mounted to that of the wire itself. The adoption of platinum-iridium alloy wire,[16] which could be safely operated at temperatures up to 300°C, made an exact match of expansion coefficients of the

[16] Hartmann-Kempf, *E.T.Z.*, **31**, 269 (1910).

wire and its mounting frame less important and largely eliminated this defect. The increase in length of the wire at the operating temperature is, of course, only a very small percentage of its total length (about 0.2 mm in a length of 17 cm in the Hartmann-Braun instrument), and various ingenious mechanical linkages have been devised to magnify this motion and convert it to motion of a pointer on a circular scale.[17] The arrangement in the Hartmann-Braun ammeter is typical and is shown schematically in Fig. 30. Magnification of the motion is accomplished by utilizing the fact that the sag at the midpoint of the heated wire is many times as great as its increase in length. Thus, an increase of 0.2 mm in the 17-cm length of the wire results in a sag of nearly 2 mm at its midpoint if the wire is kept stretched. A second sag wire, perpendicular to the heated filament and attached to its midpoint, produces a further magnification and makes available a total linear motion of 6 mm (a total magnification of thirty-fold) in a thread attached to the midpoint of the second sag wire, carried around a roller to actuate the instrument pointer, and kept under tension by a suitable leaf spring.

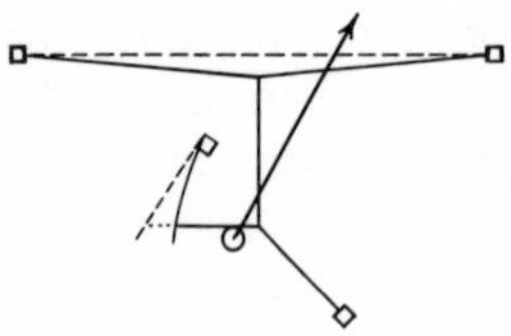

FIG. 30.

A rather curious source of error exists in the Hartmann-Braun ammeter at certain frequencies in the lower audio range. Eddy-current damping of the pointer system is accomplished by means of an aluminum disc in the air gap of a permanent magnet. This magnet is attached to the iron base plate on which the expansion element is mounted, with the result that a considerable magnetic field is present around the hot wire. At certain frequencies, corresponding to modes of vibration of the mechanical linkage system, motor action between this field and the current in the hot wire produces a resonant vibration of the wire and results in added cooling because of its motion in the surrounding air, reducing its temperature slightly. Differences of a half per cent or more between a-c and d-c indications of one such instrument have been observed at a number of frequencies below a kilocycle. Since this effect results from mechanical resonance it would not be present at high frequencies, but the behavior of such an instrument should be thoroughly explored in the lower audio-frequency range if it is to be used in "transfer" work.

The overload capacity of hot-wire instruments is very limited, the expansion element being injured or even destroyed by a moderate overload,

[17] A number of such arrangements have been described by Keinath, *Die Technik elektrischer Messgeräte*, Vol. 1, p. 218. See also Palm, *Elektrische Messgeräte*, 3rd edition, p. 96, Springer, 1948.

and their operating power is higher than that of any other type of a-c instrument.

Thermocouple Instruments. OPERATING PRINCIPLE. The essential components of a thermocouple instrument are: (1) the heater element (usually a fine wire or thin-walled tube) which carries the current to be measured; (2) a thermocouple having its hot junction in thermal contact with the heater element and its cold junction at or near room temperature; (3) a sensitive permanent-magnet, moving-coil millivoltmeter whose deflection results from the emf developed by the thermocouple. Since the emf developed by the thermocouple is approximately proportional to the temperature rise of the heater element, the deflection of the millivoltmeter is approximately proportional to the I^2R loss in the heater element. A thermocouple ammeter or voltmeter therefore has a *square-law* response; i.e. the angular deflection of the millivoltmeter is a measure of I^2 in the heater element, and the rms (effective) value of current or voltage is indicated by the scale reading. Actually the proportionality factor between heater temperature and I^2 is only approximately constant since the heater may have either a positive or a negative temperature coefficient of resistance. Also the emf of a thermocouple is not strictly proportional to the first power of the temperature difference between its junctions. These effects are usually quite small so that, if the air-gap field of the millivoltmeter is uniform, the scale of the instrument may be laid off approximately with the square of the heater current. Values of thermal emf plotted against heater current are compared in Fig. 31 for a 2-ma carbon heater element having a negative temperature coefficient of resistance and a 200-ma metallic element having a positive coefficient.[18]

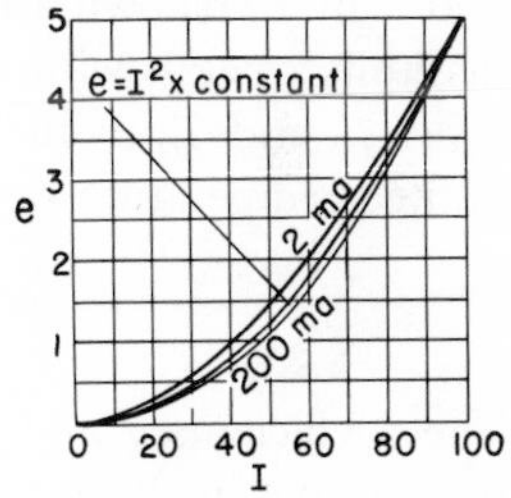

FIG. 31.

THERMAL EMF. In 1826 Seebeck reported that, if an antimony wire and a bismuth wire were connected together to form a closed circuit, a current would flow in the circuit if the junctions between the two metals were at different temperatures. The inverse of the Seebeck effect was described by Peltier in 1834. He found that, if he inserted a battery into the circuit described by Seebeck and caused a current to flow, one junction would be heated and the other cooled by the current.[19] In 1851 Lord

[18] These data, on Weston vacuum thermoelements, are reproduced by permission of the Weston Electrical Instrument Corporation. See Kunz, *Weston Engineering Notes*, **2,** No. 3, p. 4 (1947).

[19] The Peltier heating or cooling of a junction of two dissimilar metals as a result of current flow should not be confused with the I^2R or Joule heating of a wire, which depends on the resistance of the conductor and is independent of the direction of current.

Kelvin showed by thermodynamic reasoning that, in addition to the Peltier effect at a junction, another reversible effect must exist in a thermoelectric circuit. He concluded (and later showed experimentally) that there must be a reversible absorption of heat when current flows in a homogeneous conductor in which there is a temperature gradient. This has the same effect as though an emf existed in a conductor in which there is a temperature gradient. Thus, in addition to the thermal emf at the junctions of dissimilar metals at different temperatures, there are thermal emf's resulting from temperature gradients along the metals themselves.

It can be shown that the emf developed in a circuit composed of dissimilar metals with their junction points at different absolute temperatures T_1 and T_2 (with $T_2 > T_1$) may be approximately described over a limited temperature range by the equation

$$E = \alpha(T_2 - T_1) + \frac{\beta}{2}(T_2^2 - T_1^2)$$

The coefficients α and β depend on the thermoelectric power of the two metals that make up the circuit. If the temperatures are expressed in degrees centigrade, where t is the hot-junction temperature and t_0 is that of the cold junction, we have

$$E = (t - t_0)\left[\alpha + 273\beta + \frac{\beta}{2}(t + t_0)\right]$$

This equation is seen to be quadratic in t, its precise definition depending on the temperatures of the junctions. In terms of the temperature difference Δt between the junctions, we have for a particular cold-junction temperature t_0,

$$E = \Delta t\,[\alpha + \beta(t_0 + 273)] + \frac{\beta}{2}\Delta t^2$$

And if we consider t_0 to be a fixed reference point we can write

$$E = a\Delta t + b\Delta t^2$$

Thus at any fixed temperature of the reference junction the emf of a thermocouple is a parabolic function of the temperature difference between the junctions. For the combinations of metals generally used as thermocouple pairs, the coefficient a amounts to 40 to 50 μv or more per degree difference in temperature, while b is usually of the order of a few tenths or hundredths of a microvolt. If a temperature difference of 100°C results from rated current through the heater element, an emf of around 5 mv is to be expected in the thermocouple circuit. In some types of thermocouple instruments the heater is operated at a considerably higher temperature, and as much as 15 mv may be available in the millivoltmeter circuit at rated current.

HEATER ELEMENT. It is well known that the resistance of a wire is a function of the frequency of the current that it carries. If a conductor is considered to be made up of a large number of elementary parallel conducting filaments, the current through each elementary conductor will set up a field around it which will link with the other elementary conductors. It will be seen that on the interior, where the elementary filaments are surrounded by others, the number of linkages will be greater than at the surface, where the filaments are affected only by the fields from current filaments to one side. When the current changes, these flux linkages also change to produce a counter emf opposing the change in current; i.e. there is a reactance distributed throughout the section of the conductor. Since the flux linkages would be more abundant, if the current were uniformly distributed, for filaments at the center of the conductor, the reactance will be higher there. The current will be less at the center and greater toward the surface of the wire. Because of this non-uniform current distribution (skin effect) the effective resistance of the conductor increases with frequency, since the effective current-carrying section of the conductor is less. For most conductor shapes the expression of the increased resistance is very complicated. In the case of a solid, round wire at an infinite distance from any other conductor the ratio of the resistance R_f at any frequency to the d-c resistance may be expressed as a series

$$\frac{R_f}{R_0} = 1 + \frac{1}{12}\left(\frac{\pi r^2 \mu\omega}{10^3 \rho}\right)^2 - \frac{1}{12 \times 15}\left(\frac{\pi r^2 \mu\omega}{10^3 \rho}\right)^4 + \cdots$$

where r is the radius in centimeters, μ is the permeability, ω is $2\pi \times$ frequency and ρ is the resistivity in microhm-centimeters.[20] It is apparent that the skin effect will be least for a very fine wire of a non-magnetic material having high specific resistance. For a 1-mil copper wire the increase in resistance is 1% at 20 megacycles, whereas for a constantan wire of the same size the increase in resistance is only 0.0015% at 20 megacycles, and only at 500 megacycles does its resistance increase by 1%. The diameter of a constantan wire would have to be 5.3 mils in order that its 20-megacycle resistance be 1% higher than its d-c resistance (i.e. for a given percentage change in resistance at a given frequency the wire diameter is proportional to the square root of the resistivity). It will be seen that in the measurement of small currents a fine wire of suitable size and material may be used up to very high frequencies to supply energy to a thermoelectric measuring system without serious

[20] For formulas and tables of skin-effect values under a variety of conditions, see *NBS Circ.* C74, pp. 299–311, 1937. See also *Smithsonian Physical Tables*, 7th revised edition, p. 344, 1927.

frequency errors. For the measurement of higher values of current a short length of thin-walled tubing serves as a heater element.

THERMOELEMENT. The heater element and thermocouple together make up a device by which energy is converted into a form in which it can be used to operate the deflecting element of a sensitive d-c millivoltmeter. It is instructive to follow the separate steps in this process. (1) Electrical energy is converted to thermal energy in the heater element and is mostly dissipated as heat. (2) A very small fraction of this energy is converted by the Seebeck effect at one junction of the thermocouple back to electrical energy. (3) A portion of the electrical energy in the thermocouple circuit is converted to mechanical energy in deflecting the moving system of the millivoltmeter and is stored as potential energy in

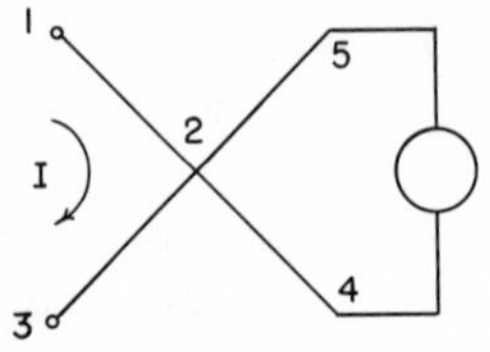

FIG. 32.

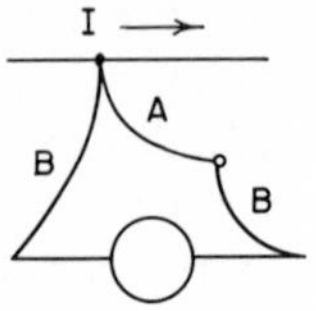

FIG. 33.

the springs of the deflected instrument. The over-all efficiency of the system is very low, a few hundredths of a per cent under the most favorable circumstances, during the time interval when the d-c instrument is being deflected. This low efficiency is significant in two respects: (1) the power consumption of a thermal ammeter is relatively high; and (2) a sensitive d-c instrument is needed as an indicating element.

The combination of heater element and thermocouple acting as an energy converter is known as a *thermoelement*; and a thermoelement, together with a permanent-magnet, moving-coil instrument, constitutes a thermocouple ammeter, milliammeter, or voltmeter.

One of the oldest and simplest types of thermoelement is the thermal cross formed by wires of two thermoelectrically dissimilar metals (e.g. platinum and constantan) soldered or welded together at their cross-over point. This arrangement is shown in Fig. 32. The current path is 1–2–3; and heat at the junction (2), resulting from the current I, gives rise to an emf which produces a current in the closed measuring circuit 5–2–4. The magnitude of this current is indicated on the permanent-magnet, moving-coil instrument whose scale may be marked in terms of the current I in the heater circuit. By proper choice of materials in the thermal cross this arrangement is usable up to currents of 5 amp without serious frequency errors up to rather high frequencies. In such an arrangement the temperature of the hot junction of the thermocouple is dependent to an important extent on the direction of current through the heater as a result of Peltier heating or cooling at the cross-over. Therefore this arrangement cannot be used as a d-c ammeter since the emf developed by a given current would be different for the two directions of current. It is quite probable, even, that the mean of reversed d-c deflections for a given current would not coincide exactly with the deflection for an equivalent alternating current.

This objection was largely overcome in the construction first used by Fleming in 1906. In his arrangement, shown schematically in Fig. 33, there is a separate heater wire, and the thermocouple *B–A–B* has one junction held in contact with the heater. In Fleming's arrangement this junction was soldered to the heater, and in the modern version the junction is welded to the heater. The Peltier effect is thus made quite small since the current being measured does not pass through the thermocouple circuit. There is a second effect (present in both the thermoelements described above) which produces a difference in indication on direct current for the two directions of heater current. Since the contact between the thermocouple and the heater cannot be a geometrical point but must necessarily have a finite volume, the heater current flowing through the resistance of this contact volume produces an *IR* drop in voltage which reverses in direction with reversal of the heater current. Since the thermal emf in the circuit does not reverse with heater current, the total voltage in the thermocouple circuit will be different for the two directions of heater current.

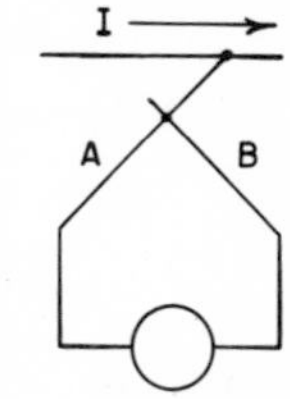

FIG. 34.

In another type of contact couple (Fig. 34) the d-c reversal effect is further reduced by welding the thermocouple wires together at a point a little removed from the heater wire. Heat is conducted to this junction by extending one of the wires (*A*) beyond the junction point and welding it to the heater wire. The *IR* drop which enters the thermocouple circuit from the contact should be negligible.

Since very early in the development of thermoelements, isolated thermocouples (with the thermocouple circuit electrically insulated from the heater) have been used to minimize the effects of capacitance currents at high frequencies, between the thermocouple circuit (including the indicating instrument) and the remainder of the circuit. In effect this insulation interposes a very small capacitance between the isolated circuits, and since it acts in series with capacitance from the instrument to ground or to other parts of the circuit, will reduce the capacitance currents which would otherwise flow through part of the heater element and produce an erroneous current indication. This is an important consideration in instruments which are used to measure small currents and in which the capacitance current might be an appreciable fraction of the total current measured.[21] In early types of isolated elements the heat transfer across the insulating bead employed to hold the hot junction in place (Fig. 35) was much less efficient than in the contact type, where the contact is welded or soldered directly to the heater. Hence, not only was the emf less for a given heater current but also the instrument response was more sluggish. However, such isolation is desirable or even necessary when small currents are to be measured with the circuit operating at a potential considerably above ground. Recently it has been possible to construct low-range thermoelements with a small insulating bead having good thermal conductivity. Such elements are now available with nearly as high sensitivity and response speed as in the contact type for currents up to about 100 ma.

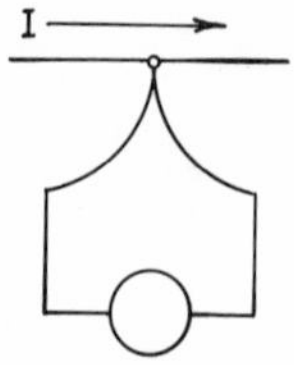

FIG. 35.

It would appear that the isolated thermocouple construction just described should entirely eliminate the d-c reversal effect found in contact elements. However, this is not generally entirely the case. Differences in thermal emf for reversed direction of heater current have been found in numerous isolated elements. These differences range from a few hundredths to a few tenths of a per cent, depending on the construction of the element. The difference will depend on the magnitudes of the Peltier and Thomson effects for the particular combination of metals used, and on the displacement of the point of attachment from the "thermal" midpoint of the heater.

VACUUM THERMOELEMENTS. For very low-range thermocouple instruments, the power absorption is necessarily low. In some cases as little as 2 mw is used in the heater element. In order to attain the temperature rise (80° to 100°C) needed to develop the required output in the thermocouple (perhaps 5 mv on open circuit) on this small heat input, the element is enclosed in an evacuated glass bulb.[22] The gas pressure is reduced in the bulb until there is no appreciable cooling of the heater by

[21] If contact-type thermoelements are used to measure small currents at high frequencies, it is important to arrange the circuit so that the instrument is at ground potential if possible.

[22] Goodwin has shown that, under the conditions existing in a vacuum thermoelement, the temperature at the attached thermocouple junction is given approximately by the formula

$$t_c = \frac{1}{1 + (R/r_c)} \times \frac{V^2}{8\kappa\rho}$$

where R is the resistance of the heater, r_c the resistance of the thermocouple, V the voltage drop across the heater, κ its thermal conductivity, and ρ its electrical resistivity: *Trans. AIEE*, **55**, 23 (1936).

convection air currents. This requires that the pressure be reduced below 0.1 μ (0.0001 mm Hg). At the operating temperature heat losses by radiation are small, and most of the heat is dissipated by conduction through the thermocouple and through the heater to the terminals. A series of vacuum thermoelements made by Weston has approximately the characteristics given in Table 3. Various materials are used in the heaters of these thermoelements, carbon filaments for the lowest ranges and metallic alloys for the higher ranges. The heater-wire diameters range from 0.4 mil to 3.6 mils.

TABLE* 3

Range-Heater Current for Open-Circuit Thermocouple emf of 5 mv, ma ± 20%	Heater Resistance at Rated Current, ohms ± 10%	Thermo-couple Resistance, ohms ± 10%	Safe Heater Current, ma	Minimum Burnout Current, ma	Power at Rated Current, mw
1.5	1365	6	3.2	20	3.1
2.0	750	6	5.0	30	3.0
5.0	82	6	10.0	20	2.0
7.5	36.2	6	16	35	2.0
10	23.4	6	25	50	2.3
15	13.0	6	40	85	2.9
20	8.4	6	50	120	3.4
25	7.0	6	62	150	4.4
30	5.8	3	75	180	5.2
37.5	4.6	3	85	210	6.5
50	3.3	3	115	260	7.5
75	1.36	3	170	330	7.7
100	1.03	3	220	380	10.3
150	0.66	3	320	540	14.9
200	0.46	3	420	700	18.4
250	0.39	3	510	900	24.4
300	0.33	3	610	1050	30
400	0.25	3	800	1300	40
500	0.2	3	1000	1900	50

* Data in this table are used by permission of the Weston Electrical Instrument Corporation, and are taken from an article on vacuum thermoelements by Kunz, *Weston Engineering Notes*, **2,** No. 3, p. 4 (1947).

THERMOCOUPLE MILLIAMMETERS. In Table 3 the thermoelements are rated in terms of their open-circuit emf. This may be determined by means of a potentiometer if precise values are needed. However, it is usually more convenient to connect a low-resistance millivoltmeter (e.g.

10 ohms, 2 mv, 200 μa at full scale) across the terminals of the thermocouple and to mark its scale in terms of heater current. The thermocouple may be considered as a d-c generator of emf E having an internal resistance r_c.[23] If an instrument of resistance r_m is connected in the thermocouple circuit the current will be

$$I = \frac{E}{r_c + r_m}$$

Energy will be dissipated in the instrument at the rate $I^2 r_m$ watts, which will be a maximum if $r_m = r_c$; i.e. if the instrument resistance equals the thermocouple resistance. Thus the *maximum* power available for the instrument is $E^2/4r_c$. Since a considerable mismatch may exist without causing a serious diminution of the power available,[24] this criterion is followed only approximately. However, it may be said that at best only about half of the open-circuit emf of a thermocouple can be made available for producing deflection in a d-c millivoltmeter connected to its terminals. The thermoelement is often mounted inside the case of the d-c instrument used with it, and may be wrapped in cotton batting, both to reduce the effect of sudden changes of ambient temperature and to protect the element against damage from mechanical shock.

Vacuum-thermocouple milliammeters are suitable for current measurements at frequencies up to 100 megacycles or more, depending on the size of the heater wire and its resistivity. For voltage measurements, difficulties are very great in constructing a satisfactory series resistor for high-frequency use. Voltmeters having resistors made of the usual type of wire-wound coils are limited in application to frequencies below 15 kc. Special multiplier construction for low-voltage ranges permits voltage measurements up to frequencies of 100 kc or more.[25]

TEMPERATURE EFFECT. This is comparatively large in thermocouple instruments. For most instruments of this type it ranges between 0.1 and 0.3%/°C. Several factors contribute to this effect. (1) The dependence on temperature of the resistance of the thermocouple circuit, largely that of the d-c millivoltmeter. (The temperature influences on springs and magnet are small in comparison with this effect.) The effect

[23] To be exact, this resistance r_c must include not only the ohmic resistance of the couple but also an equivalent resistance introduced by the Peltier effect of the current in the thermocouple circuit.

[24] H. B. Brooks, *NBS J. Research*, **4**, 297 (1930).

[25] This involves a symmetrical arrangement of shielded resistors such that the resistances and capacitances form a balanced four-arm impedance bridge. As a result no capacitance current flows in the thermoelement, and the voltmeter reading is practically independent of frequency, up to rather high frequencies. See Wilson, *Trans. AIEE*, **43**, 220 (1924); and Goodwin, *Trans. AIEE*, **46**, 479 (1927).

of the resistance change may be compensated in precision-grade instruments by a suitable network, but at the expense of an increased power consumption in the instrument. Since the power available from the thermocouple is very small this compensation is usually impractical. (2) Ambient temperature changes affect the thermocouple itself by changing the temperature base above which the hot junction operates. We have seen already that the emf-temperature relation of thermocouples is quadratic. It will be apparent from an inspection of Fig. 36 that for a given temperature difference $(T_2 - T_1)$ between hot and cold junctions the emf developed in the thermocouple will decrease as the cold-junction temperature is increased $(E' < E)$. Thus, for a given heater current, the deflection decreases as the instrument temperature is increased. (3) If the heater itself has a temperature coefficient of resistance, the I^2R power which must be dissipated for a given current will depend on the ambient temperature, and the temperature rise of the hot junction will consequently be a function of instrument temperature. The instrument correction arising from this cause may be additive or subtractive, depending on the temperature coefficient of resistance of the heater.

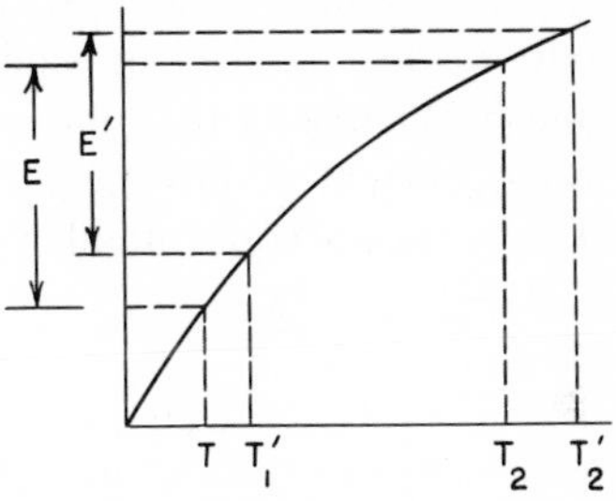

FIG. 36.

BRIDGE-TYPE THERMOELEMENTS. An arrangement of thermocouples in a bridge circuit, described by Schering in 1909, is shown in Fig. 37. This arrangement is more sensitive than the simple thermoelement since two thermocouples act in series to send current through the d-c instrument,

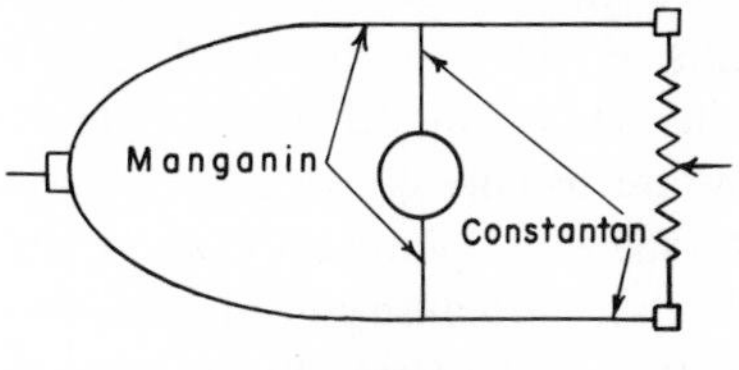

FIG. 37.

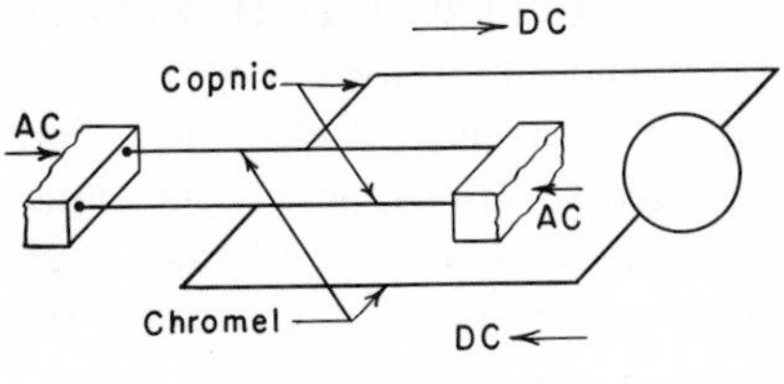

FIG. 38.

while at the same time a lower circuit resistance is secured. The slider is adjusted with a very low direct current until the bridge is balanced. This same principle is now utilized in some low-range thermocouple instruments to provide adequate operating torque without resorting to vacuum elements. The bridge arrangement used by the General Electric Company is shown in Fig. 38. Here the locations of the junctions on the heater wires are such that the resistances from the junction to either terminal block are substantially equal. An elaboration of Schering's thermocouple bridge, shown in Fig. 39, is used by several manufacturers. In this arrangement there are a number of thermocouples in series in the parallel heater elements. The cold junctions of the thermocouples are soldered or welded to heavy metal studs which are electrically insulated from the supporting base plate. At the hot junctions the thermocouple wires are butt-welded. Since the studs have considerably greater cooling surface and heat capacity than the small butt-welded joints their temperature rise when current is flowing is much less than that of the hot junctions. There are an equal number of thermocouples in each bridge arm, and they are so connected that their thermal emf's add to send current through the d-c instrument, as shown in Fig. 39. In a bridge of this type, constructed by the General Electric Company, eight couples produce an open-circuit thermal emf of 25 mv with a heater current of 120 ma. Similar bridge arrangements are used by Weston in a series of thermocouple instruments ranging from 0.1 to 0.75 amp. On direct current these instruments will have different indications for the two directions of current flow as a result of the Peltier effect. In addition any difference in the resistance of the bridge arms will result in different indications for the same value of direct current in the two directions through the bridge.

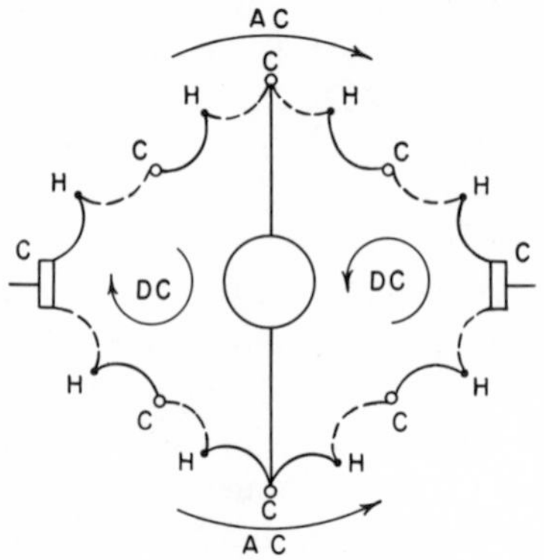

FIG. 39.

HIGHER-CURRENT INSTRUMENTS. Above the range of vacuum- and bridge-type thermoelements, short lengths of wire or thin-walled tubes in air serve as heater elements. Since the heater and thermocouple are exposed to atmospheric conditions they are usually constructed of non-corrosive alloys. Noble-metal alloys, such as platinum-iridium and gold-palladium, may be used for this purpose. Because considerable heat must be dissipated from the heater, mostly by conduction to the terminal blocks, a simple element such as that shown in Fig. 33 would have a source of error as a result of the instrument being heated by the heater element. As heat is conducted from the heater element to the terminal blocks, their temperature will rise. This will cause a further temperature rise in the heater element since, for a constant power input (I^2R), the temperature gradient from the midpoint of the heater to the terminal block will tend to remain constant. If the temperature does not rise at the same rate at the hot and cold junctions of the thermocouple, the emf developed, and hence the instrument indication, will drift with time. In an uncompensated instrument the equilibrium temperature of the hot junction will rise faster than that of the cold junction so that a greater emf will be developed. This will result in a gradual increase with time of the deflection for a constant current. Also, when the heater current is reduced to zero, heat stored in the terminal blocks flows back into the heater, keeping its temperature above its surroundings and producing an emf in the couple until the terminals have cooled to the temperature of the cold junction. This effect will be greater in higher-current ranges where the heat input is greater.

A method of cold-junction compensation, developed by Goodwin in 1917,[26] is shown in Fig. 40. The hot junction of the thermocouple is

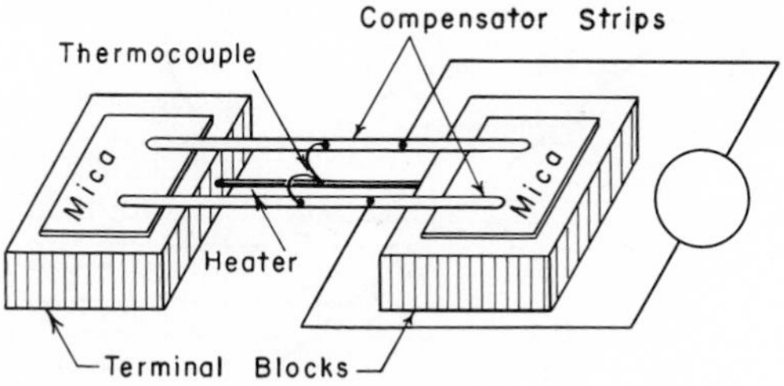

FIG. 40.

welded or hard-soldered to the midpoint of the heater in the usual manner. The cold junctions are attached to metal strips which are carried over the terminal blocks. These compensating strips are electrically insulated from the terminal blocks by mica sheets which are thin enough that heat is readily conducted to them from the terminal blocks. Then to a first approximation the compensating strips will tend to be in temperature equilibrium with the terminal blocks, and the temperature of the cold junctions will also have the same value since they are attached to the compensation strips. Thus the temperature difference between hot and cold junctions will remain constant even though the terminal blocks rise in temperature above their surroundings. Actually, the situation is more complex than is indicated by the explanation above. The compensation strips must be so proportioned that they are influenced by variations in ambient temperature and by inequalities of temperature in the terminal blocks to the same extent and at the same rate as the heater itself, in order that the temperature difference between hot and cold junctions be independent of all variables except heater current. This method of compensating cold junctions is used in thermoelements in air, designed to measure currents of 0.5 amp or more. At high values of

[26] Goodwin, *Electrical Engineering*, **55**, 23 (1936).

current, radiating fins are sometimes added to the terminal blocks to reduce their temperature rise above the ambient. For current ratings above 60 amp parallel heater elements may be used, the hot junction being attached to one of them.

General Considerations. Thermocouple instruments are primarily designed for current measurements at high frequencies. In this application they are superior to any other type of ammeter both in accuracy and in frequency range. Although they are never specifically designed

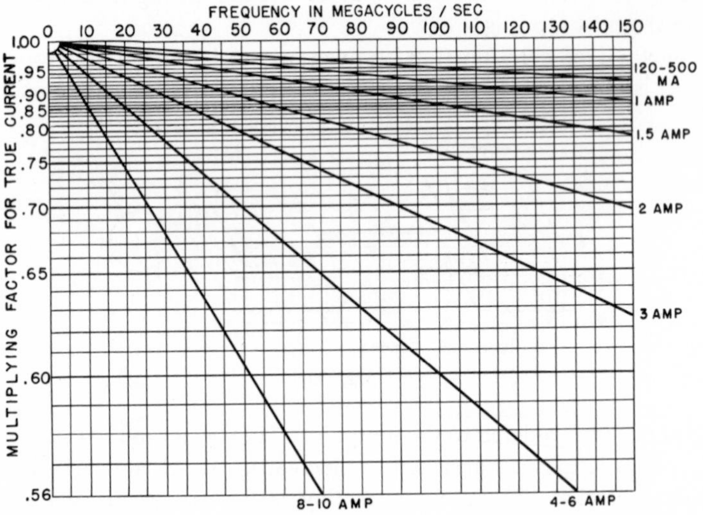

FIG. 41.

for d-c measurements, thermoelements can be selected which have a very small d-c reversal effect (a few hundredths of a per cent). Such elements may be used in transfer instruments for the calibration of other a-c instruments, provided the mean of reversed readings is employed in the d-c calibration of the thermoelement. Thermocouple transfer instruments for example, may serve to calibrate moving-iron instruments at frequencies different from their design values. In transfer work the thermoelement may be used with a deflecting instrument (millivoltmeter) or, for greater precision, with a potentiometer.

If thermocouple ammeters are arranged in such a way that the effect of capacitance currents is negligible, the upper limit of frequency at which they can be used without frequency correction is dependent on the heater dimensions and resistivity (i.e. on the frequency at which the skin effect becomes important). This will be very different for instruments of different current ranges. Figure 41 shows how the frequency error of thermocouple ammeters may be expected to vary with range for a particular type of Weston ammeter having solid heater wires. When thin-walled tubes were substituted for the solid wires, their performance for all ranges was found to be reasonably well represented by the upper curve (for milliammeters) on the graph.[27] In the construction of ammeters for high-frequency use, it is customary to connect all the internal metal parts to one live terminal of the instrument and to mark this terminal for connection to the ground side of the circuit.

Thermocouple instruments are made in the same accuracy classes as other types of a-c instruments, i.e. $\frac{1}{2}$ to $\frac{3}{4}\%$ for portable and 2% for panel-type instruments. For precise measurements the instrument temperature coefficient must be determined and used to correct the instrument indications, since the temperature coefficient is higher than in other high-grade portable ammeters. The overload capacity of thermocouple instruments is not so great as that of some other types of a-c instruments but is usually 150% or more of the full-scale current.

Electrostatic Instruments

In this type of instrument the deflecting torque results from the action of an electric field on charged conductors. Electrostatic instruments may be classified into three types: repulsion, symmetrical, and attraction. Such instruments are useful at very low voltages in cases where no appreciable current may be drawn from the circuit. Electrostatic voltmeters can also be designed for use at extremely high voltages. In fact, the total range of voltage covered, with small errors in measurement, is greater than for any other class of deflecting instruments. On direct voltage, the operating current, after the initial charging current, is only the small leakage current required by the insulation resistance of the instrument, which is generally very high. On alternating voltage the current is determined by the capacitance of the instrument and the frequency, the operating current increasing with frequency as the reactance ($X = 1/2\pi fC$) decreases. A 15,000-volt instrument having a capacitance of 20 $\mu\mu$f requires 120 μa for full-scale deflection at a frequency of 60 cycles. It is possible with fairly simple arrangements to extend the range of voltage measured to values in excess of 200 kv with negligibly small current and power requirements.

Repulsion Instruments. Among repulsion types of instruments the simplest is the gold-leaf electroscope. This is also one of the oldest

[27] This graph, reproduced by permission of the Weston Electrical Instrument Corporation, was taken from a paper on thermocouple ammeters for ultra-high frequencies: Miller, *Proc. IRE*, **24,** 1567 (1936). See also Miller, *Weston Engineering Notes*, **1,** No. 2, p. 7 (1946).

voltage-measuring devices. The charge taken by an electroscope is a function of the voltage and capacitance and is measured by the separation of the leaves. Hence the leaf separation (θ of Fig. 42) could be used as a measure of the voltage impressed between the case and the insulated electrode. Although the electroscope can be calibrated to read voltage this is rarely done in practice because the instrument is too delicate to make a satisfactory voltmeter.

A voltmeter which uses the same operating principle is the Braun type shown in Fig. 43. A very light aluminum needle is pivoted to turn about a horizontal axis. The needle support is brought through a hard-rubber, amber, or polystyrene insulating bushing in the metal case of the instrument. The support rod also carries a graduated scale which is formed

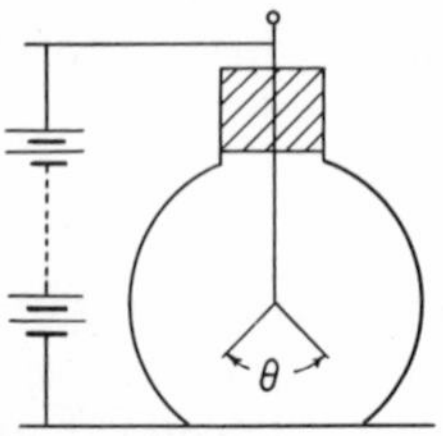

FIG. 42.

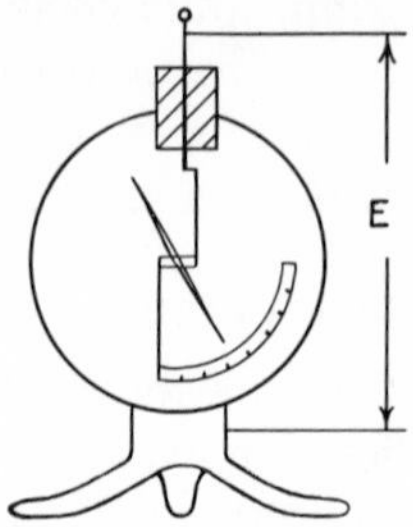

FIG. 43.

into the arc of a circle. Voltage is applied between the insulated rod and the metal case. The needle is repelled by charges on the scale support rod since the charges on it are always of the same sign as those on the needle (just as with the electroscope leaves); the equilibrium position which the needle takes up under the action of the deflecting torque and that produced by gravity is a measure of the impressed voltage. The needle also serves as a scale pointer. Such a system is not capable of high precision and is rather sensitive to level since a gravity control is used. However, the capacitance is quite small (a few micromicrofarads), and the instrument is both rugged and inexpensive. Braun-type voltmeters find some use as portable laboratory instruments for the rough measurement of voltage between a few hundred and a few thousand volts. This design is not well suited for operation at higher voltages (above 20 kv) because the insulation problem becomes more difficult and expensive and because indications may be affected by the formation of corona.

Symmetrical Instruments. Two types of symmetrical instruments, combining the attraction and repulsion principle in their operation, have found considerable use in low-voltage measurements where high sensitivity is desired. Instruments of this type are called "electrometers" rather than voltmeters.

THE STRING ELECTROMETER. In this instrument a very fine quartz fiber is stretched under tension between two metal plates as shown in Fig. 44. The fiber is made conducting by a thin metallic coating, usually of gold or platinum. A fixed voltage difference is impressed between the plates, and the voltage to be measured is impressed between the fiber and the midpoint of the plate voltage. The fiber is attracted toward the plate having charges of the opposite sign and repelled from the plate whose charges are of the same sign as that of the fiber. Fiber motion may be observed in a microscope having a scale in its eyepiece. Sensitivity is controlled by tension on the fiber and by the field between the plates. The deflection is usually not linear with voltage, and the instrument must be calibrated for each set of operating conditions. The capacitance of such an instrument is very small. One instrument of this type, made by Cambridge & Paul, has a capacitance of about 2 $\mu\mu$f and a maximum sensitivity of 100 divisions/volt with 45 volts between the plates. A string electrometer by Edelmann has sensitivities ranging from 1000 to 0.01 divisions/volt and a capacitance between 1.5 and 7 $\mu\mu$f. The insulation of such an instrument is of amber or fused quartz. The frame supporting the fiber is designed to have the same coefficient of linear expansion as the fiber itself so that the tension will be independent of temperature changes. It should be noted that, if the plates as well as the string are suitably insulated, the instrument may be operated with a fixed high potential on the string and with the unknown potential impressed between the plates. Advantages of the string electrometer are compactness, portability, insensitivity to level, and a wide range of available sensitivity. Such a device can also be used as a low-voltage, low-frequency oscillograph if a continuous record of the string position is taken.

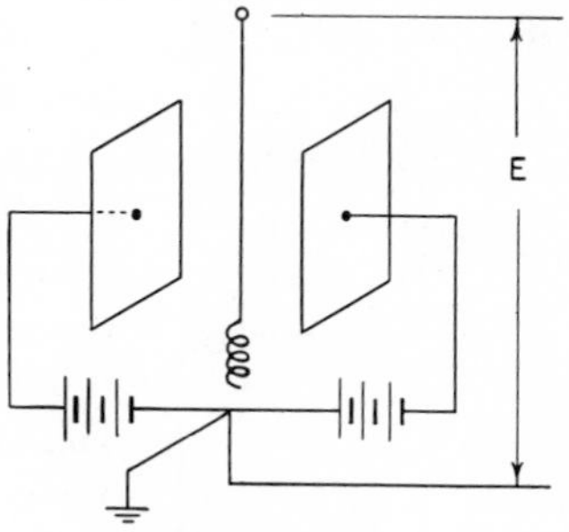

FIG. 44.

THE QUADRANT ELECTROMETER. This instrument consists of a cylindrical metal box divided into insulated quadrants with a light, metal sector disc (needle) suspended in the hollow enclosure by means of a fine gilded quartz fiber or a Wollaston wire. The quadrant and needle arrangement is shown schematically in Fig. 45. The needle carries a light mirror from which its position can be read with a lamp-and-scale arrangement similar to that used with a galvanometer. If the needle is maintained at a fixed voltage relative to the case, and a potential difference exists between the quadrant pairs, the needle is attracted to the quadrant pair having a charge opposite to it and is repelled from the quadrant pair having a like charge. As a result of these forces a torque acts, tending to rotate the needle. This is opposed by the stiffness of the suspension, and the equilibrium position is a function of the voltage differences and of the capacitances between the needle and quadrants, and of the stiffness of the suspension. The law of deflection

$$\theta = K\left[(V_1 - V_2)\left(V - \frac{V_1 + V_2}{2}\right)\right]$$

as stated by Maxwell (where V_1, V_2, and V are the potentials of the two quadrant pairs and of the needle respectively) is based on the assumption that the capacitance between the needle and case does not change with needle position ($dC_A/d\theta = 0$), and that the capacitance of one quadrant pair to the needle increases with angle at the same rate that the capacitance between the other quadrant pair and the needle decreases ($dC_B/d\theta = -\, dC_C/d\theta$). This assumes a mechanically symmetrical arrangement. The above law of deflection is still followed rather closely in cases where the departures from symmetry are small. The Dolezalek quadrant electrometer is of symmetrical construction and has a capacitance of less than 100 $\mu\mu$f and a limiting sensitivity of about 2000 mm/volt on a scale at a meter distance. In the Compton electrometer dissymmetry is deliberately introduced between the needle and the quadrants by displacing one quadrant vertically with respect to the others and by very slightly tilting the needle from the horizontal plane. The result of this dissymmetry is to change the law of deflection to the form

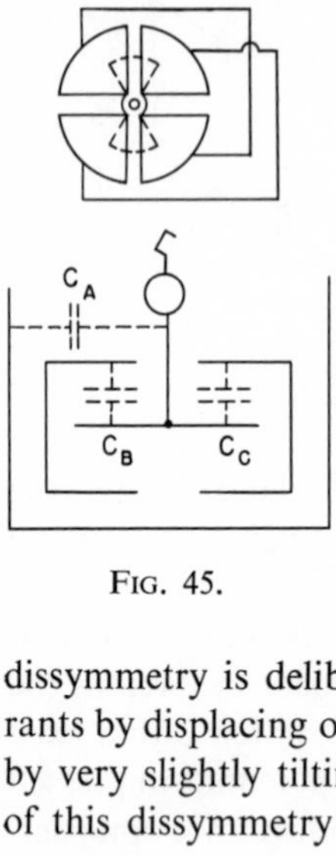

FIG. 45.

$$\theta = (V_1 - V_2)\left(\frac{KV}{U - As\delta V^2} - Bs^3\delta V^2\theta^2\right)$$

where U is the elastic constant of the suspension, s is the slope of the needle, and δ is the vertical displacement of the movable quadrant.[28] The algebraic signs of the terms containing the constants A and B depend on the relative signs of s and δ. If these parameters have the same sign, the terms in A and B are both negative and the resultant electrical control force

[28] For the development of these formulas and for a description of the technique involved in setting up and operating the quadrant electrometer the reader is referred to Laws, *Electrical Measurements*, 2nd edition, pp. 234–244.

partly neutralizes the control force from the stiffness of the suspension. Thus the sensitivity may be increased, and its limiting value is determined by the magnitudes of s and δ for which U is so nearly neutralized that the electrometer becomes unstable (i.e. the restoring torque effectively vanishes). The maximum sensitivity which has been attained with this type of instrument is of the order of 50,000 mm/volt with a capacitance of 12 to 15 $\mu\mu$f. Such an instrument is extremely sensitive to level, and great care must be exercised in setting up and operating it. Of course, the period increases as the control is diminished, becoming very long at high sensitivities. Electrometers (Hoffman) have been constructed using binants instead of quadrants and having an unsymmetrical needle position with a consequent tendency toward zero restoring torque, ending in instability. This tendency toward instability increases with increasing voltage between the binants, and at some particular voltage the system becomes completely unstable. With proper precautions regarding contact potentials and temperature effects and with operation in a partial vacuum to reduce ionization resulting from stray radiation, such a system is capable of considerably greater sensitivity than the Compton electrometer.

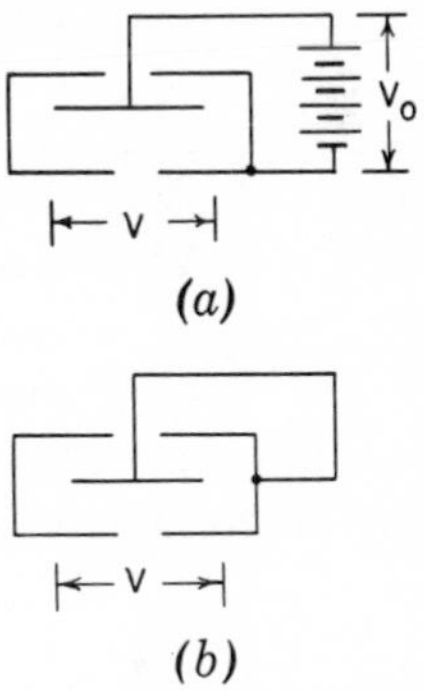

FIG. 46.

It may be noted that, if the capacitance of the measuring system is known, the rate at which voltage changes is a measure of the rate of change of electric charge, i.e. a measure of current. In the Hoffman electrometer discussed above currents of 10^{-17} amp have been measured without unusual precautions, and currents as low as 10^{-19} amp have been measured if the operating technique was sufficiently good.[29]

The Lindemann electrometer, another modification of the quadrant electrometer, is designed for portability and insensitivity to changes in level. Parallel vertical plates at a separation of 6 mm are used as quadrants, and the needle, a silvered glass fiber, is mounted on a taut quartz suspension so that it may rotate about a horizontal axis. The instrument, having a capacitance of about 1 $\mu\mu$f, is small enough to be mounted on the stage of a microscope and read by observing the motion of the end of the needle. Currents of the order of 10^{-15} amp may be observed with it.

The quadrant electrometer may be used in either of two ways. In the *heterostatic* connection, shown in Fig. 46(a), the needle is charged to a

[29] A description of the Hoffman electrometer may be found in Michels, *Advanced Electrical Measurements*, 2nd edition, pp. 73–74.

high potential V_0 and the voltage V to be measured is impressed between the quadrant pairs. The sensitivity may be controlled between wide limits by varying the needle potential, since $D \propto V_0 V$. In the *idiostatic* connection [Fig. 46(*b*)] the needle is connected to one pair of quadrants and is attracted to the opposite pair regardless of their polarity. This connection may be used to measure alternating potential differences. In this connection $D \propto V^2$.

Attraction Instruments. Portable, low-voltage electrostatic voltmeters are generally of the attraction type. The fixed and moving systems consist of flat metal sector discs or interleaved discs (Fig. 47). Since the fixed and movable discs are insulated from each other, a voltage can be impressed between them, resulting in the presence of charges of opposite sign on the two sets of plates. The force of attraction between these charges produces a torque which is opposed by a spiral spring or in some cases by the stiffness of a suspension which supports the moving system. The law of response may be seen from the following considerations. The energy stored in the capacitor formed by the fixed and movable plates is

FIG. 47.

$$W = \tfrac{1}{2}V^2C$$

where V is the potential difference impressed on the capacitance C. The torque is

$$\mathscr{T} = \frac{dW}{d\theta} = \frac{1}{2}\,V^2\frac{dC}{d\theta}$$

Since the restoring torque from the spring is proportional to angular displacement, we have

$$U\theta = \frac{1}{2}\,V^2\frac{dC}{d\theta}$$

at equilibrium. The angular deflection is proportional to V^2, and the response is *square law* so that effective values of voltage are indicated. The change of capacitance with angle ($dC/d\theta$) may be utilized to shape the scale. For example, if $dC/d\theta$ were made proportional to $1/V$, the scale would be linear with voltage. In practice, of course, this cannot be done at the low end of the scale where V is small, so that the scale is *always* compressed near zero. However, in some instruments the scale is made very nearly uniform over most of its length by suitable electrode design.

The operating torque is always small in electrostatic instruments and may be increased only within fairly narrow limits by increasing the capacitance between the fixed and moving plates. If either the number of the plates or their area is increased, the weight of the moving system will be greater, with a consequent increase in friction and period. If the capacitance is increased by decreasing the separation of the plates, a limit is reached in low-voltage instruments at the mechanical clearance needed for good operation, and at high voltages by the clearance necessary to avoid electrical breakdown or corona.

In low-voltage instruments, the capacitor consists of a number of interleaved fixed and movable plates with the minimum clearance required by mechanical considerations. In earlier instruments the moving system was suspended from a torsion filament, and damping was secured by vanes or paddles moving in an oil-filled vessel. Although suspensions are used today in some instruments which are designed for very high sensitivity, most modern instruments are pivoted in jewel bearings in order to secure greater ruggedness, portability, and insensitivity to level. Air damping is provided by light vanes moving in a sector box; or, in some instances, eddy-current damping is secured from an aluminum vane moving in the field of a permanent magnet. The torque-weight ratio is always very small in comparison with that attainable in a moving-iron or electro-dynamic instrument, and the mechanism is inherently rather delicate if the instrument has high sensitivity. A 240-volt suspension-type Kelvin electrostatic voltmeter has a moving system weighing 24 gm and a torque of 0.0023 gm-cm at a deflection of 60°, so that its torque-weight ratio is 0.0001. Its minimum capacitance is 34 $\mu\mu$f and its maximum 50 $\mu\mu$f. A line of Sensitive Research Instrument Company voltmeters has ranges from 75 volts full scale with a capacitance of 500 $\mu\mu$f to 5000 volts full scale with a capacitance of 100 $\mu\mu$f.

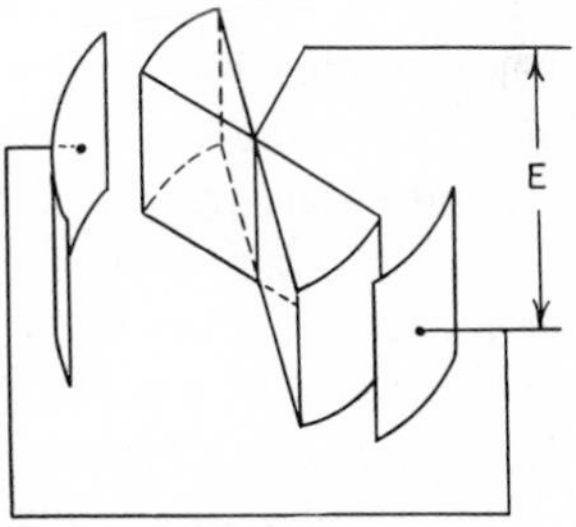

FIG. 48.

Where voltages are sufficiently high, attraction-type voltmeters may have fixed and moving elements that are sections of coaxial cylinders, as shown in Fig. 48. This construction permits the large clearances which are necessary at high voltages and is used by the General Electric Company in a series of instruments ranging from 3 to 20 kv full scale. In the 15-kv instrument the full-scale capacitance is 20 $\mu\mu$f and the full-scale current is 120 μa at 60 cycles. In order to reduce the weight and moment of inertia of the moving system, a mirror is employed with a straight-filament lamp and a translucent scale, rather than a pointer, to indicate deflection. The period of this instrument is 4 sec. Eddy-current damping is used.

The design, shown schematically in Fig. 49, is somewhat different in a series of instruments, ranging from 2 to 50 kv full scale, made by The Sensitive Research Instrument Company. The moving electrode is a section of a cylinder, and the fixed electrode is a flat disc, insulated from the metal case by means of a high-voltage bushing. A vertical scale and knife-edge pointer are used. This design permits the construction of multi-range voltmeters by a change in spacing between electrodes. The high-voltage disc electrode is arranged to slide in the high-voltage bushing, its position for each range being located by a ball-and-notch detent. Since this change in spacing alters both the capacitance and its rate of change with angle ($dC/d\theta$) a separate scale must be drawn for each voltage range.

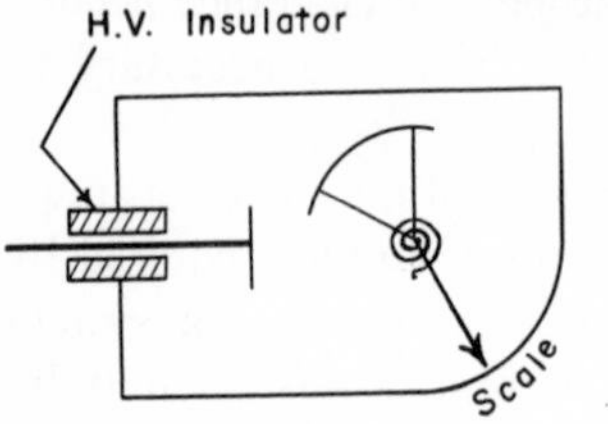

FIG. 49.

At very high voltages a third type of attraction voltmeter is sometimes employed. This is the attracted-disc voltmeter first used by Snow-Harris in the form of parallel plate electrodes. This system was modified by Lord Kelvin, who introduced a guard-ring electrode around the movable plate in order to eliminate the effect of fringing field at the edge of the disc and thus make the force between the parallel plates computable in terms of the mechanical dimensions of the capacitor. This type of construction has been carried to a high degree of refinement at the National Bureau of Standards by Brooks, Silsbee, and Defandorf, who have described such a voltmeter (as an absolute electrometer) capable of precise measurements up to voltages of 250 kv or more. Because of the large spacings required at high voltages, the guard ring of Kelvin is supplemented in this instrument by guard hoops, each connected to one section of a capacitance voltage divider, as shown in Fig. 50. By this device the voltage is graded along the guard hoops so that the field in the central volume under the attracted disc can be computed from electrode spacing and applied voltage. This voltmeter is gravity controlled, the attracted disc being suspended from one arm of a sensitive beam balance, and the attractive force is balanced by weights at the opposite end of the balance beam. Construction is such that voltages

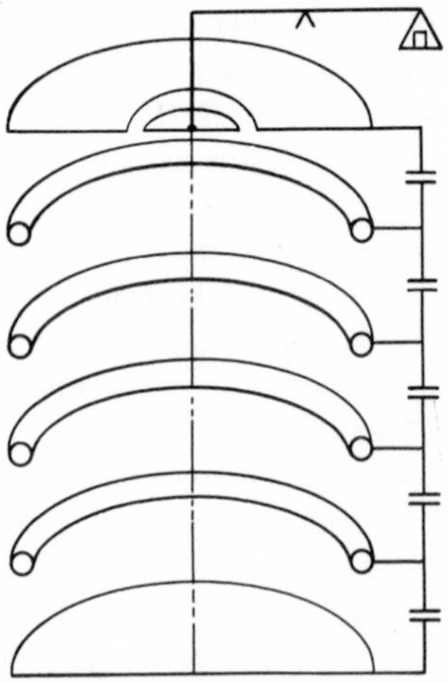
FIG. 50.

can be measured absolutely (in terms of units of length, mass, and time), by careful weighings to an accuracy of 0.02% or better. Since the operation of such an instrument is very tedious and exacting, it would be of no use in routine measurements. It is of value only in a national standardizing laboratory to provide a means of checking on other methods of high-voltage measurements.

A variation of the attracted-disc voltmeter, designed by Abraham of Everett-Edgecumbe, is useful up to 500 kv. The voltage to be measured is applied between two rounded metal bodies, each mounted on an insulating pedestal. The moving element is an attracted disc set into the face of one electrode (see Fig. 51). It is carried on a horizontal rod suspended from phosphor-bronze strips. The field between the electrodes causes the disc to travel outward from its rest position, and its motion is transmitted to the pointer by a mechanical linkage contained within the electrode. The attracted disc, moving with small clearance in a restricted space, is air damped by its piston action. The pointer position is read from a vertical scale mounted in the rear face of the electrode. Sensitivity may be varied by changing the distance between the electrodes.

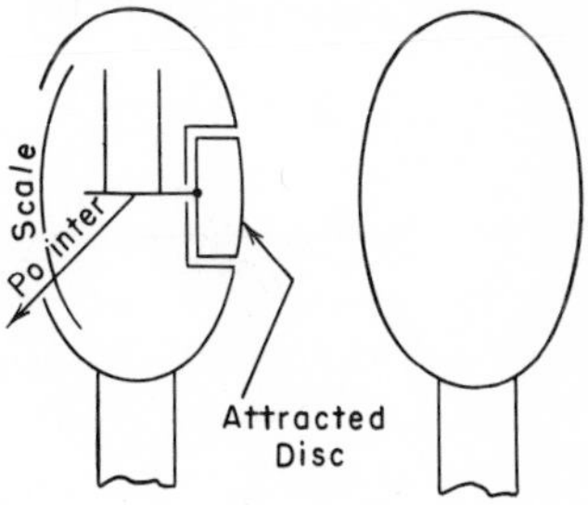

FIG. 51.

General Considerations. CORONA. Since electrostatic voltmeters will operate properly only in the complete absence of corona, sharp edges must be avoided in construction. Edges must be carefully rounded, and spacing must be sufficient to hold field gradients below the corona point in order to avoid "electric wind" reaction and air currents set up by corona discharge. This sets the lower limit to electrode spacings at high voltages. In some instances compressed gas or insulating oil is used as the dielectric material so that electrode spacings may be reduced and the available operating force increased. Both these expedients present mechanical difficulties, and neither is utilized extensively in practice. It will be apparent that the instrument must be operated at voltages well below breakdown, and that the margin of safety is considerably greater for direct voltage than for the same effective value of alternating voltage. A safety factor of at least two is necessary in order to prevent corona at crest values of voltage, or breakdown from voltage surges. In most instruments the spacing is kept as small as possible, consistent with these requirements, and the voltmeter should be protected against injury in case a spark-over occurs. Neither fuses nor parallel safety gaps can be depended on to act quickly enough to protect the instrument, but a series resistor is ordinarily employed to limit the current to a small value if breakdown occurs. This introduces no error on direct voltages or at low frequencies, but its effect on total impedance must be considered at high frequencies where the capacitive reactance is relatively low.

CAPACITANCE VOLTAGE DIVIDERS. On alternating voltages a capacitance voltage divider is often used to extend the range of an instrument. In some cases a capacitor bushing serves as a voltage divider, with an electrostatic voltmeter across the section nearest ground, to measure high voltages. This is shown schematically in Fig. 52. Voltage division is inversely proportional to the ratio of capacitances in the divider. If the values of capacitance in the divider are small, or if the divider consists of

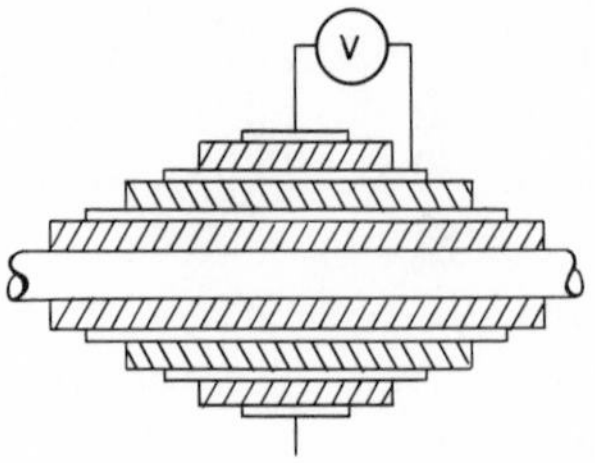

FIG. 52.

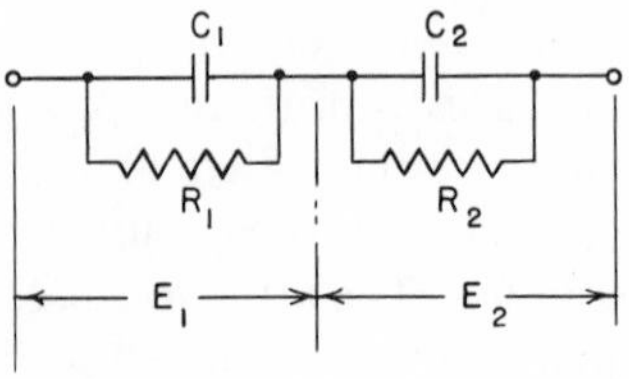

FIG. 53.

the voltmeter and a series capacitor with the capacitance of the voltmeter itself acting as one section of the divider, the change in capacitance of the voltmeter with deflection must be considered. Since the instrument capacitance always increases with deflection, the effect of the voltage divider is to compress the upper portion of the scale; i.e. the multiplying factor of the divider will be greater at full-scale deflection than at smaller deflections because of the increase in instrument capacitance. Unless the divider section in parallel with the voltmeter has a capacitance which is large compared with that of the instrument itself, a special calibration will be needed or the multiplying factor of the divider must be determined for various instrument deflections. This can, of course, be computed if the instrument capacitance is a known function of deflection.

At very low frequencies, and on direct voltage, another effect of the capacitance voltage divider must be considered. Any leakage resistance across the insulation of the capacitor may be considered as resulting from a parallel resistance. A capacitance divider *in all cases* then comprises two capacitors in series, each shunted by a high resistance, as shown in Fig. 53. The impedance of section 1 is

$$Z_1 = \frac{1}{(1/R_1) + j\omega C} = \frac{R_1}{\sqrt{1 + \omega^2 C_1{}^2 R_1{}^2}}$$

and of section 2

$$Z_2 = \frac{R_2}{\sqrt{1 + \omega^2 C_2{}^2 R_2{}^2}}$$

Then

$$\frac{E_1}{E_2} = \frac{Z_1}{Z_2} = \frac{R_1}{R_2}\sqrt{\frac{1 + \omega^2 C_2{}^2 R_2{}^2}{1 + \omega^2 C_1{}^2 R_1{}^2}}$$

On direct voltage $\omega = 0$, so that the above expression reduces to $E_1/E_2 = R_1/R_2$. In this case the voltage division is independent of the values of capacitance in the divider and is determined solely by the equivalent parallel resistance of the two sections. The general expression can be written as

$$\frac{E_1}{E_2} = \frac{C_2}{C_1}\sqrt{\frac{1 + \dfrac{1}{\omega^2 C_2{}^2 R_2{}^2}}{1 + \dfrac{1}{\omega^2 C_1{}^2 R_1{}^2}}}$$

for alternating voltages. Now

$$\frac{1}{\omega^2 C^2 R^2} = \tan^2 \delta \approx \delta^2$$

where δ is defined as the *loss* angle (the departure in phase angle of the capacitor from quadrature). Then

$$\frac{E_1}{E_2} = \frac{C_2}{C_1}\sqrt{\frac{1 + \delta_2{}^2}{1 + \delta_1{}^2}} \approx \frac{C_2}{C_1}\left(1 + \frac{\delta_2{}^2 - \delta_1{}^2}{2}\right)$$

if the capacitors are of good quality so that their losses are small. In any practical case, at power frequencies or higher, $(\delta_2{}^2 - \delta_1{}^2)/2 \ll 1$ and, to a close approximation, $E_1/E_2 = C_2/C_1$. On alternating voltages, then, a capacitance voltage divider will divide the voltage inversely with the capacitance of the component capacitors, but on direct voltages a capacitance divider cannot be used.

CONTACT POTENTIAL DIFFERENCE. In low-voltage instruments operated on direct voltage another effect must be considered. Whenever two different metals are in contact a difference of potential appears. The magnitude of this contact potential differs with different metals and depends on their surface condition. It is generally of the order of a volt or less but will produce a difference in the indications of an electrostatic voltmeter on reversed direct current, since it will add on one polarity of the external applied voltage and subtract on the other polarity. Metal combinations giving rise to substantial values of contact emf are generally avoided in the construction of electrostatic voltmeters. However, if accurate measurements are to be made with an instrument, it should be tested by taking reversed readings with a constant applied voltage. The average of such reversed readings will, of course, represent the effect of the external voltage only. This effect need not be considered in high-voltage instruments, where its magnitude is too small to constitute an appreciable percentage of the measured value of voltage.

SUMMARY. The principal advantages of the electrostatic voltmeter are its negligible current consumption, its practical independence of frequency and wave-form influences, and its ready adaptability to high-voltage applications. Its disadvantages are its low operating torque, unfavorable torque/weight ratio, and consequent lack of ruggedness. A further disadvantage, sometimes present as a result of faulty design, is the possibility of differences between d-c and a-c calibrations. At low voltages the chief contributing cause of such a difference is the presence of contact potentials. At higher voltages such a difference may result from inadequate spacing or sharp-edged electrodes. The presence of corona at high voltages introduces a torque as a result of "electric wind" and may in addition cause unsteadiness in the deflection. This effect would appear at a lower voltage (rms) on alternating current than on direct current, since the corona would first appear at the peaks of alternating voltage waves. If the instrument is unshielded, if the shields are inadequately bonded, or if insulating material is present in a strong electric field, the accumulation of charges on isolated parts of the instrument may affect the field distribution and alter the instrument calibration. Such an effect might well be different on alternating current and on direct current and might even result in a drift in the instrument indication with time at constant voltage.

Since electrostatic voltmeters are independent of frequency and indeed, if suitably constructed and operated, have no differences in indication on alternating and direct current, they can serve as transfer instruments. In fact the National Physical Laboratory of Great Britain employs electrostatic instruments as their basic transfer standards in the same way that the National Bureau of Standards uses electrodynamic instruments.

Electronic Instruments

Almost all vacuum-tube voltmeters make use of the rectifying properties of a thermionic vacuum tube and are thereby able to utilize a sensitive permanent-magnet, moving-coil microammeter as an indicating element. The two-element tube (diode) was employed first in this application in 1895 and is still popular as the sensing element of vacuum-tube voltmeters, since for many types of measurement it has certain advantages. In other cases the grid-plate characteristic of a triode (or of a more complex tube used as a triode) is utilized. In addition, the amplifying properties of vacuum-tube circuits are utilized in all except the simplest vacuum-tube voltmeters, since, by this device, the power required for operating the deflecting element can be supplied from an auxiliary source. Thus, while the circuit whose voltage is being measured controls the sensing element of the voltmeter, there is no appreciable power drain on it. This feature of vacuum-tube voltmeters is indispensable for measurements in many high-impedance circuits such as are encountered in communication equipment. Another important feature of vacuum-tube voltmeters is that with relatively simple circuits their response can be made practically independent of frequency within extremely wide limits. Some voltmeters permit the measurement of voltage from direct current to frequencies in excess of 100 megacycles. The operating principles of vacuum-tube voltmeters, together with some of the features common to many of them, will be discussed below.

Diode Voltmeters. AVERAGE INDICATION. The simplest diode voltmeter can be considered a rectifier instrument in which *average* values of

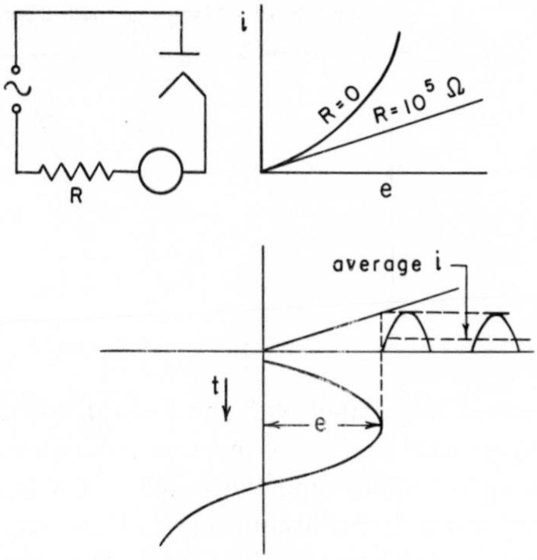

FIG. 54.

voltage are indicated. A diode, a resistor, and a d-c microammeter are connected in series across the unknown as shown in Fig. 54. A high resistance R is desirable both to limit the current and to make constant the proportionality factor between applied voltage and instrument current. If the series resistance is sufficiently high that the resistance of the tube is negligible in comparison, the voltage scale of the deflecting instrument will be practically uniform and independent of variations in the tube resistance. A resistance of 10^5 ohms or more is used for this purpose. For a sine-wave input voltage, the average current which flows during the positive half-cycle is the quotient of the average voltage during the half-cycle divided by the resistance, as in any rectifier voltmeter. Since no current flows during the negative half-cycle, the average current through the deflecting element is $I_{ave} = E_{rms}/(2 \times 1.11R)$. If the scale of such an instrument is marked in terms of rms volts, then, for any alternating voltage other than sinusoidal, its readings must be corrected for the departure of the form factor from 1.11. On direct voltage the current is $I = E/R$, so that, for a given direct voltage, the instrument deflection will be 2.22 times as great as for an equivalent rms sinusoidal voltage.

The input impedance of the voltmeter is effectively equal to the resistance R at low frequencies, but flat frequency response is limited at the high-frequency end by the distributed capacitance of the resistor.

PEAK INDICATION. By a minor modification we can greatly improve the high-frequency characteristics of the simple diode voltmeter. If a

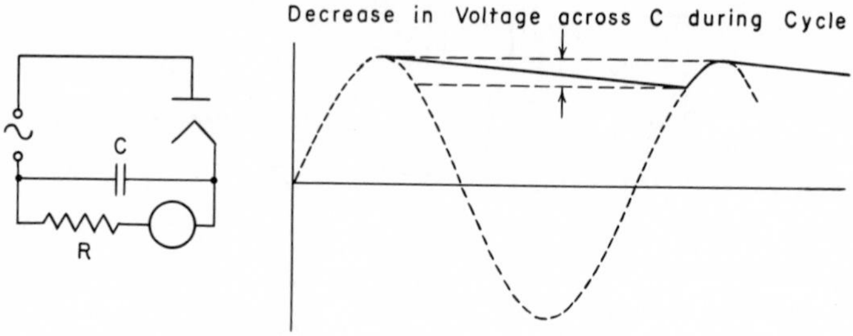

FIG. 55.

capacitor is connected in parallel with the resistor and microammeter as shown in Fig. 55, the instrument is converted from an *average* indicating to a *peak* indicating voltmeter, and the range of flat frequency response is extended to very much higher frequencies. However, a lower limit to its frequency range is set by the product CR. The time constant of this circuit must be large compared with the interval between successive peaks of the input voltage wave in order that the voltage across the capacitor will not decrease appreciably between charging impulses. Performance is usually considered satisfactory if $CR = 100/f$, as this limits the effect on instrument response to less than 1%. The input impedance depends on R and on the capacitance of the diode and leads, but not on the shunt capacitance, since it is isolated from the input circuit by the diode except for a very short interval at the positive peak of each cycle. This type of circuit, as well as the one previously described, can be used only to measure voltage in a circuit in which a complete d-c path exists through which the diode can charge the capacitor *C*.

If the circuit is rearranged so that the capacitor is in series with the two parallel branches, (*a*) and (*b*) of Fig. 56, containing the microammeter with its series resistance, and the diode respectively, a d-c circuit is provided which is independent of the voltage source that is being measured. The use of *C* as a "blocking" capacitor isolates the voltmeter from the source and makes possible the measurement of a small alternating voltage superposed on a direct voltage, since only the alternating voltage will be passed, whereas the direct voltage will be "blocked" by *C*. The behavior of this voltmeter is otherwise very similar to the one described just previously. The low-frequency-response limit is again fixed by the product *CR*. Measurement of high voltages is limited by the inverse peak voltage which the diode will withstand. If low voltages are to be measured, a tube with an indirectly heated cathode is preferred, since, in a tube which uses the heated filament as cathode, the voltage drop along the filament will produce a current and consequently a "zero" deflection of the microammeter without any voltage being impressed at the input terminals of the voltmeter. With an indirectly heated cathode, a similar but smaller effect is present. Electrons which leave the cathode with an appreciable initial velocity will reach the plate even in the absence of any applied voltage. This zero-signal current will depend on the tube design, the condition of the cathode, and the heater current, and will decrease with increasing resistance in the plate circuit. In the absence of a complete plate-cathode circuit, or if the resistance of this circuit is very high, the electrons reaching the plate will cause it to assume a potential that is slightly negative (perhaps up to a volt or so) with respect to the cathode. This may be considered as analogous to the contact difference of potential observed in low-voltage electrostatic instruments. In low-range voltmeters these effects (zero-signal current and contact potential difference) may not be negligible unless appropriate compensation is introduced into the measuring circuit.

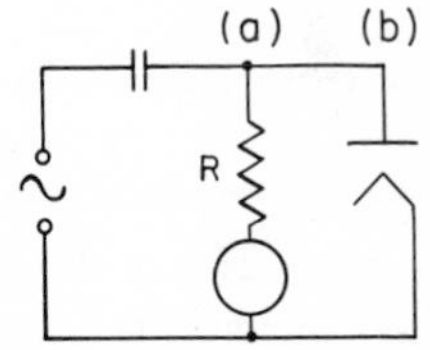

FIG. 56.

Although the voltmeter is a peak-indicating instrument, the scale of its microammeter is often marked in terms of rms volts for an assumed sinusoidal input voltage. For a scale so marked, readings will be in error for any non-sinusoidal voltage. To convert to peak voltage for any wave form, scale readings must be multiplied by 1.41. If the wave form of the measured voltage is known, its rms value may then be obtained by dividing the *peak* voltage by the ratio $E_{\mathrm{max}}/E_{\mathrm{rms}}$ for the particular wave form in question.

The potentiometer principle may be used in the diode voltmeter. This type of circuit, shown in Fig. 57, is known as "slide-back." With the input terminals shorted and the slider *a* at its extreme right position (no voltage on the voltmeter), the slider *b* is set to bring the current of the microammeter *A* to a reference value. The unknown voltage is then impressed at the input terminals, and the position of slider *a* is adjusted to bring the microammeter back to its reference indication. The reading of the voltmeter *V* then gives the peak value of the input voltage. It should be noted that the operating accuracy of a slide-back instrument will depend on the closeness to which the reference current can be set by manipulating *a*. Hence both the sensitivity and accuracy of the instrument are improved if the reference current is small and if a low-range microammeter is used.

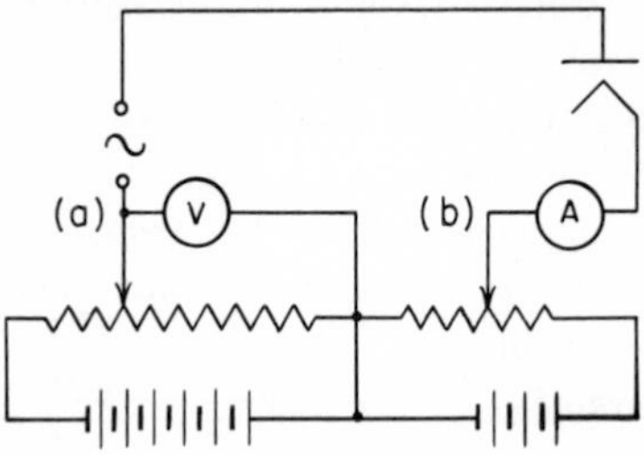

FIG. 57.

For measuring high voltages, a crest-indicating voltmeter can be made up very simply with a high-voltage diode (Kenotron) and an electrostatic voltmeter of suitable range. Since the electrostatic voltmeter is itself a capacitor, a *constant* direct voltage equal to the crest value of the impressed voltage will appear across it, and its deflection will indicate the *crest* value of this voltage just as it would for any direct voltage. An electrostatic voltmeter which incorporates a capacitance voltage divider cannot be used in this arrangement (see pp. 452–453), although a capacitance divider may be employed on the source side of the Kenotron, as indicated by the dashed lines of Fig. 58, to extend the voltage range of the measuring circuit. In the absence of a d-c return circuit this arrangement will indicate the *maximum* value attained by the crest voltage, and must be discharged before a lower voltage can be measured.

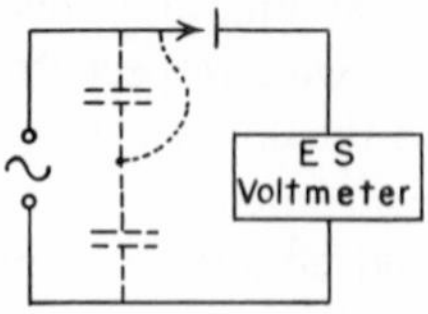

FIG. 58.

Triode Voltmeters. The grid-voltage, plate-current characteristic of a triode tube (or of a multi-element tube operating as a triode) may be used in voltage-measurement applications. This has an advantage over the simple diode voltmeter described above in that the power required for operating the indicating instrument may be drawn from an auxiliary source with the voltage under measurement serving to control the operation of the tube. In the basic circuit of the triode voltmeter, shown in Fig. 59, three types of response are possible, depending on the grid bias.

FULL-WAVE RECTIFICATION. The negative grid bias is considerably less than the cut-off value, and full-wave rectification takes place. If the grid-voltage, plate-current characteristic of the tube is assumed to be parabolic (i.e. is represented to a sufficient approximation by the first two terms of a power series: $i_p = a_1 e + a_2 e^2$), then the increase in average plate current

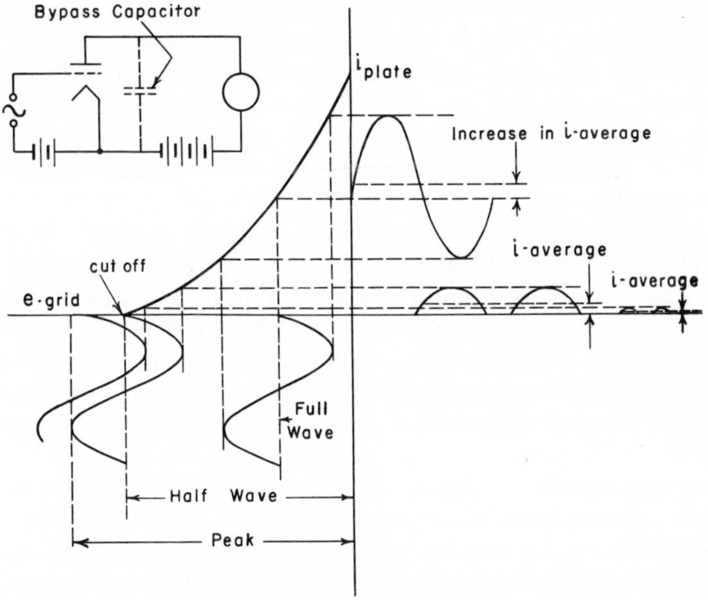

FIG. 59.

for a particular input voltage is proportional to the square of the impressed voltage,[30] and the instrument may be said to have a *square-law* response.

[30] For the bias voltage e_0 only, we have $i_0 = a_1 e_0 + a_2 e_0^2$. Let the impressed voltage be $e = e_0 + E \sin \omega t$. Then for this voltage

$$i_p = a_1(e_0 + E \sin \omega t) + a_2(e_0 + E \sin \omega t)^2$$

The average plate current for this impressed voltage is

$$I_{\text{ave}} = \frac{1}{T}\int_0^T i_p \, dt = \frac{a_1}{T}\int_0^T (e_0 + E \sin \omega t)\, dt + \frac{a_2}{T}\int_0^T (e_0 + E \sin \omega t)^2 \, dt$$

$$= a_1 e_0 - a_1 E \cos \omega t \Big|_0^{2\pi} + a_2 e_0^2 - 2a_2 e_0 E \cos \omega t \Big|_0^{2\pi} + \frac{a_2 E^2}{2}$$

$$- \frac{a_2}{4} E^2 \sin 2\omega t \Big|_0^{2\pi} = a_1 e_0 + a_2 e_0^2 + \frac{a_2 E^2}{2}$$

The scale may then be marked in terms of rms values of the external applied voltage. For a voltmeter operating with a low grid bias such that full-wave rectification occurs, there is *no wave-form error*, provided the impressed voltage that is to be measured is limited to values within which the grid-plate characteristic of the vacuum tube is parabolic.

HALF-WAVE RECTIFICATION. This takes place if the grid is biased to its cut-off value. Here only the positive half-wave is rectified, but again the response follows a *square law* and there is no wave-form error if the half-waves of the impressed signal voltage are symmetrical (i.e. if only odd harmonics are present). It should be noted that a wave-form error in the indication will result from any asymmetry of wave form of the impressed voltage, since the negative half-wave is not represented in the output, and that changes in the indication may be expected in the presence of even harmonics, when the instrument leads are reversed. With the grid biased to cut-off, the amplification is small for low signal voltages, and the accuracy of the indication depends critically on the *exact* maintenance of the grid-bias value. Voltmeter stability and low-voltage response are both better if the grid bias is reduced to the point where full-wave rectification occurs. However, the total range of voltage measurement is less for the smaller bias value, since the grid must be kept negative at all times.

PEAK RECTIFICATION. This occurs when the grid is biased past its cut-off. In practice, a high-resistance plate circuit is used with the high bias so that the characteristic curve is nearly linear and approximately *average* values will be indicated for that portion of the positive half-cycle during which plate current flows. Consequently, large wave-form errors are to be expected if the input departs from sine-wave form. The average plate current cannot be affected by the wave shape except during that portion of the positive half-cycle during which plate current flows. However, this device (bias greater than the cut-off value) may be used to extend the voltage range of the instrument. This type of operation is also utilized in some multirange instruments.

For any of the three methods employing a triode as the sensing element of a voltmeter, the input impedance is very high since the grid always remains negative. Input impedance depends on the tube and, to some extent, on the frequency but is generally at least of the order of megohms.

The change in average current,

$$I_{\text{ave}} - i_0 = \frac{a_2 E^2}{2}$$

This relation, worked out for a sinusoidal wave, will hold for the separate components of a complex wave and hence for any complex wave that can be resolved into a series of sine terms.

The "slide-back" principle can be applied to triode voltmeter circuits. The voltmeter will operate as a peak-indicating instrument, but, with a simple triode, difficulties arise from the fact that the cut-off is not sharp enough. Better results are obtained with a screen-grid tube as shown in Fig. 60.

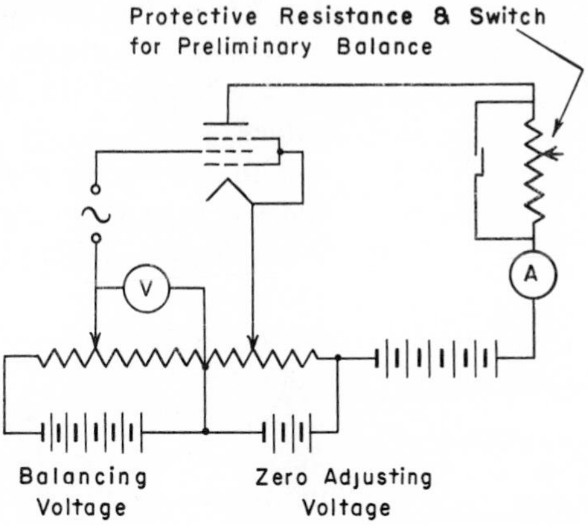

FIG. 60.

GENERAL DESIGN CONSIDERATIONS. Among the practical problems encountered in the design of a plate-detection vacuum-tube voltmeter such as those described above are: (1) to balance out the plate current for zero voltage at the input terminals so that the entire scale of the indicating instrument may be usefully employed; (2) to minimize or prevent changes in the instrument calibration resulting from variations of the supply voltage or from aging of the tube; (3) to extend the frequency range; (4) to keep the input impedance as high as possible; and (5) to design for multirange operation. The first of these objectives (elimination of zero current) is frequently accomplished by using a potentiometer circuit, as in Fig. 61(*a*), or a Wheatstone bridge circuit, either with the tube as one arm [Fig. 61(*b*)] or with two similar tubes in adjacent arms [Fig. 61(*c*)]. If a single tube is used, the zero current may be balanced by varying any one of the remaining resistances until zero current is indicated with the input terminals shorted. If two tubes are used,[31] a zero balance may be obtained by variation of *A* or *B*. Values of these resistances can be found for which small changes in the plate-supply voltage have negligible effect on the zero balance. Two similar tubes in a zero balancing arrangement have the further advantage that they respond similarly to changes in plate supply and in cathode temperature

[31] Wynn-Williams, *Phil. Mag.*, **6**, 324 (1928).

so that the zero balance is stabilized and the bridge does not readily become unbalanced from internal causes.

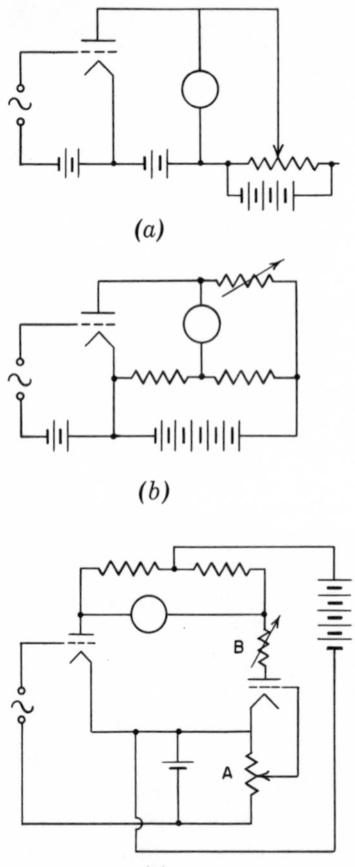

(a) (b) (c)

FIG. 61.

In single-tube circuits the effect of operating voltage on calibration can be reduced by using a common battery to supply cathode heater, grid bias, and plate voltage as indicated in Fig. 62. Adjustment of heater current to a fixed point also brings grid and plate voltages to the proper operating values.

Although the operating life of modern tubes is long, it is advisable to check the voltmeter calibration occasionally whatever circuit is used, since tube aging will generally be expected to have some effect.

Dependence of calibration on frequency, resulting from changes of impedance in the microammeter and plate-supply current, may be prevented by a by-pass capacitor, shown by dashed lines in Fig. 59, between the plate and cathode of the tube. At high frequencies the calibration may be affected by the inductance of the grid-input leads and by resonance of this inductance with the capacitance of the grid circuit. Tubes with low input capacitance should be used, and the arrangement of the conductors connected to the grid should be such as to minimize capacitance. For measurements at very high frequencies, miniature tubes are desirable. If the detector tube is mounted at the end of a shielded flexible cable so that the input voltage can be applied directly to the grid of the tube, the input capacitance is further reduced.

Sensitivity (and range) of a vacuum-tube voltmeter may be controlled by degenerative amplification. A resistor in series with the cathode of an amplifier tube (Fig. 63) will limit the plate current. The appearance of a positive voltage across the grid-cathode input terminals causes current to flow in the plate-cathode circuit. This current produces a voltage drop in the cathode resistor which (if this resistor is large) is only slightly less than the input voltage. If the resistor is sufficiently large, it effectively swamps out the tube characteristic and the plate current is then grid voltage divided by cathode resistance. Thus the voltage appearing across the cathode resistor limits the plate current and *degenerates* the amplification so that the tube is capable of handling a much greater range of grid input voltage than is otherwise possible. Multirange operation can be secured by inserting various cathode resistors in the circuit by

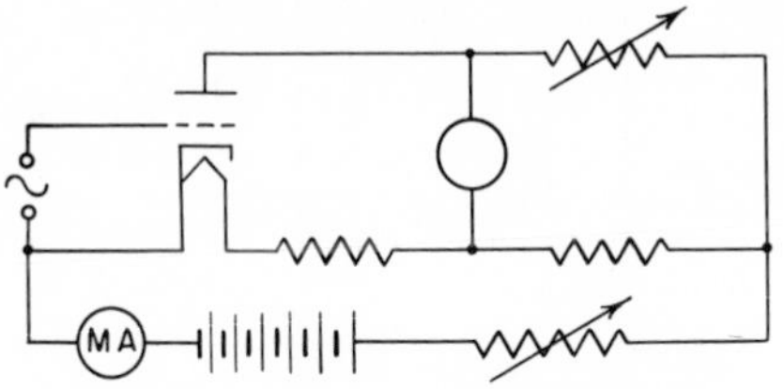

FIG. 62.

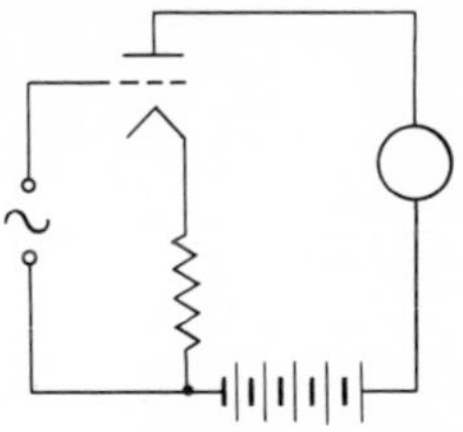

FIG. 63.

means of a selector switch. Biasing voltage must be changed, of course, whenever the value of cathode resistance is altered.

Commercial Voltmeters. Degenerative feedback is frequently used in the d-c amplifier stage of a voltmeter whose detector stage is a diode-tube circuit. The General Radio vacuum-tube voltmeters, for which simplified circuit diagrams are shown in Fig. 64, are of this type. In Fig. 64(*a*)[32] an acorn diode on a probe reduces input capacitance and frequency influence. Range selection is accomplished by changing the cathode resistor in the amplifier stage. Ranges are available in the voltmeter from 1.5 to 150 volts. Frequency influence is less than 1% at 50 megacycles, input capacitance is 6 $\mu\mu$f, and input impedance is 5 megohms at low frequencies. Over-all accuracy on a sine-wave input signal is 2%. Since this is a peak voltmeter whose scale is marked in terms of rms values for a sine-wave input, it will have a wave-form correction which is a function of the wave shape of the input signal. A regulated a-c power supply is incorporated in this instrument. Figure 64(*b*) illustrates a battery-operated voltmeter[33] which employs a sensitive two-stage, direct-coupled amplifier, using pentode tubes. Ranges are available from 0.3 to 300 volts full scale. The ranges above 10 volts use a high-resistance voltage divider and have somewhat broader accuracy limits than the low ranges because of aging drift in the resistance elements. The rectifier section is built into the instrument case rather than being extended on a

[32] This is General Radio Model 726–A voltmeter, introduced in 1937 and now obsolescent.

[33] General Radio Model 727–A. Tuttle, *GR Experimenter*, **16**, No. 12 (1942).

probe and has a higher input capacitance, 16 $\mu\mu$f. Figure 64(*c*) shows a voltmeter[34] whose amplifier consists of a twin triode tube, used in a balanced circuit. A twin diode is employed in the rectifying element

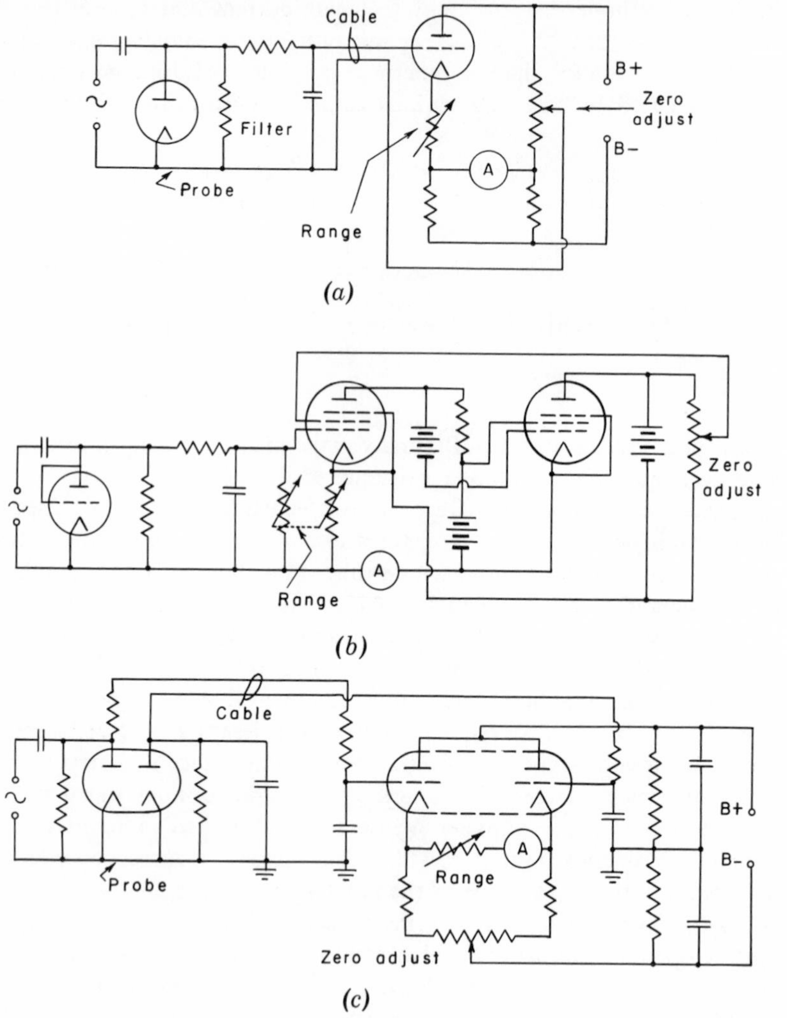

FIG. 64.

which is mounted on a probe. The inactive element of the rectifier is connected to the d-c amplifier to balance the effect of the contact potential of the active diode on the indicating microammeter. The input capacitance is 11.5 $\mu\mu$f. Regulated alternating current serves as a power supply.

[34] General Radio Model 1803–A. Woodward, *GR Experimenter*, **24**, No. 11 (1950).

It is sometimes of advantage to use a preamplifier with a vacuum-tube voltmeter and, for multirange operation, to precede the amplifier with an attenuator or voltage divider. Such an arrangement is shown in the block diagram of Fig. 65. The amplifier may be selective regarding

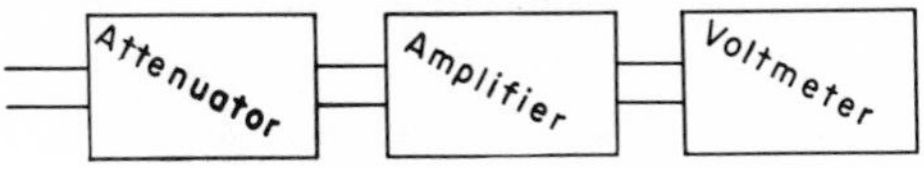

FIG. 65.

frequency if a limited range of frequencies is to be covered. Such an arrangement might be of advantage in tracing signals through a tuned circuit. If a resistance-coupled amplifier is used whose response is independent of frequency up to 10 kc, the instrument can measure voltages in the audio-frequency range. Such a voltmeter could not be used at radio-frequencies since the amplifier response falls off rapidly at high frequencies.

The Ballantine voltmeter (Model 300) is of the preamplifier type. As shown in the simplified diagram of Fig. 66, the input section is a high-impedance voltage divider. This is followed by an amplifier which is stabilized by negative feedback. Current from the final stage of the

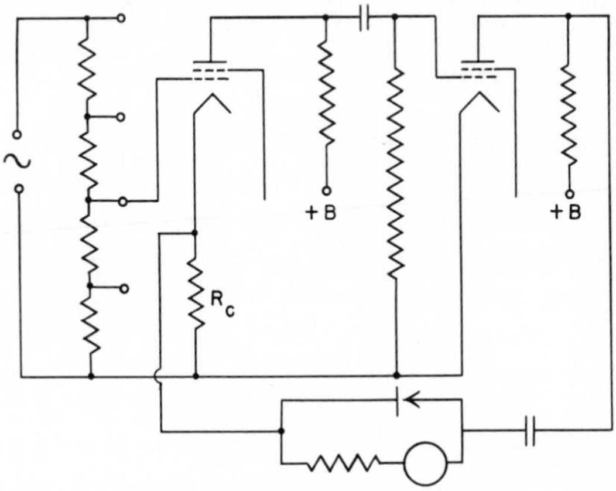

FIG. 66.

amplifier is rectified and produces deflection on the d-c instrument. The use of negative feedback reduces the over-all sensitivity and makes the output current dependent principally on the value of the resistor, R_c. This considerably reduces the effects on amplification of tubes and other circuit elements and of variations in line voltage. Since the stability, over-all sensitivity, and calibration of the voltmeter depend largely on

R_c, this resistor is constructed to have good stability as regards temperature and aging. If the resistor is properly adjusted, tube replacements and other expected changes have little effect on the voltmeter calibration. Range changing is accomplished in the input circuit. Because of the frequency range covered (10 cycles to 150 kc) the voltage divider is not made up of high-resistance units as shown, but consists actually of a resistance-capacitance network. Ranges are available by means of a selector switch from 0.01 volt to 100 volts full scale, and special pre-amplifiers and multipliers are available for range extension to lower and higher voltages. The input impedance is 0.5 megohm shunted by 20 to 30 $\mu\mu$f. The scale of the deflecting instrument is logarithmic. Instrument response is to *average* values of the input voltage as a result of the action of the cathode resistor, R_c, but the scale is marked in terms of rms values for a sine-wave input. The logarithmic scale distribution is obtained[35] by shaping the pole pieces of the d-c instrument in the manner shown in Fig. 67. The coil of the instrument moves into a weaker field as it deflects upscale, and by properly controlling the length of the air gap the sensitivity may be decreased with increasing deflection by the amount necessary to produce a logarithmic scale.

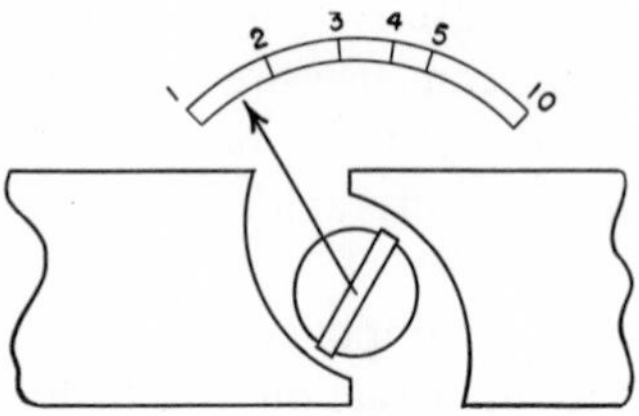

FIG. 67.

Current Measurements with Electronic Circuits

Except for the measurement of peak values, vacuum-tube circuits are not used for the measurement of currents within the range of the ammeter types previously discussed. For measuring crest values of current some form of peak-indicating vacuum-tube voltmeter may be employed to measure voltage drop across a known resistor carrying the current. However, special vacuum-tube circuits are useful in measuring very small direct currents. As we have seen previously, a sensitive method for measuring small direct currents is based on determining the rate of change of potential across a small capacitor (having negligible leakage) which is being charged by the current. This method increases in sensitivity as the value of the capacitance is reduced, and the sensitivity should be very high when the capacitor consists of the grid-cathode capacitance of a vacuum tube. Precision of results obtained by such a method depends on reducing leakage currents to a negligible value. Such leakage currents result from (1) leakage over grid supports inside the tube, across the

[35] For other methods of obtaining logarithmic response see Reich, *Theory and Applications of Electron Tubes*, 1st edition, p. 569, McGraw-Hill.

surface of the glass outside the tube, and between conductors connected to the grid and cathode; (2) electrons emitted by the grid and carried to other electrodes; (3) ionization of residual gas in the tube; and (4) (at low biasing voltages) current from electrons emitted by the cathode with sufficient velocity to reach the grid. Special tubes designed to minimize these effects are called *electrometer* tubes. One such tube (FP-54) is capable of d-c measurements down to 10^{-17} amp. To prevent leakage currents, the grid is mounted on fused quartz supports, the tube is thoroughly evacuated, and the electrode structure is such that electron emission from the grid is not present at the low operating voltages. A

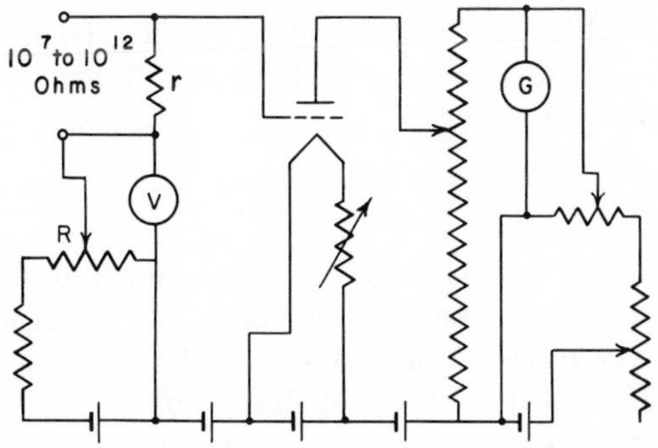

FIG. 68.

space-charge grid, between the cathode and the control grid, is operated at a positive potential to dissipate space charge in the neighborhood of the cathode and thus increase plate current for a given voltage. The amplification factor of the FP-54 is unity, and it cannot be used for voltage amplification.

Small currents may be measured by means of an electrometer tube in a circuit such as that shown in Fig. 68. If the unknown current i is allowed to flow through a high resistance r, the voltage drop ir (producing a grid potential) can be used to measure the current. A null method of measurement is indicated in the figure. With no current flowing in r, and with the slider R at its extreme right position so that no voltage is introduced into the grid circuit from this source, the galvanometer G is set to zero by means of the balancing resistors in the plate circuit. When the unknown current flows in r, the resulting ir drop may be balanced by adjusting the position of R so that an equal opposing voltage is inserted into the grid circuit and the galvanometer deflection returns to zero. This voltage may be read on V, and, since it is equal to ir, i may be computed. The characteristics of the tube are not involved, and the method is suitable for measuring currents as small as 10^{-13} amp.

For smaller currents a rate of charge method may be used. Suppose r to be an infinite resistance. The current i will then charge the capacitance C of the grid-filament system in the electrometer tube. The rate of change of grid voltage then becomes a measure of current, for $CV_g = Q$, and hence

$$\frac{dV_g}{dt} = \frac{1}{C}\frac{dQ}{dt} = \frac{i}{C}$$

The change in V_g produces a change in the galvanometer deflection and can be measured in terms of galvanometer drift. If no current is flowing in the input circuit, the rate of drift will result solely from the leakage current i_0 in the tube. If time is measured for the galvanometer deflection to change by a fixed amount with and without the unknown current (t and t_0 respectively), we have

$$\frac{t}{t_0} = \frac{i_0}{i + i_0}$$

Thus if either C or i_0 is known, the circuit can be calibrated and the current i be measured. DuBridge[36] states that currents as small as 10^{-16} amp can be measured in this way. The sensitivity of the simple electrometer-tube circuit is limited by fluctuations of battery voltages and by difficulties in exactly balancing the steady component of plate current. A number of stabilized electrometer-tube circuits have been devised in which essential features are the use of a single battery to supply all voltages, and the use of such operating voltages of the electrodes that small fluctuations tend to compensate each other. Large-capacity storage batteries are advisable for the voltage supply as they are more stable than small cells. It is also important that the circuits be carefully shielded against the effects of external fields.

[36] DuBridge, *Phys. Rev.*, **37**, 392 (1932). See also McDonald, *Physics*, **7**, 265 (1936) for a general discussion of the measurement of small currents by means of vacuum-tube circuits.

CHAPTER 11

THE MEASUREMENT OF POWER

Power may be defined as the rate at which energy is transformed or made available. The power in a circuit at any instant equals the product of the current in the circuit and the voltage across its terminals at that instant. In a d-c circuit, if the current and voltage are constant, $P = EI$, so that it is necessary only to determine the current and the voltage and to take their product in order to obtain the value of power in the circuit. Alternatively, if the circuit resistance is known, power may be computed from one of the equivalent formulas, $P = E^2/R = I^2R$.

Power in D-C Circuits

In almost all cases the power in a d-c circuit is best measured by separately measuring two of the three quantities, E, I, and R, and by computing power by the appropriate formula rather than by measuring the power directly with a wattmeter. If simultaneous voltage and current measurements are made, it must be remembered that the voltmeter and the ammeter require power for their operation and that allowance must be made for this. Either of the two connections shown in Fig. 1 may be used for the simultaneous measurement of current and voltage: (*a*) the ammeter is connected between the voltmeter and the load; or (*b*) the voltmeter is connected between the ammeter and the load. In case (*a*) the voltmeter indicates not only the voltage V_L across the load but in addition the voltage $V_a = IR_a$ across the ammeter. Power in the load is

$$P = V_L I = (E - IR_a)I = EI - I^2R_a$$

In case (*b*) the ammeter reading includes not only the load current I_L, but also the current $I_v = V_L/R_v$, taken by the voltmeter, so that power in the load is

$$P = I_L V_L = \left(I - \frac{V_L}{R_v}\right) V_L = V_L I - \frac{V_L^2}{R_v}$$

In either case the product of the instrument readings (assuming that they correctly indicate the quantity at their terminals) includes the power in the load and also the power in the instrument connected next to the load. In order to obtain the *true* load power, the power in the instrument nearest the load must be subtracted from the product of the instrument readings. If the power delivered by the source is to be measured, then the power taken by the instrument nearest the source must be added to the product of the instrument readings. Of course the power loss in the ammeter or in the voltmeter is often very small compared to the load power and may be safely neglected, but if this point is doubtful it should

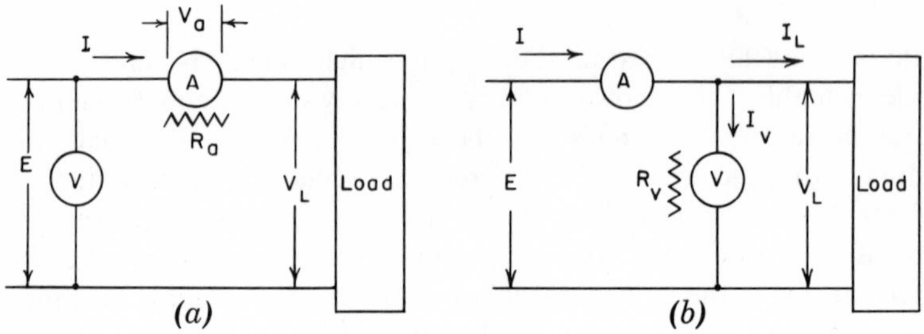

FIG. 1.

be checked from the instrument constants and the measured current or voltage. Even where instrument losses are to be ignored, it is often well to estimate roughly the expected instrument loss and to use the connection for which this loss will be a minimum. If a correction is to be made, connection (*b*) (Fig. 1) is preferable when, as is often the case, we know the resistance of the voltmeter but not of the ammeter. However, where the ammeter is known to have a 50-mv drop at full scale (or some other known value) the operating power can easily be computed from its deflection so that, in this case, connection (*a*) may be used.

Another source of error, which also applies to d-c as well as to a-c measurements, is encountered when the source of power is of high resistance or of limited output, so that the power required to operate the voltmeter and ammeter may amount to an appreciable fraction of the available power. In such cases the voltage, current, and power may be altered by the introduction of the instruments into the circuit. Under these circumstances one should, if possible, choose instruments requiring minimum operating power. It is often possible to extrapolate, from a knowledge of the circuit and of the instruments used, to obtain the value of power which existed in the circuit before the instruments were introduced.

Power in A-C Circuits

In the case of alternating currents the instantaneous power varies continuously as the current and voltage go through a cycle of values. This cyclic variation of power has a period so short that it can be followed only by special instruments such as oscillographs. However, we are not usually interested in the instantaneous power (except where transient phenomena are being studied) but in its time *average*, $P = (1/T)\int_0^T ei\,dt$, since the average power multiplied by time measures energy transfer over an interval if steady-state conditions exist. We will therefore confine our discussion to the measurement of average power, and the smallest interval that will concern us is the period of the alternating current, since the average power for 1 cycle is the same as for any integral number of cycles under steady-state conditions. If the voltage and current are both sinusoidal the average power over a cycle may be simply derived. From our definition of average power we have

$$P = \frac{1}{T}\int_0^T ei\,dt = \frac{1}{2\pi}\int_0^{2\pi} E_M \sin\theta \cdot I_M \sin(\theta - \phi)d\theta$$

where E_M and I_M are the maximum values of current and voltage, and ϕ is the phase angle by which the current lags behind the voltage. Since $\sin(\theta - \phi) = \sin\theta\cos\phi - \cos\theta\sin\phi$, we may write

$$P = \frac{E_M I_M}{2\pi}\left(\int_0^{2\pi} \sin^2\theta\cos\phi\,d\theta - \int_0^{2\pi} \sin\theta\cos\theta\sin\phi\,d\theta\right)$$

$$= \frac{E_M I_M}{2\pi}\left[\left(\frac{\theta}{2} - \frac{\sin 2\theta}{4}\right)\Big|_0^{2\pi} \cdot \cos\phi - \left(\frac{1}{2}\sin^2\theta\right)\Big|_0^{2\pi}\sin\phi\right] = \frac{E_M I_M}{2}\cos\phi$$

Now, with our assumption of sinusoidal voltage and current, their rms values are

$$E = \frac{E_M}{\sqrt{2}} \quad \text{and} \quad I = \frac{I_M}{\sqrt{2}}$$

If these values are substituted in our equation we have

$$P = EI\cos\phi$$

Under these conditions we could, if E, I, and ϕ were determined, take the indicated product as a measure of the average power.

Another case which is of considerable interest is that in which an a-c ripple is superposed on a steady d-c value. We will say that the voltage is made up of a steady d-c value E_0 with a sinusoidal ripple $E_1 \sin\theta$

superposed on it. Then $e = E_0 + E_1 \sin \theta$. Similarly $i = I_0 + I_1 \sin \theta$. From our definition the average power may be written as

$$P = \frac{1}{T}\int_0^T ei\, dt = \frac{1}{T}\int_0^T \frac{e^2}{R}\, dt$$

where R is the resistance of the circuit. Then

$$P = \frac{1}{T}\int_0^T \frac{e^2}{R}\, dt = \frac{1}{2\pi}\int_0^{2\pi} \frac{(E_0 + E_1 \sin \theta)^2\, d\theta}{R}$$

$$= \frac{1}{2\pi R}\int_0^{2\pi} (E_0^2 + 2E_0E_1 \sin \theta + E_1^2 \sin^2 \theta)\, d\theta$$

$$= \frac{1}{R}\left(E_0^2 + \frac{E_1^2}{2}\right) = \frac{E_0^2}{R}\left[1 + \frac{1}{2}\left(\frac{E_1}{E_0}\right)^2\right]$$

and by a similar development

$$P = RI_0^2\left[1 + \frac{1}{2}\left(\frac{I_1}{I_0}\right)^2\right]$$

E_0 and I_0 are the average values of voltage and current which will be indicated by d-c (average-reading) instruments. It is evident from the equations above that, if the indicated average value of voltage or current is used with the resistance to compute average power, the computed value of power will be only slightly in error for quite large values of ripple. For example, if the ripple is 10%, the power computed from resistance and average value of current or voltage will be in error by only $\frac{1}{2}$%.

If both current and voltage contain harmonics the situation is somewhat more complex. If the voltage is given by

$$e = \sqrt{2}E_1 \cos(\omega t + \alpha_1) + \sqrt{2}E_2 \cos(2\omega t + \alpha_2) + \cdots + \sqrt{2}E_r \cos(r\omega t + \alpha_r) + \cdots$$

and if the current is given by

$$i = \sqrt{2}I_1 \cos(\omega t + \beta_1) + \sqrt{2}I_2 \cos(2\omega t + \beta_2) + \cdots + \sqrt{2}I_r \cos(r\omega t + \beta_r) + \cdots$$

there will be in our expression for average power, $(1/T)\int_0^T ei\, dt$, two types of terms. If the term involves the same harmonic of current and voltage, we have as a typical term

$$\frac{1}{2\pi}\int_0^{2\pi} 2E_rI_r \cos(r\theta + \alpha_r) \cdot \cos(r\theta + \beta_r)\, d\theta$$

$$= \frac{2E_rI_r}{2\pi}\int_0^{2\pi}[\cos^2 r\theta \cos \alpha_r \cos \beta_r + \sin^2 r\theta \sin \alpha_r \sin \beta_r - \sin r\theta \cos r\theta \sin(\alpha_r + \beta_r)]\, d\theta$$

$$= \frac{2E_rI_r}{2\pi}\left[\left(\frac{1}{2}r\theta + \frac{1}{4}\sin 2r\theta\right)\Bigg|_0^{2\pi} \cos \alpha_r \cos \beta_r + \left(\frac{1}{2}r\theta - \frac{1}{4}\sin 2r\theta\right)\Bigg|_0^{2\pi} \sin \alpha_r \sin \beta_r - \frac{1}{2}\sin^2 r\theta\Bigg|_0^{2\pi} \sin(\alpha_r + \beta_r)\right]$$

$$= E_rI_r \cos(\alpha_r - \beta_r)$$

If the term involves different harmonics of current and voltage, we have as a typical term

$$\frac{1}{2\pi}\int_0^{2\pi} 2E_rI_q[\cos(r\theta + \alpha_r)\cos(q\theta + \beta_q)]\, d\theta$$

$$= \frac{2E_rI_q}{2\pi}\int_0^{2\pi}[\cos r\theta \cos q\theta \cos \alpha_r \cos \beta_q - \sin r\theta \cos q\theta \sin \alpha_r \cos \beta_q - \cos r\theta \sin q\theta \cos \alpha_r \sin \beta_q + \sin r\theta \sin q\theta \sin \alpha_r \sin \beta_q]\, d\theta$$

$$= \frac{2E_rI_q}{2\pi}\left[\left(\frac{\sin(r-q)\theta}{2(r-q)} + \frac{\sin(r+q)\theta}{2(r+q)}\right)\Bigg|_0^{2\pi} \cos \alpha_r \cos \beta_q + \left(\frac{\cos(r-q)\theta}{2(r-q)} + \frac{\cos(r+q)\theta}{2(r+q)}\right)\Bigg|_0^{2\pi} \sin(\alpha_r - \beta_q) + \left(\frac{\sin(r-q)\theta}{2(r-q)} - \frac{\sin(r+q)\theta}{2(r+q)}\right)\Bigg|_0^{2\pi} \sin \alpha_r \sin \beta_q\right] = 0$$

since each of the definite integrals is separately zero if $r \neq q$. We have then finally for the average power over a cycle

$$P = \sum_{r=1}^{\infty} E_rI_r \cos(\alpha_r - \beta_r) = \sum_{r=1}^{\infty} E_rI_r \cos(\beta_r - \alpha_r)$$

which may be designated as "active" power. By analogy with this expression convention has established a complementary quantity, designated "reactive" power, which is defined by the equation

$$Q = \sum_{r=1}^{\infty} E_rI_r \sin(\beta_r - \alpha_r)$$

The combination of active power and of reactive power (in the complex plane) by the equation $\mathbf{V} = \mathbf{P} + j\mathbf{Q}$ is designated "vector" power. The magnitude of vector power is of course given by $V = \sqrt{P^2 + Q^2}$. The term "apparent" power is used to designate the product of the effective value of current multiplied by the effective value of voltage,

$$S = EI = \sqrt{(E_1^2 + E_2^2 + \cdots)(I_1^2 + I_2^2 + \cdots)}$$

The apparent power and the magnitude of the vector power become identical only if both the current and voltage have the same wave form. The above definitions can be extended[1] to cover more complicated circuits, such as three-wire and polyphase circuits.

Although the measurement of reactive power is important in some applications and will be discussed later, its exact evaluation is not usually as significant as the precise measurement of active power, which is defined in general by the expression $P = (1/T)\int_0^T ei\,dt$. We have seen that, where both voltage and current are sinusoidal, power is given by the expression $P = EI\cos\phi$, where ϕ is the angle by which current and voltage vectors are separated. Cos ϕ is designated as *power factor* and represents the ratio of the average power to the product of the effective voltage and the effective current. In the more general case the power factor is the ratio of the active to the apparent power, and it should be noted that it does not in general represent the cosine of an actual angle between vectors except where both current and voltage are sinusoidal. It may be further noted that, if a certain harmonic is present in either the current or the voltage but not in the other, it *does not contribute* to the average (or active) power.

Single-Phase Power Measurement

Electrodynamic Wattmeter. The wattmeter is an instrument designed to measure average power, not only in the special case where $P = EI\cos\phi$, but in the more general case defined by $P = (1/T)\int_0^T ei\,dt$. Electrodynamic[2] instruments are particularly well adapted to this purpose at power frequencies and are generally used with the fixed (field) coils connected in series with the load so that they carry the load current, and with the moving coil (together with a series resistance) in parallel with the load so that its current is proportional to the load voltage (Fig. 2). The torque on the moving system is proportional to the product of the currents in the fixed and moving coils, $\mathscr{T} = K_1 i_m i_f (dM/d\theta)$, where M is the mutual inductance between the fixed and moving coils for the given relative position of these coils. Since the current in the moving coil (i_m) is

[1] For this extension see American Standard Definitions of Electrical Terms (C42—1942, Sec. 05.21).

[2] See discussion of electrodynamic instruments in Chapter 10.

proportional to the instantaneous voltage across the load, and the current in the fixed coils (i_f) is the load current, the instantaneous torque $\mathscr{T} = K_2 ei$. The period of the instrument is very long compared with the period of the alternating voltage; and, since the moving system of the instrument cannot follow in detail the rapid variations in torque, it will take up a balance position for which the average driving torque is equal to the restoring torque of the springs. In other words the deflection will represent the average torque $D = (K_2/T)\int_0^T ei\ dt$, which is identical

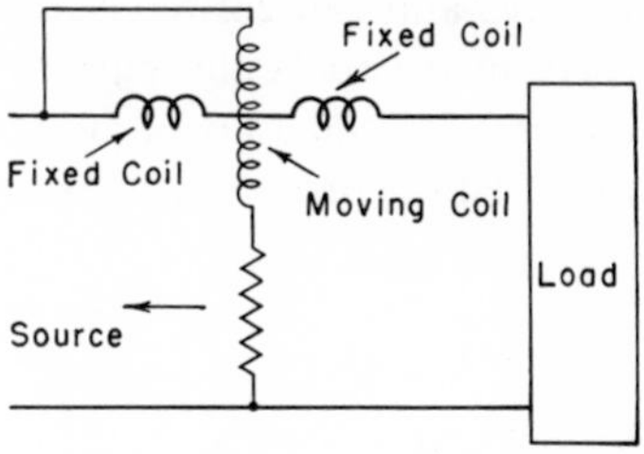

FIG. 2.

with our definition of average power, $P = (1/T)\int_0^T ei\ dt$, multiplied by an appropriate constant. The deflection of such an idealized instrument would be proportional to the average power in the load, with the proportionality factor depending on the spring constant (countertorque of the instrument springs) and the rate of change with angle of the mutual inductance between the fixed coils and the moving coil. The response follows the "first-power" law, and the scale is essentially uniform over the range in which $dM/d\theta$ is constant. Departures from a uniform scale distribution are a result of changes in the value of $dM/d\theta$ with angle. By suitable design the mutual inductance between the coils can be made to vary nearly linearly with angle over an angular range of 40 to 50° on either side of the position of zero mutual inductance as shown in Fig. 3. If the position of zero mutual inductance is at about the midscale point, the scale will be uniform over most of its length, with perhaps a noticeable concentration at each end. In some wattmeter designs the position of zero mutual inductance is displaced from the midpoint so that one end of the scale is quite uniform whereas the distribution at the other end of the scale is very noticeably non-uniform.

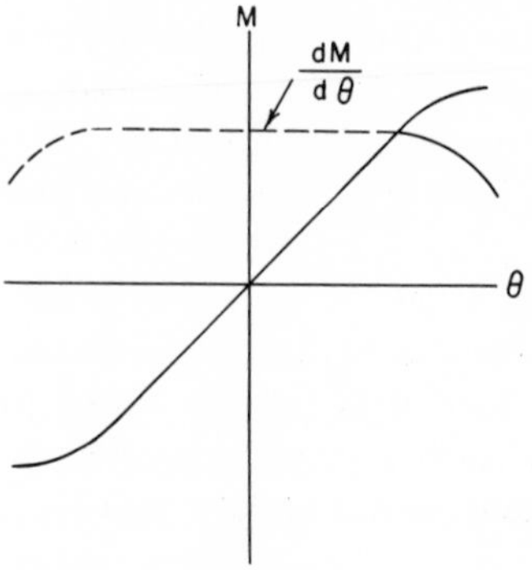

FIG. 3.

The use of the moving coil as a voltage element, and of the fixed coils as the current element of a wattmeter, is a natural consequence of design requirements. Since the current to the moving coil is normally carried by the instrument springs it is limited to values which can be carried by the springs without appreciable heating. A series resistor is used in the voltage circuit, and the current is limited to a small fraction of an ampere (usually between 10 and 50 ma). The fixed coils can be made more massive and can easily be constructed to carry considerable current. In early instruments the current coils were sometimes built to carry load currents of 100 amp or more. In such construction it was difficult to avoid eddy currents. Also the use of heavy current leads to the instrument introduced stray-field errors whose magnitude depended on the position of the leads and the current in them. Because of these and other errors, modern practice usually limits the maximum current ranges of wattmeters to about 20 amp. For power measurements involving large load currents it is usually better practice to use a wattmeter having a current range of 5 amp combined with a current transformer of suitable range. The voltage range of wattmeters is usually limited to about 300 volts (unless a separate, external multiplier is added) by the power requirements of the voltage circuit since most of the power is absorbed in the multiplier in series with the moving coil and considerable heat must be dissipated. Therefore voltage ranges are likewise extended by instrument transformers with which the 125- or 150-volt range of the wattmeter is employed. Methods of connecting instrument transformers and the corrections necessitated by their use in power measurements will be discussed in the chapter on instrument transformers. The use of instrument transformers for range extension is, of course, limited to alternating current at power frequencies. However, since it is usually better to measure d-c power by other methods, the restriction of wattmeters to comparatively low current and voltage ranges does not unduly limit their field of service.

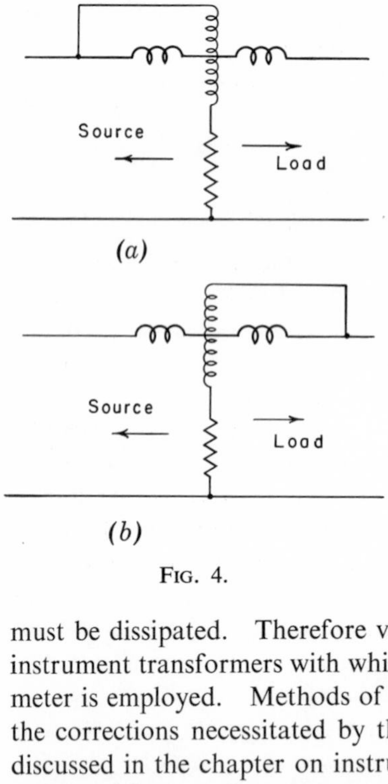

FIG. 4.

By analogy to the previous discussion of d-c power measurements it will be seen from Fig. 4 that there are two ways of connecting a wattmeter into a circuit to measure power. With connection (*a*) the wattmeter measures the power taken by its own current coils in addition to that in the load. This is true since the voltage drop in the current coils plus the voltage drop in the load is impressed on the voltage circuit of the wattmeter while the current in the field coils is the load current. With connection (*b*) the current in the field coils is the load current plus the current taken by the voltage circuit, and hence the power taken by the voltage circuit of the wattmeter is included in the instrument reading. If the error resulting from wattmeter losses measured with the load is to be neglected, then for a load current which is small compared with the current rating of the wattmeter coils the power taken by the current coils is small and connection (*a*) is preferable. If the current approaches the rating of the wattmeter the power taken by the current coils increases, and in some instances connection (*b*) may be preferable. In any event it should be noted that the power taken in the circuit which is connected

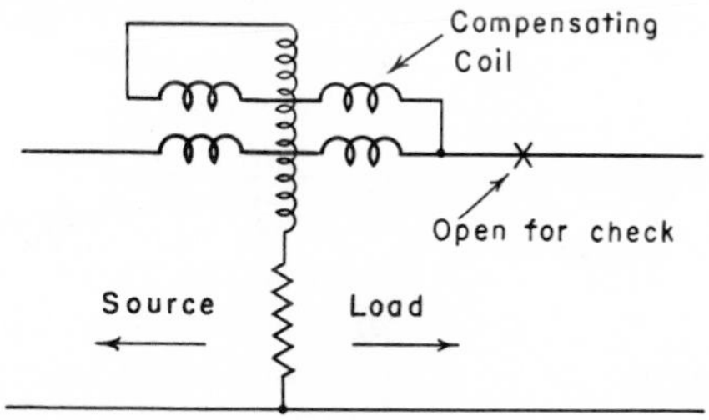

FIG. 5.

nearest to the load is included in the reading of an uncompensated wattmeter. If the desired accuracy requires that the power loss in the instrument be taken into account, connection (*b*) is usually preferable since, for a constant voltage, it introduces a constant error which is easily applied as a correction.[3] Where the resistance of the voltage circuit is known and that of the current circuit is not known, connection (*b*) must be used in order to correct the reading for instrument loss. Unless the regulation of the source is poor, the power taken by the voltage circuit in connection (*b*) may often be readily measured, by opening the load circuit and observing the wattmeter reading. (See Fig. 5.)

THE COMPENSATED WATTMETER. The power taken by the voltage circuit is constant if the voltage is constant, but becomes a smaller percentage of the total as a larger amount of power is measured. However, in cases where the load current is large and the load power factor is small, connection (*b*) may result in a large percentage correction since the total power measured may be small. Hence in wattmeters which are designed for low-power-factor measurements, a compensating coil is sometimes incorporated in the instrument. This is shown schematically in Fig. 5. A pair of coils of relatively fine wire connected in series with the voltage circuit is wound with the current coils so that it has the same number of

[3] See section on wattmeter uses, p. 488.

turns similarly located and is so connected that its field opposes the field from the current coils. That part of the main field which results from the current taken by the voltage circuit is thus neutralized by the counter-field set up by the compensating coil. The reading [for connection (*b*)] is a measure of the load only and does not include the power taken by the voltage circuit. The compensation may be checked by opening the circuit on the load side of the wattmeter. If the compensation is perfect the wattmeter reading should be zero.

SELF-INDUCTANCE OF THE VOLTAGE CIRCUIT. It was implied in the discussion of the idealized wattmeter that the current in the moving coil of the instrument was in phase with the impressed voltage. If the voltage

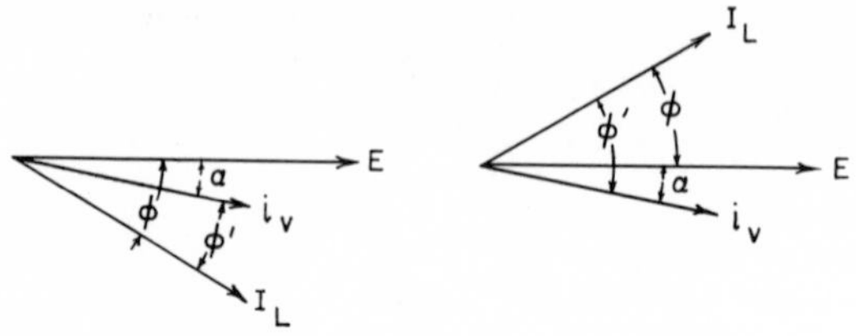

FIG. 6.

circuit of a wattmeter is inductive, its current (i_v) lags behind the impressed voltage as shown in Fig. 6. It will be seen from the vector diagram that for lagging power factor the apparent power-factor angle (i.e. the angle ϕ' between the current in the moving coil and the current in the fixed coils) is less than the angle ϕ by which the load current lags the impressed voltage, that is $\phi' = \phi - \alpha$. Hence the apparent power factor is greater than the true power factor, and the instrument reading is too high. For a leading current in the load the apparent power factor is less than the true power factor, and the wattmeter reading is too low. If we define $\alpha = \tan^{-1}(\omega L_v/R_v)$ in terms of the reactance and resistance of the voltage circuit, we may write for a lagging load:

$$\text{Wattmeter reading} = KI_L i_v \cos(\phi - \alpha) = \frac{KI_L E}{Z_v} \cos(\phi - \alpha)$$

But $Z_v = R_v/\cos\alpha$. Hence

$$\text{Wattmeter reading} = \frac{KI_L E}{R_v} \cos\alpha \cdot \cos(\phi - \alpha)$$

If there were no inductance in the voltage circuit of the instrument we would have $Z_v = R_v$ and (in the absence of other errors)

$$P_{\text{true}} = \frac{KI_L E}{R_v} \cos\phi$$

Then we may say

$$P_{\text{true}} = \frac{\cos \phi}{\cos \alpha \cdot \cos (\phi - \alpha)} \times \text{wattmeter reading}$$

$$= \frac{1 + \tan^2 \alpha}{1 + \tan \phi \tan \alpha} \times \text{reading}$$

Now α is always small, at most only a few minutes of angle, and $\tan^2 \alpha \ll 1$, so we may write

$$P_{\text{true}} \approx \frac{\text{wattmeter reading}}{1 + \tan \phi \tan \alpha}$$

This approximation is inconvenient to use where the power factor is low, since $\tan \phi$ becomes very large. In fact the expression becomes indeterminate at zero power factor. However, the correction may be expressed more conveniently in an equivalent subtractive form as

$$P_{\text{true}} = \text{wattmeter reading} - EI \tan \alpha \sin \phi$$

It may be noted from this last expression that the correction varies from zero at unity power factor to a maximum of $EI \tan \alpha$ at zero power factor. Furthermore, since at 50% power factor $\sin \phi = 0.866$, the correction is already 87% of the maximum value it can attain for the given value of volt-amperes EI, the value at 50% power factor may usually be taken as a sufficient approximation at lower power factors. In most wattmeter applications, measurements of voltage and current as well as power are made so that ϕ can usually be calculated and a correction applied if α is known. It should also be noted that the latter formula is equally applicable to lagging or leading power factor if we consider that ϕ is positive if the current lags and negative if the current leads. In the latter case the correction to the wattmeter reading becomes positive.

Many wattmeters are compensated for this source of error by means of a capacitor shunting a portion of the multiplier, as shown in Fig. 7(*a*). In this circuit the impedance may be written as

$$Z = R\left(\frac{N-1}{N}\right) + j\omega L + \frac{\dfrac{R}{N} - j\dfrac{\omega C R^2}{N^2}}{1 + \dfrac{\omega^2 C^2 R^2}{N^2}}$$

If the circuit constants are so chosen that for power frequencies we may write $\omega^2 C^2 R^2 / N^2 \ll 1$, we have approximately

$$Z \approx R + j\omega\left(L - \frac{CR^2}{N^2}\right)$$

and, if $L = CR^2/N^2$, then

$$Z \approx R \quad \text{and} \quad \alpha = 0$$

This type of compensation is affected by frequency only very slightly up to frequencies high enough that $\omega^2C^2R^2/N^2$ is no longer negligible compared with 1. It is preferable to use a relatively large capacitance in parallel with a small fraction of the resistance in the voltage circuit (i.e. N large) since the effect of the capacitance in increasing the moving-coil current is then relatively slight, and also because failure of the capacitor will not result in burning out the moving-coil circuit.

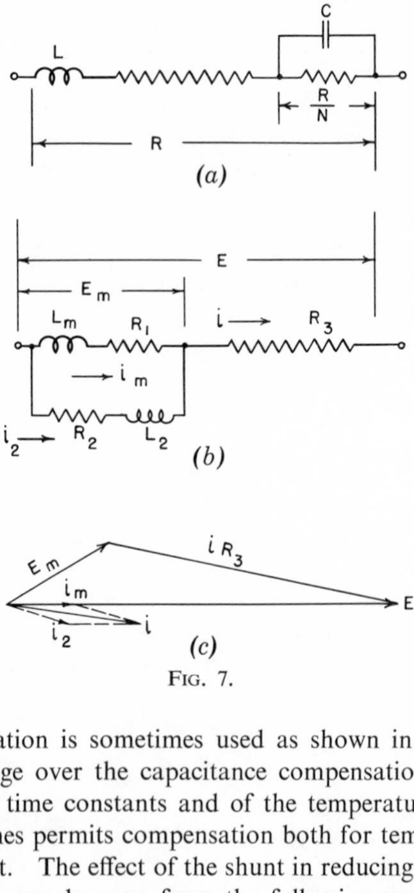

FIG. 7.

Shunt compensation is sometimes used as shown in Fig. 7(*b*). This has some advantage over the capacitance compensation in that proper adjustment of the time constants and of the temperature coefficients of the parallel branches permits compensation both for temperature and for phase displacement. The effect of the shunt in reducing temperature and self-heating errors may be seen from the following considerations. As the temperature of the moving coil rises from any cause, such as heat radiated from the field coils, I^2R loss in the coil itself, or a rise in ambient temperature, its resistance increases, and, if the shunt is of lower-temperature-coefficient material than the moving-coil branch of the circuit, a larger portion of the current will flow in the shunt. The larger current will result in a higher voltage drop E_m across the combination so that the current in the moving coil will not decrease as rapidly as would be anticipated from its resistance rise alone.[4] It will be noted that this device cannot be expected to result in complete compensation but only in a reduction of temperature effects. However, it has the advantage that the shunt may be so located that the heat which it dissipates may be applied where needed to equalize the temperature of the moving coil and spring system.[5] If the shunt is wound inductively and if its time constant (L/R) is higher than that of the moving-coil branch of the circuit, it can be used to compensate the self-inductance error in the voltage circuit of the wattmeter. This may be seen from the vector diagram [Fig. 7(*c*)]. The current $\mathbf{i}_2$ in the shunt will lag $\mathbf{E}_m$ (the voltage across the combination) by an angle which is greater than the lag angle of $\mathbf{i}_m$ (the current in the moving coil). Their vector sum ($\mathbf{i}$) will be the current in the series resistor R_3, and the voltage $\mathbf{E}$ impressed on the voltage circuit will be the vector sum of $\mathbf{E}_m$ and $\mathbf{iR}_3$. It is possible, by choosing properly the time constant of the inductive shunt and the magnitude of its impedance relative to that of the moving-coil branch of the circuit, to bring $\mathbf{i}_m$ into exact phase coincidence with $\mathbf{E}$ for some particular chosen frequency and to make its phase departure from $\mathbf{E}$ very small over a considerable range of frequency.[6]

EDDY-CURRENT EFFECTS. Eddy currents in metal coil supports or other structures and even within the thickness of the wires in the winding themselves will produce a component of flux in the wattmeter field which lags the main flux produced by the current in the field coils (i.e. the load current). Since the resultant flux lags the load current it will affect the angle between fields which react to produce torque in the moving system. It is similar in principle to the self-inductance error of the voltage circuit discussed above, except that the "apparent" lag of the current is greater than the true lag, so that the wattmeter will read low for a lagging power factor and high for a leading power factor. This error is therefore opposite in sign to the self-inductance error. In a well-designed instrument it is quite small and becomes important only at low power factors. Actually the effect of eddy currents, of self-inductance in the voltage circuit, and of distributed capacitance in the voltage circuit resistor can be lumped together as a single angle α and once determined may be used to correct the wattmeter reading in accordance with the formula developed in the preceding section. It should be noted that eddy-current losses, and hence the error that they introduce, increase with the square of the

[4] Werner Skirl, *Wechselstrom-Leistungsmessungen*, Vol. 2, pp. 19–23, J. Springer, 1923.

[5] See discussion (p. 417) of self-heating errors in electrodynamic voltmeters.

[6] This system of compensation was originally patented by Siemens and Halske and has been used by them in precision wattmeters.

frequency. It is important that eddy currents be eliminated or held to small values in precision wattmeters which are to be used at low power factors or at high frequencies. Current coils in such instruments are held in frames made of insulating material or of alloys having a high specific resistance. If the current coils are to carry large currents they are made of stranded conductors to minimize eddy currents in the coils themselves.

MUTUAL INDUCTANCE EFFECTS. Mutual inductance between the fixed and moving coils also introduces an error, which is usually quite small at commercial power frequencies but becomes more important as the frequency is increased. Because of the coupling between fixed and moving coils, an emf is induced in each by the flux in the other. Rigorous expressions showing the combined effect of self- and mutual-inductance have been developed by Silsbee[7] for the two possible wattmeter connections shown in Fig. 4. If the voltage circuit of the wattmeter is connected nearest the load, we have

$$P_a = I_m{}^2R_v + I_l{}^2R_l\left[1 + \frac{\omega^2(L_m + M)(L_l - M)}{R_vR_l}\right]\left[1 + \frac{\omega^2(L_m + M)^2}{R_v{}^2}\right]^{-1}$$

and if the current circuit of the wattmeter is connected nearest the load

$$P_a = I_l{}^2(R_l + R_f)\left[1 + \frac{\omega^2(L_m - M)(L_l + L_f - M)}{R_v(R_l + R_f)}\right]\left[1 + \frac{\omega^2(L_m - M)^2}{R_v{}^2}\right]^{-1}$$

P_a is the a-c indication of a wattmeter which reads correctly on direct current; M is the mutual inductance between fixed and moving coils (positive for pointer positions above the position where $M = 0$); I_l and I_m are respectively the load current and the moving-coil current; R_v is the resistance of the voltage circuit and L_m is its inductance; R_f and L_f are respectively the resistance and inductance of the current coils. For almost any condition, the last factor in brackets in the formulas is so close to 1 that it may be neglected. Also M and L_f are small relative to L_l, except when the power factor of the load is very nearly unity, in which case R_l is large and the factor $\omega M/R_l$ or $\omega(L_f - M)/(R_l + R_f)$ is small. With these approximations Silsbee's equations reduce to

$$P_a \approx P_l + I_m{}^2R_v + E_lI_l \sin\theta_l \frac{\omega(L_m + M)}{R_v}$$

and

$$P_a \approx P_l + I_f{}^2R_f + E_lI_l \sin\theta_l \frac{\omega(L_m - M)}{R_v}$$

[7] Unpublished notes of F. B. Silsbee. The reader may refer to a discussion of mutual-inductance effects in wattmeters and the development of very similar formulas in a paper entitled, The Accuracy of Commercial Electrical Measurements, by H. B. Brooks, *Trans. AIEE*, **39**, 495 (1920).

It will be seen that the effect of M is to increase the phase angle[8] α for the connection in which the voltage circuit of the wattmeter is nearest the load, and to decrease α for the alternative connection by the amount $\tan^{-1}(\omega M/R_v)$. For most wattmeters this contribution to error of indication is exceedingly small at power frequencies but increases linearly with frequency. For a typical 5-amp, 150-volt wattmeter ($R_v = 5000$ ohms, $M = 0.2$ mh) the contribution of M to the error at rated volt-amperes and 60 cycles is only 0.01 watt even at zero power factor. Instruments of the same design, wound for other rated currents or voltages, would have the same error in watts due to mutual inductance when operated at rated volt-amperes.

STRAY MAGNETIC FIELDS. Since the electrodynamic wattmeter has a relatively low operating field it is particularly affected by stray magnetic fields and must be carefully shielded. Laminated iron shields are used in portable laboratory instruments, and steel cases sometimes provide shielding in switchboard instruments. Transfer wattmeters of the highest grade, in which shielding is avoided both to keep down eddy currents and to avoid the small d-c errors which may result from the permanent magnetism of a shield, are made astatic by the use of two complete measuring systems. The coils of these systems are so arranged and connected that their torques are in the same direction for the power which is being measured, whereas the torques resulting from external fields are opposed and completely cancel if the external field is uniform within the volume of the elements.[9] Astatic systems are also used in some portable instruments in lieu of shielding, but it should be borne in mind that such construction is completely effective only against uniform fields and is not a satisfactory substitute for shielding in cases where the stray field is not uniform. On the other hand, shields are not completely effective and may not be of zero retentivity, so that shielding may not completely eliminate stray-field errors and may even introduce a small error in some cases.

VIBRATION OF THE MOVING SYSTEM. Still another source of error, found occasionally on alternating current, arises from the fact that the mechanical torque varies cyclically with a frequency twice that of the voltage. If the pointer, spring, or some other portion of the moving system has a mode of vibration which is in approximate resonance with the frequency of the torque pulsation, vibrations of considerable amplitude may occur. Not only would such a vibration make the pointer position difficult to read accurately but also the mean position of the pointer may be displaced from that corresponding to the average value of the power. If the torque constant of the instrument varies with position (i.e. if $dM/d\theta$ is

[8] See discussion of self-inductance above.

[9] See discussion of electrodynamic ammeters and voltmeters in Chapter 10.

not constant over the range of angles involved in the vibration), the moving system may fail to integrate properly and its mean position be displaced because of the vibration. Also vibration of the instrument springs may result in mechanical torques which displace the moving system. It is, of course, true that mechanical resonance of the moving system or of some portion of it will occur at one frequency or another, but manufacturers usually try to avoid having any mode of vibration of the moving system close to 120 cps. A convenient procedure for locating such mechanical resonant frequencies is to apply direct current to the fixed coils and alternating current of adjustable frequency to the moving coil. The pointer is then observed for vibration while the frequency is slowly varied over a wide range. If vibration is found at a frequency about double that at which the wattmeter will be used, the resonance frequency can usually be shifted by replacing the balancing weights on the moving system with others of different weight and by rebalancing the system with the new weights in appropriate positions.

TEMPERATURE EFFECTS. Changes in room temperature may affect the indication of a wattmeter as a result of changes in the resistance of the moving coil and because of the temperature coefficient of stiffness of the instrument springs. These effects would nearly compensate[10] if the voltage circuit were composed of copper and of a resistance alloy having a negligible temperature coefficient, in the ratio of 1:10. Usually the requirement that the power taken by the voltage circuit be small leads to a design in which the proportion of alloy of low temperature coefficient is much higher than 10:1. Compensation may then be obtained by adding series resistance of high temperature coefficient so placed that it will attain the temperature of the coil and springs, or by shunting the coil by a resistor of low temperature coefficient. As has already been pointed out,[11] the use of an inductive shunt and the proper adjustment of the time constant of the parallel circuits will also result in compensation of the phase angle, α, of the voltage circuit as well.

Wattmeter Testing. The calibration of an electrodynamic wattmeter is most readily checked on direct current. Preferably the current and voltage circuits of the wattmeter should be supplied from independent sources, since in this case the current and voltage can be separately determined by potentiometer methods or other suitable means and their product used to determine the expected indication of the wattmeter. In this way the actual power requirements on the sources are simply those of the current and voltage circuits of the instrument under test, together with the necessary control circuits, whereas if an actual load were set

[10] See discussion of temperature effects on ammeters and voltmeters, Chapter 10.

[11] See discussion of self-inductance effect on p. 480.

up the power which the source would be required to furnish would be that corresponding to the wattmeter indication. Furthermore if the separate sources are used—phantom loading—no correction need be made to the indication for power absorbed in either the current or the voltage element of the wattmeter. It should be noted that it is essential in such a test that the current and voltage circuits be connected together at one point so that no difference of potential will develop between them to give rise to electrostatic forces or to cause insulation breakdown in the windings. This electrostatic tie between the circuits should be located at the voltage terminal of the wattmeter which is connected directly to the moving coil itself,[12] so that the potentials of the fixed and moving coils will be the same. The tie should be of fairly low resistance, although its actual value is not important since it carries no appreciable current.[13] It should also be noted that if a compensated wattmeter is tested or used with separately excited circuits the compensating coil should not be included in the voltage circuit since the wattmeter indication does not include the losses in the voltage circuit.

Since most of the sources of wattmeter error enumerated above are effective only on alternating current, the d-c check on the calibration should be supplemented by comparing the a-c performance of the wattmeter under test with that of some standard instrument which is known to be reliable. Normally such a comparison test may be made by connecting the wattmeter under test and the standard wattmeter with their current circuits in series and their voltage circuits in parallel. The voltage and current circuits are preferably excited from separate sources which on direct current may be two storage batteries or a battery for the current supply and rectified alternating current for the voltage supply, and on alternating current two alternators which are mechanically coupled but whose outputs are independently controlled.[14] It is advantageous to use a test procedure in which the indications of the test and standard instruments are alternately compared on alternating and direct current as indicated below. Alternating current is supplied to both circuits of both instruments and adjusted until the instrument under test is brought to a definite reading. Direct current is then supplied to both instruments and adjusted to restore the reading of the instrument under test. The direct current and voltage are then reversed, and the test instrument is again

[12] This terminal is usually marked either $\pm$ or 0.

[13] A voltmeter might be used to advantage as the electrostatic tie. Its deflection would indicate the presence of a potential difference between the circuits, and its resistance would be low enough to prevent damaging voltages.

[14] Other satisfactory separate supply systems for the current and voltage circuits can be constructed with the aid of isolating transformers, variacs, and a suitable phase shifter.

brought to the same reading. After this the original a-c adjustment is repeated. For each of the four adjustments the reading of the standard instrument is observed. Usually two or more sets of such readings are made in quick succession. The average of all the a-c readings, and the average of all the d-c readings on the standard instrument, are then computed and the difference in performance on alternating and direct current (as shown by the difference in the averages) is computed as a percentage of the mean a-c reading. This difference is a measure of the various a-c errors discussed above, and the procedure described effectively eliminates the effects of heating and of spring fatigue in either the test or the standard instrument. By reading the pointer position of the instrument under test with a low-power microscope a precision approaching 0.01% of full scale can be obtained in the observed difference.

Since some of the a-c errors are a function of scale position or of power factor, the transfer test just described should be made not only at full scale on the instrument under test but also at one or more other points distributed over the scale, and should be made both at unity power factor and at 50% power factor with the current lagging. This power factor is suggested since it is the universal practice of the public utility industry to adjust watthour meters at 50% power factor, current lagging. If the wattmeter is to be used for other purposes it may be desirable to make transfer tests at other power factors. In particular, a comparison of the wattmeter with the standard instrument at zero power factor, where its residual indication is expressed as a fraction of that which would correspond to the product of the test current and voltage, affords a convenient way of obtaining the net phase displacement, α, for use in the correction formula discussed above under the heading, Self-Inductance of the Voltage Circuit. It should be noted that the contributions to α resulting from eddy currents and from mutual inductance are automatically included in the experimentally determined value of α.

It should be borne in mind that a transfer test such as that described above, in which a standard instrument of known, reliable performance is compared with the instrument under test, is inherently capable of greater accuracy than that which is normally associated with a single measurement of power, since some of the errors of individual determinations tend to cancel out. It is therefore profitable to take considerable pains to minimize the uncertainty of reading, and similar random errors. The "Laboratory Standard" type of wattmeter is intended for just such high-precision measurements, and its long pointer and carefully divided scale permit close reading.

Use of Wattmeters. The wattmeter errors discussed above are generally small if the instrument is well designed, properly constructed, and intelligently used. In fact they may be expected to be negligible in many cases where high precision is not required, but they do set the limits of accuracy attainable with the electrodynamic wattmeter. Leading manufacturers build wattmeters having guaranteed accuracies ranging from 0.1% to 2%.

It should always be borne in mind that a wattmeter has three ratings: current, voltage, and power, and that excessive deflection occurs *only* when the power rating is exceeded. If the current or voltage rating is exceeded, this is made evident only after injury has progressed to the

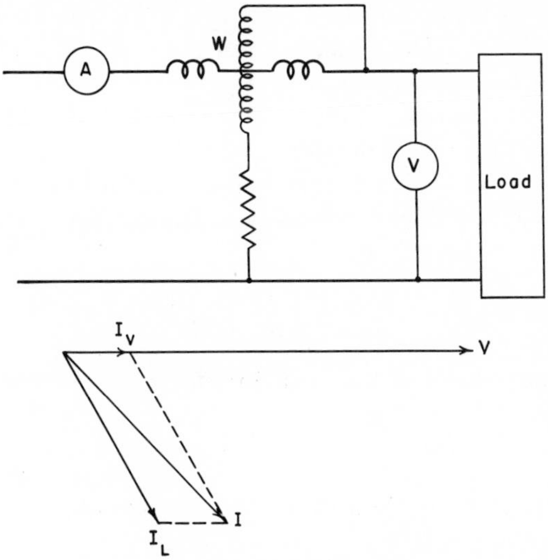

FIG. 8.

point where smoke or odor is present or where an actual burnout has occurred. In *any* measurement it is necessary to make certain, either from a knowledge of circuit conditions or from independent current and voltage measurements,[15] that none of the ratings will be exceeded. In the majority of cases in which power measurements are made, a determination of current and voltage is also desired in order that power factor may be computed. If current, voltage, and power are simultaneously measured it is essential to consider the effect of the instruments on the indicated quantities. We shall take as an example the instrument arrangement shown in Fig. 8, and shall assume that the load current lags

[15] It is, of course, also necessary to ensure that the voltage between the fixed and moving coils is low and that the voltage of neither circuit to the case or to ground is excessive, since insulation failure or errors resulting from electrostatic forces may otherwise result. The use of electrostatic ties between the circuits and to the case is always indicated when the circuits are separately excited from independent sources or when they are isolated through instrument transformers.

the applied voltage. Here the voltmeter indicates the true voltage at the load. The wattmeter reading is too high by the amount of power taken by the voltmeter and by the voltage circuit of the wattmeter. The power in the load is

$$P = W - V^2\left(\frac{1}{R_w} + \frac{1}{R_v}\right)$$

where W is the wattmeter reading, and R_w and R_v are the resistances of the voltage circuits of the wattmeter and of the voltmeter respectively. If the wattmeter is compensated, its reading is still too high since it includes the voltmeter power. The ammeter does not read the load current, but the vector sum $\mathbf{I}$ of the load current $\mathbf{I}_L$ and the sum of the currents $\mathbf{I}_v$ taken by the voltage circuit of the wattmeter and by the voltmeter. This may be seen from the vector diagram of Fig. 8. Since the voltage circuits are practically non-inductive their combined current $\mathbf{I}_v$ may be considered to be in phase with the load voltage $\mathbf{V}$. The current I_v is given by the expression

$$I_v = V\left(\frac{1}{R_w} + \frac{1}{R_v}\right)$$

The in-phase component of the load current is

$${}_pI_L = \frac{P}{V} = \frac{W}{V} - V\left(\frac{1}{R_w} + \frac{1}{R_v}\right)$$

and the quadrature component of the load current is

$${}_qI_L = \sqrt{I^2 - \left(\frac{W}{V}\right)^2}$$

Then the total current in the load is

$$\begin{aligned} I_L &= \sqrt{{}_pI_L^2 + {}_qI_L^2} \\ &= \sqrt{\left(\frac{W}{V}\right)^2 - 2W\left(\frac{1}{R_w} + \frac{1}{R_v}\right) + V^2\left(\frac{1}{R_w} + \frac{1}{R_v}\right)^2 + I^2 - \frac{W^2}{V^2}} \\ &= \sqrt{I^2 + V^2\left(\frac{1}{R_w} + \frac{1}{R_v}\right)^2 - 2W\left(\frac{1}{R_w} + \frac{1}{R_v}\right)} \end{aligned}$$

Special Types of Electrodynamic Wattmeters. (*a*) TORSION-HEAD WATTMETERS. In the Siemens electrodynamometer[16] (1878) the moving coil was coupled to a torsion head by means of a helical spring. The torsion head could be turned to restore the moving coil to a fixed operating position so chosen that the mutual inductance between fixed and moving

[16] Frolich, *E.T.Z.*, **1**, 199 (1880).

coils was zero. An angle scale attached to the torsion head indicated the operating torque. A somewhat similar arrangement was used in the Westinghouse torsion-head wattmeter. In this instrument a pair of moving coils at opposite ends of a pivoted horizontal arm interacted with fixed coils in a manner analogous to the current balance but with the axis of motion vertical. A spiral spring coupled the moving system to the torsion head, which was rotated to restore the balance between spring torque and electrodynamic torque.[17] Both these instruments had a long, nearly uniform scale and were free from mutual-inductance effects. However, the balancing operation was slow compared with the response time of a deflecting wattmeter, and as they were usually constructed the self-inductance and eddy-current effects were comparatively large. Both these instruments are largely of historical interest today, although a considerable number of the Westinghouse instruments are still in use as precision wattmeters. A Hartmann and Braun astatic, torsion-head wattmeter of the suspension type and with a scale 40 cm long has also been described (1933). An accuracy of 0.1% was claimed for this instrument, which was called a "Promille"[18] wattmeter.

(*b*) IRON-CORED WATTMETERS. A very large increase in operating torque is obtained by using a laminated iron core. Also, by properly shaping the parts, angular motion up to 270° may be made available for the scale. This construction introduces difficulties from eddy currents and hysteresis in the iron, and the calibration is generally useful only over a rather narrow frequency range. Such instruments must be calibrated in terms of an air-cored wattmeter. The construction is employed both by Westinghouse and by General Electric in their long-scale switchboard instruments and is also used at times in switchboard instruments having conventional scales. A laboratory instrument of this type of special construction and with a mu-metal core was found by the National Physical Laboratory[19] to have a transfer error of less than 0.01% at 50 cps. This instrument had twenty-eight ranges extending from 25 watts to 2500 watts. It used a light-beam pointer and its stated precision was 0.05%.

(*c*) COMPOSITE-COIL WATTMETERS. Silsbee[20] has described an instrument (used either as an ammeter or a wattmeter) in which the upscale torque produced by the a-c current or power being measured is opposed by a nearly equal torque produced by an adjustable direct current in a set

[17] This arrangement may be considered as a Kelvin balance turned on edge, with a spring rather than weights to supply the restoring force.

[18] The term "Promille," meaning parts per thousand, is used by the Germans and would be a welcome addition to our own language.

[19] Spilsbury and Felton, *J. IEE*, **89**, II, p. 135 (1942).

[20] Silsbee, *NBS J. Research*, **8**, 17 (1932).

of windings which are intermingled with the a-c windings. It is of the suspension type and has a mirror and light beam to indicate the deflection resulting from the residual unbalanced torque. The result is equivalent to an instrument having a scale 375 cm long with 2500 divisions.

Shotter and Hawkes[21] have described a similar instrument in which the d-c countertorque for balancing the average a-c torque is obtained from a d-c milliammeter movement, whose moving coil is attached to the same shaft as the moving coil of the wattmeter. The d-c balancing current is measured by a potentiometer. The component instruments are magnetically shielded from each other. A built-in current transformer provides current ranges from 0.5 to 5 amp.

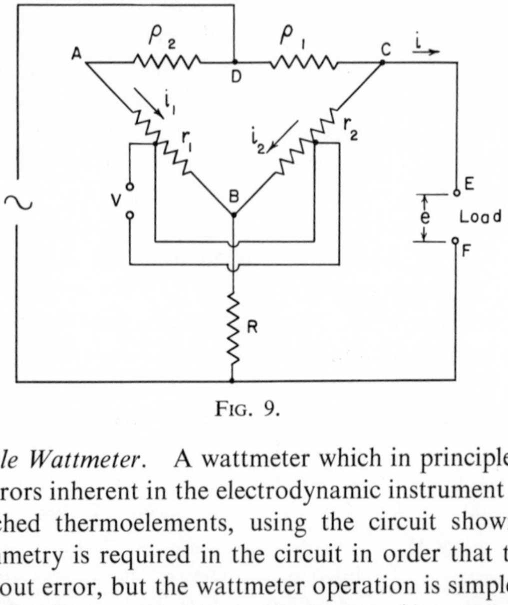

FIG. 9.

Thermocouple Wattmeter. A wattmeter which in principle is free from some of the errors inherent in the electrodynamic instrument can be made up with matched thermoelements, using the circuit shown in Fig. 9. Complete symmetry is required in the circuit in order that the power be indicated without error, but the wattmeter operation is simple in principle and a sufficiently close approach to symmetry can be achieved[22] that its indication will be in error by less than 0.1%. Branches *AB* and *BC* consist of the heater elements of a matched pair of thermoelements so constructed that the voltages produced at the thermocouple junctions are identical if equal currents flow in the heaters. In the circuit shown the heater currents i_1 and i_2 are functions of the voltage e across the load and of the load current i, and are of the form

$$i_1 = c_{11}e + c_{12}i$$
$$i_2 = c_{21}e + c_{22}i$$

[21] Shotter and Hawkes, *J. IEE*, **93,** II, p. 314 (1946).
[22] Goffin and Marchal, *Bull. Schweiz. elektrot. Verein*, **37,** 595 (1946).

The thermocouples are connected in opposition, and their combined output is of the form $V = k(i_1^2 - i_2^2)$, where k is a constant common to the two elements of the matched pair. Now, if the constants in the current equations satisfy the conditions $c_{11} = -c_{21}$ and $c_{12} = c_{22}$, the output has a value $V = 4c_{11}c_{22}kei = Kei$, which is precisely our definition of power in the load. It has been shown[23] that, if the current equations are written in the form

$$i_1 = i_{1L} + i_{1K}$$
$$i_2 = i_{2L} + i_{2K}$$

where $i_{aL} = c_{a1}e$ is the current in branch a when the load terminals (E, F) are open-circuited, and $i_{aK} = c_{a2}i$ is the current in branch a when the

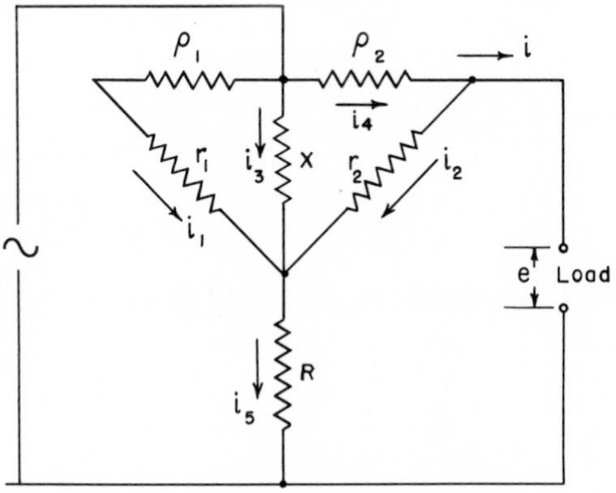

FIG. 10.

load terminals are short-circuited, then our conditions for wattmeter operation become $i_{1L} = -i_{2L}$ and $i_{1K} = i_{2K}$. Physically this means precisely that on open circuit (no load at terminals E, F) the heater currents i_1 and i_2 must be equal and in the same direction, and that on short circuit (at E, F) they must be equal and in opposite directions. The open-circuit condition may be realized if the resistances of the two branch circuits DAB and DCB are equal, i.e. $r_1 + \rho_1 = r_2 + \rho_2$. The short-circuit condition of symmetry cannot be realized in the simple circuit of Fig. 9, since when EF is shorted the resistance, R, of the voltage circuit is in parallel with r_2. The condition may, however, be realized if we connect a compensating resistance X between the points BD such that

$$X = \frac{r_1 + \rho_1}{r_2} R$$

as shown in Fig. 10. The adjustments needed to achieve the conditions required for wattmeter operation are simple if the thermoelements are so

[23] Bader, *Arch. für Elektrot.*, **29**, 809 (1935).

matched that their output is identical for equal heater currents. With the "load" terminals open, ρ_1 may be adjusted to bring the emf, V, of the combined thermocouples to zero. Then $\rho_1 + r_1 = \rho_2 + r_2 = R'$. Next, with the "load" terminals short-circuited, X is adjusted until V is again zero, so that

$$X = \frac{\rho_1 + r_1}{r_2} R = \frac{R'R}{r_2}$$

The wattmeter is now ready for use.

Subject to the conditions of symmetry, $\rho_1 + r_1 = \rho_2 + r_2 = R'$ and $X = R'R/r_2$, it can be shown that the output V of the opposed thermocouples is a measure of the load power.

We have

$$i_1 + i_2 + i_3 = i_5$$
$$i_4 - i_2 = i$$
$$r_2 i_2 + R i_5 = e$$

and

$$i_3 X = i_1 R' = i_4 \rho_2 + i_2 r_2$$

The currents i_1 and i_2 may be expressed in determinant form as:

$$i_1 = \frac{\begin{vmatrix} 0 & 1 & 1 & 0 & -1 \\ i & -1 & 0 & 1 & 0 \\ e & r_2 & 0 & 0 & R \\ 0 & 0 & X & 0 & 0 \\ 0 & r_2 & -X & \rho_2 & 0 \end{vmatrix}}{\begin{vmatrix} 1 & 1 & 1 & 0 & -1 \\ 0 & -1 & 0 & 1 & 0 \\ 0 & r_2 & 0 & 0 & R \\ -R' & 0 & X & 0 & 0 \\ 0 & r_2 & -X & \rho_2 & 0 \end{vmatrix}}, \quad \text{and} \quad i_2 = \frac{\begin{vmatrix} 1 & 0 & 1 & 0 & -1 \\ 0 & i & 0 & 1 & 0 \\ 0 & e & 0 & 0 & R \\ -R' & 0 & X & 0 & 0 \\ 0 & 0 & -X & \rho_2 & 0 \end{vmatrix}}{\begin{vmatrix} 1 & 1 & 1 & 0 & -1 \\ 0 & -1 & 0 & 1 & 0 \\ 0 & r_2 & 0 & 0 & R \\ -R' & 0 & X & 0 & 0 \\ 0 & r_2 & -X & \rho_2 & 0 \end{vmatrix}}$$

and the solutions are

$$i_1 = \frac{X[eR' + i\rho_2(R + r_2)]}{2RR'^2 \cdot \dfrac{(R + r_2)}{r_2}} = \frac{e}{2(R + r_2)} + i\frac{\rho_2}{2R'}$$

$$i_2 = \frac{eR'X - i\rho_2 R(X + R')}{2RR'^2 \cdot \dfrac{(R + r_2)}{r_2}} = \frac{e}{2(R + r_2)} - i\frac{\rho_2}{2R'}$$

The combined output of the thermocouples is

$$V = K \cdot \frac{1}{T}\int_0^T (i_1^2 - i_2^2)\, dt$$

if we assume that the period during which e and i go through a complete cycle of values is short compared to the response time of the thermoelements (i.e. the thermocouple response is a measure of the *average* square of the heater current). If now we substitute our values of i_1 and i_2 in this expression we have

$$V = \frac{K\rho_2}{R'(R + r_2)} \cdot \frac{1}{T}\int_0^T ei\,dt = K' \times \text{power}$$

since by definition the power in a circuit is $(1/T)\int_0^T ei\,dt$.

It should be noted that in the compensated thermocouple wattmeter no indication results from the power taken by either the current or the voltage circuit. The adjustments required for compensation, and the

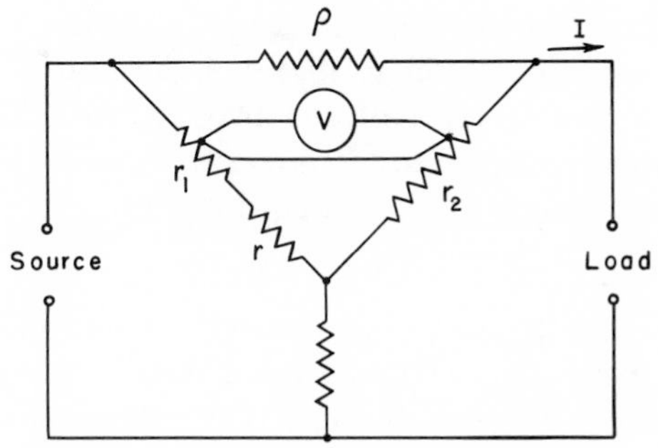

FIG. 11.

calibration of the wattmeter, can be accomplished on direct current by methods which are inherently of high precision. On alternating current the indication is independent of frequency up to values at which the distributed capacitance of the resistance network becomes important. If suitable elements are used there should be no appreciable frequency error up to perhaps 10 kc.

Another thermocouple wattmeter, designed for measuring small amounts of power at high frequencies, is shown schematically in Fig. 11. In this instrument a small resistance r, in series with one of the heater elements r_1, is used to compensate for inequality of the thermoelements. However, the thermocouple output contains a term which is proportional to the power loss in the shunt, ρ, which carries the load current. A low-range millivoltmeter indicates the load power, and full-scale deflection corresponds to 120 mw of which about 1% represents power in the shunt. The wattmeter is accurate up to about 1 megacycle.[24] Power consumption in the heaters and the series resistor amounts to 56 mw.

[24] Kuhnel, *Zeits. für Instrumentenk.*, **48,** 127 (1928).

A polyphase thermal wattmeter having a response time of about $\frac{1}{2}$ sec has been described[25] by John H. Miller of the Weston Electrical Instrument Corporation. Derived currents, obtained through suitably connected transformers, are sent through a pair of heaters which are so arranged that one is heated by the algebraic sum of the currents and the other by their difference. One of the derived currents (i_1) is in phase with and proportional to the circuit current; the other (i_2) is in phase with and proportional to the circuit voltage. The current in one heater is

$$I_1 = \sqrt{i_1^2 + 2i_1 i_2 \cos\theta + i_2^2}$$

and in the other

$$I_2 = \sqrt{i_1^2 - i_1 i_2 \cos\theta + i_2^2}$$

θ being the angle by which the circuit current lags the voltage. The two heaters are made up of a number of thermocouples connected in series in the manner shown in Fig. 39, Chapter 10, and their output emf's are opposed across a millivoltmeter so that its indication is proportional to the difference in temperatures of the two heaters. Since the heater temperatures are proportional to the power (I^2R) which is dissipated, the difference in temperatures will be proportional to

$$I_1^2R - I_2^2R = Ki_1 i_2 \cos\theta$$

R being the resistance (equal in the heaters) of each heater, and K being a proportionality constant. Thus, since i_1 and i_2 are proportional to circuit current and voltage respectively, the millivoltmeter indication is proportional to circuit power.

Electrostatic Wattmeter. This is a special-purpose instrument which has been much used in the past to measure power at very low power factors, particularly at high voltages, as, for example, in cable dielectric-loss measurements. In this application it has been largely superseded by bridge methods, but it requires less expensive apparatus than does the Schering bridge,[26] and, in the hands of a skilled operator, it is capable of very accurate results. It is also useful in studying the behavior and errors of electrodynamic wattmeters at power factors approaching zero, where many of the errors of the electrodynamic instrument are most troublesome. At the National Physical Laboratory[27] a very carefully constructed instrument of this type serves as the basic standard for checking the calibration of other wattmeters.

A conventional type of quadrant electrometer[28] may be used to measure

[25] Miller, *Trans. AIEE,* **60,** 37, 633 (1941).

[26] See Chapter 15.

[27] Paterson, Rayner, and Kinnes, *Collected Researches NPL,* **11,** 117 (1914).

[28] See description in Chapter 10.

power when connected as shown in Fig. 12. A resistor R, which carries the load current i, serves as a shunt to supply a potential difference to the quadrant pairs. Needle potential is supplied by the voltage across the load. The torque developed is then a function of the load power, as will be seen from the following considerations. Let v_1 and v_2 be the instantaneous quadrant potentials and v be the instantaneous needle potential.

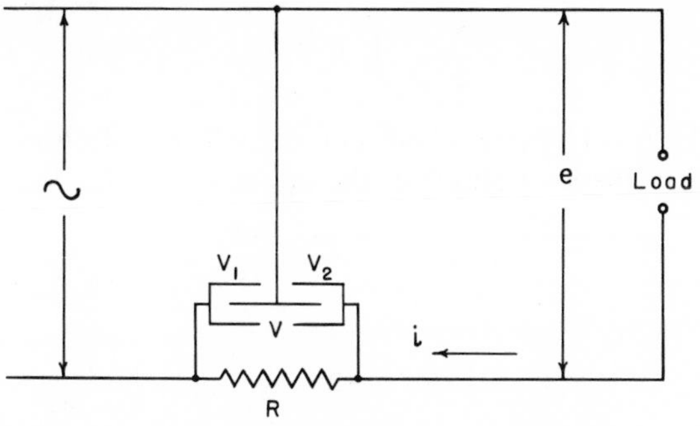

FIG. 12.

The energy stored in the electric fields between the needle and the quadrant pairs is

$$W = (v - v_1)^2 C_1 + (v - v_2)^2 C_2$$

where C_1 and C_2 are the capacitances between the needle and the quadrant pairs. The torque is

$$\mathcal{T} = \frac{dW}{d\theta} = (v - v_1)^2 \frac{dC_1}{d\theta} + (v - v_2)^2 \frac{dC_2}{d\theta}$$

If we may assume symmetrical construction in the electrometer, then $dC_2/d\theta = -(dC_1/d\theta)$, since any rotation of the needle will increase the capacitance between the needle and one quadrant pair at the same rate that the capacitance is decreased between the needle and the second quadrant pair. We may also assume that the restoring torque from the suspension is proportional to the angular deflection so that

$$K\theta = \frac{1}{T}\int_0^T [(v - v_1)^2 - (v - v_2)^2]dt$$

Now from Fig. 12

$$v - v_2 = e$$

the instantaneous load voltage; and

$$(v - v_1) = (v - v_2) - (v_1 - v_2) = e + iR$$

the sum of the instantaneous load voltage and the voltage across the non-inductive shunt R. From this we have

$$K\theta = \frac{1}{T}\int_0^T [(e + iR)^2 - e^2]dt = 2R \cdot \frac{1}{T}\int_0^T ei\,dt + R^2 \frac{1}{T}\int_0^T i^2\,dt$$

If $2R$ is combined with the constant K, we have

$$K'\theta = \frac{1}{T}\int_0^T ei\,dt + \frac{R}{2} \cdot \frac{1}{T}\int_0^T i^2\,dt = \text{average power} + \frac{I^2R}{2}$$

where I is the rms (effective) load current. The deflection is a measure of the power in the load plus half the power loss in the shunt resistor R.

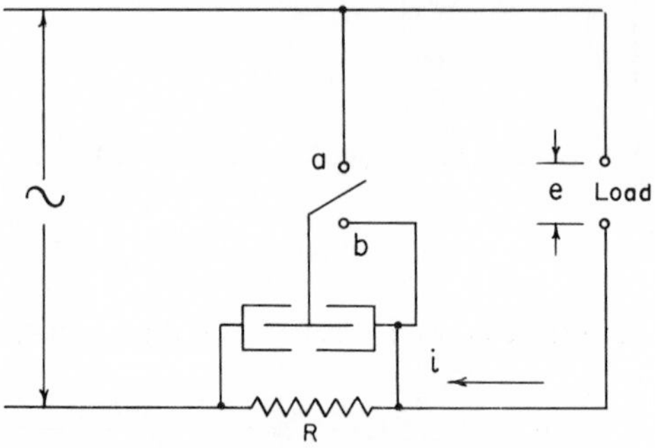

FIG. 13.

If the power factor is very small so that the power in the shunt is a significant part of the total, an independent measurement is needed of the losses in the shunt. This may be accomplished by a second measurement, using the electrometer in its idiostatic connection, as shown in Fig. 13. Connection (a) is the case just discussed (with the electrometer in a heterostatic connection). For connection (b) we have $v - v_2 = 0$ and $v - v_1 = iR$. Then

$$K\theta_b = \frac{1}{T}\int_0^T (iR)^2\,dt = 2R \cdot \frac{I^2R}{2}$$

or

$$K'\theta = \frac{I^2R}{2}$$

The average power in the load is therefore

$$P = K'(\theta_a - \theta_b)$$

If the load is such that $\theta_a - \theta_b$ is small, then the measurement will be of low precision.

The electrometer may be connected to measure load power only, without responding to shunt losses, by using the connection of Fig. 14. A large non-inductive resistance is connected as a voltage divider across the source with the needle connected to its midpoint. In this case

$$v - v_1 = \frac{e + iR}{2}$$

and

$$v - v_2 = \frac{e + iR}{2} - iR = \frac{e - iR}{2}$$

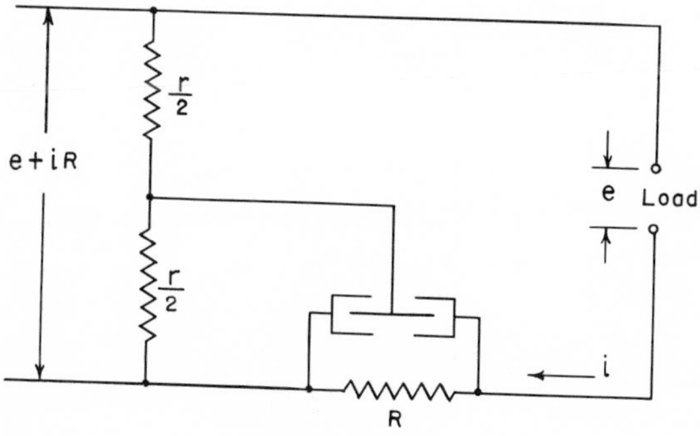

FIG. 14.

Then

$$K\theta = \frac{1}{T}\int_0^T \left[\frac{e^2 + 2eiR + i^2R^2}{4} - \frac{e^2 - 2eiR + i^2R^2}{4}\right] dt$$

$$= R \cdot \frac{1}{T}\int_0^T ei\, dt$$

so that $K''\theta$ = average power in load.

In high-voltage measurements, where the load voltage is too high to impress directly on the needle, the needle voltage may be obtained from the line voltage by means of a voltage divider having a ratio N of line voltage to needle voltage. When the ratio of voltage division is other than 2, the compensation for shunt losses just discussed is no longer valid. However, compensation may now be obtained by inserting in the line a resistance of proper value, between the voltage divider and the load, as shown in Fig. 15. Here

$$v - v_1 = \frac{e + i\rho + iR}{N}$$

and

$$v - v_2 = \frac{e + i\rho + iR}{N} - iR$$

Then

$$K\theta = \frac{1}{T}\int_0^T \left[\left(\frac{e + i\rho + iR}{N}\right)^2 - \left(\frac{e + i\rho + iR}{N} - iR\right)^2\right] dt$$

$$= \frac{2R}{N} \cdot \frac{1}{T}\int_0^T ei\, dt + \left(\frac{2\rho R + 2R^2}{N} - R^2\right) \cdot \frac{1}{T}\int_0^T i^2\, dt$$

If we divide by $2R/N$ we may write

$$K'\theta = \frac{1}{T}\int_0^T ei\, dt + \left(\rho + R - \frac{RN}{2}\right) \cdot \frac{1}{T}\int_0^T i^2\, dt$$

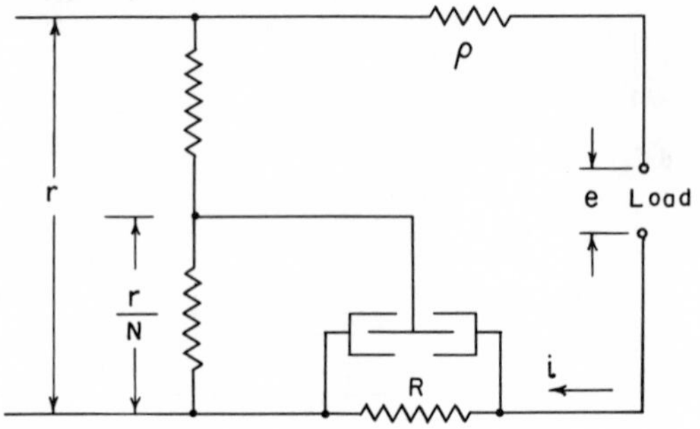

FIG. 15.

The last term vanishes if

$$\rho = \frac{RN}{2} - R = \frac{R}{2}(N - 2)$$

and we have

$$K'\theta = \frac{1}{T}\int_0^T ei\, dt = \text{average load power}$$

It should be noted that the compensated case previously discussed becomes a special case of the more general compensating network, in which $N = 2$ and hence $\rho = 0$.

An important application of the electrostatic wattmeter is in the measurement of errors of the electrodynamic wattmeter at low power factors. This can be accomplished in the arrangement shown in Fig. 16. We will assume that the current and voltage circuits of the wattmeters are supplied from separate, synchronous sources. Two separate alternators coupled to the same motor may be used. Alternatively, if only one source is available, the current and voltage circuits must be isolated from each other by means of transformers and the voltages supplied to the circuits must be separately variable. We will also require that the phase relation between the supply voltages may be varied as desired. If the tie between the current and voltage circuits is at the midpoint of the shunt, we have

$$v - v_1 = \frac{e}{N} + \frac{iR}{2}$$

and

$$v - v_2 = \frac{e}{N} - \frac{iR}{2}$$

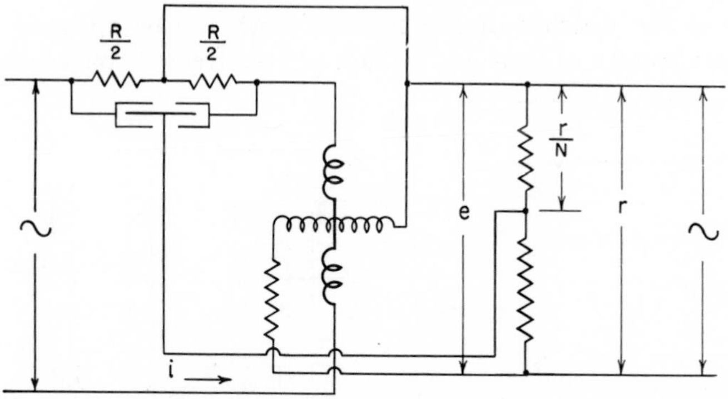

FIG. 16.

Then for the electrostatic wattmeter,

$$K = \frac{1}{T}\int_0^T \left[\left(\frac{e}{N} + \frac{iR}{2}\right)^2 - \left(\frac{e}{N} - \frac{iR}{2}\right)^2\right] dt = \frac{2R}{N}\cdot\frac{1}{T}\int_0^T ei\,dt$$

or

$$K'\theta = \frac{1}{T}\int_0^T ei\,dt$$

If the electrodynamic wattmeter were free from errors, its deflection would also be

$$K\theta = \frac{1}{T}\int_0^T ei\,dt$$

as we have previously seen.

If the phase relation between the current and voltage sources is adjusted until the electrostatic wattmeter has zero deflection, the indication of the electrodynamic wattmeter is a direct measure of its own low-power-factor errors. At power factors other than zero the electrodynamic instrument may be calibrated in terms of the electrostatic instrument. In such a calibration, N may be selected to adjust the electrometer sensitivity to a suitable value. At zero power factor the sensitivity should be high and N may be 1.

Electronic Wattmeters. A number of circuits have been devised using vacuum tubes in power measurements. The vacuum-tube wattmeter[29] whose circuit is shown in Fig. 17 is typical of such arrangements. The basic operating circuit is similar to those already discussed for the thermocouple and electrostatic wattmeters. A non-inductive shunt carries the load current, and the resulting voltage drop, together with a voltage related to the load voltage, produces a response which is proportional to the product of load current and voltage. The circuit requires the use of two matched double triodes, which will be operated on the non-linear portion of their grid-voltage plate-current characteristic. We

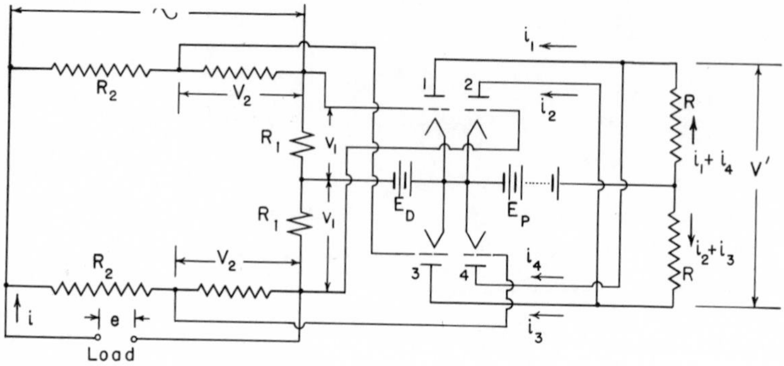

FIG. 17.

will assume this characteristic to be represented by the relation $i_p = K(v_g + v_0)^2$, where v_0 is the negative cut-off potential, v_g is the grid potential, and i_p is the plate current. We will further assume for simplification that the tubes are exactly matched so that K and v_0 are identical for all four electrode assemblies, that the voltage drop in the shunt ($2v_1$) is negligible compared with the load voltage e, and that the currents taken by the matched voltage dividers (R_2) are negligible compared with the load current i. A common grid-biasing voltage E_0 is applied to each tube to secure operation in the proper portion of its characteristic curve between zero and the cut-off value. We may write for the grid potentials of the four tube circuits

$$v_1 = -E_0 - V_1; \quad v_2 = -E_0 + V_1; \quad v_3 = -E_0 - V_1 + V_2;$$
$$v_4 = -E_0 + V_1 + V_2$$

Now the voltage appearing in the plate circuit across R–R is

$$V' = R(i_1 - i_2 - i_3 + i_4)$$

[29] Myers and Clothier, *J. Sci. Inst.*, **16**, 302 (1939).

and we will assume that this is very small compared with the total voltage in the plate circuits (i.e. the plate voltages are constant and equal). If the tube characteristics are identical, we may write

$$i_1 = K(-E_0 - V_1 + v_0)^2; \quad i_2 = K(-E_0 + V_1 + v_0)^2;$$
$$i_3 = K(-E_0 - V_1 + V_2 + v_0)^2; \quad i_4 = K(-E_0 + V_1 + V_2 + v_0)^2$$

so that

$$i_1 - i_2 = 4KV_1(E_0 - v_0)$$

and

$$i_4 - i_3 = 4KV_1(-E_0 + V_2 + v_0)$$

Then

$$i_1 - i_2 - i_3 + i_4 = 4KV_1V_2$$

and

$$V' = 4KRV_1V_2$$

Since we have assumed that R_1 and R_2 have negligible effects on the load circuit, V_1 is proportional to the instantaneous load current, and V_2 to the load voltage, so that V' is proportional to the instantaneous power in the load. Its average value is therefore a measure of the average load power.

The above development assumed identical performance of all four tube circuits, but in practice the tubes cannot be exactly matched. The circuit must therefore be modified to eliminate measurement errors resulting from imperfect matching of the tubes. For details of the adjustments by which Myers and Clothier compensated for imperfect tube matching, and for the voltage drop in the load-current shunt, the reader should refer to the original paper. An accuracy of $1\frac{1}{2}\%$ of full-scale value was claimed by Myers and Clothier for their arrangement on direct current and on alternating current up to 20 kc, with an error of 7% at 50 kc. The frequency error results principally from distributed capacitance in the voltage dividers and in other parts of the circuit. Compensation of these capacitances would be expected to extend the useful frequency range of the instrument by a considerable amount.

Polyphase Power Measurements

Blondel's Theorem. If a network is supplied through N conductors, the total power is measured by summing the readings of N wattmeters so arranged that a current element of a wattmeter is in each line and the corresponding voltage element is connected between that line and a common point. If the common point is located on one of the lines, then the power may be measured by $N - 1$ wattmeters. Suppose that the circuit is as shown in Fig. 18, with the voltage elements of the wattmeters P_1, P_2, P_3 connected to a common point c, whose potential differs by a voltage v from that of the neutral point o of the load. By definition the instantaneous power in the load is

$$P = e_1 i_1 + e_2 i_2 + e_3 i_3$$

Now

$$e_1 = v + e_1'; \quad e_2 = v + e_2'; \quad e_3 = v + e_3'$$

so that

$$\begin{aligned} P &= (v + e_1')i_1 + (v + e_2')i_2 + (v + e_3')i_3 \\ &= v(i_1 + i_2 + i_3) + e_1'i_1 + e_2'i_2 + e_3'i_3 \end{aligned}$$

But by Kirchhoff's law $i_1 + i_2 + i_3 = 0$, so that

$$P = e_1'i_1 + e_2'i_2 + e_3'i_3$$

This last expression is the total instantaneous power measured by the three wattmeters. Hence the sum of their readings measures total power

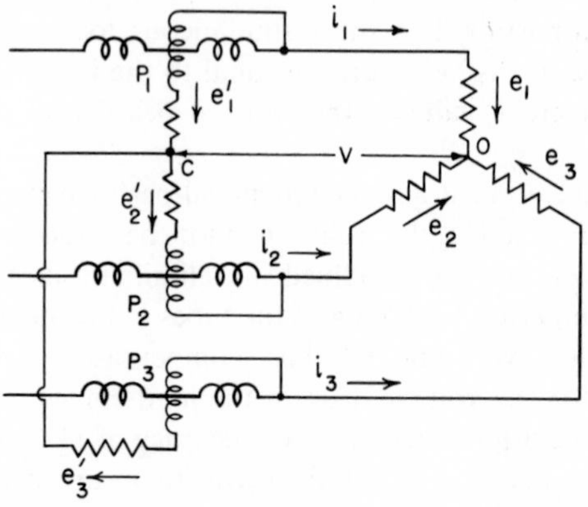

FIG. 18.

in the load. Now suppose the common point c coincides with one of the lines, say line 3. Then $e_3' = 0$, and $P = P_1 + P_2$ represents the total power in the load. It will be seen that the above proof of Blondel's theorem may be extended to any number of lines and is independent of load conditions.

Three-Phase Power Measurement. If in the above case we assume a balanced load, the vector relations of currents and voltages may be represented by Fig. 19. We have

$$\alpha = 30° + \phi, \quad \text{and} \quad \beta = 30° - \phi$$

$$P_1 = E_{13}I_1 \cos \alpha \quad \text{and} \quad P_2 = E_{23}I_2 \cos \beta$$

Now

$$E_{13} = E_{23} = \sqrt{3}E, \quad \text{and} \quad I_1 = I_2 = I$$

where E and I are the phase voltage and current in the balanced load. The power in the load is

$$P = P_1 + P_2 = \sqrt{3}EI(\cos\alpha + \cos\beta)$$

$$= \sqrt{3}EI(\cos 30° \cos\phi - \sin 30° \sin\phi + \cos 30° \cos\phi + \sin 30° \sin\phi)$$

$$= \sqrt{3}EI(2\cos 30° \cos\phi) = 3EI\cos\phi$$

which is the total power in the load. We also have that

$$P_2 - P_1 = \sqrt{3}EI(2\sin 30° \sin\phi) = \sqrt{3}EI\sin\phi$$

Then

$$\frac{P_2 - P_1}{P_1 + P_2} = \frac{\sqrt{3}EI\sin\phi}{3EI\cos\phi} = \frac{\tan\phi}{\sqrt{3}}, \quad \text{or} \quad \tan\phi = \frac{\sqrt{3}(P_2 - P_1)}{P_2 + P_1}$$

from which expression the power factor ($\cos\phi$) of the load may be obtained.

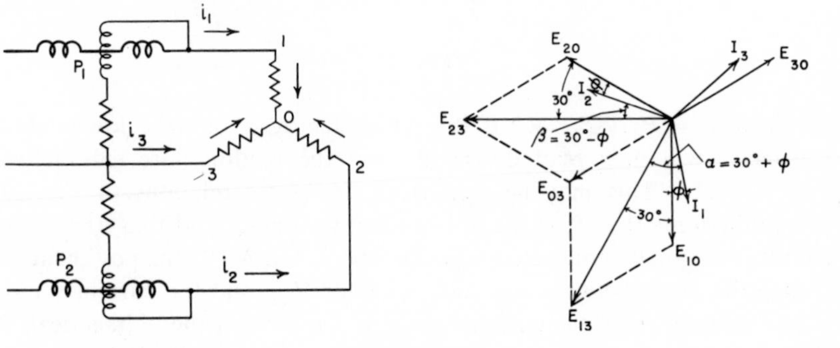

FIG. 19.

It should be noted that, if the power factor of the load is $0.5 (\phi = 60°)$, then $\alpha = 90°$ and $P_1 = 0$, so that the entire load is indicated by P_2. For a power factor less than 0.5 ($\phi > 60°$), P_1 would read downscale and its current connections would have to be reversed to obtain an upscale reading. In this case the load power would be given by the difference in the wattmeter readings, $P = P_2 - P_1$. This raises the following question: If we are measuring three-phase power with two wattmeters and the connections are such that both instruments read upscale, do we take the sum or the difference of the wattmeter readings as the total power? It is apparent that a polarity check is needed and that it is the algebraic sign of the low-reading wattmeter which is in question, since if the power factor is less than 0.5 its reading is subtractive, and if greater than 0.5, additive. When, on a balanced load with an unknown power factor and with both wattmeters reading upscale, we wish to determine whether their readings are additive or subtractive (power factor $\gtrless 0.5$) a very simple test can be made. If, on the low-reading wattmeter, we open the voltage circuit at the common line and reconnect it to the line containing the current element of the other wattmeter, there are two possibilities: (1) if the power factor > 0.5, the low-reading wattmeter will continue to read upscale and the power is the sum of the original

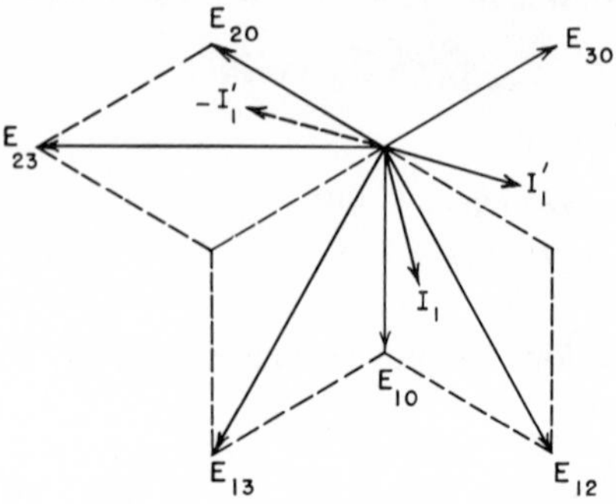

FIG. 20.

readings, $P = P_2 + P_1$; (2) if the power factor < 0.5, the low-reading wattmeter will now read downscale and the readings are subtractive, $P = P_2 - P_1$. This may be seen from the phase relations of Fig. 20. We will assume that P_1 is the low-reading wattmeter and that its voltage circuit is originally connected between lines 1 and 3. If the power factor > 0.5, the angle between the voltage vector, E_{10}, and the current vector is less than 60° (say the current vector is I_1). When the voltage lead is shifted so that the voltage E_{12} is impressed on the circuit the reading is still upscale, and there has been no reversal. Now suppose the angle between E_{10} and I_1 is greater than 60°; i.e. the current vector is I_1'. The angle between I_1' and E_{13} is greater than 90°, and if the instrument is to read upscale the current connections must be reversed and the vector $-I_1'$ must be used with E_{13}. Then when the voltage lead is shifted the instrument reads downscale, since the angle between E_{12} and $-I_1'$ is greater than 90°, and the current connections must again be reversed to obtain an upscale reading; i.e. in this case I_1' would be used.

Polyphase Wattmeters. The above discussion applies to the general case of power measurement in a three-phase, three-wire system with two single-phase wattmeters. Polyphase wattmeters are constructed for this purpose, incorporating two single-phase elements within the same case and on a single shaft. In the design of such instruments care must be taken that the two elements have no mutual action; i.e. field from one element must not produce torque in the other. This may be checked by exciting the current circuit of one element and the voltage circuit of the other. There should be no deflection for this connection.[30] Also the two elements must be matched in their characteristics. This may be checked by connecting the elements with the voltage circuits in parallel and the current circuits in series opposing. Again there should be no deflection. If these requirements are satisfied the wattmeter calibration may be checked by connecting the voltage coils in parallel and the current coils in series aiding, and checking the calibration of the instrument as though it were a single-phase wattmeter.

In connecting a polyphase wattmeter to a circuit to make power measurements one must be careful to follow the polarity markings exactly in order that the instrument will read the load power correctly. A convenient rule to follow is to connect the instrument so that, as current flows from the source, it enters both the current and voltage circuits of the wattmeter at the marked ($\pm$ or zero) terminals. This rule can also be used in connecting two single-phase wattmeters to measure three-phase power, with the additional note that, if one wattmeter reads downscale when so connected, its current coil must be reversed and the resulting upscale reading subtracted from the reading of the other wattmeter to obtain total power.

Three-Phase Power Measurement with One Wattmeter. On balanced three-phase loads a number of devices are available whereby power may be measured with one single-phase wattmeter. One such method is shown in Fig. 21. The wattmeter is connected with its current coil in one line. Its voltage circuit is connected to the other two lines in turn (A and B), and the sum of the two readings thus obtained represents the total power in the load.

[30] This test can be applied conveniently only at the zero of the scale, or at most only over the limited scale range which can be reached by the zero adjuster. Unfortunately no comparable test is possible for interaction at other upscale positions of the moving system without breaking the instrument seal, opening the case, and setting the equilibrium position of the moving system upscale by loosening the spring abutments and reclamping them in the desired position. Since opening the instrument case will generally invalidate the maker's guarantee, such a procedure cannot usually be undertaken in the laboratory but is more properly a factory test. Generally a test for interaction at the zero scale position is sufficient; however, cases have arisen in which there was no interaction at the zero position but there was a substantial interaction at some other position of the moving system.

Here we have

$$P_A = \sqrt{3}EI \cos(30° + \phi)$$
$$P_B = \sqrt{3}EI \cos(30° - \phi)$$
$$P_A + P_B = \sqrt{3}EI[\cos(30° + \phi) + \cos(30° - \phi)]$$
$$= 3EI \cos\phi = P$$

As with the two-wattmeter method previously discussed, it will be seen that, if the current coil of the instrument has to be reversed to obtain an

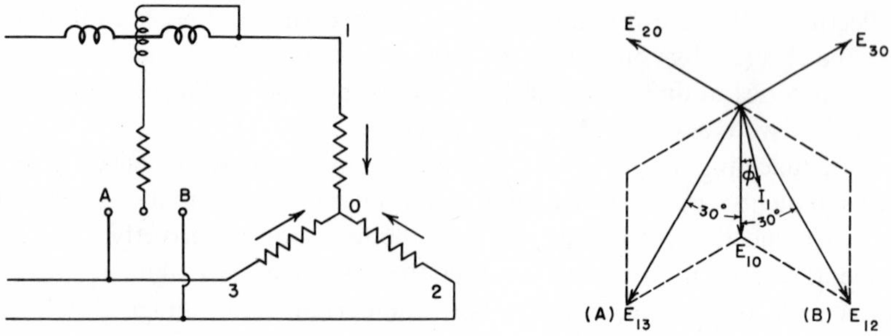

FIG. 21.

upscale reading for either position, that wattmeter reading is subtracted from the other.

BARLOW'S TRANSFORMER METHODS. Two methods utilizing transformers can be used with a single wattmeter to measure three-phase power in a

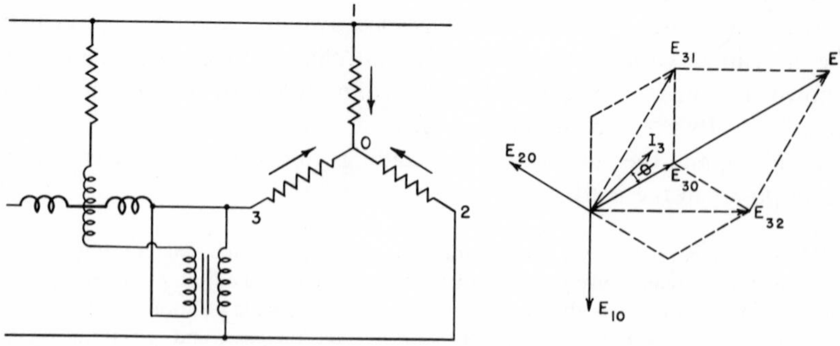

FIG. 22.

balanced load. *Barlow's voltage-transformer method* makes use of a 1/1 voltage transformer in addition to the wattmeter. The connections are shown in Fig. 22. The primary of the voltage transformer is connected between two of the lines, one of which carries the current coil of the wattmeter, and its secondary is connected through the voltage circuit of the wattmeter between the line which carries the current coil, and the third line. Thus two line-to-line voltages are added, and the resultant is in phase with the phase voltage from the line carrying the current coil of the wattmeter. Here we have

$$E_{32} = E_{31} = \sqrt{3}E; \quad E' = \sqrt{3}E_{32} = 3E$$

Then

$$P = E'I \cos \phi = 3EI \cos \phi$$

since E' is in phase with E_{30}. The wattmeter sums the power directly, and its reading equals the total power in the load.

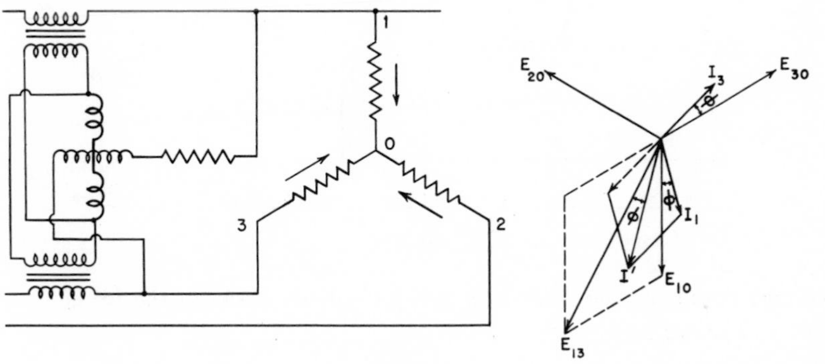

FIG. 23.

Barlow's current-transformer method uses two 1/1 current transformers to add the phase currents from two phases in the current coil of the wattmeter. The connections are shown in Fig. 23. The phase voltages from the same phases are added across the voltage circuit of the wattmeter. In the voltage circuit $E_{31} = \sqrt{3}E$, and in the current circuit $I' = \sqrt{3}I$. Each of these vectors is displaced 30° in the same direction from the corresponding phase vector so that their phase difference ϕ is equal to the angle between E and I in a single phase. Then

$$P = \sqrt{3}E \cdot \sqrt{3}I \cos \phi = 3EI \cos \phi$$

Here also the wattmeter sums the power directly, and its reading is the total power in the load.

Y-BOXES. These arrangements are also employed with a single-phase wattmeter to read the power in a balanced three-phase load. If, in Fig. 24, $r = R$ (the resistance of the voltage circuit of the wattmeter), the connection is identical with one in which the wattmeter is connected in one phase with its voltage circuit connected between line and neutral point. Here the wattmeter reads the power in a single phase, and the total power is three times the wattmeter reading. The Y-box consists of the resistances $(r - r)$ and is usually constructed to match the resistance R of a particular wattmeter. However, it can still be used to measure power in cases where $r \neq R$, i.e. with wattmeters other than that for which it is designed. In this case the instantaneous current i_v in the

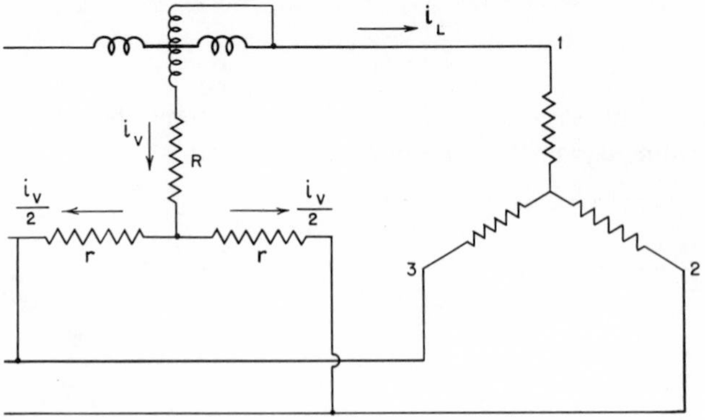

FIG. 24.

voltage circuit of the wattmeter divides equally between the branches of the Y, and we have

$$i_v R + \frac{i_v}{2} r = e_{12} = e_{13}, \quad \text{or} \quad (2R + r)i_v = e_{12} + e_{13},$$

and

$$i_v = \frac{e_{12} + e_{13}}{2R + r}$$

Now the instantaneous torque in the wattmeter is represented by $\mathcal{T} = i_L \cdot R i_v$, and its average value, the wattmeter reading, is

$$R \cdot \frac{1}{T} \int_0^T i_L \cdot i_v \, dt = \frac{R}{2R + r} \frac{1}{T} \int_0^T i_L(e_{12} + e_{13}) \, dt$$

$$= \frac{R}{2R + r} \{I \cdot \sqrt{3} E[\cos (30 + \phi) + \cos (30 - \phi)]\}$$

$$= \frac{R}{2R + r} (3EI)$$

But $3EI = P$ is the total power in the load, so that the power in the load is given by

$$P = \frac{2R + r}{R} \times \text{wattmeter reading}$$

It should be noted that the multiplying factor $(2R + r)/R$ to be used with the Y-box reduces to 3 if $R = r$, as we have already seen.

It will be apparent that it is easier to connect a Y-box with a wattmeter for three-phase power measurements than to apply either of Barlow's transformer methods. However, it should be pointed out that Barlow's methods permit the direct reading of the total power, whereas a multiplying factor is needed to totalize power when a Y-box is used. It should also be realized that *none* of the single-wattmeter methods described above will correctly indicate total power in the load *unless the load is balanced.*

Summation of Power. It is sometimes necessary or convenient to measure the total power in a number of three-phase branch circuits and

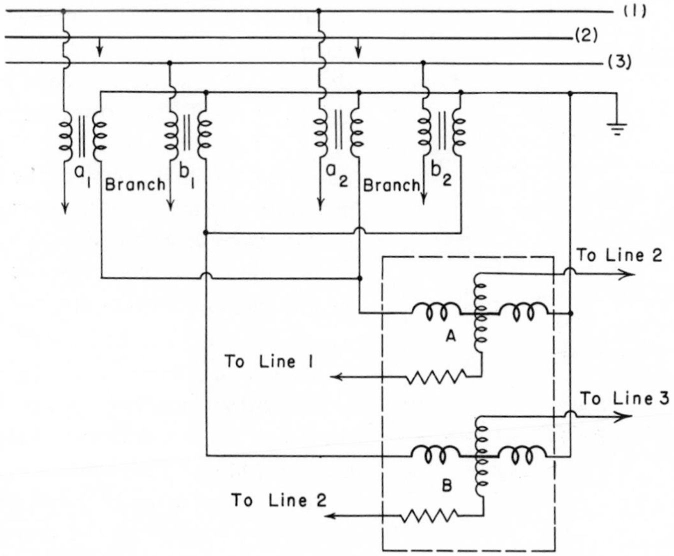

FIG. 25.

to indicate this summation on a single instrument. This can be done with a polyphase wattmeter, together with current transformers to add the currents from the various branches, as is indicated schematically in Fig. 25. The current transformers $a_1, a_2, \cdots$ sum the currents in phase 1 from the various branch circuits and supply the current coil of element *A* of the polyphase wattmeter. The corresponding voltage circuit of the wattmeter is connected between lines 1 and 2 of the system (through a voltage transformer if the voltage is too high for direct connection). Similarly the current transformers $b_1, b_2, \cdots$ sum the currents in phase 3 from the various branch circuits and supply the current coil of element *B* of the wattmeter. The corresponding voltage circuit of the wattmeter is connected between lines 2 and 3 of the system. If we neglect the very small phase angles introduced by the current transformers, the indication of the wattmeter is then

$$P = E_{12} \cdot \Sigma I_1 \cos \phi_1 + E_{23} \Sigma I_3 \cos \phi_3$$

which is the total power in the branch circuits.

Measurement of Reactive Power

It is often convenient or even essential that the reactive power ($Q = EI \sin \phi$) be measured. For example, in load monitoring, such a measurement gives the operator or load dispatcher information concerning the nature of the load and serves as a check on power-factor measurements, since the ratio of reactive to active power is the tangent of the power-factor angle ($Q/P = \tan \phi$). Also the apparent power EI (which determines the line and generator capacity needed for carrying a load) may be determined from measurements of active and reactive power (assuming that the current and voltage are sinusoidal), i.e. $EI = \sqrt{P^2 + Q^2}$.

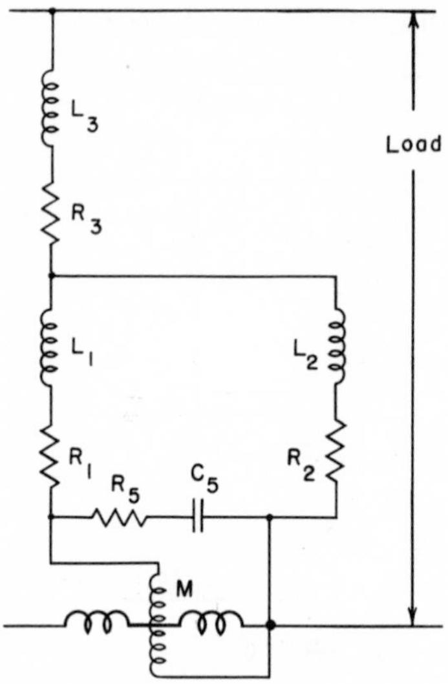

FIG. 26.

Single-Phase Varmeters. In a single-phase circuit reactive power can be measured by a varmeter. This is an electrodynamic instrument in whose voltage circuit a large inductive reactance is in series with the moving coil. A wattmeter may serve as a varmeter by substituting inductive reactance for resistance in the voltage circuit so that the moving-coil current is in quadrature with the impressed voltage. The reactor circuit of the Weston varmeter is shown in Fig. 26. The current in the moving coil can be brought into exact quadrature with the voltage by making the time constant, L_2/R_2, of the shunt circuit enough less than L_1/R_1 to compensate the effects of the resistances R_3 and R_1 necessarily present in the reactor. The mutual inductance between the fixed and moving coils tends to introduce an error except at the midscale position (i.e. the position of zero mutual inductance). A shunting circuit[31] R_5C_5

[31] Unpublished notes of J. H. Miller and R. F. Estoppey of Weston Electrical Instrument Corporation.

can be used to ensure that the circulating current induced by this mutual inductance is in quadrature with the current in the fixed coil and produces no torque. It should be noted that such an instrument does not indicate correctly except at the frequency for which it is adjusted, nor will it indicate correctly the reactive power if harmonics are present. The greater impedance of the inductive voltage circuit at higher frequencies diminishes the current in the voltage circuit and hence reduces the contribution of harmonics to the net torque of the instrument. The effect of harmonics would be magnified if a capacitive reactor were employed.

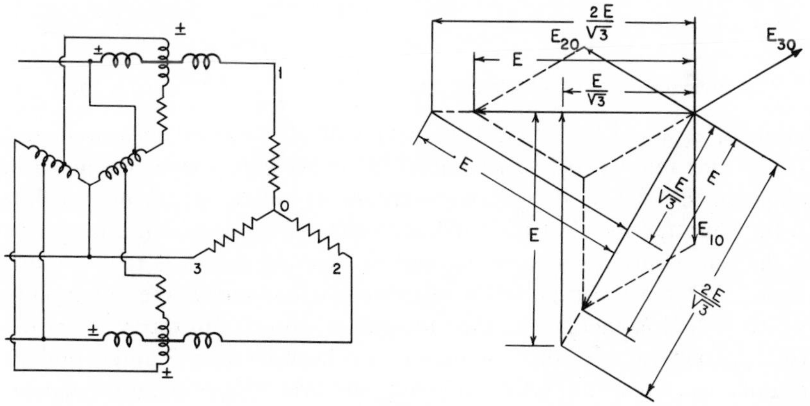

FIG. 27.

Polyphase Varmeters. These differ from wattmeters only in that their voltage circuits are supplied by voltages which are in quadrature with the line-to-line voltages which would be supplied to the same element in the wattmeter connection. One device for accomplishing this is shown in Fig. 27. Two auto-transformers, connected in open delta, are used to obtain the quadrature voltages. Connections to these transformers are brought out at the points 0, $E/\sqrt{3}$, E, $2E/\sqrt{3}$, indicated in the vector diagram. The voltage circuit of a wattmeter element is supplied between the point $E/\sqrt{3}$ on one leg of the delta and the point $2E/\sqrt{3}$ on the other leg. The voltage between these points is equal to and in quadrature with the line-to-line voltage as will be seen from the vector diagram. Such an arrangement is called a "phasing transformer." It should be noted that the phase relations and magnitudes of these voltages are correct only when the line-to-line voltages are symmetrical. Any lack of symmetry will cause the voltages supplied to the voltage circuits of the wattmeters to be incorrect in phase and magnitude and will result in an error in the reading of the varmeter.

CHAPTER 12

ENERGY MEASUREMENTS

The measurement of electrical energy $\left(W = \int_{t_1}^{t_2} ei\, dt\right)$ is, from the viewpoint of economics, the most important of all electrical measurements. If the time interval $(t_2 - t_1)$ is measured in seconds, e in volts, and i in amperes, the energy, W, is in watt-seconds or joules. If the unit of time is the hour and the electrical units are volts and amperes, the energy unit is the watt-hour. A more usual unit in metering energy is the kilowatt-hour. When electric power is generated or consumed, the commodity which is sold is energy, the time integral of power. In recent years the total market value of this commodity has been between 3 and 4 billions of dollars per year in the United States, and over 80% of the total population of the country are consumers. The various steps leading up to the precise measurement of electrical energy have already been discussed, starting with the primary standards of voltage, resistance, and time, and the methods by which they are used in turn to measure current, voltage, power, and energy.[1]

The need for an integrating meter was recognized as soon as electrical energy first became a salable commodity, in commercial arc lighting. The first integrating meter (1872) used to measure such service was a spring-driven clock mechanism whose operation was normally arrested except when an electromagnet in series with the line was energized and released the mechanism. It was not a true energy meter but simply measured the total time during which the circuit was energized. With the advent of incandescent lighting, Edison devised an electrolytic meter (1881) in which the passage of direct current deposited metal on an electrode.

[1] It is interesting to note that if the entire cost of maintaining the electrical standards at the National Bureau of Standards, together with the work which the Bureau does in disseminating these standards and making them available on a nation-wide basis, were assessed against the electrical industry, it would amount to less than 0.005% of the total annual value of the commodity whose accurate measurement is completely dependent on the continuing validity of these standards.

The gain in weight of one electrode was actually a measure of the total number of coulombs ($\int i\,dt$) which flowed in the line between weighings, but could be translated into kilowatt-hours if multiplied by a factor involving the assumed line voltage.[2]

Thomson Watthour Meter

The first true electrical energy meter was the commutator meter developed by Elihu Thomson in 1889. Oddly enough, although the purpose of the inventor was to develop an a-c watthour meter, the Thomson meter has been and still is used primarily for the metering of d-c energy. It was employed very little in a-c metering, because its development was so closely followed (1890–1895) by the induction watthour meter which, as we shall see, is much better adapted to the measurement of a-c energy than is the commutator meter. Thomson's meter is essentially a small motor which is provided with a magnetic brake. As shown in Fig. 1, its field consists of a few turns of heavy copper wire carrying the current of the load being metered, so that its field strength is proportional to the load current; the armature current is proportional to the line voltage. In these respects it resembles an electrodynamic wattmeter, and its driving torque is $\mathscr{T}_d = KEI$. (No iron is used in the fields or armature.) The armature is provided with a silver commutator and silver- or gold-tipped brushes, and is carried on a jewel bearing to minimize friction. As it turns it drives a gear train that registers the total number of revolutions (or this number multiplied by a suitable factor) by means of a set of dials or a cyclometer. If, as we shall see, the speed of rotation is proportional to the driving torque (KEI), the rate of rotation can be used as a measure of power (EI), and the total number of revolutions in a given time is a measure of the energy taken by the load in that time $\left(\int_{t_1}^{t_2} EI\,dt\right)$. In order that the motor speed be proportional to power in the load it is necessary that the counter emf generated in the armature be very small,[3] and hence

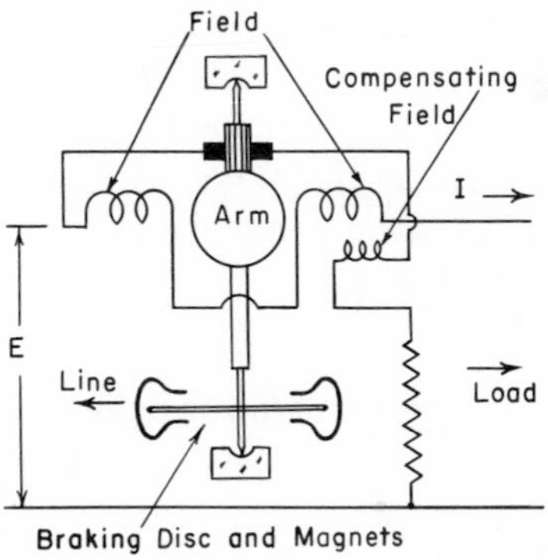

FIG. 1.

[2] "Bills were figured in 'lamp-hours,' the basis being a 16 candle-power, 110 volt, 0.75 ampere lamp. This was easy for the customer to understand, and motors had not yet entered the picture." H. B. BROOKS.

[3] In practice this may amount to 0.1 to 0.2 volt at full-load speed in a 110-volt meter.

a retarding or braking torque, of sufficient magnitude to keep the speed of rotation small, must be provided. An aluminum disc is attached to the motor shaft and intercepts the flux of a permanent magnet. As the disc rotates, eddy currents are induced in it by the flux that it intercepts, and a countertorque results from the reaction between these currents and the field of the magnet. The voltage e induced in the disc by its motion in the field is proportional to its speed of rotation S and to the flux ϕ which it intercepts: $e = K_1 S\phi$. The current i in the disc is inversely proportional to the resistance ρ of the eddy-current path, and the braking torque $\mathscr{T}_b$ at an effective radius r from the axis of the disc is

$$\mathscr{T}_b = K_2\phi i r = K_3\phi \frac{e}{\rho} r = K_4\phi^2 \frac{S}{\rho} r$$

Since the retarding torque of the magnetic brake (used to absorb the output of the motor) is proportional to the speed of rotation, and since at constant speed the driving and retarding torques must be equal, we will have

$$\mathscr{T}_d = \mathscr{T}_b, \quad \text{or} \quad K_d EI = K_b S$$

On integrating this equation we have

$$K_d \int EI\,dt = K_b \int S\,dt$$

which may be written as

$$K_d \times (\text{energy into load}) = K_b \times (\text{total revolutions})$$

Proportionality of speed of rotation to driving torque is fundamental to the proper operation of any watthour meter. Since it is necessary that the braking torque be equal to the driving torque at relatively low speeds, it is advantageous that the disc resistance be low and that ϕ and r be large. An aluminum disc is generally preferred to copper since for a given weight its resistance will be less. Restrictions on weight and size also limit the radius of the disc. Strong magnets, having a large pole area, are used, and the air gap is kept as small as practical mechanical clearance requirements will permit. Magnets are frequently used in pairs, arranged as shown in Fig. 2, with unlike poles adjacent. In this way the flux through the disc establishes eddy currents in shorter paths than if like poles were adjacent.[4] Thus the resistance of the eddy-current

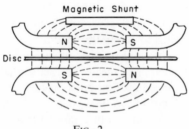

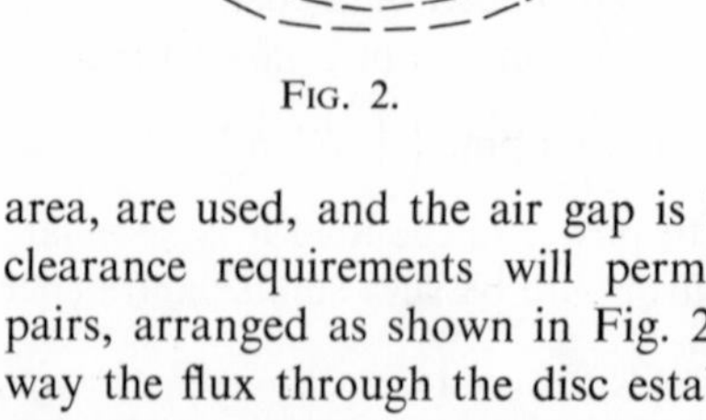

Fig. 2.

[4] This will be apparent if the flux paths are sketched in for the latter arrangement.

circuit is less and the braking torque greater for the arrangement shown. In some meters the braking torque is adjusted by the use of a soft-iron magnetic shunt (shown in Fig. 2), whose distance from the magnet poles can be varied to by-pass a greater or lesser portion of the flux. Its shunting action increases as it is moved closer to the pole pair, reducing the flux which threads the braking disc and therefore reducing the braking torque. It will be noted from the torque equation that torque varies with ϕ^2, so that a 1% change in flux produces a 2% change in braking torque at constant speed, or a 2% change in speed for a constant driving torque.

There are a number of sources of mechanical friction in the Thomson watthour meter: (1) bearings, (2) gear train and meter register, (3) brush pressure on the commutator, and (4) windage. Friction may amount to as much as 1% of full-load driving torque, and brush friction may be $\frac{3}{4}$ of the total. Since the friction (except windage) is practically constant at all rotor speeds, it follows that the frictional torque might be nearly 10% of the driving torque at a 10% load and that the meter would be considerably in error when it operates under light loads unless compensation for the friction is provided. This is accomplished by means of the compensating field coil (shown in Fig. 1) in series with the armature. Its flux adds to that of the field coils which carry the load current, and, since its current is proportional to line voltage, its reaction with the armature current (constant at constant voltage) will contribute a substantially constant driving torque to the motor. Its torque contribution may be adjusted by changing its position relative to the armature to alter the portion of its flux which the armature intercepts.

This type of meter is adjusted by varying the braking torque so that its rate is correct at rated load. In some meters this is accomplished by moving the magnet assembly radially and so changing the lever arm (r) at which the braking force operates. In other meters the magnet position is left unchanged but the magnitude of the braking force is altered by means of the magnetic shunt described above. The field adjustment to compensate friction is usually made at 10% of rated load and is called the "light-load" adjustment. The "light-load" and "full-load" adjustments having been properly made, the meter rate is correct at 10% and 100% load, and the average meter will start at a load somewhat less than 1% of its rated load. Since the friction (especially windage) will vary somewhat with speed, compensation at light loads does not ensure correct registration at other loads. The characteristic performance of a commutator meter is shown in Fig. 3. If the errors resulting from self-heating under sustained loads are not considered, a meter which is correctly adjusted at 10% and 100% load will run fast at intermediate loads and slow under overload conditions. Self-heating errors tend in general to increase the rate in the intermediate range and to decrease it for large loads. An error in the full-load adjustment (braking torque) would result in a constant percentage error at all loads so that the curve of Fig. 3 would be shifted vertically but would remain parallel to itself. An error in the light-load (friction) adjustment would result in a rate error of decreasing relative importance at increasing loads since the friction is roughly constant; i.e. an incorrect light-load adjustment which

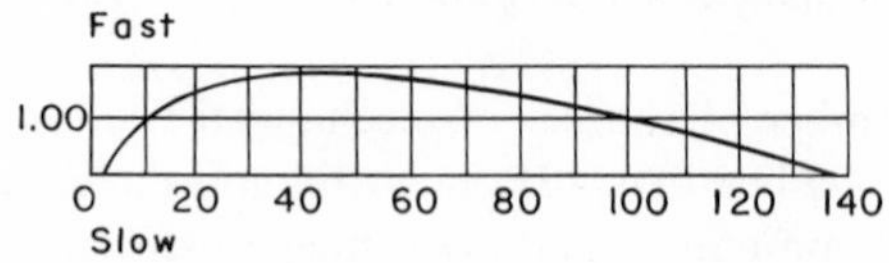

FIG. 3.

would cause a 1% error in the rate at 10% load would result in an error of only 0.1% in the full-load rate.

Mercury Meter

The weight of the moving system of a commutator meter is necessarily large (100 to 150 gm) and the torque-weight ratio is low (0.1 to 0.2 gm-cm/gm). Also the friction is large because of the brush pressure required for good commutation. Both these disadvantages are largely overcome in the mercury meter, in which the rotor is a copper disc floated in mercury and operated as a Barlow wheel.[5] Current is introduced through the mercury near the rim of the disc and enters the disc through an amalgamated zone. The current leaves the disc at a second amalgamated zone near the axis of the disc or at a point on the rim diametrically opposite the entrance point. Radial slots in the disc largely confine current flow to a radial direction. A magnetic field perpendicular to the direction of the current is provided so that a torque is produced which causes the disc to rotate. Thus the relatively high friction of brushes on a commutator is avoided and is replaced by the much lower friction of the copper disc turning in mercury.[6] Also the weight of the entire moving system is supported by the mercury and is adjusted so that there is a very light upward pressure (about 3 gm in the Sangamo meter) against the upper bearing. Bearing friction is thus practically eliminated, and

[5] Barlow's wheel is a rudimentary motor. Descriptions of its action will be found in almost any elementary physics textbook.

[6] In time the mercury may become contaminated, and its friction against the disc may increase to such an extent as to render the meter inoperative. It may, however, be replaced by clean mercury to restore the meter to operation.

the torque-weight[7] ratio is very much higher (about 10 times) than in the commutator meter.

The essential features of the Sangamo mercury watthour meter are shown schematically in Fig. 4. The electromagnet *M* is supplied from the line. Light-load adjustment is obtained by connecting, in series with the voltage circuit, a heater element *H* which supplies heat to a thermo-junction *T*. This thermocouple supplies a small current to the disc in the same direction as the load current. The resistance of the thermo-couple circuit is altered by changing the position of the clamp *S* in order to bring the meter rate to its correct value at 10% load. Compensation for increased fluid friction between the disc and the mercury at high speeds is obtained by an auxiliary winding *W* on the electromagnet, which supplies added flux when the load current is large. For meters operating on load currents above 10 amp, a shunt is used in the current circuit, as indicated in Fig. 4. To adjust the multiplying factor of the shunt, resistance is varied at *N* in the lead from the shunt to the current element of the meter. An internal 60-mv shunt is used with currents up to 80 amp, and an external 75-mv shunt with currents of 100 amp or more. The higher-voltage shunt is needed because of additional lead resistance, and the meter may be located at any distance up to 25 ft from the current bus. The position of the brake magnets is fixed, and the full-load adjustment is made by means of a magnetic shunt of the type previously described. Mercury *ampere-hour* meters are of similar construction except that a permanent magnet is used with the disc in place of an electromagnet to provide driving torque.

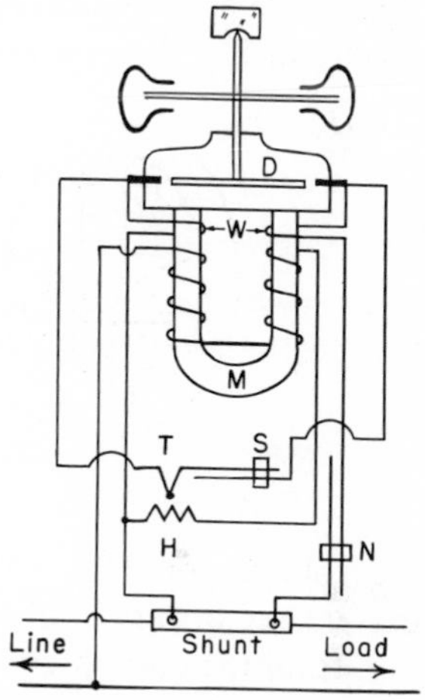

FIG. 4.

The Induction Watthour Meter

This is essentially an induction motor whose output is largely absorbed by its braking system and dissipated as heat. The basic principles of the induction meter, utilizing two magnetic fields displaced in space and time, were worked out by Shallenberger (1888) in an induction ampere-hour meter, quite independently of the invention of the induction motor (Tesla, 1886). Shallenberger was also the first (1895) to realize a means for bringing the operating flux from the voltage circuit of the watthour

[7] The upward thrust of the rotor rather than its weight must be considered here.

meter into quadrature with the impressed voltage, making it possible to measure a-c energy precisely at any load power factor.[8] Subsequent developments by a great number of workers have resulted in design simplifications, improvement of operating characteristics, and better performance both at overloads and over a wide temperature range. As a result the modern induction watthour meter is an inexpensive and accurate device which is expected to retain its accuracy over a very wide range of loads and ambient conditions for long periods of time, with little or no maintenance.

The pole arrangement of an induction watthour meter is shown schematically in Fig. 5. Two current poles (2, 4) are displaced in space from

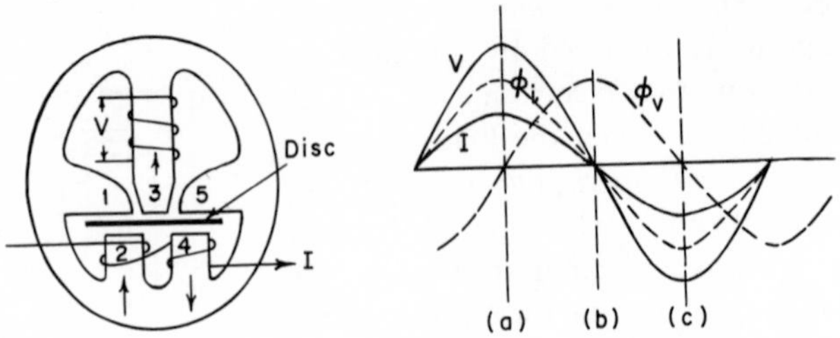

FIG. 5.

the voltage pole (3). Consider first the case in which the voltage and current vectors are in phase (i.e. unity power factor), and assume that the flux from the current coils is in phase with the current, and that the flux from the voltage coil is in quadrature with the voltage, as shown in the figure. At time (*a*) the current is maximum, the current flux ϕ_i is also maximum, and the voltage flux ϕ_v is zero. The flux paths which intercept the disc are upward from 2 to 1 and from 2 to 3, and downward from 3 to 4 and from 5 to 4. A quarter-cycle later, at time (*b*), when I and V are zero, ϕ_v is maximum and the flux paths intercepting the disc are upward from 2 to 3 and from 4 to 3. After another quarter-cycle, at time (*c*), when ϕ_v is again zero, the flux paths are downward from 1 to 2

[8] A history of the development of the watthour meter may be found in an AIEE Committee Report, Progress in the Art of Metering Electric Energy, published in *Electrical Engineering*, **60** (1941). Dr. Blathy (of Ganz and Company, Hungary), in a letter to the editor of *Electrical Engineering*, June 1937, claims the invention of the induction watthour meter on the basis of a U.S. Patent issued in 1889. This patent described a watthour meter with shunt and series coils, in which the shunt coils were made highly inductive. It did not have a lag adjustment (see below), but depended on the inductance of the shunt coil to minimize errors at low power factors. Blathy states that one of his meters was in error by only 2.5% at 0.5 power factor (lagging) and 100% load. Thus it was a reasonably good meter. However, Shallenberger's meter was the first in which correct registration independent of power factor was theoretically attainable.

and from 3 to 2, and upward from 4 to 3 and from 4 to 5. The upwardly directed flux has in effect moved across the disc from left to right. This shifting field induces voltages and sets up eddy currents in the disc. The reaction of these eddy currents with the field produces a torque which tends to rotate the disc in the direction of motion of the field. Although this simplified analysis gives a qualitative picture of the meter action, it does not show how the meter measures energy.

The Torque Equation. A more complete analysis must take into account the fact that, when a current-carrying conductor is acted on by

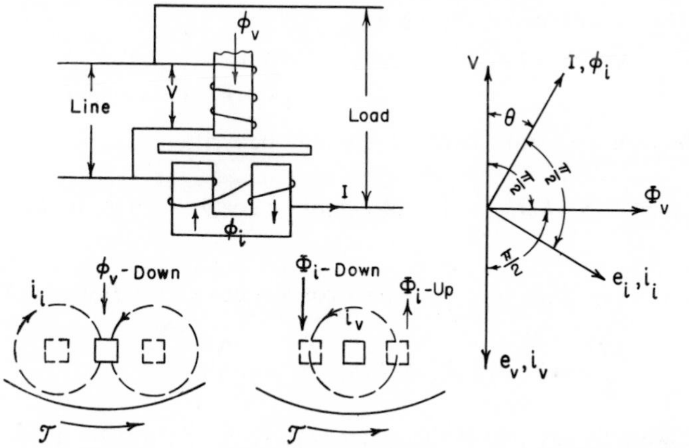

FIG. 6.

a magnetic field, the force which it experiences is proportional to the product of the current and the field. The motor torque can be expressed as $\mathscr{T} = K\phi i$, where K is a geometrical factor that depends on the configuration of the conductor and of the field. We will assume for simplicity that the effective eddy currents produced by the current-pole flux can be approximated by an equivalent eddy current i_i whose path links the flux from the voltage pole, and that the equivalent eddy current i_v from the voltage flux has a path which links the flux from the current poles, as shown in Fig. 6. We will also assume that the active flux from the voltage pole lags by 90° behind the impressed voltage, and that the eddy currents in the disc are in phase with the voltages induced in the disc, i.e. lag by 90° the currents in the voltage and current coils respectively of the meter.[9] The instantaneous disc torque may be written as

$$\mathscr{T} = K(\phi_v i_i - \phi_i i_v)$$

[9] This is, of course, a somewhat idealized case since in practice the eddy-current circuits have some inductance associated with them. This situation will be considered later.

There are no components of average torque from $\phi_v \cdot i_v$ or $\phi_i \cdot i_i$, since each is a product of vectors which are in quadrature. Now

$$e = V \sin \omega t; \quad i = I \sin (\omega t - \theta)$$

$$\phi_i = K_1 I \sin (\omega t - \theta); \quad \phi_v = K_2 V \cos \omega t$$

Also

$$i_i = K_3 \frac{d\phi_i}{dt} = K_3 I \omega \cos (\omega t - \theta)$$

$$i_v = - K_4 V \sin \omega t$$

Then the instantaneous torque is

$$\mathcal{T} = K[K_2 K_3 \omega VI \cos \omega t \cdot \cos (\omega t - \theta) + K_1 K_4 \omega VI \sin \omega t \cdot \sin (\omega t - \theta)]$$

and the average torque over a cycle may be written as

$$\mathcal{T}_{\text{ave}} = VIK \left[K_2 K_3 \frac{1}{2\pi} \int_0^{2\pi} \cos \omega t (\cos \omega t \cos \theta + \sin \omega t \sin \theta)\, d(\omega t) + K_1 K_4 \cdot \frac{1}{2\pi} \int_0^{2\pi} (\sin \omega t \cos \theta - \cos \omega t \sin \theta) \sin \omega t\, d(\omega t) \right]$$

$$= \frac{VI}{2} \cos \theta \cdot K(K_2 K_3 + K_1 K_4) \propto \text{power}$$

Hence we may say that if the meter is to register correctly at any power factor it is essential that the active voltage flux lag the applied voltage by 90°, as we had assumed.

Lag Adjustment. It will be realized that the current in the voltage coil cannot lag the applied voltage by 90°, since resistance as well as inductance will be present in the winding. However, by introducing a magnetic shunt circuit which will allow the main portion of the voltage-coil flux to by-pass the gap in which the disc is located, it is possible to introduce a magnetómotive force in the proper phase relation to bring the flux in the disc air gap into quadrature with the voltage. This is shown in Fig. 7. The required mmf is obtained from a "lag coil" which is located on the potential pole very close to the disc gap, and which links the flux that the disc intercepts. A voltage e_L is induced in this coil (as in the secondary of a transformer), and the current i_L in the coil will lag behind the induced voltage by an angle α which depends on the reactance and the resistance R_L of the lag-coil circuit. The flux ϕ_g in the potential-pole gap of the magnetic circuit will arise from the combined action of the main mmf $\mathcal{F}_s$ in phase with I_V and the lag-coil mmf $\mathcal{F}_L$ in phase with i_L, and will be in phase with their resultant $\phi_g \mathcal{R}_g$, where $\mathcal{R}_g$ is the reluctance of this branch of the magnetic circuit. It will be seen that the phase of this flux can be adjusted by varying either R_L or the coupling of this coil with the magnetic circuit. Both methods have been used. In some meters a few turns of wire are placed around the voltage pole and the resistance of this circuit is altered to adjust the lag angle of the active flux. An increase in resistance decreases the current and mmf in the lag coil and therefore decreases the lag angle. In other meters a single-turn lag coil consisting of a punched "lag plate" is used (see Fig. 8). The material and cross section of the lag plate are such that appropriate values of impedance and of mmf are obtained. The lag plate is situated in the air gap directly

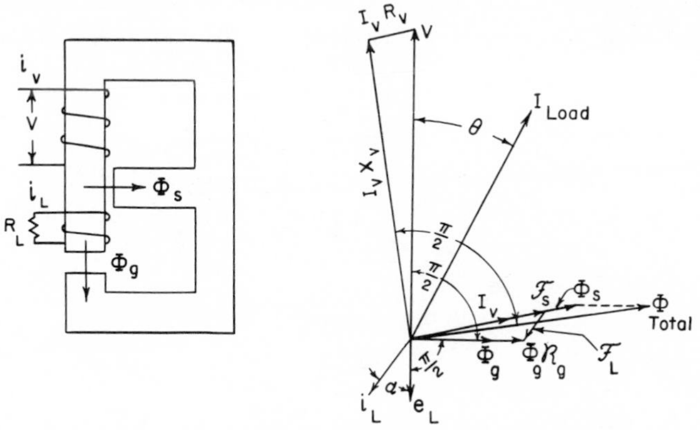

FIG. 7.

beneath the voltage pole, and the lag angle is adjusted by moving the plate either radially with respect to the axis of the disc or parallel to the axis of the disc, so that it links with more or less of the active flux. Thereby its induced voltage is altered with a corresponding change in its current and mmf.[10]

In order to simplify the discussion of lag adjustment it has been assumed that the active voltage flux should be brought into exact quadrature with the impressed voltage. Actually the current flux will lag very slightly behind the current because of copper and iron losses in the current circuit of the meter. Also some inductance will of necessity be associated with the eddy-current paths in the meter disc, so that these currents will lag the induced voltages in the disc by a small angle. Hence it would be more exact to say that, if the electromagnetic structure were so compensated that at a unity-power-factor load the voltage flux was in phase with the eddy currents induced in the disc by the load current in the

[10] A similar plate, movable in a direction tangential to the disc, is used to compensate frictional torque so that the meter rate may be adjusted at light load. This adjustment will be discussed later.

current coils, the torque reactions of fluxes and eddy currents would be proportional to cos θ at all power factors, and the meter would be correctly lagged.[11] However, the approximation already made (i.e. that the flux in the voltage pole should lag the impressed voltage by 90°) describes the situation reasonably well. The angle between the induced voltage and current in the disc is substantially constant at a fixed frequency; and it can be shown[12] that, if the lag-angle compensation is correctly made, the contribution of the eddy-current lag angle to the meter torque is not appreciably a function of power factor but may be considered a constant multiplier in the torque equation. It is therefore automatically compensated if the regular adjustments of the meter are correct. In practice the lag adjustment is usually made so that the rate is correct at a 50% power-factor load, since the effect of an incorrect lag adjustment is greater at low than at high power factors.[13]

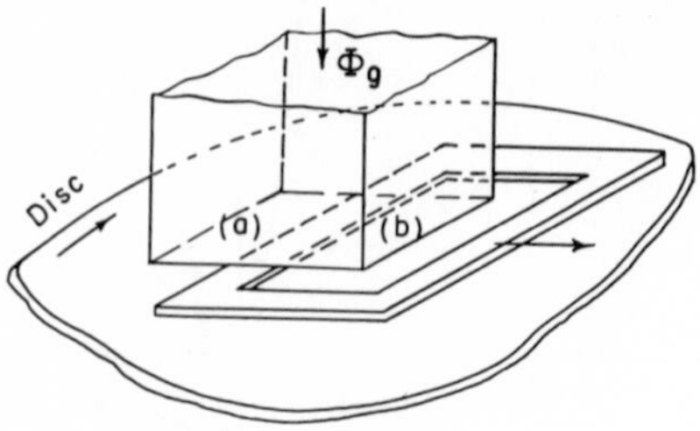

FIG. 8.

The Light-Load Adjustment. Friction is compensated in the induction watthour meter by lagging the flux in a portion of the voltage pole by means of a stamped lag plate or "single-turn winding" as shown in Fig. 8. The voltage pole is "shaded" by displacing the stamping in a direction parallel to the direction of motion of the disc, and the resulting contribution to the driving torque is adjusted to compensate the frictional torque. The action of the shading coil may be explained as follows. In the position shown, the light-load plate links only a portion of the active flux ϕ_g from the voltage pole. During the part of the cycle in which ϕ_g is increasing, an emf will be induced and a current will circulate in the plate in such a direction that (by Lenz's law) its mmf opposes the increase in the inducing flux which links it. Hence the flux density will be less in

[11] This statement could, of course, be completely correct only for a single voltage and a particular value of load current because of the non-linear character of the magnetic circuit.

[12] See Knowlton, *Electric Power Metering*, p. 139, McGraw-Hill, 1934.

[13] See Chapter 11 for a discussion of the effect of lag angle in the voltage circuit of a wattmeter, an analogous case.

region (*b*) of Fig. 8 than in region (*a*), where no counter mmf from the plate acts. When ϕ_g reaches a maximum value and $d\phi_g/dt = 0$, no voltage is induced in the light-load plate and no counter mmf is present from this source, so that the flux density in region (*b*) is equal to that in region (*a*). When ϕ_g decreases, the current in the plate is in such a direction that its mmf opposes the decrease, and the flux density is higher at (*b*) than at (*a*). Thus a shift in flux takes place from left to right (in the direction of motion of the disc) and contributes to the driving torque. The dimensions and resistance of the light-load plate are chosen so that its torque contribution is sufficient to compensate any expected value of frictional torque. It should be noted that this torque will increase with an increase in ϕ_g, and hence will rise with increasing voltage, so that if the line voltage is abnormally high the disc may have a tendency to "creep" under no-load conditions because the frictional torque is overcompensated.

The *rate adjustments* of the induction watthour meter, accessible to the operator, may be summarized as: (1) the *full-load* adjustment, made at rated load by changing the radial position or effective strength of the braking magnets; (2) the *light-load* adjustment, made at 10% of rated load by moving a stamping in a direction parallel to the direction of motion of the meter disc; and (3) the *lag* adjustment, usually made at 50% power factor by adjusting the resistance of a special lag winding or by moving a lag plate in a radial direction.

Factors Influencing Operation. LOAD CURRENT. The motion of the disc past the current and voltage poles of the watthour meter induces eddy currents in addition to those induced by the changing fluxes. These eddy currents react with the fluxes present to produce a braking effect in the same way that it is produced by the permanent magnets used for braking the disc. Similarly the braking torque is proportional to the disc speed and to the square of the active flux.[14] The braking torque contributed by the voltage pole is proportional to the speed since, under most practical use conditions, the line voltage fluctuates over a rather small range and the voltage-pole flux is therefore nearly constant. Thus, at constant line voltage, the contribution of the voltage-pole flux is constant and quite like that of the damping magnets, and does not cause an error in registration. On the other hand, the current-pole flux varies with the load; and, since the braking is proportional to ϕ^2, its contribution to damping becomes unduly large with increasing loads where the load current is large. The braking resulting from the action of the current-pole flux is, in fact, the most important limitation to the accuracy of the meter under overload conditions. The braking effect of the current-pole flux is minimized by reducing the number of ampere-turns

[14] See p. 514.

in the current coils (with a corresponding increase in ampere-turns in the voltage coil), and by decreasing the disc speed for a given value of power in the load (with a corresponding increase in the strength of the braking magnets). However, these expedients are not sufficient to meet present requirements for accurate overload metering[15] (up to 400% of rated current), and an overload-compensating device is used in modern meters to extend their range of accurate operation. This consists of a magnetic shunt between the current poles, which approaches saturation and decreases in permeability at overload currents. Thus at large currents the shunt diverts less of the current-coil flux, so that a larger portion of the flux appears in the air gap and contributes to the driving torque. Figure 9 shows the performance of a typical modern watthour meter

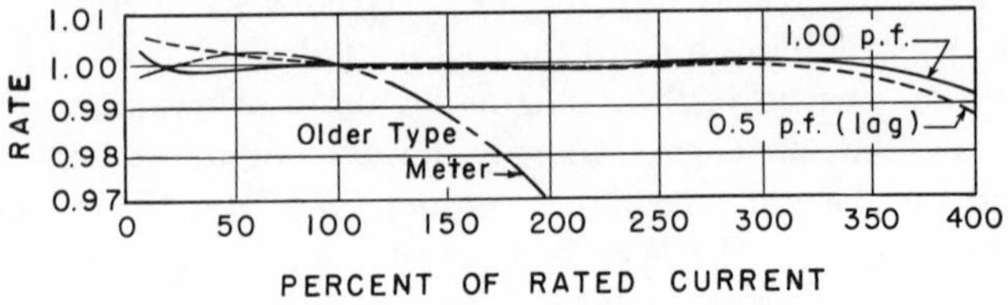

FIG. 9.

under varying load, together with that of an earlier meter in which the "load shunt" was not used. Actually, in many applications, correct operation at light loads is most important since the meter will operate under these conditions most of the time. The overload correction is provided for the occasional heavy loads that will be encountered, but it is not expected that the meter will be operated regularly under severe overload conditions since the disc speed would be high and the resulting bearing wear would be excessive.

VOLTAGE VARIATION. The voltage flux will increase with an increase in voltage. This results in an increased braking, and a tendency for the meter to run slow at higher than normal voltages and fast at reduced voltages, since the driving torque increases with the first power of the flux, whereas the braking torque increases with the square of the flux. In addition to the effect on braking, an increase in voltage will increase the power consumption in the voltage coil so that its temperature and

[15] The maximum load which the meter is required to register in residential service is increasing with increasing use of electrical appliances in the home. However, large loads are usually of an intermittent nature, and the meter operates under small loads much of the time. Thus it is essential that the light-load performance of the meter be good, and meters having a high current rating are precluded. Therefore it is necessary to continue the use of low-range meters with their inherently better performance on very small loads and to improve their performance on large overloads.

resistance will rise. This will reduce the lag angle somewhat, resulting in an increased rate at low power factors (current lagging). The driving-torque contribution of the shaded pole will also increase with voltage, as has already been stated, so that, at light loads, the meter rate may tend to be high when the voltage is high. All these effects are small and, for most meters, can be expected to be not more than 0.2 to 0.3% for a voltage change of 10% from rated value. In some modern meters the principal effect, that of increased braking with increased voltage, has been compensated by proportioning the magnetic circuit of the voltage flux (see Fig. 7) so that the portion which carries the shunted flux ϕ_s is operating in a region of decreasing permeability, whereas the return path for the gap flux ϕ_g operates in a region of increasing permeability. Thus,

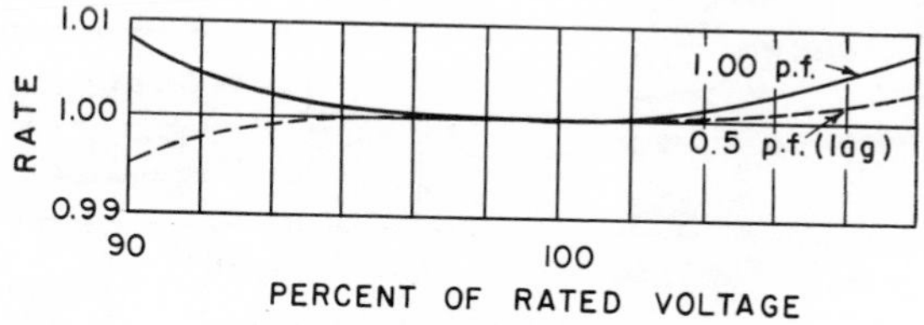

FIG. 10.

when the voltage rises, a larger fraction of the flux traverses the disc and the added driving torque compensates the increased braking torque; i.e. the driving torque increases faster than the first power of the voltage. Figure 10 shows the effect of changes in voltage for operation at rated load both at unity power factor and at 50% power factor (current lagging).

FREQUENCY VARIATION. The voltage coil is highly inductive, so that its current and flux will decrease with increasing frequency. The current coils are nearly non-inductive, and the current-coil flux will be nearly independent of frequency. The eddy currents established in the disc by the current flux will therefore be proportional to frequency, and their reaction with the voltage flux (which is inversely proportional to frequency) should be very nearly independent of frequency since the torque is proportional to the product of the reacting quantities. The eddy currents established in the disc by the voltage flux should be very nearly independent of frequency, since the voltage flux varies inversely with frequency, and the induced voltage in the disc (for a given value of flux) varies directly with frequency. The torque contribution from the reaction of the "constant" current-pole flux with the "constant" eddy currents from the voltage-pole flux should also be nearly independent of frequency. Thus at a unity-power-factor load one would expect the meter rate to be independent of frequency to a first approximation. The above analysis is overly simplified, and certain other factors must be considered. The division of the voltage-coil flux between the disc gap and the shunt path (see Fig. 7) alters with changing frequency as a result of the change in relative reluctance of the alternative paths with changing flux density, and the useful voltage flux decreases more rapidly than $1/f$ decreases. Also the impedance of the eddy-current paths is increased with increasing frequency,[16] and the eddy currents are relatively less than our first approximation implied. The consequence of both these factors is a reduction in the driving torque with increasing frequency, so that the meter would tend to run slow on a unity-power-factor load at a frequency above normal. For loads at power factors other than unity the effect of frequency on the lag adjustment must also be considered. Although the current in the voltage coil decreases with increasing frequency, the iron

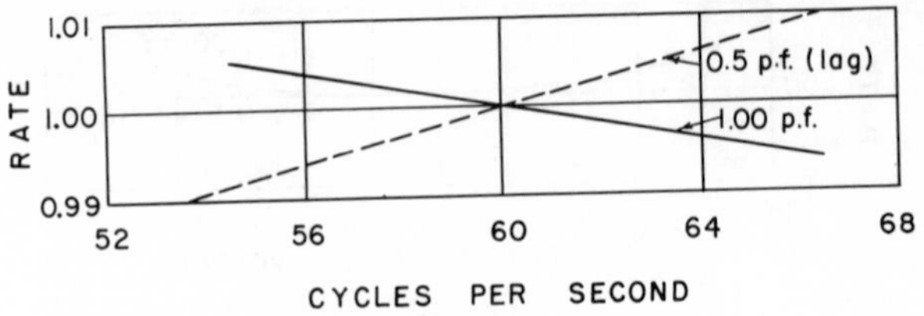

FIG. 11.

losses in the electromagnet increase more rapidly than the copper losses decrease, so that the lag angle of the voltage flux decreases somewhat. The increased inductive reactance (with increasing frequency) of the lag coil or lag plate causes its current to lag further behind the voltage induced in it. The net result is usually that the lag-defect angle is overcompensated, and the meter tends to run fast on inductive loads at elevated frequencies. Figure 11 shows the frequency influence on the performance of a modern watthour meter.

HARMONICS. An analysis of the effect of harmonics in the voltage and current wave forms would be exceedingly complicated and cannot be undertaken here. An extension of the analysis of the effect of frequency variation should yield a qualitative answer. If we neglect the distortion introduced by the iron in the magnetic circuit of the watthour meter, we may say that, unless a particular harmonic is present in both the voltage and current wave forms, it will have no effect on the meter registration.[17] If a particular harmonic were present in both waves and in phase with

[16] The inductance of the eddy-current paths is greater if the iron of the voltage and current poles is close to the disc than if it is moderately far away. This is one reason that a relatively large air gap is used even though it results in some sacrifice of driving torque.

[17] For a discussion of this point, see p. 473, Chapter 11.

each other, it would tend to make the registration low (see Fig. 11). Similarly, if the harmonic in the current wave lagged behind the phase of the same harmonic in the voltage wave, it would tend to increase the registration. As a practical matter this simplified picture is inadequate since an appreciable third harmonic does exist in the voltage flux for a sinusoidal applied voltage, this distortion being introduced by the varying permeability of the magnetic circuit. Hence a torque can result from the presence of a third harmonic that appears only in the current wave. An experimental and theoretical analysis by Ennis[18] has shown that the modern watthour meter is relatively insensitive to distortions. For example, the maximum observed error caused by a third harmonic of current equal in magnitude to the fundamental was less than 2%.

TEMPERATURE. Since watthour meters are frequently required to operate in outdoor installations and are subject to extreme temperatures that may range from more than 100°F to well below 0°F, the effects of temperature and their compensation are very important. The resistance of the disc, of the potential coil, and of the lag plate are all affected, as well as the characteristics of the magnetic circuit and the strength of the braking magnets. Both the magnitudes and the phase relations of the active fluxes are altered with temperature, and consequently the registration both at unity power factor and at low power factors is influenced by temperature variation.

Temperature influences can be conveniently grouped into two classes. Factors which affect the magnitudes of the various fluxes (both driving and braking) are grouped together as *Class I* temperature effects. Those which affect the lag angle between the voltage and current fluxes are grouped as *Class II*. Obviously Class II errors will be present only when the metered load is reactive,[19] whereas Class I errors may affect the meter rate at all loads, regardless of power factor. Experimentally, the largest source of Class I errors is the change in strength of the braking magnets with temperature. The air-gap flux of an uncompensated magnet may be expected to decrease 0.02 to 0.03%/°C rise in temperature. Since braking torque depends on the square of the flux, this would result in 0.4 to 0.6% decrease in braking for a 10°C rise in temperature and a corresponding rise in disc speed. Changes in the resistance of the voltage

[18] This work, by A. G. Ennis, was reported in a dissertation, "The Effect of Distortion on Registration of Watthour Meters," The Johns Hopkins University (1941), but has not yet been published.

[19] This statement applies only to single-phase metering. In polyphase metering, where the angles between voltage and current in the separate elements do not correspond to the load-power-factor angle, Class II errors may be present in the individual meter elements even though the load power factor is unity. See the discussion of polyphase power measurements, p. 502, in Chapter 11.

coil and in the permeability of the magnetic circuit will also cause changes in the magnitude of the driving flux, but these changes are small. It might be thought that the large temperature coefficient of the aluminum disc (0.4%/°C) would cause large errors by changing the magnitudes of the eddy currents. However, since the driving and braking torques act on the same disc, any change in disc conductivity will affect both by equal amounts and there will be no resultant error.

Since the principal source of Class I temperature errors is the change in strength of the braking magnets, compensation can be readily introduced at the magnets to minimize this error. One method that has been used in the past for this compensation is to mount the magnets on a supporting structure having a suitable temperature coefficient of expansion to keep the torque at its required value by automatically increasing the radial distance from the axis of the disc as the air-gap flux decreases with increasing temperature. However, this type of compensation has been almost universally superseded by the use of magnetic shunts.[20] Certain alloys of nickel and copper with small added amounts of manganese and iron decrease in permeability very rapidly with increasing temperature in the range over which compensation is desired. These materials, called "thermalloys," have Curie temperatures[21] not far above normal ambient temperatures. The Curie point is dependent on the copper content of the alloy, being depressed by the addition of copper. Two blocks of such material, one having a Curie point around 100°C and the other a Curie point about 20°C, are inserted in the braking-magnet assembly as shown in Fig. 12. Since the permeability of these "shunts" decreases more rapidly than does the material of the magnets themselves, some of the flux which they carry at low temperature is forced through the air gap as the temperature increases, maintaining the air-gap flux at the required value despite the decreasing strength of the magnets. One element of the shunt is effective in the higher temperature range, and the other at low temperatures (below 20°C). In this way Class I temperature errors are compensated over a very wide range of ambient temperatures.

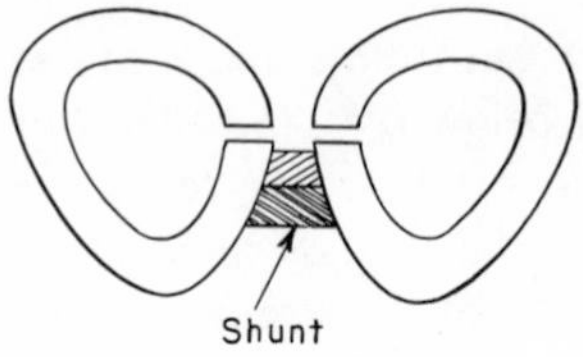

FIG. 12.

The principal source of Class II temperature errors is the change in resistance of the voltage coil, which changes the lag angle of the voltage flux. The lag plate (or lag coil) also changes in resistance, but this effect is smaller. The net result is to decrease the lag angle of the voltage flux

[20] Kinnard and Faus, *Trans. AIEE*, **44**, 275 (1925).

[21] See p. 346, Chapter 9.

at higher temperatures and therefore (see Fig. 6) to decrease the driving torque and rate of the meter on a lagging power factor. Two methods of Class II temperature compensation are used in modern watthour meters. Thermalloy strips are fastened around one side of the lag plate so that the plate is linked with a temperature-sensitive core. As the temperature increases, the permeability of this core decreases, the impedance is reduced, and more current flows in the lag plate. The increased mmf which results brings the active flux into the proper phase relation with the applied voltage (see Fig. 7). Another method of compensating Class II errors involves overlagging the voltage flux with a lag coil having a low temperature coefficient of resistance. The current flux is also lagged, with lag coils having a high temperature coefficient of resistance (say copper)

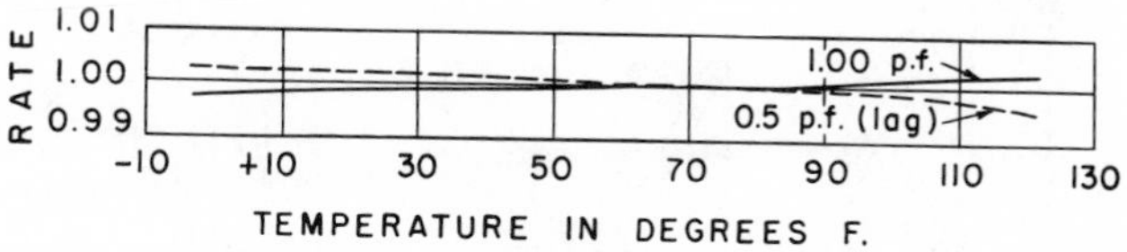

FIG. 13.

placed around the current poles, to reduce the equivalent lag angle to 90°. An increase in temperature, which increases the resistance of the voltage coil and decreases the lag angle of the voltage flux, also decreases the lag angle of the current flux. By properly proportioning the two lag circuits, the resultant net change in angle can be made very small. The variation of meter rate with temperature is shown in Fig. 13 for a modern meter having good compensation for both Class I and Class II temperature errors. Without compensation the changes of rate with temperature might be expected to be 10 to 20 times as great as those shown in the figure.

Meter Stability. Long-time accuracy (or stability) of a meter is an important consideration. Because of the very great number of meters in service, and the time and expense that are involved in periodically adjusting them, it is obviously very advantageous that their construction be such as to ensure commercially negligible changes in their accuracy over a period of several years under normal use conditions. General design and construction features must be such as to ensure ruggedness of the working parts and ability to withstand the hazards of service. Two possible sources of trouble are bearings and brake magnets. If excessive friction develops, the meter will tend to run slow, particularly at light loads; if the magnets decrease in strength, the meter will tend to run fast at all loads. In a test of 40,000 meters, after a 4-year period of operation, it was found that at rated load 78% of them had errors of 1% or less, while 99% had errors of less than 4%; at light loads 67% had errors smaller than 1 %, while 97 % had errors less than 4 %. More meters ran slow than fast, and excessive friction was the most common source of error.

Three types of load-carrying bearings are in current use and are shown schematically in Fig. 14. Construction (*a*) has a conventional pivot and sapphire jewel used as a lower bearing. Construction (*b*) has a lower bearing consisting of a hardened ball rolling between a fixed lower jewel and a rotating upper jewel carried at the bottom of the shaft. This latter bearing has shown better wear characteristics in general than the conventional pivot-jewel bearing and is used in many modern meters.[22] Construction (*c*) has a magnetic suspension developed by the General

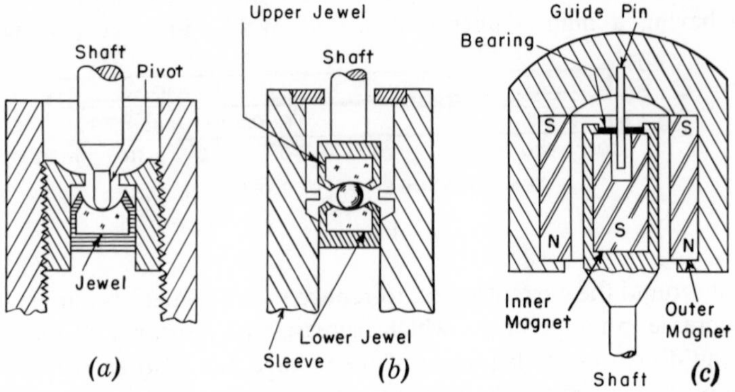

FIG. 14.

Electric Company and incorporated in their I-50 meter.[23] In this construction the suspension consists of coaxial cylindrical magnets, the inner magnet being carried at the upper end of the meter shaft and the outer magnet attached to the frame. A stainless-steel guide pin, attached to the stationary magnet assembly, engages a graphite guide bushing in the rotating magnet assembly. This, together with a similar pin and bushing arrangement at the lower end of the shaft, maintains the axial alignment of the rotating system and, since the entire weight of the moving system is "floated" by the magnetic suspension, serves merely to absorb the side thrust of the rotor.[24] The concentric magnetic flotation is made possible

[22] In constructions (*a*) and (*b*), which have jeweled lower bearings, an upper sleeve bearing is used to maintain alignment of the rotor. This upper bearing is lubricated in some instances and is operated dry in others.

[23] Trekell, Mendelsohn, and Wright, *Trans. AIEE*, **67**, 1180 (1948); Kinnard, *Electrical Engineering*, **67**, 627 (1948).

Some early types of magnetic suspensions have been described by Drysdale and Jolley, *Electrical Measuring Instruments*, Vol. 2, p. 69, Benn, 1924.

[24] The thrust load on these pin-bushing assemblies is of the order of 100 psi, whereas the combined weight and thrust loading of the jewel bearings previously described is

by the use of Cunico, a machinable magnetic alloy of high coercivity. The inner and outer cylinders are machined to close tolerances from bar stock and are assembled in die castings to maintain accurate concentricity. The die casting carrying the outer, stationary magnet is adjustable in height, as is the casting carrying the pin at the lower sleeve bearing, in order that the air-gap clearances at the disc may be set correctly. The outer and inner magnets are magnetized so that their poles appear on their end faces, and are assembled as shown in Fig. 14 so that the north pole of the inner magnet is adjacent to the south pole of the outer magnet.

Loss of strength in the braking magnets of a meter is minimized by using properly aged and stabilized magnets. One hazard which is encountered, particularly on rural lines, is their demagnetization as a result of transient mmf's set up in the current coils of the meter by surge currents from lightning strokes. Although this is actually a rather rare occurrence, it may result in considerable customer ill-will by causing the meter to run fast; i.e. the strength of the magnets cannot be greatly increased but can be considerably decreased by a surge. Shielding against such effects is possible by making the structure that supports the main assembly of steel and locating it between the electromagnet and braking magnets to provide electromagnetic shielding between them. Danger of accidental demagnetization is further reduced by using a high-coercivity material such as Alnico for the braking magnets. Additional shielding may be provided by heavily copper-plating the magnets so that the eddy currents set up in the copper by the surge field will produce a counter mmf that helps to neutralize the field incidental to the surge. Equivalent shielding is obtained in the G.E. I-50 meter, whose Alnico brake magnets are completely surrounded by the metal of the die casting in which they are assembled.

Polyphase Meters

Polyphase energy could, of course, be metered by a group of single-phase meters connected as required by Blondel's theorem,[25] the total energy being the algebraic sum of the readings of all the watthour meters

of the order of 200,000 psi. The construction utilizing magnetic suspension does, of course, greatly reduce the hazards of bearing damage in handling and operation, since the static loading of jewel bearings is only a moderate amount lower than the elastic limit of the materials. Also it is to be expected that development of excessive friction from bearing wear would be less of a problem in the suspension-type bearing than in the jewel bearing. However, it should not be assumed that, for bearings which are in good condition, the total friction load is much less in a meter having suspension-type bearings than in one having a jewel bearing, particularly since much of the friction resides in the gear train in either case.

[25] See Chapter 11.

(a negative sign being applied to the reading of any meter which runs backward). However, this is never done commercially as it would be both more expensive and more troublesome than the use of polyphase meters. Such meters have two or more single-phase meter elements within the same case, driving a single shaft and register. In some meters separate discs are used with each electromagnet; in others two electromagnets drive the same disc, which is slotted or laminated in sectors to prevent eddy currents set up by one element from interacting with the other. In any event the elements must be so arranged and shielded that there is no interaction. The adjustments of a polyphase meter are the same in principle as those of a single-phase meter. Full-load adjustment is made with braking magnets. Where separate discs are used with the elements, each has its own braking magnets but the adjustment of either affects the entire system. Similarly the light-load adjustment of one element provides driving torque (if its voltage coil is energized) even though the entire load current is carried by the other element. However, for light-load accuracy the compensating torque should be shared equally by the light-load adjustments of the separate elements. It is more important that the lag adjustments and the Class II temperature compensation be correct in a two-element polyphase meter than in a single-phase meter since, even if the load power factor is unity, the current and voltage at the elements will not be in phase.[26] The elements must be "balanced" so that each contributes its proper share to the registration, since otherwise the registration will not be correct on an unbalanced load. This balancing is done by adjusting the elements to have the same speed under identical load conditions. Such an adjustment is made in some meters by means of taps on one of the voltage coils; in others by adjusting the disc air gap. Only after the elements are balanced should the full-load rate be adjusted by means of the braking magnet. The balancing adjustment is most conveniently made with the voltage coils connected in parallel and the current coils in series opposition. If the elements are balanced there will be no rotation of the disc for this condition.

Watthour-Meter Testing

Two methods which differ in principle are available for determining the correctness of registration of a watthour meter. The electrical energy into a system over a time interval $(t_2 - t_1)$ is $\int_{t_1}^{t_2} ei\,dt$, while the average power is $\dfrac{1}{(t_2 - t_1)} \int_{t_1}^{t_2} ei\,dt$. If the power is constant and known over the

[26] For a balanced, unity-power-factor load, one element will operate at an 0.866 leading power factor, and the other at 0.866 lagging.

entire interval, its value may be multiplied by the elapsed time to obtain energy, and the value of energy so determined may be compared with the meter registration. Alternatively, the meter rate can be compared directly with the rate of a meter which is known to integrate correctly (or whose rate corrections are known), provided the meters are operated on identical loads for equal times. The latter method does not require that the load be constant during the test interval, but it does require that the meters whose rates are being compared "see" precisely the same load during the interval. Both methods are of value and will be discussed briefly.

Portable Standard Watthour Meters. These are precisely constructed and accurately adjusted watthour meters having special registers which permit readings to be taken to within 0.01 revolution of the disc, while revolutions up to 100 are totalized by accumulator dials. These meters are usually provided with multiple current and voltage ranges to permit their use in testing a variety of meters, and are equipped with a switch and a mechanical brake in the voltage circuit so that the meter operation may be started and stopped quickly. Such meters are employed in the routine determination of the rates of service meters. The voltage circuits of the two meters are connected in parallel and their current circuits in series, and their rates may be compared by measuring the total number of revolutions made by each in a measured time interval. Alternatively, the potential circuit of the standard meter may be energized while the disc of the meter under test is observed to make a certain number of revolutions, the passage of a mark on the meter disc past a fixed reference point serving to mark revolutions. If identical manual manipulations can be employed to close and open the switch which operates to energize the voltage circuit of the reference meter, starting and stopping errors which depend on the observer's reaction time will be minimized. In setups where large numbers of meters must be tested on a routine basis, for example in the meter laboratory of a power company, various devices have been used to facilitate the testing operations. For example, the switching can be controlled by a photoelectric cell operated by a light beam through a hole in the meter disc or alternatively by the passage of a painted mark on the meter disc through the light beam. In some instances a photoelectric cell intercepts light from a mirror carried on an accurate seconds pendulum, and controls switching through cam or relay arrangements which permit the accumulation of a preselected time interval. In one ingenious stroboscopic arrangement the disc of the reference meter is notched at regular intervals. Light passing through these notches strikes a photoelectric cell which actuates a neon lamp, illuminating a pattern of marks on the disc of the meter under test. If the disc rates are the same, the pattern appears to be stationary. If the meter under test is slow, its disc appears to be turning backward, or forward if its rate is fast. This method has the decided advantage that it gives a continuous indication of the comparative meter rates and permits adjustment of the meter while operating. By such means the time required for testing and adjustment of a meter may be substantially reduced.

Power-Time Measurements. Direct comparison of the rate of a meter with that of a standard presupposes that the rate of the reference meter is correct. Determination of the rates of reference meters must ultimately be made in terms of measurements of power and time. As a practical matter the calibration of a watthour meter may be accomplished by taking the product of a measured time interval, and a *constant* value of power as measured with a wattmeter. Of course power is also a derived quantity, but the definition of average power $\left(\frac{1}{T}\int_0^T ei\,dt\right)$ enables one to base the measurements on quantities which are readily determined in terms of fundamental electrical quantities. All electrical measurements must eventually be referred to our electrical standards, the ohm and the volt. It must be realized, therefore, that the accuracy of the wattmeter must itself be investigated, and that it is merely a link in a chain of measurements. The wattmeter may be considered a device for transferring to alternating current the average product of current and voltage, which may be accurately determined separately on direct current by means of a potentiometer, a standard cell, and a standard resistor. In practice the calibration of a wattmeter is checked on direct current by potentiometer methods, and the difference between its indications on direct current and on alternating current may be determined by comparison with a transfer instrument whose construction is such that either its indications are the same on direct and alternating current, or the differences are accurately known. Of course, many laboratories are not equipped to carry out all the steps which are essential in determining the rate of a watthour meter in terms of the fundamental electrical standards, and therefore must depend on the manufacturer or on a standardizing laboratory to supply some of the information needed. Fortunately, since the difference in the alternating and direct current indications of an electrodynamic instrument (such as the usual laboratory grade of wattmeter) depends only on details of its construction, such differences need be determined only once during the life of the instrument. Having once determined the alternating and direct current differences of a wattmeter, it is necessary only to check the continued accuracy of its calibration from time to time on direct current by potentiometer methods, a task for which facilities are available in most meter laboratories.

If the test value of power is established with a good laboratory-grade wattmeter and can be held constant during the test interval, accuracies of the order of $\frac{1}{4}$ to $\frac{1}{2}$% may reasonably be expected. If the wattmeter is used simply as a transfer instrument (with a d-c calibration at the time of test and with an appropriate correction applied for its alternating and direct current difference) the test accuracy may be as good as 0.1 to 0.2%, provided the time interval is accurately determined. Such accuracies cannot be attained if a stop watch is used, unless the time interval is very long. The intermittent motion of the sweep-second hand, together with the observer's reaction time in starting and stopping the watch at the ends of the interval, may easily amount to 1% in 100 sec and is proportionately larger for shorter intervals. Nor is a synchronous clock operated from the commercial power supply very much better since, over short time intervals, the frequency may depart from standard by several tenths of a per cent, and departures of as much as 1%, although unusual, are observed from time to time. A precision source of time signals, such as an accurate pendulum clock, a tuning fork, or a crystal-controlled oscillator[27] is essential for the accurate determination of meter rates in terms of measured power and time.

Phantom Loading. This consists in supplying the voltage and current circuits of the watthour meter (or wattmeter) from sources which, though synchronous, are insulated from each other except at one point and are independently adjustable. Such a procedure has a number of advantages over the use of actual resistive and reactive loads: (1) greater ease and flexibility are attained in the adjustment of voltage, current, and power factor to desired values; (2) a source having much smaller volt-ampere rating is adequate; and (3) the need is eliminated for taking account of losses in the current or voltage circuits of the test and reference instruments. Since the voltage circuits of the instruments or meters are supplied in parallel from one source, and the current circuits are supplied in reries from another, one can be sure that the voltage, current, and phase selations are the same in each. Figure 15 illustrates two simple methods of phantom loading, applicable to the testing of watthour meters. In (*a*) the current circuits of the test and reference instruments are connected in series and supplied through a step-down transformer, which isolates the current circuit[28] and permits the use of a smaller resistor for adjusting the load current, with the expenditure of correspondingly less energy than in a rheostat that would be required to handle the actual load being

[27] See discussion of frequency standards in Chapter 14.

[28] Unless the meter circuits are connected internally, the current and voltage circuits should be connected together by means of a high resistance in order that no large difference of potential develop between them. See the discussion of electrostatic ties in Chapter 11.

simulated. This method is employed principally to simulate a unity-power-factor load, and the low-side voltage of the current-supply transformer must be high enough that the resistance used as a current control will "swamp" the reactance of the current circuits of the meters. With an appropriate combination of resistance and reactance in the current circuit, a low-power-factor load may be simulated. Figure 15(*b*) shows a method by which 50% power-factor loads may be simulated if a three-phase supply is available. In this instance the current supply is taken

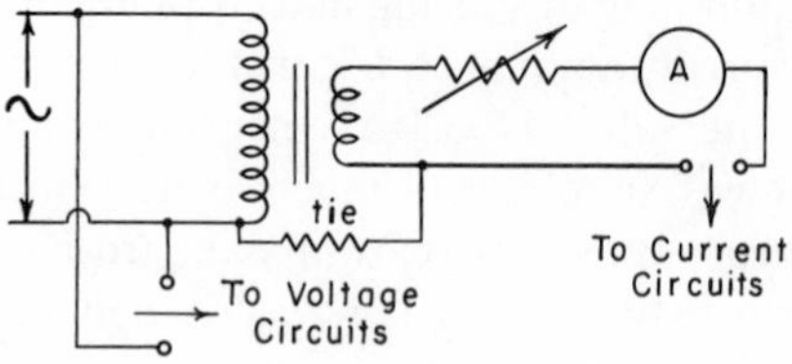

(*a*)

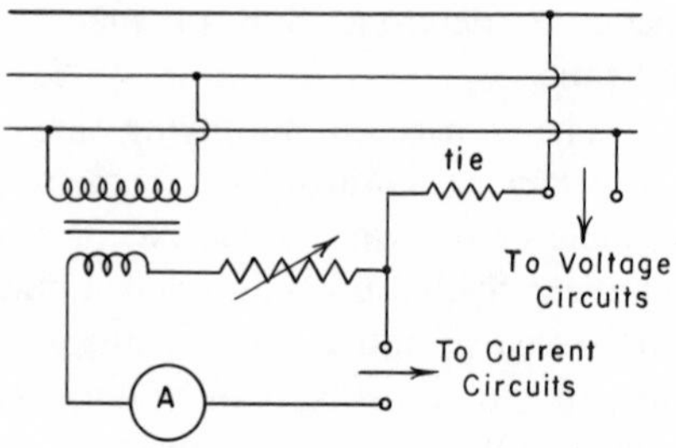

(*b*)

FIG. 15.

from one phase and the voltage supply from another. If the phase sequence is known, the phase for the voltage supply can be selected to lead or lag the current in the secondary of the current-supply transformer by 60°. If a wattmeter is included in the circuit, a simple test for leading or lagging power factor can be made. When a capacitor of suitable size (perhaps a microfarad) is connected momentarily across the resistor in the current circuit, the deflection of the wattmeter will increase if the current is lagging since the introduction of a capacitance component of current will cause the total current to lag by a smaller amount. On leading current the deflection will decrease since the capacitance component will cause the current to lead by a greater angle. A somewhat more elaborate but much more flexible method of phantom loading employs a phase-shifting transformer and a separate variable-ratio transformer[29]

[29] Such as a "variac" or a "powerstat."

for regulating the current, voltage, and phase relations independently in the meter circuit. Alternatively, separate synchronously driven generators (coupled mechanically to the same driving motor) can be employed to supply the voltage and current circuits. One of the generators must be so constructed that its stator can be shifted mechanically through 180 electrical degrees in order that leading and lagging power factors may be simulated. Generator-field control is convenient for changing voltage and current in the meter circuits. Specially constructed sine-wave alternators are available and should be used in precision testing where the harmonic content of the voltage and current circuits must be small.[30]

Demand Meters

Since an electric power company must be prepared to supply energy at whatever rate is needed to meet the operating requirements of its customers, generating and distribution equipment must be installed which will provide for the maximum demand for electrical energy, rather than merely the average demand. The additional capacity that must be installed in order to take care of this maximum demand represents an investment which would produce revenue only a portion of the time unless proper allowance were made for it in setting up rate schedules. One method by which stand-by equipment can be made to produce the revenue needed to amortize its cost and yield a return on the money invested in it is to base a portion of the charges for electric service on the maximum requirements of the customer, in addition to the regular charge for energy consumption. Demand billing also encourages the customer to diversify his load where possible so that his energy consumption is more uniform. In order that charges based on demand be equitable, demand metering must take account of energy requirements over an appreciable time interval since momentary overloads do not require reserve capacity, and the thermal capacity of supply equipment is usually the factor which limits its use. The demand intervals which are most frequent in metering are 15, 30, or 60 min, the 15-min period being used most often.

Maximum demand meters are of three distinct types: (1) recording wattmeters, (2) integrating-demand meters, and (3) lagged-demand meters. Although the chart from a recording wattmeter can be utilized in estimating demand charges, the labor required in its examination and in the

[30] Voltage regulators of the saturable-core type must be used with some caution since their harmonic content may not be negligible. The purely electrical regulators may have an appreciable content of odd harmonics, while both even and odd harmonics may be present in the output of an electronic regulator.

computation of energy consumed during specified demand intervals is costly, so that it is less often used for this purpose than are other devices. Two types of integrated-demand meters are popular, both being modifications of the usual watthour meter. In the first of these, the total energy consumed in a fixed time interval is measured, and in some instances recorded on a chart or strip. In the second type of integrated-demand meter a record is made on a chart each time a predetermined amount of energy is consumed, the maximum demand coinciding with the demand interval during which the greatest number of equal blocks of energy was consumed. In lagged-demand meters a certain time interval is required for the indication to reach a point corresponding to the load; the indication lags behind the load in somewhat the same manner as the temperature rise in the supply equipment lags behind the load imposed on it. Of the many types of mechanisms employed in demand meters, a simple type of the integrated-demand meter and of the lagged-demand meter will be described.

In its simplest form the block-interval type of *integrated-demand* meter requires an auxiliary gear train driven by the watthour-meter disc. This moves an arm, which in turn pushes a pointer around an indicating dial at a rate proportional to the disc speed. At the end of the demand interval (usually 15 min) a reset mechanism, operated from a small synchronous motor, returns the pusher arm to its zero position, leaving the pointer at the maximum position reached. In subsequent time intervals the pusher arm again moves upscale, but does not reach the pointer position unless a larger energy consumption occurs during a demand interval. Thus the pointer indicates the maximum demand which has occurred since the meter reader last returned the pointer to zero, but does not show when the demand occurred nor does it give indication of the smaller demands which occurred during the period between meter readings. In a modification of this system a line is drawn on a chart during each demand interval, the length of the line being proportional to the total energy consumption in the interval. Such a record shows not only the maximum demand but also the time when it occurred, as well as the frequency and time of occurrence of other smaller demands. Meters of this type have one serious disadvantage. If the maximum rate of energy consumption occurs some time after the start of one time interval and continues over only a part of the succeeding interval, the *maximum* demand is not indicated, since it is split between two blocks.

Block splitting is avoided in the lagged-demand meter, whose indication does not depend on preselected times but whose integration is continuous. The *thermal lagged-demand* meter is essentially a thermal wattmeter with a very long response time. Its deflecting torque is obtained from the differential action of two bimetallic springs which are heated by currents in two equal resistors (R, R) of a circuit arranged as shown in Fig. 16. A small transformer is connected across the line, and its secondary supplies to each of the heaters (R) a current Ke proportional to the line voltage. The load current i is taken from the junction point between the heaters so that half flows through each resistor. Thus the current in one

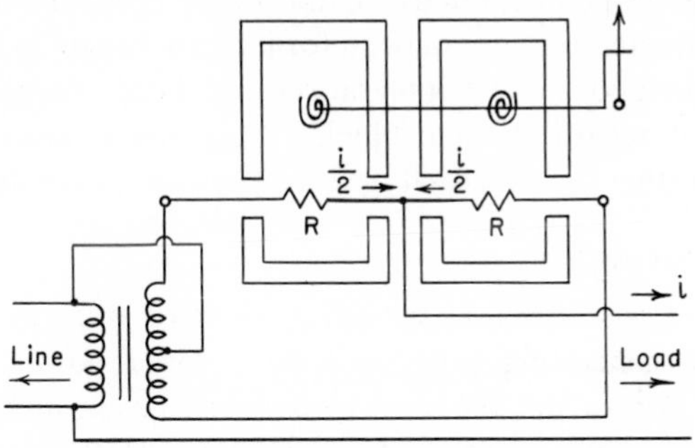

FIG. 16.

heater is $Ke + (i/2)$, while the current in the other heater is $Ke - (i/2)$. The rate of heat production in the first resistor can be written as

$$H_1 = \left(K^2e^2 + Kei + \frac{i^2}{4}\right) R$$

and in the second,

$$H_2 = \left(K^2e^2 - Kei + \frac{i^2}{4}\right) R$$

Their difference is

$$H_1 - H_2 = 2KRei$$

which is proportional to the instantaneous power in the load. Heat from the resistors raises the temperatures of the oppositely coiled bimetallic springs, and any difference in their expansion (corresponding to a temperature difference between them) rotates a pusher arm and advances the indicating pointer upscale. The springs and their housings are of massive construction and have considerable thermal-storage capacity so that their temperatures change slowly under a constant load. The temperature rise is exponential, so that the deflection may be expressed as

$$D = (1 - \varepsilon^{K_1t}) \cdot K_2 \times \text{power}$$

K_1 being a function of the thermal-storage capacity. Final deflection under a constant load is approached asymptotically, and the design is such that the practical attainment of final temperature corresponds reasonably well with the demand interval. Actually, the definition of the demand interval is somewhat arbitrary in this type of meter. If 90% of the temperature rise occurs in 15 min and 99% in 30 min under constant load, either interval may be selected as the demand interval. The deflection at any time depends on the integrated effect of load over a period of time, and it should be noted that the integration starts when the load starts. As contrasted with the integrated-demand meter previously described, the lagged-demand meter does not depend for its response on assigned instants of time to begin and end its integration and hence registers maximum demand without regard to time blocks. Lagging is also accomplished by mechanical rather than thermal means in some types of demand meters.

Reactive Metering

Load power factor as well as maximum demand must be considered in establishing the generating capacity needed for a power system, since more iron and copper are required to deliver a given amount of power at a low than at a high power factor. Design allowance must be made for any reactive volt-amperes in addition to the designed power load. For low-power-factor loads the transmission losses are higher and voltage regulation is poorer. Since the presence of a low-power-factor load in a system represents added cost in the delivery of energy to it, the consumer must be expected to pay for any contribution that he makes to low power factor, as well as for his demand and for the actual energy consumed. Reactive metering is used to obtain an estimate of the average power factor of a fluctuating load over a period of time. It requires a meter whose response is proportional to $EI \sin \theta = EI \cos (90^\circ - \theta)$, where θ is the power-factor angle. If then by some device the voltage impressed on the voltage coil of the watthour meter can be shifted into quadrature with the line voltage at the load, the meter will automatically register kilovar-hours rather than kilowatt-hours. In polyphase circuits this is accomplished by means of a phasing transformer and has already been explained in discussing the polyphase varmeter.[31] It must be realized that reactive metering is inherently considerably less accurate than energy metering in the presence of unbalanced voltages, currents, and loads. The procedures by which the required phase shift is accomplished in the voltage circuit are in theory exact only for balanced conditions, and are generally attained only as a reasonable approximation. However, high accuracy is not needed for reactive metering since the information required is merely for the establishment of an acceptable power-factor index for

[31] See Chapter 11. In a single-phase meter the desired phase shift can be approximately accomplished by a suitable combination of resistance, capacitance, and inductance.

estimating service costs. Strictly speaking, unless the power factor is constant, the power-factor index obtained by taking the ratio

$$\cos \bar{\theta} = \frac{\text{KWH}}{\sqrt{(\text{KWH})^2 + (\text{KVH})^2}}$$

where KWH and KVH are the watthour-meter and varhour-meter readings respectively, is not a true average and does not correspond to the average of successive values of power factor during the same period. It is simply an acceptable way of arriving at a suitable index for billing purposes.

Volt-Ampere Metering

Volt-ampere hours are sometimes metered (where the added expense is justified) to arrive more directly at an evaluation of the circuit quantities which can be only approximated by conventional reactive metering. A detailed discussion of the methods of evaluating kilovolt-ampere-hours is beyond the scope of this book. There are two types of volt-ampere-hour meters. In one the effect of the phase angle between voltage and current is neutralized or compensated so that response is in terms of EI rather than $EI \cos \theta$. In the other type the principle of vector addition is used. Two watthour meter elements, whose speeds correspond to active and reactive power respectively, are coupled by some mechanical device which sums their speeds vectorially, in accord with the expression

$$\text{volt-amperes} = \sqrt{(\text{watts})^2 + (\text{vars})^2}$$

CHAPTER 13

INSTRUMENT TRANSFORMERS

The extension of instrument range, so that current, voltage, power, and energy can be measured with instruments or meters of moderate size and capacity, is of very great importance not only in laboratory work but, even more, in commercial metering. Here power is frequently handled in large blocks at high currents and voltages. It is of particular importance that the performance of devices for range extension be of good quality and quite accurately known in cases where energy is sold in such amounts that a relatively small percentage error in its measurement would result in considerable monetary loss to the producer or to the consumer. Tie points where different utility companies connect to the same power grid are an illustration of this. Another is the metering of energy at the service lines of a large industrial consumer. In both these cases the metering must be done at currents and voltages which are far too large for any meter of reasonable size and cost.

It might appear that range extension could be conveniently accomplished by the use of shunts for current, and multipliers for voltage measurement, as is done in d-c measurements. However, such a method would be very difficult to realize, and would be practical only for relatively small values of current and voltage. We have already seen that the use of shunts in a-c measurements requires that the time constants of the shunt and instrument be closely matched. Thus a different shunt would be needed for each instrument. Furthermore this method would be limited to shunts having capacities of a few hundred amperes at most, since the power which would be taken by the shunt would be quite large for large currents. Also the problem of adequate instrument insulation would be very difficult of solution if the current to be measured were at a potential of several hundred or thousand volts above ground. Although multipliers for voltage measurements do not present any serious difficulties below 1000 volts, their general use as instrument auxiliaries becomes impracticable at voltages much above this level. Actually it is not uncommon to find self-contained voltmeters, particularly in high-sensitivity types, up to 750 volts, and voltmeters with external multipliers up to 1500 volts. A 750-volt multiplier for a voltmeter having a sensitivity of 100 ohms/volt would dissipate 7.5 watts. This represents about the limit of power which should be dissipated in a self-contained instrument. Care is needed to keep leakage currents in high-voltage multipliers down to negligible values, but such designs are quite feasible. Insulation of multipliers against appreciable leakage currents and the reduction of distributed capacitance to avoid appreciable shunt capacitance currents become rapidly more difficult and very expensive above a few thousand volts. Also it is often desirable or necessary to insulate the measuring circuit from the power circuit.

These are among the reasons that the use of instrument transformers for range extension followed very soon after the development of a-c power circuits. Such transformers were developed by a number of workers during the last decade of the nineteenth century and by 1900 had come into fairly general use. Today current and voltage transformers are employed in very precise measurements as well as in routine metering, and their performance quality may be sufficiently high and predictable that they can be safely used without correction in ordinary metering.

Current-transformer ratings have been standardized at 5 amp secondary current, and voltage transformers at from 100 to 120 volts secondary. This makes it possible to standardize the measuring instruments around these fixed ratings and so to reduce greatly the over-all cost of both transformers and instruments. Some lines of current transformers having a rated secondary current of 1 amp or less have been built recently. This has certain advantages in some applications, particularly in metering at a distance from the transformer, since lighter conductors are feasible between transformers and meters. The use of transformers for range extension is, then, of advantage since it permits: (1) standardization of instruments and meters at secondary ratings of 100–120 volts and 5 or 1 amp; (2) insulation of instruments from line voltage, so that they may be grounded; (3) operation of several instruments from a single transformer; (4) low power consumption in the measuring circuit.

In using instrument transformers for current or voltage measurements we must know the ratio of the magnitudes of the primary quantities to the corresponding secondary quantities. These ratios furnish a multiplying factor to use with the instrument reading in order to obtain the corresponding primary magnitude. For power or energy measurements we must know not only the ratio of transformation but also the phase angle between the primary and the secondary vectors since this introduces a further correction to the reading. This latter correction depends on the power factor of the load, as may be seen from the following considerations.[1] As a simplification we will assume that in the vector diagram shown in Fig. 1 the phase angles, β, of the current transformer, and γ, of the voltage transformer, are both positive and that the current, $\mathbf{i}_v$, in the voltage circuit of the wattmeter lags behind the instrument voltage, $\mathbf{E}_{sec}$, by an angle, α, whose value is determined by the inductance and

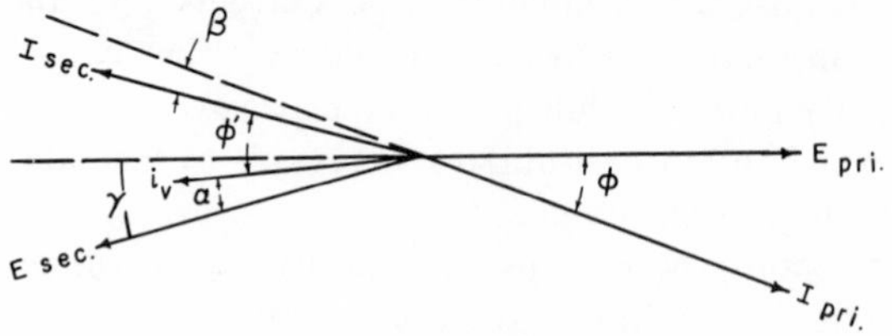

FIG. 1.

resistance of the voltage circuit. The phase angle between the field current and the voltage-coil current in the wattmeter is

$$\phi' = \phi + \gamma - \alpha - \beta$$

Now let us call the combined phase-angle corrections

$$\alpha + \beta - \gamma = \delta$$

so that

$$\phi = \phi' + \delta$$

Then the instrument reading is

$$P_R = E_s I_s \cos \phi'$$

and the true load power is

$$\begin{aligned} P_T &= E_p I_p \cos \phi = E_p I_p \cos (\phi' + \delta) \\ &= \frac{E_p I_p}{E_s I_s} \cdot E_s I_s \cos \phi'(\cos \delta - \tan \phi' \sin \delta) \\ &= \frac{E_p}{E_s} \cdot \frac{I_p}{I_s} \cdot P_R (1 - \tan \phi' \tan \delta) \cos \delta \approx \frac{E_p}{E_s} \cdot \frac{I_p}{I_s} \cdot P_R (1 - \tan \phi' \tan \delta) \end{aligned}$$

since δ is always a small angle (usually less than 2°). Thus the true average power in the load is given by the wattmeter reading, multiplied by the product of the current and voltage ratios of the transformers, and by a correction factor which is a function of the apparent power-factor

[1] See also Inductance Error of Wattmeter, p. 479.

angle and of the combined phase angles of the transformers and the lag angle of the voltage circuit of the wattmeter.

In an ideal transformer the vector ratio would equal the turn ratio and the phase angle would be zero. However, as a result of physical limitations inherent in the magnetic and electric circuits of the transformer there are always some departures from this ideal. This fact will be apparent from the following considerations: (1) primary ampere-turns are required to produce flux in the transformer core; (2) the flux density in the core is not a linear function of the magnetizing force; (3) the transformer input must have a component which supplies the eddy-current and hysteresis losses in the core and the I^2R losses in the transformer windings; (4) there is always leakage present in the magnetic circuit so that the primary and secondary flux linkages are never equal.

The convention universally adopted for the sign of the phase angles of both current and voltage transformers is that the angle shall be considered positive when the reversed secondary vector leads the primary vector. This is shown in Fig. 2. There are certain other conventions and definitions which we shall adopt in the discussion which follows. The *transformer ratio* is the ratio of the magnitude of the primary to the secondary vector:

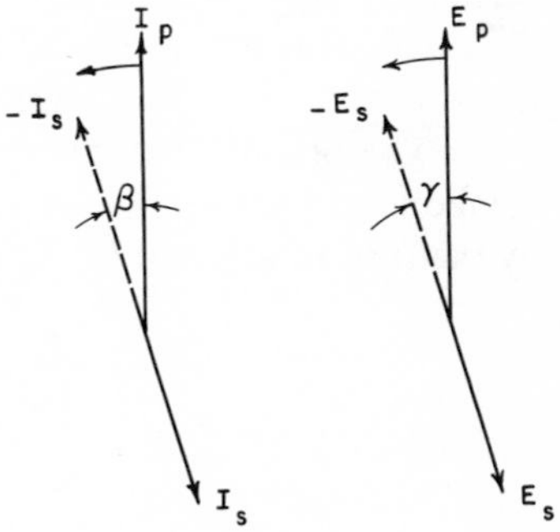

FIG. 2.

$$\text{Ratio} = \frac{|\text{primary vector}|}{|\text{secondary vector}|}$$

The *nominal ratio* is the ratio of the rated primary to the rated secondary current (or voltage). It may be stated as a fraction, either in terms of these quantities directly (e.g. 500/5) or as the equivalent reduced fraction (100/1); or it may be written simply as the number representing the numerator of the reduced fraction (100). The *ratio factor* of a transformer is the transformer ratio divided by the nominal ratio (Transformer ratio = ratio factor × nominal ratio). The *turn ratio* is the ratio of primary to secondary winding turns for a voltage transformer ($N_t = T_p/T_s$); and for the current transformer is the ratio of secondary to primary turns.

Current Transformers

Ratio and Phase-Angle Formulas. The current transformer is used with its primary winding connected in series with the line carrying the current to be measured as shown in Fig. 3. The instrument load (ammeter, current coil of wattmeter or watthour meter, etc.) is connected to the terminals of the secondary winding, and with its connecting wires will be designated as the transformer burden. A current transformer operates with its secondary under nearly short-circuit conditions. The secondary circuit is connected to ground in many cases. The transformer burden (usually somewhat inductive), together with the secondary resistance and leakage reactance of the transformer, constitutes the total secondary impedance Z_s at a phase angle ϕ_s. Then, in order to circulate the secondary current I_s [Fig. 4(*a*)], there is required an induced secondary voltage $E_s = I_s Z_s$, which is produced by the flux Φ in the magnetic circuit of the transformer. This flux leads the induced secondary voltage by an angle $\pi/2$. The primary current I_p may be considered to be made up of two components: (1) $I_p' = -N_t I_s$, the reversed secondary current multiplied by the turn ratio; and (2) I_0, the current needed to supply magnetization

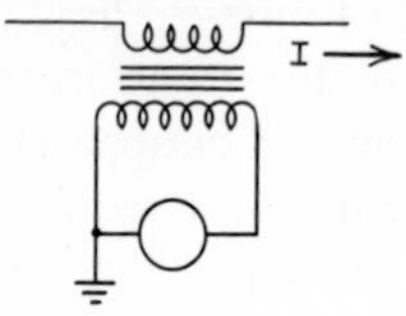

FIG. 3.

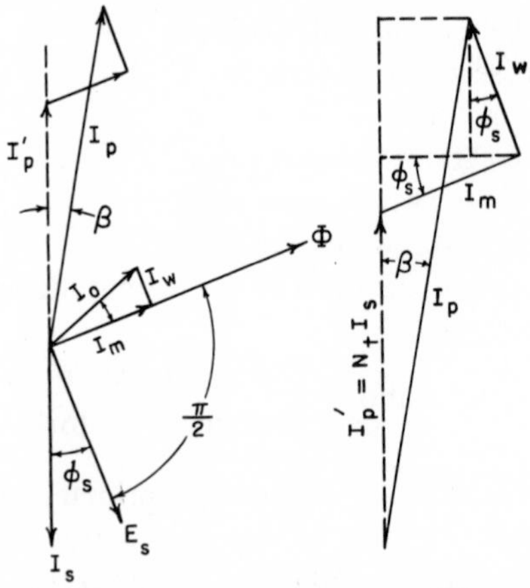

(*a*) (*b*)

FIG. 4.

and core losses. We will consider that I_0 is itself made up of two components: (1) I_m, the magnetizing current in phase with Φ; and (2) I_w, the loss current leading Φ by $\pi/2$. On this basis we can construct the essential parts of the vector diagram of a current transformer: Figs. 4(*a*), (*b*).[2]

[2] It must be understood that the magnitudes and phase relations of some of the vectors are exaggerated in order to separate them on the diagram. No scale is intended in Fig. 4.

From Fig. 4(*b*) we have, on resolving I_p along I_p' and perpendicular to it, that

$$I_p \cos \beta = I_p' + I_m \sin \phi_s + I_w \cos \phi_s = I_s N_t + I_m \sin \phi_s + I_w \cos \phi_s$$

and

$$I_p \sin \beta = I_m \cos \phi_s - I_w \sin \phi_s$$

On squaring and adding these equations, we have

$$\begin{aligned} I_p^2 &= I_s^2 N_t^2 + I_m^2 \sin^2 \phi_s + I_w^2 \cos^2 \phi_s + 2I_m I_w \sin \phi_s \cos \phi_s \\ &\quad + 2I_s N_t (I_m \sin \phi_s + I_w \cos \phi_s) + I_m^2 \cos^2 \phi_s \\ &\quad + I_w^2 \sin^2 \phi_s - 2I_m I_w \sin \phi_s \cos \phi_s \\ &= I_s^2 N_t^2 + I_m^2 + I_w^2 + 2I_s N_t (I_m \sin \phi_s + I_w \cos \phi_s) \end{aligned}$$

But $I_m^2 + I_w^2 = I_0^2$, so that we have, on dividing by I_s^2 and taking the square root,

$$\begin{aligned} \left| \frac{I_p}{I_s} \right| &= \text{transformer ratio} \\ &= N_t \left[1 + \frac{2(I_m \sin \phi_s + I_w \cos \phi_s)}{I_s N_t} + \frac{I_0^2}{I_s^2 N_t^2} \right]^{1/2} \end{aligned}$$

Now in a well-designed current transformer $I_0 \ll I_p$ (usually less than 1% of the primary current), and $I_p \approx I_s N_t$. We can then expand our expression for ratio, and, neglecting squares and higher powers of small quantities, we can say that the

$$\text{Ratio} \approx N_t \left(1 + \frac{I_m \sin \phi_s + I_w \cos \phi_s}{I_s N_t} \right)$$

or, since $I_m = I_0 \cos \theta$ and $I_w = I_0 \sin \theta$, our expression may be written

$$\text{Ratio} \approx N_t \left[1 + \frac{I_0}{I_p} \sin (\phi_s + \theta) \right]$$

Going back to the original equations, we have, on dividing the second by the first,

$$\frac{I_p \sin \beta}{I_p \cos \beta} = \tan \beta = \frac{I_m \cos \phi_s - I_w \sin \phi_s}{I_s N_t + I_m \sin \phi_s + I_w \cos \phi_s} = \frac{I_0 \cos (\phi_s + \theta)}{I_s N_t + I_0 \sin (\phi_s + \theta)}$$

and this may be approximated as

$$\beta \approx \frac{I_0 \cos (\phi_s + \theta)}{I_s N_t} \approx \frac{I_0}{I_p} \cos (\phi_s + \theta)$$

Let us write our equations in the form

$$\text{Ratio} \approx N_t \left[1 + \frac{I_m \sin \phi_s + I_w \cos \phi_s}{I_p} \right]$$

and

$$\beta \approx \frac{I_m \cos \phi_s - I_w \sin \phi_s}{I_p}$$

and examine the dependence of the transformer ratio and phase angle on the phase angle of the secondary circuit. It may be observed that for all inductive burdens the secondary current lags the induced secondary voltage, so that ϕ_s is positive. Under these conditions the ratio is always greater than the turn ratio; the phase angle β is positive for small values of ϕ_s (high power factor) but becomes negative as the secondary burden becomes more inductive and ϕ_s approaches 90°. For burdens which are sufficiently capacitive that I_s leads E_s, ϕ_s is negative and the ratio decreases, becoming less than the turn ratio for values of ϕ_s approaching $-$ 90°. For negative values of ϕ_s, β is always positive. The dependency of transformer ratio and phase angle on the phase angle of its secondary circuit is shown graphically in Fig. 5.

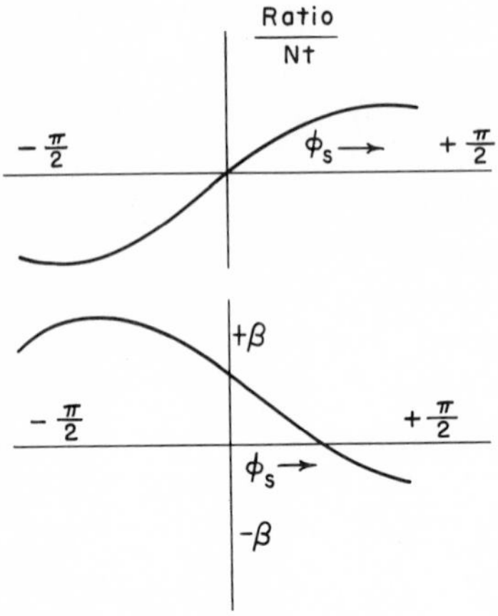

FIG. 5.

It should be noted that the ratio and phase angle are functions of magnetizing and loss currents as well as secondary phase angle, so that the above statements and curves apply only for an impedance of constant magnitude.

The usual instrument burden is largely resistive, with some inductance so that the secondary impedance is inductive, and ϕ_s is positive and generally small. In this case we can, to a rough approximation, write

$$\text{Ratio} \approx N_t \left(1 + \frac{I_w}{I_p} \right), \quad \text{and} \quad \beta \approx \frac{I_m}{I_p}$$

From this it follows that, for the usual type of burden, the departure of the transformer ratio from the turn ratio depends largely on the component of current supplying the core loss, and the transformer phase angle depends largely on magnetizing current. If the ratio is to be close to the turn ratio and the phase angle is to be small, I_m and I_w must be small compared to I_p.

Design Features. The magnetizing current, I_m, is minimized by using core material having high permeability, large cross section, and short magnetic path length, and by operating at a low flux density. The reluctance of the magnetic circuit is kept small by having tight, accurately fitted lap joints and by reducing the number of joints by the use of L- or E-shaped strips. In the highest grades of transformers the core is built up of ring-shaped laminations or from a continuous, spiral-wound strip of sheet material so that joints are completely eliminated. The loss current, I_w, is kept small by choosing material having low hysteresis and eddy-current losses and by operation at low flux densities.

Silicon steel (4% silicon) is much used as the core material, but some precision-type transformers have cores of high-permeability nickel-iron alloys such as Hipernik (50% nickel) or Permalloy (78% nickel), with thin laminations to minimize the magnitude of eddy currents. Since these high-permeability materials saturate at relatively low magnetizing forces, they offer no advantages in transformers designed for the operation of overload relays or for other overload operations. In such transformers silicon steel may actually be preferable from the viewpoint of performance as well as being less expensive, since it ensures approximately normal ratio at large overcurrents. The oriented-grain silicon steels,[3] commercially developed during the past few years, are finding increasing use in instrument transformers, because of both their greater permeability (up to one-third more than ordinary silicon steel) and the somewhat higher maximum flux density at which they can be worked.

In order that the exciting current I_o be small compared with the primary current I_p, it is necessary that the total ampere-turns be large, preferably 800 to 1000. For window-type transformers using a bus bar as a single turn primary, this requirement would limit the application of this type of transformer to ratings of 500 amp or more. However, the advent of improved magnetic materials and the development of methods for biasing the core (see p. 553) to improve its effective permeability allow the construction of window-type transformers for primary ratings as low as 100 amp. Reasonable design figures for current transformers of the usual type might call for 1000 ampere-turns at rated current, excitation not more than 1% of rated current, flux density in the core less than 1000 gausses. Figure 6(*a*) represents the magnetizing and loss components of the excitation of a modern, high-quality current transformer having a nominal 5/5 amp ratio. These data, plotted against secondary open-circuit voltage, were obtained with an a-c potentiometer, using the method described in a later section of this chapter.[4] The secondary

[3] Goss, *American Soc. Metals*, **23,** 511 (1935).
[4] See p. 598.

resistance of this transformer was 0.196 ohm, and its secondary leakage reactance at 60 cycles was 0.16 ohm. The values of excitation may be compared to the secondary current (and hence to the primary) in the following way for any particular burden. The total secondary impedance (transformer + burden) is multiplied by the secondary current to obtain the total voltage drop. The excitation current is that corresponding to the same value of open-circuit voltage. For example, with ASA Burden

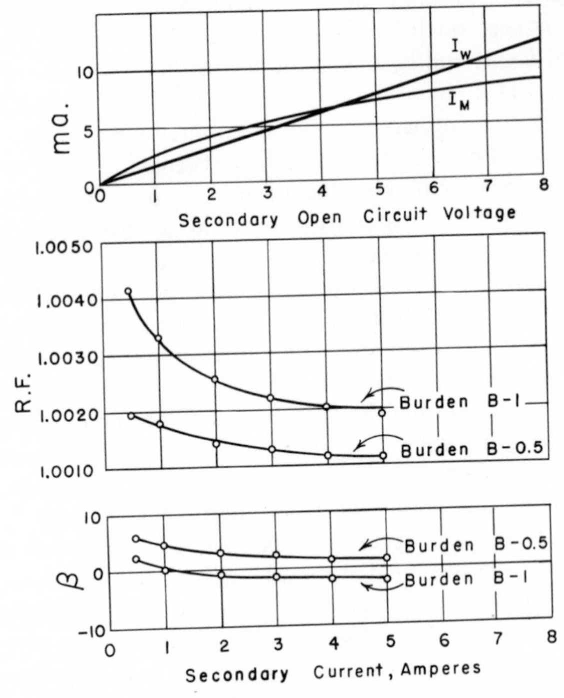

FIG. 6.

B-0.5[5] (0.45-ohm resistance and 0.58-millihenry inductance) the total secondary impedance is 0.5 ohm at 60 cycles, and the voltage values range from 0.375 volt at 0.5 amp to 3.75 volts at 5 amp. It will be noted that the excitation is less than 1% of the total current (0.3% at 0.5 amp to 0.13% at 5 amp) throughout the current range. Figure 6(*b*) shows the agreement between experimentally determined values of ratio factor and phase angle and those computed from the excitation data on this transformer[6] for ASA Burdens B-0.5 and B-1. It may be observed that the

[5] See p. 564.

[6] The formulas of p. 567 were used in these computations, and an effective turn ratio of 0.9995 was assumed.

experimental and computed values do not differ by more than 0.01 % in ratio factor and 1 min in phase angle at any point.

The mechanical construction of a current transformer must allow for the forces encountered under any short-circuit condition that may be met in operation. The coils and insulation must be well braced and the assembled core securely clamped. Since the transformer may be subjected to the voltage between line and ground, the insulation of the primary winding will determine the voltage level at which the transformer may be operated. For low voltages, impregnated tape may be used. For higher voltages the transformer may be filled with solid insulating compound or may be oil-immersed, and the primary may be additionally insulated by a Bakelite, fiber, or porcelain tube. For very high voltages a porcelain bushing and oil filling are used; or, in some cases, the voltage and insulation are divided into two or more stages by a cascade arrangement.

Limitations of Ratio and Phase-Angle Formulas. The ratio and phase angle of a current transformer may be computed with good accuracy by the formulas developed above for any condition of use in which we know the magnetizing and loss components of the excitation current in terms of the induced secondary voltage, the total resistance and total reactance of the secondary circuit, and the effective turn ratio of the transformer. The magnetizing and loss components of the excitation can be measured by methods which will be described later; the turn ratio may be known from manufacturer's data or can be measured; the resistance of the secondary winding and the reactance of the external burden can be measured directly. However, in most cases the leakage flux which may be represented by a reactance associated with the secondary winding of the transformer cannot be determined easily. The total leakage reactance of the transformer can be determined from short-circuit data, but the fraction of this reactance which should be assigned to the secondary circuit varies greatly with the construction of the transformer. In a series of measurements on a variety of transformers[7] the secondary leakage reactance was found to be nearly half of the total leakage reactance for a transformer having primary and secondary windings formed of superposed, link-shaped coils on one leg of a rectangular core, and negligible for a transformer having a uniformly distributed secondary and a bar primary on a circular, ring-shaped core. In general the secondary leakage reactance was much less than half the total. The value of the secondary leakage reactance is, then, the element whose uncertainty limits the usefulness of formulas in predicting the performance of a current transformer. It is generally much more satisfactory as well as

[7] Price and Duff, *Univ. Toronto Engineering Research Bull.*, **2**, p. 167, 1921.

less laborious to measure the transformer performance directly under the condition of operation than to attempt its computation. However, for design purposes and for relaying transformers whose accuracy requirements are not so high, computations of performance are very useful. Such computations, by methods that take into account the variation of leakage flux along the core, have been described by Sinks[8] and by Wentz.[9]

Current-Transformer Performance. An examination of the transformer equations will show that the ratio and phase angle are functions of N_t, I_s, I_m, I_w, and ϕ_s. Hence the transformer corrections will depend on both the secondary current and the secondary impedance. In practical measurements, instrument or meter impedances are usually inductive. The internal secondary impedance of the transformer is also inductive

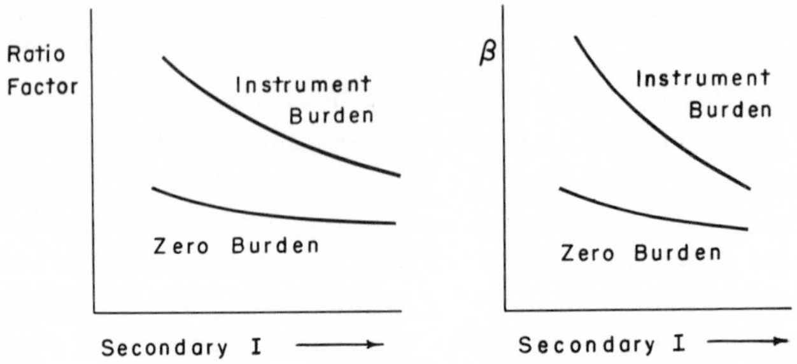

FIG. 7.

(being made up of winding resistance and secondary leakage reactance) and fixes the values of the transformer corrections on short circuit (zero external burden). Generally speaking, an increase in the external burden increases the ratio for all currents and shifts the phase angle toward more positive values.[10] It is therefore essential that in precise work the transformer corrections be determined with an external secondary impedance equivalent to the instrument burden with which the transformer will be used. It is, of course, advantageous in applying corrections that they be small and constant over the entire operating current range of the transformer, but this is in general not possible except in the highest grade of current transformers. Figure 7 gives qualitative correction curves which are typical of a large class of current transformers.

RATIO ADJUSTMENT. Since the impedance of the secondary circuit is inductive in almost all cases which are of practical interest in measurements

[8] Sinks, *Trans. AIEE*, **59**, 663 (1940).

[9] Wentz, *Trans. AIEE*, **60**, 949 (1941).

[10] This statement is usually true for instrument burdens. If the burden is very inductive the phase-angle shift may be toward negative angles. See Figs. 5 and 6.

(i.e. both the transformer impedance and that of the instrument burden are inductive), the *transformer ratio* will generally be greater than the *turn ratio*. If the *transformer ratio* is to coincide with the *nominal ratio*, the *turn ratio* must be less than the *nominal ratio*.[11] It is common manufacturing practice to decrease the turn ratio by using fewer secondary turns. Dropping a secondary turn moves the ratio factor curves of Fig. 7 downward approximately parallel to themselves but has almost no effect on the phase angle of the transformer. Where the removal of a single secondary turn results in too coarse an adjustment of ratio, some method of adjustment must be used which is equivalent to removing a fraction of a turn. This may be done by threading the final turn through a hole drilled in the core so that it links only part of the flux, as shown

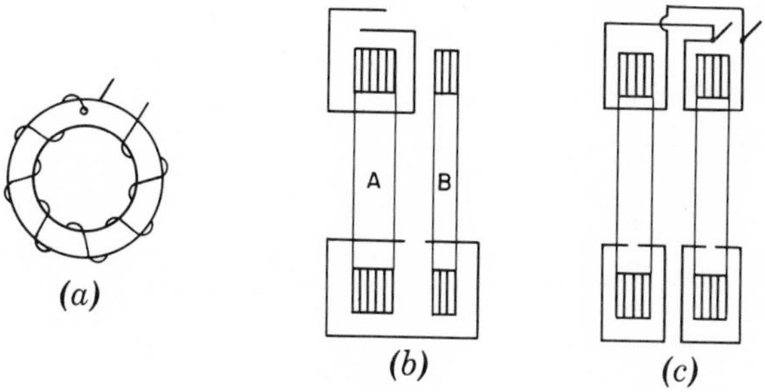

FIG. 8.

in Fig. 8(*a*). This method has the disadvantage that drilling a hole in the core reduces its effective cross section. A better method of fractional-turn adjustment is to divide the core laminations into two stacks (*A*, *B*) as shown in Fig. 8(*b*). The nearest whole number of turns is wound around both stacks, and the last (fractional) turn around *A* or *B* only. If the turns are properly proportioned[12] this method has the important advantage of improving the performance of the transformer by biasing the core in somewhat the same manner as the Wilson compensation method described below (p. 557). Another method is to divide the core into two equal parts [Fig. 8(*c*)] and to wind each uniformly as a 2.5-amp secondary (i.e. with double the nominal turns). These two windings are then connected in parallel to form the 5-amp secondary. An adjustment of one turn on either section then has only one-fourth of the effect resulting

[11] In an ideal transformer, having a core of infinite permeability and requiring zero exciting current, the primary and secondary ampere-turns would be equal so that the nominal and turn ratios would be identical and would coincide with the transformer ratio.

[12] Specht, *Trans. AIEE*, **64**, 635 (1945).

from one turn on a simple winding since each section has twice the turns wound over half the core area. Another device which has been used is to connect the transformer secondary to the instrument burden through an auxiliary transformer made up with a 5/5 amp ratio, and having a large number of turns in both its primary and secondary windings. If 1000 turns are used in each winding a single turn adjustment would amount to 0.1% in ratio.

PHASE-ANGLE ADJUSTMENT. None of the methods described for ratio adjustment has much effect in reducing phase angle, and it is quite

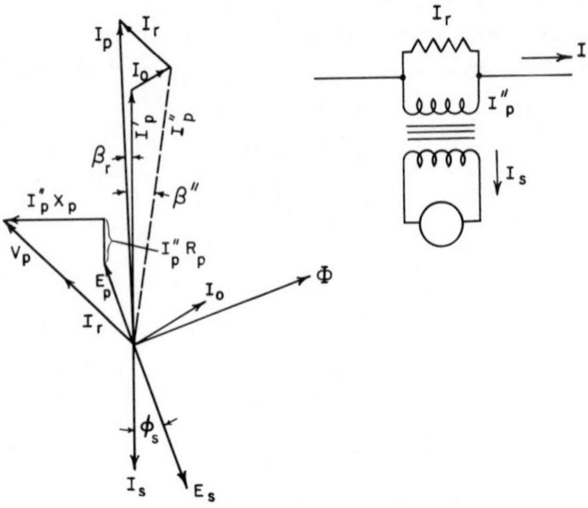

FIG. 9.

important in power or energy measurements at low power factors that the transformer phase angle be small. β can be held to small values by using a core of large cross section (low reluctance) and by keeping the total number of turns high. Also, it can be brought to zero by making the secondary circuit sufficiently inductive. Referring to Fig. 5, we see that, for a certain value of ϕ_s, β reverses its sign. ϕ_s may be brought near this value by introducing the proper amount of leakage reactance into the secondary winding. In general it may be said that the presence of a moderate leakage reactance results in a smaller phase angle. However, adjustment of β by increasing leakage reactance might have an undesired effect on ratio.

It can be shown that the ratio of a transformer may be changed and its phase angle decreased by the use of a shunt in either the primary or the secondary circuit. We will first consider a resistance shunt across the primary winding of the transformer. Referring to Fig. 9, Φ, I_0, E_s, I_s, and I_p' of Fig. 4 are unchanged. I_p'' is the current in the primary winding and is the vector sum of $I_p' = -I_sN_t$ and I_0. E_p is the induced primary voltage, and V_p is the primary terminal voltage, made up of E_p together with the impedance drop in the primary winding. I_r is in phase with V_p and adds to I_p'' to make up I_p, the primary line current. The phase angle, β_r, of the shunted transformer is less than the uncompensated phase angle β'', but the ratio is increased since $I_p > I_p''$. The effect of a primary shunt resistance is then to increase the ratio and to decrease the phase angle of a current transformer.

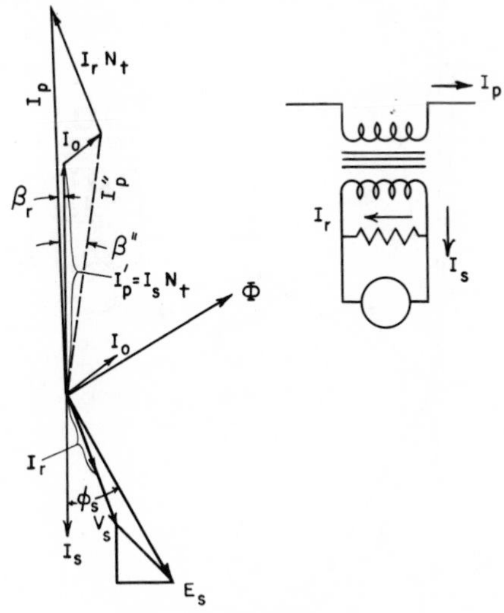

FIG. 10.

That the effect of a secondary shunt resistance is similar will be seen from Fig. 10. Φ, I_0, E_s, I_s, I_p' are as before. The useful ratio is the ratio of the primary *line* current to the current in the secondary *instrument* burden. Hence I_s must be considered to be the instrument current and not the total secondary current. V_s is the voltage appearing across the secondary transformer terminals and is E_s minus the impedance drop in the secondary winding. The current I_r in the shunt is in phase with V_s. I_p'' is made up of $I_p' = -I_sN_t$ plus I_0, and is at an angle β'' with I_p' (the uncompensated phase angle of the transformer). I_p is the vector sum of I_p'' and $-I_rN_t$, and is at an angle β_r from I_p'. The shunt compensation has decreased the phase angle of the transformer and increased the ratio. In using either a primary or a secondary shunt resistance for phase-angle correction, the *turn* ratio is first adjusted until the *transformer* ratio is less than the *nominal* ratio. Then when the shunt is added the ratio is increased by an amount which in the first case is approximately the ratio of the transformer resistance to the shunt resistance, and in the second case is the ratio of the burden resistance to the shunt resistance.

The use of a shunt capacitance across the secondary (or primary) terminals of the transformer has the advantage that the compensating current adds at a small angle to I_0 and therefore changes the transformer ratio less than does the shunt resistance for a given change in β. This will be seen from the vector diagram of Fig. 11. It must be noted, however, that, since the impedance of a capacitor is a function of frequency,

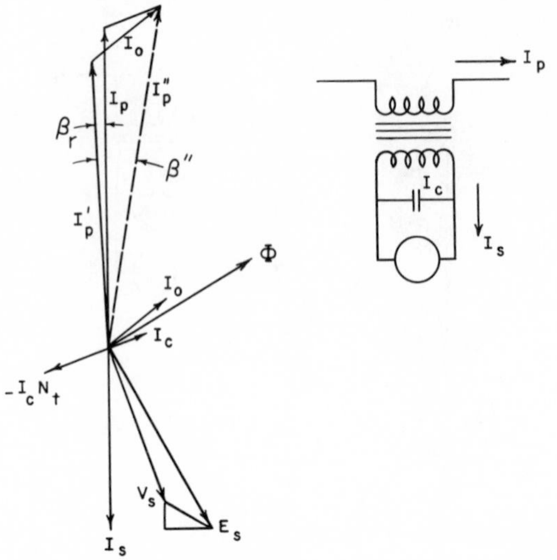

FIG. 11.

the compensation obtained with a shunt capacitance will be more sensitive to frequency and to wave form than compensation by a shunt resistance. An improvement on the shunt compensation described above is obtained by connecting the resistor or capacitor to a separate tertiary winding of the transformer rather than to the secondary terminals. When the shunt is connected to the secondary terminals its current is determined by the terminal voltage of the winding, which is in turn influenced by the impedance of the winding and by the parallel external burden. Hence its current does not follow changes in flux as closely as would be the case if it were supplied by a separate winding having no other load. Ockenden[13] has constructed a current transformer with a nickel-iron core, having a capacitance load connected to a separate tertiary winding. The value of β was constant at 0.8 min from 10% to full rated current, and the ratio

[13] Ockenden, *J. IEE*, **68**, 720 (1930).

change was less than 0.01% over the same current range. A short-circuited single-turn tertiary winding, formed of a resistance alloy, of proper proportions, is used by one manufacturer for compensation by this method.

A magnetic shunt has also been effective for error compensation.[14] The transformer ratio can be brought to a desired value by secondary-turn adjustment for some particular operating condition. However, the transformer ratio tends to decrease as the secondary current is increased. (See Fig. 7.) If by some means the effective turn ratio could be increased as the current increases, the variation of transformer ratio would be lessened. A method of doing this is shown in Fig. 12. The secondary

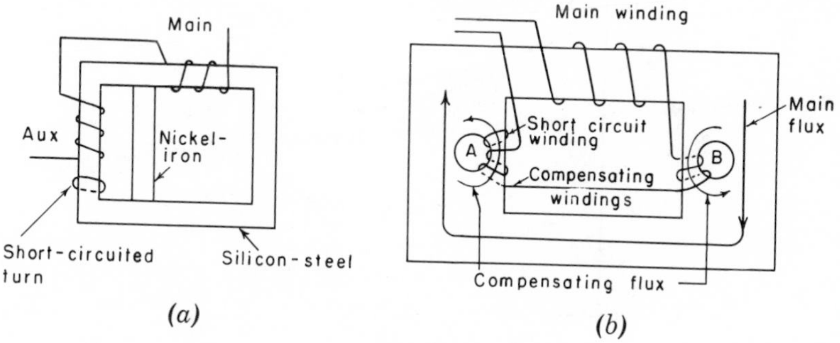

FIG. 12.

is wound in two sections. The winding marked "aux" contains 1 or 2% of the total turns. The main core is of silicon steel, and the magnetic shunt, of nickel-iron, is placed as shown so that a portion of the flux is by-passed around the auxiliary winding. Since the nickel-iron saturates more quickly than the main core, more flux will link the auxiliary winding as the current is increased. This device alone will decrease the variation of ratio but will have very little effect on the phase angle. If a short-circuited turn is placed around the section of the core holding the auxiliary winding, a lag angle is introduced into the main flux and therefore into the secondary voltage and current with respect to the primary current, thus reducing the angle β by which the reversed secondary current leads the primary (see Fig. 4). This lag angle decreases as the limb of the core on which the short-circuited turn is placed approaches saturation, so that β is decreased more for small currents than for large and less variation of β with current results.

Although the magnetic shunt described above is effective, its construction is troublesome and is not commercially feasible. However, the same

[14] Wilson, *Trans. AIEE*, **48**, 179 (1929).

result can be secured, using silicon steel alone, if the magnetic circuit is arranged in two parts, such that one operates in the region of increasing and the other in the region of decreasing permeability. Figure 12(*b*) shows the arrangement adopted commercially. Holes are drilled in the core at *A* and *B*, and a small number of turns (1 or 2% of the total secondary turns) are threaded through them in such a direction that the auxiliary flux produced by the compensating ampere-turns is in the same direction as the main flux within the portion of the core enclosed by the compensating winding and opposes the main flux in the remainder of the core section. The flux density is therefore higher in the area enclosed

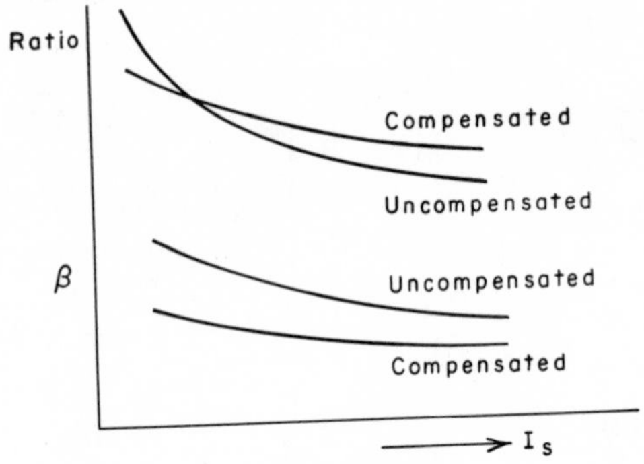

FIG. 13.

by the compensating flux than in the remainder of the core. The compensating winding and the area it encloses are so chosen that, as the secondary current is increased, these portions operate in the region of decreasing permeability while the remainder of the coil is still in the region of increasing permeability. The ampere-turns[15] of the compensating winding subtract from the ampere-turns of the main winding; and, since their effect is relatively greater at low currents than at high currents, the *effective* ampere-turns of the total winding increase with increasing current. Consequently the *effective* turn ratio of the transformer is greater at high than at low currents. Thus the effect on transformer ratio is precisely the same as that of the magnetic shunt previously described. A short-circuited turn, indicated in Fig. 12, is used for phase-angle compensation. The transformer construction is normal except for the holes, which do no harm to the mechanical strength and other properties of the transformer. The effect on ratio and phase angle of magnetic shunt compensation is shown in Fig. 13.

[15] Strictly speaking, one must consider not the ampere-turns but the flux linkages involved, i.e. the product of ampere-turns with the flux linked by the turn.

Two-stage transformers, specially loaded tertiary windings, auxiliary transformers with saturable cores, and various other devices have been used with varying success in attempts to compensate the errors of current transformers. Most of these methods involve additional expense in transformer construction and can in general be justified only where the correction must be held to very small values.

EFFECT OF PRIMARY CONDUCTOR POSITION. A source of error which is sometimes considerable in high-range transformers results from the magnetic field set up by the current-carrying conductor. This error may appear in a number of ways. The ratio and phase angle of the transformer may be influenced to a significant extent by the position of the return lead from the primary circuit or by other conductors in the neighborhood carrying heavy currents. In through- (window-) type transformers the corrections may be influenced by the position of the primary turns when more than one turn of a flexible conductor is threaded through the window as a primary winding. (The nominal ratio is halved by using two primary turns, etc.) If the core has joints, the position of these primary conductors with respect to the core joints may change the corrections. This effect is greatest if the secondary is wound on only one leg of the core and the primary turns are wrapped around the other, since the leakage reactance is greatest in this case. The situation is considerably improved if the secondary winding is divided into halves and wound on both legs. If a single primary turn is used, the ratio and phase angle may be changed if the primary turn is not centered in the window. For a jointless core of ring-shaped laminations, with a secondary uniformly distributed around the core, there is usually very little effect from the position of the primary turns. However, in any event care should be taken in testing transformers to arrange the primary circuit so that the effect of primary conductor position is minimized,[16] or, if a lack of symmetry will be encountered in operation, to duplicate as nearly as possible the conductor arrangement which is to be used.

A similar effect of dissymmetry is revealed, to a much smaller extent, in multirange transformers with wound primaries. Figure 14 shows this for a transformer having sixteen ranges obtained by taps on the primary winding. The same secondary winding is used on all ranges. Ratio factors and phase angles are plotted against secondary current at a constant impedance burden, for the two extreme ranges, 5/5 and 150/5 amp. The corresponding curves for the intermediate ranges lie between the plotted curves. The primary and secondary windings are on the same leg of the core, and the core joints are well fitted and tightly clamped. It may be seen that with this favorable arrangement the influence on ratio

[16] J. H. Park, *NBS J. Research*, **14**, 367 (1935).

factor and phase angle of the number of primary turns and their position is small. (In the case cited the extreme differences amount to 0.1% in ratio factor and 3 min in phase angle.) This influence is even smaller in a transformer which has a distributed secondary wound on a jointless, ring-type core.

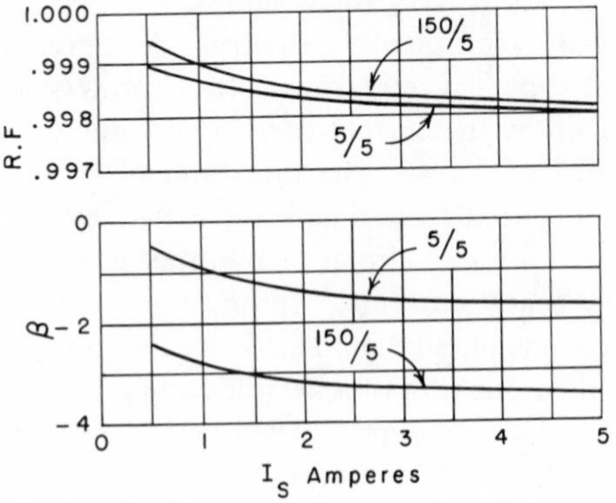

FIG. 14.

EFFECT OF PERMANENT MAGNETIZATION. The presence of permanent magnetization in the core of a current transformer may reduce its permeability at the flux densities at which it is normally operated and thus increase both its ratio and its phase angle. Permanent magnetization may arise from any of a number of causes. If the secondary circuit of the transformer is opened while its primary is energized, there will be no back mmf present and the flux density in the core will continue to rise until saturation is reached. If now the primary circuit is opened, the core may be left permanently magnetized, the magnitude of the magnetization depending on the instantaneous magnitude of primary current at the instant of interruption. Permanent magnetization may also result from direct current in either winding, for example, as a consequence of the measurement of winding resistance in a Wheatstone bridge or the use of a d-c polarity check. It may also arise from a transient short-circuit current in the line, since such a current may have a unidirectional component which has the same effect as a direct current. Such permanent magnetization may be removed and the transformer restored to its normal condition by demagnetizing the transformer core. The demagnetization procedure in general assures that saturation be established by the magnetizing current which is then gradually reduced to zero, using a current reversal or cycling process to ensure gradually diminishing magnetizing forces. Demagnetization of a transformer can be accomplished in a number of ways. If one circuit is open so that no counter mmf is set up, the core can be saturated by sending current through the other winding. If the primary circuit is open, alternating current may be sent through the secondary winding to perhaps twice the rating and then gradually reduced to zero by inserting resistance in the secondary circuit. A continuously adjustable rheostat may be used for this purpose. The transformer may also be demagnetized by passing enough alternating current through the primary winding to first saturate the core and then gradually reducing it to zero. Or rated current may be passed through the primary with a large resistance connected across the secondary terminals. This secondary resistance is then reduced gradually to zero. Of these methods of demagnetization, the first will probably be the most convenient on the test bench because of the lower currents involved. The third method may be useful for demagnetizing a transformer which cannot be removed from service.

EFFECT OF SECONDARY OPEN CIRCUIT. A precaution which should *always* be observed in using a current transformer is the following: NEVER OPEN THE SECONDARY CIRCUIT OF A CURRENT TRANSFORMER WHILE ITS PRIMARY IS ENERGIZED. The number of primary ampere-turns is fixed by the primary current and is not reduced when the secondary is opened. The opening of the secondary circuit reduces the secondary ampere-turns to zero, so that no counter mmf is present to oppose the mmf from the primary ampere-turns, and the flux density rises until the core saturates. As a consequence of the saturation flux acting on the large number of secondary turns, the voltage induced in the secondary winding may be large. This induced voltage may, in fact, be dangerously high to the operator who has opened the circuit and may also damage or destroy the insulation of the transformer. Also considerable heating may result from the core losses at saturation which, in extreme cases, may be sufficient to damage the transformer. As already mentioned, if the primary circuit is opened while this condition exists, the core is apt to be magnetized with a consequent change in ratio and phase angle.

Current Transformer Standards.[17] The American Standards Association has been instrumental in the adoption of certain conventions and has set up classes under which the performance of current transformers may be rated. These conventions and ratings are almost universally followed by American manufacturers. The following conventions and definitions are pertinent to this discussion:

(*a*) *Polarity*: Primary and secondary transformer leads are said to have the same polarity if at a given instant the current enters the primary lead in question and leaves by the secondary lead in question as though the two leads formed a continuous circuit.

[17] ASA C57.13—1948, pp. 8–12.

(*b*) *Ratio Correction Factor* (*RCF*) is the factor by which the *nominal* ratio must be multiplied to obtain the *true* ratio of the transformer (i.e. the ratio of magnitude of the primary to the secondary vector).

(*c*) *Phase-Angle Correction Factor* is the factor by which the reading of a wattmeter (or watthour meter) must be multiplied to correct for phase displacement. This factor equals the ratio of the true to the apparent power factor, assuming that no phase error is present except that introduced by the transformer.

(*d*) *Transformer Correction Factor* (*TCF*) is the factor by which the reading of a wattmeter (or watthour meter) must be multiplied to correct for the combined effects of the ratio correction factor and the phase-angle correction factor.

The accuracy classes into which instrument transformers are divided for measurement applications are based on the maximum value which the transformer correction factor may have with loads of lagging power factors between 1.00 and 0.6. The rating is then based on the accuracy class of the transformer at a specified burden. We will first examine the relation between transformer correction factor TCF and transformer phase angle β.

If we assume that the only error in a wattmeter reading W is that introduced by the current transformer,[18] we may say that the load power divided by the nominal transformer ratio is

$$\frac{P}{\text{Nom. ratio}} = W \cdot \text{TCF} = W \frac{\cos \phi}{\cos (\phi - \beta)} \cdot \text{RCF}$$

so that

$$\text{TCF} = \text{RCF} \frac{\cos \phi}{\cos (\phi - \beta)}$$

Now

$$\frac{\cos \phi}{\cos (\phi - \beta)} = \frac{1}{\cos \beta(1 + \tan \phi \tan \beta)} \approx \frac{1}{1 + \beta \tan \phi}$$

since β is a very small angle. In this expression β is in radians, and $\tan \phi = 1.33$ since by definition the limiting value of the correction corresponds to a lagging power factor of 0.6 (i.e. $\cos \phi = 0.6$). If now β is expressed in minutes (β'), its value must be divided by 3438 to reduce it to radians. So we may write

$$\text{TCF} \approx \text{RCF} \left[\frac{1}{1 + \dfrac{\beta' \times 1.33}{3438}} \right] \approx \text{RCF} \left[1 - \frac{\beta'}{2600} \right] \approx \text{RCF} - \frac{\beta'}{2600}$$

since RCF does not depart greatly from unity.

[18] See Fig. 1 of this chapter.

Hence

$$\beta' = 2600(\text{RCF} - \text{TCF}) \text{ min}$$

If, for example, TCF = 1.012 and RCF = 0.988, $\beta' = -2600 \times 0.024 = -62'$; using the opposite limits, if RCF = 1.012, β' must be $+62'$ in order that TCF = 0.988.

The ASA accuracy classes are as follows:

Accuracy Class	TCF Limits				
	At 100% Rated Current		At 10% Rated Current		For Lagging Power Factor between
	min	max	min	max	
1.2	0.988	1.012	0.976	1.024	0.6 and 1.00
0.6	0.994	1.006	0.988	1.012	,,
0.3	0.997	1.003	0.994	1.006	,,
0.5	0.995	1.005	0.995	1.005	,,

The limiting values of ratio correction factor and phase angle which correspond to a particular transformer-correction factor can be shown graphically as a parallelogram. The parallelograms corresponding to the accuracy class 0.3 are shown in Fig. 15. In this instance we can say

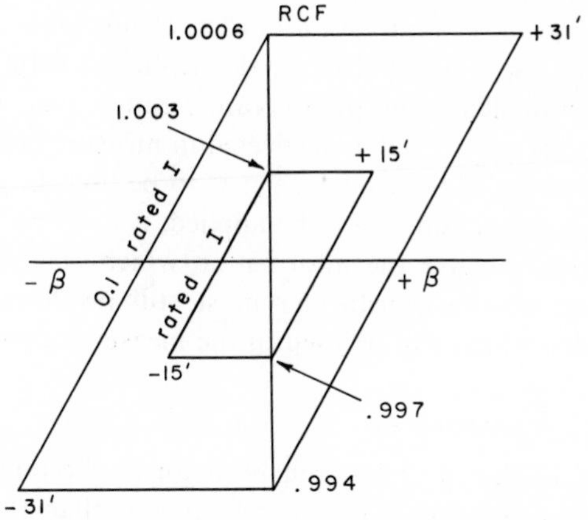

FIG. 15.

that the error in power or energy measurements resulting from neglecting the corrections introduced by a current transformer will not be greater than 0.3% at rated current if the ratio correction factor and phase angle of the transformer are within the inner parallelogram; and that the error will not be greater than 0.6% at 0.1 rated current if they are within the outer parallelogram at this current. Of course, the ratio and phase angle will depend on the instrument burden, so that transformers are rated in terms of the accuracy classes that they meet with certain specified maximum secondary burdens. The ASA burdens for rating purposes are as follows:

Burden	Characteristics		For 60 cycles and 5 amp			For 25 cycles and 5 amp		
	R, ohms	*L*, mh	*Z*, ohms	VA	PF	*Z*, ohms	VA	PF
B–0.1	0.09	0.116	0.1	2.5	0.9	0.0918	2.3	0.98
B–0.2	0.18	0.232	0.2	5.0	0.9	0.1836	4.6	0.98
B–0.5	0.45	0.580	0.5	12.5	0.9	0.4590	11.5	0.98
B–1	0.5	2.3	1.0	25	0.5	0.617	15.4	0.81
B–2	1.0	4.6	2.0	50	0.5	1.234	30.8	0.81
B–4	2.0	9.2	4.0	100	0.5	2.468	61.6	0.81
B–8	4.0	18.4	8.0	200	0.5	4.936	123.2	0.81

It will be recognized that the ASA rating merely specifies a minimum transformer performance under a specified maximum burden; i.e. Class 0.3 with B-0.1 simply states that the transformer in question will not have a TCF that departs from unity by more than 0.3% at rated current or 0.6% at 10% current if used with a burden of not more than that represented by B-0.1. Such a performance description is helpful in a purchase specification, or to determine the operating range over which the transformer corrections may be safely neglected in measurements of a specified precision. However, if the transformer is to be used in precise measurements for which corrections are to be applied, it must be realized that the ASA rating does not give the information which is needed. The ratio and phase angle of the transformer must still be determined with the particular burden which will be used in the measurements.

The Voltage Transformer

This is quite similar in design and behavior to the power transformer, and in both these respects is very much simpler than the current transformer, since the voltage and hence the flux density in the core are nearly constant, whereas the flux density in the core of a current transformer varies with current. Its primary winding is connected between lines (Fig. 16) so that the full line voltage is impressed on it, in contrast to the current transformer, whose primary is connected in one line and carries the full line current. The voltage transformer may be considered a "parallel" transformer with its secondary operating under virtual open-circuit conditions,[19] whereas the current transformer may be thought of as a "series" transformer whose secondary operates under virtual short-circuit conditions.[20] Since in normal operation the line voltage is nearly constant, voltage-transformer excitation varies only over a restricted range, whereas the primary current and excitation of a current transformer vary over wide limits in normal operation.

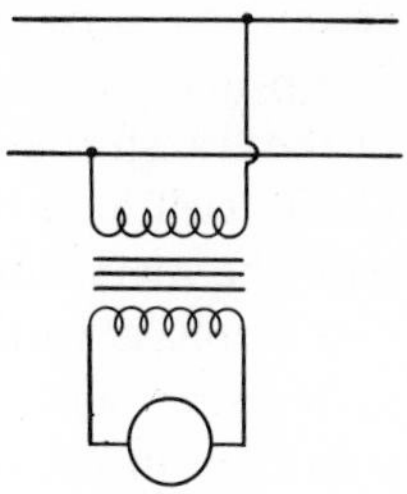

FIG. 16.

The secondary winding of a voltage transformer is usually designed so that in normal operation a voltage between 100 and 120 volts is delivered to the instrument load. Insulation problems are very similar to those in a power transformer of comparable voltage rating, but the loading of a voltage transformer is always small, sometimes only a few volt-amperes, and consists of the voltage circuits of instruments, meters, or relays. Since the power requirements are small, the design is usually controlled by considerations of adequate insulation and good regulation rather than by economies in the use of iron and copper.

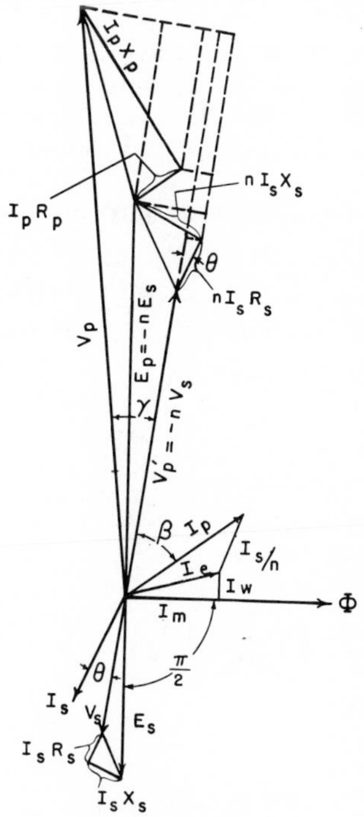

FIG. 17.

Ratio and Phase-Angle Formulas. The vector diagram of a voltage transformer is shown in Fig. 17. Starting with the main flux Φ in the core,[21] which links the primary and secondary windings, the induced secondary voltage E_s lags this flux by 90°. This voltage causes a current I_s to flow in the secondary circuit and a terminal voltage V_s to appear at the secondary terminals and across the secondary burden. This terminal voltage will be less than E_s because of the voltage drop I_sZ_s in the secondary winding.

The primary terminal voltage V_p may be divided into two parts: the primary impedance drop, I_pZ_p, and the primary induced voltage, $E_p = -nE_s$ (n being the ratio of primary to

[19] Most voltage-transformer burdens are of relatively high impedance.

[20] Most current-transformer burdens are of relatively low impedance.

[21] No scale is intended in Fig. 17. The relative magnitudes and phase relations of the various vectors are distorted to separate them in the figure.

secondary turns in the transformer), leading the main flux Φ by 90°. The primary current I_p contains two components: I_e, the exciting current of the transformer, and $-I_s/n$, the reflection of the secondary current. I_e will itself have two components: I_m, the magnetizing current in phase with the main flux, and I_w, the core-loss current leading the flux by 90° and in phase with $E_p = -nE_s$.

In using such a transformer as an instrument transformer, we are interested in the ratio of primary to secondary *terminal* voltages and in the phase angle γ between the primary and reversed secondary terminal voltages. R_s, X_s and R_p, X_p are the resistance and leakage reactance of the secondary and primary windings respectively; V_s and V_p are the corresponding terminal voltages; and θ is the phase angle of the secondary burden—the instrument load on the transformer.

If we resolve V_p along V_s reversed and ignore the signs associated in the vector diagram with the reversed secondary vectors, we have:

$$V_p \cos \gamma = nV_s + nI_s(R_s \cos \theta + X_s \sin \theta) + I_p(R_p \cos \beta + X_p \sin \beta)$$

Now, $\gamma < 1°$ for a well-designed voltage transformer at any burden within its rating, and we can say that

$$\cos \gamma \approx 1; \quad I_p \cos \beta \approx I_w + \frac{I_s}{n} \cos \theta; \quad \text{and} \quad I_p \sin \beta \approx I_m + \frac{I_s}{n} \sin \theta$$

Then

$$V_p \approx nV_s + nI_s(R_s \cos \theta + X_s \sin \theta) + R_p \left(I_w + \frac{I_s}{n} \cos \theta\right) + X_p \left(I_m + \frac{I_s}{n} \sin \theta\right)$$

$$\approx nV_s + I_s \cos \theta \left(nR_s + \frac{R_p}{n}\right) + I_s \sin \theta \left(nX_s + \frac{X_p}{n}\right) + I_w R_p + I_m X_p$$

$$\approx n \left[V_s + I_s \cos \theta \left(R_s + \frac{R_p}{n^2}\right) + I_s \sin \theta \left(X_s + \frac{X_p}{n^2}\right) + \frac{I_w R_p + I_m X_p}{n}\right]$$

We will write

$$R_s + \frac{R_p}{n^2} = R_{ts}; \quad X_s + \frac{X_p}{n^2} = X_{ts}$$

and note that R_{ts}, X_{ts} are the equivalent *total* resistance and reactance of the transformer referred to its secondary circuit. Substituting these values in the equations above and dividing by V_s, we have

$$\text{Ratio} = \frac{V_p}{V_s} \approx n\left[1 + \frac{I_s(R_{ts}\cos\theta + X_{ts}\sin\theta) + \dfrac{I_wR_p + I_mX_p}{n}}{V_s}\right]$$

Going back to the vector diagram of Fig. 17, if we write the component of V_p perpendicular to V_s, we have

$$V_p \sin\gamma = I_pX_p\cos\beta - I_pR_p\sin\beta + nI_sX_s\cos\theta - nI_sR_s\sin\theta$$

But under the conditions of our approximation $\sin\gamma \approx \gamma$ and $V_p \approx nV_s$. Also the accepted sign convention on phase angles of instrument transformers requires that the angle shall be considered positive when the reversed secondary vector *leads* the primary vector. This convention requires that the sign of γ in our vector diagram and equation be negative. Then, on making the indicated substitutions, we may write

$$-\gamma \approx \frac{X_p\left(I_w + \dfrac{I_s}{n}\cos\theta\right) - R_p\left(I_m + \dfrac{I_s}{n}\sin\theta\right) + nI_s(X_s\cos\theta - R_s\sin\theta)}{nV_s}$$

or

$$\gamma \approx \frac{R_pI_m - X_pI_w}{nV_s} - \frac{I_s}{V_s}\left[\left(\frac{X_p}{n^2} + X_s\right)\cos\theta - \left(\frac{R_p}{n^2} + R_s\right)\sin\theta\right]$$

$$\approx \frac{R_pI_m - X_pI_w}{nV_s} - \frac{I_s}{V_s}(X_{ts}\cos\theta - R_{ts}\sin\theta)$$

At no load (secondary circuit open so that $I_s = 0$) we have for the ratio and phase angle

$$R_0 = n\left(1 + \frac{I_wR_p + I_mX_p}{nV_s}\right) \quad \text{and} \quad \gamma_0 = \frac{R_pI_m - X_pI_w}{nV_s}$$

Now we will define a ratio factor $F = R/n$ (i.e. the true ratio divided by the turn ratio of the transformer), and will attach the subscript I_θ to R, F, and γ to indicate their values for a particular secondary current I having a particular phase angle θ referred to the secondary terminal voltage. The subscript I_0 will represent a pure resistance burden for which the current is I and the phase angle zero at the voltage V_s. Also we will designate the no-load values (as above) with the subscript 0 (i.e. $I_\theta = 0$). The relations for no load (secondary circuit open) become

$$F_0 = \frac{R_0}{n} = 1 + \frac{I_wR_p + I_mX_p}{nV_s} \quad \text{and} \quad \gamma_0 = \frac{I_mR_p - I_wX_p}{nV_s}$$

For the general case (burden current I at a phase angle θ) we may write

$$F_{I_\theta} = F_0 + \frac{I_\theta}{V_s}(R_{ts}\cos\theta + X_{ts}\sin\theta)$$

and

$$\gamma_{I_\theta} = \gamma_0 - \frac{I_\theta}{V_s}(X_{ts}\cos\theta - R_{ts}\sin\theta)$$

For the case where the burden is purely resistive, so that $\theta = 0$ and $I_\theta = I_0$, these expressions become

$$F_{I_0} = F_0 + \frac{I_0}{V_s}R_{ts} \quad \text{and} \quad \gamma_{I_0} = \gamma_0 - \frac{I_0}{V_s}X_{ts}$$

Then we may say

$$R_{ts} = \frac{V_s}{I_0}(F_{I_0} - F_0) \quad \text{and} \quad X_{ts} = \frac{V_s}{I_0}(\gamma_0 - \gamma_{I_0})$$

These values may be substituted in our general equations, and we have

$$F_{I_\theta} = F_0 + \frac{I_\theta}{V_s}\left[\frac{V_s}{I_0}(F_{I_0} - F_0)\cos\theta + \frac{V_s}{I_0}(\gamma_0 - \gamma_{I_0})\sin\theta\right]$$

or

$$F_{I_\theta} = F_0 + \frac{I_\theta}{I_0}[(F_{I_0} - F_0)\cos\theta + 0.000291(\gamma_0 - \gamma_{I_0})\sin\theta]$$

if γ is in minutes, since it must be converted into radians. (There are 3438 minutes in a radian.) Similarly

$$\gamma_{I_\theta} = \gamma_0 - \frac{I_0}{V_s}\left[(\gamma_0 - \gamma_{I_0})\frac{V_s}{I_0}\cos\theta - (F_{I_0} - F_0)\frac{V_s}{I_0}\sin\theta\right]$$

$$= \gamma_0 - \frac{I_\theta}{I_0}[(\gamma_0 - \gamma_{I_0})\cos\theta - 3438(F_{I_0} - F_0)\sin\theta] \text{ min}$$

From these last equations we can compute the ratio and phase angle of a transformer at a given voltage, for any load conditions at any power factor, if we know F and γ at no load and at a single unity-power-factor load for the same voltage. If we know the equivalent total resistance R_s and reactance X_s of the transformer, we may compute ratio and phase angle for any load whatever from the no-load values at the same voltage. R_s is readily obtained. The primary and secondary resistances may be separately measured in a Wheatstone bridge and $R_{ts} = \left(\frac{R_p}{n^2} + R_s\right)$. X_{ts} may be obtained from short-circuit data. If the primary of the transformer is short-circuited and a low voltage (a few per cent of rated voltage) is applied to the secondary winding with an ammeter, voltmeter, and wattmeter connected to measure voltage E, current I, and power P, then

$$\frac{E}{I} = Z_{ts}, \quad \frac{P}{EI} = \cos\theta, \quad \text{and} \quad Z_{ts}\cos\theta = X_{ts}$$

Design Features. At no load the actual ratio exceeds the turn ratio by an amount $(I_w R_p + I_m X_p)/V_s$, i.e. because of the drop in voltage resulting from the exciting current in the resistance and leakage reactance of the primary winding. Hence the actual ratio can be brought to nominal if we reduce the turn ratio by this amount. The manner in which the leakage reactance is divided between the primary and secondary circuits cannot be precisely evaluated. For most purposes it is satisfactory to assign half of the total equivalent reactance to the primary circuit. With any inductive or resistive load there is a further increase of ratio because of the voltage drop resulting from the load current in the equivalent total impedance of the primary and secondary transformer windings. This would require a further reduction in turn ratio to bring the actual ratio to nominal. Thus the ratio factor of a voltage transformer can be brought to unity for some particular combination of load and voltage by adjusting the turn ratio. This may be done either by adding secondary turns or by removing an equivalent percentage of primary turns. It will be seen from the equations developed above that the no-load phase angle, γ_0, could be made zero if $I_m R_p = I_w X_p$. However, it is not generally practical to design for this condition, and the no-load phase angle is generally positive because $I_m R_p > I_w X_p$. The means which can be taken to reduce R_p will increase I_m, and a compromise must be made. Low values of R and X are of importance in decreasing the errors under load, and accordingly the best design is usually one with a minimum number of turns and as high a flux density in the core as is feasible without approaching too closely to saturation. Designers are not altogether in agreement as to the proper value of flux density to use, but high permeability (low I_m) is more important than low loss (low I_w). It is generally agreed that the newer oriented-grain steels which allow a working flux density of 15,000 gausses are of great value compared with the older materials that were limited to flux densities below 12,000 gausses.

Although the design and construction of voltage transformers are basically the same as those of power transformers, the design requirements are usually determined by the performance desired in constancy of ratio and smallness of phase angle, and by the space necessary for proper insulation. Since the power output of a voltage transformer is always small, the design may depart considerably from that which would be most economical in a power transformer of similar voltage rating. The core is usually of the "open window" type of construction, and the windings may be either entirely on one leg or divided between the legs of the core. The primary and secondary windings are usually coaxial to reduce leakage to a minimum, with the low-voltage winding inside next to the core in order to simplify the problem of insulation. The primary winding may be a single coil in low-voltage transformers but must be subdivided into a number of short coils in high-voltage transformers in order to reduce the insulation needed between coil layers. Multirange transformers may have both primary and secondary windings divided into two or more equal sections for series and parallel connection, or may have taps brought out on a continuous winding. (In the latter case it is usually, although not necessarily, the secondary winding which is tapped.) Cotton tape and varnished cambric are much used for insulation in coil construction with hard fiber separators between coils. At low voltages transformers are usually filled with solid compound, whereas oil is used at higher voltages.[22] At very high voltages the solid insulation and cloth employed in coil construction must be carefully dried and the assembly vacuum-impregnated to eliminate moisture, voids, and entrapped air which would reduce the quality of the insulation. Dry-type, porcelain-insulated transformers have been developed in European practice for use up to 45 kv.

For very high voltages, 100 kv and greater, oil-filled transformers of the conventional type are very large and costly because of insulation requirements. For example, a 110-kv voltage transformer built by one of the leading manufacturers has an over-all height of 14 ft, requires nearly 800 gal of oil, and weighs almost 5 tons. The power rating of such transformers is so far in excess of instrument requirements that exceedingly uneconomical use is made of the materials utilized in the transformer construction. In recent years a number of high-voltage instrument transformer designs have incorporated radical departures from the usual features of power transformers in order to reduce size and cost. Two interesting European designs eliminate the high-voltage lead-in bushings which contribute considerably to the size and cost of the regular type of transformer. Both designs are intended to measure line-to-ground voltages in a three-phase system: (1) a transformer built within an insulating casing; and (2) cascaded transformer sections.

Economies of space and material over the conventional design are achieved by building the transformer entirely within an oil-filled high-

[22] Non-flammable chlorinated liquid compounds (askarels, such as Pyranol or Inerteen) which have been much used recently in power transformers have been employed to a limited extent in voltage transformers. However, they have some disadvantages in this application, and it is not expected that their use will become general.

voltage insulator. In the design shown[23] in Fig. 18, one leg of the core is used for the windings. The primary, a stack of flat coils, extends almost the full length of the insulator and the core is connected to the midpoint of the winding. The ends of the winding are connected to the metal end caps of the insulator, which serve as high-voltage and ground connections. The core is insulated from both end caps, and the potential is graded uniformly from top to bottom by a series of metal rings, fixed near the inner surface of the insulator and connected to successive primary

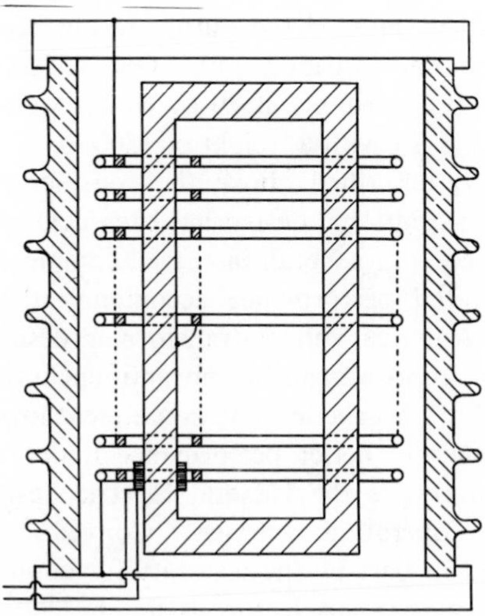

FIG. 18.

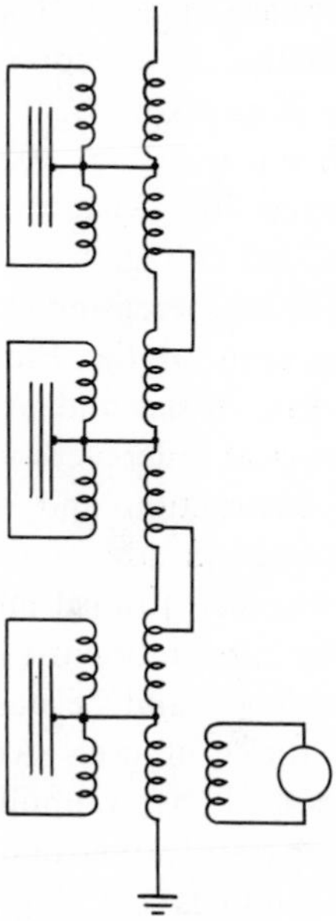

FIG. 19.

coils. The secondary coil is near the lower end of the core, and leads are brought out through the lower end cap. Such transformers are constructed to give 0.5% accuracy for loads up to 200 volt-amperes. A 150-kv Brown-Boveri transformer of this type has a height of 8 ft and occupies about one-ninth of the floor space required by the conventional type of transformer having the same rating. However, it is suitable only for line-to-ground use, and presents manufacturing difficulties due to the large size of the porcelain bushing needed to enclose the transformer.

In the cascade arrangement of Fig. 19 the voltage is divided among n transformers so that each takes $1/n$ of the total. In this way each unit requires insulation corresponding to the lower voltage, with a consequent

[23] Meyerhans, *Elecktrot. Zeits.*, **51**, 17 (1930).

over-all economy of space and material. If the sections were not coupled magnetically the potential distribution of the system (considered as a reactor) would not be uniform. Each unit is therefore provided with an auxiliary winding by means of which it is coupled to the next lower unit. Use of the autotransformer principle for the coupling turns (as shown in Fig. 19) results in economy of winding. Because of the rather high leakage reactance inherent in this construction short-circuited leakage-compensating windings (shown in the figure) are sometimes used to reduce the phase angle. This auxiliary winding can be adjusted to correct flux unbalance in the core, its ampere-turns being utilized to add or subtract flux as needed. Such transformers can be built in a $\frac{1}{2}\%$ accuracy class with an output of 100 volt-amperes or more,[24] the output rating being lowered somewhat with each additional cascaded unit. One series of cascaded voltage transformers employs two units at 70 kv with a weight of 450 lb, increasing to six units at 210 kv with a weight of 1500 lb.

In each of the European designs described above the considerable decrease in size and weight over a conventional design has been achieved by radical differences in methods used. In general, increased complexity of construction and somewhat limited performance accompany these decreases in size and weight. In America voltage-transformer designs have tended toward modification or improvement of conventional transformers, both because of their simpler construction and consequent lower labor cost, and because of the generally better performance under all conditions of use. An example of this is the General Electric design developed by Camilli[25] for high operating voltages. Conventional power-transformer design is dictated in part by the necessity for cooling the windings. It should be apparent that this feature is not needed in high-voltage instrument transformers. For example, the copper loss in the primary of a 138-kv transformer having a resistance of 10,000 ohms is less than 1 watt with a load of 500 volt-amperes. The liquid cooling ducts provided in the power transformer are therefore not needed. Now, in an insulating structure comprising oil in series with solid insulation, the dielectric stress is inversely proportional to the dielectric constant. Since the dielectric constant of the solid material is approximately twice that of the oil, the dielectric strength of the solid is not generally fully utilized. If solid dielectric were used in place of a structure which is half liquid and half solid, the spacing would need to be only two-thirds as great. Camilli's design has a layer winding (Fig. 20) with the layers separated by solid insulation. The separators between layers consist of several sheets of paper with their edges folded forward over the coil. The

[24] Reiche, *Arch. für tech. Mess.*, Z387–1 (January 1933).
[25] Camilli, *Trans. AIEE*, **62**, 483 (1943).

assembly is impregnated with liquid (oil or Pyranol). In this way a uniform solid insulating structure is formed, having a dielectric constant intermediate between that of the oil and the paper, and a strength about equal to that of impregnated paper in an oil-filled cable. The core is formed from spirally wound strip material and encloses the high- and low-voltage coils with small clearance so that the coil structure substantially fills the window of the core. The transformer case is made liquid-tight and an oil expansion chamber is located at the top of the oil-filled bushing. The lower part of the bushing (inside the tank) is eliminated, and an insulating shield protects the high-voltage lead at the entrance to the bushing. A cross-sectional drawing of the assembly is shown in Fig. 21. The over-all height, largely that of the bushing, is about half that needed in the conventional design, the weight is about 40%, and the oil volume is about 15%. The transformer has performance characteristics equal to those obtained in transformers of the conventional type.

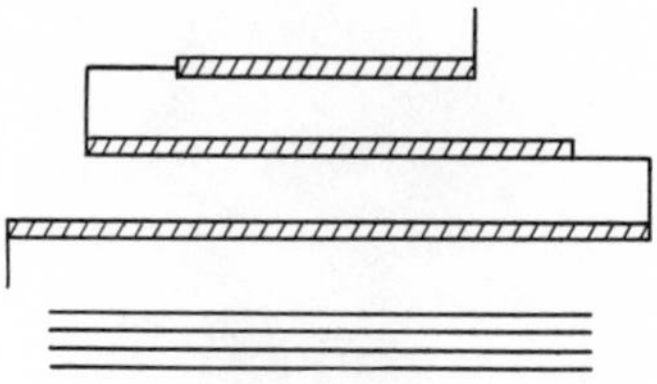

FIG. 20.

Another American design (Westinghouse), which is similar in some respects to that just described, also achieves about the same saving in weight and space without limiting performance and without excessive labor cost. In this design also, shown in Fig. 22, the conventional type of lead-in bushing has been eliminated. The major coil insulation, of paper tape, has been extended smoothly and continuously along the high-voltage lead up into a porcelain weather casing mounted on the tank. The porcelain bushing is permanently sealed to the transformer case and is oil-filled. The primary coils of the transformer are "pie-wound" as in the conventional design, and oriented-grain silicon steel is used as the core material. Because of the "pie" construction of the primary winding the case is slightly larger than for the layer-wound primary described previously. Either of these designs can be adapted to line-to-ground operation with a single high-voltage bushing, or line-to-line operation with two bushings.

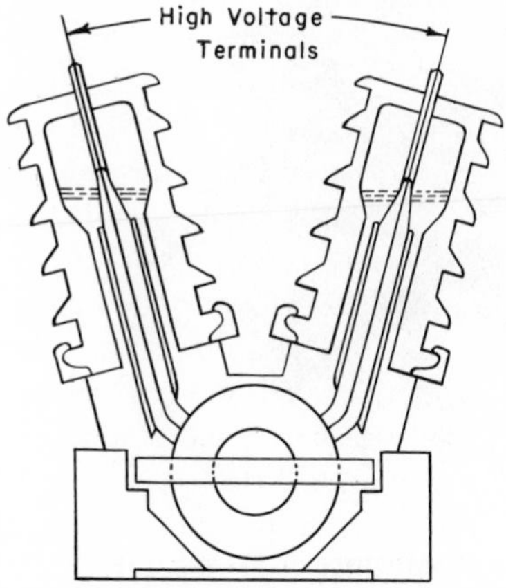

FIG. 21.

Voltage-Transformer Standards. Standards for American use have been sponsored by the American Standards Association to specify the performance of transformers for metering service. These standards are

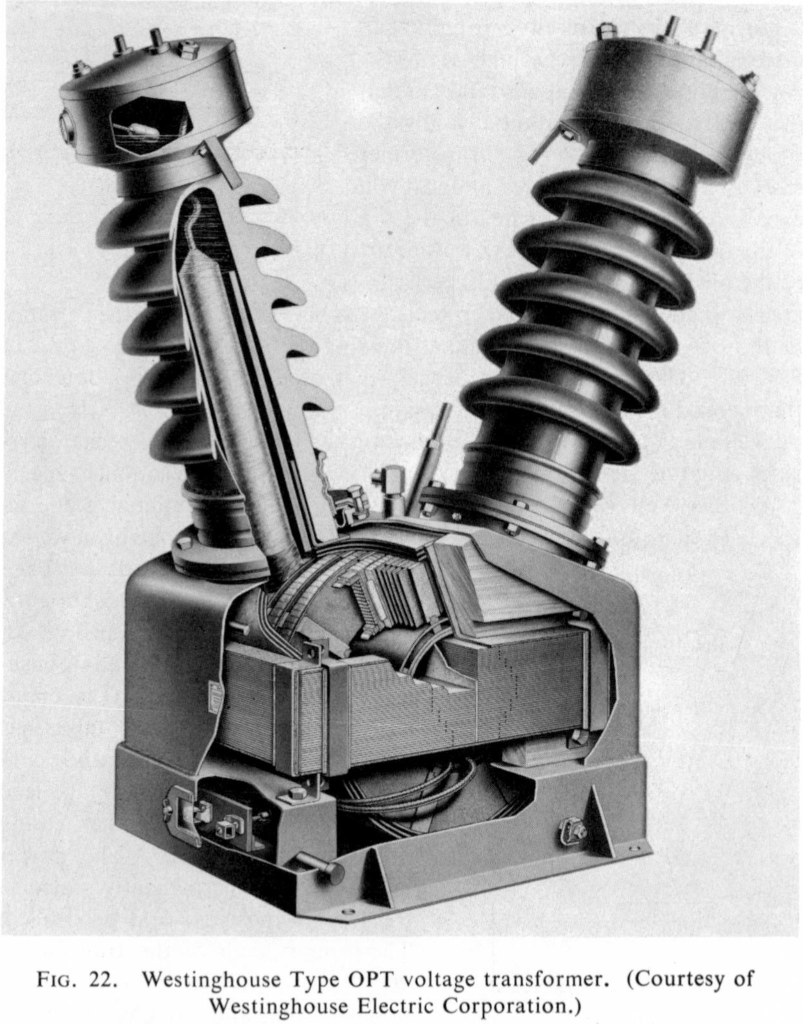

FIG. 22. Westinghouse Type OPT voltage transformer. (Courtesy of Westinghouse Electric Corporation.)

similar in form and content to those already discussed for current transformers.[26] For details the reader should refer to sections of the current ASA Standard C57 dealing with instrument transformers. The standard burdens used for describing performance are given in the table at top of page 575. The burden is stated in terms of volt-amperes and power factor

[26] See p. 561 of this chapter.

Designation of Burden	*Sec. Volt-Amperes*	*Power Factor of Burden*
W	12.5	0.10
X	25	0.70
Y	75	0.85
Z	200	0.85

at 120 volts and rated frequency, except for transformers rated for service at a secondary voltage of 69.3 volts, where the burdens are specified at the rated voltage. The resistance and inductance of the burden are assumed to remain constant over the entire range of voltages on which the transformer will be used.

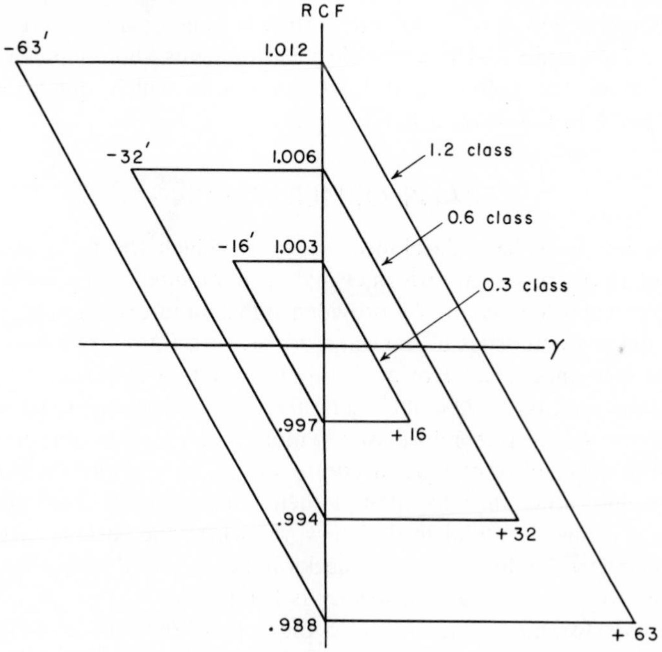

FIG. 23.

The standard accuracy classes stating the limiting transformer correction factor[27] (TCF) over a range of voltage departing as much as $\pm 10\%$ from rated voltage are given in the table below. The phase-angle limits corresponding to particular ratio correction factors (RCF) may be found from the formula $\gamma = 2600(\text{TCF} - \text{RCF})$ and are shown in Fig. 23.

Accuracy Class	*Limits of TCF*	*PF (lag.) Limits of Metered Load*
1.2	1.012–0.988	0.6–1.00
0.6	1.006–0.994	,,
0.3	1.003–0.997	,,

[27] See p. 562 for explanation.

An accuracy-class statement, referred to a particular standard burden (viz. Z-0.6), indicates that the transformer correction factor is within the stated limits 0.6% for any burden from zero (open circuit) up to the stated standard burden, and for any power factor of the metered load from 0.6 lagging to unity.

Although the name-plate statement of the accuracy classes of a transformer for various standard burdens indicates the maximum error introduced into a power or energy measurement by neglecting the transformer corrections, and therefore the types of measurement for which they are suitable without correction, the *precise determination* of ratio and phase angle remains important if the transformer is to be used for more exacting work. Such ratio and phase-angle measurements should preferably be made under the voltage and load conditions which duplicate those encountered in the work at hand.

TRANSFORMER TESTING

Formulas have been developed above by which the ratio and phase angle of an instrument transformer may be computed with good accuracy for a particular load condition provided sufficient information is available about the characteristics of the transformer, turn ratio, excitation, losses, leakage reactance, etc. However, this information is generally unavailable to the user, or may be obtained only after a rather elaborate series of measurements. It is therefore usually more economical of time and effort, as well as productive of more accurate values, to measure the ratio and phase angle rather than to attempt their computation. Such computations are primarily useful in design work, where the various factors are controllable within limits, or as a check on measured values in cases where an exhaustive study of a transformer is being made.

Methods for measuring the ratio and phase angle of an instrument transformer may be broadly classified into two groups: *direct* and *comparative*. In a *direct* method the ratio and phase relation of the primary and secondary vectors (current or voltage) in which we are interested are determined by their direct comparison or by the comparison of two quantities which are related in a known way, one to the primary and one to the secondary vector current or voltage. In a *comparative* method the secondary vector current or voltage (or a related quantity) of the transformer under test is compared to the secondary output of a known or reference transformer, the unknown and reference transformers being operated under such conditions that their primary vector inputs are known to be identical. From the measured relations between the two secondary vectors, and from the known relations between the primary and secondary vectors of the reference transformer,[28] the ratio and phase angle of the unknown may be computed. Each of these two types of test methods (direct and comparative) can be further classified, according to the measurement technique utilized, as *deflection* and *null* methods. Deflection methods make use of the deflections of suitable instruments such as electrodynamic wattmeters[29] for measuring quantities related to the vectors under consideration or to their difference. The required ratio and phase angle are computed from the magnitude of the deflection. In some instances scales of the instruments can be marked in terms of ratio factor and phase angle so that the methods become "direct reading." Null methods make use of a network in which the appropriate vector quantities are balanced against one another, or in which their differences are compensated, balance or compensation being indicated by the null indication of an appropriate detector. The ratio and phase angle are then computed from the impedance elements of the network; or the method may sometimes be made "direct reading" in terms of calibrated scales on adjustable elements of the network. Such networks may be generally considered special-purpose a-c potentiometers, the two elements of the potentiometer balance usually corresponding to ratio and phase-angle determination. We shall examine some of the methods of transformer testing, typical of the various general classes. It should be borne in mind that the secondary burden of the transformer is an essential element in all such tests and that for results of the highest accuracy the impedance of this burden should correspond to the impedance of the circuit connected to the secondary terminals of the transformer when it is used.

Current-Transformer Testing

Direct Deflection Methods. A simplified method for determining the ratio and phase angle of a current transformer in terms of the readings of two electrodynamic wattmeters is shown schematically in Fig. 24(*a*). The current coil of one wattmeter is in series with the primary winding of the transformer, and carries the primary current I_p. The current coil of the other wattmeter is connected in the secondary circuit and carries the secondary current I_s. The voltage circuits of the two wattmeters are

[28] It will be realized that the calibration of the reference transformer must eventually be made in terms of a direct determination of ratio and phase angle, either on the reference transformer itself or by comparison with another transformer that has been so calibrated. Most manufacturers are equipped to furnish ratio and phase-angle data on their transformers, and there are a number of laboratories in the United States that have facilities for making such direct tests.

[29] Integrating meters such as watthourmeters may also be used for this purpose.

supplied, at constant voltage V, from an auxiliary source whose phase can be varied with respect to the transformer supply. The indicated burden may include instruments or equivalent impedance elements used to fix the condition under which the transformer is tested, and it should be remembered that the current coil of the secondary wattmeter is part of the total secondary burden.[30] If the phase of the voltage supply, V,

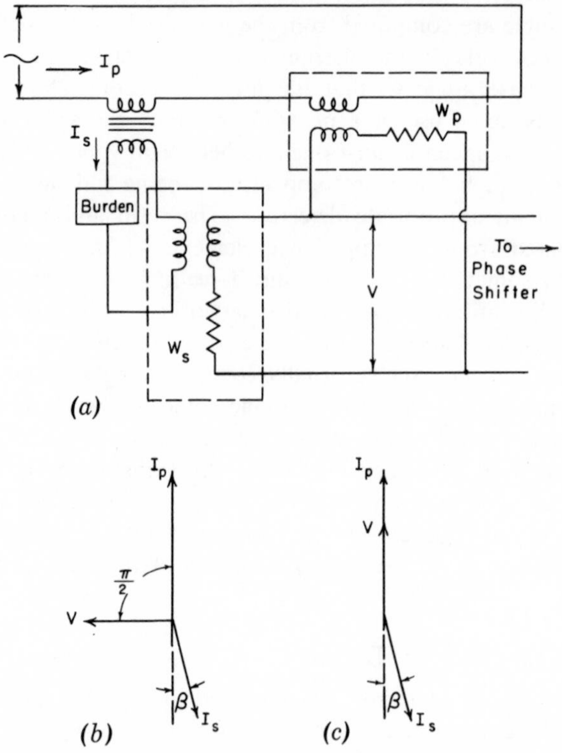

FIG. 24.

to the wattmeters is adjusted until the wattmeter W_p in the primary circuit reads zero, V and I_p will be in quadrature as shown in Fig. 24(*b*), and the reading of the secondary wattmeter will be

$$_1W_s = VI_s \cos\left(\frac{\pi}{2} + \beta\right) = -VI_s \sin\beta$$

Now, if the phase of V is shifted through $\pi/2$ so that the reading of W_p

[30] It will be generally true for the methods to be discussed that any current-carrying element in the secondary circuit of the transformer forms part of the burden.

is maximum,[31] V will be in phase with I_p and the secondary wattmeter reading will be

$$_2W_s = VI_s \cos(\pi + \beta) = -VI_s \cos\beta$$

Under these conditions the reading of the primary wattmeter will be $_2W_p = VI_p$.

Now

$$\frac{_2W_p}{\sqrt{_1W_s^2 + {_2W_s^2}}} = \frac{VI_p}{V\sqrt{I_s^2 \sin^2\beta + I_s^2 \cos^2\beta}} = \left|\frac{I_p}{I_s}\right| = \text{ratio of the transformer}$$

or, since $_2W_s \gg {_1W_s}$, we have approximately

$$\text{Ratio} \approx \frac{W_p}{_2W_s}$$

Also

$$\frac{_1W_s}{_2W_s} = \frac{VI_s \sin\beta}{VI_s \cos\beta} = \tan\beta$$

or, since β is always small,

$$\beta \approx \frac{_1W_s}{_2W_s}$$

Thus the ratio and phase angle of the transformer are determined in terms of the wattmeter readings. Although this test method is quite simple and straightforward in theory, there are a number of practical disadvantages to its use. At best, when the wattmeters are being operated at nearly full-scale deflection for the "in-phase" setting, the results can be no more accurate than the wattmeter readings (perhaps 0.2 to 0.5%, depending on the quality of the instruments) and both the sensitivity and accuracy fall off with the first power of the current, so that if they are suitable for determinations at rated current they are relatively insensitive at low currents. Since the wattmeter in the primary circuit must carry the primary current, the method is adaptable only to comparatively low-range transformers. Finally, since the current coils of a wattmeter represent a fairly large burden (perhaps 5 volt-amperes or more) a rather high lower limit is set on the secondary burden at which such tests may be made.

Comparative Deflection Methods. A deflection method capable of considerable precision has been described by Silsbee[32] and is shown

[31] Since the wattmeter setting near maximum is very insensitive to phase shifts ($\cos\phi \approx 1$) it is always better where possible to first determine the quadrature position (where wattmeter response is very sensitive to small changes in phase) and then to shift the phase through 90°, rather than to set up an "in-phase" relation by adjusting the phase directly in terms of the maximum reading of the instrument.

[32] Silsbee, *Bull. Bur. Standards*, **14**, 317 (1919).

schematically in Fig. 25(a). Here the ratio and phase angle of a transformer X are determined, in terms of a reference transformer S having the same nominal ratio, from the readings of a wattmeter W_2 (or an equivalent, separately excited electrodynamic instrument). W_1 is a wattmeter whose current coil is connected to carry the secondary current of the reference transformer. The current coil of W_2 carries the difference

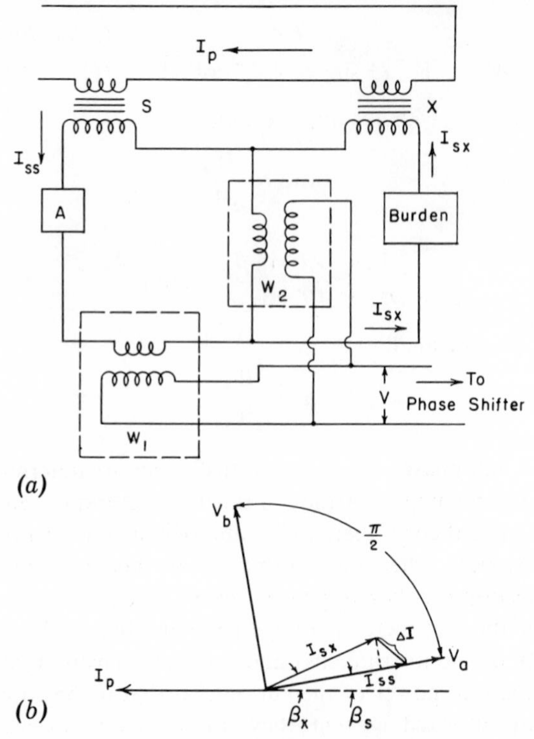

FIG. 25.

ΔI between the secondary currents of the reference and test transformers. The voltage circuits of the wattmeters are supplied in parallel from a phase shifter at a constant voltage V. W_1 is used to adjust the phase of V to quadrature or in phase with I_{ss}, the secondary current of the reference transformer. The phase relations are as shown in Fig. 25(b). When V is in quadrature with I_{ss} we have

$${}_1W_2 = VI_{sx} \cos \left[\frac{\pi}{2} - (\beta_x - \beta_s)\right] = VI_{sx} \sin (\beta_x - \beta_s)$$

and when V is in phase with I_{ss}, we have

$${}_2W_2 = VI_{ss} - VI_{sx} \cos (\beta_x - \beta_s)$$

In this case ${}_2W_1 = VI_{ss}$, and we could determine the secondary current as $I_{ss} = {}_2W_1/V$. Now the ratio of the test transformer is $R_x = I_p/I_{sx}$, and that of the reference transformer is $R_s = I_p/I_{ss}$, so that

$$\frac{R_x}{R_s} = \frac{VI_{ss}}{VI_{sx}} \approx \frac{VI_{ss}}{VI_{ss} - {}_2W_2} = \frac{1}{1 - \dfrac{{}_2W_2}{VI_{ss}}} \approx 1 + \frac{{}_2W_2}{VI_{ss}}$$

or

$$R_x \approx R_s\left(1 + \frac{{}_2W_2}{VI_{ss}}\right)$$

Also

$$\tan(\beta_x - \beta_s) \approx \beta_x - \beta_s = \frac{{}_1W_2}{VI_{ss} - {}_2W_2} \approx \frac{{}_1W_2}{VI_{ss}}$$

since

$${}_2W_2 < V\Delta I \ll VI_{ss}$$

Then we have

$$\beta_x \approx \beta_s + \frac{{}_1W_2}{VI_{ss}}$$

The ratio and phase angle of the test transformer have been stated in terms of the reference transformer and the wattmeter readings. It should be noted that, whereas W_1 carries the full secondary current and must therefore be a 5-amp instrument, W_2 carries only the difference ΔI between the nominally equal secondary currents and may be a wattmeter of low current range. For adequate sensitivity it is better to use an electrodynamic instrument designed especially for the purpose (i.e. a current range of perhaps 0.1 amp or less). It should also be noted that the current coil of W_2 has a minor effect on the burden of the test transformer. Let Z_x be the impedance of the burden exclusive of the current coil of W_2, Z_e be the impedance of the effective burden, and Z_w be the impedance of the wattmeter coil. Then

$$Z_e \cdot I_{sx} = Z_x I_{sx} - Z_w \cdot \Delta I$$

so that

$$Z_e = Z_x - \frac{\Delta I}{I_{sx}} \cdot Z_w$$

The effective burden is less by a small amount than the burden set up as Z_x. This, of course, sets a limit on the maximum value of impedance that the current coil of W_2 may have if $Z_w \cdot (\Delta I/I_{sx})$ is to be negligible compared to Z_x.

A modification of Silsbee's method has been constructed[33] in which ratio error and phase angle are direct-reading in terms of instrument

[33] Sieber, *Siemens-Zeits.*, **9**, 845 (1929).

deflection. The stated accuracy of the modified arrangement is 0.1% in ratio and 5 min in phase angle.

Comparative deflection methods have been devised making use of watthour meters in place of wattmeters. It is possible in this way to attain good accuracy in the determination of ratio and phase angle, since the small measured differences between the test and reference transformer may be allowed to accumulate over an interval of time. Agnew's method[34]

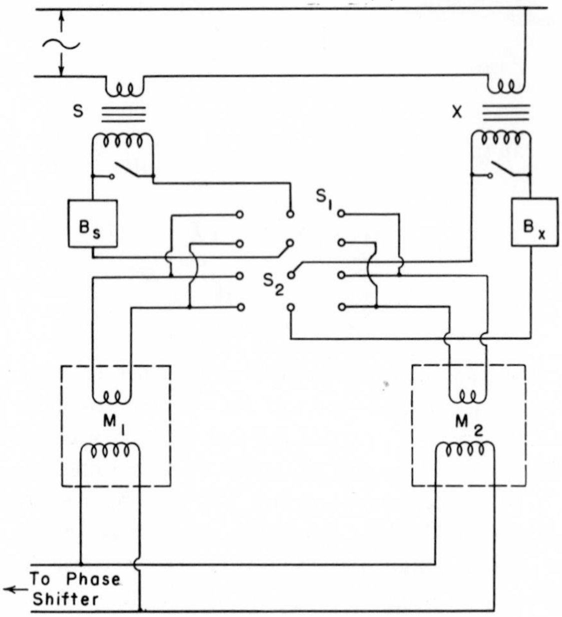

FIG. 26.

will serve to illustrate this type of test. We will assume that the two watthour meters are of the same type and are both adjusted to operate correctly on full load at unity and 50% power factor, and that the nominal watt-hours per revolution are the same for each meter. The wiring diagram is shown in Fig. 26. The ratio of recorded watt-hours to true watt-hours will be m_1 and m_2 respectively for the meters. Now, if a meter is connected to a circuit having a power factor ϕ, through a current transformer having a ratio R, a nominal ratio R_N, and a phase angle β, then for a revolutions the true energy will be

$$\frac{R}{R_N} \cdot \frac{\cos \phi}{\cos (\phi - \beta)} \cdot \frac{Ka}{m} \approx \frac{R}{R_N} \cdot \frac{Ka}{m(1 + \tan \phi \tan \beta)}$$

since β is a very small angle and $\cos \beta \approx 1$.

[34] Agnew, *Bull. Bur. Standards*, **11**, 347 (1915).

We will operate M_1 on the secondary of the reference transformer and M_2 on the secondary of the test transformer (i.e. with S_1 connected to the left and S_2 to the right) at a known power factor; and then under the same conditions operate M_1 on the test and M_2 on the reference transformer,[35] for the same total time. Let the watthour-meter readings be a_{1s}, a_{2x} in the first run and a_{1x}, a_{2s} in the second. Then, since the nominal ratios of the transformers are equal and the same total energy should be registered by each of the meters on a run, we have

$$\frac{R_s K a_{1s}}{m_1(1 + \tan\phi \tan\beta_s)} = \frac{R_x K a_{2x}}{m_2(1 + \tan\phi \tan\beta_x)}$$

and

$$\frac{R_x K a_{1x}}{m_1(1 + \tan\phi \tan\beta_x)} = \frac{R_s K a_{2s}}{m_2(1 + \tan\phi \tan\beta_s)}$$

at any power factor.

At unity power factor (i.e. the auxiliary voltage in phase with the current) $\tan\phi = 0$, and our expressions reduce to

$$\frac{R_s a_{1s}}{m_1} = \frac{R_x a_{2x}}{m_2}, \quad \text{and} \quad \frac{R_x a_{1x}}{m_1} = \frac{R_s a_{2s}}{m_2}$$

from which we may say that

$$\frac{R_x}{R_s} = \sqrt{\frac{a_{1s} \cdot a_{2s}}{a_{1x} \cdot a_{2x}}}, \quad \text{or} \quad R_x = R_s \sqrt{\frac{a_{1s} \cdot a_{2s}}{a_{1x} \cdot a_{2x}}}$$

With the phase of the auxiliary voltage shifted so that the power factor is low (e.g. if the meter rates have been adjusted at a pf $= 0.5$, this value may be used), a new set of observations is made with the meters interchanged between the circuits. Let the readings be a'_{1s}, a'_{2x} in the first run, and a'_{1x}, a'_{2s} when the meters are interchanged. Then for these conditions

$$\frac{R_s \cdot a'_{1s}}{m_1(1 + \tan\phi \tan\beta_s)} = \frac{R_x \cdot a'_{2x}}{m_2(1 + \tan\phi \tan\beta_x)}$$

and

$$\frac{R_x \cdot a'_{1x}}{m_1(1 + \tan\phi \tan\beta_x)} = \frac{R_s \cdot a'_{2s}}{m_2(1 + \tan\phi \tan\beta_s)}$$

Dividing the first of these equations by the second, we have

$$\frac{R_s \cdot a_{1s}(1 + \tan\phi \tan\beta_x)}{R_x \cdot a_{1x}(1 + \tan\phi \tan\beta_s)} = \frac{R_x \cdot a_{2x}(1 + \tan\phi \tan\beta_s)}{R_s \cdot a_{2s}(1 + \tan\phi \tan\beta_x)}$$

[35] It should be recalled that the secondary circuit of a current transformer should not be opened while the transformer is energized. Thus in Fig. 26 short-circuiting switches are shown for use when the meters are being interchanged.

from which

$$\frac{(1 + \tan \phi \tan \beta_x)^2}{(1 + \tan \phi \tan \beta_s)^2} = \left(\frac{R_x}{R_s}\right)^2 \cdot \frac{a'_{1x} \cdot a'_{2x}}{a'_{1s} \cdot a'_{2s}}$$

Since β_x and β_s are both small, we can neglect squares and higher-order terms, and say

$$1 + 2 \tan \phi (\tan \beta_x - \tan \beta_s) \approx \left(\frac{R_x}{R_s}\right)^2 \cdot \frac{a'_{1x} \cdot a'_{2x}}{a'_{1s} \cdot a'_{2s}}$$

or

$$\tan \beta_x - \tan \beta_s \approx \frac{1}{2 \tan \phi} \left(\frac{a_{1s} \cdot a_{2s}}{a_{1x} \cdot a_{2x}} \cdot \frac{a'_{1x} \cdot a'_{2x}}{a'_{1s} \cdot a'_{2s}} - 1\right)$$

Then

$$\beta_x = \beta_s - \frac{1}{2 \tan \phi} \left(1 - \frac{a_{1s} \cdot a_{2s}}{a_{1x} \cdot a_{2x}} \cdot \frac{a'_{1x} \cdot a'_{2x}}{a'_{1s} \cdot a'_{2s}}\right)$$

By allowing sufficient time on each run so that a is large, good accuracy can be attained: 0.03% in ratio and 1 or 2 min in phase angle. It should be noted as a disadvantage of the method that considerable time is required to test a transformer. Results are, however, very nearly independent of fluctuations in line current, and no special apparatus is needed for the test.

Direct Null Methods. Such methods in general utilize specialized potentiometer networks in which the voltage drop across a four-terminal resistor in the primary circuit is opposed to the voltage drop across a four-terminal resistor in the secondary circuit. The phase difference between these voltages may be compensated by capacitance, or by self- or mutual-inductance appropriately placed in the network. The method of Sharp and Crawford,[36] as modified by Agnew and Silsbee[37] for use at the National Bureau of Standards, will serve to illustrate the general procedure. Actually the simplicity, precision, flexibility, and speed of operation of this method make it very attractive, and it is widely used on this account. The arrangement is shown schematically in Fig. 27(*a*), and the corresponding vector diagram in 27(*b*).

For simplicity it will be assumed that the voltage drops across the primary and secondary shunts are precisely in phase with the corresponding current vectors. Then from the vector diagram we may write

$$\tan \beta = \frac{\omega I_s M}{I_s R_s}, \quad \text{and} \quad \cos \beta = \frac{I_s R_s}{I_p R_p}$$

[36] Sharp and Crawford, *Trans. AIEE*, **29**, 1517 (1911).

[37] Agnew and Silsbee, *Trans. AIEE*, **31**, 1635 (1912); also Silsbee, Smith, Forman, and Park, *NBS J. Research*, **11**, 93 (1933).

From these relations we have

$$\beta \approx \frac{\omega M}{R_s}$$

and

$$\text{Ratio} = \frac{I_p}{I_s} = \frac{R_s}{R_p \cos \beta}$$

If we take account of the phase angle θ_p of the primary shunt[38] and θ_s of the secondary shunt our phase-angle formula must be modified to

$$\beta = \frac{\omega M}{R_s} + \theta_p - \theta_s$$

Actually in the setup at the National Bureau of Standards, $(\theta_p - \theta_s)$ is around 3 min at 60 cycles in the extreme case and, for most of the shunt

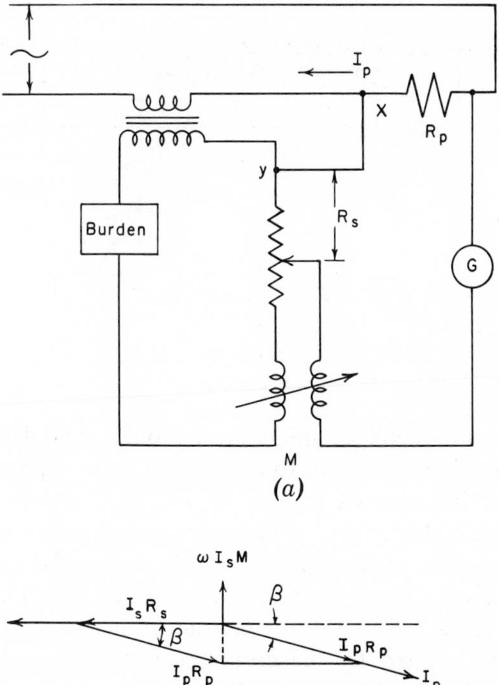

(a)

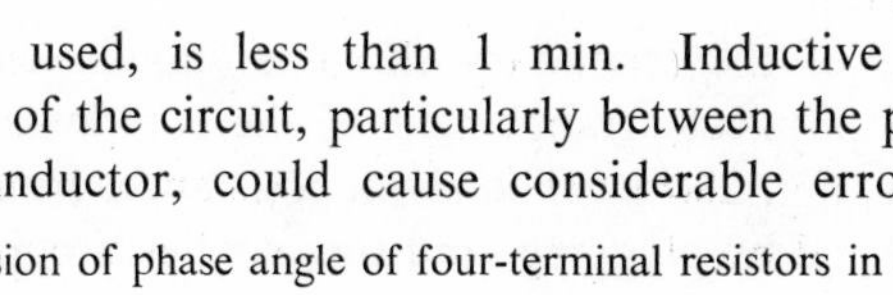

(b)

FIG. 27.

combinations used, is less than 1 min. Inductive coupling between various parts of the circuit, particularly between the primary circuit and the mutual inductor, could cause considerable error. Such coupling

[38] See discussion of phase angle of four-terminal resistors in Chapter 7.

should be avoided by using coaxial conductors where possible in the secondary circuit, by keeping the going and return leads as closely together as possible and twisting them together as a pair where coaxial construction is impossible, and by keeping the primary and secondary circuits separated to the maximum extent possible. The presence of inductive coupling can be detected by connecting both potential leads of the primary shunt to point x of Fig. 27, and both secondary potential leads to point y, and, with rated current in the primary circuit, observing the detector deflection.

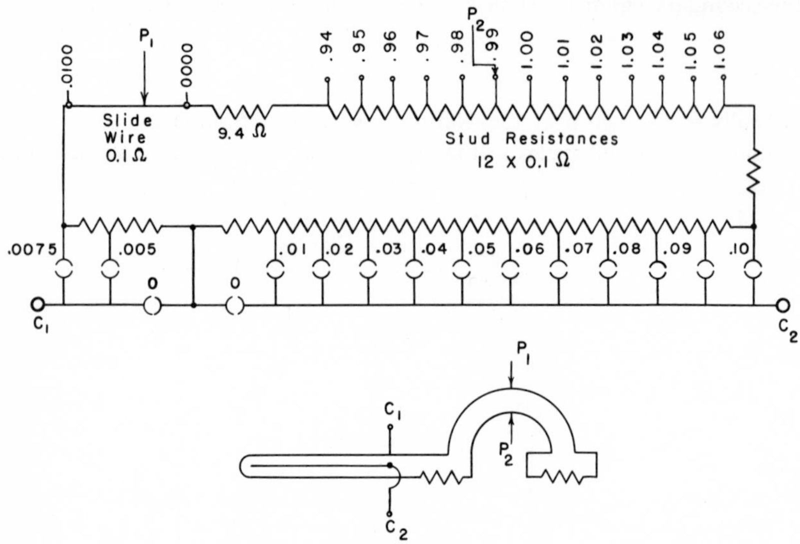

FIG. 28.

In the absence of inductive coupling there should be no detector response when the mutual inductor is set to zero. If there is appreciable response with the mutual inductor set to zero, the circuit should be rearranged so that the coupling is eliminated. The burden introduced into the secondary circuit by R_s and the primary of M is of the order of 0.1 ohm (2.5 volt-ampere) and sets the lower limit to burden values which can be used in testing. The upper limit to ratios of transformers which can be tested by this method is fixed by the current capacity of available primary shunts. In the National Bureau of Standards setup this limit is 2500/5 amp. An accuracy of 0.01% in ratio and 0.3 min in phase angle is attainable in this setup.

The arrangement of the secondary shunt is shown schematically in Fig. 28(a), and the physical arrangement of the components is approximately indicated in Fig. 28(b). The shunt resistance, from 0.0075 ohm to 0.10 ohm, is selected by plugging, and the parallel circuit arrangement is so made that the four-terminal resistance R_s may be varied continuously over a range of $\pm 6\%$ from the nominal value by altering the positions of P_1 and P_2, this variation of R_2 being required for balancing the potentiometer. It will be noted that the main shunt which carries the secondary current of the transformer, together with the parallel circuit (having a resistance about 100 times as great), forms a closed loop of constant total resistance S. Now let the resistance plugged in the main shunt be R_c, and the resistance between the sliders be R_p. The total resistance of the shunt between the current terminals is then

$$\frac{R_c(S - R_c)}{S}$$

and the total voltage drop across the shunt is

$$\frac{IR_c(S - R_c)}{S}$$

The voltage drop between P_1 and P_2 is

$$\frac{IR_c(S - R_c)}{S} \cdot \frac{R_p}{(S - R_c)}$$

so that the four-terminal resistance, using C_1, C_2 as current terminals and P_1, P_2 as potential terminals, is

$$R_s = R_c \cdot \frac{R_p}{S}$$

The resistances are adjusted so that a shift of P_2 from one stud position to the next changes R_s by 1%, while the slide wire under P_1 has a total range of 1% and is equal to a step of P_2. Thus the four-terminal resistance of the secondary shunt is continuously variable, and its setting at balance is direct-reading in terms of transformer ratio factor for any resistance within the range of the apparatus.

Comparative Null Methods. NBS METHOD. A comparative null method used at the National Bureau of Standards for transformer tests between 2500/5 and 12,000/5 amp is shown in Fig. 29. The transformer, S, employed as a reference standard has a laminated ring core. Primary and secondary windings are each uniformly distributed about the core, and a large number of ratios are available by using various parallel and series combinations of the sectionalized windings. The construction of this transformer is such that its ratio error and phase angle are the same if the number of primary turns is changed by a shift from a series to a parallel arrangement, while the secondary turns, burden, current, and frequency are left unchanged. Similarly, the ratio error and phase angle are unchanged if the number of secondary turns is changed by a shift from a parallel to a series arrangement and the external burden is changed at the same time by a factor equal to the square of the ratio of the new to the old number of series secondary turns, while the number of primary turns, the frequency, and the secondary current are left unchanged. Physically these criteria are based on the assumed constancy of the coupling (or mutual inductance) between the primary and secondary windings. In other words, the ratio of primary to secondary flux linkages is assumed to be constant for any particular value of ampere-turns, whatever the combination of amperes and turns used to produce the

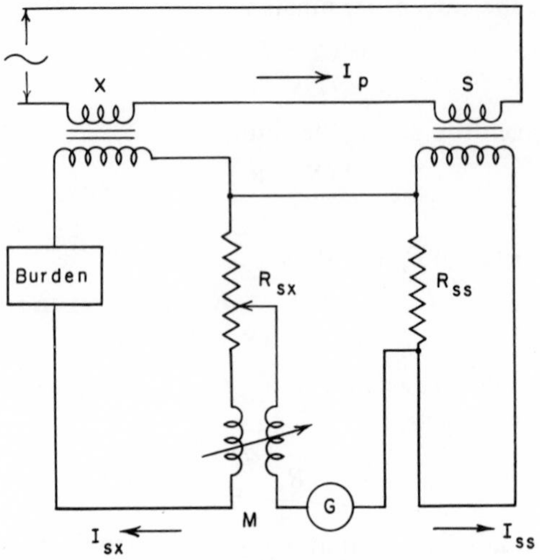

FIG. 29.

value. This assumption is justified to a high degree of precision when both the primary and the secondary windings are uniformly distributed around a jointless core. It must, of course, be further assumed that the impedance per turn of the sections that are to be connected in parallel or in series is nearly enough alike that the current distribution between the sections is not materially altered in the change. (Tests have shown that these criteria have been satisfied to within 0.02% in ratio error and 1 min of phase angle for all the primary and secondary turn combinations used in the National Bureau of Standards standard transformer.) Hence the transformer can be calibrated on a low ratio (2500/5 amp or less) by the direct method described above, and used as a reference standard at the larger ratios (above 2500/5 amp).

Now, if the ratio of the standard transformer is N_s and its phase angle is β_s, we have

$$I_{ss} = \frac{I_p}{N_s}(\cos \beta_s + j \sin \beta_s) \approx \frac{I_p}{N_s}(1 + j\beta_s)$$

If we say that the four-terminal resistance of the shunt in the standard transformer secondary circuit is R_{ss} and its phase angle is θ_{ss}, also that the corresponding values for the shunt in the secondary circuit of the test transformer are R_{sx} and θ_{sx}, we have for the voltage drop across R_{ss}

$$E_{ss} = I_{ss} \cdot R_{ss}(1 + j\theta_{ss}) = \frac{I_p}{N_s} R_{ss}[1 + j(\theta_{ss} + \beta_s)]$$

and for the voltage drop across R_{sx}

$$E_{sx} = I_{sx}R_{sx}(1 + j\theta_{sx})$$

The voltage drop inserted by the mutual inductance to produce balance is

$$E_m = j\omega M I_{sx}$$

The equation of balance is

$$E_{ss} = E_{sx} - E_m$$

or

$$\frac{I_p}{N_s} R_{ss}[1 + j(\theta_{ss} + \beta_s)] = I_{sx}R_{sx}\left[1 + j\left(\theta_{sx} - \frac{\omega M}{R_{sx}}\right)\right]$$

From this equation we have that

$$\frac{I_p}{I_{sx}} \approx \frac{R_{sx}N_s}{R_{ss}}\left[1 + j\left(\theta_{sx} - \frac{\omega M}{R_{sx}} - \theta_{ss} - \beta_s\right)\right]$$

The phase angle of the test transformer (the angle by which the reversed secondary vector *leads* the primary) is then

$$\beta_x = \frac{\omega M}{R_{sx}} + \beta_s + \theta_{ss} - \theta_{sx}$$

and we may write

$$\frac{I_p}{I_{sx}} = \frac{R_{sx}N_s}{R_{ss}}(1 - j\tan\beta_x) = \frac{R_{sx}N_s}{R_{ss}}\left(\frac{\cos\beta_x - j\sin\beta_x}{\cos\beta_x}\right)$$

whence the ratio of the test transformer is

$$N_x = \left|\frac{I_p}{I_{sx}}\right| = \frac{R_{sx}N_s}{R_{ss}} \cdot \frac{1}{\cos\beta_x}$$

SILSBEE CURRENT-TRANSFORMER TESTING SET. This is a portable apparatus made by the Leeds and Northrup Company for testing current transformers in terms of a calibrated reference transformer having the same nominal ratio and is the basis of one of the most widely used null comparative test methods. The circuit of the early Leeds and Northrup apparatus (on the market before 1936), shown schematically in Fig. 30(*a*), was a modification of the circuit originally described by Silsbee[39] and is direct-reading at 25 and 60 cycles. The difference in ratio error and phase angle between the reference and test transformers is read at balance from the dial settings, balance being obtained by adjustment of the

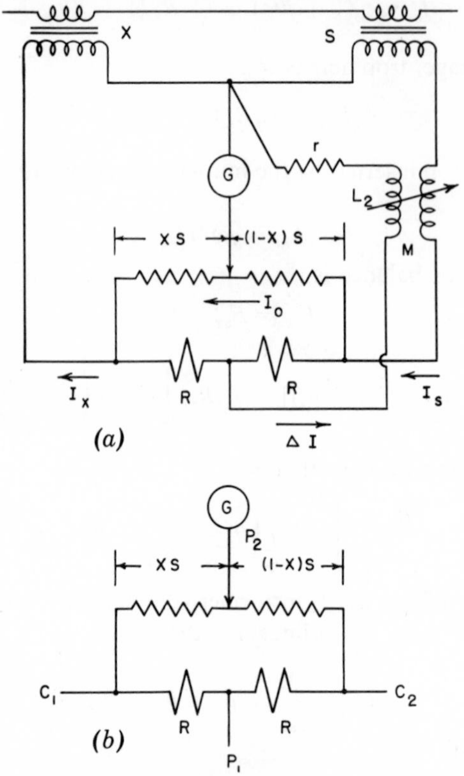

FIG. 30.

slide-wire resistor S and the mutual inductor M. The total range is $\pm$ 5% in ratio and $\pm$ 3° in phase angle.

The equation of balance may be written as

$$(1 - x)SI_0 = (I_s - I_0)R + \Delta I(r + j\omega L_2) + I_s j\omega M$$

Also at balance (when the galvanometer current is zero)

$$\Delta I = I_s - I_x$$

and

$$I_0 S = R(I_s - I_0) + R(I_x - I_0) = R(I_x + I_s - 2I_0)$$

[39] Silsbee, *Bull. Bur. Standards*, **14**, 317 (1919).

so that

$$I_0 = \frac{R(I_s + I_x)}{2R + S}$$

Now let the four-terminal resistance shown in Fig. 30(*b*) be σ, using C_1, C_2 as current terminals and P_1, P_2 (the midpoint of the fixed resistor R, R and the contactor on the parallel slide wire) as potential terminals. Then

$$\sigma = \frac{R(1 - x - x)S}{2R + S} = \frac{RS(1 - 2x)}{2R + S}$$

so that

$$(1 - x) = \frac{2R + S}{2RS}\sigma + \frac{1}{2}$$

If we substitute for $(1 - x)$, ΔI, and I_0 in the balance equation, we have

$$S\left[\frac{2R + S}{2RS}\sigma + \frac{1}{2}\right] \cdot \frac{R(I_s + I_x)}{2R + S}$$

$$= I_s R - \frac{R^2(I_s + I_x)}{2R + S} + (r + j\omega L_2)(I_s - I_x) + j\omega M I_s$$

or

$$I_s\left[r + \frac{R}{2} - \frac{\sigma}{2} + j\omega(L_2 + M)\right] = I_x\left[r + \frac{R}{2} + \frac{\sigma}{2} + j\omega L_2\right]$$

If we let

$$\frac{\sigma}{r} = a, \quad \frac{\omega M}{r} = b, \quad \frac{\omega L_2}{r} = c, \quad \frac{R}{2r} = d$$

we may write

$$\frac{I_s}{I_x} = \frac{1 + \dfrac{a}{2} + d + jc}{1 - \dfrac{a}{2} + d + j(b + c)}$$

If we expand this expression, retaining all second-order terms and neglecting terms of the third and higher orders, we have

$$\frac{I_s}{I_x} \approx 1 + a - ad + \frac{a^2}{2} - b^2 - bc - j\left(b + ac + \frac{3ab}{2} - bd\right)$$

The effective current ratio

$$\left|\frac{I_s}{I_x}\right| \approx 1 + a - ad + \frac{a^2}{2} - \frac{b^2}{2} - bc$$

and the phase angle

$$\delta = -b + bd - \frac{ab}{2} - ac$$

which is the angle by which I_s leads I_x. Now the phase-angle scale of the test set is marked to read the angle by which I_x leads I_p, and we may write

$$\alpha = -\delta = b(1-d) + a\left(\frac{b}{2} + c\right)$$

It should be noted that there are terms in the ratio equation which depend on b and terms in the phase-angle equation which depend on a; i.e. the reading of the ratio dial must be corrected for the setting of the phase-angle dial, and the reading of the phase-angle dial must be corrected for the setting of the ratio dial. If the ratio dial is marked to read

$$R = 1 + a + \frac{a^2}{2} - ad$$

the true ratio is

$$R - b\left(\frac{b}{2} + c\right)$$

Similarly, if the phase-angle dial is marked to read

$$\beta = b(1-d) = \frac{3438\omega M}{r} \times 0.975 \qquad (d \approx 0.025)$$

the true

$$\text{Phase angle} = \beta + a\left(\frac{b}{2} + c\right)$$

Correction tables are supplied with these test sets, giving the corrections for each dial in terms of the settings of the other. These corrections range upward to 0.22% in ratio at a phase angle of 180 min, and 3 to 7 min in phase angle for a ratio setting of 0.95 or 1.05.

In 1936 Leeds and Northrup adopted a further modification[40] of the circuit, in which the secondary of the mutual inductor is connected in series with the detector. The modified circuit shown in Fig. 31(*a*) has two advantages: (1) the resistors which carry the difference current $(I_s - I_x)$ between the transformer secondaries can be made of a material having a low temperature coefficient; (2) the second-order terms are so changed that it is possible to correct the ratio scale simply by using an index mark which is shifted slightly in position for changes in the phase-angle setting, and no correction is needed for the phase-angle reading as a result of the ratio dial setting. The ratio dial comprises two slide wires, Q and S, which are moved together, S being in parallel with the shunts R, R which carry the currents I_s and I_x, and Q being in parallel with a

[40] This modification (suggested by Dr. Leo Behr) was incorporated in all test sets having L & N serial numbers higher than 275179.

resistor r_2 which carries the difference current $(I_s - I_x)$. We must therefore consider two four-terminal resistors. As before

$$\sigma = \frac{RS(1 - 2x)}{2R + S}$$

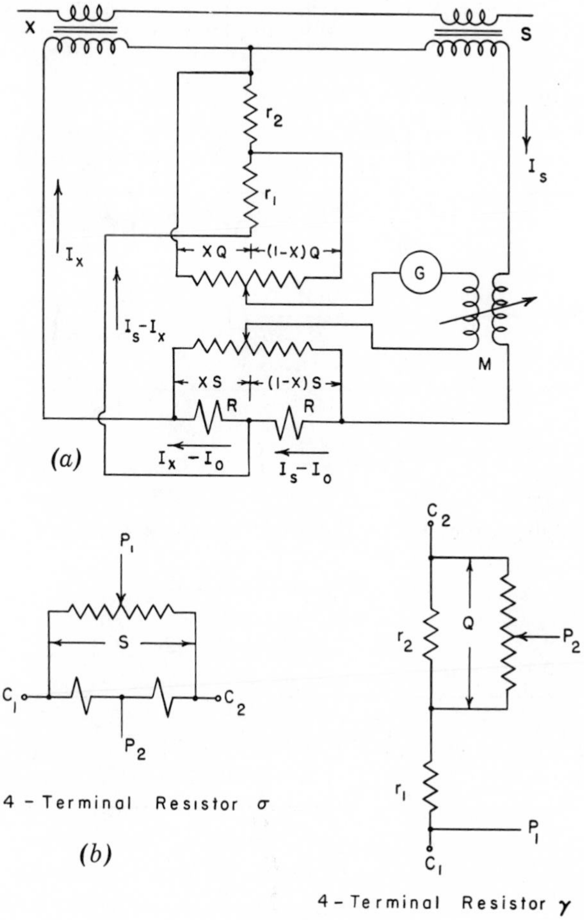

FIG. 31.

[see Fig. 31(*b*)]; while

$$\gamma = \frac{(1 - x)Qr_2}{r_2 + Q} + r_1$$

Also, as before,

$$I_0 = \frac{R}{2R + S}(I_s + I_x)$$

At balance, when the potential difference across the detector is zero, we have

$$I_0 xS - (I_x - I_0)R + (I_s - I_x)\gamma + j\omega M I_s = 0$$

If we substitute for I_0 and regroup terms, we have

$$I_s\left[\gamma + \frac{R(R + Sx)}{2R + S} + j\omega M\right] = I_x\left[\gamma + R - \frac{R(R + xS)}{2R + S}\right]$$

This may be arranged as

$$\frac{I_s}{I_x} = \frac{\gamma + \dfrac{R}{2} + \dfrac{1}{2}\left[\dfrac{RS(1 - 2x)}{2R + S}\right]}{\gamma + \dfrac{R}{2} - \dfrac{1}{2}\left[\dfrac{RS(1 - 2x)}{2R + S}\right] + j\omega M} = \frac{\left(\gamma + \dfrac{R}{2} - \dfrac{\sigma}{2}\right) + \sigma}{\left(\gamma + \dfrac{R}{2} - \dfrac{\sigma}{2}\right) + j\omega M}$$

$$= \frac{1 + \dfrac{\sigma}{\gamma + \dfrac{R}{2} - \dfrac{\sigma}{2}} - \dfrac{j\omega M}{\gamma + \dfrac{R}{2} - \dfrac{\sigma}{2}}\left(1 + \dfrac{\sigma}{\gamma + \dfrac{R}{2} - \dfrac{\sigma}{2}}\right)}{1 + \dfrac{\omega^2 M^2}{\left(\gamma + \dfrac{R}{2} - \dfrac{\sigma}{2}\right)^2}}$$

Neglecting higher-order terms, the angle by which I_x leads $\dot{I}_s$ is given by

$$\tan \alpha \approx \alpha = \frac{\omega M}{\gamma + \dfrac{R}{2} - \dfrac{\sigma}{2}}$$

while the ratio is

$$\frac{\sqrt{\left(1 + \dfrac{\sigma}{\gamma + \dfrac{R}{2} - \dfrac{\sigma}{2}}\right)^2 + \dfrac{\omega^2 M^2}{\left(\gamma + \dfrac{R}{2} - \dfrac{\sigma}{2}\right)^2}\left(1 + \dfrac{\sigma}{\gamma + \dfrac{R}{2} - \dfrac{\sigma}{2}}\right)^2}}{1 + \dfrac{\omega^2 M^2}{\left(\gamma + \dfrac{R}{2} - \dfrac{\sigma}{2}\right)^2}}$$

$$= \left(1 + \frac{\sigma}{\gamma + \dfrac{R}{2} - \dfrac{\sigma}{2}}\right)\frac{1}{\sqrt{1 + \dfrac{\omega^2 M^2}{\left(\gamma + \dfrac{R}{2} - \dfrac{\sigma}{2}\right)^2}}}$$

$$= \left(1 + \frac{\sigma}{\gamma + \dfrac{R}{2} - \dfrac{\sigma}{2}}\right)\cos \alpha$$

It will be noted that our expression for phase angle may be made independent of the ratio dial setting if $(\gamma + R/2 - \sigma/2)$ is constant. [Actually it is sufficient that $\left(\gamma + \frac{R}{2} - \frac{\sigma}{2}\right)$ will not vary by more than 1% for any dial setting.] The ratio correction resulting from the setting of the phase-angle dial is made simple by providing three index marks for reading the ratio dial setting: one for use if the phase angle is less than 84 min, one for angles between 84 and 153 min, and one for angles exceeding 153 min.

DOUBLE-RANGE SILSBEE SET. It is clear that the range over which ratio errors and phase angles can be measured depends on the value of the constant resistance $\left(\gamma + \frac{R}{2} - \frac{\sigma}{2}\right)$. In the usual apparatus this resistance is 0.2 ohm and the ratio scale ranges from 95 to 105%, while the phase-angle scale covers ± 180 min. An added resistance of 0.8 ohm in series with r_1 [Fig. 31(*a*)] would make $\left(\gamma + \frac{R}{2} - \frac{\sigma}{2}\right) = 1.0$ ohm and would reduce the range of both the ratio and phase-angle dial by a factor of 5, to ± 1% in ratio and ± 36 min in phase angle, with a corresponding increase in precision of setting. If this added resistance is arranged so that it can be removed from the circuit by means of a short-circuiting plug, two ranges will be available in the test set: (1) the normal range of ± 5% and ± 180 min when $\left(\gamma + \frac{R}{2} - \frac{\sigma}{2}\right) = 0.2$ ohm; and (2) the low range of ± 1% and ± 36 min. The low range is of advantage in that it permits more accurate testing of high-grade current transformers. A number of such two-range test sets have been built by Leeds and Northrup.

Baker's Test-Ring. This method[41] of testing current transformers is an interesting example of the direct use of mmf's in effecting a balance between the primary and secondary vector currents. This method does not exactly fit into our classification of test methods. It is a direct method, since quantities which are functions of the primary and of the secondary currents are used, but it represents an intermediate condition between a null and a deflection method, the balance between primary and secondary quantities being only approximate and their residual being measured by a deflection method.

The circuit is shown in Fig. 32(*a*). A special "test" ring of laminated transformer steel is provided with two windings which are similar to those of the current transformer. A third winding, consisting of a large number of turns (perhaps 6000), is placed next to the test-ring core and is connected

[41] Baker, *Trans. AIEE*, **37**, 1173 (1918); Silsbee, *Trans. AIEE*, **43**, 282 (1924).

to the voltage coil of a wattmeter, the current coil of the wattmeter being supplied from an auxiliary source whose phase can be shifted by a known amount. The primary and secondary windings of the test ring carry the corresponding transformer currents and are connected so that their mmf's are in opposition. Any difference between these mmf's (I_pT_p and I_sT_s) produces a flux in the test ring and induces an emf in the tertiary winding connected to the wattmeter coil. The secondary turns on the test ring are varied until the wattmeter reading is a minimum. Since the secondary turns can be varied only by integral steps, an exact balance

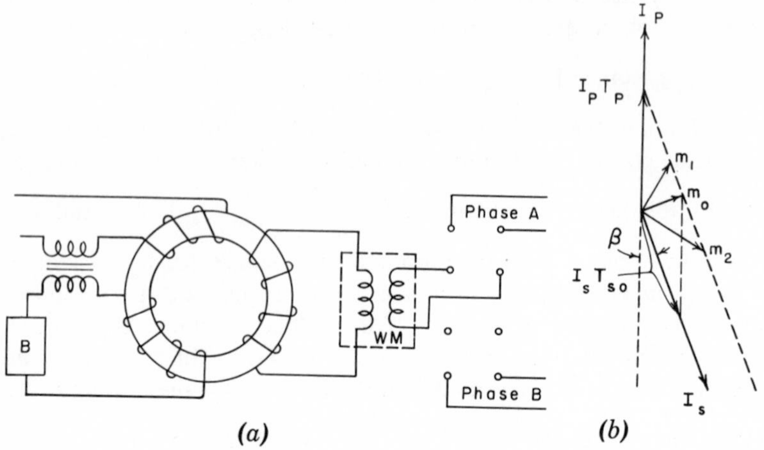

FIG. 32.

cannot be secured, but turn values can be found which bracket the minimum value. Two or more wattmeter readings corresponding to particular numbers of secondary turns (near the balance point) are taken and the operation is repeated for the same numbers of turns with the phase of the auxiliary wattmeter circuit shifted by a known amount. From these data the relative magnitudes and directions of the residual mmf's m_1 and m_2 are computed. Now on the vector diagram [Fig. 32(*b*)] the locus of the ends of these vectors is a straight line, parallel to the vector I_s and passing through the end of the vector I_pT_p. This is true since the primary mmf (I_pT_p) is constant, the secondary mmf I_sT_s varies in magnitude as T_s is changed but remains in phase with I_s, and the vector sum ($I_pT_p + I_sT_s$) must always be m. This locus may be constructed from the measured values ($m_1, m_2, \cdot\cdot\cdot$), and the value m_0 interpolated at which the mmf's most nearly balance. This will correspond to a secondary mmf (I_sT_{s0}) which may now be found graphically. (In general, T_{s0} will involve a fractional turn, together with the whole number of secondary turns at which m was found to be most nearly a minimum.) Then from the vector diagram we have very approximately

$$I_p T_p \approx I_s T_{s0}$$

or

$$\text{Ratio} = \frac{I_p}{I_s} \approx \frac{T_{s0}}{T_p}$$

and

$$\frac{m_0}{I_p T_p} = \tan \beta \approx \beta$$

The method has the advantages that it requires only very simple and relatively inexpensive apparatus, and is quite flexible in range, the windings

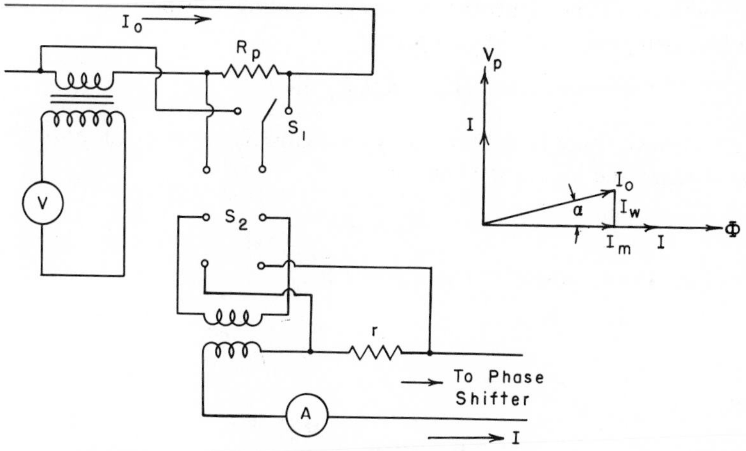

FIG. 33.

on the test ring being easily changed. Computation of results is, however, complicated; blunders may easily be made in the graphical solution; and results are not as accurate as with the null methods already described.

Measurement of Excitation. Cases occasionally arise in which it is of interest to know the excitation of a current transformer and its magnetizing and loss components, as well as the ratio and phase angle. The standard open-circuit test for determining the excitation of power or voltage transformers is of little use here, since the quantities to be measured are small and cannot be accurately measured with portable instruments. For this purpose a number of special wattmeter methods have been developed which utilize sensitive electrodynamic instruments. Agnew's method[42] will serve to illustrate the procedure. Agnew's arrangement is shown schematically in Fig. 33. A sensitive high-resistance voltmeter is used to

[42] Agnew, *Bull. Bur. Standards*, 7, 423 (1911).

set and measure the secondary voltage of the transformer. Since the resistance of V is high, the transformer will be operating on virtually open-circuit conditions. With switch S_1 to the left and S_2 in the up position, the phase of the auxiliary current source is adjusted until the wattmeter reads zero. This brings the phase of the auxiliary current I in quadrature with the primary voltage of the transformer and hence in phase with the flux. Then, with S_1 to the right, the wattmeter reading will be proportional to the magnetizing component I_m of the excitation; i.e.

$$W_1 = KII_0R_p \cos \alpha$$

If the phase of I is then shifted 90°, it will be in quadrature with the flux, and, with S_1 to the right, the wattmeter reading will be proportional to the loss component of the excitation:

$$W_2 = KII_0R_p \sin \alpha$$

The wattmeter may be calibrated by changing S_2 to the down position so that it reads the loss in the shunt r:

$$W_3 = KI^2r$$

From the three wattmeter readings we may say

$$I_0 \cos \alpha = I_m = \frac{W_1}{W_3} \cdot \frac{r}{R_p} I$$

and

$$I_0 \sin \alpha = I_W = \frac{W_2}{W_3} \cdot \frac{r}{R_p} I$$

If an a-c potentiometer[43] is available, the components of the excitation can be very simply measured by a method devised by Spooner.[44] The arrangement is shown in Fig. 34. The two components of the potentiometer A, B are supplied in quadrature with each other through a phase shifter. If B is set to zero and the switch S is in its left position, balance is obtained by adjustment of A and of the phase shifter. Then A reads the open-circuit secondary voltage of the transformer; i.e. A is in phase with the transformer secondary voltage, and the dial reading A_1 gives its value. Then switch S is changed to its right-hand position, and the potentiometer rebalanced by adjusting both components (new readings A_2, B_2), without altering the phase shifter setting. The vector sum of $A_2 + B_2 = RI_0$, the voltage drop across the shunt in the transformer

[43] See Chapter 6.

[44] Spooner, *J. Sci. Inst.*, **3**, 214 (1926).

primary circuit. The voltage V_{A_2} corresponding to reading A_2 is in phase with the induced voltage in the transformer and is therefore proportional to the loss component of the excitation. The voltage V_{B_2} corresponding to B_2 is in quadrature with the induced transformer voltage and hence

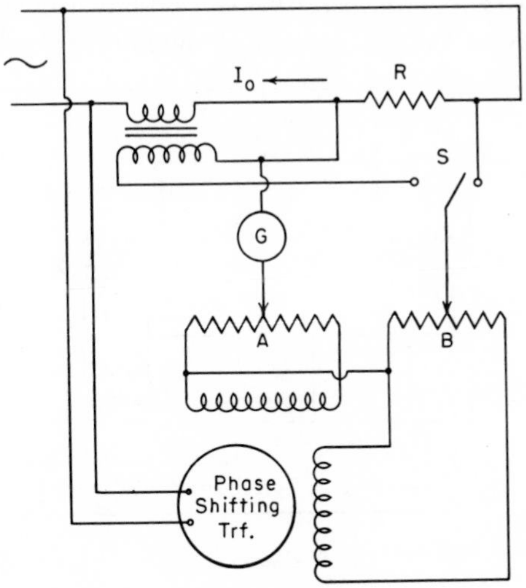

FIG. 34.

in phase with the flux. It is therefore proportional to the magnetizing component of excitation. Then

$$I_w = \frac{V_{A_2}}{R}, \quad \text{and} \quad I_m = \frac{V_{B_2}}{R}$$

Voltage-Transformer Testing

The methods available for determining the ratio and phase angles of voltage transformers are analogous to those already discussed for current transformers and may be broadly classified in the same way: direct and relative, deflection and null. In general, null methods are more precise than deflection methods and, where possible, should be used if the results are critical. Relative methods are most frequently employed in routine testing but require reference transformers having known performance characteristics. Hence all tests must depend eventually on values obtained by a direct method, which will also usually be a null method. A few illustrative examples of various types of test methods will be discussed.

Deflection Methods. Direct deflection methods, in which the primary and secondary voltage vectors are directly measured or compared, are completely analogous to the corresponding method described for current transformers, and two wattmeters may be used for this purpose. However, without highly specialized instruments and multipliers the method is limited in application to relatively low voltages and so is not generally useful. A *comparative wattmeter method* is shown schematically in Fig. 35. The analogy to the corresponding method for current-transformer

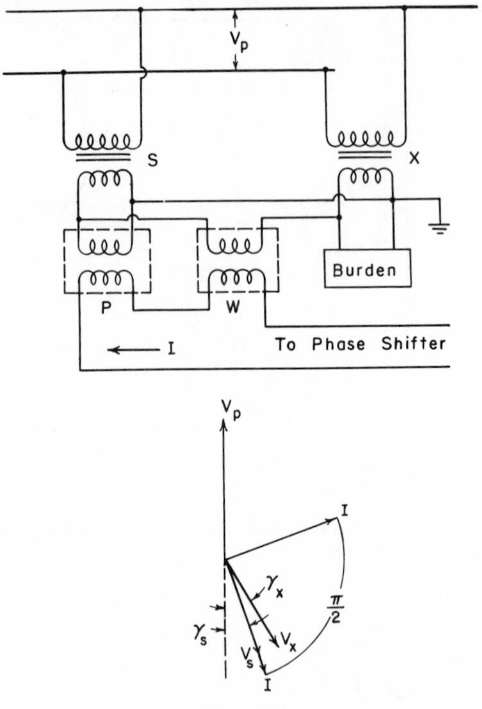

FIG. 35.

testing will be apparent. The wattmeter P is used to set the current I from the auxiliary source (i.e. zero indication on P) in quadrature with V_s. Then the indication of wattmeter W is

$$W_1 = IV_x \cos\left[\frac{\pi}{2} - (\gamma_x - \gamma_s)\right] = IV_x \sin(\gamma_x - \gamma_s)$$

Then, if the phase of I is shifted 90° so that it is in phase with V_s, the indication of W will be

$$W_2 = I[V_s - V_x \cos(\gamma_x - \gamma_s)]$$

Now the ratio of the reference transformer is $N_s = V_p/V_s$, and that of the test transformer is $N_x = V_p/V_x$, so that $N_x/N_s = V_s/V_x$. Then, from the quadrature and in-phase indications of the wattmeter, we have

$$IV_x \cos(\gamma_x - \gamma_s) = IV_s - W_2$$

and

$$IV_x \sin(\gamma_x - \gamma_s) = W_1$$

so that

$$\tan(\gamma_x - \gamma_s) = \frac{W_1}{IV_s - W_2} \approx (\gamma_x - \gamma_s)$$

or

$$\gamma_x = \gamma_s + \frac{W_1}{IV_s - W_2} \approx \gamma_s + \frac{W_1}{IV_s}$$

Also

$$\frac{N_x}{N_s} = \frac{V_s}{V_x} = \frac{IV_s}{IV_s - W_2}$$

since $\cos(\gamma_x - \gamma_s) \approx 1$. Then

$$N_x \approx N_s \left[\frac{1}{1 - (W_2/IV_s)}\right] \approx N_s \left[1 + \frac{W_2}{IV_s}\right]$$

The wattmeter should preferably be one having a very low voltage range, since only the vector difference $(V_s - V_x)$ is impressed on its moving-coil circuit. Also it should be of a precision type, but under the most favourable conditions the precision of the method is limited, as it is in any deflection method of testing, by the inherent limitations of the deflection instrument.

Considerably higher precision can be attained with watthour meters than is possible by a wattmeter method. In effect this is the practical equivalent of the use of a wattmeter with an enormously expanded scale, since the quantity measured can be accumulated (i.e. integrated) over a comparatively long time interval. The method is an adaptation of Agnew's watthour-meter method already described for current transformer testing. The circuit is shown in Fig. 36. As before, the watthour meters M_1, M_2 will be assumed to be of the same type, and to be adjusted to operate correctly at unity power factor and at 50% power factor. The procedure is also the same. Runs are made in pairs with the meters interchanged, at unity power factor and at a low power factor. It may be shown that

$$N_x = N_s \sqrt{\frac{a_{1s} \cdot a_{2s}}{a_{1x} \cdot a_{2x}}}$$

and that

$$\gamma_x = \gamma_s - \frac{1}{2 \tan \phi}\left[1 - \frac{a_{1s} \cdot a_{2s}}{a_{1x} \cdot a_{2s}} \cdot \frac{a'_{1x} \cdot a'_{2x}}{a'_{1s} \cdot a'_{2s}}\right]$$

where a_{1s}, a_{2x} are the meter readings accumulated in the first run at unity power factor, a_{1x}, a_{2s} are the readings with the meters interchanged, and the "primed" values are the corresponding readings in the low-power-factor runs. As in the current-transformer case high precision can be attained but only at the cost of a considerable expenditure of time.

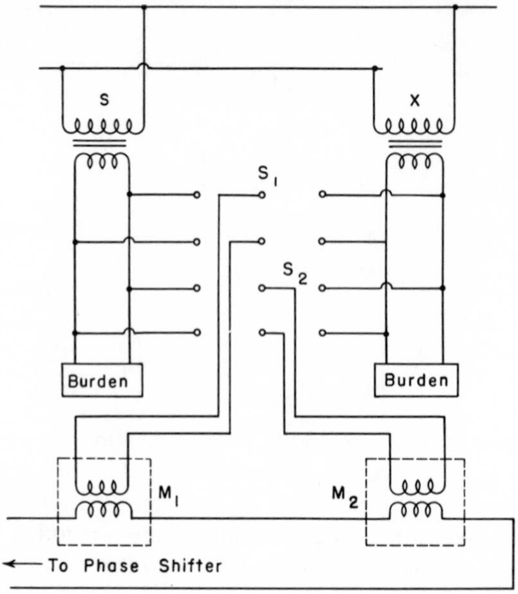

FIG. 36.

Direct Null Methods. These generally involve a potentiometer type of network. A suitable fraction of the primary voltage brought out at a tap point of a voltage divider is opposed to the secondary voltage, and the ratio and phase angle of the transformer are determined by impedance adjustments needed to attain balance in the network. At low and moderate voltages, resistance voltage dividers are usually employed, while at very high voltages capacitance networks are more practical. In either case a combination of resistance with self-inductance, mutual inductance, or capacitance can be used to obtain the quadrature component of voltage needed for phase-angle compensation.

RESISTANCE METHODS. In general the resistance in the divider should be high in order that its power dissipation (E^2/R) be low. However, high resistances are inherently less stable than low resistances, and workers have usually chosen to use a resistance of around 20 ohms/volt in the construction of the divider. Apart from the power requirements of such a resistor, a practical limit is set to the voltage for which such a resistor can be constructed, by its distributed capacitance. As the design voltage is increased this type of resistor becomes very bulky, and its distributed capacitance becomes great enough that it can no longer be considered a pure resistance. To reduce the phase angle produced by capacitance effects in such a resistor, shielding is used, and the usual solution of the problem involves dividing the resistor into sections and enclosing the sections in individual shields, the shields being maintained at such potentials as to reduce the effects of capacitance to a minimum.[45] Qualitatively we may say that, if the shield of each section is maintained at a potential midway between the terminal potentials of the section, the effect of capacitance will be very nearly a minimum. The capacitance currents are from the shield to the resistor in half of each section, and from the resistor to the shield in the other half. Since they are very nearly equal they will tend to neutralize each other and the resultant phase angle of the section will be quite small. In the shielded resistor designed by Silsbee[46] for voltage-transformer testing, each shielded section consists of twenty 1000-ohm card-wound resistors enclosed in a brass box and immersed in oil to obtain a large heat capacity. The shield potentials are maintained at their proper values by means of a guard resistor made up of identical resistance sections tapped to the shields at their midpoints. The potential distribution along the guard resistor is itself affected by distributed capacitance as well as by resistance, and, at high voltages, the effect of capacitance is enough that the guard resistor is no longer capable of maintaining the shield at a potential identical with the midpotential of the shielded section. Thus the system cannot be extended indefinitely for use at higher voltages. Silsbee determined that 30 kv was about the practical limit to which a resistor of this type should be extended, but pointed out that if the shield potentials were maintained by taps from a suitable transformer the shielding could be extended to considerably higher voltages. Weller[47] of the General Electric Company used this device in constructing a shielded resistor for transformer testing up to 132 kv.

The use of resistance voltage dividers at high voltages for transformer testing is confined to relatively few laboratories because of their bulk and cost, but since the transformer test method based on such a resistor is one of the primary means of extending precise voltage measurements to high values, the direct null method used at the National Bureau of Standards will be described. The circuit arrangement is shown in Fig. 37. The balancing procedure consists of adjusting r, the resistance connected across the secondary of the transformer, and the mutual inductance M,

[45] For a detailed analysis of such shielding see Chapter 7.

[46] Silsbee, *Bull. Bur. Standards*, **20**, 489 (1926).

[47] Weller, *J. AIEE*, **48**, 312 (1929).

so that no current flows through the detector G. An auxiliary balance of the guard circuit is also required to bring the lower end of the shielded resistor and the corresponding point of the guard circuit to the same potential, as indicated by the detector shown with dashed lines. We will assume that the equivalent inductance of the resistor R, which is connected across the primary of the transformer, is L'; and that L' takes account

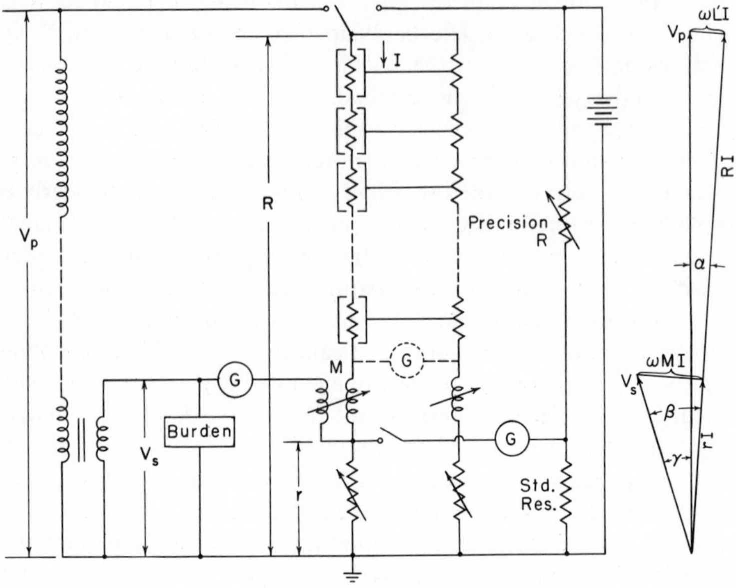

FIG. 37.

of the residual phase angle of the shielded resistor as well as the self-inductance of the primary of the mutual inductor M. Then from the vector diagram we may write

$$\tan \beta = \frac{\omega M}{r} \approx \beta = \alpha + \gamma; \quad \tan \alpha = \frac{\omega L'}{R} \approx \alpha$$

and, since $\beta = \alpha + \gamma$, we have

$$\gamma = \frac{\omega M}{r} - \frac{\omega L'}{R}$$

Also

$$V_s \cos \beta = V_p \frac{r}{R}$$

or

$$\text{Ratio} = \frac{V_p}{V_s} = \frac{R}{r} \cos \beta$$

As considerable energy is absorbed in the shielded resistor during the time required to obtain a balance, its temperature rise may be sufficient to affect its resistance value. Hence to obtain an accurate value of transformer ratio, the voltage divider is removed from the high-voltage source and connected into a Wheatstone bridge where the resistance ratio $(R - r)/r$ is measured before the temperature has fallen appreciably. The components of the network are sufficiently well known that the transformer ratio can be measured to 0.01% and its phase angle to 0.3 min.

CAPACITANCE METHODS. Methods of this type, which are used in transformer testing at high voltages, avoid a number of the objectionable features of the resistance methods. The shielding is simple and is easily accomplished; the method is capable of extension to very high voltages; the apparatus is less bulky and requires much less power for its operation than does a resistance network operating at the same voltage. Capacitance methods require a high-voltage capacitor capable of withstanding the entire operating voltage, together with a network of resistance, inductance, or capacitance elements in such combinations and so arranged that the secondary voltage may be compared with a known, adjustable fraction of the primary voltage. In most of the methods described in the literature, the capacitance of the high-voltage capacitor is assumed to be computable from its dimensions (some coaxial cylinder and parallel plate capacitors using free air as dielectric can be so computed) or is separately measured and assumed to remain constant. (This assumption is necessary in some types of enclosed capacitors which use compressed gas as a dielectric and which may suffer dimensional changes with changing pressure.) Thus the precision of the method is limited by the accuracy with which the high-voltage capacitor is known. Alternatively, in some arrangements the ratio of two capacitances can be used to measure the ratio of the transformer, and this capacitance ratio can be measured in a suitable bridge at the time of the test, just as the resistance ratio of a resistance voltage divider may be measured in a Wheatstone bridge. This should eliminate the uncertainty in capacitance values which results from temperature coefficients of the capacitors, as well as from their long-time and accidental changes, and should increase the accuracy of the transformer test by a considerable factor. We will examine one of each of these general methods.

Yoganandam's[48] method is a good example of the first type, and the circuit arrangement is shown in Fig. 38. C_1 is a fixed-value, high-voltage capacitor, and C_2 is a precision adjustable capacitor. C_1 is a three-terminal air capacitor and is assumed to be free from losses. C_2 is a

[48] Yoganandam, *J. IEE*, **68**, 192 (1930).

high-quality mica capacitor whose losses are small. R_3 and R_4 are known resistors of about the same nominal value. R_3 has an adjustable slide-wire section. Actually in our equations ρ will represent the resistance between the capacitor C_2 and the detector junction point. It will be considered to include a resistance equal to the equivalent series loss resistance of the capacitor. C_4 is adjustable and may contain both air capacitors and mica capacitors. In measuring transformer ratio and phase angle C_2 is set to such a value that C_2/C_1 is approximately equal to the nominal ratio of the transformer. Balance is accomplished by

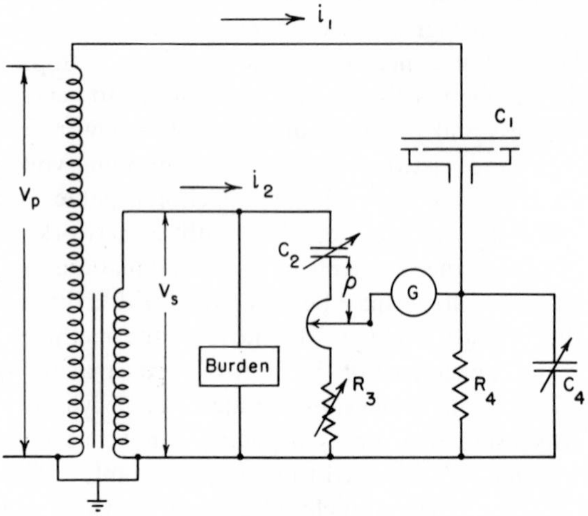

FIG. 38.

adjusting R_3, ρ, and C_4. The balance equation is $i_1Z_4 = i_2R_3$; i.e. the voltage drops in the two resistance branches of the network are equal so that no voltage difference appears across the detector. The impedance across which V_p is impressed is

$$Z_p = \frac{1}{j\omega C_1} + \frac{R_4}{1 + j\omega C_4R_4} = \frac{1 + j\omega R_4(C_1 + C_4)}{j\omega C_1(1 + j\omega C_4R_4)}$$

and for V_s the impedance is

$$Z_s = \rho + R_3 + \frac{1}{j\omega C_2} = \frac{1 + j\omega C_2(\rho + R_3)}{i\omega C_2}$$

Our balance equation may be written as

$$\frac{V_p}{Z_p} \cdot \frac{R_4}{(1 + j\omega C_4R_4)} = \frac{V_s}{Z_s} \cdot R_3$$

and we have, on rearranging,

$$\frac{V_p}{V_s} = \frac{Z_p}{Z_s} \cdot \frac{R_3(1 + j\omega C_4 R_4)}{R_4} = \frac{R_3}{R_4} \cdot \frac{\dfrac{1 + j\omega R_4(C_1 + C_4)}{j\omega C_1(1 + j\omega C_4 R_4)}(1 + j\omega C_4 R_4)}{\dfrac{1 + j\omega C_2(\rho + R_3)}{j\omega C_2}}$$

$$= \frac{R_3 \cdot C_2}{R_4 \cdot C_1} \cdot \frac{1 + j\omega R_4(C_1 + C_4)}{1 + j\omega C_2(\rho + R_3)}$$

The transformer ratio is

$$\left|\frac{V_p}{V_s}\right| = \frac{R_3 C_2}{R_4 C_1}\left[\frac{1 + \omega^2 R_4{}^2(C_1 + C_4)^2}{1 + \omega^2 C_2{}^2(\rho + R_3)^2}\right]^{1/2} \approx \frac{R_3 C_2}{R_4 C_1}$$

if terms of the type $\omega^2 C^2 R^2 \ll 1$. Also the phase angle is

$$\gamma = \tan^{-1}[\omega R_4(C_1 + C_4)] - \tan^{-1}[\omega C_2(\rho + R_3)]$$
$$\approx \omega R_4(C_1 + C_4) - \omega C_2(\rho + R_3)$$

If C_1 is 100 $\mu\mu$f, the sensitivity at 110 kv permits balances to 0.01% and 0.3 min in phase angle with the detector used by Yoganandam. It should be noted that shielding of the various network components is omitted from our diagram in order to simplify it. Complete shielding and the use of auxiliary impedance elements to maintain correct shield potentials are essential if accurate results are to be obtained. Also the various components of the network have to be accurately known and constant if the accuracy permitted by the high sensitivity is to be realized.

Bousman and Ten Broeck's[49] capacitance method of transformer testing, developed for use in the laboratories of the General Electric Company, employs a Schering bridge[50] to measure the ratio of the capacitances, in terms of an accurately known resistance ratio. Thus we do not need to know accurately the value of either the high-voltage or the low-voltage capacitor, nor are we required to make any assumptions concerning their long-time stability, since their ratio is determined as a ratio of resistances at the time the transformer is tested. Such a resistance ratio can be far more stable over a period of time than a capacitance ratio since its temperature coefficient will be very small. Also its value is not dependent on the constancy of mechanical dimensions and clearances. The circuit arrangements are shown in Fig. 39(*a*). As in the previous case the shielding arrangements are not shown. If we assume that both C_1 and C_2 are loss-free capacitors, the balance equation of the Schering

[49] Bousman and Ten Broeck, *Trans. AIEE*, **62**, 541 (1943).

[50] See Chapter 15.

bridge of Fig. 39(*b*) which results when switch S is closed downward may be written as

$$\frac{1}{i\omega C_1} \cdot \frac{R_3}{1 + j\omega C_3 R_3} = \frac{1}{j\omega C_2} \cdot \frac{R_4}{1 + j\omega C_4 R_4}$$

If we make the simplifying assumption[51] that terms of the type $\omega^2 C^2 R^2 \ll 1$, then on separating reals and imaginaries in the balance equation we have $C_2/C_1 = R_4/R_3$, and $\omega C_3 R_3 = \omega C_4 R_4$. In balancing the bridge we will initially set up the resistance ratio $R_4/R_3 = \sqrt{n}$, where n is the nominal ratio of the transformer to be tested. We will then balance the bridge by adjusting C_2, so that $C_2/C_1 = R_4/R_3 = \sqrt{n}$. C_1 is the fixed-value, high-voltage capacitor, and C_2 is assumed to remain at the value set up in the bridge balance during the subsequent transformer test. Also, as we shall see later, a particular value of C_4 is initially set up and C_3 is adjusted to complete the bridge balance. Now, if we interchange arms 3 and 4 by means of the reversing switch, and connect C_2 to the secondary and C_1 to the primary of the transformer under test, by closing S upward we will have the transformer test circuit of Fig. 39(*c*). The balance equation in this case is $i_1 Z_3 = i_2 Z_4$. The impedance operator connected across V_p is

$$Z_p = \frac{1}{j\omega C_1} + \frac{R_3}{1 + j\omega C_3 R_3} = \frac{1 + j\omega R_3(C_1 + C_3)}{j\omega C_1(1 + j\omega C_3 R_3)}$$

and across V_s we have

$$Z_s = \frac{1 + j\omega R_4(C_2 + C_4)}{j\omega C_2(1 + j\omega C_4 R_4)}$$

The balance condition for the transformer test circuit may be written as

$$\frac{V_p}{Z_p} \cdot \frac{R_3}{1 + j\omega C_3 R_3} = \frac{V_s}{Z_s} \cdot \frac{R_4}{1 + j\omega C_4 R_4}$$

Then

$$\frac{V_p}{V_s} = \frac{Z_p}{Z_s} \cdot \frac{R_4}{R_3} \cdot \frac{1 + j\omega C_3 R_3}{1 + j\omega C_4 R_4} = \frac{C_2}{C_1} \cdot \frac{R_4}{R_3} \cdot \frac{1 + j\omega R_3(C_1 + C_3)}{1 + j\omega R_4(C_2 + C_4)}$$

The transformer ratio is

$$\left|\frac{V_p}{V_s}\right| = \frac{C_2 R_4}{C_1 R_3} \left[\frac{1 + \omega^2 R_3^2 (C_1 + C_3)^2}{1 + \omega^2 R_4^2 (C_2 + C_4)^2}\right]^{1/2} \approx \frac{C_2 R_4}{C_1 R_3}, \quad \text{if } \omega^2 C^2 R^2 \ll 1$$

and the phase angle is

$$\gamma = \omega[R_3(C_1 + C_3) - R_4(C_2 + C_4)]$$

[51] It should be realized that in practical cases this assumption may not always be justified, and that the effect of these terms may have to be carried as small correction factors.

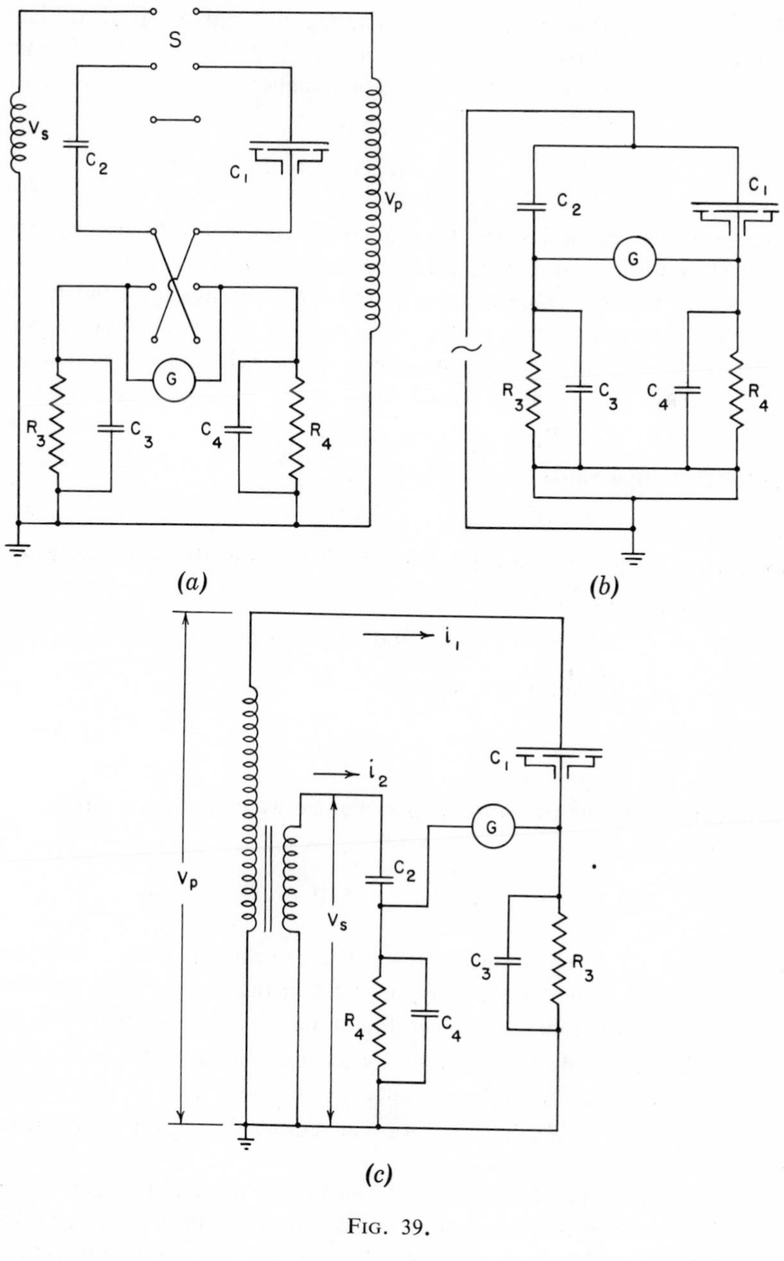

S
V_s
C_2
C_1
V_p
G
R_3
C_3
C_4
R_4
(a)
C_1
C_2
G
R_3
C_3
C_4
R_4
~
(b)
i_1
i_2
V_p
V_s
C_1
G
C_2
C_3
R_3
R_4
C_4
(c)

FIG. 39.

We will suppose that we may leave C_1, C_2, C_3, and R_3 fixed at their Schering-bridge values. We will assume further that the transformer ratio is $K = n(1 + \delta)$, and that the ratio balance is made by changing R_4 to $R_4' = R_4(1 + \delta)$, so that

$$K = \frac{C_2}{C_1} \cdot \frac{R_4'}{R_3} = \sqrt{n} \cdot \sqrt{n}(1 + \delta) = n(1 + \delta)$$

Since in most practical cases the actual transformer ratio is adjusted rather closely to the nominal, δ will be small compared to 1. We will now assume that the value of C_4 required for the phase-angle balance is C_4', that if the transformer phase angle were zero it would have a particular value C_4'', and that the value used in the Schering-bridge balance was C_4. Then for $\gamma = 0$ we would have

$$R_3(C_1 + C_3) = R_4'(C_2 + C_4'')$$

and for any other value of phase angle,

$$\gamma = \omega R_4'(C_4' - C_4'') = \omega R_4(C_4' - C_4'')(1 + \delta)$$

Now, if both C_1 and C_2 are loss-free, we have from the Schering-bridge balance $C_3R_3 = C_4R_4$, so that

$$C_3 = \sqrt{n} \cdot C_4, \quad \text{and} \quad C_2 = \sqrt{n} \cdot C_1$$

If we may assume that $\delta \ll 1$, we have

$$C_4'' = \frac{1}{\sqrt{n}}(C_1 + \sqrt{n} \cdot C_4) - \sqrt{n} \cdot C_1, \quad \text{or} \quad C_4 - C_4'' = \frac{n - 1}{\sqrt{n}} \cdot C_1$$

i.e. in computing the transformer phase angle we must use as a reference value of C_4 the value

$$C_4'' = C_4 - \frac{n - 1}{\sqrt{n}} C_1 = \frac{1}{\sqrt{n}} [C_3 - (n - 1)C_1]$$

where C_3 or C_4 is the setting at the Schering-bridge balance. It is not important what values of C_3 or C_4 are used in the initial bridge balance, but the reference point of C_4 for the transformer-phase-angle balance must be less than the bridge value by an amount $(n - 1)C_1/\sqrt{n}$. This necessitates that in the bridge balance we use, as a part of C_4, a fixed capacitance $(n - 1)C_1/\sqrt{n}$, which we will remove during the transformer balance.

The arrangement of Bousman and Ten Broeck appears to have several advantages over other capacitance test methods which have been described in the literature. Not only is the transformer ratio referred to a resistance ratio which can be accurately measured but, by the device of interchanging arms, the actual ratio that we deal with is $\sqrt{n}$ rather than n. This smaller ratio can be determined more easily with high accuracy than a larger one, particularly at very high voltages. For example, for a transformer whose ratio is 240,000/120 volts, $n = 2000$, whereas $\sqrt{n} \approx 45$.

Comparative Null Methods. These methods are used to determine the ratio and phase angle of a transformer in terms of the performance of a reference transformer by comparing their secondary voltages (the primaries being supplied in parallel) in a potentiometer network.

NBS METHOD. As a first example we will take the precision transformer comparator which has been used at the National Bureau of Standards

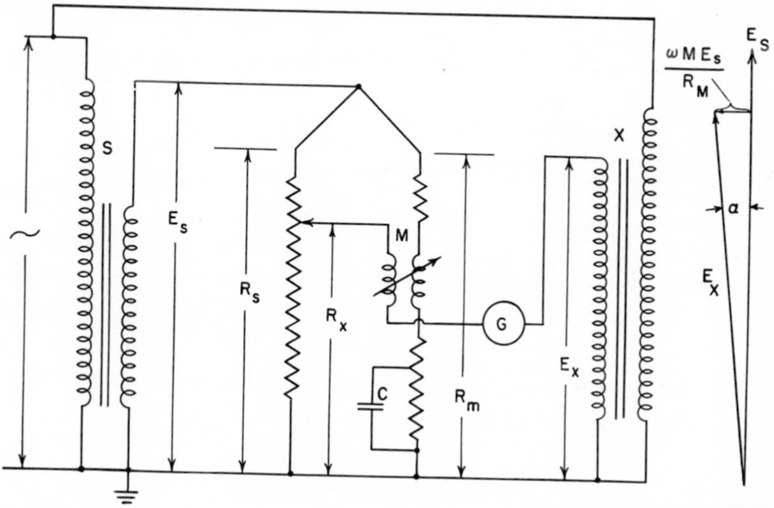

FIG. 40.

for several years. The circuit arrangement is shown in Fig. 40. Two circuits are supplied from the secondary of the reference transformer. R_s is constructed to have as small residuals as possible. Coils of 100 ohms and larger are of woven wire and are mounted on ceramic forms. The upper portion of this resistor carries a continuously adjustable tap point to which the secondary of the test transformer is connected as shown in the figure. The second, parallel resistance R_m includes the primary of the mutual inductor M, and is made non-inductive by shunting a portion of the resistance with a capacitance so that the current in the primary of the mutual inductor is in phase with the voltage[52] E_s. R_m is also used to supply shield potentials for sections of R_s and for the shielding in the galvanometer branch of the network. The construction is such that in most tests the phase angle introduced in the R_s branch is negligible. (If

[52] See inductance compensation in the voltage circuit of a wattmeter, Chapter 11.

$R_s/R_x = 2/1$, a combination used in testing 2/1 transformers, the phase-angle correction introduced by the resistances is 0.1 min at 60 cycles and is less for any other combination.) The balance equations may be written by inspection from the vector diagram:

$$\tan \alpha = \frac{\omega M E_s}{R_m E_x}, \quad \text{and} \quad E_s \cdot \frac{R_x}{R_s} = E_x \cos \alpha$$

Now for the reference transformer, the ratio is $N_s = E_p/E_s$, and for the test transformer $N_x = E_p/E_x$, so that

$$N_x = N_s \cdot \frac{E_s}{E_x}$$

This relation may be substituted into our balance equation and we have

$$N_x = N_s \cdot \frac{R_s}{R_x} \cos \alpha$$

Also $\gamma_x - \gamma_s = \alpha$, so that

$$\gamma_x = \gamma_s + \frac{\omega M R_s}{R_m R_x}$$

or, since in all cases $R_m = R_s$, we have

$$\gamma_x = \gamma_s + \frac{\omega M}{R_x}$$

In this phase-angle formula γ is in radians if M is in henrys and R is in ohms. To convert to minutes, we may write

$$\gamma_x = \gamma_s + 3438 \frac{\omega M}{R_x}$$

The sensitivity and precision of the method are such that ratio can easily be determined to 0.01% and phase angle to 0.3 min. The accuracy of the determination is, of course, dependent on the accuracy with which N_s and γ_s are known.[53] A group of reference transformers are available in the National Bureau of Standards laboratory in terms of which transformers having any ratio from 1/1 to 2000/1 can be calibrated. It should be noted that an inherent limitation of the method is that the R_s and R_m circuits must be supplied from the reference transformer. Hence balance conditions require that $E_x \leqslant E_s$, i.e. that the ratio of the reference transformer be less than (or at most equal to) the ratio of the test transformer. This requirement is met in the National Bureau of Standards setup by using reference transformers whose ratios have been adjusted to values 2% less than the integral values usually encountered as nominal ratios in commercial transformers.

[53] In the case of the National Bureau of Standards standard reference transformers this is usually of about the same order: 0.01% and 0.3 min.

LEEDS AND NORTHRUP VOLTAGE-TRANSFORMER TEST SET. This is a portable apparatus in which the secondary voltage of a transformer is compared with that of a reference transformer having the same nominal

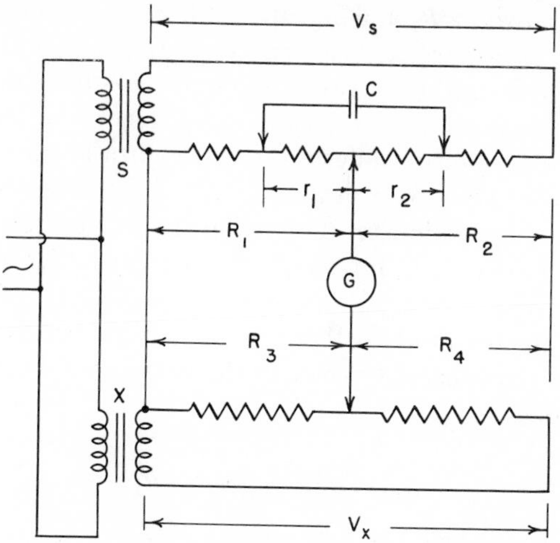

(*a*)

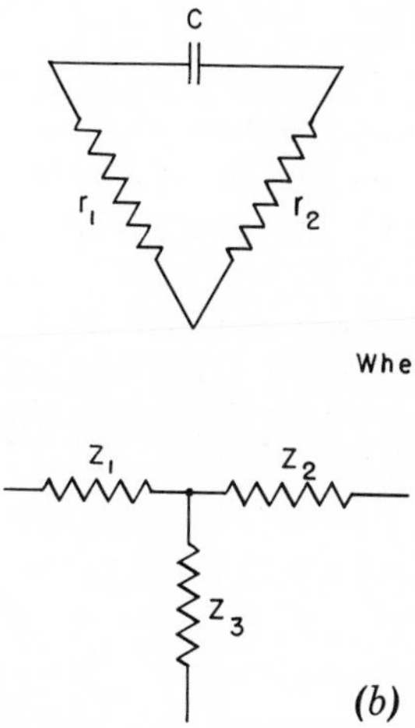

Where

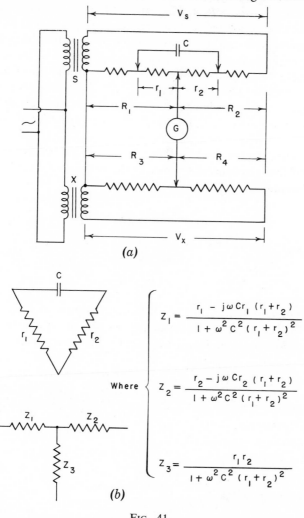

$$Z_1 = \frac{r_1 - j\omega C r_1 (r_1 + r_2)}{1 + \omega^2 C^2 (r_1 + r_2)^2}$$

$$Z_2 = \frac{r_2 - j\omega C r_2 (r_1 + r_2)}{1 + \omega^2 C^2 (r_1 + r_2)^2}$$

$$Z_3 = \frac{r_1 r_2}{1 + \omega^2 C^2 (r_1 + r_2)^2}$$

(*b*)

FIG. 41.

ratio. The range of adjustment covered is $\pm$ 5% in ratio and $\pm$ 120 min in phase angle. Ratio balances are made by adjusting a ratio of resistances, and phase angle by a capacitance shunting a resistance. The circuit arrangement is shown in Fig. 41(*a*). The slide wire for adjusting the ratio balance is in the *X*-circuit, and the slide wire for adjusting phase-angle balance is in the S-circuit. The capacitor C is connected across a constant resistance $(r_1 + r_2)$, the slider contacts at the extremities of r_1 and r_2 being rigidly connected together. Since, as we shall see, the position of C relative to R_1 and R_2 affects the ratio balance, a compensating slide wire is inserted at the junction of r_1 and r_2 and its slider is rigidly connected to the other two. With this compensation the ratio and phase-angle balances are very nearly independent, and for most work no corrections to the dial readings are required as a result of the setting of the other dial. The compensation is not quite complete, however, and the ratio dial correction resulting from the phase-angle dial setting may amount to nearly 0.1% for phase angles of the order of 100 min or more.

If we assume for the moment that the phase angle between V_s and V_x is zero and that the capacitor is not in the circuit, we would have as a balance condition

$$V_s \frac{R_1}{R_1 + R_2} = V_x \frac{R_3}{R_3 + R_4}$$

or, since $R_1 = R_2$, we may say

$$\frac{V_s}{V_x} = \frac{2R_3}{R_3 + R_4}$$

Hence the ratio of V_s to V_x may be balanced, and read from the slide-wire position in the X-circuit. Now in the actual case, if we use the Δ-Y transformation [see Fig. 41(b)], we have for the unrestricted equation of balance

$$V_s \frac{\left[(R_1 - r_1) + \dfrac{r_1 - j\omega C r_1(r_1 + r_2)}{1 + \omega^2 C^2 (r_1 + r_2)^2}\right]}{(R_1 + R_2) - (r_1 + r_2) + \dfrac{r_1 - j\omega C r_1(r_1 + r_2) + r_2 - j\omega C r_2(r_1 + r_2)}{1 + \omega^2 C^2 (r_1 + r_2)^2}}$$

$$= V_x \cdot \frac{R_3}{R_3 + R_4}$$

This may be written as

$$V_s \cdot \frac{R_1}{R_1 + R_2} \left[\frac{\dfrac{1}{(r_1 + r_2)^2} + \left(1 - \dfrac{r_1}{R_1}\right) \omega^2 C^2 - \dfrac{j\omega C}{(r_1 + r_2)} \cdot \dfrac{r_1}{R_1}}{\dfrac{1}{(r_1 + r_2)^2} + \left(1 - \dfrac{r_1 + r_2}{R_1 + R_2}\right) \omega^2 C^2 - j\omega C \cdot \dfrac{1}{R_1 + R_2}} \right]$$

$$= V_x \frac{R_3}{R_3 + R_4}$$

We will let

$$\frac{r_1}{R_1} = a; \quad \frac{r_1 + r_2}{R_1 + R_2} = b; \quad \text{and } \omega C(r_1 + r_2) = \alpha$$

If we make the indicated substitutions, rationalize, and approximate the resulting expression by omitting terms in the third and higher powers of α, it can be shown that the balance condition is approximately given by the expression

$$V_s \cdot \frac{R_1}{R_1 + R_2} [1 + (b - a)(1 - b)\alpha^2 + j\alpha(b - a)] = V_x \cdot \frac{R_3}{R_3 + R_4}$$

Then the ratio may be written (assuming $R_1 = R_2$) as

$$\left|\frac{V_s}{V_x}\right| = \frac{2R_3}{R_3 + R_4}\left[1 - (b - a)\left(1 - \frac{b + a}{2}\right)\alpha^2\right]$$

and the phase angle is given by

$$\tan \beta \approx \beta = \frac{\alpha(b - a)}{1 + (b - a)(1 - b)\,\alpha^2}$$

It will be seen from these expressions that the phase-angle dial may be directly marked in terms of the phase angle between V_s and V_x and that no correction is needed for the setting of the ratio dial, since β is not a function of R_3 and R_4. However, the ratio is a function of r_1 and r_2, which change with the position of the phase-angle dial, only their sum $(r_1 + r_2)$ remaining constant. This correction term can, however, be very nearly compensated over most of the range of the phase-angle dial by a linear slide wire, interlocked with the phase-angle dial, whose sliding contact is in the galvanometer circuit. It should be noted, of course, that all sliding contacts in the set are either in the galvanometer branch of the network or in a branch whose impedance is so high that contact resistance is negligible.

The Leeds and Northrup voltage-transformer testing set can be calibrated most simply by impressing voltages which bear to each other a ratio and phase relationship known to the full accuracy of the measurement, across the X and S circuits, and noting the dial positions at which the set balances. In contrast to this it is possible to calibrate the Silsbee current-transformer testing set by measuring with only the accuracy needed in the difference current ΔI, the mutual inductance, and the one or the two four-terminal resistances corresponding to the various dial settings. The corresponding corrections can then be computed by means of the formulas derived from the balance equation.

CHAPTER 14

WAVE-FORM AND FREQUENCY MEASUREMENTS

WAVE-FORM MEASUREMENTS

Any single-valued periodic function can be resolved into sine and cosine terms which have the same period as the function, or simple fractional multiples of this period, i.e. can be expressed as a series of sine and cosine terms whose frequencies are simple whole-number multiples of the frequency of the function. Thus a periodic function[1]

$$f(\theta) = A_1 \sin \theta + A_2 \sin 2\theta + \cdots + \frac{B_0}{2} + B_1 \cos \theta + B_2 \cos 2\theta + \cdots$$

where

$$A_k = \frac{1}{\pi}\int_0^{2\pi} f(\theta) \sin K\theta \, d\theta, \quad \text{and} \quad B_k = \frac{1}{\pi}\int_0^{2\pi} f(\theta) \cos K\theta \, d\theta$$

An equivalent, alternative form of this series can be written by combining the corresponding sine and cosine terms, for

$$A \sin \theta + B \cos \theta = \sqrt{A^2 + B^2} \sin \left(\theta + \tan^{-1}\frac{B}{A}\right) = C \sin (\theta + \phi)$$

Then we have

$$f(\theta) = \frac{B_0}{2} + C_1 \sin (\theta + \phi_1) + C_2 \sin (2\theta + \phi_2) + \cdots$$

where

$$C_k = \sqrt{A_k^2 + B_k^2}, \quad \text{and} \quad \phi_k = \tan^{-1}\frac{B_k}{A_k}$$

[1] Such a series is called a Fourier series after its inventor (Fourier, 1812). The student should consult a suitable mathematical textbook for proof of the theorem and discussion of its general application. For example, see Byerly, *Fourier Series and Spherical Harmonics*, Ginn, 1893; Reddick and Miller, *Advanced Mathematics for Engineers*, Wiley, 1947.

Now any alternating voltage or current under steady-state conditions is a periodic single-valued function and hence can be expressed as a Fourier series. Thus

$$e(t) = E_0 + E_1 \sin(\omega t + \phi_1) + E_2 \sin(2\omega t + \phi_2) + \cdots$$

Here $\omega = 2\pi f$, where f is the fundamental frequency of the voltage, E_0 is any direct (constant) component it may have, and $E_1, E_2, E_3, \cdots$ are the maximum values of the fundamental and the various harmonic components. An alternating voltage or current then can be represented as a composite of sine-wave terms whose frequencies are all whole-number multiples of the fundamental frequency.

Generally, alternating-current and voltage wave forms contain only the fundamental and odd harmonics. The presence of even harmonics would be associated with a lack of symmetry in the positive and negative halves of the wave, and this is not to be expected in voltages produced by rotating machinery. Voltage or current wave forms having any even-harmonic content are likely to be produced only in circuits which make use of electronic tubes. For example, the output of certain types of amplifiers may have a considerable amount of second harmonic present. However, circuit conditions may greatly influence the wave form, particularly of the current. A circuit which is largely inductive (with small resistance and capacitance) will tend to suppress higher harmonics in the current wave form since inductive impedance increases with increasing frequency. On the other hand the presence of capacitance (in the absence of appreciable resistance and inductance) will tend to increase the amplitudes of the higher harmonics that may be present in the current wave. If both inductance and capacitance in series are present in such amounts as to produce resonance for a particular harmonic, this harmonic will be accentuated in the current wave. In fact series resonance may be used to detect the presence of a particular harmonic in an emf, by an examination of the current wave form when the emf is impressed on a circuit that is adjusted to resonate at the frequency of the harmonic. The magnetic saturation of any iron which is linked with a circuit will also affect the current wave form, resulting principally in a third harmonic component.

Analysis of the steady-state conditions in any electrical circuit in which alternating emf's are present is most readily carried out on the basis that the emf varies sinusoidally, or by superposing the effects of sinusoidal components of a complex wave. It is therefore frequently desirable to determine the wave form of a voltage or current and to analyze this wave form for the presence, magnitude, and phase relationships of its various harmonic components. The analysis of wave forms and the methods of computation used in such analyses are outside the scope of the present work. For this purpose various methods are available, in which computation schedules are set up for systematizing and reducing the labor involved, and the student should acquaint himself with these operations.[2] However, the methods by which wave forms may be determined will be considered.

Point-by-Point Methods

These methods of wave-form determination make use of a contactor or switch which is operated synchronously with the source being measured, and which closes the circuit during an interval so short in comparison with the repetition time of the voltage or current wave that no significant

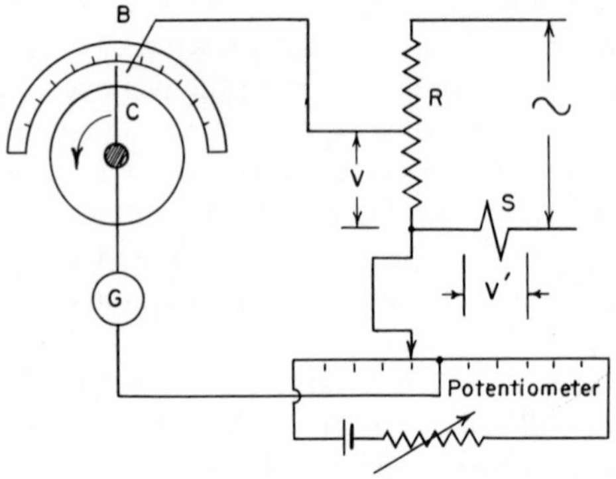

FIG. 1.

change takes place before the circuit is again opened. Various means are available for measuring the voltage present in the circuit during the interval that it is closed, and a series of such determinations is made for points distributed over the cycle of repetition. This method requires that circuit conditions be steady during the time needed for the entire series of determinations and that the wave form repeat itself precisely during this time. Under these conditions point-by-point methods of wave-form determination are capable of considerable precision and are limited primarily by the constancy of the voltage source and of the circuit conditions.

Such a method is shown in Fig. 1. A contactor (C) is mounted on a shaft which is driven synchronously from the source whose wave form is to be determined. A brush (B) makes contact with the contactor once

[2] Such schedules are developed and discussed in detail in numerous engineering texts and elsewhere. For example see Laws, *Electrical Measurements*, p. 677, McGraw-Hill, 1938; Kerchner and Corcoran, *Alternating-Current Circuits*, p. 131, John Wiley, 1938; Grover, *Bull. Bur. Standards*, **9**, 567 (1913).

each revolution, and its angular position at the time of contact is read from the divided circle on which it is mounted. The voltage (V) which is present on the voltage divider (R) at the instant of contact is measured by opposing to it a potential drop from a potentiometer (indicated in the figure as a slide wire), balance between these voltages being indicated by the galvanometer (G). A series of such measurements is taken, the brush being moved along the divided circle between successive measurements until the entire wave has been surveyed. The arc of the circle which must be used depends on the number of pole pairs in the synchronous motor which drives the contactor. With a two-pole motor, whose synchronous speed in revolutions per second equals the frequency, an arc of 360° is required; with a four-pole motor, whose synchronous speed is half the frequency, an arc of 180° is sufficient to cover the entire wave form. Current wave form in the circuit may be determined in a similar manner by measuring the instantaneous voltages V' which appear across a non-inductive shunt (S). If the wave form of a very high voltage is to be determined, a capacitance voltage divider may sometimes be used to advantage in place of the resistance voltage divider (R) shown in Fig. 1, and a quadrant electrometer or other suitable detector substituted for the galvanometer.

Harmonic Analyzers

These instruments, in which the various components of a complex wave can be separated and measured, can be employed to determine the

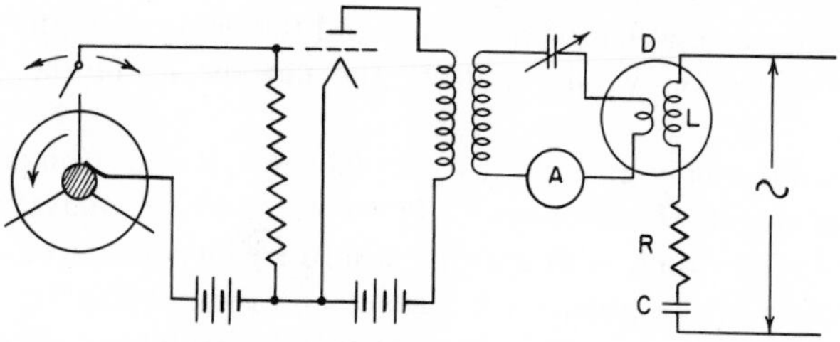

FIG. 2.

magnitudes of the fundamental and of the harmonics. Such an analysis is useful where there is interest only in the magnitudes of the harmonics but where their phase relations are not significant. Such an analyzer, utilizing an electrodynamic instrument,[3] is shown schematically in Fig. 2. The moving coil of the instrument is supplied from the source whose wave form is to be analyzed. The field coils of the instrument are separately excited at the frequency of the particular harmonic under investigation.

[3] Cockcroft, *J. IEE*, **63**, 69 (1925).

The operation of the method depends on the fact that a net torque capable of producing deflection in the instrument is present only when its fixed and moving coils are excited at the same frequency. Hence there is a deflection only if the harmonic is present in the wave form.[4] Excitation at the desired frequency may be furnished from a tuned circuit, driven as indicated, by a synchronous contactor. The number of contacts per revolution would determine the order of the harmonic excited, and separate contact rings would have to be available for each harmonic. The phase of the field excitation in the electrodynamic instrument could be varied by changing the position of the contact brush until the instrument deflection was maximum, when the deflection would be $D = KI_fI_m$. The field-coil current I_f could be measured by a suitable ammeter, and the component of current I_m in the moving coil, corresponding to the harmonic being measured, could be determined from the deflection and the constant K of the instrument. The voltage corresponding to this harmonic would then be

$$V_n = I_m \sqrt{R^2 + \left(n\omega L - \frac{1}{n\omega C}\right)^2}$$

A capacitor in the moving-coil circuit magnifies the current for the higher harmonics and thus increases the sensitivity of the method. Alternatively a variable-frequency generator could supply field current for the electrodynamic instrument. If the frequency of this generator were very nearly that of the harmonic, the instrument deflection would go through a cycle of values from a positive to a negative maximum with a frequency equal to the difference between the harmonic and the field-coil frequency. The maximum deflection would indicate the current I_m in the same way as before.

A harmonic analyzer built by the General Radio Company has a different principle of operation.[5] The voltage to be analyzed is mixed in a heterodyne circuit with a signal whose frequency can be controlled. When the sum of this auxiliary frequency and the frequency of one of the components of the unknown voltage is exactly 50,000 cps, their resultant can pass through a highly selective quartz-crystal filter and its amplitude is measured. The circuit is shown schematically in Fig. 3. The heterodyne method makes it possible to use a fixed-frequency filter while varying the response frequency. The pass band of the filter is only about 4 cycles wide, the response being down 15 db at 5 cycles away from the center of the band (voltage response down to 18% of peak response) and 60 db at 30 cycles from the peak (voltage response down to 0.1%). A wide range

[4] See Chapter 11.

[5] Arguimbau, *G.R. Experimenter*, **7**, 12 (1933).

of input voltages can be measured by employing an attenuator in the input and an adjustable gain control in the final amplifier. Calibration is accomplished by inserting a known 60-cycle voltage in the system and adjusting the amplifier gain to give a standard output. A frequency range of 20 to 16,000 cps is covered by this apparatus.

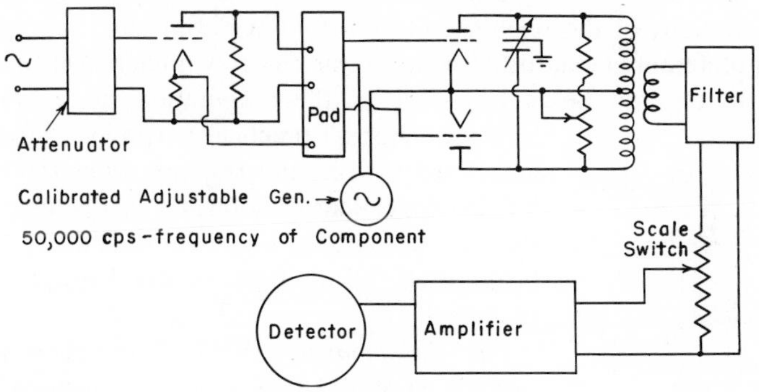

FIG. 3.

Oscillographs

The point-by-point method of wave-form determination previously discussed can be used only where conditions are completely steady for an extended period of time, and wave analyzers do not indicate phase relations among the component harmonics. Where the wave form must be observed in a relatively short time or where conditions are not sufficiently stable to permit the use of the more accurate point-by-point method, an oscillograph is needed. Oscillographic methods have the advantage of greater convenience of operation, and, since they permit continuous recording or observation, are useful in following transients and other short-time variations of voltage and current in a circuit. However, since their operation depends on observing the motion of an illuminated spot on a screen (or, in some types of recording oscillographs, a trace drawn on paper), the accuracy with which their recordings can be read is inherently low, being limited by the ratio of trace width to deflection, and is not better than 1 to 2% under the most favorable circumstances.

An oscillograph is essentially an instrument designed for recording or observing[6] rapid variations in voltage or current. These variations are automatically plotted (usually against time) on a suitable screen or, if a permanent record is to be made, on a photographic film or paper. Two

[6] It has been suggested that the term *oscilloscope* be applied to an instrument for visually observing wave forms and similar phenomena, while the term *oscillograph* be reserved for an instrument with which a permanent record of the phenomenon is made.

types of oscillograph are extensively used at the present time, which differ basically in the nature of the element which responds to voltage or current variations. The response element may be either a mechanical moving system (in the galvanometer oscillograph) or an electron beam (in the cathode-ray oscillograph). If a mechanical moving system is used, its inertia must be small, its response time must be short compared with the time variations of the phenomenon under observation, and its damping should preferably be adjusted within rather narrow limits. On the other hand, an electron beam has none of these limitations as a response element. For all practical purposes no inertia is associated with it, and response time and damping are dependent only on the characteristics of the electrical circuits used with it, and not on the beam itself. Both types of oscillograph will be discussed.

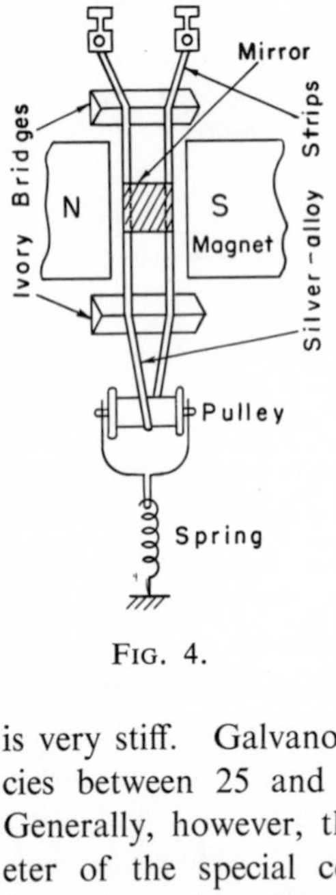

FIG. 4.

The Galvanometer Oscillograph. This instrument is employed only at low frequencies. The response element may be considered a damped harmonic oscillator whose mechanical characteristics limit its performance to frequencies well below the resonant frequency of the oscillator. For applications in which only very low frequencies are of interest and high sensitivity is desired, the response element may be a d'Arsonval galvanometer whose coil is very narrow to keep its moment of inertia small and whose suspension is very stiff. Galvanometer elements having natural (resonant) frequencies between 25 and 1000 cps have been used in oscillograph work. Generally, however, the response element is a rudimentary galvanometer of the special construction shown in Fig. 4. A single loop of thin silver-alloy ribbon[7] is stretched over ivory bridges and a pulley, and is attached to the binding posts. Between the upper and lower bridges the two sides of the loop are parallel and are situated between the pole pieces of a permanent magnet.[8] Tension (usually adjustable) is applied to the loop by means of a spring and screw arrangement attached to the pulley, and a mirror is cemented to the loop in the straight portion

[7] Aluminum ribbon has been used in some instances.

[8] Electromagnets were used in early models but have been universally abandoned in favor of small permanent magnets, with a considerable reduction in weight and with the advantage of not requiring a d-c source. Another disadvantage of the older electromagnets was the fact that they dissipated considerable heat, changing the temperature of the response elements and seriously modifying the damping characteristics of the fluid in which the element was immersed.

between the bridges. The galvanometer with its mounting is usually immersed in a liquid to provide damping, and is removable as a unit for adjustment and repair. The light source is usually a low-voltage incandescent lamp which is normally operated at about rated voltage, but whose brightness is increased, when taking photographic records, by applying a momentary overvoltage. The light beam, focused by a suitable lens system, passes through a slit and shutter arrangement to a photographic film for recording, or is intercepted by a rotating or oscillating mirror and projected on a screen for visual observation. The linear velocity of the film past the slit, or the angular velocity of the intercepting mirror, determines the time scale.

Galvanometers of the design described above have been constructed to have natural frequencies up to 10,000 cps. The accuracy with which such a high-frequency galvanometer will follow short-time variations in current or voltage depends on the natural frequency of the galvanometer and on its damping. In order to establish, in terms of natural frequency and damping, the frequency range over which the galvanometer response is satisfactory, we will examine the galvanometer equation of motion for the case in which the driving torque is produced by a sine-wave voltage. As a reasonable approximation to the actual physical structure, we may consider that the galvanometer is a damped harmonic oscillator with one degree of freedom, in forced vibration.

THEORY. The differential equation of motion may be stated, from our previous discussion of the galvanometer,[9] as

$$P\frac{d^2\theta}{dt^2} + A\frac{d\theta}{dt} + U\theta = \frac{GE}{R}\sin(\omega t + \beta)$$

where P is the moment of inertia about the axis of rotation, A is the total damping (including both the dissipative or frictional damping and the conservative or circuit damping), U is the restoration constant or stiffness of the system, G is its motor constant, R is the resistance of the circuit in which it operates, and $E\sin(\omega t + \beta)$ is the sinusoidal voltage in the circuit. The particular solution (representing the steady-state response) may be written as

$$\theta = \frac{\dfrac{GE}{RP}\sin(\omega t + \beta)}{D^2 + \dfrac{A}{P}D + \dfrac{U}{P}}$$

$$= \frac{GE}{RP(m_1 - m_2)}\left[\varepsilon^{m_1 t}\int \varepsilon^{-m_1 t}\sin(\omega t + \beta)\,dt - \varepsilon^{m_2 t}\int \varepsilon^{-m_2 t}\sin(\omega t + \beta)\,dt\right]$$

[9] See Chapter 3, p. 47, *et seq.*

where

$$m_1 = -\frac{A}{2P} + \sqrt{\frac{A^2}{4P^2} - \frac{U}{P}}, \quad \text{and} \quad m_2 = -\frac{A}{2P} - \sqrt{\frac{A^2}{4P^2} - \frac{U}{P}}$$

After integrating and collecting terms, we have

$$\theta = \frac{GE}{RP(m_1 - m_2)}\left[\left(\frac{m_2}{m_2^2 + \omega^2} - \frac{m_1}{m_1^2 + \omega^2}\right)\sin(\omega t + \beta) + \omega\left(\frac{1}{m_2^2 + \omega^2} - \frac{1}{m_1^2 + \omega^2}\right)\cos(\omega t + \beta)\right]$$

$$= \frac{GE}{RP(m_2^2 + \omega^2)(m_1^2 + \omega^2)}[(m_1 m_2 - \omega^2)\sin(\omega t + \beta) + \omega(m_1 + m_2)\cos(\omega t + \beta)]$$

We will define an angle ϕ, such that

$$\tan\phi = \frac{\omega(m_1 + m_2)}{m_1 m_2 - \omega^2}$$

Then

$$\cos\phi = \frac{m_1 m_2 - \omega^2}{\sqrt{(m_1^2 + \omega^2)(m_2^2 + \omega^2)}}$$

and

$$\sin\phi = \frac{\omega(m_1 + m_2)}{\sqrt{(m_1^2 + \omega^2)(m_2^2 + \omega^2)}}$$

Our particular solution is then

$$\theta = \frac{GE}{RP\sqrt{(m_2^2 + \omega^2)(m_1^2 + \omega^2)}}\sin(\omega t + \beta + \phi)$$

Now

$$m_1 m_2 = \frac{U}{P}, \quad \text{and} \quad (m_1 + m_2) = -\frac{A}{P}$$

Then

$$P\sqrt{(m_2^2 + \omega^2)(m_1^2 + \omega^2)} = P\sqrt{(m_1 m_2)^2 + [(m_1 + m_2)^2 - 2m_1 m_2]\omega^2 + \omega^4}$$

$$= P\sqrt{\left(\frac{U}{P}\right)^2 + \left[\left(\frac{A}{P}\right)^2 - 2\frac{U}{P}\right]\omega^2 + \omega^4}$$

$$= U\sqrt{1 + \left[\left(\frac{A}{U}\right)^2 - 2\frac{P}{U}\right]\omega^2 + \omega^4\left(\frac{P}{U}\right)^2}$$

Now

$$\frac{P}{U} = \frac{T_0^2}{4\pi^2} = \frac{1}{\omega_0^2}$$

where ω_0 is the natural (undamped) frequency of the moving system. Introducing relative damping, we have $\gamma = A/A_c$, where $A_c = 2\sqrt{UP}$. Then

$$\left(\frac{A}{U}\right)^2 = 4\gamma^2 \frac{P}{U} = \frac{4\gamma^2}{\omega_0^{\,2}}$$

We will define $\omega/\omega_0 = \eta$, the ratio of forced frequency to natural frequency. These values may be substituted into our particular solution to give

$$\theta = \frac{GE}{RU} \cdot \frac{1}{\sqrt{1 + 2(2\gamma^2 - 1)\eta^2 + \eta^4}} \sin(\omega t + \beta + \phi)$$

Also

$$\tan \phi = \frac{\omega(m_1 + m_2)}{m_1 m_2 - \omega^2} = \frac{-\omega(A/P)}{(U/P) - \omega^2} = \frac{-2\gamma\omega\omega_0}{\omega_0^{\,2} - \omega^2} = \frac{-2\gamma\eta}{1 - \eta^2}$$

If we define

$$\psi = \tan^{-1} \frac{2\gamma\eta}{1 - \eta^2}$$

and recall that $GE/RU = \theta_{dc}$, the d-c deflection of the galvanometer for a voltage E, we may write for our final *steady-state* solution for the galvanometer in forced vibration

$$\theta = \frac{\theta_{dc}}{\sqrt{1 + 2(2\gamma^2 - 1)\eta^2 + \eta^4}} \sin(\omega t + \beta - \psi)$$

It will be observed that the amplitude of the deflection is a function of frequency and damping, and that the deflection lags behind the applied voltage by an angle ψ which is also a function of frequency and damping. If then the oscillograph galvanometer can be approximated as a galvanometer with one degree of freedom (pure rotation about an axis of symmetry), we can see that for steady-state response it has two types of distortion in following the variations of a voltage or current (amplitude and phase distortion), which are both functions of frequency and damping. These will be defined in terms of "magnification":

$$M = \frac{\theta_{max}}{\theta_{dc}} = \frac{1}{\sqrt{1 + 2(2\gamma^2 - 1)\eta^2 + \eta^4}}$$

and phase displacement:

$$\text{"lag"} = \psi = \tan^{-1} \frac{2\gamma\eta}{1 - \eta^2}$$

i.e. by comparing the maximum response at any particular frequency to the steady-state response for a direct voltage of the same magnitude, and by stating the angle by which the response for a particular frequency lags behind the applied voltage.

The complete solution, which includes both the steady-state response of the galvanometer and its transient response, may be written as

$$\theta = C_1\varepsilon^{m_1t} + C_2\varepsilon^{m_2t} + \theta_{dc} \cdot M \cdot \sin(\omega t + \beta - \psi)$$

The constants of integration may be evaluated in terms of the usual boundary conditions

$$\left\{\begin{aligned} \theta &= 0 \\ \frac{d\theta}{dt} &= 0 \end{aligned}\right|_{t=0}$$

i.e. the galvanometer being initially at rest in its equilibrium position. If we apply these conditions to the *underdamped* galvanometer (the only case which is of practical importance in oscillograph applications), the *complete* solution for the galvanometer in forced vibration can be shown to be

$$\frac{\theta}{\theta_{dc}} = M\left[\sin(\omega t + \beta - \psi) - \frac{\varepsilon^{-\omega_0\gamma t}}{\sqrt{1-\gamma^2}} \left\{\begin{matrix}\gamma \sin(\omega_0\sqrt{1-\gamma^2}\, t + \sin^{-1}\sqrt{1-\gamma^2}) \sin(\beta - \psi) + \\ \eta \sin(\omega_0\sqrt{1-\gamma^2}\, t) \cos(\beta - \psi)\end{matrix}\right\}\right]$$

Thus in the most general case we have three types of distortion in the oscillogram (*amplitude*, *phase*, and *transient*) which arise from the characteristics of the recording element. The conditions which will minimize any one of these distortions will not be precisely those which will reduce the other types of distortion to minimum values. It is not difficult to arrive at a compromise which will be satisfactory in most oscillograph applications. But it must be realized that cases may arise in practice in which one or another of the distortions may have to be minimized at the expense of added distortion of another type.

AMPLITUDE DISTORTION. Magnification

$$M = \frac{1}{\sqrt{1 + 2(2\gamma^2 - 1)\eta^2 + \eta^4}}$$

is shown in Fig. 5 as a function of frequency for a number of values of relative damping. For small damping this function first rises to a maximum and then decreases with a further increase of frequency. The maximum completely disappears for $\gamma = 0.707$, $2\gamma^2 - 1 = 0$, and for higher values of damping the function has a negative slope at all frequencies. The maximum range of frequency for which the departure of magnification from unity is not significant is obtained by using a value of relative damping somewhat less than the value ($\gamma = 0.707$) at which the maximum disappears. If we consider that under favorable conditions (narrow trace line and good contrast), the ordinates of an oscillogram cannot be read to better than 1%, it will be seen that a distortion (departure of magnification from unity) of 1% or less will be insignificant.

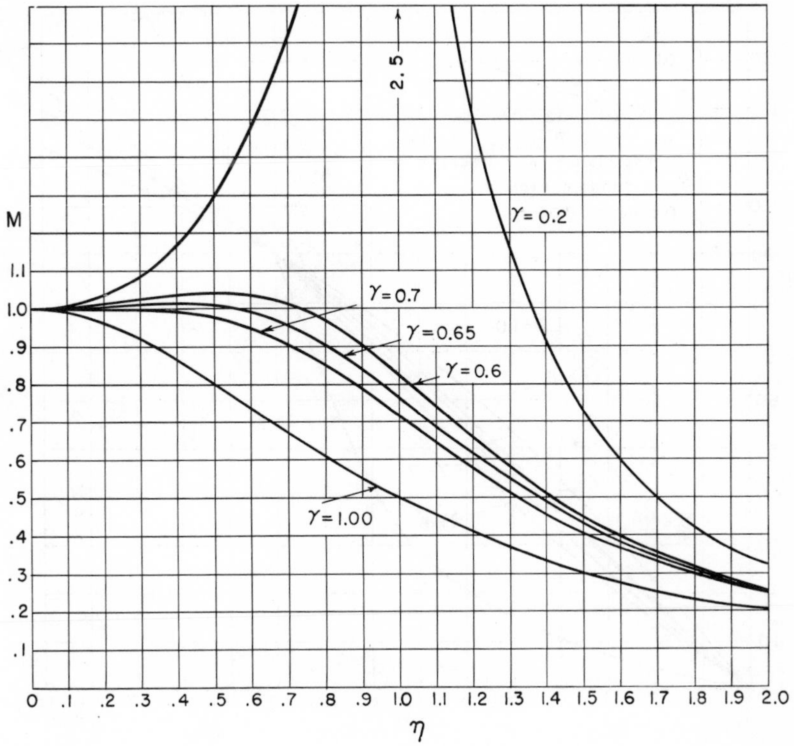

FIG. 5.

From Fig. 5 it will be seen that for $\gamma = 0.65$ the maximum is approximately 1% above the value at zero frequency, and the range over which the distortion is 1% or less extends from direct current to a frequency 0.6 of the natural frequency, whereas the distortion will exceed 1% at 0.4 of the natural frequency if $\gamma = 0.7$.

PHASE DISTORTION. The angle ψ by which the galvanometer deflection lags the applied voltage is shown in Fig. 6 as a function of frequency for a number of values of relative damping, and it may be noted that the lag angle is 90° at the natural frequency for any value of damping. If this lag angle were linear with frequency, there would be no phase distortion and all harmonic components in an oscillogram would appear in their correct time relation with respect to each other; i.e. for a phase displacement proportional to frequency the displacement in time on an oscillogram is constant. We may say, then, that a value of relative damping which would give the best approximation to a straight line over the useful range of frequencies (when lag angle is plotted against frequency) would

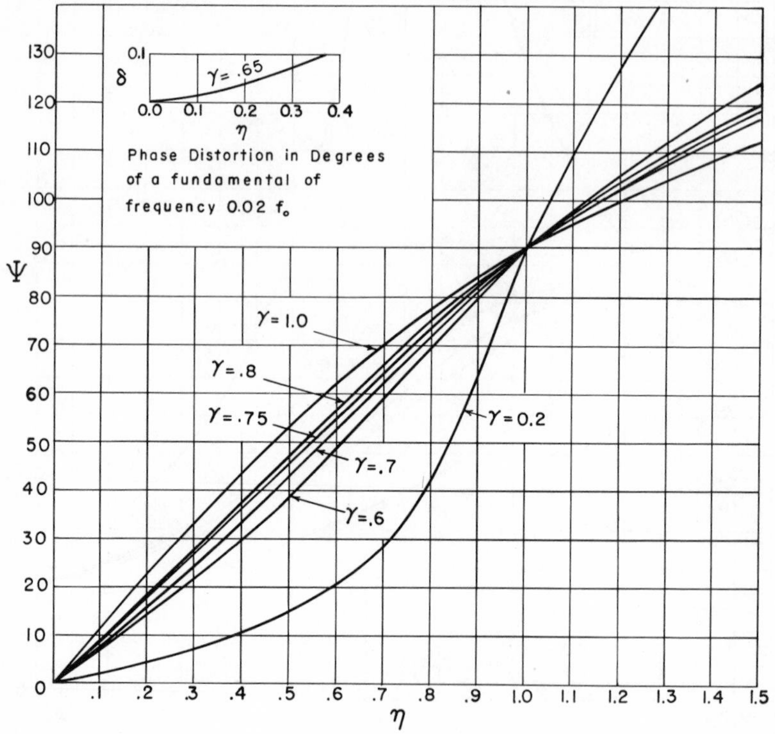

FIG. 6.

result in minimum phase distortion. This value of damping ($\gamma = 0.75$) is somewhat higher than the damping required for minimum amplitude distortion. However, in many applications the phase distortion resulting from lower damping does not result in any measurable error on oscillograms. For example, if we were recording a wave form having a 60-cycle fundamental, with an oscillograph having a natural frequency of 3000 cps, the phase displacement of harmonics with respect to the fundamental (measured in degrees of the fundamental) would be

$$\delta = \frac{0.02}{\eta}\,\psi_\eta - \psi_{0.02}$$

These values are plotted for a relative damping of $\gamma = 0.65$, in the insert curve of Fig. 6, and it will be seen that the phase distortion for any harmonic up to the 19th is less than 0.1° of the fundamental. This phase distortion is entirely negligible and could not be measured on an oscillogram. The situation will, of course, not be nearly so favorable if the fundamental frequency in an oscillogram is a large fraction of the natural frequency of the galvanometer. However, the case cited is typical of much of the work for which a galvanometer oscillograph is used, and for such applications any reasonable value of damping will result in a rather small phase distortion (δ).

TRANSIENT DISTORTION. A third type of distortion arises from the transient response of the galvanometer. This cannot be analyzed as

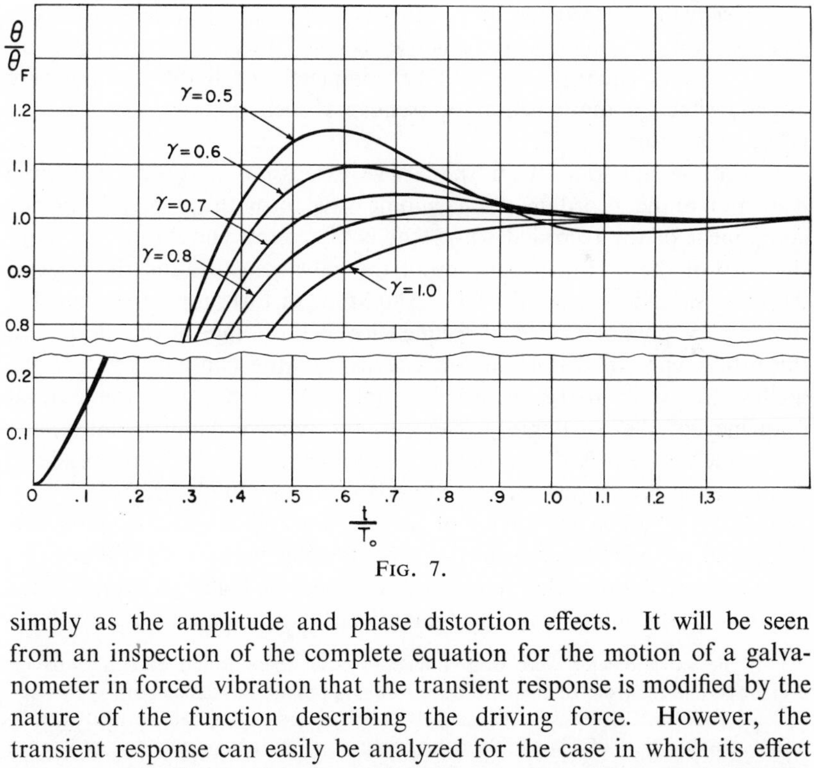

FIG. 7.

simply as the amplitude and phase distortion effects. It will be seen from an inspection of the complete equation for the motion of a galvanometer in forced vibration that the transient response is modified by the nature of the function describing the driving force. However, the transient response can easily be analyzed for the case in which its effect is greatest, i.e. for a suddenly applied voltage of constant magnitude. In this case the transient response is that which has already been derived for the d-c galvanometer.[10] This is shown in Fig. 7 as a function of time for a series of values of relative damping. It will be noted that the

[10] See Chapter 3, p. 53.

transient response has become less than 1% of the total in a time equal to the free period ($2\pi/\omega_0$) of the galvanometer for any relative damping between 0.6 and 1.0. An oscillogram of a *square* wave would show a "pip" or overshoot[11] at the beginning of the wave, but the record would be free from transient distortion for any time greater than T_0. This provides a convenient method for determining the oscillograph damping since the relation between proportional overshoot and final deflection can be expressed as a function of damping[12]

$$-\log \frac{\theta_1 - \theta_F}{\theta_F} = \frac{\pi\gamma}{\sqrt{1-\gamma^2}}$$

Now in the usual applications of the galvanometer oscillograph the transient term will be less at any time than the "maximum" transient distortion discussed for the square-wave response, as may be seen from an inspection of the general equation. It will be completely negligible for the case already cited—a fundamental of frequency such that $\eta = 0.02$, and a relative damping of 0.65.

It will be apparent from the above discussion that, for negligible distortion in the recording of a harmonic wave form, the highest frequency component of the recorded wave that is of interest should not be more than 0.6 of the natural frequency of the galvanometer, and the relative damping should be around 0.65. Amplitude distortion is minimized for the greatest possible range of frequencies at this value of damping, and the other types of distortion are usually of little consequence. If the highest frequency to be recorded is not more than 0.4 of the natural frequency of the oscillograph element, the relative damping may have any value between 0.65 and 0.70. For lower frequencies the latitude in damping for distortion-free recording is correspondingly greater.

SENSITIVITY. The sensitivity of an oscillograph element is quite low compared to that of the usual d-c galvanometer because its stiffness (U) must be large in order that its natural frequency be high. A typical value of current sensitivity[13] is 0.4 radian/amp for commercially available

[11] If the galvanometer were overdamped ($\gamma > 1$), there would of course be no overshoot, and the front of a square wave would appear to be rounded off.

[12] See p. 54 of Chapter 3. Alternatively the relative damping can be read directly from a graph (Fig. 7 of Chapter 3) if the proportional overshoot on a square wave is known.

[13] Statement of sensitivity θ/I in radians per ampere may appear somewhat unusual but has been adopted here in order to permit direct comparison of elements used in different oscillographs. The optical path lengths in various oscillographs are widely different, and a statement of sensitivity in millimeters of deflection per ampere is significant on a comparative basis only if the optical path length is also specified. To reduce these sensitivities to more familiar terms one has only to recall that an angular

elements having a natural frequency in air of 5000 cps. Higher-sensitivity elements are usually available, but at the cost of reduced natural frequencies; for example, a sensitivity of 12 radians/amp was found for an element having a natural frequency in air of 1200 cps. Multiturn galvanometers of the d'Arsonval type are also used in some oscillographs. These have much higher sensitivities, but their moments of inertia are quite large and their natural frequencies correspondingly low. As examples of the latter construction an element having a sensitivity of 25 radians/amp has a natural frequency of 200 cps, while an element having a sensitivity of 900 radians/amp has a natural frequency of 50 cps.[14] Such oscillograph elements are, of course, suitable only for recording at low frequencies since, as we have seen, amplitude distortion begins to be appreciable for frequencies greater than 0.6 of the natural frequency.

DAMPING. Damping control is usually accomplished for very low-frequency elements by shunting the galvanometer with a resistance of suitable value. This will reduce the current sensitivity of the element somewhat but the effect is not as serious for low-frequency elements as is the effect of damping by immersion of the element in a viscous fluid. Fluid damping, which is commonly used with high-frequency elements, markedly reduces the effective natural frequency of the element, since an appreciable volume of the liquid moves with the element and consequently the effective inertia of the moving system is increased to a very considerable extent. In fact the natural frequency of a fluid-damped oscillograph element may be as little as 40 to 60% of its natural frequency in air.[15] Another disadvantage of fluid damping is the fact that the viscosity of most damping fluids changes considerably with temperature, and consequently their damping characteristics are temperature-sensitive.[16] Hence, for oscillograms of high quality, the temperature of the element should be held within rather narrow limits, or, if the element must be exposed to extreme temperatures, a damping fluid should be selected such that the value of damping may be correct at the temperature of operation.

---

deflection of 1 radian corresponds to a deflection of 2000 mm on a circular scale at a meter distance, since angular displacement of the spot on the scale is twice the angular motion of the galvanometer mirror.

[14] These latter figures are quoted from a recent catalog of the Hathway Instrument Company.

[15] The user should keep this fact in mind when considering the range of applicability of a particular element, since the natural frequency stated by the maker is usually the frequency in air.

[16] The damping fluids ordinarily used are rather highly refined mineral oils whose viscosity variation with temperature is large. Certain silicone fluids which have been recently developed have much less variation of viscosity with temperature and may be expected to prove useful as damping fluids in some applications.

Special shunting networks have been developed for use with the galvanometer oscillograph, in order to avoid the necessity for fluid damping. Such a circuit is shown in Fig. 8 and is known as Irwin's resonant shunt.[17] The shunt is tuned to the resonant frequency of the galvanometer so that $\omega_0 = 1/\sqrt{LC}$, and a value of resistance (R) is used which will bring the damping to a suitable value (e.g. $\gamma = 0.65$ to 0.70). Since the usual high-frequency element consists of a single loop stretched across bridges, as shown in Fig. 4, its behavior is only approximately described as that of a d'Arsonval galvanometer. Actually the individual strips forming the sides of the loop have their own resonant frequencies, and the system is coupled mechanically by the mirror which is cemented to both strips between the bridges. In one type of resonant shunt,[18] shown in Fig. 9, a separate resonant shunt is provided for each of the strips, and the shunts are electrically coupled by mutual inductance. Another variation of circuit damping makes use of a single resonant shunt across the entire element but accomplishes part of the damping by immersing the element in kerosene. The decrease in natural frequency is only about half as great as if the entire damping were accomplished by means of fluid, and the damping characteristics of kerosene are affected by temperature to only a moderate extent.

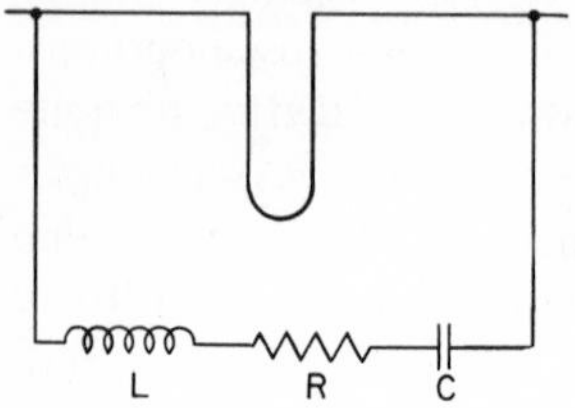

FIG. 8.

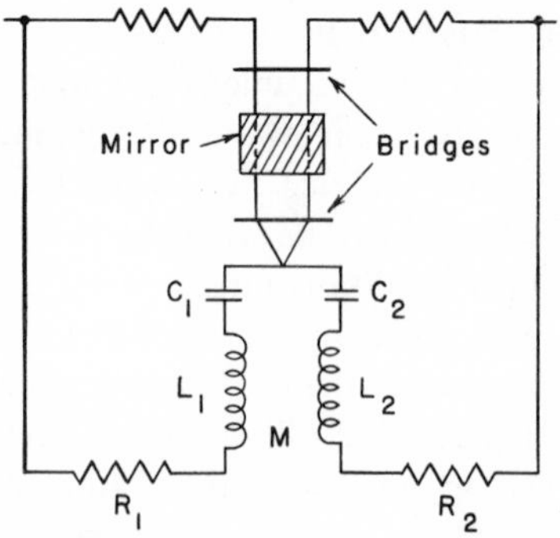

FIG. 9.

The Cathode-Ray Oscillograph. The response element in a cathode-ray oscillograph is a beam of electrons, and, since there are no mechanical moving parts, there is no practical limit to the frequencies for which wave-form traces can be formed.[19]

[17] Irwin, *Oscillographs*, p. 91, Pitman, 1925; Butterworth, *J. Sci. Inst.*, **4**, 8 (1926–27).

[18] Martin and Caris, *Rev. Sci. Inst.*, **3**, 598 (1932).

[19] There is a type of distortion (different from those discussed above) which may be present at very high frequencies. It may be called "transit-time" distortion, and will occur if there is any appreciable change in the voltage on the deflecting plates of the oscillograph in the time interval during which individual electrons in the beam are "in transit" in the deflecting field. As will be seen from the discussion this transit time is a function of the length of the deflecting plates, and of the voltage used to generate the electron beam. However it is significant only at extremely high frequencies and need not be considered in the present discussion.

The earliest demonstration of the use of an electron beam to delineate wave forms was made by Braun in 1897, but it has been only since about 1925 that cathode-ray oscillographs have been developed as practical, general-purpose laboratory instruments.

OPERATING PRINCIPLE. The basic operating principle depends on the deflection of electrons in electric or magnetic fields. If an electron beam passes between parallel plates between which there is a difference of potential [Fig. 10(a)], the electrons will be accelerated toward the positive plate and away from the negative plate. While in the electric field they will follow a curved path (since their acceleration is perpendicular to the direction of motion) and when they leave the field (so that they are no longer accelerated), they will again travel in a straight line in a direction tangent to the curved path. They will strike a fixed target at the end of their path in a spot which is displaced from their terminal position for no voltage on the deflecting plates (i.e. for no accelerating field normal to the direction of motion). The deflection sensitivity of a cathode-ray tube may be defined as the displacement of the spot on the target or screen for unit potential difference between the deflecting plates. It may be written approximately as $S = lL/2Vd$, where l is the length of path traversed in the electric field between the deflecting plates, L is the distance from the plates to the screen, d is the separation of the plates (all in centimeters), and V is the potential in volts used to generate the electron beam.

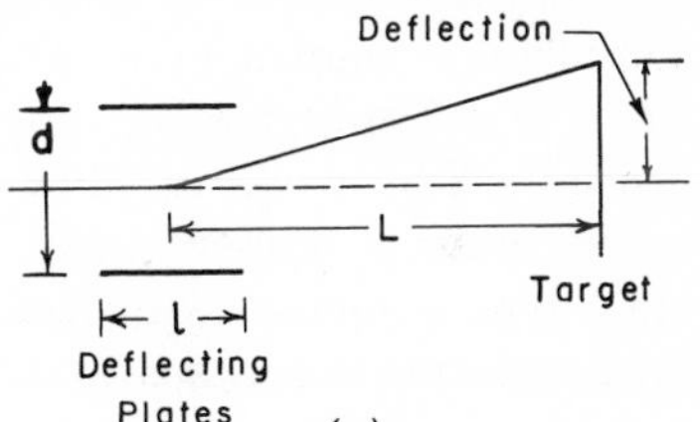

(a)

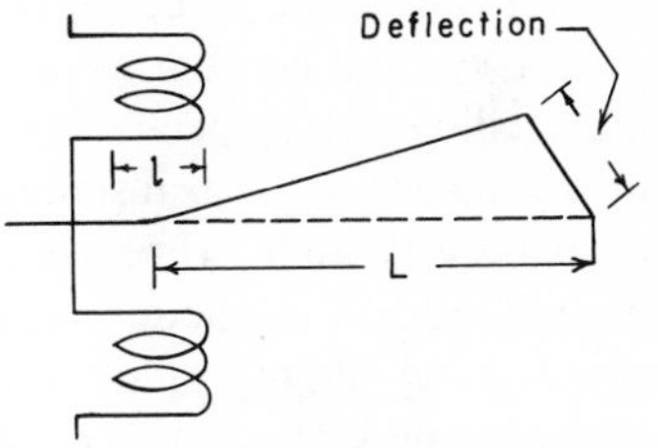

(b)

FIG. 10.

The electron-beam path is also curved when it passes through a magnetic field. Here, however, the acceleration is perpendicular both to the direction of the field and to the direction of motion of the electrons in the beam. In the arrangement shown in Fig. 10(b), the deflection would be perpendicular to the plane of the paper. The displacement of the spot on the screen from its undeflected position would be perpendicular to the plane of the paper. The displacement of the spot on the screen from its undeflected position may be written approximately as $X = 0.3BlL/\sqrt{V}$, where X is the displacement in centimeters, B is the field in gausses, l is the path length in the magnetic field, and the other symbols are the same as in the previous case.[20] It will be noted that in the case of the electric field the sensitivity is inversely proportional to the beam voltage. In the usual type of low-voltage tube ($V \approx 2000$ volts) the sensitivity may amount to 0.2 to 0.3 mm/volt. Electrostatic rather than magnetic deflecting systems are ordinarily used in cathode-ray oscillographs. The plate system involves a capacitance of a few micro-microfarads at most, and with any reasonable value of series resistance the time constant of the deflecting circuit will be quite small. In contrast, if a magnetic deflecting system were set up by current in field coils, a considerable amount of inductance and resistance would be associated with the deflection circuit, so that the current in the deflecting coils, and hence the sensitivity, would be a function of frequency.

Two general types of tubes are used in measurement work. In the older type a high-voltage electron beam is generated in a gas-discharge tube operating at perhaps 50 to 60 kv. The beam passes through a small hole in the anode and may be focused by using axial magnetic fields.[21] Such a tube must be continuously pumped to maintain the different but proper vacuum conditions in the discharge tube and in the main body of the oscillograph respectively. The principal application of such tubes is in the recording of transient phenomena, where the speed of recording must be very high. The photographic film for recording oscillograms is placed inside the vacuum chamber so that the electron beam directly strikes the photographic emulsion. For this type of oscillograph, operating under favorable conditions, no practical limit to recording speed can be stated. Records have been taken in which the recording spot moved across the film at a velocity of 2.3×10^{10} cm/sec (three-fourths of the velocity of light). Sealed tubes utilizing a hot cathode as an electron source were first introduced as practical commercial equipment around 1925 and are used for general-purpose oscillography at all frequencies. In early tubes the ionization of residual gas was utilized to focus the electron beam. However, this was not satisfactory because the tube life was short as a result of bombardment of the cathode by positive ions and because of so-called "zero distortion" resulting from positive space charge.[22]

[20] For the basic equations from which these expressions are derived the student may refer to a textbook on electricity and magnetism. For example, see Loeb, *Fundamentals of Electricity and Magnetism*, p. 396, Wiley, 1938.

[21] For a description of such a cathode-ray oscillograph, see Ackermann, *Trans. AIEE*, **49**, 49 (1930).

[22] Because of the relatively large mass of positive ions, they will move much more slowly than electrons and an appreciable electric field is required to prevent their accumulation. Therefore, when the potential difference between deflecting plates is small, positive ions will accumulate between them in sufficient numbers to partly

Present-day cathode-ray tubes are highly evacuated and depend only on the action of electric fields between axially spaced electrodes to focus the electron beam. Figure 11(*a*) shows an arrangement of accelerating and focusing electrodes (used in DuMont tubes) which is typical of the electron-gun structures of modern cathode-ray tubes. The indirectly heated cathode is surrounded by an electrode which is kept negative with respect to it. This negative electrode acts in the same way as a grid in an electron tube and controls the intensity of the beam. As this "grid"

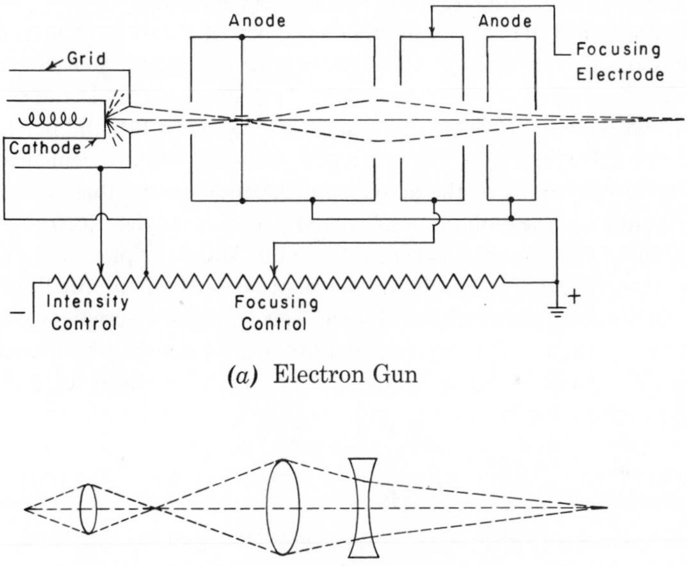

(*a*) Electron Gun

(*b*) Optical Analogue

FIG. 11.

is made more negative, fewer electrons escape to enter the beam until, at some critical voltage, the beam is completely extinguished. The succeeding electrodes serve to accelerate the electrons in the beam and to focus them into a very small spot at the fluorescent screen where their paths terminate. The electric field near the axis, in the neighborhood of

---

neutralize the deflecting field, and the deflection sensitivity will be reduced. Above a certain critical value of voltage these ions will be swept out of the field and collected on the negative deflecting plate. With the removal of the positive space charge the ratio of effective field to potential difference between plates will be greater and the deflection sensitivity will be increased. The net result will be a low sensitivity for small deflections, an increased sensitivity for larger deflections, and a constant sensitivity for deflections which correspond to fields greater than the critical value. Thus the oscillogram will be distorted for small values of deflection.

plane-parallel electrodes with central apertures, modifies the paths of electrons whose directions are at small angles to the axis, in much the same way that optical lenses modify the paths of paraxial light rays. An optical system whose action is closely analogous to that of the electrodes in the cathode-ray tube is shown in Fig. 11(*b*). It may be noted that the function of the intermediate electrode marked "focusing electrode" in Fig. 11(*a*) is to adjust the effective focal length of the electron-optical lenses that it forms with the two anodes, in order to focus the beam to a spot of minimum size on the fluorescent screen.

FLUORESCENT SCREENS. A number of types of fluorescent screens are used in cathode-ray tubes. All of them have the property of converting the kinetic energy of the electron beam into radiant energy at the point of impact, but they differ widely in the spectral characteristics and persistence of the emitted light. For any particular phosphor (fluorescent material) the relative brightness of the active spot depends on the thickness of the material and on the voltage and current density of the electron beam. A number of the screen materials adopted as standard phosphors by the Radio Manufacturers Association have proved useful in oscillographic work. Complete descriptions of their spectral characteristics and persistence may be found in the technical literature published by the various tube manufacturers. Some of their important characteristics are summarized in the table below.

Phosphor (RMA Designation)	*Color of Spot*	*Use*	*Persistence*
P–1	Green	Visual observation	Medium
P–2	Blue-green fluorescence* Yellow phosphorescence	,, ,,	Long
P–5	Blue	Photography	Short
P–7	Blue fluorescence Yellow phosphorescence	Visual observation	Long (but shorter than P–2)
P–11	Blue	Photography (higher activity than P–5)	Short (but longer than P–5)

* Fluorescence designates the luminescence during the stimulus period. Phosphorescence designates the luminescence after the stimulus is removed.

The recording of recurrent patterns does not usually present any serious problem regardless of the screen used, since, if the pattern can be made stationary on the screen, it can be photographed by time exposures. However, where the pattern is traced only once or where it is to be photographed on a moving film, the linear speed at which the spot moves over the screen must be considered. In the case of photography on a moving film the record will also be affected by the persistence of phosphorescence in the activated area. No general statement is possible which will adequately cover all the situations that arise in practice, and the user must correlate his operating conditions with the technical information supplied by the tube maker. However, it will be apparent that for any particular type of screen, beam voltage, and current density there will be an upper limit of trace speed beyond which records cannot be made from a single trace. This limit will, of course, depend also on the sensitivity of the photographic film and on the characteristics of the camera lens. Records have been obtained, under favorable conditions and with high beam voltages, of traces in which the trace speed was as much as 400 in./μsec (one-thirtieth of the velocity of light).

OPERATING CIRCUITS. Three basic types of circuits are used in cathode-ray oscillographs. (1) A high direct-voltage source must be provided for generating and focusing the beam. This must be tapped as indicated in Fig. 11(*a*), and controls provided for focusing the beam and for adjusting its intensity. It is desirable that the deflecting plate potential be about the same as that of the anode, since any large difference of potential in this region would affect both the focusing and the deflection sensitivity. Hence the anode is operated at ground potential as indicated in the figure. In some tubes an additional electrode or series of electrodes is located between the deflecting plates and the fluorescent screen and is positive with respect to ground. Its function is to accelerate the beam after deflection so that the spot on the screen may be made brighter while retaining most of the deflection sensitivity associated with a low-voltage beam at the deflecting plates. The high-voltage supply circuit consists essentially of a voltage regulator, transformer, rectifier, and filter. Voltages from 1 to 5 kv are commonly employed. For post-deflection acceleration, voltages up to 20 kv or more are used.[23] Figure 12(*a*) shows a DuMont tube, and Fig. 12(*b*) is a complete oscillograph. The various controls for the associated circuits are mounted on the front panel of the instrument.

(2) The voltage sensitivity of a cathode-ray tube is inherently low, and some hundreds of volts may be required for deflection to cover the entire width of the screen. It is necessary therefore to provide amplifiers in

[23] Where voltages of 20 kv or more are used, there is a possibility that X-rays will be radiated. Precautions must be taken to avoid exposure. Also, since the screen is at the potential of the final accelerating electrode (20 kv from ground), suitable precautions must be taken to avoid contact with this high voltage at the exposed end of the tube. A substantial transparent screen over the end of the tube will protect the operator from flying fragments of glass in the event that the tube implodes.

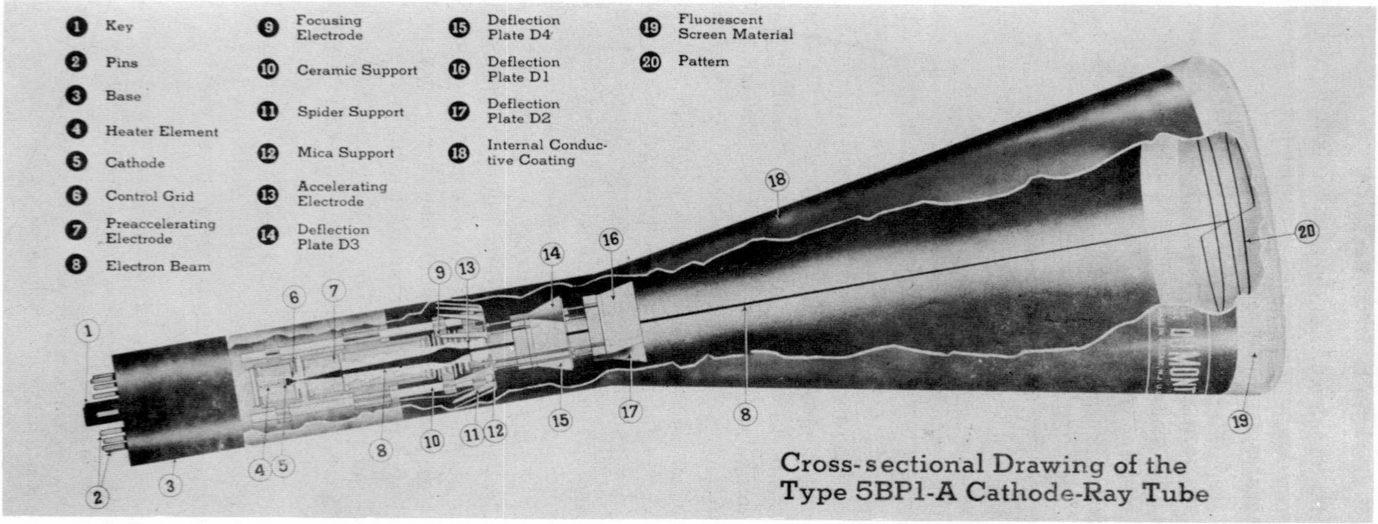

FIG. 12 (*a*). (Courtesy of Allen B. DuMont Laboratories.)

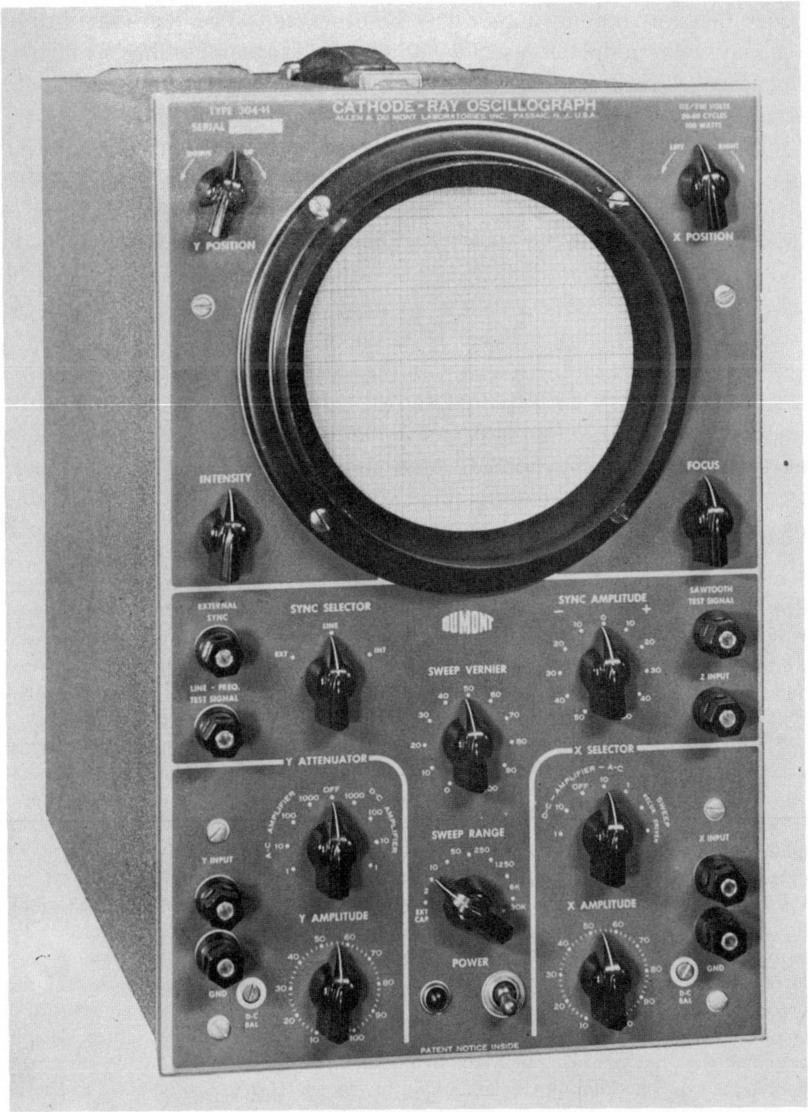

FIG. 12 (*b*). DuMont's Type 304-H oscillograph. (Courtesy of Allen B. DuMont Laboratories.)

order that low input voltages may be observed. The characteristics of the particular amplifier used will limit the range of voltages and frequencies[24] over which the signal voltage is faithfully reproduced[25] at the screen of the oscillograph.

(3) Most cathode-ray tubes are provided with two pairs of deflecting plates which are at right angles with each other. By impressing the signal to be examined on one pair of plates and a voltage which varies linearly with time on the other plate-pair, the signal may be traced on the screen in cartesian coordinates against time. Such a system can be used for presenting the oscillogram of a transient voltage as a single isolated event or, if the signal is a function which repeats itself, as a stationary pattern on the screen. In the latter case a voltage wave having a sawtooth pattern such as that shown in Fig. 13(*a*) would have to be impressed on the timing plates and synchronized with the signal voltage at the same frequency or at some submultiple of the signal-voltage frequency. The basic features of a simple relaxation oscillator capable of generating such a voltage wave are shown in Fig. 13(*b*). The voltage

[24] An amplifier having a flat response characteristic from 20 cycles to 2 megacycles/sec, with a gain of 300 and an input impedance of 5 megohms and 20 $\mu\mu$f, is used in DuMont's Type 241 oscillograph. An amplifier having a flat response characteristic from 2 cycles to 100 kc/sec, with a gain of 2000 and an input impedance of 2 megohms and 50 $\mu\mu$f, is used in the DuMont Type 304H oscillograph and is representative of general-purpose equipment.

[25] The cathode-ray oscillograph, as generally used, cannot be considered a precise measuring instrument unless both the horizontal timing sweep and the vertical deflection sensitivity are properly calibrated. If the amplitude and frequency of voltages represented by stationary wave patterns are to be measured, the calibration can be made quite simply. The total time interval of the timing sweep and its uniformity can be directly established by impressing a sine-wave voltage of known frequency on the vertical plates with the sweep in operation, and measuring known time intervals along the horizontal base line. The vertical deflection sensitivity can be calibrated by measuring the deflection produced by known input voltages. When transients are involved and an accuracy approaching 1 to 2% of maximum deflection is desired, the procedure is somewhat more complicated. In this case it is often convenient to disconnect the sweep circuit and use only the vertical deflection plates with a suitable amplifier, the time axis being provided by photographing the vertical excursions of the fluorescent spot on a film moving at a uniform velocity. Care must be taken to ensure that the deflection is accurately perpendicular to the direction of motion of the photographic film. Immediately after the transient is recorded, a series of known calibration voltages may be impressed on the input of the deflecting circuit and the resulting deflections recorded. This is necessary in accurate work in order to avoid changes in the deflection sensitivity as a result of drift in the amplifier or changes in the beam voltage in the oscillograph tube. A method for obtaining and applying such a series of calibrating voltages has been described in a paper by Roberts and Curtis, An Instrument for the Rapid Production of a Decimal Series of Potentials and Its Application to Ballistic Measurements, *NBS J. Research*, **41**, 45 (1948).

rises across the capacitor C as it is charged from the source E. This rise is exponential with time, but if only a small portion of the charging curve is used the departure from a straight line function is not serious. At the breakdown voltage of the gas triode, the capacitor is discharged, the voltage across it quickly falls to such a value that the discharge in the gas tube is extinguished, and the charging interval starts again. If the

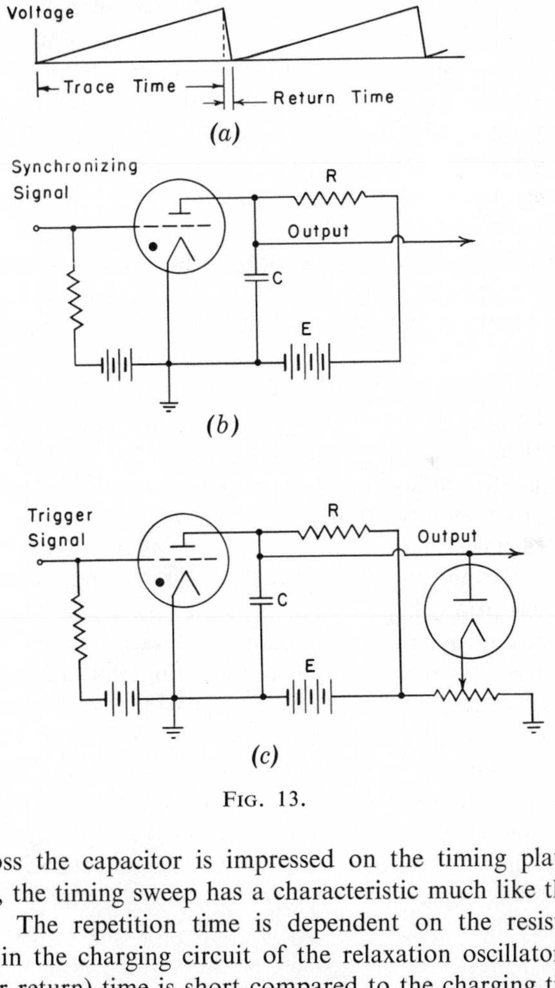

FIG. 13.

voltage across the capacitor is impressed on the timing plates of the oscillograph, the timing sweep has a characteristic much like that shown in Fig. 13. The repetition time is dependent on the resistance and capacitance in the charging circuit of the relaxation oscillator, and the discharge (or return) time is short compared to the charging time. The frequency of the timing signal is adjusted by changing the values of R and C in the circuit. The synchronizing voltage is superposed on the biasing voltage of the grid circuit and may be provided either from the signal voltage under observation or from some external source. The synchronizing voltage initiates the discharge in the gas triode and thus controls the timing with respect to the signal under observation, holding the pattern on the screen stationary. Such a relaxation oscillator has a useful frequency range from a few cycles to 50 kc/sec or more. Its upper limit is determined by the deionization time of the gas triode which controls the discharge portion of the timing cycle, and its lower limit by leakage resistance of the capacitor. Leakage resistance prevents the voltage on the capacitor from rising as rapidly as it otherwise would and slows down the timing sweep during the latter portion of the charging interval. During the discharge interval the fluorescent spot returns to the initial position that it occupied at the start of the timing sweep, and this return trace may sometimes be seen on the screen. It may be blanked out by applying a synchronized negative biasing voltage on the grid electrode (intensity control) of the cathode-ray tube.

The same basic circuit can be adapted to produce a single sweep for the study of transients, as shown in Fig. 13(*c*). A diode is placed across the output circuit of the oscillator, and its cathode voltage is adjusted so that conduction will occur in the diode at an output voltage less than that required to fire the gas triode. The sweep is initiated by a triggering pulse on the grid of the triode to discharge the capacitor. The sweep voltage is then generated by the charging of the capacitor through the resistor, but the conduction of the diode prevents the capacitor voltage from rising to a point where the triode will again be fired; i.e. the cycle is not repeated unless another triggering pulse is impressed on the grid of the triode. Various modifications of this timing circuit are used in practice, and the sweep voltage may be generated by discharging the capacitor at a fixed rate through a constant-current device.

Alternatively, for work with high-speed transients, a charged capacitor may be discharged through a resistor to provide a logarithmic time scale, or through a constant-current device to provide a linear time scale. In high-speed oscillography, such as is required in the study of impulse voltages and lightning surges, hydrogen-Thyratron tubes may be used to initiate the sweep voltage, and the timing of the triggering pulse be controlled through *R–C* circuits. In this way fast sweeps can be generated and their timing controlled to a tenth of a microsecond or better. Time markers may be superposed on an oscillogram by impressing suitably timed pulse voltages on the intensity-control electrode of the cathode-ray tube. In this case the time marker appears on the oscillogram as a brighter or darker interval in the trace.

TRANSIENT RECORDING. In photographing high-speed transients it is frequently necessary to open the camera shutter an appreciable time before the transient is initiated. In order to prevent fogging the film, it may be necessary to deflect the electron beam entirely off the fluorescent screen or to blank it out by impressing a sufficient negative voltage on the intensity-control electrode. In this case the blanking voltage must be removed when the transient is initiated and imposed again at the termination of the desired record.[26] A similar problem must be solved in using the high-voltage, cold-cathode oscillograph in which the film is inside the vacuum chamber. The Norinder relay[27] affords a very ingenious method of blocking the beam from the photographic film except during the interval when the transient is being recorded. This is shown in Fig. 14. The beam, generated in the discharge tube, passes through a small hole in the anode and is blocked from the photographic film by striking a metal target. A voltage is impressed on the relay plates simultaneously with the start of the timing sweep. The upper pair of relay plates deflects the beam away from the axis of the tube, and the second pair (of opposite polarity) deflects the beam in the opposite direction so that it is again parallel to the axis but displaced from it enough that it no longer strikes the target. The two lower plate pairs of the relay, below the target, reverse the actions of the upper plates and return the beam to the axis so that it passes between the deflecting plates and strikes the photographic film. When the sweep has completed its traverse the voltage is removed from the relay plates and the beam returns to the intercepting target.

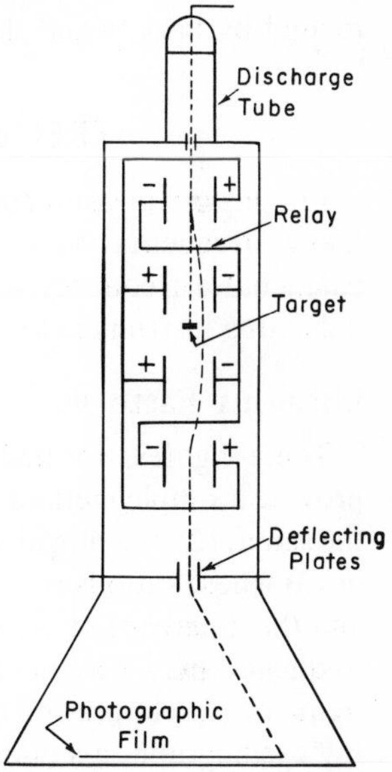

FIG. 14.

The recording of high-voltage transients requires rather specialized knowledge and techniques and cannot appropriately be discussed here, except to indicate some of the problems that are involved. Resistance voltage dividers, which are used to obtain a relatively low voltage for the oscillograph, introduce distortions when the rate of change of voltage is large (steep wave fronts) because of their distributed capacitance, residual inductance, and capacitance to ground. The use of capacitance

[26] For details about the circuits required for synchronizing and performing these operations, the reader may refer to a paper by Keuhni and Ramo, A New High-Speed Cathode-Ray Oscillograph, *Trans. AIEE*, **56**, 721 (1937). This paper also has a bibliography of eighty-one references.

[27] See Ackermann, *op. cit.*

dividers requires special oscillograph arrangements and techniques. No completely satisfactory solution to this problem is known at the present time. The signal voltage is usually carried to the oscillograph by a coaxial cable. Attenuation of the signal, and the proper termination of such a cable to avoid reflections, must be considered. The recording of current surges also involves special considerations. The design and construction of suitable four-terminal resistors for measuring current surges without distortion are difficult problems. The design of such shunts has been treated by Park,[28] and the reader should refer to his paper.

FREQUENCY MEASUREMENTS

Frequency measurements are usually made by comparison with a known frequency, by counting cycles over a measured time interval, by balancing a frequency-sensitive bridge, or by means of various types of indicating instruments.[29] Each of these methods will be briefly discussed.

Lissajous Patterns

These figures, formed on the screen of a cathode-ray oscillograph, provide a simple method for comparing two frequencies (1) that are nearly the same; (2) one of which is an exact whole-number multiple of the other; or (3) whose ratio is commensurable. If one of the frequencies is known, and the difference or the ratio of the frequencies is determined, the second frequency may be calculated. If equal sine-wave voltages of the same frequency are impressed on the vertical and horizontal plates of a cathode-ray oscillograph, a standing pattern is formed on the oscillograph screen. The shape of this pattern will depend on the phase difference between the voltages, as shown in Fig. 15(*a*). As the phase difference increases, the pattern changes as shown until, at a phase difference of 2π, it is again identical with the pattern for zero phase difference. If one frequency is slightly different from the other, the pattern changes progressively as the phase difference increases from 0 to 2π. When the pattern has progressed through the entire sequence of shapes, one voltage has gained a complete cycle on the other. Hence the repetition rate of the sequence of patterns can be used as a measure of frequency difference. The elapsed time in seconds required for completion of the sequence of patterns is the

[28] Park, *NBS J. Research*, **39**, 191 (1947).

[29] Methods which are used primarily at high frequencies do not come within the scope of the present study and will not be discussed. Such methods, involving wave meters, heterodyning against an oscillator whose frequency is stable and known, the production and measurement of standing waves in a tuned line, etc., will be found in textbooks dealing with radio-frequency measurements.

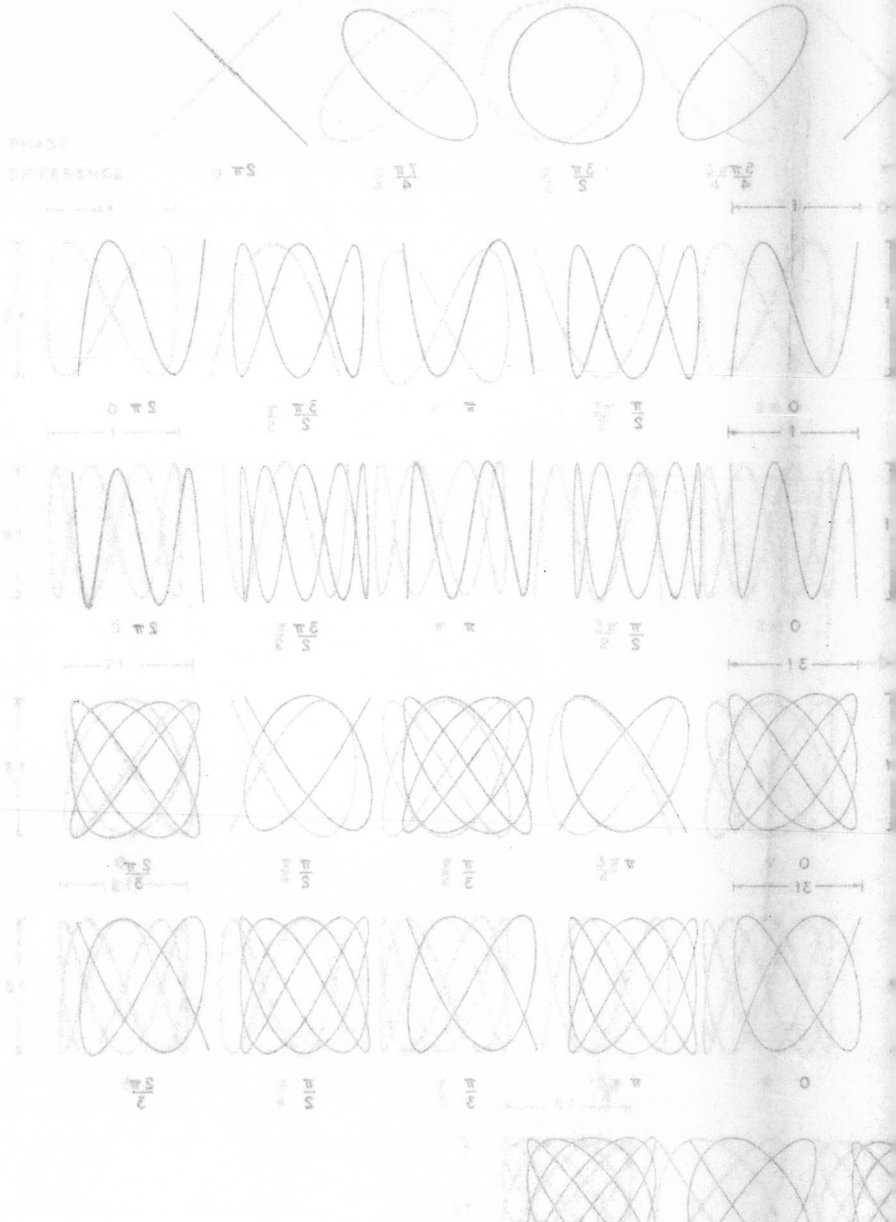

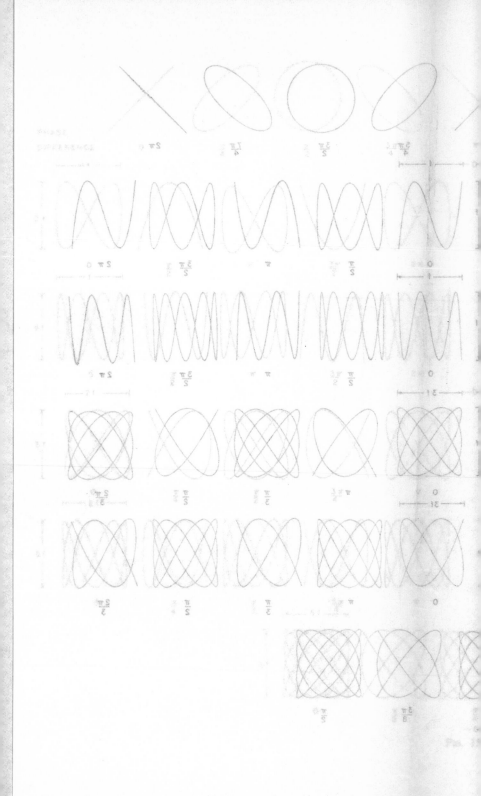

reciprocal of the difference in frequencies between the signals. Obviously the precision of this method of measuring frequency differences can be increased by measuring the total elapsed time for a number of cycles of repetition of the patterns. The accuracy with which a frequency can be determined in this way will, of course, depend on the accuracy with which the reference frequency is known. The method can be extended to the measurement of frequencies whose ratios are commensurable with the known frequency.

The pattern remains fairly simple if one frequency is a small whole-number multiple of the other, as will be seen from Fig. 15(*b*). In the cases plotted, the emf's causing the vertical deflections have frequencies 2, 3, 4, and 5 times the frequency of the emf producing the horizontal deflection. The sequence of patterns for various phase differences is shown in each case with the phase of the vertical emf progressively advanced. Progressive shift through the sequence of patterns on the oscillograph indicates a frequency different from the exact whole-number multiple. The repetition rate of the sequence shown is a measure of the time required for the higher frequency to gain 1 cycle; for example, if in the first series of patterns in Fig. 15(*b*), the ratio of frequencies being 2/1, the repetition time is 1 sec and the reference frequency is 60 cps, the higher frequency is 121 cps. It should be apparent that the time will be the same but the order of the sequence will be reversed if the higher frequency were 119 cps. It will also be seen from the figure that there is no way of distinguishing between the two cases. If the frequencies are constant, the slip frequency may be measured but it cannot be determined whether it is to be added or subtracted. If one of the frequencies can be increased (or decreased) slightly, the sign of the slip frequency can then be determined by observing whether the time required for the sequence of patterns is increased or decreased. It may be noted that the sequence involves the expansion of a simple pattern into one of more complex appearance and its subsequent collapse into another simple form which may be the reverse or the inversion of the original pattern, depending on whether the frequency ratio is odd or even. It may be further noted that the number of points of tangency of the expanded pattern to a horizontal line at the base and to a vertical line at the edge of the figure is equal to the ratio of the frequencies of the emf's producing vertical and horizontal deflection; for example, if the ratio of frequencies is 5/1, there are 5 points of tangency to a horizontal base line and 1 point of tangency to a vertical line.

If the ratio of frequencies is a simple fraction the pattern becomes somewhat more complicated, as will be seen from Fig. 15(*c*). Here again the number of points of tangency to horizontal and vertical boundary lines drawn on the expanded figure can be used to measure the ratio of frequencies; for example, when the ratio of frequencies of the vertical to the horizontal emf is 5/4, there are 5 points of tangency to a horizontal boundary line drawn on the expanded pattern and 4 points of tangency to a vertical line. The repetition rate of the sequence of patterns for frequencies slightly different from the simple fraction is no longer a measure of 2π advance in phase of the higher frequency with respect to the lower, but represents a smaller phase advance. This may be precisely stated if we consider the phase difference of one vector voltage with respect to

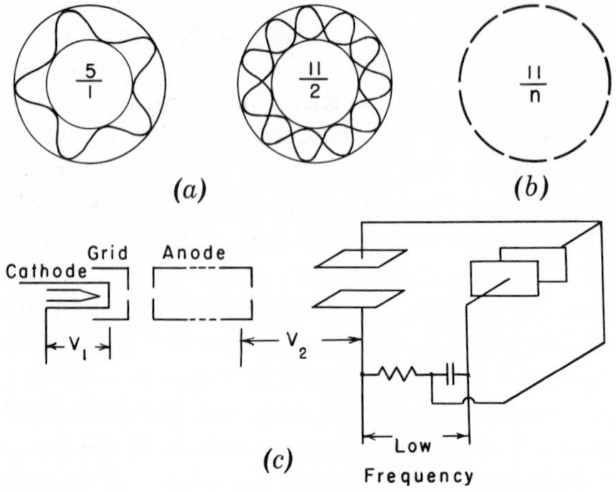

FIG. 16.

the other at a given instant. The phase differences stated in Fig. 15 represent the phase angle ϕ in the expression for the vertical emf, $E_V = E \sin (n_v\omega t + \phi)$, when the horizontal emf is given by $E_h = E \sin n_h\omega t$. Thus ϕ represents the angle between the vector voltages at a time $t = 0$. For the frequency ratio 3/2, the pattern sequence repeats after a phase shift of π—if the reference frequency were 60 cps the pattern sequence would repeat in 1 sec for a frequency of 89.5 or 90.5 cps. It will be seen from the figure that the phase shift, ϕ, of the higher frequency, represented by a complete sequence of patterns, is $2\pi/N$, where N is the denominator of the fraction stating the ratio of the higher frequency to the lower. Thus, for the ratio 5/4, the pattern repeats when ϕ is increased by $\pi/2$. If, in this case, the reference frequency were 60 cps, the pattern sequence would repeat in 1 sec for a frequency of 74.75 or 75.25 cps.

The patterns rapidly become more complicated and difficult to interpret as n_h and n_v are increased, but can be simplified by separating the forward and return traces as shown in Fig. 16.[30] If the lower frequency is impressed on both pairs of oscillograph deflecting plates through a phase splitting device, as shown in Fig. 16(*c*), it will form a circular pattern if the voltages across the resistor and capacitor are equal, and an elliptical pattern if they are unequal. The higher frequency can be superposed on this pattern as shown in Fig. 16(*a*) by impressing the high-frequency voltage between the final anode and the deflecting plates (V_2) so that it modulates the deflection sensitivity, or as alternate bright and dark spaces [Fig. 16(*b*)] by impressing it between the cathode and grid of the oscillograph (V_1) so that it modulates the intensity of the beam.

Cycle Counters

Counters provide one of the simplest methods of frequency measurement, particularly if the frequency is low. A very light relay which will operate on each cycle of a low-frequency voltage is arranged so that it actuates a counter through an escapement or linkage mechanism. A *constant* frequency within the operating range of the relay can be measured by counting the total number of cycles during a measured time interval. Such mechanical cycle counters are limited in range by the inertia of the moving system and are not generally satisfactory at frequencies as high even as 60 cps. At frequencies above the range of mechanical counters, electronic counter circuits can be used. A number of such counter circuits have been described in the literature,[31] and some are commercially available. In one scheme of operation a number of Thyratron tubes are arranged in a ring circuit so that when one Thyratron is fired by an impulse applied to its grid the resulting flow of current primes the succeeding tube and extinguishes the preceding one. The firing of one particular tube in the ring may be made to actuate a mechanical counter relay in addition to the regular sequence of operations, so that in effect the range of the mechanical counter is multiplied by the number of elements in the ring. For more rapid counts, circuits have been devised which eliminate the mechanical counter entirely.[32] It should be emphasized that such methods of frequency measurement are applicable only if the frequency is constant during the measured time interval, or if only an average value of frequency is required.

[30] Rasmussen, *Trans. AIEE*, **45**, 1256 (1926).

[31] For example, two such circuits, one a binary and the other a ring type, are described by Reich, *Theory and Applications of Electron Tubes*, p. 460, McGraw-Hill, 1939.

[32] For example, Manley and Bulkley, *Electronics*, **23**, 84 (1950), describe a counter using neon tubes and germanium diodes, capable of registering up to 30,000 counts per minute.

See also Regener, *Rev. Sci. Inst.*, **17**, 185 (1945).

Frequency Bridges

Any bridge whose balance equations are a function of frequency can, in theory, be used to measure frequencies if the impedance elements of the bridge arms are known. One of the bridges which is most commonly employed for this purpose is the Wien bridge,[33] shown schematically in Fig. 17. The balance conditions which must be met simultaneously can be shown to be

$$\omega = \frac{1}{\sqrt{R_3 R_4 C_3 C_4}}, \quad \text{and} \quad \frac{R_1}{R_2} = \frac{R_3}{R_4} + \frac{C_3}{C_4}$$

By proportioning the bridge so that $R_3 = R_4$ and $C_3 = C_4$, we have $f = 1/2\pi R_4 C_4$. From the second balance equation it will be seen that

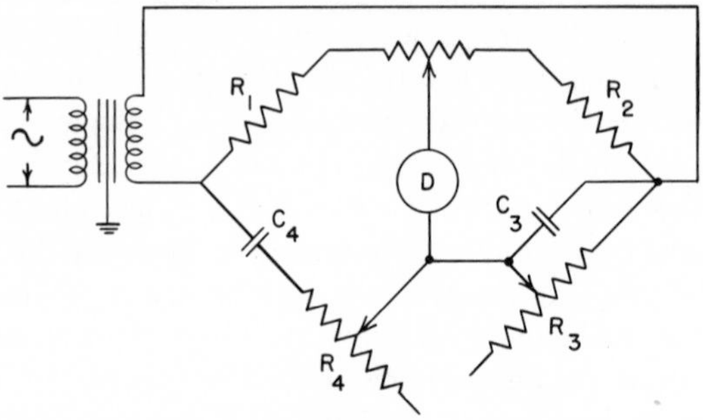

FIG. 17.

under these conditions we must also have $R_1/R_2 = 2$. In practice R_3 and R_4 may be identical slide-wire resistors mounted on a single shaft so that they may remain continuously equal. The range of these resistors may be such that a 10/1 range of frequencies may be covered, and decimal multiples of this base range may be obtained by appropriate changes in C_3 and C_4.[34] Since it is very difficult to construct the slide-wire resistors so that they are precisely equal for all slider positions, a low-resistance slide wire (1 to 2% of R_2) is inserted between R_1 and R_2 to correct for slight inequalities in R_3 and R_4, so that a sharper balance point may be obtained. This has very little effect on the frequency calibration of the bridge. Any harmonics present in the input voltage will appear in the detector arm at balance, since the bridge is in balance only for one particular frequency. Even small harmonics, therefore, will become

[33] See p. 718, Chapter 15.

[34] General Radio's Type 1141–A frequency meter is a bridge of this type and covers the range 20 to 20,000 cps with three pairs of capacitors and a single pair of slide-wire resistors.

quite prominent in the output of the detector branch as balance is approached. At audio-frequencies where headphones can be used, particularly in the range where the ear is most sensitive, it is usually possible to balance the fundamental in the presence of harmonics. However, when an indicating instrument is used as a detector an appropriate filter is needed ahead of it to eliminate spurious indications from harmonics of the frequency being measured.[35] The Wien bridge has the advantage over those described below that its circuit is made up entirely of resistors and capacitors, so that there is no inductive coupling with other sources of emf.

The resonance bridge, shown in Fig. 18, is also used for frequency measurements. Since three of the arms are pure resistances, there can

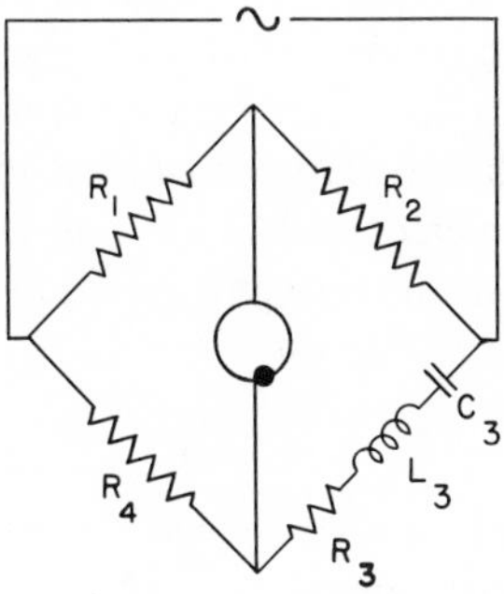

FIG. 18.

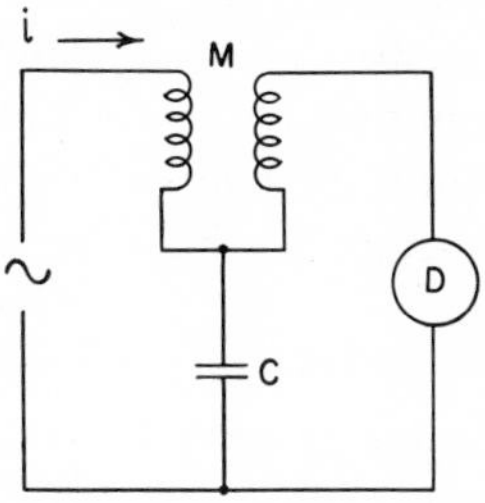

FIG. 19.

be no balance unless the fourth arm is also a pure resistance; i.e. the balance conditions are

$$\frac{R_1}{R_2} = \frac{R_4}{R_3}, \quad \text{and} \quad \omega L = \frac{1}{\omega C}$$

whence

$$= \frac{1}{2\pi\sqrt{LC}}$$

R_3, of course, includes the resistance associated with the inductor and the equivalent resistance corresponding to any loss in the capacitor.

Another type of circuit, which makes use of mutual inductance and capacitance, is Campbell's[36] frequency bridge, shown in Fig. 19. At balance, with no current in the detector, the voltage ωMi induced in the

[35] This difficulty is, of course, common to all frequency bridges.

[36] See Hague, *A-C Bridge Methods*, p. 471, Pitman, 1946; also see Hague, pp. 510–516, for a general discussion and classification of frequency bridges.

secondary of the mutual inductor must balance the voltage drop $i/\omega C$ in the capacitor. Hence at balance

$$\omega M i = \frac{i}{\omega C}, \quad \text{or} \quad \omega^2 = \frac{1}{MC}$$

whence

$$f = \frac{1}{2\pi\sqrt{MC}}$$

These voltages will be in phase and will result in a *null* balance only if both the capacitance and the mutual inductance are pure,[37] so that the voltage of each is precisely 90° out of phase with the current i. This bridge is most useful at frequencies above 1 kc since for low frequencies the product MC becomes inconveniently large. In addition to the usual balance requirement, that the harmonic content of the supply voltage be small, it has already been observed that for exact balance it is necessary that the capacitor have very low losses and that the mutual inductor be free from impurities. This requires a mica capacitor of good quality and, in order to limit the effect of impurity in the inductor, restricts the upper limit of frequency at which the bridge may be used.[38]

Frequency Meters

Such instruments may be classified into two general types: reed or vibration instruments, and deflection instruments.

Vibrating-Reed Type. Reed-type frequency meters depend for their indication on the mechanical resonance of thin, flat steel reeds. If such a reed is excited at its resonant frequency by an electromagnet, it will vibrate with an amplitude which increases until the rate at which it dissipates energy in molecular and air friction is equal to the rate at which it receives energy from the electromagnet. Since the reeds in a frequency meter are arranged to be viewed end on, they have a portion bent over at the free end to serve as a flag or target, as shown in Fig. 20(a). The targets are painted white to afford maximum contrast against their black background. As the excitation frequency departs from the resonant frequency the amplitude of the vibration decreases rapidly (i.e. the tuning is sharp and the damping is small), becoming negligible for a frequency perhaps 1 to 2% away from resonance. Thus, in a reed frequency meter having

[37] See p. 671, Chapter 15.

[38] For modifications to adapt this bridge to the measurement of high frequencies see Butterworth, *Proc. Phys. Soc.*, **33**, 337 (1921).

For modifications adapting the bridge to low-frequency measurements, see Chiba, *J. IEE* (*Japan*), No. 405, p. 294 (1922).

See also Hague, *op. cit.*, pp. 470 and 557.

a series of reeds tuned $\frac{1}{2}$ cycle apart, some vibration of the 59.5- and 60.5-cycle reeds may be noticed when the 60-cycle reed is vibrating at its maximum amplitude, but very little vibration will be seen on the 59- and 61-cycle reeds [Fig. 20(*b*)]. For a frequency exactly midway between that of two reeds, both would vibrate at amplitudes which are equal, but considerably less than the maximum amplitude at resonance [Fig. 20(*c*)]. The entire set of reeds may be attached to a common armature which is vibrated by the electromagnet energized by the current whose frequency is to be determined. Only the reed whose resonance frequency is equal to the armature frequency will be set into appreciable oscillatory motion.

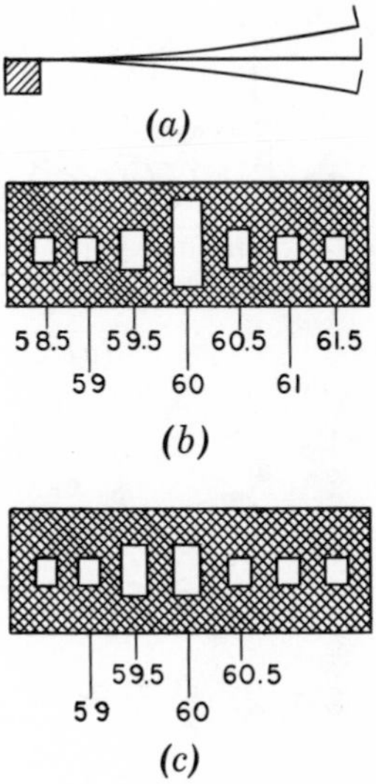

FIG. 20.

The frequency range of a set of reeds may be doubled in a simple manner. In the presence of an alternating flux alone, the reeds receive two impulses per cycle and the reed whose natural frequency is twice that of the current in the electromagnet will respond. If, however, the electromagnet is polarized by a direct flux superposed on the alternating flux and equal to it in magnitude, the fields will cancel during one half-cycle and reinforce during the opposite half-cycle, so that the reeds will receive only one impulse per cycle. A reed will therefore indicate the frequency of the exciting current if the electromagnet is polarized, and half the frequency of the exciting current if unpolarized. In some frequency meters this polarization is accomplished by using a d-c winding on the electromagnet in addition to the a-c winding. The polarization can also be accomplished by a permanent magnet, but care must be taken to ensure that it is not demagnetized by the a-c field. With polarization available, a bank of reeds can be used for a low-frequency range with the a-c field acting alone, and for a high-frequency range (double the other) with both fields acting. An advantage of the reed type of frequency meter is that the indication is virtually independent of the wave form of the applied voltage and of the magnitude of the voltage, except that the voltage must be high enough to provide sufficient amplitude in the reed vibrations for reliable readings. Such an instrument cannot, however, be read much closer than half the frequency difference between adjacent reeds, and is also limited by the accuracy with which the reeds can be tuned to a given frequency.

Deflection Type. Deflecting frequency meters are of two kinds—those depending on electrical resonance, and those depending on the frequency variation of current distribution between an inductive circuit and a parallel resistive circuit. The *General Electric* frequency meter is of the resonant type. The essential features of the instrument are shown in Fig. 21(*a*). The field coils, *A* and *B*, are alike and are connected so that

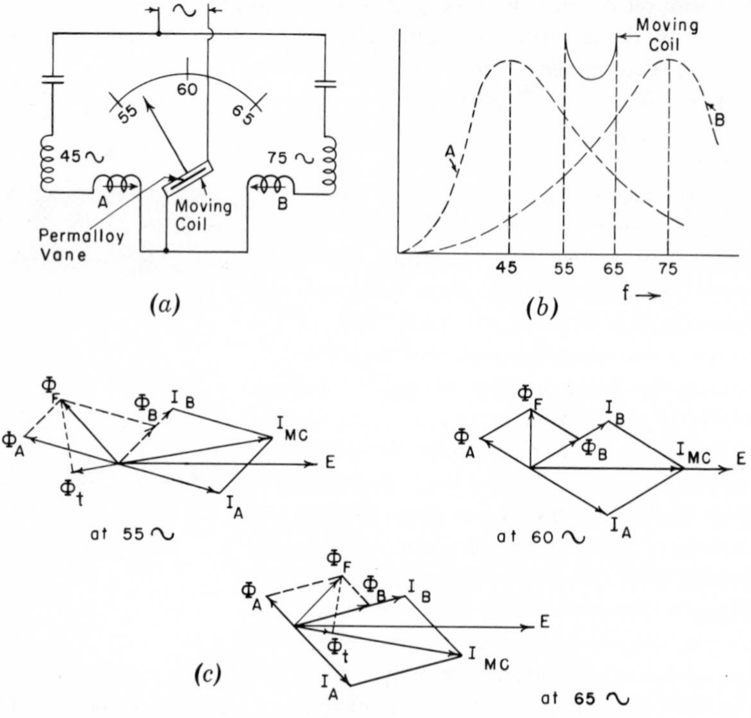

FIG. 21.

their fields are opposed. Coil *A* is supplied from an *L-C* circuit which is tuned to series resonance at a frequency below the instrument range, while coil *B* is in a circuit that resonates at a frequency above the instrument range. The moving coil is connected to the junction of the field-coil circuits and carries the current of both. Connections to the moving coil are made through spiral conductors whose contribution to the torque is negligible. The field-coil and moving-coil currents are shown graphically in Fig. 21(*b*) as functions of frequency. It may be noted that in the operating range the current in field coil *A* lags the applied voltage and decreases rapidly with increasing frequency, whereas that in *B* leads the applied voltage and increases rapidly. Deflecting torque is produced by the reaction of the field of the moving coil with the in-phase component of the resultant field from coils A and B. These flux vectors are shown in Fig. 21(c) for the low, middle, and high points of the range. It will be noted that there is no deflecting torque at the midpoint (60 cycles) since the flux vectors are in quadrature, while the directions of the flux vectors are such as to produce a downscale torque at frequencies below 60 cycles and an upscale torque at frequencies above 60. The counter-torque required to establish a definite equilibrium position for the moving system at any frequency is supplied by a Permalloy vane in the plane of the moving coil rigidly attached to its shaft. This vane produces a torque, oppositely directed to the deflecting torque, as a result of its tendency to align itself in the physical direction of the field-coil flux regardless of the time-phase relations. As long as the Permalloy vane is in a weak magnetic field, so that its flux density is approximately proportional to the field, the deflection is a function of the ratio and phase difference of the field-coil currents but is independent of their magnitudes. A change from rated voltage (115 volts) of as much as $\pm$ 20 volts will result in a change in deflection of less than 0.3% of midscale value. By suitable design modifications such instruments can be made to cover a very narrow range (59 to 61 cycles) or a wide range (20 to 90 cycles).

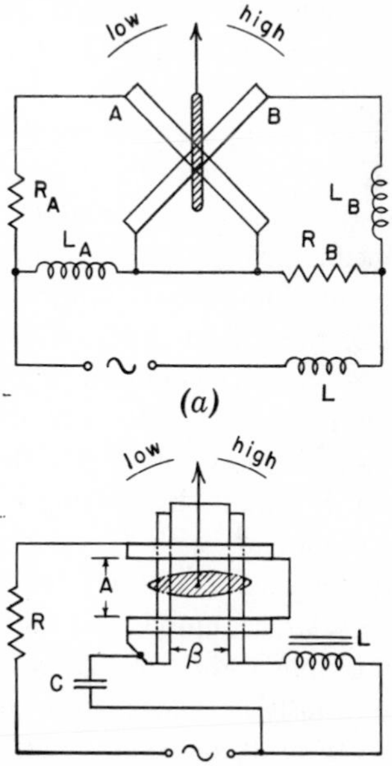

(a)

(b)

FIG. 22.

One type of *Weston* frequency meter makes use of the fields of two perpendicular coils connected as shown in Fig. 22(a). The branch circuit which includes coil A has a resistor R_A in series, while coil B has an inductive reactance L_B in series. Circuit A is in parallel with an inductance L_A, while B is in parallel with a resistance R_B. Hence when the frequency is increased the current through coil A increases whereas that through B decreases. The moving element, a pivoted soft-iron needle, tends to align itself along the resultant magnetic field of the coils A and B and therefore turns more nearly parallel with the axis of coil A at high frequencies, and more nearly parallel with the axis of coil B at low frequencies. The series inductance L acts to suppress higher harmonics in the current wave form of the instrument and therefore tends to minimize wave-form errors in its indication. This instrument also can be designed to cover a broad or a narrow range of frequencies, depending on its circuit parameters. Another type of *Weston* frequency-meter circuit is shown in Fig. 22(*b*).

Frequency Standards

All frequency standards are derived from the standard of time (the second) which is in turn derived from the motion of the earth. The standard second is the 1/86,400 part of a *mean solar day*, which is the average interval between passages of the sun through a given meridian. The length of a solar day varies somewhat through the year, but its average taken over a year's time is very nearly constant. Actually the sidereal day derived from observations by the U.S. Naval Observatory of the passage of fixed stars through the vertical meridian is used to check and regulate the standard of time. It is interesting to note that any mechanically driven standard of time available to us depends on the oscillation or rotation of some device (pendulum, tuning fork, piezoelectric crystal, etc.) which is used to maintain a *constant* frequency. The primary standard of frequency consists of one of a group of 100-kc quartz-crystal oscillators maintained at the National Bureau of Standards under conditions of constant temperature and pressure, and is checked for constancy by causing it to drive a clock whose rate is determined by comparison with Naval Observatory time. Thus it is checked almost directly against "star" time.

A large number of frequencies are obtained from this crystal through multiplier and divider circuits. Standard frequencies, which are continuously broadcast from the National Bureau of Standards radio station (WWV) at Beltsville, Maryland, a suburb of Washington, D.C.,[39] and monitored against the primary standard, include 2.5, 5, 10, 15, 25 megacycles, each modulated at 440 cycles (A above middle C on the international musical scale) and 600 cycles. These two audio-frequencies are given alternately, starting with 600 cycles on the hour for 4 min, interrupted for 1 min, followed by 440 cycles for 4 min, and interrupted for 1 min. Each 10-min period during the hour is the same. In addition there is a pulse 0.005 sec in duration and consisting of 5 cycles of 1-kc frequency, on each carrier frequency to mark second intervals. This pulse is omitted at the beginning of the last second of each minute. The second signals are accurate to 1 μsec, and the standard frequencies (including the audio-frequencies) are accurate as transmitted to 1 part in 50 million. Momentary errors in the signals as received may amount to

[39] A somewhat more limited schedule of standard frequencies and time signals is broadcast from the Bureau's auxiliary station (WWVH) on the island of Maui, Territory of Hawaii.

1 part in a million as a result of motions of the reflecting layers of the ionosphere. Time announcements are broadcast during the minute intervals when the signal is not modulated by one of the audio-frequencies. These signals from the station in Beltsville or the one in Maui can usually be received anywhere in the world.

Tuning forks may be used as laboratory frequency standards at power and audio-frequencies. Such forks may be driven by a low-voltage storage battery or by feedback from a vacuum-tube amplifier. They are somewhat sensitive to temperature, to barometric pressure, and to the driving voltage. A precision vacuum-tube driven fork,[40] operating at a constant, controlled temperature, may have a frequency which is stable to 10 parts in 10^6 and, when corrected for barometric pressure, to 1 part in 10^6. A battery-driven fork, operating without temperature control, may be expected to have a temperature coefficient of less than $-0.015\%/°C$, and a voltage coefficient of less than 0.01%/volt. It should provide a frequency which may be known to better than 0.1% under any specified laboratory conditions. The output of such a fork must, of course, be filtered if its harmonic content is to be kept low.

The frequency of 60-*cycle power* in most localities affords a convenient reference point. However, it must be realized that, even in locations where power is supplied from a grid that includes many large generating stations operating over an area of hundreds of square miles, the frequency is not continuously kept precisely at 60 cps. It may depart from this frequency by 0.1 or 0.2 cps quite frequently, and occasionally by as much as a half-cycle per second. Also, when such a large departure occurs, the frequency can be corrected only slowly because of the very large system inertia. (This may require a half hour or more.) The average frequency over an extended time interval will be very close to 60 cycles, and synchronous clocks will usually keep time within a few seconds (except in the event of power failure), but the frequency cannot be reliably employed as a reference standard to much better than 1%, and therefore cannot be used to operate synchronous clocks for timing short intervals to better than 1%.

Oscillators

Adjustable-frequency vacuum-tube oscillators are of great convenience in frequency measurements. The three general types are: (1) *resonant circuit*, in which the frequency of oscillation is maintained by a tuned circuit of inductive and capacitive elements; (2) *beat frequency*, in which the output frequency is the difference between the frequencies of two oscillators, one of fixed and the other of adjustable frequency; (3)

[40] General Radio's Type 816 fork.

resistance-capacitance, in which the frequency of oscillation is controlled through a resistance-capacitance filter in a circuit which is highly degenerative except at the pass frequency of the filter.

The resonant-circuit type of oscillator is a conventional oscillator which is stabilized by a feedback resistance connected between the plate and the tuned circuit. Such oscillators are characterized by good wave shapes and substantial independence of tube voltages. However, at audio-frequencies this circuit is not generally used since the array of capacitors and inductors needed for continuous tuning over a wide range of frequencies is bulky and expensive.

In the beat-frequency oscillator the output of two r-f oscillators is fed to a mixer circuit and the resulting difference frequency is amplified. The chief value of this type of oscillator arises from the fact that a relatively small change in the frequency of the adjustable oscillator (obtainable through a variable capacitor) may be used to vary the difference frequency from a few cycles per second through the entire audio-frequency range. Hence a wide band of frequencies can be covered by a single control. Performance is affected by the stability of the individual oscillators, and, since the inductors and capacitors of the tuned circuits will change in value with temperature variation, temperature differences between the oscillators must be avoided. The oscillators must be matched as closely as possible in both electrical and thermal characteristics, and other heat-producing elements in the circuit must be so arranged that their effects on the oscillators are small. Because of the temperature dependence of the oscillator frequency, adjustment is required, as the oscillator is used, to bring the scale to a correct reading. This is usually accomplished by setting the scale to a reference frequency and adjusting the frequency of the "fixed-frequency" oscillator with a small variable capacitor until the output frequency of the oscillator is correct. A fixed-frequency, vibrating reed may be used to establish the reference frequency, or, in some cases, the frequency dial may be set to zero and the oscillator adjusted to zero beat frequency. At very small frequency differences the two oscillators will tend to synchronize and lock together, unless they are well shielded and isolated. Wave form in the output is largely determined by distortion in the mixer circuit. For low distortion, the fixed-frequency oscillator should be free from harmonics and its output voltage considerably smaller than that of the variable-frequency oscillator.

The "*R-C* filter controlled" oscillator utilizes the frequency sensitivity of a Wien bridge. This may be seen from the circuit diagram of Fig. 23. In this circuit the frequency is determined by the frequency-sensitive network $R_1C_1R_2C_2$ with $R_1C_1 = R_2C_2$. This circuit is regenerative; the maximum ratio of input to output voltage (E_i/E_0) occurs at a frequency

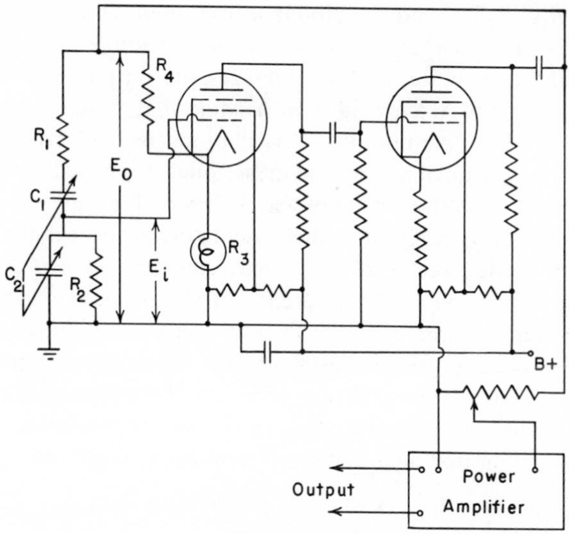
R4
R1
E0
C1
C2
R2
Ei
R3
B+
Output
Power
Amplifier

FIG. 23.

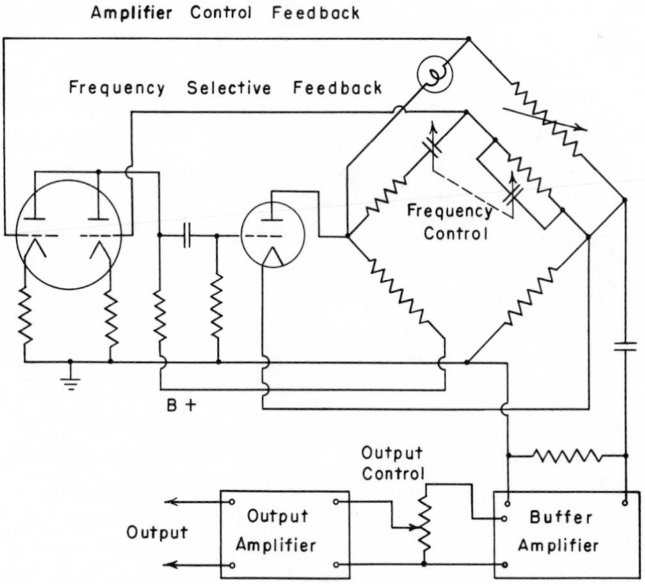
Amplifier Control Feedback
Frequency Selective Feedback
Frequency
Control
B +
Output
Control
Output
Output
Amplifier
Buffer
Amplifier

FIG. 24.

$f = 1/2\pi\sqrt{R_1C_1R_2C_2}$; and the circuit will oscillate at this frequency. A lamp resistor R_3 provides additional degeneration in case the output voltage tends to increase, and so stabilizes the output.[41] Another *R-C* oscillator, using the Wien bridge in a somewhat different manner,[42] is shown in Fig. 24. Amplitude of oscillations is held constant by the feedback from the auxiliary bridge arms, one of which contains a non-linear resistance. A buffer amplifier is inserted ahead of the output control to minimize reaction. Such oscillators have a constant output voltage over a wide range of frequencies and are quite stable after an initial warm-up period. The frequency of the output voltage is not as sensitive to temperature as is the case in the beat-frequency oscillator. Another advantage of this arrangement over the beat-frequency oscillator is that it does not require that the scale zero be adjusted each time the oscillator is used. For accurate frequency measurements the scale must, of course, be calibrated against known frequency standards.

[41] Terman *et al.*, *Proc. IRE*, **10,** 649 (1939). This is the circuit in a series of audio-frequency oscillators made by Hewlett-Packard.

[42] This is the circuit in General Radio's *R–C* oscillators.

CHAPTER 15

ALTERNATING-CURRENT BRIDGES

Definition

A bridge circuit is a network which is so arranged that, when an emf is present in one branch, the response of a suitable detecting device in another branch may be made zero by a suitable adjustment of the electrical constants of still other branches; and which is characterized by the fact that, if the emf and the detecting device are interchanged, after completing the adjustment, the response of the detecting device is still zero.[1] This definition emphasizes the fact that the operation of a bridge implies the adjustment of one or more of the impedance elements making up the branches of the bridge circuit in order that the potential difference across a particular branch (containing the detector) may be brought to zero, and further points out the fact that in any balanced bridge the source of emf and the detector may be interchanged without affecting the balance relations. Both these features which distinguish a bridge circuit from other networks should be kept in mind in the discussion which follows.

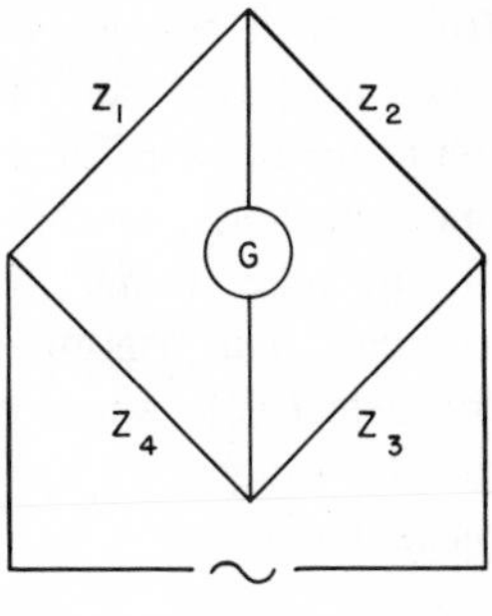

FIG. 1.

By far the commonest type of bridge circuit is the four-arm impedance bridge, which is a generalization of the Wheatstone bridge already discussed in connection with resistance measurements and shown in Fig. 1. The relation which must exist at balance between the impedances is $Z_1Z_3 = Z_2Z_4$. The individual branches may themselves be series or parallel combinations, and may include resistance, inductance, and capacitance elements, separately or in combination. Bridges are generally used for the purpose of determining the characteristics of an impedance

[1] This is one of a group of definitions of electrical terms written under the sponsorship of the American Institute of Electrical Engineers, ASA C42—1941, paragraph 05.45.090.

in one branch in terms of the known characteristics of other impedances in the same branch or other branches of the circuit or for comparing the characteristics of similar impedances in terms of the others. Thus, if one branch consists of an unknown impedance while the impedances of the other branches are known, the unknown may be determined. Likewise, if an unknown and a similar known impedance are substituted in turn in one branch, the unknown can be determined in terms of the substituted standard and the known changes in the balance condition required by the substitution. Another important use for certain types of bridges is the determination of the frequency of the source of emf by the use of impedances of known characteristics in each of the branches.

There are other useful bridge networks which are more complicated than the four-arm Wheatstone bridge, and, indeed, in many cases where the four-arm network is used one must consider the effect of capacitive or inductive coupling which may be either deliberately introduced or unavoidable between various branches. Both the simple four-arm impedance bridge and certain other useful bridge networks of greater complexity will be discussed below. We will first consider the elements from which bridges are constructed. It will be apparent from the discussion above that the individual branches of the bridge network are made up of resistance, capacitance, self-inductance, and mutual inductance elements, and that the usefulness of a particular bridge depends, among other things, on the accuracy with which individual elements are known. The usefulness of a bridge also depends on the sensitivity of the detector to small changes of adjustment near the balance point and on the range of impedances which may be conveniently employed or measured in it.

BRIDGE COMPONENTS

Before discussing individual bridge arrangements we will consider the characteristics of self- and mutual inductors and of capacitors which are used in bridges. The reader should also refer to the discussion in a previous chapter on the resistance elements which are employed in bridges. Discussion of detectors and of suitable sources of emf will be deferred to a later section.

Self-inductors

Two kinds of inductors, fixed-value and adjustable, are utilized in bridge measurements.

Fixed-Value Inductors. These are, in some instances, so constructed that their inductance can be accurately computed from measured dimensions. Such inductors are made and used by the national laboratories, such as the National Bureau of Standards, in establishing the values of electrical units, and are known as primary or absolute standards of inductance. They are not, however, practical for general measurements, not only because of the care and expense involved in their construction and in the determination of their inductance, but also because they make very inefficient use of the wire with which they are wound; i.e. the time constant, L/R, is relatively low. Computable standards are generally single-layer solenoids. Marble, electrical porcelain, low-expansion glass or fused quartz, accurately ground to cylindrical shape, is employed as a winding form, and in the best absolute inductors a screw thread is lapped into the face of the finished cylinder so that the pitch of the winding can be held to a constant value. Details concerning the construction, mechanical measurement, and computation of such a standard are not appropriate here, and the reader should refer to papers on absolute measurements, where detailed discussions will be found.[2]

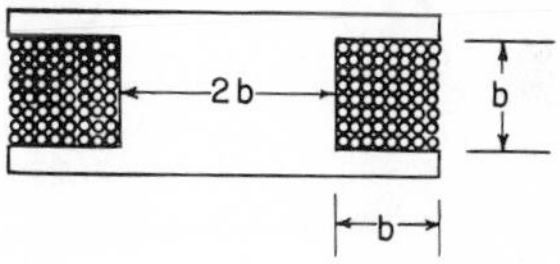

FIG. 2.

LABORATORY INDUCTORS. The type of fixed-value inductor which is generally used in laboratory work is one in which, for a given size and length of wire, the inductance is maximum; i.e. the time constant is as large as possible. This requirement being set up, it has been shown that if the coil is wound in a rectangular groove on a cylindrical coil form, as shown in Fig. 2, the inductance is maximum for a given length and size of wire if the winding section is square and if the inside diameter of the coil is twice the side of the square section.[3] In this case the inductance can be computed with sufficient accuracy for design purposes from the formula

$$L = 24.5bn^2 \times 10^{-9} = \frac{24.5b^5}{d^4} \times 10^{-9} \text{ henry}$$

where b is the side of the square, d is the wire diameter over the insulation (both in centimeters), and n is the number of turns in the winding. The form on which the coil is wound should, of course, be free from magnetic impurities and should be dimensionally stable. Marble has been frequently used for this purpose; serpentine was employed in early work but has been shown to be slightly magnetic and should be avoided; electrical porcelain has been used in some cases and is particularly well adapted for coil forms provided a variety is chosen whose coefficient of

[2] See Curtis, *Electrical Measurements*, McGraw-Hill, 1937; Curtis, Moon, and Sparks, *NBS J. Research*, **21**, 371 (1938).

[3] H. B. Brooks, *NBS J. Research*, **7**, 293 (1931).

linear expansion matches that of the copper winding. Bakelite and hard rubber have been used, but their coefficients of expansion are higher than that of copper and they are both liable to plastic deformation under pressure, particularly at an elevated temperature. For ordinary laboratory work, coil forms of mahogany, thoroughly dried and impregnated with paraffin, have much to recommend them. The construction is inexpensive, and, if the wood is thoroughly impregnated, it is quite stable. However, its coefficient of expansion varies from a value about double that of copper in a direction across the grain to a value about 0.1 of this amount in the direction of the grain, so that a considerable temperature coefficient of inductance may be expected.

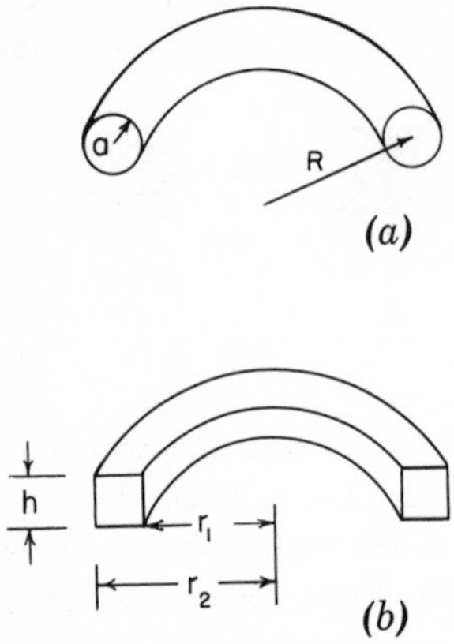

FIG. 3.

Another form of winding which is sometimes used as a fixed-value inductor is the toroidal coil, i.e. a single-layer winding on a ring-shaped form. This has two advantages over the flat cylindrical coil: its external field is very small, and it is less affected by external fields from other sources. (If the winding is uniformly distributed on the torus its coupling with a uniform external field is effectively that of a single turn having the mean radius of the torus.) However, such a coil is tedious and difficult to wind. Also its inductance and time constant will be much less than those of a cylindrical coil using the same wire and having the dimensions of a Brooks coil. For a torus of round section as shown in Fig. 3(*a*), having a uniform, closely spaced single-layer winding, the inductance is approximately given by the formula

$$L = 0.01257n^2(R - \sqrt{R^2 - a^2}\,) \times 10^{-6} \text{ henry}$$

and for a toroidal winding whose turns are rectangular, as shown in Fig. 3(*b*), the inductance is approximately[4]

$$L = 0.002n^2h \log_\varepsilon \frac{r_2}{r_1}$$

REQUIREMENTS. There are certain general conditions which should be met by an inductor, regardless of its shape, if it is to serve as a reference standard: (1) its value should be definite and permanent; (2) its resistance should be low; i.e. its time constant should be large; (3) its temperature

[4] For precise formulas, corrected for the space between turns, the reader is referred to p. 170 of Grover's *Inductance Calculations*, Van Nostrand, 1946.

coefficient of inductance should be small; (4) its value of inductance should be independent of current; (5) its change of inductance with frequency should be small. In addition, for many applications it is desirable that it be as nearly astatic as possible with respect to external fields. The permanence of an inductor depends on stability of the winding form, the wire, and its insulation. The form is generally put under considerable stress in winding, and the wire is under tension. If this stress results in plastic flow in the form, or if the wire elongates under tension and relieves the stress to some extent, or if the insulation on the wire yields, dimensional changes will occur in the coil and in the relative position of the turns with respect to one another, so that the value of the inductance will change. A similar effect occurs if the form is made of a material which suffers a permanent dimensional change when carried through a temperature cycle. In many cases there is also a small but definite change of inductance with humidity, resulting from dimensional changes in the structure. This may amount to a few tenths of a per cent. Indefiniteness in the value of inductance may result from improperly placing the leads connecting the inductor to other parts of the circuit. Most laboratory inductors are provided with binding posts to which leads may be attached, and if these leads are not always in the same position the change in coupling results in a change in the total inductance. The binding posts should be close together and should be located so that there will be no appreciable mutual inductance between the coil and the leads. In the case of the cylindrical coil (the usual form) the binding posts should be located close to the outer edge of the winding form, preferably on the rim itself. The leads should be brought away as a twisted pair or coaxially or, if neither of these arrangements is possible, should be kept close together so that the loop which they form will have as small an area as feasible.

The desirable property of low resistance and high time constant may be best met by using cylindrical coils of square winding cross section having the dimensional relations stated by Brooks. For this construction the time constant may be expected to range between 1 and 10 msec. Cases will, of course, arise in which this desideratum must be sacrificed to obtain astaticism or for some other reason. The temperature coefficient of inductance of a coil results from changes in the dimensions with changing temperature. The linear coefficients of the form and the insulation seldom match that of the wire, so that the tension of the winding will be affected by changes in temperature. Thus the temperature coefficient of inductance depends not only on the linear coefficients of the wire, insulation, and winding form but also on the compressibility of the form and the insulation and on the tension in the winding. It is therefore difficult to predict a temperature coefficient of inductance. It may be either positive or negative, and in the usual construction may be expected to be of the order of 10 parts per million/°C. In order that the inductance be independent of current it is necessary that no magnetic materials be used in the coil construction.

The effective inductance and resistance of the coil are functions of frequency as a result of (1) eddy currents, (2) distributed capacitance between coil turns, and (3) imperfect insulation between turns. Eddy currents may be reduced by using stranded conductor with the strands insulated from each other. If the coil is to be employed at high frequencies the separate strands must be fine in order that skin effect be minimized. The binding posts for attaching leads should be placed in the weakest part of the field and should be small and of a high-resistance material to reduce eddy-current effects. Also the winding form and its supports should be assembled without metal, or if screws must be used they should be small, non-magnetic, and made of high-resistance material.

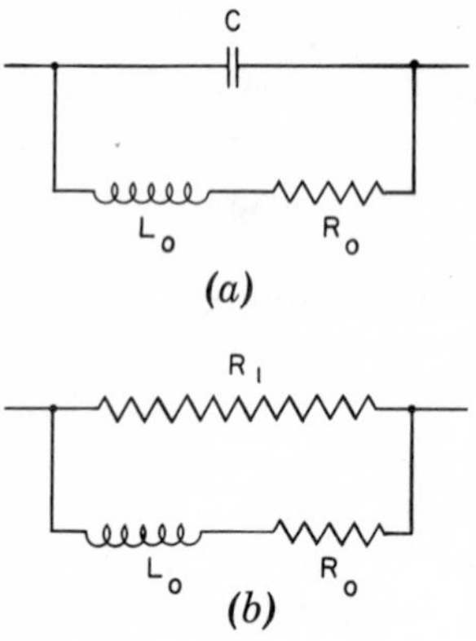

FIG. 4.

EQUIVALENT CIRCUITS. The capacitance between turns and layers of the coil can be approximately represented by a capacitor connected across the terminals of the coil as shown in Fig. 4(*a*). The impedance of this parallel combination can be developed as follows:

$$\frac{1}{Z} = \frac{1}{R_0 + j\omega L_0} + j\omega C$$

$$Z = \frac{R_0 + j\omega L_0}{1 - \omega^2 L_0 C + j\omega R_0 C} = \frac{R_0 + j\omega[L_0(1 - \omega^2 L_0 C) - R_0{}^2 C]}{(1 - \omega^2 L_0 C)^2 + \omega^2 R_0{}^2 C^2}$$

Since in any practical case C will be very small we may write the equivalent resistance as

$$R_{\text{eq}} = R_0(1 + 2\omega^2 L_0 C)$$

and the equivalent inductance as

$$L_{\text{eq}} = L_0(1 + \omega^2 L_0 C)$$

In practice C may be calculated from values of equivalent inductance L_{eq} measured at two frequencies. The effect of distributed capacitance is seen to be proportional to the square of the frequency. Actually for small inductances it will usually be negligible except at high frequencies, but for a large inductor (say of the order of a henry) the change in effective inductance may amount to several per cent within the audio-frequency range. The impedance of an inductor having distributed capacitance can be expressed in another form which may be more convenient. If we define $Q = \omega L_0/R_0$ and $\omega_0 = 1/\sqrt{L_0C}$, the impedance of the parallel combination may be written as

$$Z = \frac{R_0 + j\omega L_0\left[1 - \left(\frac{\omega}{\omega_0}\right)^2\left(1 + \frac{1}{Q^2}\right)\right]}{1 - 2\left(\frac{\omega}{\omega_0}\right)^2 + \left(\frac{\omega}{\omega_0}\right)^4\left(1 + \frac{1}{Q^2}\right)}$$

If ω_0 (2π times the natural frequency of the coil) is known, and if Q is known for the operating frequency, the equivalent inductance and resistance may be computed from the above expression. For the case where Q is large, we have as approximations,

$$R_{eq} \approx R_0\left[1 + 2\left(\frac{\omega}{\omega_0}\right)^2\right], \quad \text{and} \quad L_{eq} \approx L_0\left[1 + \left(\frac{\omega}{\omega_0}\right)^2\right]$$

It will be seen that these approximations are identical with those previously derived. The insulation resistance of an inductor may be represented as a parallel resistance connected across its terminals as shown in Fig. 4(*b*). The impedance of this combination may be written as

$$Z = \frac{R_1(R_0 + j\omega L_0)}{R_1 + R_0 + j\omega L_0} = \frac{R_1[R_0(R_1 + R_0) + \omega^2 L^2{}_0 + j\omega L_0 R_1]}{(R_1 + R_0)^2 + \omega^2 L_0{}^2}$$

Then the effective resistance is

$$R_{eq} = R_1\frac{R_0(R_1 + R_0) + \omega^2 L_0{}^2}{(R_1 + R_0)^2 + \omega^2 L_0{}^2}$$

and the effective inductance is

$$L_{eq} = L_0\frac{R_1{}^2}{(R_1 + R_0)^2 + \omega^2 L_0{}^2} = L_0\frac{1}{\left(1 + \frac{R_0}{R_1}\right)^2 + \frac{\omega^2 L_0{}^2}{R_1{}^2}}$$

It must be realized that the term R_1 is the a-c resistance of the insulation, which may itself be a function of frequency and is not necessarily related in a simple way to the d-c insulation resistance. If now R_1 is very large compared to R_0, we have

$$L_{eq} \approx L_0\frac{1}{1 + \frac{\omega^2 L_0{}^2}{R_1{}^2}} \approx L_0\left(1 - \frac{\omega^2 L_0{}^2}{R_1{}^2}\right)$$

and

$$R_{eq} \approx R_0\left(1 + \frac{\omega^2 L_0{}^2}{R_0 R_1}\right)$$

Thus the effective inductance is decreased and the effective resistance increased by faulty insulation. Hence it is important that the insulation of the winding, and of the terminal block on which the binding posts are mounted, be of good quality.

Adjustable Inductors. In applications where inductance must be varied or be set to a precise value, the adjustment provided by fixed steps of inductance is often inadequate. Adjustable or continuously variable inductors are therefore required. The simplest form which such an inductor can take is an arrangement of two circular coils (one within the other), the inner coil being pivoted so that it may be rotated about a diameter of the outer, fixed coil.[5] Such an arrangement can obviously be used either as a mutual or a self-inductance. If we consider the outer coil as the primary of a mutual inductor, the mutual inductance may be varied from a maximum when the coils are coplanar, through zero when they are perpendicular, to a negative[6] maximum when they are again coplanar.

It should be apparent that if the two coils are connected in series to form a self-inductance the mutual coupling between them will add to the inductance in one of the coplanar positions and subtract from it in the other in which the movable coil has been rotated through 180°. As a variable self-inductance, then, the value ranges continuously from a maximum $L_1 + L_2 + 2M$ to a minimum $L_1 + L_2 - 2M$, where L_1 and L_2 are the self-inductances of the coils and M is their mutual inductance in the coplanar position. Such an arrangement has some serious disadvantages. If, as is usually the case, the two coils are as nearly as feasible equal in radius, so that their coupling may be as large as possible, the rate of change of mutual inductance with angle is very far from constant,[7] and a scale of inductance (either self- or mutual) marked on the arc of a circle will be quite non-uniform. Also it will be apparent that the simple arrangement described is not astatic. It is, however, an inexpensive design and has been much used in laboratory work.

Both defects of the Ayrton-Perry inductometer (non-linearity of scale and lack of astaticism) were very largely corrected in the Brooks[8] inductometer,

[5] This arrangement was described by Ayrton and Perry in 1895 and is known as the Ayrton-Perry inductometer, although it had been used previously by other investigators both as a self- and as a mutual inductance.

[6] The concept of positive and negative mutual inductance forms a convenient way of distinguishing the direction of the induced emf in the secondary winding with reference to the primary and to one of the secondary terminals. (Also see p. 671.)

[7] Lord Rayleigh has shown that a nearly uniform scale results if the radius of the inner coil is 0.548 that of the outer coil.

[8] Brooks and Weaver, *Bull. Bur. Standards*, **13**, 569 (1917).

An improved design [Brooks and Lewis, *NBS J. Research*, **19**, 493 (1937)] has been described but has never been available commercially.

which is shown schematically in Fig. 5. There are four stator coils arranged in pairs above and below the rotor coils. The system is connected astatically, and the link-shaped coils are so proportioned that the inductance scale is very nearly uniform with angle except at its extreme ends. With this arrangement a higher time constant can be secured than is feasible in the inductor previously described. Another important

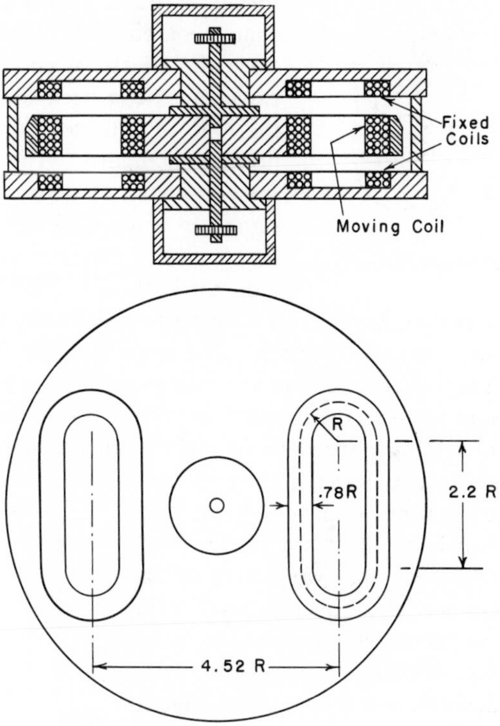

FIG. 5.

consideration is the fact that small axial displacements of the rotor with respect to the stators change the inductance by an exceedingly small amount, so that the calibration does not change appreciably with bearing wear.

Mutual Inductors

In addition to the continuously adjustable inductors described above, which can be used either as self- or mutual inductors, fixed-value mutual inductors are frequently required in laboratory work. In general, the requirements which they should satisfy in order to make acceptable reference standards are very similar to those for self-inductors.

Primary Standards. Primary standards of mutual inductance, calculable from measured dimensions, have been designed and constructed at various national laboratories. It may be noted that such standards can be calculated somewhat more precisely than the corresponding absolute self-inductors because of the higher theoretical accuracy of the mutual-inductance formulas used. Also they show less change of effective value with frequency since the effects of eddy currents and of capacitance can be made smaller than in the type of self-inductors employed as a primary standard. The best known of these primary standards is the one designed by Campbell[9] and constructed at the National Physical Laboratory. This inductor is shown schematically in Fig. 6.

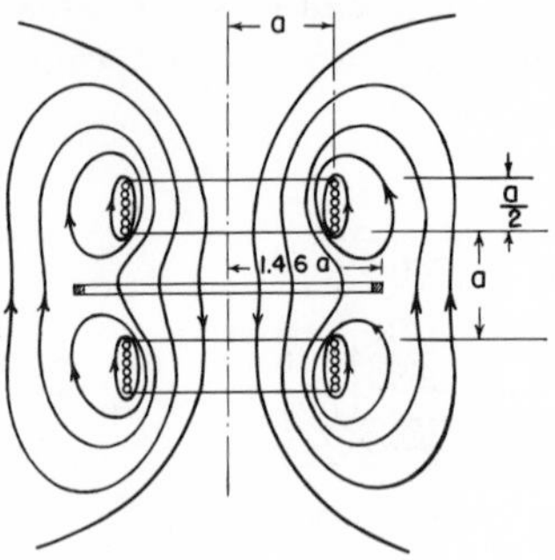

FIG. 6.

The primary is divided into two equal sections helically wound in a screw thread, cut on a marble cylinder. The secondary has a large number of turns wound in a channel of square cross section cut in a marble ring and spaced midway between the primary sections and coaxial with them. By properly proportioning the radii (R_p, R_s) of the primary and secondary windings and the axial spacing h, the mutual inductance is maximum, and the secondary coil lies in a very weak magnetic field which results from the presence of the gap between the two halves of the primary winding. Consequently small axial and radial displacements of secondary turns have a minimum effect on the value of the mutual inductance, and it is thus possible to use a multilayer secondary coil and obtain a comparatively large value of mutual inductance.

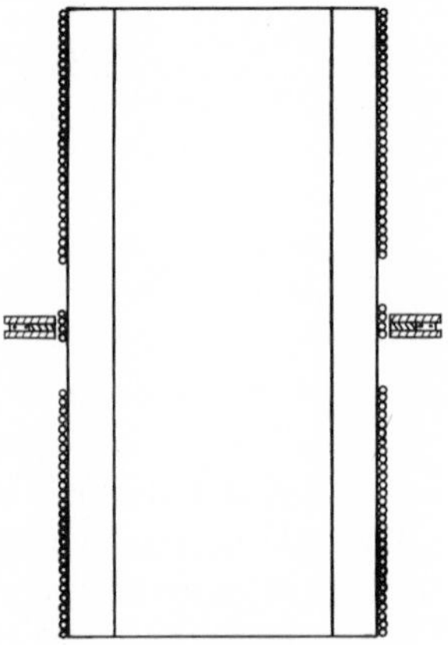

FIG. 7.

A modification of the Campbell mutual inductor has been designed and constructed at the National Bureau of Standards by Wenner and his coworkers.[10] In this design, shown in Fig. 7, there are two gaps in the primary helix, resulting in two annuli of zero field. By properly proportioning the primary radius and the gap widths, a relatively large annular space, within which the field is very small, is available for the secondary

[9] Campbell, *Proc. Roy. Soc.*, A**79**, 428 (1907).
[10] Thomas, Peterson, Kotter, and Cooter, *NBS J. Research*, **43**, 325 (1949).

winding. This mutual inductor probably has the most precisely known value of inductance of any which has ever been built. Such inductors are useful only as primary reference standards and so are maintained only at national laboratories.

Laboratory Mutual Inductors. Several factors should be considered in the design of fixed inductors for laboratory work. The inductor should be as permanent and as definite in value as possible; the winding should make economical use of the wire (i.e. the time constant should be large); capacitance should be small between the windings; and eddy currents should be minimized in order that the change in the effective

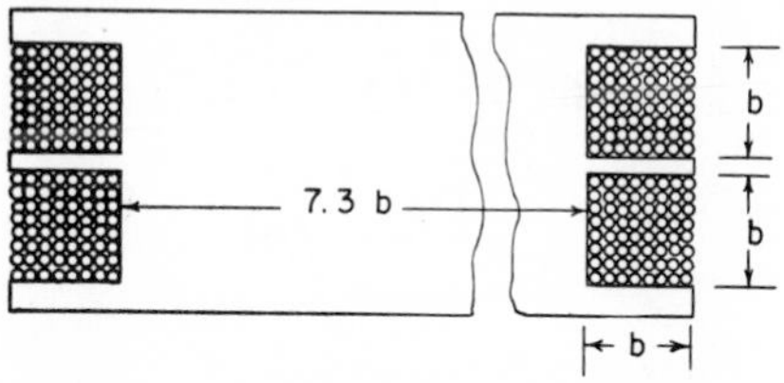

FIG. 8.

value of inductance with frequency be small. Some of these characteristics and constructions which promote them have already been discussed in connection with self-inductors. A common type of mutual inductor is made by winding two wires side by side in a circular coil of rectangular cross section. The primary and secondary windings have the same inductance, and since the coupling is high between the windings the mutual inductance is only slightly less than the self-inductance. If the Brooks proportions[11] are used the mutual inductance is thus very nearly a maximum for a given length and diameter of wire. However, the capacitance between windings is very large in this construction, since the windings are closely intermingled, and the effective inductance would be expected to change rather rapidly with changing frequency. The capacitance between windings will be much less if the construction makes use of two coaxial coils of rectangular cross section, wound side by side on a form as shown in Fig. 8. Unless there is some reason for making the intercoil capacitance very small the coils may be placed as close together as possible. The mutual inductance of such a coil pair with windings of square cross section is given very approximately by the formula[12]

$$M = 4\pi a n^2 \left[\log_\varepsilon \frac{8a}{d}\left(1 + \frac{3d^2}{16a^2}\right) - \left(2 + \frac{d^2}{16a^2}\right)\right]$$

[11] See p. 661 above.

[12] Rosa and Cohen, *Bull. Bur. Standards*, **5**, 10 (1908).

where n is the number of turns per coil, a is the mean radius of a turn, and d is the distance between centers of the two coils. If the coils are very close together so that $d \approx b$, we have as an approximation

$$M = 4\pi a n^2 \left(\log_\varepsilon \frac{8a}{b} - 2\right)$$

The maximum mutual inductance for a given length of wire, l, per coil can be determined as follows,[13] if D = diameter of the wire over its insulation:

$$n = \frac{b^2}{D^2} = \frac{l}{2\pi a}$$

and our approximate formula for M becomes

$$M = \frac{l^2}{2\pi a}\left(\log_\varepsilon \frac{128\pi a^3}{lD^2} - 4\right)$$

Then

$$\frac{dM}{da} = \frac{l^2}{2\pi a^2}\left(\log_\varepsilon \frac{128\pi a^3}{lD^2} - 7\right)$$

and for a maximum value of M,

$$\frac{64a^2}{b^2} = \varepsilon^7, \quad \text{or} \quad \frac{a}{b} = 4.139$$

Under these conditions the diameter of the winding form is $2a - b = 7.279b$. The mutual inductance is, from our approximation, $M = 78bn^2 \times 10^{-9}$ henry. Using Perry's formula,[14] the self-inductance of each coil is

$$L = \frac{4\pi n^2 a^2}{0.2317a + 0.83b} = 120bn^2 \times 10^{-9} \text{ henry}$$

Such coils on marble or impregnated mahogany forms are useful in many laboratory measurements, subject to the same limitations as are imposed on similar self-inductors. They are, of course, not astatic, and care must be exercised in placing them so that coupling with external fields is reduced to a minimum. Where astaticism is required special windings are required. If a toroidal winding with the wires of the primary and secondary side by side is objectionable because of the large capacitance between windings, a relatively simple solution is the use of two equal sets of coils such as those described above, mounted either coaxially or side by side, and oriented so that the coils have fields of opposite instantaneous

[13] Curtis, *op. cit.*, p. 82.
[14] Rosa and Cohen, *op. cit.*, p. 46.

polarity when viewed from the same side. Of course, in such an arrangement the mutual coupling between the coil pairs will have to be taken into account.

Frequency Effects. At low frequencies it may be assumed, very approximately, that the emf which appears in the secondary circuit of a mutual inductor as a result of a current i in its primary winding is $e = \pm j\omega Mi$, where M is the mutual inductance; i.e. the secondary voltage is in exact quadrature with the primary current. The sign to be given the induced emf is arbitrary, but will be reversed, depending on whether the self- and mutual fluxes aid or oppose. We shall consider that the induced emf is positive if the self- and mutual fluxes aid, and negative if they are opposed.[15] At higher frequencies this simple relation is no longer valid because of the effects of (1) distributed capacitance in the windings and inter-capacitance between them, (2) eddy-current losses, (3) losses in the insulation, and (4) resistance which is common to both primary and secondary circuits when they are connected to a common point. Assuming for the moment that the common resistance σ is the only source of impurity, we have, from Fig. 9, for the two meshes[16]

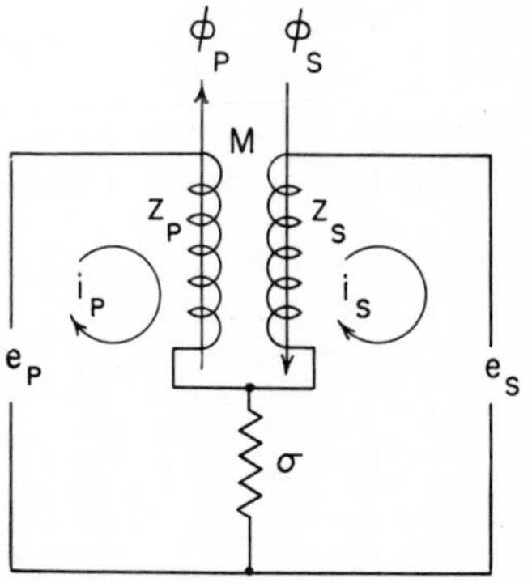

FIG. 9.

$$i_pZ_p + (i_p - i_s)\sigma + j\omega i_sM = e_p$$

and

$$i_sZ_s + (i_s - i_p)\sigma + j\omega i_pM = e_s$$

which may be arranged as

$$(Z_p + \sigma)i_p = e_p - (j\omega M - \sigma)i_s$$
$$(Z_s + \sigma)i_s = e_s - (j\omega M - \sigma)i_p$$

The secondary emf resulting from current in the primary is $(j\omega M - \sigma)i_p$, and its departure from exact quadrature with the primary current vector is $\delta = \tan^{-1}(\sigma/\omega M)$. In the general case of an impure mutual inductance σ may be considered an equivalent resistance which is common to the primary and secondary circuits.

[15] This convention is a common one but is not universally used. The reader must keep this fact in mind and is cautioned to examine the sign convention employed, in applying the results of any particular writer's work.

[16] For the use of Maxwell's cyclic currents in network equations see p. 688.

The most important source of impurity is capacitance. In the general case the capacitances which act on the circuit may be represented by those of Fig. 10(*a*). However, when the primary and secondary of the inductor have a common point, the equivalent network is much simplified and may be represented by Fig. 10(*b*). The latter case has been investigated by Butterworth,[17] who, through a series of Δ-Y transformations, arrived at the approximate expressions

$$M = M_0 - C_{ps}R_pR_s + \omega^2[C_pL_pM_0 + C_sL_sM_0 + C_{ps}(L_p + M_0)(L_s + M_0)]$$

and

$$\sigma_c = -\omega^2\{C_pR_pM_0 + C_sR_sM_0 + C_{ps}[R_p(L_s + M_0) + R_s(L_p + M_0)]\}$$

where M_0 is the mutual inductance at low frequency, M is the equivalent mutual inductance at a frequency $\omega/2\pi$, σ_c is the impurity resulting from

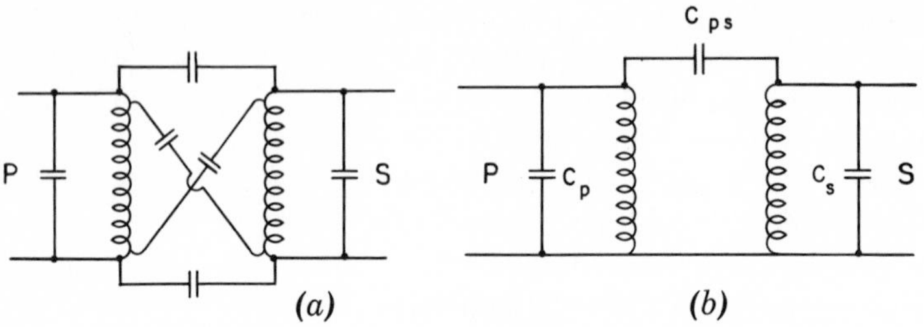

FIG. 10.

the presence of capacitance, and the assignments of the various L, R, and C terms are designated by their subscripts. If, as is usually the case, the term $C_{ps}R_pR_s$ is negligible, the frequency coefficient of mutual inductance is

$$\frac{\Delta M}{M_0} = \omega^2\left[C_pL_p + C_sL_s + C_{ps}\frac{(L_p + M_0)(L_s + M_0)}{M_0}\right]$$

The terms resulting from the self-capacitances of the primary and secondary ($\omega^2C_pL_p$ and $\omega^2C_sL_s$) will always be positive. The term resulting from intercapacitance $\left[\omega^2C_{ps}\frac{(L_p + M_0)(L_s + M_0)}{M_0}\right]$ will be positive or negative, depending on the sign of M_0 and on the relative magnitudes of L_p, L_s, and M_0. $\Delta M/M_0$ will be largest for given capacitance values when M_0 is positive, i.e. when the self- and mutual fluxes aid. Hence it is better to use a mutual inductance with the fluxes opposed, provided

[17] Butterworth, *Proc. Phys. Soc.* (*London*), **33**, 312 (1921); Hartshorn, *Proc. Phys. Soc.* (*London*), **38**, 302 (1926).

the capacitance values are the same. For, if M_0 is negative (as is the case in most bridge arrangements), then numerically,

$$\frac{\Delta M}{M_0} = \omega^2 \left[C_p L_p + C_s L_s - C_{ps} \frac{(L_p - M_0)(L_s - M_0)}{M_0}\right]$$

If L_p and L_s are both greater than M_0, the intercapacitance term is negative. If $L_p > M_0 > L_s$ the intercapacitance term is positive but less than if M_0 is positive.

The phase defect (departure from quadrature) resulting from capacitance is

$$\delta_c = \tan^{-1} \frac{\sigma_c}{\omega M} \approx \frac{\sigma_c}{\omega M_0}$$

$$\approx -\left\{\omega C_p R_p + \omega C_s R_s + C_{ps} \left[\frac{\omega R_p(L_s + M_0)}{M_0} + \frac{\omega R_s(L_p + M_0)}{M_0}\right]\right\}$$

It will be observed here also that δ_c is smaller for M_0 negative than for M_0 positive with equal values of capacitance. It should be noted, however, from Fig. 10(*a*) that the intercapacitances do not necessarily remain the same when the common point is altered, so that in practice the frequency coefficient of mutual inductance and phase defect angle may change with a change of common point.

Because of the inherent impurities of mutual inductors, which are largely proportional to the square of the frequency, it is usually inadvisable to use them in bridge circuits above the lower audio-frequency range unless the effective mutual inductance and phase defect angle are known at the frequency to be employed. These factors should, of course, be known for a variable inductor over its entire scale range.

Capacitors

Absolute capacitors (calculable from dimensions) are usually in the form of concentric spheres, coaxial cylinders, or parallel plates, with air as the dielectric. They are ordinarily of small capacitance and are not generally useful in bridge measurements. Most of the useful capacitors which are available for this work are of a type whose capacitance must be experimentally determined. Ideally, a standard capacitor should have the following properties: (1) On a sine-wave voltage, the current should be in quadrature with the impressed voltage; (2) the value of capacitance should be permanent and definite; (3) the dielectric should be free from losses and absorption; (4) the value of capacitance should not be affected by temperature or frequency; (5) insulation resistance should be very great. In addition it is frequently desirable that the capacitor be capable of withstanding a high voltage. Depending on construction and dielectric material, these requirements are met to a greater or less degree. Air or other gases, mica, oils, impregnated paper, glass, and ceramics have all served as the dielectric material. In precision capacitors only gas and mica are suitable dielectrics. Where requirements are not severe impregnated paper is sometimes used. Other dielectric materials are ordinarily employed only for special-purpose capacitors, i.e. as components of filter circuits, electronic circuits, etc.

Low-Voltage Air Capacitors. Air capacitors, except high-voltage types, usually have parallel plate electrodes. The dielectric constant of air is small (about 1.0006 under ordinary atmospheric conditions) so that, to obtain large capacitance, the electrode area must be large and the spacing between electrodes small. At the same time the dielectric strength of air is small, and capacitors with small electrode separation, using air as a dielectric at atmospheric pressure, can be operated only at relatively low voltages. Most of the common laboratory types of air capacitors utilize multiple-plate electrodes, interleaved and having a spacing of not much less than 1 mm between successive plates. Where the spacing is close care must be taken in keeping the electrode surfaces clean and dry since dust or fibers present might bridge the gaps between electrodes, introducing losses because of the conducting paths across the fibers and reducing the breakdown voltage of the capacitor. Usually parallel plate capacitors are enclosed in a dust-tight metal container. The set of plates forming one electrode is very often mounted on the base of this container and is in electrical contact with it so that the container acts as a part of the electrode assembly. The set of plates forming the other electrode is insulated from it by means of solid dielectric supports. These supports are generally of fused quartz, Pyrex glass, or some ceramic material such as isolantite. Plastic materials such as hard rubber and polystyrene cannot be used except in very light assemblies because of the danger of deformation under load, thus changing the electrode spacing and the capacitance value. It is important that the solid insulation supporting the insulated electrode assembly be of low-loss material and be located in a weak electric field since losses in the solid insulation contribute very largely to the total losses of the capacitor. A metal container completely enclosing the insulated electrode assembly makes the capacitance value much more definite than that of an open capacitor since the container acts as a shield to screen the insulated electrode from outside fields. The manner in which electrical connection is made between the insulated electrode and its external terminal may contribute an indefinite and uncertain amount of capacitance to the system, but this can usually be made very small in comparison with the definite value of capacitance which can be assigned to the remainder of the system.

Fixed-value air capacitors having a capacitance of 10,000 $\mu\mu$f have been used for many years at the National Bureau of Standards. The electrode assemblies are made up from rectangular brass plates, interleaved as shown in Fig. 11. Fused quartz supports the insulated electrode assembly. Most laboratory air capacitors used at low voltages are of a continuously variable type. In the usual construction one set of plates, mounted on a shaft in bearings, is arranged to rotate, the individual plates being interleaved between the plates of the fixed, insulated electrode assembly. Both sets of plates are approximately semicircular in shape, and the active area of the capacitor, where the fixed and moving plates face each other (see Fig. 12), is continuously variable,

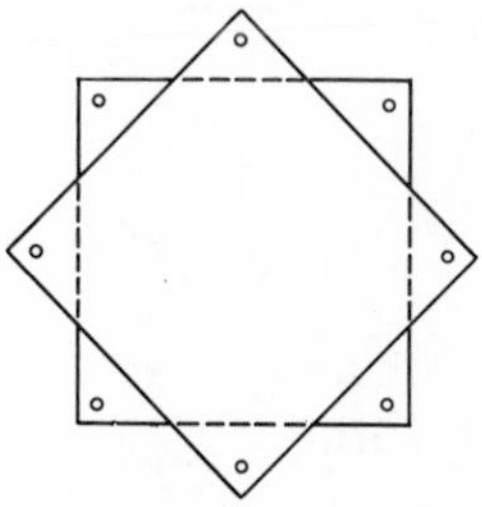

FIG. 11.

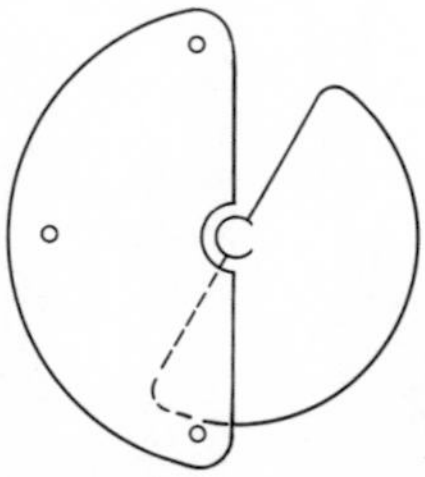

FIG. 12.

going from a minimum to a maximum as the rotor is moved through 180°. The capacitance scale of such a variable capacitor is very nearly uniform with angle except near the ends, where the rotor plates are just beginning to interleaf, or are almost wholly interleaved between the fixed plates. The capacitance changes less rapidly at the ends of the scale, and a certain minimum capacitance will exist in the rotor position where there is no interleaving of the electrode plates. In precision capacitors of this type, great care is taken, in the bearing construction of the rotor assembly, that there be no looseness or play between the bearings and the rotor shaft, the design being such that the effect of bearing wear is minimized. In some precision variable air capacitors the rotor is moved through a worm and gear arrangement so that finer adjustment of capacitance is possible. The General Radio capacitor shown in Fig. 13 is of this type.

High-Voltage Air Capacitors. These present very different problems. The spacing between electrodes must be enough that the electric field is considerably less than the breakdown value (30 kv/cm), and sharp edges, points, and corners which would produce local breakdown stress must be avoided in order that there be no corona with consequent losses. Because of the large spacing required, such capacitors are quite bulky and are usually of rather low capacitance. Parallel plate arrangements have been used at times, but difficulties of construction and shielding are such that a coaxial cylinder electrode arrangement is usually preferred. The latter construction also lends itself readily to the use of compressed gas (usually nitrogen or carbon dioxide) as a dielectric. Since the dielectric strength of a gas is directly proportional to pressure over a wide range, smaller electrode spacings and a considerable over-all reduction in bulk are possible for a given voltage if the gas is compressed to perhaps 10 to 15

FIG. 13. Precision type of variable air capacitor. (Courtesy of General Radio Company.)

atmospheres pressure. This requires a gas-tight pressure enclosure for the electrode assembly and makes the problem of the high-voltage bushing somewhat more difficult than for a free-air capacitor.

FREE-AIR CAPACITORS. Figure 14 shows schematically the construction[18] of a free-air capacitor designed for operation at 150 kv. The outer cylinder, a machined cast-iron cylinder supported on compression insulators, is used as the high-voltage electrode. The inner cylinder, also machined from cast iron, is divided into three sections. The end sections serve as grounded guard electrodes and are insulated from the middle section by hard-rubber discs. The capacitance between the outer cylinder

[18] Churcher and Dannatt, *World Power*, **5**, 238 (1926).

and the middle section of the inner cylinder is thus computable with moderate precision from dimensions, since the electric field in this section is very nearly that which would be present between infinite coaxial cylinders. Capacitance between the outer cylinder and the end sections of the inner cylinder, where the field is much distorted, cannot be computed with precision. However, this is immaterial since these capacitances are

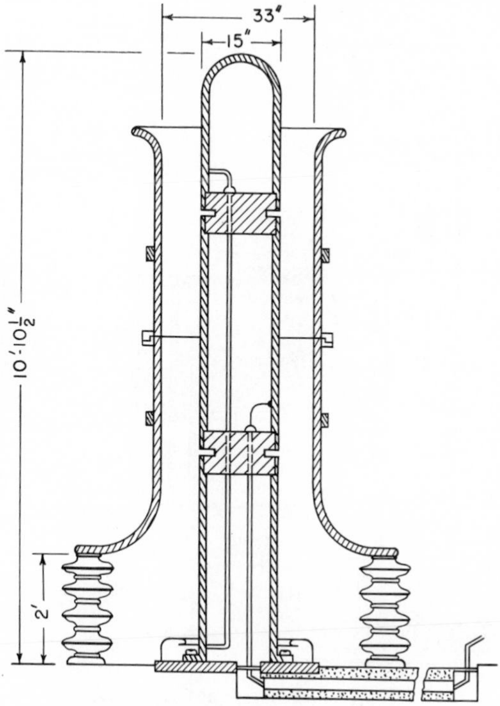

FIG. 14.

not in the measuring circuit.[19] Also the guard sections of the inner cylinder, together with the outer cylinder, serve to screen the working capacitor from the effects of external objects and so tend to make its capacitance definite.[20] The ends of the cylinders are rounded so that the electric field will not at any point exceed the breakdown voltage of air, in order that the capacitor be entirely free from corona losses at the operating voltage.

COMPRESSED-GAS CAPACITORS. Two basic designs have been developed for compressed-gas capacitors. In the first of these, shown schematically

[19] See discussion of shielding, p. 734.

[20] See discussion of three-terminal capacitors, p. 679.

in Fig. 15(*a*),[21] the walls of the pressure chamber are of insulation add support the high-voltage electrode, so that a high-voltage bushing is not required. The low-voltage electrode is supported from the base, and its lead is brought out through a pressure seal. In the second type, shown in Fig. 15(*b*),[22] a steel cylinder is used as the pressure chamber, and the high-voltage electrode is suspended from a high-voltage bushing which

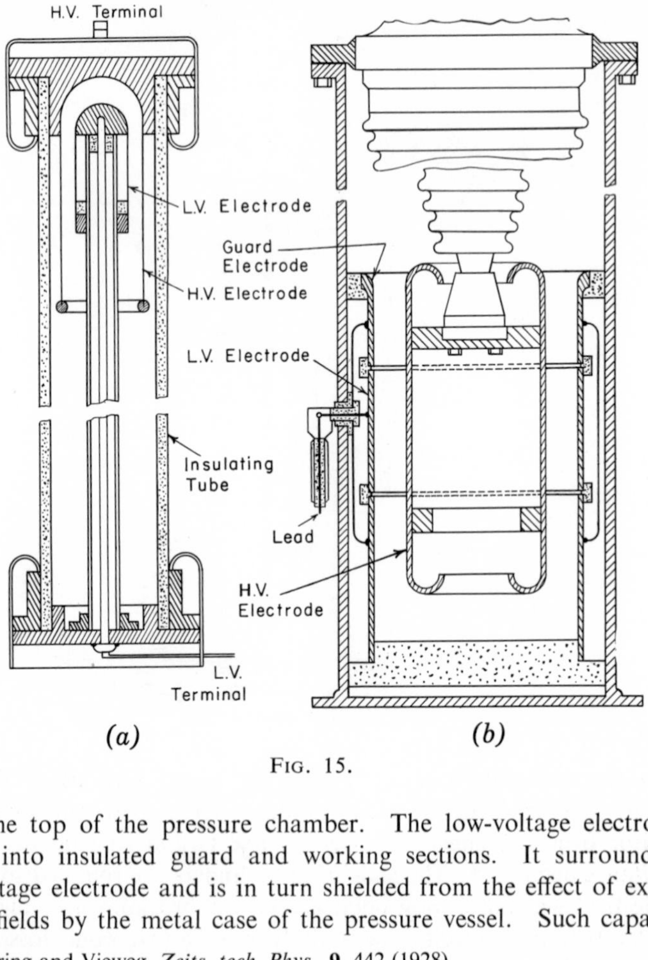

FIG. 15.

forms the top of the pressure chamber. The low-voltage electrode is divided into insulated guard and working sections. It surrounds the high-voltage electrode and is in turn shielded from the effect of external electric fields by the metal case of the pressure vessel. Such capacitors

[21] Schering and Vieweg, *Zeits. tech. Phys.*, **9**, 442 (1928).

[22] The particular design that is sketched is that of Bousman and Ten Broeck. A number of such arrangements have been described. See Palm, *Elektrot. Zeits.*, **47**, 873, 904 (1926); also Kouwenhoven and Berberich, *Trans. AIEE*, **52**, 521 (1933). The latter is a completely shielded and guarded arrangement.

Defandorf [*J. Washington Acad. Sci.*, **38**, 41 (1948)] has indicated how the Bousman-Ten Broeck arrangement may be modified to obtain complete shielding.

usually have a capacitance of 100 $\mu\mu$f or less and have been constructed for use up to 500 kv.

Defects of Air Capacitors. If we consider the capacitor as a system of isolated electrodes, its total capacitance is generally dependent on the capacitance between the individual electrodes and ground as well as the direct capacitance between the electrodes themselves. Thus, in Fig. 16, if we consider the capacitor having electrodes 1 and 2 [completely enclosed within a shield (3) which will be assumed at ground potential] we have the direct capacitance C_{12} between the electrodes and the capacitances $C_{13}C_{23}$ between the separate electrodes and the shield. The total capacitance of the system consists of C_{12} in parallel with the series combination of C_{13} and C_{23}, or

$$C = C_{12} + \frac{C_{13}C_{23}}{C_{13} + C_{23}}$$

the *working* capacitance differs from the *inter-capacitance* by an amount equal to the shield capacitances in series. Most air capacitors are constructed so that the electrode system is as nearly as possible completely enclosed within a metal shield. In many cases both electrodes are insulated from the shield and brought out to terminals on the outside of the shield, a separate terminal being provided for the shield. Such an arrangement is known as a three-terminal capacitor, as distinguished from a two-terminal capacitor, which, if shielded, has the shield permanently connected electrically to one of the electrodes. Depending on its connection, a three-terminal capacitor may have a number of values of capacitance. One of these has already been discussed. When the shield (3) is not connected to either electrode the capacitance of the system is

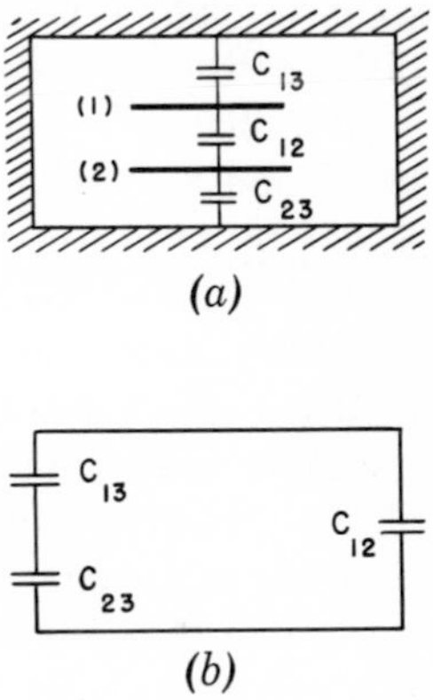

FIG. 16.

$$C = C_{12} + \frac{C_{13}C_{23}}{C_{13} + C_{23}}$$

If the shield is connected to electrode 1, the capacitance is $C = C_{12} + C_{23}$; and if electrode 2 is connected to the shield, the capacitance is $C = C_{12} + C_{13}$. The separate capacitances can easily be measured; for, if we connect terminals 1 and 3 together, the measured capacitance will be $C_{12} + C_{23}$; if we connect 2 and 3 together, the measured capacitance will be $C_{12} + C_{13}$; and if we connect 1 and 2 together, the capacitance measured between them and the shield will be $C_{13} + C_{23}$. From these values the separate capacitances may be computed so that it is possible to allow for them in any connection used.

In the discussion above it was assumed that the shield completely enclosed the other electrodes. In practice this is not exactly true since a connection to each electrode must be brought through the shield by means of an insulating bushing. Capacitance will be present between these conductors and outside objects, or ground, and to this extent the capacitance is indefinite. This indefiniteness may amount to a micro-microfarad or more. A three-terminal capacitor can frequently be connected into the measuring circuit and shielded in such a way that its working capacitance is completely definite.[23]

Another defect of air capacitors results from the necessity of using solid insulating material to support the electrodes. Wherever solid dielectric is present there will be some losses. In well-designed capacitors solid insulation is held to a minimum amount, is of high quality with low losses and high leakage resistance, and is so placed that it is in a weak field. By means of the guard-ring principle[24] the solid insulation supporting the electrodes can be removed entirely from the field of the working capacitor and be wholly in the guard capacitor, where its losses need not affect measurements. Another source of loss is the electrical resistance of the connections to the electrodes and of the metallic circuit of the capacitor. In a variable capacitor the contact to the movable electrode is sometimes a source of trouble. This can be almost entirely eliminated by a suitable brush and disc contact to the rotary electrode. In a precision General Radio variable capacitor, designed for use at high frequencies, contact to the rotor is made by silver-alloy brushes bearing on a silver-plated disc. In this capacitor the total metallic series resistance is about 0.008 ohm at 1 megacycle and increases with the square root of the frequency as a result of skin effect.

Another defect of air capacitors, analyzed by Astin,[25] appears to reside in the electrodes themselves. In the presence of moisture the surface of the electrodes adsorbs a very thin film whose thickness and conductivity are functions of humidity. We have then in effect a composite capacitor made up of the surface film which represents a capacitor having appreciable losses, in series with the pure capacitance between the electrodes themselves. This situation is shown schematically in Fig. 17(a), and the equivalent circuit in Fig. 17(b). If we have the condition that $t \ll d$, or that $C_1 \ll C_2$, Astin has shown that we may write approximately

$$C \approx C_1 \left(1 - \frac{\omega^2 R_2^{\,2} C_1 C_2}{1 + \omega^2 R_2^{\,2} C_2^{\,2}}\right)$$

[23] See discussion of shielded bridges, p. 716.

[24] See p. 682.

[25] Astin, *NBS J. Research*, **22**, 673 (1939).

and

$$\phi \approx \frac{\omega R_2 C_1}{1 + \omega^2 R_2^2 C_2^2}$$

Here C is the total equivalent capacitance of the system, and ϕ is the phase defect angle (the departure of the capacitor current from true quadrature). It may therefore be considered the contribution of the surface film to the power factor of the capacitor. Astin found in general that: (1) The power factor of a two-electrode air capacitor was of the form $A + (B/C)$ (C being capacitance), where A depends on electrode material, frequency, and humidity, and B depends on solid insulating material of the electrode supports, frequency, and humidity. (2) The power factor of a two-electrode capacitor cannot be defined unless the capacitor is in equilibrium with the atmosphere and the conditions of measurement are precisely stated. (3) The power factor of a three-electrode capacitor of the guard-ring type, so constructed that solid insulation is excluded from the measured capacitance, is inversely proportional to electrode separation. The losses are a function of relative humidity. (4) The losses observed in guard-ring capacitors may be explained in terms of layers of oxide or water or both on the electrode surfaces.[26] (5) The contribution of surface films to power factor is greater in a non-uniform than in a uniform electric field.

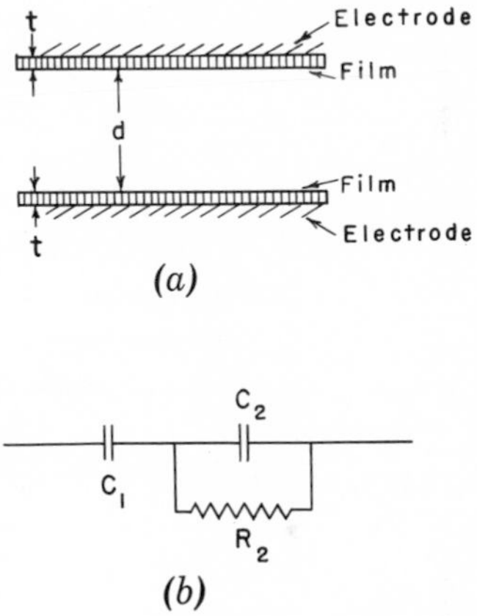

FIG. 17.

[26] The contribution of oxide films to the power factor of three-terminal capacitors has also been observed by Koops [*Philips Tech. Rev.*, **5**, 300 (1940)], using an equal-arm bridge in which phase displacements could be measured with an accuracy of 3×10^{-8} radian. Koops states that "the evils of oxide film could be very much limited when the plates were made of aluminium or were covered with a layer of aluminium. An oxide film is then formed, it is true, but it is much thinner than with other metals and, thanks to its poor conductivity, has only a very small phase displacement." Astin, on the other hand, observed larger phase displacements with aluminium electrodes than with other metals such as nickel and stainless steel, as well as with silver-, chromium-, and gold-plated brass electrodes. He also found that the power factor increased with humidity (up to 50% r.h.).

It is probable that the surfaces of the aluminium electrodes used by Astin were not as carefully prepared as those of Koops, but such conflicting results indicate the need for further work on this point. In any event it may be stated that the phase-defect angle of a properly designed and constructed three-terminal capacitor will not be in excess of 1 microradian and may be considerably less.

Small Capacitors. Small, accurately known standards of direct capacitance are needed for the calibration of bridges and test sets which are used to measure the interelectrode capacitances of electron tubes. A series of such standard capacitors, ranging from 5 $\mu\mu$f to 0.001 $\mu\mu$f, has been described by Moon,[27] together with decade-type and continuously adjustable three-terminal capacitors in the same range, which he has found useful in measurement work.

GUARD-RING CAPACITORS. Moon's primary standards of capacitance (computable from their dimensions) down to 0.1 $\mu\mu$f are of the conven-

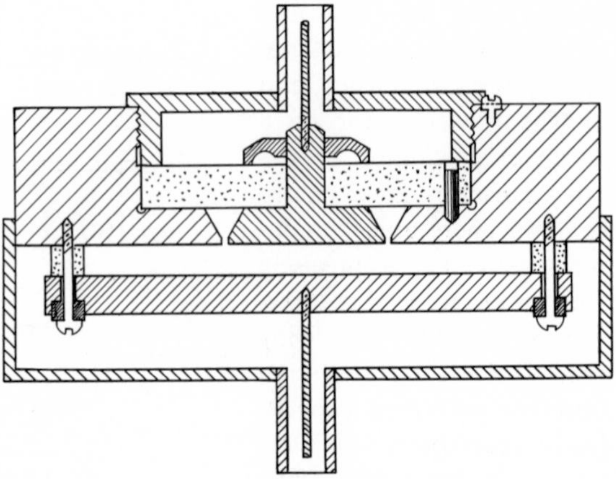

FIG. 18.

tional guard-ring type. Their design, shown in Fig. 18, is such that they can be very precisely made, with accurately known dimensions. The guarded electrode is rigidly held and accurately centered in the guard ring by a Pyrex-glass disc, which is held in place by a spring clamping ring. The high-voltage electrode is held at a fixed distance from the guard ring by equal-length Pyrex spacers whose ends are plane and parallel. The common surface of the guarded electrode and the guard ring is ground and lapped optically flat. Locating pins ensure that the capacitor can be taken apart and reassembled without sensible loss of accuracy. The accuracy with which the capacitance can be computed is limited principally by accuracy of measurements of the mechanical dimensions. For the 1-$\mu\mu$f capacitor this limit was found to be about 0.1%. Any displacement of the guarded electrode from the plane of the guard ring would result in an error in the computed value of capacitance. The change in capacitance is approximately linear with displacement (for small displacements), but is considerably larger than would be computed by treating

[27] Moon and Sparks, *NBS J. Research,* **41**, 497 (1948).

the displacement as if it were merely a change in the distance between the parallel plate electrodes.[28] It was found that, in the case of the 1-$\mu\mu$f capacitor, departure from coplanarity would cause a change of 0.05% capacitance per micron displacement of the guarded electrode. Displacements observed in the actual capacitors amounted to about $\frac{1}{2}$ micron. Another correction of a similar nature but of smaller magnitude arises from the presence of the gap between the guarded electrode and the guard ring. A formula for computing capacitance is available[29] which takes account of the air-gap width

$$C = K\left[\frac{\bar{a}^2}{4d} - \frac{\pi\bar{a}}{2}\left(\frac{a_2 - a_1}{2\pi d}\right)\coth\frac{\pi\bar{a}}{d}\right]$$

where C is the capacitance in cgs electrostatic units (statfarads), a_1 is the radius of the guarded electrode, a_2 is the radius of the hole in the guard ring, $\bar{a} = (a_1 + a_2)/2$, d is the separation of the electrodes (all in centimeters), and K is the dielectric constant of air. The gap-width correction amounts to only 10 parts per million for the widest gap used.

GUARD-WELL CAPACITORS. Construction of primary standards of capacitance as conventional three-electrode, guard-ring capacitors becomes impractical for values less than 0.1 $\mu\mu$f, since either the guarded electrode must be reduced in area to such an extent that its mechanical dimensions can no longer be measured with the required accuracy, or the electrode spacing must be so large that an unreasonably wide guard ring would be required to keep the field uniform in the central, guarded portion. A new type of capacitor, which Moon calls a "guard-well" capacitor, was developed for values of 0.1 $\mu\mu$f and less.[30] The construction used for primary standards of fixed value is shown in Fig. 19(*a*), a continuously adjustable capacitor of range 0.1 to 0.001 $\mu\mu$f in Fig. 19(*b*), and capacitance as a function of well depth in Fig. 19(*c*) for a capacitor whose essential dimensions [referred to Fig. 19(*b*)] are $a = 1.680$ cm, $c = 0.2098$ cm, d is adjustable. This design, in which the electrode is at the bottom of a recess or well, permits the building of primary standards whose capacitance is as small as desired while keeping linear dimensions large enough for precise construction and accurate measurement.

[28] It will be realized that a displacement of this sort results in the exposure of a sharp edge at the guard-ring gap, with a consequent concentration of field along the exposed edge. Hence the formula for the parallel plate capacitor is no longer strictly applicable, since it assumes the presence of a uniform field.

[29] This is an unpublished formula developed by Dr. C. Snow of the National Bureau of Standards.

[30] This construction was suggested by Dr. F. B. Silsbee, and formulas for its computation were developed by Dr. C. Snow. *NBS J. Research*, **42,** 287 (1949).

ADJUSTABLE CAPACITORS. Moon also constructed a low-range adjustable capacitor with which small differences between fixed-value capacitors could be compensated, and a three-electrode "decade" capacitor which had accurately adjusted steps between 0.1 and 1 $\mu\mu$f. The adjustable capacitor was a modification of a design by Zickner,[31] and is shown in

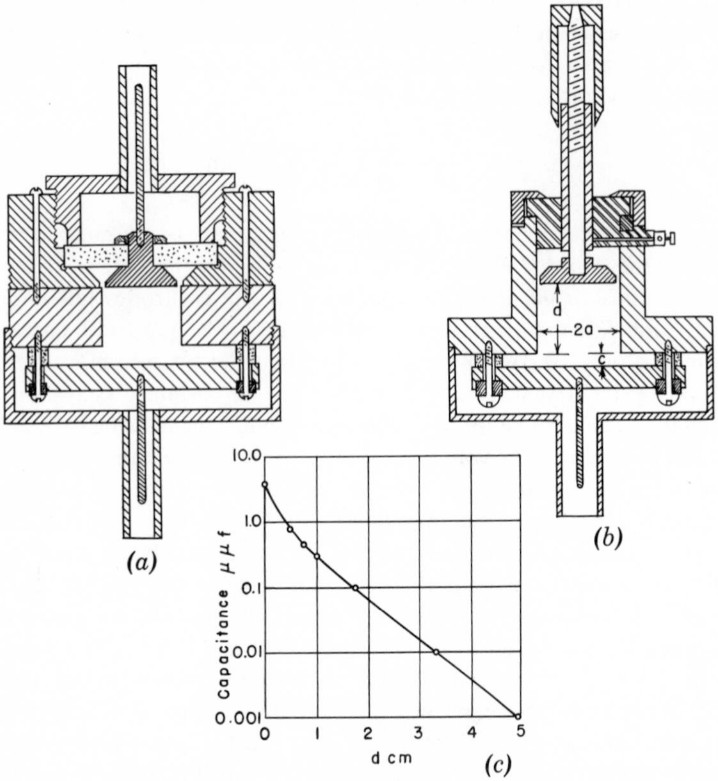

FIG. 19.

Fig. 20. It consists of two active electrodes separated by a shielding electrode in which a semicircular slot is cut. The capacitance is varied by rotating a semicircular plate (connected to the shield) so that it covers more or less of the slot. The advantages of this type of unit are that the minimum capacitance is *exactly* zero, the scale is linear, and full-scale value can be made as small as desired by proper choice of slit width and electrode spacing. As an accurate means of stepping from 0.1 to 1 $\mu\mu$f a decade capacitor free from "switching" errors was constructed. It consists of five units: two of 0.1 $\mu\mu$f; two of 0.2 $\mu\mu$f; and one of 0.4 $\mu\mu$f.

[31] Zickner, *Elek. Nachr.-Tech.*, **7**, 443 (1930).

They are arranged symmetrically in a circle and connected to central coaxial terminals, as shown in Fig. 21. Each unit consists of a pair of insulated plates and a shutter which is connected to the housing. This shutter is pivoted so that it can be interposed between the plates, making their direct capacitance zero. A rough adjustment of the capacitance of a unit was made by adjusting the distance between plates, and then a very close adjustment by means of a screw whose end extends outward from the center of one electrode. In this way the units were adjusted to be

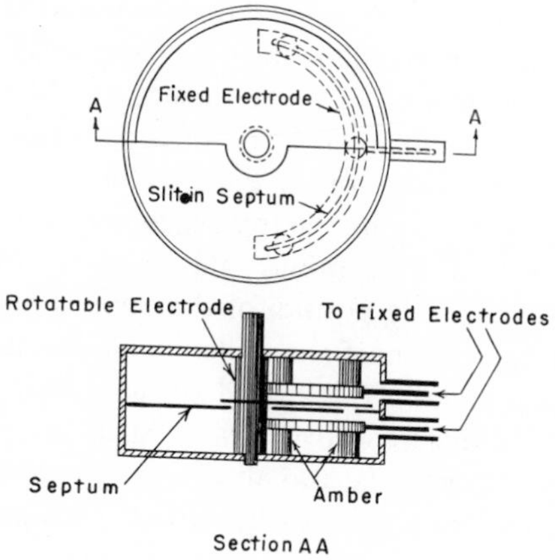

FIG. 20.

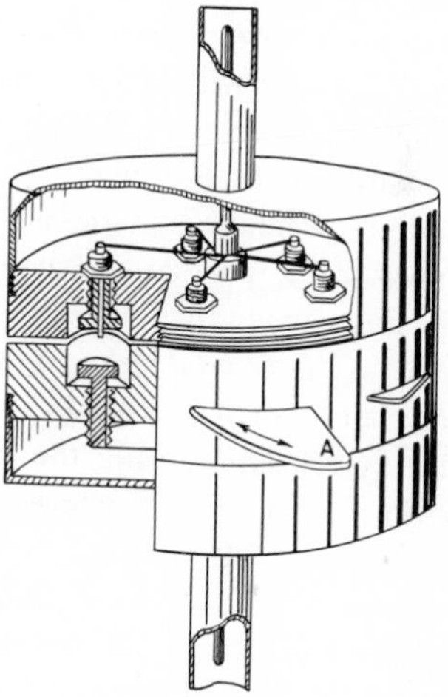

FIG. 21.

exactly equal, or exact multiples (within the limit of sensitivity of the bridge used to measure them), and have been found to hold their adjustment very closely.

Moon states that an accuracy of about 0.1% can be realized (with a suitable bridge[32]) in the measurement of direct capacitance down to about 0.1 $\mu\mu$f. His estimated error is 0.5% at 0.01 $\mu\mu$f, and 2% at 0.001 $\mu\mu$f.

Capacitors with Solid Dielectric. These are required if the value of capacitance must be large. Since the dielectric constant of air is small (requiring large electrode area) and its dielectric strength is low (requiring large electrode separation), air-capacitor construction is practical only for units of comparatively small capacitance. An air capacitor of 1-μf or even 0.1-μf capacitance would be enormously bulky. However, solid material having a high dielectric strength and a large dielectric constant permits very small electrode separation to be used and also reduces the electrode area needed so that capacitors of large capacitance and small

[32] See p. 727.

physical size are feasible. However, capacitors with solid dielectrics have certain inherent defects in addition to those present in an air capacitor. If a capacitor is discharged, all of the charge is not instantaneously released. There is a "bound" or absorbed charge which is given up only very slowly. The relative amount of charge which is given up instantly on short circuit, and that which is given up over a period of time, vary enormously with different dielectric materials, but the phenomenon is generally a characteristic of solids. When a capacitor is cyclically charged and discharged, the quantity of electricity which is alternately stored and released per unit difference of potential between the electrodes will depend more or less strongly on the time required to complete the cycle. Hence the capacitance of an absorbing capacitor, measured by an a-c method, will be a function of the frequency at which the measurement is made, and of the wave form of the impressed voltage. Since, for a particular capacitor, the absorption is quite definite, the effective capacitance will also be definite if we fix the frequency and wave form. There is a second a-c effect of absorption: the quantity of electricity which is stored during the charging portion of the cycle is not entirely released during the discharge portion of the cycle. This results in the dissipation of energy when a capacitor is cycled on alternating current, and by analogy is known as dielectric hysteresis. Such losses increase with increasing frequency. Energy is also dissipated by conduction through the dielectric and by leakage across its surface between the electrodes. Thus both the capacitance and the power factor of a capacitor having a solid dielectric are to some extent a function of the frequency.

Although air and other gases are almost entirely free from absorption (as are some liquids), this phenomenon is present to a greater or less degree in solid dielectrics. Only those solids are suitable for precision capacitors in which absorption is very small and which in addition are readily available in thin uniform sheets. Thus the available materials are limited to mica and purified cellulose paper free from filler. Paper capacitors, formed by laying one or more sheets of paraffined paper between sheets of tinfoil, compressing and impregnating the resulting assembly, are, of course, much cheaper and are often used where large values of capacitance are needed; but, although paraffined paper capacitors are convenient and readily available in larger sizes than mica, they are generally of very much poorer quality and should not be employed as standards. Grover[33] has made the following observations concerning paper capacitors: (1) The changes of capacitance with frequency and temperature are greater than for mica capacitors. (2) The capacitance

[33] Grover, *Bull. Bur. Standards*, **7**, 495 (1911).

usually decreases with increasing frequency, the rate of change being greater at higher temperatures. (3) For capacitors having low losses, the temperature coefficient of capacitance at constant frequency is usually negative and may amount to 0.05%/°C. (4) The loss angle (and power factor) depend greatly on the materials used and are particularly sensitive to the dryness of the paper. Loss angles ranging from 6 min to 2° or more in the lower audio-frequency range were found in paraffined paper capacitors.

Mica capacitors, made from selected clear ruby mica, show very much better performance than paper, but are seldom made in sizes larger than 1 μf. The best-quality mica capacitors are assembled with melted wax at an elevated temperature and under conditions such that moisture and air are excluded. The assembly consists of thin sheets of clear mica, free from blemishes and scratches, with tin-foil electrodes. After assembly and adjustment the capacitor is clamped between heavy metal blocks under pressure. The pressure is such (2000 psi or more) that almost all the wax is squeezed out.[34] This is important, since not only in an unclamped mica capacitor unstable with time and temperature, but its losses and temperature coefficient are adversely affected by the presence of excess wax. Also the capacitance of an unclamped mica capacitor is sensitive to changes in atmospheric pressure. The completed capacitor must be sealed from contact with air and moisture. Mica capacitors of high quality[35] may have phase defect angles of 1 or 2 min in the power and audio-frequency ranges. The temperature coefficient is usually negative and may lie between 0.005 and 0.03%/°C. It should be noted that, since both mica and wax are rather poor heat conductors, such capacitors should be kept at a constant temperature for several hours before precise measurements are attempted. Properly made mica capacitors are very stable, their capacitance value remaining fixed within 0.01 or 0.02% over a period of many years.

BRIDGE CHARACTERISTICS

Balance Equations

Most of the common bridge networks that are used in capacitance and inductance measurements are four-arm impedance bridges which are essentially similar to the Wheatstone bridge.[36] However, it is often convenient or necessary to consider more complicated networks, and a general method of analysis is needed for their solution, in order to derive

[34] Thiessen, *G.R. Experimenter*, **7**, 1 (1933).
[35] Curtis, *Bull. Bur. Standards*, **6**, 431 (1910).
[36] See p. 258.

their balance equations. We will illustrate the development of this method with the four-arm impedance bridge of Fig. 22(*a*), in which a source of emf *e* is present in one diagonal and a voltage-sensitive detector in the opposite diagonal. We could, by applying Kirchhoff's laws, establish the relations needed to specify completely the behavior of the network. Thus

$$\left.\begin{array}{ll}(1) & Z_6 i_6 + Z_3 i_3 + Z_4 i_4 = e \\ (2) & Z_2 i_2 + Z_5 i_5 - Z_3 i_3 = 0 \\ (3) & Z_1 i_1 - Z_4 i_4 - Z_5 i_5 = 0\end{array}\right\} \text{ and } \left\{\begin{array}{ll}(4) & i_6 - i_2 - i_3 = 0 \\ (5) & i_2 - i_1 - i_5 = 0 \\ (6) & i_1 + i_4 - i_6 = 0\end{array}\right.$$

could be used. Here we have six independent equations in six unknowns which, taken together, completely specify each of the branch currents in

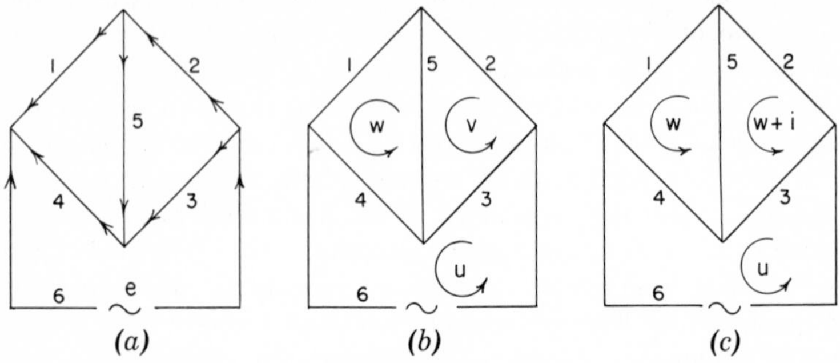

FIG. 22.

terms of the impedances and the impressed emf, but the labor involved in the solution of these relations is considerable. It can be greatly reduced by a mathematical device suggested by Maxwell. We will assume a hypothetical "cyclic" current flowing in each mesh of the network, such that the current in each branch is the difference of the "cyclic" currents in the adjacent meshes. It must be realized that such cyclic currents have no physical reality but are a purely mathematical device by which we may reduce the labor involved in solving the network. Thus we can write an equation for each of the three meshes of the network as shown in Fig. 22(*b*).

$$(1) \quad u(Z_6 + Z_3 + Z_4) - vZ_3 - wZ_4 = e$$

$$(2) \quad v(Z_2 + Z_5 + Z_3) - uZ_3 - wZ_5 = 0$$

$$(3) \quad w(Z_1 + Z_4 + Z_5) - uZ_4 - vZ_5 = 0$$

and we have reduced our system from six equations in six unknowns to three equations in three unknowns.

In deriving balance equations we are usually interested only in the current in one conductor—the detector branch—since at balance this current is reduced to zero. In this case we can further simplify the algebra by assigning values to the cyclic currents in the adjacent meshes such that this branch current appears directly in our equations. Since the branch currents are assumed to be the difference between the cyclic currents in the adjacent meshes we may write $i_5 = v - w$, or $v = w + i_5$. [See Fig. 22(*c*).] On making this substitution for *v* and rearranging our equations, we have

$$\begin{aligned}
&(1)\quad u(Z_3 + Z_4 + Z_6) - w(Z_3 + Z_4) - i_5 Z_3 && = e \\
&(2)\quad -uZ_3 \qquad + w(Z_2 + Z_3) + i_5(Z_2 + Z_3 + Z_5) && = 0 \\
&(3)\quad -uZ_4 \qquad + w(Z_1 + Z_4) - i_5 Z_5 && = 0
\end{aligned}$$

and can write the solution for i_5 directly from these equations as

$$i_5 = \frac{\begin{vmatrix} Z_3 + Z_4 + Z_6 & -(Z_3 + Z_4) & +e \\ -Z_3 & +(Z_2 + Z_3) & 0 \\ -Z_4 & +(Z_1 + Z_4) & 0 \end{vmatrix}}{\begin{vmatrix} (Z_5 + Z_4 + Z_6) & -(Z_3 + Z_4) & -Z_3 \\ -Z_3 & +(Z_2 + Z_3) & +(Z_2 + Z_3 + Z_5) \\ -Z_4 & +(Z_1 + Z_4) & -Z_5 \end{vmatrix}} = e\,\frac{-Z_3(Z_1 + Z_4) + Z_4(Z_2 + Z_3)}{D} = \frac{e(Z_2 Z_4 - Z_1 Z_3)}{D}$$

When the bridge is balanced, we have, from our definition,[37] $i_5 = 0$, so that the balance condition becomes $Z_1 Z_3 = Z_2 Z_4$. The equation for balance in the four-arm impedance bridge is quite general since Kirchhoff's laws may be generalized to include any linear impedance *Z*, for any voltage *e* which can be constructed from sinusoidal components.

If we write our impedance operator $Z = \mathbf{Z}\underline{/\phi}$, we have at balance[38]

$$\mathbf{Z}_1\underline{/\phi_1} \cdot \mathbf{Z}_3\underline{/\phi_3} = \mathbf{Z}_2\underline{/\phi_2} \cdot \mathbf{Z}_4\underline{/\phi_4}$$
$$\mathbf{Z}_1\mathbf{Z}_3\underline{/\phi_1 + \phi_3} = \mathbf{Z}_2\mathbf{Z}_4\underline{/\phi_2 + \phi_4}$$

We now see that there are really two balance conditions which must be satisfied simultaneously in the four-arm impedance bridge:

$$(1)\quad Z_1 Z_3 = Z_2 Z_4 \quad \text{for magnitude balance}$$

and

$$(2)\quad \phi_1 + \phi_3 = \phi_2 + \phi_4 \quad \text{for phase-angle balance}$$

[37] See p. 659.

[38] See Kerchner and Corcoran, *Alternating-Current Circuits*, p. 70, John Wiley, 1938.

These relations may be seen from the vector diagram which is associated with the balanced bridge. In Fig. 23, we have

$$Z_1 I_B = Z_4 I_D \quad \text{and} \quad Z_2 I_B = Z_3 I_D$$

or

$$\frac{Z_1}{Z_2} = \frac{Z_4}{Z_3}$$

whence $Z_1 Z_3 = Z_2 Z_4$. Also

$$\phi_1 - \phi_4 = \phi_2 - \phi_3$$

or

$$\phi_1 + \phi_3 = \phi_2 + \phi_4$$

by construction.

Let us consider a simple bridge in which two of the arms will be assumed to be pure resistances. From the balance relations it is apparent that

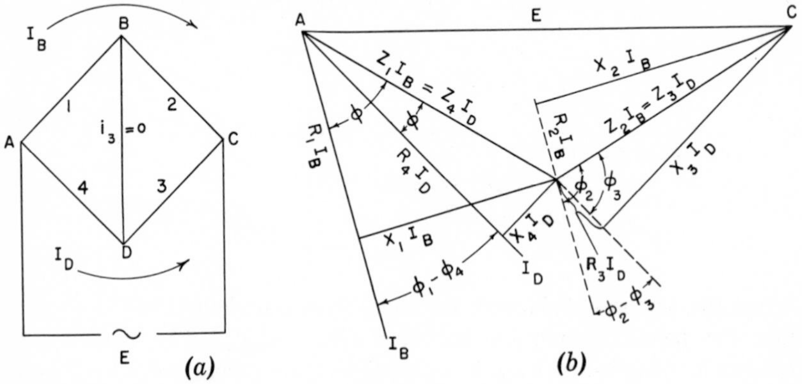

FIG. 23.

the phase balance depends on the remaining two arms. Thus, if Z_1 is inductive, its positive phase angle ϕ_1 can be compensated in either of two ways: (1) an impedance with an equal positive phase angle can be used in either of the adjacent arms ($\phi_1 = \phi_2$, or $\phi_1 = \phi_4$) the remaining two arms having zero phase angle; or (2) an impedance with an equal negative phase angle can be used in the opposite arm ($\phi_1 + \phi_3 = 0$). In other words, an inductance can be measured in terms of another inductance (of equal time constant), placed in either adjacent arm; or the inductance can be measured in terms of a combination of resistance and capacitance (of equal time constant) in the opposite arm. Similarly a capacitance in one arm can be measured in terms of a capacitance in an adjacent arm, or of an inductance in the opposite arm. In each case the time constants of the impedors must be matched.

We will suppose that two inductances are to be compared and that one of them is $Z_1 = R_1 + j\omega L_1$. The phase balance condition may be met by making either Z_2 or Z_4 inductive, the other arms being pure resistances. Suppose that the comparison inductance is put in arm 4, so that $Z_4 = R_4 + j\omega L_4$, and so that we have the bridge of Fig. 24. Now since $\phi_2 = \phi_3 = 0$ we must have $\phi_1 = \phi_4$; i.e. a resistance will have to be

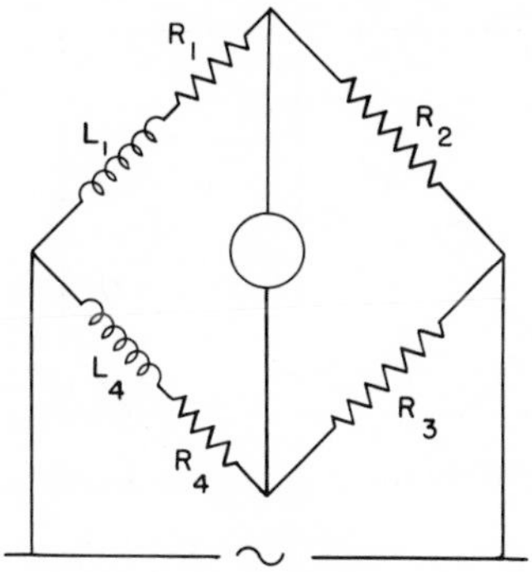

FIG. 24.

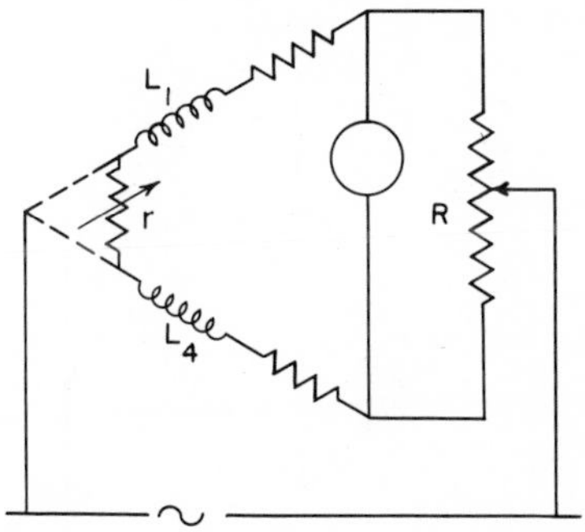

FIG. 25.

inserted in the arm (1 or 4) with the inductor having the smaller time constant. The balance condition $Z_1Z_3 = Z_2Z_4$ may be written

$$(R_1 + j\omega L_1)R_3 = R_2(R_4 + j\omega L_4)$$

On separation of real and imaginary components we have

$$R_1R_3 = R_2R_4, \quad \text{or} \quad \frac{R_2}{R_3} = \frac{R_1}{R_4}$$

and

$$\omega L_1R_3 = \omega L_4R_2, \quad \text{or} \quad L_1 = L_4 \cdot \frac{R_2}{R_3}$$

We can also write

$$L_1 = L_4 \cdot \frac{R_1}{R_4}$$

(from the relation between resistances) so that $L_1/R_1 = L_4/R_4$; i.e. the time constants of Z_1 and Z_4 must be matched for balance. The ratio of inductances is given by R_2/R_3, so that Z_2 and Z_3 may be considered ratio arms. Such a bridge could be constructed as shown in Fig. 25, with a resistance r to be introduced into arm 1 or 4 as required by the time constants of the inductor, and a slide-wire resistor R could be used to form the ratio arms.

If we wish to compare capacitors a similar situation exists. The capacitors must be in adjacent arms. In Fig. 26 we will suppose that C_1 is not a pure capacitance but may be represented by a capacitance in series with a resistance R_1. In this case, if C_4 is a capacitor with a smaller loss angle, series resistance must be added in arm 4 to achieve balance. We will assume that R_4 includes not only the added resistance but also the

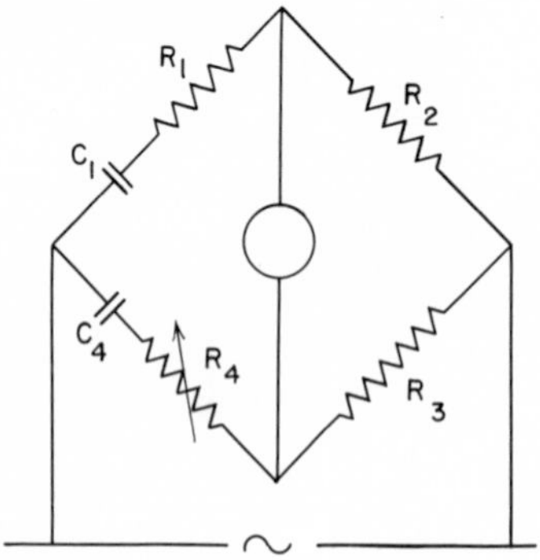

FIG. 26.

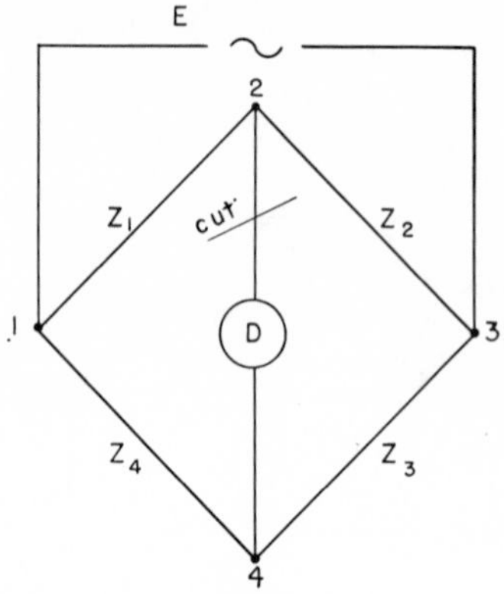

FIG. 27.

equivalent series resistance required to represent the losses of the capacitor C_4. The balance equation can be written

$$\left(R_1 - \frac{j}{\omega C_1}\right) R_3 = R_2 \left(R_4 - \frac{j}{\omega C_4}\right)$$

which separates as

$$R_1 R_3 = R_2 R_4 \quad \text{and} \quad \frac{R_3}{\omega C_1} = \frac{R_2}{\omega C_4}$$

from which

$$C_1 = C_4 \cdot \frac{R_3}{R_2}$$

If we define the loss angle (the amount that the capacitor departs from quadrature), we have

$$\tan \delta_1 = \omega R_1 C_1 = \omega R_1 \cdot C_4 \frac{R_3}{R_2} = \omega \frac{R_2 R_4}{R_3} \cdot C_4 \frac{R_3}{R_2} = \omega C_4 R_4 = \tan \delta_4$$

and again we have equality of time constants: $C_4 R_4 = C_1 R_1$.

The Unbalanced Impedance Bridge

We will assume that the impedance of the source is negligible and that a voltage E is impressed between points 1 and 3 of Fig. 27. We will also assume that the unbalance present results from an impedance ΔZ_4, defined as the departure of Z_4 from the value required to satisfy the balance equation $Z_1Z_3 = Z_2Z_4$. Then, if the detector branch of the circuit were opened, the voltage drop between points 1 and 2 would be

$$E_{12} = E\frac{Z_1}{Z_1 + Z_2}$$

and the drop between points 1 and 4 would be

$$E_{14} = E \cdot \frac{Z_4 + \Delta Z_4}{Z_4 + \Delta Z_4 + Z_3}$$

Then the open-circuit voltage of unbalance appearing at a cut in the detector branch (i.e. between points 2 and 4) would be

$$e = E_{14} - E_{12} = E\left(\frac{Z_4 + \Delta Z_4}{Z_3 + Z_4 + \Delta Z_4} - \frac{Z_1}{Z_1 + Z_2}\right)$$

But

$$\frac{Z_4}{Z_3 + Z_4} = \frac{Z_1}{Z_1 + Z_2} \quad \text{at balance}$$

so that

$$e = E\left[\frac{Z_4\left(1 + \dfrac{\Delta Z_4}{Z_4}\right)}{(Z_3 + Z_4)\left(1 + \dfrac{\Delta Z_4}{Z_3 + Z_4}\right)} - \frac{Z_1}{Z_1 + Z_2}\right]$$

$$= \frac{EZ_4}{Z_3 + Z_4}\left(\frac{1 + \dfrac{\Delta Z_4}{Z_4}}{1 + \dfrac{\Delta Z_4}{Z_3 + Z_4}} - 1\right)$$

$$= \frac{EZ_4}{Z_3 + Z_4}\left[\left(1 + \frac{\Delta Z_4}{Z_4}\right)\left(1 - \frac{\Delta Z_4}{Z_3 + Z_4} + \frac{\overline{\Delta Z_4}^2}{(Z_3 + Z_4)^2} - \cdots\right) - 1\right]$$

$$\approx \frac{EZ_3\Delta Z_4}{(Z_3 + Z_4)^2}$$

if the departure from balance is small, so that terms in $\overline{\Delta Z_4}^2$ and higher orders may be neglected.[39] If we express the departure of Z from its balance value in terms of proportional parts, we have

$$Z + \Delta Z = Z(1 + p), \quad \text{or} \quad p = \frac{\Delta Z}{Z}$$

[39] See also the unbalanced Wheatstone bridge in Chapter 7.

Using this designation, and using the subscript 4 to indicate that the voltage of unbalance results from an incorrect value of Z_4, we may write

$$e_4 = E \cdot p_4 \frac{Z_3 Z_4}{(Z_3 + Z_4)^2}$$

Similarly, an unbalance impedance in Z_3 will result in an identical expression for the open-circuit voltage in the detector branch, provided we say that $p_3 = \Delta Z_3 / Z_3$; thus

$$e_3 = E \cdot p_3 \frac{Z_3 Z_4}{(Z_3 + Z_4)^2}$$

For unbalance impedances in the other arms of the bridge we have similar expressions for the voltage of unbalance; thus

$$e_1 = E \cdot p_1 \frac{Z_1 Z_2}{(Z_1 + Z_2)^2}; \quad \text{and} \quad e_2 = E \cdot p_2 \frac{Z_1 Z_2}{(Z_1 + Z_2)^2}$$

Bridge Sensitivity. If the detector is essentially a high-impedance device (i.e. if its impedance is very large compared to the impedance of

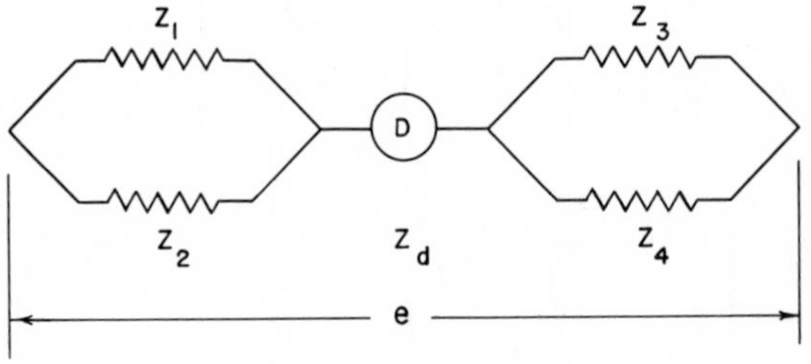

FIG. 28.

the bridge arms connected across it), its response can be determined directly in terms of the voltage of unbalance and the voltage sensitivity of the detector. If, however, its impedance is low or comparable to that of the bridge arms, we must consider the impedance of the entire circuit. Assuming that the impedance of the source is negligible, we have, from Thévenin's theorem, that the voltage of unbalance acts in the equivalent circuit of Fig. 28. If we know the current sensitivity of the detector, or its voltage sensitivity for the given circuit conditions, its response can be calculated. For the simple case in which the detector impedance is very large, we can make use of the expressions developed in the preceding section for unbalance voltage in the detector branch, to show that sensitivity is maximum in an *equal-arm* bridge. If we let $Z_2 = KZ_1$, our expression for the voltage in the detector branch becomes[40]

$$e = E \cdot p \frac{KZ_1^2}{(1 + K)^2 Z_1^2} = E \cdot p \frac{K}{(1 + K)^2}$$

The maximum value of e is found by differentiating with respect to K and equating the result to zero:

$$\frac{de}{dK} = E \cdot p \frac{(1 + K)^2 - 2K(1 + K)}{(1 + K)^4} = 0, \quad \text{or} \quad 1 + K = 2K$$

so that $K = 1$ and $Z_1 = Z_2$ at the maximum. Similarly $Z_3 = Z_4$ at the maximum, and if we interchange the detector and voltage source we can also show by similar procedures that $Z_1 = Z_4$ and $Z_2 = Z_3$ for the maximum sensitivity. Thus we may say that, for a proportional departure $p = \Delta Z/Z$ in any arm of the bridge, the maximum open-circuit voltage will appear in the detector branch of the circuit if $Z_1 = Z_2 = Z_3 = Z_4$, or the sensitivity will be maximum if the magnitudes of the impedance of the bridge arms are equal. It may be noted that the open-circuit voltage in the detector branch decreases as K departs from unity in accordance with the expression

$$e \text{ (for bridge ratio } K) = e \text{ (for equal-arm bridge)} \times \frac{4K}{(1 + K)^2}$$

if we assume that the impressed voltage, E, and the proportional departure from the balance, p, remain constant. It may be noted from this expression that the bridge sensitivity, expressed in terms of the voltage of unbalance, decreases rather slowly as K departs from unity. For example, if $K = 5$, the open-circuit voltage in the detector branch has dropped only to half the value it would have if $K = 1$; and if $K = 20$, the voltage is still one-fifth of that for $K = 1$. It also follows as a corollary of this discussion that the detector position which will yield the highest bridge sensitivity is at the junction of adjacent arms whose ratio (K) is nearest unity. If the impedance of the detector is not very high compared to that of the bridge arms, so that the situation of Fig. 28 must be considered, the actual analysis of sensitivity relations is very much more complicated. However, it is still true in general that the maximum sensitivity to a proportional unbalance is obtained in an equal-arm bridge, and that the sensitivity decreases rather slowly as the bridge ratio departs from unity, for any detector which will be reasonable to employ in the case under consideration.[41]

[40] K may be either a real or a complex number, depending on the nature of Z_1 and Z_2, but will always be a pure number.

[41] It must be borne in mind that the maximum power is available for operating the detector if its impedance equals the impedance of the circuit connected to its terminals.

Approach to Balance. While the expressions developed in the preceding sections may be used to evaluate the relative effects of proportional departures of the various bridge elements from the values required for balance, the actual situation which is present is not so simple when we adjust bridge elements in order to approach a balance condition. The approach to balance is generally made through the adjustment of two bridge elements which may not, in general, be independent.[42] We will assume that *both* of the adjustable elements are initially at values which differ from their "balance" values. The voltage of unbalance may be written as

$$e = E\left(\frac{Z_4}{Z_3 + Z_4} - \frac{Z_1}{Z_1 + Z_2}\right) = E\,\frac{Z_2Z_4 - Z_1Z_3}{(Z_3 + Z_4)(Z_1 + Z_2)}$$

Near the balance point, small variations of the bridge elements will change the value of the numerator of this expression, since it must vanish at balance, but will have a relatively minor effect on the value of the denominator. In examining the approach to balance we can, therefore, consider the denominator as having a fixed value, and, since the detector response is proportional to the voltage of unbalance, we may write

$$\xi = Z_2Z_4 - Z_1Z_3 = (R_2 + jX_2)(R_4 + jX_4) - (R_1 + jX_1)(R_3 + jX_3)$$

where ξ is a quantity proportional to detector response. It will be seen that, if we vary *only one* resistance or reactance term, our expression for ξ is linear in terms of this variable and its locus may be shown graphically as a straight line.[43] The graphical analysis of approach to balance may be illustrated with the bridge of Fig. 29(*a*), in which the ratio arms Z_1 and Z_2 are pure resistances and the remaining arms are

$$Z_3 = R_3 + j\omega L_3 = R_3 + jX_3$$

and

$$Z_4 = R_4 + j\omega L_4 = R_4 + jX_4$$

Our general response equation becomes

$$\xi = R_2(R_4 + jX_4) - R_1(R_3 + jX_3)$$

We will first examine the response near balance as R_1 is varied, and we may write the response equation as

$$\xi = A_{24} - R_1(R_3 + jX_3)$$

ξ may be represented in the complex plane as the vector difference of a constant vector $A_{24} = R_2(R_4 + jX_4)$, having a slope X_4/R_4, and a variable

[42] In the bridges conforming to Ferguson's classification (see the section immediately following this) the balance condition is approached by successive adjustments of two elements which are independent.

[43] Kupfmuller, *Elek. und Masch.*, **51,** 204 (1933); Hague, *Alternating-Current Bridge Methods*, 5th edition, pp. 299–305, Pitman, 1946.

vector whose length depends on the values of R_1, R_3, and X_3 and whose slope ($\phi_3 = \tan^{-1} X_3/R_3$) is constant. The variation of ξ with R_1 is shown in Fig. 29(*b*). As R_1 is varied through a range such that ξ varies from ξ_1 to ξ_2, the response decreases to a minimum and again increases, minimum response corresponding to the vector ξ_0, normal to the locus $R_1(R_3 + jX_3)$. In other words, the value of R_1 for which $\xi = \xi_0$ is the nearest approach we can make to balance with the values present in the other elements of the bridge. It will also be apparent that, for a certain

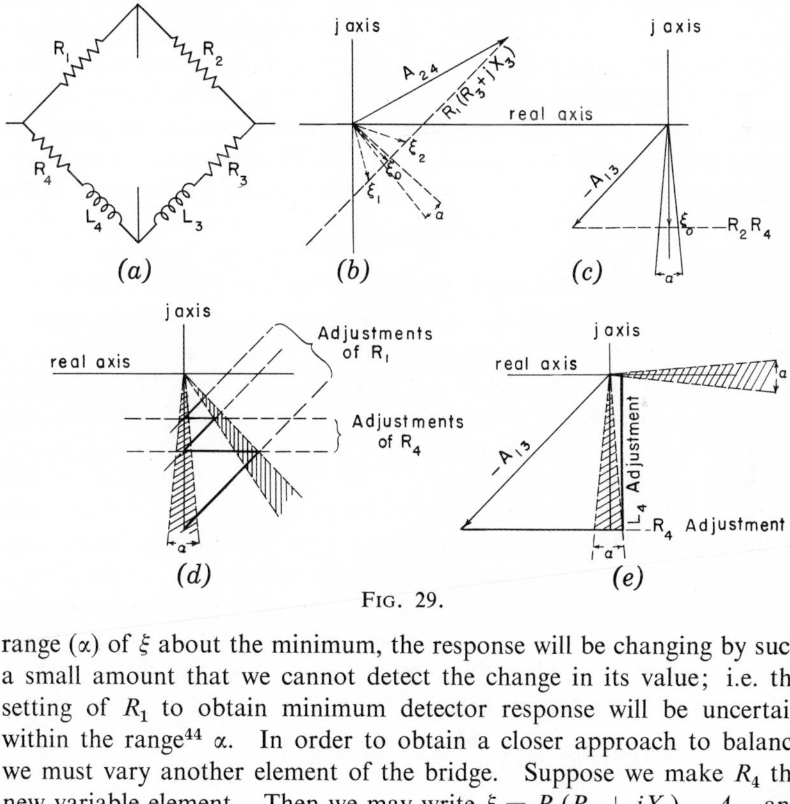

FIG. 29.

range (α) of ξ about the minimum, the response will be changing by such a small amount that we cannot detect the change in its value; i.e. the setting of R_1 to obtain minimum detector response will be uncertain within the range[44] α. In order to obtain a closer approach to balance we must vary another element of the bridge. Suppose we make R_4 the new variable element. Then we may write $\xi = R_2(R_4 + jX_4) - A_{13}$, and we see that our variable vector $R_2 \cdot R_4$ is real and of zero slope. This is shown in Fig. 29(*c*), the minimum response again being normal to the locus.

If we approach the balance condition by successive adjustments of R_1 and R_4, our progress can be plotted graphically in Fig. 29(*d*). If we assume that the least observable change in the detector response is a

[44] The angular range of α will depend on the type of detector used. At the extreme of the range we may write $\xi \cdot \cos(\alpha/2) = \xi_0$. If, for example, the detector is such that a 2% change in its response is detectable, we will have $\cos(\alpha/2) = 0.98$, or $\alpha = 23°$.

constant percentage of that response,[45] the shaded areas subtended by the angle α indicate the uncertainty in each of the successive adjustments. It will be apparent that, in this particular case, the balance will be approached more rapidly if our adjustments actually overshoot the area of uncertainty, as shown by the dotted line in the figure.

If instead of selecting R_1 and R_4 as the adjustable elements we had used R_4 and L_4, it will be seen from our expression for detector response that the locus of ξ is parallel to the real axis for the R_4 adjustment, and parallel to the j-axis for the L_4 adjustment. The progress of our approach to balance might then appear as in Fig. 29(*e*). In this case our balancing adjustments are independent of each other,[46] and the approach to balance is more rapid than for that which used R_1 and R_4. It is, in fact, a condition for which the approach to balance is the most rapid possible.[47] The realization of this condition in the actual bridge chosen as an illustration obviously depends on the availability of an adjustable self-inductor of suitable range.

Ferguson's[48] Classification of Four-arm Bridges

It will be apparent, if we consider the general four-arm bridge, that a very great number of circuits are available for measurement purposes. Each of the four arms could, for example, contain either resistance, capacitance, inductance or some parallel or series combination of two or more of them. Of course many of these combinations would be impractical, and with many of them it would even be impossible to achieve balance. The four-arm bridges which are most useful for general measurements can be classified into a few types if we make certain restrictions concerning the operations needed for achieving balance. In the general bridge of Fig. 1, we will assume that Z_3 is the unknown to be measured. We can then write $Z_3 = Z_2Z_4/Z_1$, which is a complex equation. If the impedances are replaced by their complex equivalents (for the present we will consider only series elements), we may write

$$(R_3 + jX_3) = \frac{(R_2 + jX_2)(R_4 + jX_4)}{(R_1 + jX_1)}$$

[45] This is approximately true for some types of detectors but not for others.

[46] See Ferguson's classification, p. 702.

[47] In general, the optimum condition for speed of approach to balance is that the loci of the response vectors for the two adjustable elements be at right angles to each other. It will be apparent from inspection that they need not, however, in general, be parallel to the j-axis and the real axis respectively. Similarly, it will be apparent that as the angle decreases between the two loci successive adjustments approach the balance condition more slowly, and, in the limiting case, where the loci are parallel, balance cannot be achieved in terms of the chosen elements.

[48] Ferguson, *Trans. AIEE.* **52,** 861 (1933).

R_3 and X_3 may, in general, be evaluated in terms of the six parameters on the right-hand side of the equation, and any or all of these quantities may be varied to arrive at balance.

Now it is desirable, from the point of view of speed and convenience of operation and cost of the bridge, that only two parameters be varied (adjustable) in the balancing operation. It is also desirable that these adjustments be independent in their effect on the bridge unbalance. If we consider *only* bridges which make use of these two desirable features, we can reduce our expression to the form $R_3 + jX_3 = A + jB$, where A and B are both real. One of the adjustable elements appears in A but not in B; the other appears in B but not in A. If both components of Z_2 or both components of Z_4 are chosen as the adjustable elements and the remaining two arms are chosen so that their ratio is a pure real or a pure imaginary number (i.e. not complex) our original equation reduces to the desired form. No other combinations will meet the requirements in the present form of the equation. Since there is no difference in the type of bridge whether Z_2 or Z_4 is used as the adjustable arm, there is in reality only one method of adjustment that will meet our requirements—namely, that the arm adjacent to the unknown contain both of the adjustable elements.

We have, up to now, considered only series components in the bridge arms. If we include also the case in which the bridge arms may be made up of parallel components, we can rewrite our equation as

$$(R_3 + jX_3) = (R_4 + jX_4)(R_2 + jX_2)(G_1 - jB_1)$$

where $(G_1 - jB_1) = Y_1 = 1/Z_1$. Now we can again reduce our equation to the desired form, provided the product $(Z_2 \cdot Z_4)$ is either a pure real or a pure imaginary number.

Thus two methods of balance are possible within the stated conditions—that the bridge be balanced by means of adjustments on only two elements and that the effects of adjustments of these elements be independent. We may make the balance (1) in terms of series elements in an arm adjacent to the unknown, or (2) in terms of parallel elements in the opposite arm. For case (1) we have

$$R_3 + jX_3 = \frac{Z_2}{Z_1} \underline{/\phi_2 - \phi_1} \cdot (R_4 + jX_4)$$

and we may say that the vector ratio of Z_2/Z_1 must be either real or imaginary but not complex; i.e. $(\phi_2 - \phi_1)$ must be either $(0, \pi/2, \pi)$. For case (2) we have

$$R_3 + jX_3 = Z_2 \cdot Z_4 \underline{/\phi_2 + \phi_4} \cdot (G_1 - jB_1)$$

and the vector product $Z_2 \cdot Z_4$ must be either real or imaginary but not complex; i.e. $\phi_2 + \phi_4 = 0, \pi/2$, or π. In case (1) the fixed arms[49] always enter the balance equation as a ratio, and bridges of this type may be called *ratio-arm* bridges. In case (2) the fixed arms enter the balance equation as a product, and bridges of this type may be called *product-arm* bridges.

Ratio-arm bridges and *product-arm* bridges may be further classified, depending on whether the term involving the fixed arms is real or imaginary. Some of the combinations which are mathematically or theoretically possible are not practical, as we shall see. The bridges which meet our requirements are then

(1) ratio arm: ratio real
(2) ratio arm: ratio imaginary
(3) product arm: product real
(4) product arm: product imaginary

and we shall examine each category in turn.

(1) RATIO-ARM TYPE—REAL RATIO. If Z_2/Z_1 is real, then $\phi_2 - \phi_1 = 0$ or π, and we have $Z_2/Z_1 = R_2/R_1 = X_2/X_1$. This may be substituted in our ratio-arm balance equation, giving

$$(R_3 + jX_3) = \frac{R_2}{R_1}(R_4 + jX_4) = \frac{X_2}{X_1}(R_4 + jX_4)$$

and, on separating reals and imaginaries,

$$R_3 = \frac{R_2}{R_1} \cdot R_4 = \frac{X_2}{X_1} \cdot R_4$$

and

$$X_3 = \frac{R_2}{R_1} \cdot X_4 = \frac{X_2}{X_1} \cdot X_4$$

Here the resistive component of the unknown is balanced by the resistive element in the adjustable arm, and the reactive component by the reactive element.

(2) RATIO-ARM TYPE—IMAGINARY RATIO. Here[50] $\phi_2 - \phi_1 = \pm(\pi/2)$ and $Z_2/Z_1 = jX_2/R_1 = -(jR_2/X_1)$.

[49] The term *fixed arms* refers only to the fact that the components are fixed during the measurement. Their impedances may be functions of frequency and may be arbitrarily adjustable to change the ratio and hence the range of the bridge, but they are not altered in making the bridge balance.

[50] If $\phi_2 - \phi_1 = \pi/2$, then

$$\frac{jZ_2}{Z_1} = \frac{R_2 + jX_2}{R_1 + jX_1}$$

so that

$$jR_1Z_2 - Z_2X_1 = R_2Z_1 + jZ_1X_2$$

and

$$\frac{Z_2}{Z_1} = j\frac{X_2}{R_1} = -j\frac{R_2}{X_1}$$

Substituting, we have

$$R_3 + jX_3 = \frac{jX_2}{R_1}(R_4 + jX_4) = -\frac{jR_2}{X_1}(R_4 + jX_4)$$

Then

$$R_3 = -\frac{X_2}{R_1} \cdot X_4 = \frac{R_2}{X_1} \cdot X_4$$

and

$$X_3 = \frac{X_2}{R_1} \cdot R_4 = -\frac{R_2}{R_1} \cdot R_4$$

The components of Z_3 are balanced by means of the corresponding quadrature elements in Z_4.

(3) PRODUCT-ARM TYPE—REAL PRODUCT. $\phi_2 + \phi_4 = 0$ or π, and $Z_2Z_4 = Z_2/Y_4 = R_2/G_4 = -(X_2/B_4)$. Substituting in the balance equation of the product bridge, we have

$$R_3 + jX_3 = \frac{R_2}{G_4}(G_1 - jB_1) = -\frac{X_2}{B_4}(G_1 - jB_1)$$

Then

$$R_3 = \frac{R_2}{G_4} \cdot G_1 = -\frac{X_2}{B_4} \cdot G_1$$

and

$$X_3 = -\frac{R_2}{G_4} \cdot B_1 = \frac{X_2}{B_4} \cdot B_1$$

Each component of Z_3 is balanced by the element of Y_1 which is in the same phase, G_1 balances R_3, and B_1 balances X_3.

(4) PRODUCT-ARM TYPE—IMAGINARY PRODUCT. $\phi_2 + \phi_4 = \pm(\pi/2)$ and $Z_2Z_4 = Z_2/Y_4 = j(R_2/B_4) = j(X_2/G_4)$. Substituting, we have

$$R_3 + jX_3 = j\frac{R_2}{B_4}(G_1 - jB_1) = j\frac{X_2}{B_4}(G_1 - jB_1)$$

so that

$$R_3 = \frac{R_2}{B_4} \cdot B_1 = \frac{X_2}{G_4} \cdot B_1$$

and

$$X_3 = \frac{R_2}{B_4} \cdot G_1 = \frac{X_2}{G_4} \cdot G_1$$

The components of Z_3 are balanced by the quadrature elements of Y_1: B_1 balances R_3, and G_1 balances X_3.

These results are summarized in the following table.

Component of Unknown	Balancing Element of Standard			
	Ratio-Arm		Product-Arm	
	Real	Imaginary	Real	Imaginary
R_3	R_4	X_4	G_1	B_1
X_3	X_4	R_4	B_1	G_1
G_3	G_4	B_4	R_1	X_1
B_3	B_4	G_4	X_1	R_1

Practical Considerations. We may now consider the practical bridge forms which meet the requirement that balance be achieved by the independent adjustment of two elements in one arm. The fixed arms might, of course, be made up of simple resistances or reactances or of complex impedances, provided they met the phase-angle requirements stated above. However, usually no practical advantage is derived from using a complex impedance rather than a simple resistance or reactance, so that it is generally best to keep the fixed arms as simple as possible. The simple elements are resistance, capacitance, and inductance. Resistors and capacitors can be selected which are very nearly free from impurities, but inductors always have resistance associated with them and therefore cannot be considered pure reactances. We could, for example, use a resistance in one fixed arm and capacitance in the other to meet quite accurately the requirement that the phase difference be $\pi/2$. On the other hand, a phase difference of $\pi/2$ cannot be set up by using an inductance and a resistance in the fixed arms. We would have to bring the resistance arm into quadrature with the inductive impedance by shunt or series capacitance. At low frequencies, where the effective inductance is not itself a function of frequency (and is therefore useful), this would generally require such a large capacitor as to be rather impractical. Also the phase difference of π, which meets the phase requirements mathematically for some of the bridge types, is impossible to realize in practice since it would require a pure capacitance and a pure inductance as the fixed-arm elements. If, then, we are to restrict our attention to practical bridges in which the fixed arms are simple elements, there are only six types of bridges which meet all our requirements. These are shown in Fig. 30.

From the theoretical point of view there are no essential differences in bridges *a*, *b*, and *c*. Any of them can be used to compare impedances of a similar nature, and all three are so used. Resistance ratio arms (*a*) are

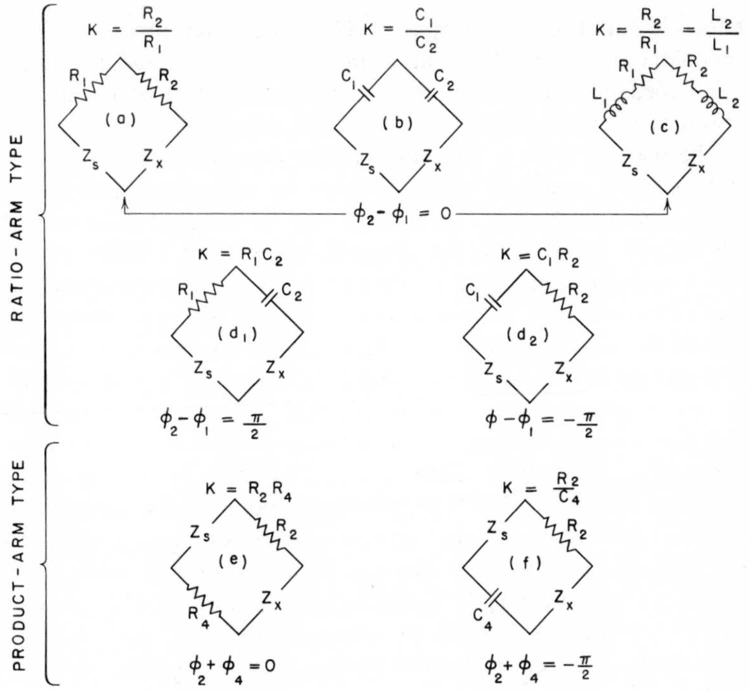

BALANCE EQUATIONS

Unknown	RATIO-ARM TYPE			PRODUCT-ARM TYPE	
	(a,b,c)	(d_1)	(d_2)	(e)	(f)
$R_x =$	KR_s	KL_s	$\frac{K}{C_s}$	KG_s	KC'_s
$L_x =$	KL_s	– –	KR_s	KC'_s	– –
$C_x =$	KC_s	$\frac{1}{KR_s}$	– –	KL'_s	$\frac{1}{KG_s}$
$G_x =$	KG_s	$\frac{1}{KL'_s}$	$\frac{C'_s}{K}$	$\frac{R_s}{K}$	$\frac{1}{KC_s}$
$L'_x =$	KL'_s	– –	$\frac{K}{G_s}$	$\frac{C_s}{K}$	– –
$C'_x =$	KC'_s	$\frac{G_s}{K}$	– –	$\frac{L_s}{K}$	$\frac{R_s}{K}$

Where R, L, C are series components of complex arms
G, L', C' are parallel " " " "

K has the value indicated in the corresponding bridge diagram

FIG. 30.

preferable for a general-purpose bridge since they are usually readily available and readily adjustable to meet various ratio requirements, and have impedances which are very nearly independent of frequency. In some measurements, capacitance ratio arms (*b*) are of advantage. They may be selected to have high impedances, an advantage in the measurement of small capacitors at low frequencies. Also, when high voltages must be used, capacitance ratio arms may be designed to withstand the high voltages without dissipating appreciable energy. Where alternating current must be superposed on direct current in a measurement, capacitance ratio arms may be used to ensure that all the direct current passes through the unknown, and that there is no energy dissipation from the direct current in the ratio arms. Where heavy currents must pass through the bridge, the inductance ratio-arm type (*c*) may be desirable since inductances can be designed to carry heavy currents with relatively small dissipation. These three direct comparison type bridges (*a*, *b*, *c*) are more used than any other type and have good accuracy, especially when the ratio arms are equal. In this case a check for equality of ratio arms may be made by simply interchanging them, and by this means the errors of measurement are largely eliminated. Bridges d_1 and d_2 are complementary, d_1 being employed to measure capacitive, and d_2 inductive impedances. Of the product-arm bridges, type *e* is suitable for measuring any type of impedance in terms of an impedance of the opposite kind, and type *f* may be used for capacitance measurements.

This classification by no means exhausts the possibilities of bridges which have been devised and used with success in various measurement problems. It does set up a useful criterion for independence of the adjustments required to achieve balance in the four-arm impedance bridge. However, it should be borne in mind that, even in the operation of a bridge which complies with Ferguson's classification, independence of balancing adjustments is frequently not the only point which must be considered. Convenience of manipulation, availability of suitable bridge elements, or the necessity for eliminating or compensating some residual error may make another balancing procedure desirable, for which the adjustments are not independent. We will consider a few of the numerous bridge circuits which have been described in the literature,[51] choosing as examples some bridges which have been generally useful and some which will serve to illustrate general classes of networks or types of operating procedures.

[51] A very complete survey of bridges and of their particular fields of usefulness will be found in Hague, *op. cit.*

BRIDGE CIRCUITS

The Maxwell-Wien Bridge. This bridge is designed for the measurement of inductance in terms of capacitance. It was originally described by Maxwell as a ballistic method and was first used as an a-c bridge by Wien. The circuit arrangement is shown in Fig. 31, and it will be seen that this is a product-arm bridge of the type described in Fig. 30(*e*). Here

$$Z_1 = \frac{R_1}{1 + j\omega C_1 R_1}; \quad Z_2 = R_2; \quad Z_3 = R_3 + j\omega L_3; \quad Z_4 = R_4$$

so that the balance equation is

$$\frac{R_1(R_3 + j\omega L_3)}{1 + j\omega C_1 R_1} = R_2 R_4$$

or

$$R_1 R_3 + j\omega L_3 R_1 = R_2 R_4 + j\omega C_1 R_1 R_2 R_4$$

Separating reals and imaginaries, we have

$$R_1 R_3 = R_2 R_4 \quad \text{and} \quad L_3 R_1 = C_1 R_1 R_2 R_4$$

or finally

$$L_3 = C_1 R_2 R_4 \quad \text{and} \quad R_3 = \frac{R_2 R_4}{R_1}$$

In practice R_1, R_2, and R_3 are non-inductive resistors. If both C_1 and L_3 have fixed values, balance must be approached by adjustments of the resistance elements R_1, and R_2 or R_4. These adjustments are not independent, and the balancing procedure may be very tedious. If C_1 and R_1 are adjustable, the criterion of independence is satisfied and the balance may be easily made. Similarly a fixed capacitor could be measured in terms of an adjustable inductor, in which case the balancing adjustments would be independent if L_3 and R_3 were the adjustable elements.

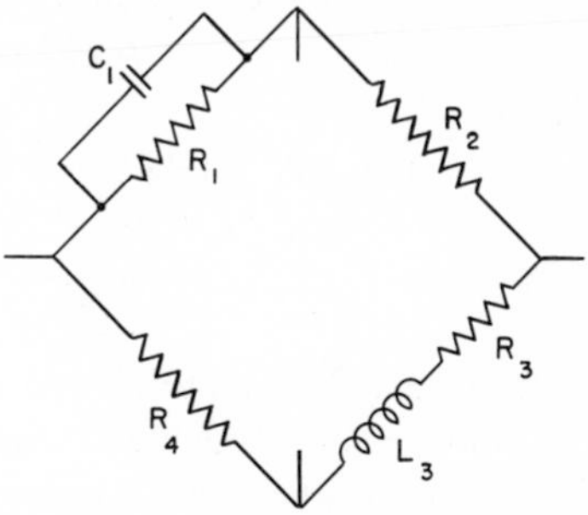

FIG. 31.

RESIDUALS IN BRIDGE ARMS. This bridge was used by Curtis[52] in precision measurements, and he made a complete analysis of the effect on balance conditions of residuals in the arms. Since the effects of impurities in the elements must be considered for any bridge that is to be used in

[52] Curtis, *Electrical Measurements*, p. 113, McGraw-Hill, 1937.

precise work, and since the analysis in this case is typical of such procedures, we will review it in some detail. We will assume that the resistances have residual inductances l_1, l_2, l_3, l_4 (l_3 will be considered to be the inductance of only that part of R_3 which is not included in the inductor L_3), and that the power factor of the capacitor C_1 is $\cos\theta$. Since the impedance of the capacitor can be stated as

$$Z_c = \frac{\cos\theta - j}{\omega C}$$

to a high degree of approximation, we may write

$$\frac{1}{Z_1} = \frac{1}{R_1 + j\omega l_1} + \frac{\omega C}{\cos\theta - j} = \frac{1}{R_1 + j\omega l_1} + \frac{\omega C(\cos\theta + j)}{1 + \cos^2\theta}$$

and

$$Z_1 = \frac{(R_1 + j\omega l_1)(1 + \cos^2\theta)}{[1 + \cos^2\theta + \omega C_1(\cos\theta + j)(R_1 + j\omega l_1)]}$$

Also

$$Z_2 = R_2 + j\omega l_2; \quad Z_3 = R_3 + j\omega(L + l_3); \quad \text{and} \quad Z_4 = R_4 + j\omega l_4$$

The exact balance equation is then

$$\begin{aligned}(1 + \cos^2\theta)&(R_1 + j\omega l_1)[R_3 + j\omega(L + l_3)]\\ &= [1 + \cos^2\theta + \omega C_1(\cos\theta + j)(R_1 + j\omega l_1)](R_2 + j\omega l_2)(R_4 + j\omega l_4)\end{aligned}$$

Separating reals and imaginaries, we obtain

$$\begin{aligned}(1 + \cos^2\theta)&\{R_1R_3 - R_2R_4 + \omega^2[l_2l_4 - l_1(L + l_3)]\}\\ &= \omega C_1[R_1R_2R_4\cos\theta - \omega(R_2R_4l_1 + R_1R_4l_2 + R_1R_2l_4)\\ &\quad - \omega^2(R_1l_2l_4 + R_4l_1l_2 + R_2l_1l_4)\cos\theta + \omega^3l_1l_2l_4]\end{aligned}$$

and

$$\begin{aligned}(1 + \cos^2\theta)&[R_1(L + l_3) + R_3l_1 - R_4l_2 - R_2l_4]\\ &= C_1[R_1R_2R_4 + \omega(R_1R_4l_2 + R_1R_2l_4 + R_2R_4l_1)\cos\theta\\ &\quad - \omega^2(R_1l_2l_4 + R_4l_1l_2 + R_2l_1l_4) - \omega^3l_1l_2l_4\cos\theta]\end{aligned}$$

Only the latter equation need be considered in determining the inductance L, and we can make certain simplifying assumptions. For air capacitors, or for mica capacitors of high quality, $\cos\theta < 10^{-3}$, so that $\cos^2\theta < 10^{-6}$ and hence is negligible compared to unity. Now let

$$\frac{\omega l_1}{R_1} = \alpha; \quad \frac{\omega l_2}{R_2} = \beta; \quad \frac{\omega l_4}{R_4} = \gamma$$

and we have

$$\begin{aligned}R_1(L + l_3) &+ R_3l_1 - R_2l_4 - R_4l_2\\ &= C_1R_1R_2R_4[1 + (\alpha + \beta + \gamma)\cos\theta - (\alpha\gamma + \alpha\beta + \beta\gamma) - \alpha\beta\gamma\cos\theta]\end{aligned}$$

If the time constant l/R of each of the resistors is less than 10^{-6}, and if $\omega \leqslant 1000$ ($f \leqslant 150$), α, β, and γ will each be less than 10^{-3}, and

$$[(\alpha + \beta + \gamma)\cos\theta - (\alpha\beta + \alpha\gamma + \beta\gamma) - \alpha\beta\gamma\cos\theta] < 3 \times 10^{-6}$$

and is therefore negligible compared to unity. Under these conditions, for low frequencies, we will have

$$L = C_1R_2R_4 + \frac{1}{R_1}(R_4l_2 + R_2l_4 - R_1l_3 - R_3l_1)$$

Now, if the bridge were arranged so that the resistances of the arms were approximately equal ($R_1 \approx R_2 \approx R_3 \approx R_4$), we can interchange R_1 and R_2, and obtain a new balance by changing C_1 to $(C_1 + \Delta C_1)$ and R_3 to $(R_3 + \Delta R_3)$, the changes ΔC_1 and ΔR_3 being small compared to C_1 and R_3, and l_3 being unchanged by the small change in R_3. For the new balance we will have

$$L = (C_1 + \Delta C_1)R_1R_4 + \frac{1}{R_2}[R_4l_1 + R_1l_4 - R_2l_3 - (R_3 + \Delta R_3)l_2]$$

Since we have $R_2 \approx R_1$ and $R_3 \approx R_4$ nearly enough that they may be used interchangeably in the correction terms, we may add our expressions for L and divide by 2 to obtain

$$L = R_4\left(\frac{R_1 + R_2}{2}\right)\left(C_1 + \frac{\Delta C_1}{2}\right) + l_4 - l_3 - \Delta R_3\frac{l_2}{R_2}$$

in which the final term will usually be negligible since both ΔR_3 and l_2/R_2 are very small.

It has been tacitly assumed in the discussion above that capacitance (except C_1, of course) in parallel with any bridge element may be treated as a part of the residual inductance of the element. This assumption is valid for all elements except the inductor. If there is a capacitance C_3 in parallel with the inductor (resulting from leads to the coil, binding posts, etc.) then the inductance equation must be modified and we have very approximately[53]

$$L = R_4\left(\frac{R_1 + R_2}{2}\right)\left(C_1 + \frac{\Delta C_1}{2}\right)(1 - \omega^2LC_3) + l_4 - l_3$$

Curtis states that in his bridge C_3 could usually be kept less than 10 $\mu\mu$f, so that (with $\omega \leqslant 1000$) inductances as large as 0.1 henry could be measured to a part in a million without requiring a correction for C_3. For larger inductances or for higher frequencies the correction for C_3 must be examined. Of course, in this case ($\omega > 1000$) the other correction terms which were omitted in our simplified formula might also require consideration.

[53] See p. 664.

SUBSTITUTION METHOD. It will be noted that the method of balance just described eliminates the correction terms resulting from residuals in the equal resistance elements which were interchanged, but requires that account be taken of the residuals in the remaining arms (l_3 and l_4). This can be avoided by use of a substitution method in which a resistor of such form that its inductance can be calculated is substituted for the inductance L.[54] The bridge is first balanced in the usual way with L in place. Then L is removed, and the substitution inductor l is connected in its place. A new balance is obtained by changing C_1 to C_1'. For the first balance we have

$$L = C_1R_2R_4(1 - \omega^2C_3L) + \frac{1}{R_1}(R_4l_2 + R_2l_4 - R_3l_1 - R_1l_3)$$

and for the substitution standard

$$l = C_1'R_2R_4 + \frac{1}{R_1}(R_4l_2 + R_2l_4 - R_3l_1 - R_1l_3)$$

Subtracting, we have

$$L = l + (C_1 - C_1')R_2R_4(1 - \omega^2C_3L)$$

the negligibly small quantity ($\omega^2C_3LC_1'R_2R_4$) having been added to the resulting expression. It will be noted that the effect of the residuals in all the resistance elements of the bridge have been eliminated by leaving these elements unchanged while a known standard is substituted for the unknown. Such a procedure may frequently be employed with profit in bridge measurements to eliminate the effects of residuals in bridge elements which are not disturbed by the substitution.

The Anderson Bridge. This is a very important and useful modification of the Maxwell-Wien bridge. It was described by Anderson as a ballistic method in 1891, and by Rowland as an a-c bridge in 1898. It is commonly used for the determination of inductance in terms of capacitance and resistance, and is shown in Fig. 32(*a*).

Making use of the Y-Δ transformation of Fig. 32(*b*), it will be seen that the Anderson bridge of Fig. 32(*a*) is the equivalent of the Maxwell-Wien bridge of Fig. 32(*c*). (The resistance R_{AC} in parallel with the voltage source contributes nothing to the balance, of course.) The

[54] The substituted resistor usually takes the form of a parallel loop of resistance wire, the wires being small and spaced about 1 cm apart. The inductance of such a loop is given approximately by the formula

$$l = 4a\left(\frac{1}{4} + \log_\varepsilon \frac{b}{d}\right) \times 10^{-9} \text{ henry}$$

a being the length of the loop (half the total length of the resistance wire), *b* the spacing between wires, and *d* the wire diameter, all in centimeters.

equations of balance can be obtained by substitution in the balance equations of the Maxwell-Wien bridge.[55] The balance equations are

$$R_1R_3 = R_2R_4, \quad \text{and} \quad L = CR_2\left[R_5\left(1 + \frac{R_4}{R_1}\right) + R_4\right]$$

The balancing adjustments are independent if R_3 and R_5 are made the adjustable elements. It has been shown[56] that for maximum sensitivity to changes in R_5 we should have $L/C = 2R_3^2$, and $R_1 = R_4 = R_3/2 = R_2/2$.

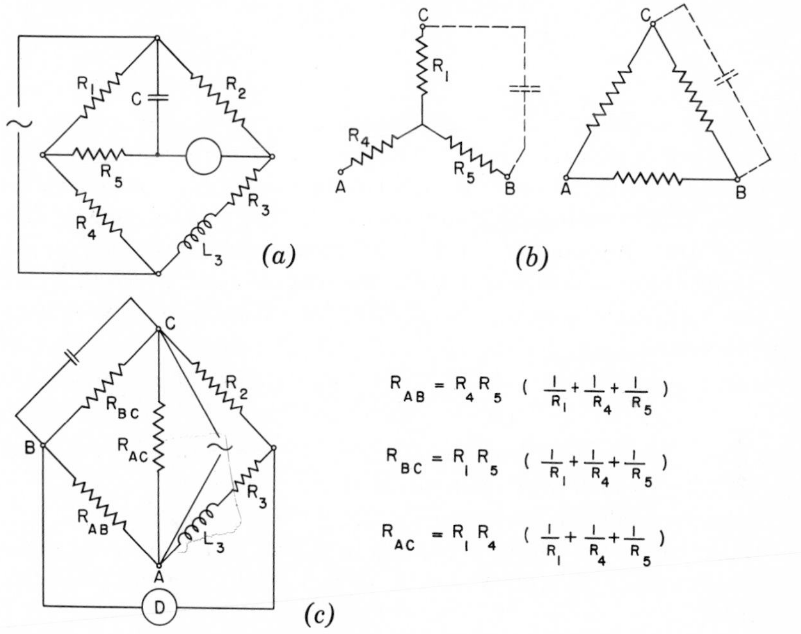

FIG. 32.

This bridge is capable of high precision, and may be used to measure a wide range of inductances with reasonable values of C and R_5. If the value of R_5 becomes very large, the sensitivity may be increased by interchanging the detector and voltage supply,[57] and by increasing the supply voltage which will now be in series with R_5.

The exact equations of balance, taking account of the residuals in the resistance elements and the power factor of the capacitor, can be computed

[55] These equations can, of course, also be derived directly by using Maxwell's cyclic currents. See p. 688.

[56] Butterworth, *Proc. Phys. Soc. (London)*, **24,** 83 (1912).

[57] This conjugate Anderson bridge is known as the Stroud and Oates bridge.

by the same process that was used for the corresponding equation of the Maxwell-Wien bridge, and we obtain

$$L = CR_2\left[R_5\left(1+\frac{R_4}{R_1}\right)+R_4\right]\cdot[1+(\alpha+\beta+\gamma+\delta+\text{similar terms})\cos\theta$$

$$-(\alpha\beta+\alpha\gamma+\alpha\delta+\text{similar terms})-(\alpha\beta\gamma+\alpha\beta\delta+\text{similar terms})\cos\theta]$$

$$+\frac{R_2l_4+R_4l_2-R_3l_1-R_1l_3}{R_1}$$

where

$$\alpha=\frac{\omega l_1}{R_1};\quad \beta=\frac{\omega l_2}{R_2};\quad \gamma=\frac{\omega l_3}{R_3};\quad \delta=\frac{\omega l_5}{R_5}$$

(the phase angles of the various resistance elements), and $\cos\theta$ is the power factor of the capacitor C. It may be seen that, for low frequencies, all terms of the types $\alpha\cos\theta$, $\alpha\beta$, $\alpha\beta\gamma\cos\theta$ are negligibly small compared to unity, subject to the same limitations as in the case of the Maxwell-Wien bridge. It should be noted further that all the terms which involve the power factor of the capacitor and the residual associated with R_5 are of this type. Then at low frequencies the balance equation is very approximately

$$L = CR_2\left[R_5\left(1+\frac{R_4}{R_1}\right)+R_4\right]+\frac{R_2l_4+R_4l_2-R_3l_1-R_1l_3}{R_1}$$

and is not affected by the power factor of the capacitor if it is of good quality (pf < 0.001) or by the residual of R_5.

Under the conditions of symmetry stated above, $R_1 \approx R_4 \approx R_3/2 \approx R_2/2$, we can eliminate the effect of residuals in R_1 and R_4 by taking the mean of two balances with arms R_1 and R_4 interchanged. For this procedure we have

$$CL = R_2\left[\left(R_5+\frac{\Delta R_5}{2}\right)\left(1+\frac{R_4}{R_1}+R_4\right)\right]+l_2-l_3$$

Not only can the Anderson bridge (together with its conjugate, the Stroud and Oates bridge) be used to measure inductances from very small to very large values, but it has also been employed to measure the residuals of resistors.[58] In this case a substitution method similar to the one already described may be used to eliminate the effects of residuals in the bridge elements. The substitution standard will take the form of a loop resistance wire with calculable residuals, adjusted to have as nearly as possible the same resistance as the unknown resistor. The ratio arms R_1 and R_4 should be equal, and the balances are made by adjustments of R_3 and R_5. If necessary, a small inductor can be added to branch 3 of

[58] Grover and Curtis, *Bull. Bur. Standards*, **8**, 461 (1913).

the bridge in order that R_5 may have a reasonable value, and left in place during the measurement of both the unknown and the substituted standard. Then, if $R_1 = R_4$, we have

$$\Delta L = 2CR_2\Delta R_5 - \Delta l_3$$

where ΔL is the difference in inductance of the standard and the unknown, ΔR_5 is the change in resistance of R_5, and Δl_3 is the change in the inductance of the adjustable portion of R_3 between balances.

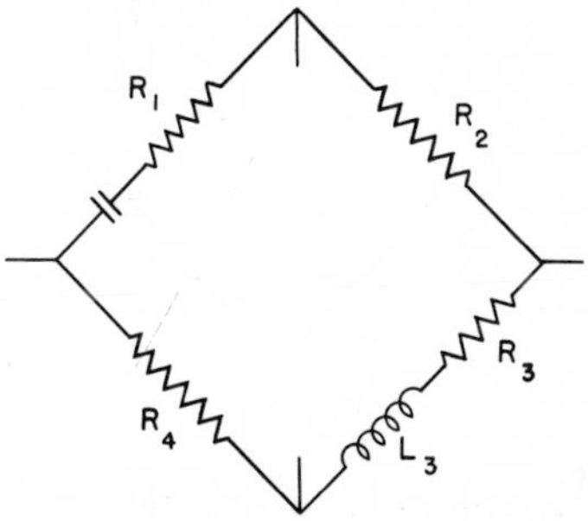

FIG. 33.

The Hay Bridge. This is another modification of the Maxwell-Wien bridge which may be used to advantage if the phase angle of the inductor ($\tan^{-1} \omega L/R$) is large. The circuit arrangement is shown in Fig. 33. In this arrangement the resistance element R_1 is in series with the capacitor C_1, and a smaller value of resistance is required than would be the case for a parallel resistor. The balance equation is

$$\left(R_1 - \frac{j}{\omega C_1}\right)(R_3 + j\omega L_3) = R_2R_4$$

Separating reals and imaginaries, we have

$$R_1R_3 + \frac{L_3}{C_1} = R_2R_4$$

and

$$\omega L_3R_1 - \frac{R_3}{\omega C_1} = 0$$

These equations may be solved simultaneously to obtain

$$L_3 = \frac{C_1R_2R_4}{1 + \omega^2R_1^2C_1^2}, \quad \text{and} \quad R_3 = \frac{\omega^2C_1^2R_1R_2R_4}{1 + \omega^2R_1^2C_1^2}$$

It will be noted that the final equations of balance contain terms in ω^2, so that the balance condition is a function of frequency. However, the frequency need not be accurately known to determine L since ω appears only in a term which will be small compared to unity in cases where use of the Hay bridge is indicated (i.e. where $\omega L/R$ is large).[59]

[59] It is of interest to note that a commercial, direct-reading bridge, General Radio Type 650A impedance bridge, makes use of the Maxwell-Wien circuit for measuring coils of low Q (small $\omega L/R$), and the Hay circuit for coils of high Q (large $\omega L/R$).

This bridge is also of Ferguson's product-arm type [Fig. 30(*e*)], and it could be balanced by making R_1 and C_1 adjustable, so that the balance adjustments are independent. However, in practice it is often more convenient to use a capacitor of fixed value and to make R_1 and either R_2 or R_4 adjustable.

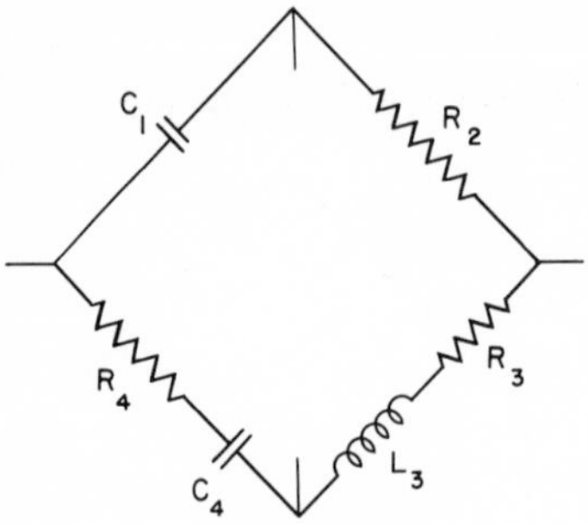

FIG. 34.

The Owen Bridge. This is another arrangement which has been much used for the determination of inductance in terms of resistance and capacitance. Its circuit is shown in Fig. 34, and it will be seen to be a ratio-arm bridge of the type illustrated in Fig. 30(*d*).[60] It has the advantage of being useful over a very wide range of inductances with capacitors of reasonable size, and the effects of residuals in the elements can be largely eliminated by a balancing procedure which will be described later. The balance equation may be written as

$$\frac{-j}{\omega C_1}(R_3 + j\omega L_3) = R_2\left(R_4 - \frac{j}{\omega C_4}\right)$$

Separation of terms yields the equations

$$R_3 = \frac{C_1}{C_4}R_2, \quad \text{and} \quad L_3 = C_1R_2R_4$$

If C_4 and R_4 are made the adjustable elements, the balancing adjustments are independent. Since ω does not appear in the final balance equations the bridge is insensitive to frequency and wave form.

The residuals of the bridge elements must be considered in precise measurements. The impedances of the arms may be written as

$$Z_1 = \frac{\cos\theta_1 - j}{\omega C_1}; \quad Z_2 = R_2 + j\omega l_2; \quad Z_3 = R_3 + j\omega(L + l_3);$$

$$Z_4 = R_4 + j\omega l_4 + \frac{\cos\theta - j}{\omega C_4}$$

The expression for L, taking account of the residuals, is then

$$L = C_1R_2R_4 - l_3 - \frac{R_3\cos\theta_1}{\omega} + \frac{C_1R_2}{\omega C_4}\cos\theta_4 - l_2\frac{C_1}{C_4}(\omega^2 l_4C_4 - 1)$$

[60] A shielded Owen bridge for precise measurements of inductance was developed at the Bell Telephone Laboratories and has been described by Ferguson, *Bell System Tech. J.*, **6**, 375 (1927). A modified Owen bridge for core-loss and permeability measurements has been discussed previously in Chapter 9.

If an auxiliary balance is taken with L removed from the circuit or shorted out (making the necessary balancing adjustments by changing R_4 to R_4' and R_3 to R_3'), we will have

$$0 = C_1R_2R_4' - l_3' - \frac{R_3'}{\omega}\cos\theta_1 + \frac{C_1C_2}{\omega C_4}\cos\theta_4 - \frac{l_2C_1}{C_4}(\omega^2 l_4 C_4 - 1)$$

The difference between these expressions is

$$L = C_1R_2(R_4 - R_4') - (l_3 - l_3') - \frac{R_3 - R_3'}{\omega}\cos\theta_1$$

Now, since the adjustment of arm 3 consists merely of adding resistance to compensate for the resistance which was removed from the circuit with the inductor, and since the change in R_4 has no effect on the value of R_3, the difference $(R_3 - R_3')$ will be exceedingly small. The correction term involving R_3 will then be negligible, and our expression for inductance becomes

$$L = C_1R_2(R_4 - R_4') - (l_3 - l_3')$$

If the resistor used in R_3 is so constructed that its inductance is not altered as its resistance is changed,[61] the correction term in l_3 becomes negligible also. It will be noted that this procedure, which in principle is a substitution method, eliminates the effects of residuals in the bridge arms except for the residual associated with the change in the resistor R_3, required to restore balance.

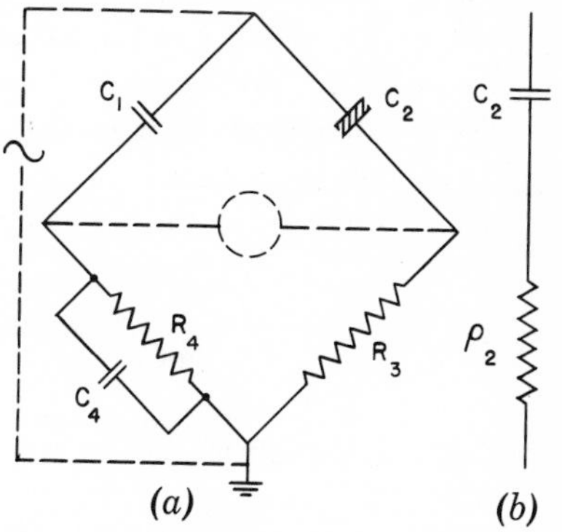

FIG. 35.

The Schering Bridge.[62] This is one of the most important and useful circuits available for the measurement of capacitance and dielectric loss. It is very generally used, both for precision measurements on capacitors at low voltages and for the study of insulation and insulating structures at high voltages. Its circuit, shown in Fig. 35(a), will be seen to be a product-arm bridge of the type shown in Fig. 30(f). It may be considered a device for comparing an imperfect capacitor [represented in

[61] Such resistance boxes are available; for example, the General Radio No. 670 compensated decade resistor is stated to change inductance by less than 0.05 μhenry for a total change of 111 ohms in resistance.

[62] Actually the circuit was first described by Thomas in a patent application filed in 1913 (U.S. Patent 1,166,159), but its usefulness was not generally realized until after the work of Schering and his associates at the P.T. Reichsanstalt, starting in 1920.

Fig. 35(*b*) in terms of its equivalent capacitance C_2 and series resistance ρ_2] with a standard capacitor, assumed to be free from losses. In high-voltage applications, voltage is applied at the junction between arms 1 and 2 and between arms 3 and 4, with the latter junction grounded, as shown in the figure. Since the impedances of the capacitance arms are enormously higher at power frequencies than those of the resistance arms, most of the voltage will appear across the capacitors, so that the detector and resistance arms will not be more than a few volts from ground potential. This arrangement is ideal from the point of view of safety, since the operator will not be exposed to high-voltage hazards when making the balancing adjustments in arms 3 and 4. The sensitivity of the bridge is, of course, much less for this arrangement than for its conjugate (with the source and detector interchanged), but at high voltages the sensitivity, with a good detector, will usually be ample for all practical purposes.[63] In precise measurements at low voltages the conjugate bridge is often used since in this case K will be much smaller and the sensitivity much greater.

The impedances of the Schering-bridge arms are

$$Z_1 = \frac{-j}{\omega C_1}; \quad Z_2 = \rho_2 - \frac{j}{\omega C_2}; \quad Z_3 = R_3; \quad Z_4 = \frac{1}{(1/R_4) + j\omega C_4} = \frac{R_4}{1 + j\omega C_4 R_4}$$

The balance equation may be written as

$$\frac{-jR_3}{\omega C_1}(1 + j\omega C_4 R_4) = R_4\left(\rho_2 - \frac{j}{\omega C_2}\right)$$

from which

$$C_2 = C_1 \frac{R_4}{R_3}, \quad \text{and} \quad \rho_2 = \frac{C_4}{C_1} \cdot R_3$$

The quality of a capacitor is frequently stated in terms of its phase defect angle (the angle by which the current departs from exact quadrature with the voltage, i.e. the complement of the phase angle). If the phase defect angle is δ and the phase angle is θ, we have $\theta + \delta = \pi/2$, and for small values of δ, $\tan\delta \approx \sin\delta = \cos\theta$. Tan δ is frequently called the *dissipation factor* (D) for a series R-C circuit, so that we have, for low

[63] In the expression for voltage of unbalance (see p. 695)

$$e = E \cdot p \frac{K}{(1 + K)^2}$$

K is very large so that $e \approx E \cdot p/K$, but, since E is also large, e will have a reasonable value.

power factors, dissipation factor ≈ power factor. The dissipation factor[64] (and approximate power factor) of C_2 is then

$$\tan \delta = \omega \rho_2 C_2 = \omega C_4 R_4 \approx \cos \theta$$

BRUCKMANN'S MODIFICATION. The simple Schering bridge of Fig. 35 can be used to measure the losses of only small and moderate-sized capacitors at high voltages. For large capacitors (for example, a reel length of cable) the charging current may exceed the rating of the adjustable non-inductive resistor (R_3). In this case R_3 can be paralleled by a low-resistance shunt (S), constructed to carry the expected charging

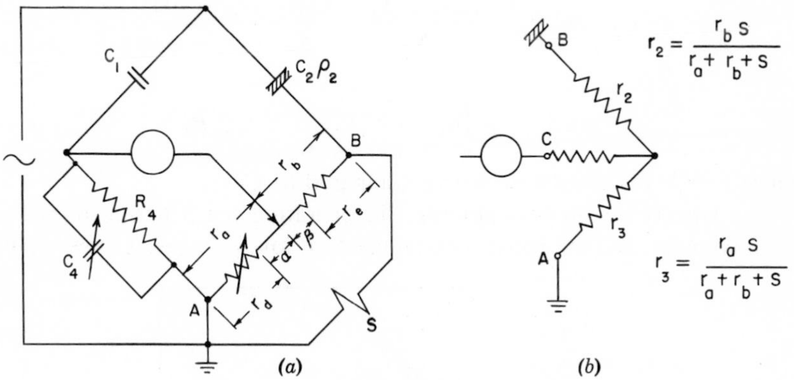

FIG. 36.

current. If the detector junction point of the bridge remained the same, the new value of resistance in arm 3 would be

$$R_3' = \frac{R_3 S}{R_3 + S} \approx S$$

and the range of balancing adjustment available by permissible variations of R_3 would be too restricted for practical use. If, however, the large resistance R_3, in parallel with the low-resistance shunt, is tapped at some intermediate point which can be varied along the resistor, the range of balancing adjustment may be increased to the extent required for satisfactory operation. An arrangement of this type, which has been used in commercial bridges,[65] is shown in Fig. 36(a). For convenience the adjustable section of the high resistance is made up of a slide wire and a

[64] If R_4 is fixed at a value $10^6/\omega$ (i.e. 2652.6 ohms for 60-cycle operation) the balance value of the capacitance C_4, in microfarads, is equal to the dissipation factor. Thus a direct-reading "dissipation-factor" scale can be constructed for the bridge. In this case the adjustable elements would be R_3 and C_4.

[65] Bruckmann, *Rev. gén. de l'élec.*, **17**, 881 (1925).

non-inductive decade resistor, the upper portion of the resistance being fixed in value. The resistance (r_b) above the detector junction is made up of a fixed resistor (r_e) and β, the upper portion of the slide wire. The resistance (r_a) below the junction is the lower portion (α) of the slide wire and the decade resistance box (r_d). Switching arrangements are incorporated into the commercial bridge such that one of a number of shunts can be selected, while the total resistance of $S + r_e + \alpha + \beta$ remains fixed at 100 ohms. If we make the Δ-Y transformation indicated in Fig. 36(b), and substitute the resulting equivalent resistances into the bridge equation, we have

$$C_2 = C_1 R_4 \frac{(r_a + r_b + S)}{r_a \cdot S} = \frac{C_1 R_4}{S} \cdot \frac{(r_d + 100)}{(r_d + \alpha)}$$

and

$$\tan \delta = \omega C_4 R_4 - \omega C_1 R_4 \cdot \frac{r_b}{r_a} \approx \omega C_4 R_4$$

since $C_1(r_b/r_a)$ is usually negligible compared to C_4.

THE SHIELDED SCHERING BRIDGE. In operating the Schering bridge at high voltages, and in precise measurements at low voltages, it is extremely

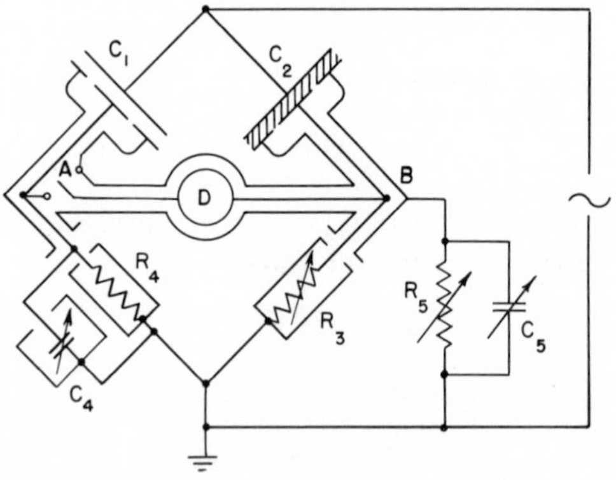

FIG. 37.

important that the effect of stray capacitances between the bridge elements be eliminated. This can be done by enclosing the vulnerable portions of the network within electrostatic shields and by maintaining these shields at suitable potentials.[66] Such a shielded bridge, suitable for high-voltage operation, is shown in Fig. 37. Both the standard air capacitor (C_1) and the test capacitor (C_2) are shown as three-electrode capacitors. The guard electrode in each case is connected to the shield system which

[66] The general question of shielding bridge components will be taken up in a later section.

completely encloses the detector branch of the circuit and the conductors between the low-voltage electrodes of C_1 and C_2 and the resistors R_3 and R_4. This shield is maintained at the same potential as the detector by means of the auxiliary bridge arm R_5–C_5, equality of potentials being adjusted and checked by means of an auxiliary bridge balance, with the detector connected between the shield and a junction point of the main bridge. (In Fig. 37 the switch at A is used either to connect the detector in the main bridge circuit for the regular balance, or between the shield and the junction point B for the auxiliary balance.) The low-voltage arms R_3 and R_4–C_4 are enclosed in shields which are directly grounded. There will be no direct capacitance between high-voltage leads and the detector branch of the circuit or the leads to the low-voltage arms, because of the enclosing shield; or to the low-voltage elements themselves since they are enclosed in grounded shields. Capacitance current between the high-voltage conductors and the detector shield flows to ground through the auxiliary arm R_5–C_5 and does not enter the measuring circuit. Capacitance between the high-voltage portion of the circuit and the ground shields around the low-voltage arms (or to other grounded objects) is in parallel with the supply voltage and acts as an additional load on the source but does not affect the measurements. Capacitance between the detector branch and its shield has no potential difference across it and so does not affect the measuring circuit. This implies, of course, an equality of instantaneous potentials, and not merely of mean potentials, so that provision must be made for phase adjustment as well as magnitude adjustment in the auxiliary arm. (This explains the need for a capacitor shunting the resistor R_5.) Thus, only the direct capacitances between the guarded electrodes of C_1 and C_2 and the corresponding high-voltage electrodes act in the measuring circuit, when both the main bridge and the auxiliary arm are balanced.

The grounded shields enclosing the resistors R_3 and R_4 protect them from influence by external fields but at the same time increase their own residuals; and in precise measurements these residuals must be taken into account. If we have $(R_3 + j\omega l_3)$ and $(R_4 + j\omega l_4)$ as the impedances of these resistors, the complete equation of the Schering bridge becomes

$$\frac{-j}{\omega C_1}(R_3 + j\omega l_3) = \left(\rho_2 - \frac{j}{\omega C_2}\right)\left(\frac{R_4 + j\omega l_4}{1 - \omega^2 l_4 C_4 + j\omega C_4 R_4}\right)$$

Now, recalling that $\tan\delta = \omega\rho_2 C_2 \approx \delta$, and letting $\phi_3 = \omega l_3/R_3$ and $\phi_4 = \omega l_4/R_4$, our equation may be separated and reduced to the form

$$C_2(1 - \phi_3\delta) = C_1\frac{R_4}{R_3}$$

and

$$\tan \delta = \omega C_4 R_4 (1 - \phi_3 \phi_4) + \phi_3 - \phi_4$$

or, since δ, ϕ_3, and ϕ_4 are all quite small

$$C_2 = C_1 \frac{R_4}{R_3}$$

and

$$\tan \delta = \omega C_4 R_4 + \phi_3 - \phi_4$$

The corrections resulting from residuals in R_3 and R_4 can be made negligible if the resistors are of the same construction and the bridge is arranged so that $R_3 \approx R_4$. In the absence of such equality the effect of residuals in R_3 and R_4 can be eliminated by a substitution method. We will suppose that both C_1 and C_2 have loss angles ϕ_1 and ϕ_2, and that the phase angles of R_3 and R_4 are ϕ_3 and ϕ_4 respectively. Also we will connect a capacitor C_3 in parallel with R_3. The balance conditions are now

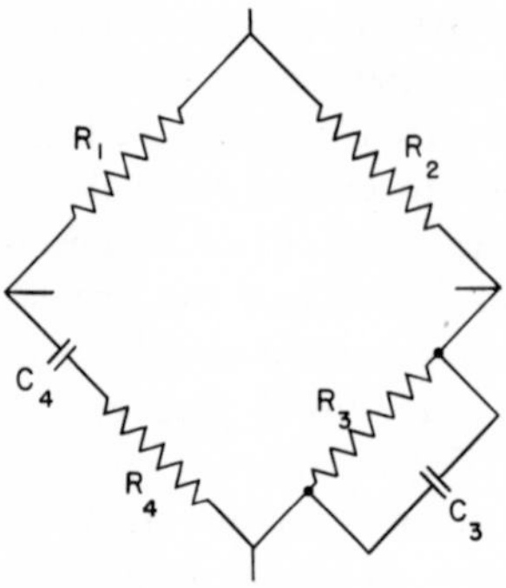

FIG. 38.

$$C_2 = C_1 \frac{R_4}{R_3}$$

and

$$\phi_2 - \phi_1 = \omega C_4 R_4 - \omega C_3 R_3 + \phi_3 - \phi_4$$

If we replace C_2 by an adjustable standard C_2' whose loss angle is known to be ϕ_2' (or better, which is known to be loss free), and rebalance the bridge by adjusting C_2 and C_4, leaving all other elements at their previous values, the balance conditions become

$$C_2' = C_1 \frac{R_4}{R_3}$$

and

$$\phi_2' - \phi_1 = \omega R_4 C_4' - \omega R_3 C_3 + \phi_3 - \phi_4$$

Thus $C_2' = C_2$, and $\phi_2 - \phi_2' = \omega R_4 (C_4 - C_4')$, and the effects of constant residuals in the other elements are completely eliminated.

The Wien Bridge. This bridge, shown in Fig. 38, was widely used for measuring capacitors and their losses, even at high voltages, until the advantages of the Schering bridge were generally realized. This circuit is frequency sensitive, and its principal applications at the present time are in the determination and control of frequency. We have

$$Z_1 = R_1; \quad Z_2 = R_2; \quad Z_3 = \frac{R_3}{1 + j\omega R_3 C_3}; \quad Z_4 = R_4 - \frac{j}{\omega C_4}$$

The balance equation is

$$\frac{R_1R_3}{1+j\omega R_3C_3} = R_2R_4 - \frac{jR_2}{\omega C_4}$$

or

$$\omega R_1R_3C_4 = \omega R_2R_4C_4 + \omega R_2R_3C_3 - jR_2 + j\omega^2R_2R_3R_4C_3C_4$$

so that we have, on separating, $\omega^2R_3R_4C_3C_4 = 1$, and $R_1/R_2 = R_4/R_3 + C_3/C_4$. Then

$$\omega^2 = \frac{1}{R_3R_4C_3C_4}, \quad \text{or} \quad f = \frac{1}{2\pi\sqrt{R_3R_4C_3C_4}}$$

If we make $R_1 = 2R_2$, and also $R_3 = R_4$ and $C_3 = C_4$ at balance, the expression for frequency reduces to $f = 1/2\pi R_3C_3$. Under these conditions, if C_3 and C_4 are held at fixed values, R_3 and R_4 can be operated from a single shaft in order that their equality can be assured at all times, and balance is possible from a single control. This control dial could, if desired, be calibrated to read directly in frequency units, and decade steps could be made available by a switching arrangement to change C_3 and C_4 by suitable amounts. Balancing the bridge would be difficult unless the wave form of the applied voltage was fairly pure, since, when the fundamental is balanced, the bridge is not balanced for harmonics, and the minimum indication of the detector would tend to be masked in the presence of any considerable harmonic content.[67]

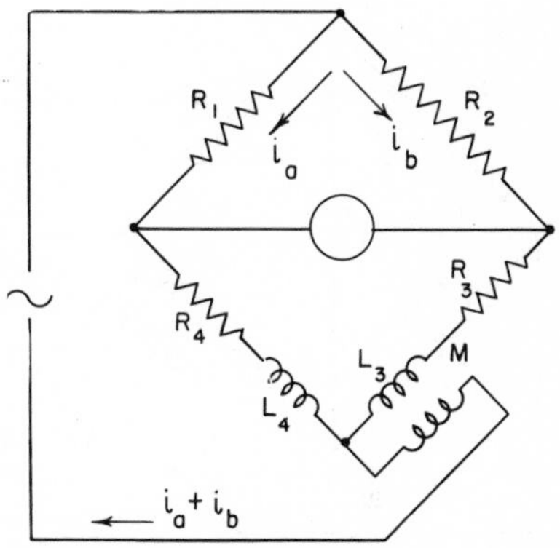

FIG. 39.

Mutual-Inductance Bridges

The Heaviside-Campbell Bridge. This bridge, shown in Fig. 39, is designed for the comparison of self- and mutual inductances, and differs from the bridges previously discussed in that coupling between bridge arms (in this case between arm 3 and the diagonal arm containing the source of voltage) is deliberately present, and is important in establishing balance conditions. If there is to be no current in the detector branch

[67] This characteristic is sometimes used to control the frequency of vacuum-tube oscillators, by supplying degenerative control from the output of a Wien bridge to prevent the circuit from oscillating at any frequency except that for which the bridge is balanced.

of the network, there must be no potential difference across it. Then at balance we will have

$$i_a R_1 = i_b R_2, \quad \text{and} \quad i_b(R_3 + j\omega L_3) + (i_a + i_b) j\omega M = i_a(R_4 + j\omega L_4)$$

From the first relation $i_a = i_b(R_2/R_1)$, which may be substituted in the second relation to give

$$R_3 + j\omega L_3 + \left(1 + \frac{R_2}{R_1}\right) j\omega M = \frac{R_2}{R_1}(R_4 + j\omega L_4)$$

This expression separates to $R_1 R_3 = R_2 R_4$, and

$$M = (R_2 L_4 - R_1 L_3)/(R_1 + R_2)$$

It will be noted that the self-inductance (L_3) of one winding of the mutual inductor must be known in order to determine M. Naturally with a calibrated standard of mutual inductance the value of a self-inductance could also be measured in this bridge.

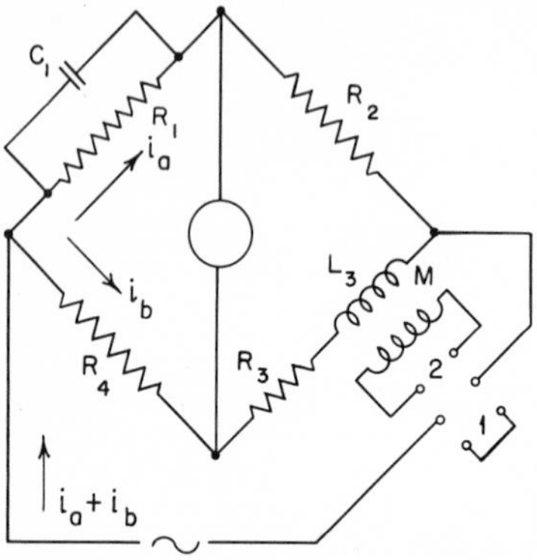

FIG. 40.

The Modified Maxwell-Wien Bridge. A modification of the Maxwell-Wien bridge can conveniently be used to determine mutual inductance in terms of resistance and capacitance.[68] This modification, shown in Fig. 40, also requires the determination of the self-inductance of one coil of the mutual inductor, preferably that having the higher inductance. This is done with the double-pole, double-throw switch of Fig. 40 in position 1. It will be seen that this circuit is identical with the Maxwell-Wien bridge already discussed,[69] and the same balance conditions apply. With the switch in position 2 the second coil of the inductor is connected in series with the source of voltage, and its connection should be such that the emf induced in arm 3 of the bridge opposes the emf resulting from the self-inductance L_3. For the balance in which M is included in the measuring circuit, we have

$$i_a \cdot \frac{R_1}{1 + j\omega C_1 R_1} = i_b R_4, \quad \text{and} \quad i_a R_2 = i_b(R_3 + j\omega L_3) - (i_a + i_b) j\omega M$$

These equations can be combined to give

$$\frac{R_2 R_4}{R_1}(1 + j\omega C_1 R_1) = (R_3 + j\omega L_3) - \left[1 + \frac{R_4}{R_1}(1 + j\omega C_1 R_1)\right] j\omega M$$

[68] Curtis, *Electrical Measurements*, p. 117, McGraw-Hill, 1937.
[69] See p. 705.

Separating reals and imaginaries, we have

$$L_3 = M\left(1 + \frac{R_4}{R_1}\right) + C_1R_2R_4$$

or, if we consider the effects of residuals in the resistance elements,

$$L_3 = M\left(1 + \frac{R_4}{R_1}\right) + C_1R_2R_4 + \frac{1}{R_1}(R_4l_2 + R_2l_4 - R_1l_3 - R_3l_1)$$
$$+ \text{higher-order terms}$$

Now suppose that in the self-inductance balance (switch in position 1) the values for the various elements were the same except that the capacitance was changed to C_1' and the resistance in arm 3 was changed to R_3' (i.e. C_1 and R_3 are used as the balancing adjustments). The balance equation can be stated from our previous analysis as

$$L_3 = C_1'R_2R_4 + \frac{1}{R_1}(R_4l_2 + R_2l_4 - R_1l_3' - R_3'l_1) + \text{higher-order terms}$$

If we equate the two values for L_3 and solve the resulting expression for M, we obtain

$$M = (C_1' - C_1)\cdot\frac{R_1R_2R_4}{R_1 + R_4} + \frac{(l_3 - l_3')}{R_1 + R_4}R_1 + l_1\frac{(R_3 - R_3')}{R_1 + R_4}$$
$$+ \text{higher-order terms}$$

The higher-order terms which have not been stated involve products of residuals together with terms in ω^2, so that the equation for M can be considered precise only at low frequencies.

The Carey-Foster (Heydweiller) Bridge. This bridge, designed for the comparison of capacitance with mutual inductance, was described as a ballistic method by Carey-Foster in 1887 and modified for a-c use by Heydweiller in 1894. The circuit is usually drawn in the conventional form of Fig. 41, where it must be understood that arm 3 is of *zero* impedance. As in the previous mutual-inductance bridges, we have[70]

$$i_a\left(R_1 - \frac{j}{\omega C_1}\right) = i_bR_2$$

and

$$i_a(R_4 + j\omega L_4) - (i_a + i_b)j\omega M = 0$$

[70] It will be apparent from inspection that the emf produced in arm 4 from the mutual inductance must oppose that resulting from the self-inductance in order that a balance be possible.

Combining these equations, we have

$$\frac{R_2(R_4 + j\omega L_4)}{R_1 - \dfrac{j}{\omega C_1}} = \left(1 + \frac{R_2}{R_1 - \dfrac{j}{\omega C_1}}\right) \cdot j\omega M$$

from which

$$M = C_1 R_2 R_4, \quad \text{and} \quad L_4 = M\left(1 + \frac{R_1}{R_2}\right) = C_1 R_4 (R_1 + R_2)$$

or, if C_1 and R_1 are to be determined in terms of inductance and resistance,

$$C_1 = \frac{M}{R_2 R_4}, \quad \text{and} \quad R_1 = \frac{R_2}{M}(L_4 - M)$$

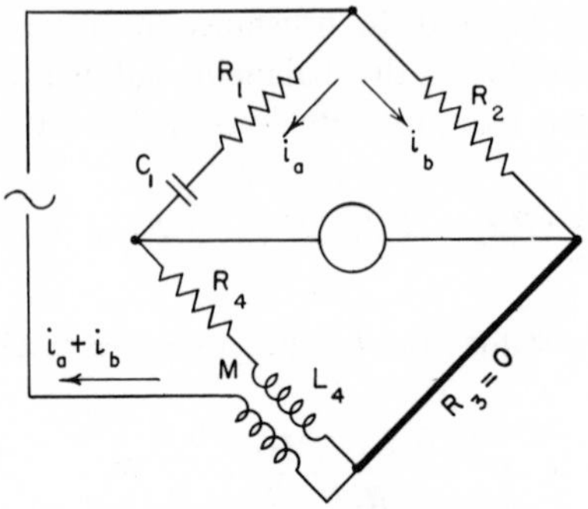

FIG. 41.

If, in addition, we consider the residuals l_1 and l_2 in R_1 and R_2, we obtain the following expression for mutual inductance

$$M = C_1 R_2 R_4 \left\{1 - \frac{\omega^2}{R_2 R_4}\,[l_2 L_4 - (l_1 + l_2)M]\right\}$$

and, since this correction term is small unless the frequency is high, we can write approximately

$$C_1 \approx \frac{M}{R_2 R_4}\left\{1 + \frac{\omega^2}{R_2 R_4}\,[l_2 L_4 - (l_1 + l_2)M]\right\}$$

and

$$R_1 = R_2\left(\frac{L_4}{M} - 1\right) + \frac{l_2 R_4}{M}$$

Since R_1 may be considered to be made up of a resistor R_1' in series with the equivalent series resistance (ρ) of the capacitor, we have

$$\rho = R_2\left(\frac{L_4}{M} - 1\right) + \frac{l_2 R_4}{M} - R_1'$$

The Campbell Bridge. This bridge, designed for the comparison of mutual inductances,[71] is shown in Fig. 42. We will assume that one of the mutual inductors is an adjustable standard in terms of which the other is to be determined. Two balances are needed: (1) as a self-inductance bridge the balance conditions are $L_1/L_2 = R_1/R_2 = R_4/R_3$; (2) as a

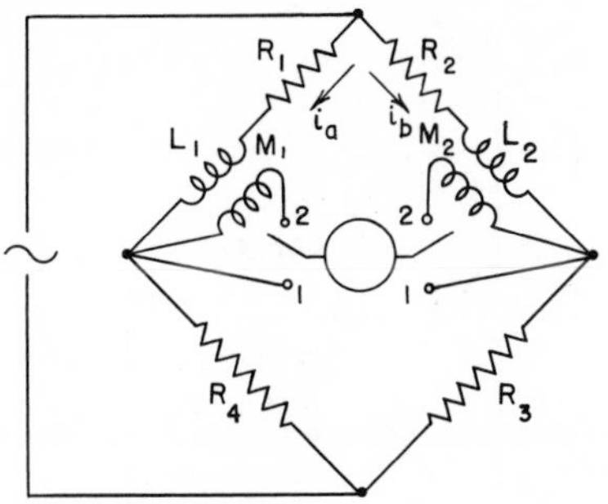

FIG. 42.

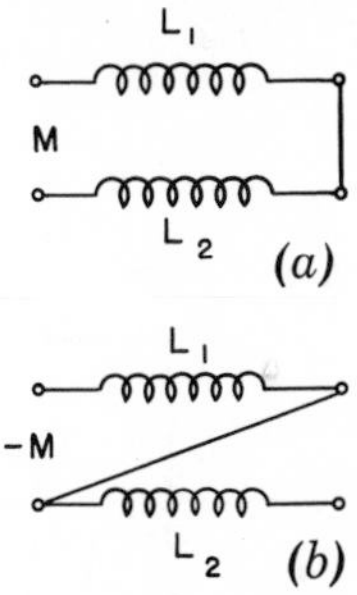

FIG. 43.

mutual-inductance bridge, retaining all the element values of the first balance and varying M_1 for the balancing adjustment, we have

$$i_a[R_1 + j\omega(L_1 - M_1)] = i_b[R_2 + j\omega(L_2 - M_2)]$$

and

$$i_a R_4 = i_b R_3$$

Then

$$R_3[R_1 + j\omega(L_1 - M_1)] = R_4[R_2 + j\omega(L_2 - M_2)]$$

and finally

$$\frac{R_1}{R_2} = \frac{R_4}{R_3} = \frac{L_1}{L_2} = \frac{M_1}{M_2}$$

Determination of Mutual Inductance as Self-Inductance. If all four terminals of a mutual inductor are accessible, the mutual inductance can be determined by any method which is available for the measurement of self-inductance. If the coils are connected in series, as in Fig. 43(*a*), so that the emf resulting from the mutual inductance aids the emf of self-inductance, the apparent inductance will be $\lambda_a = L_1 + L_2 + 2M$; and, if the coils are reconnected, so that the mutual opposes the self, the apparent inductance is $\lambda_b = L_1 + L_2 - 2M$. If now λ_a and λ_b are measured by any suitable method, we have

$$\lambda_a - \lambda_b = 4M, \quad \text{or} \quad M = \frac{\lambda_a - \lambda_b}{4}$$

[71] Campbell, *Proc. Phys. Soc.* (*London*), **21**, 79 (1910).

Inductive Ratio Bridge

A bridge with closely coupled ratio arms has advantages over the conventional four-arm bridge in some types of measurement. This bridge is generally used with a 1:1 ratio, but the balance conditions will be worked out for the general case. The circuit arrangement is shown

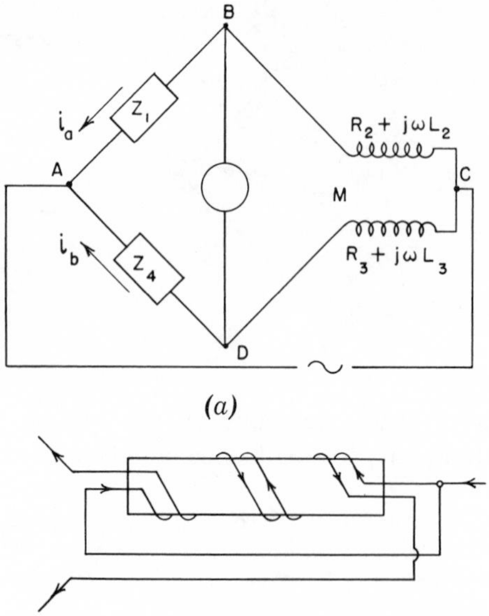

(a)

(b)

FIG. 44.

in Fig. 44(*a*), and details of the connection of the inductive arms in 44(*b*). At balance we have

$$i_a Z_1 = i_b Z_4$$

and

$$i_a(R_2 + j\omega L_2) - i_b j\omega M = i_b(R_3 + j\omega L_3) - i_a j\omega M$$

from which

$$\frac{Z_1}{Z_4} = \frac{R_2 + j\omega(L_2 + M)}{R_3 + j\omega(L_3 + M)}$$

If the circuits are so closely coupled that there is no appreciable leakage flux, then $M^2 = L_2 L_3$. Now let $L_2 = N^2 L_3$. Then $M^2 = N^2 L_3^2$, or $M = NL_3$. Substituting, we have

$$R_2 + j\omega(L_2 + M) = R_2 + j\omega(N^2 L_3 + NL_3) = R_2 + j\omega NL_3(1 + N)$$

and

$$R_3 + j\omega(L_3 + M) = R_3 + j\omega(L_3 + NL_3) = R_3 + j\omega L_3(1 + N)$$

Then, if $R_2 = NR_3$, we have

$$\frac{Z_1}{Z_4} = \frac{R_2 + j\omega(L_2 + M)}{R_3 + j\omega(L_3 + M)} = \frac{N[R_3 + j\omega L_3(1 + N)]}{R_3 + j\omega L_3(1 + N)} = N$$

Suppose now that the leakage flux cannot be made negligible, so that $M^2 = K^2L_2L_3$, where K is a factor less than unity. As before we will assume that $L_2 = N^2L_3$, and $R_2 = NR_3$. Then $M^2 = K^2N^2L_3{}^2$, so that $M = KNL_3$. Then we have

$$\frac{Z_1}{Z_4} = \frac{NR_3 + j\omega NL_3(N + K)}{R_3 + j\omega L_3(1 + KN)}$$

$$= N\left[\frac{R_3 + j\omega L_3(K + N)}{R_3 + j\omega L_3(1 + KN)}\right]$$

which is not equal to N except for the special case of $N = 1$. In this case $Z_1/Z_4 = 1$ for any value of K. For other values of N, $(R \ll \omega L)$ the ratio may be approximated. In this case the balance condition may be written as

$$\frac{Z_1}{Z_4} \approx N\left[\frac{K + N}{1 + KN}\right]$$

The most important case is the one for which $N = 1$, so that $R_2 = R_3$. This can be accomplished by winding a twisted pair of conductors on a toroidal coil of silicon steel (or, better, of Permalloy), with the windings connected [as shown in Fig. 44(*b*)] so that the voltage induced by the mutual inductance opposes that of the self-inductance in each arm. Then we have at balance that the total reactance drop in each of the ratio arms is very nearly zero, and the impedances of the elements are very nearly equal to their resistances: $Z_2 = Z_3 \approx R_2 = R_3$. If these resistances are low, points B, C, D are all at very nearly the same potential and the point C can be directly grounded without serious error from stray capacitance to ground from points B and D. When the bridge is unbalanced, so that unequal currents flow, the emf's contributed to the arms by the mutual inductances are no longer exactly equal to the emf's contributed by the self-inductances and the impedances are large. Thus, for the unbalanced bridge the inductive ratio arms act as a high-impedance ratio but at balance the ratio arms have a low impedance.[72]

Differential Elements

In many cases the characteristics of an unknown impedance can be determined from the difference in settings of bridge elements before and

[72] Walsh, *Phil. Mag*. (7th Series), **10**, 49 (1930).

after the unknown is introduced. In the measurement of small capacitances this method is most easily applied by using a differential capacitor which adds capacitance to one arm and subtracts an equal amount from an adjacent arm. Such a capacitor may be made up with a single bank of movable plates which turn into separately insulated banks of fixed

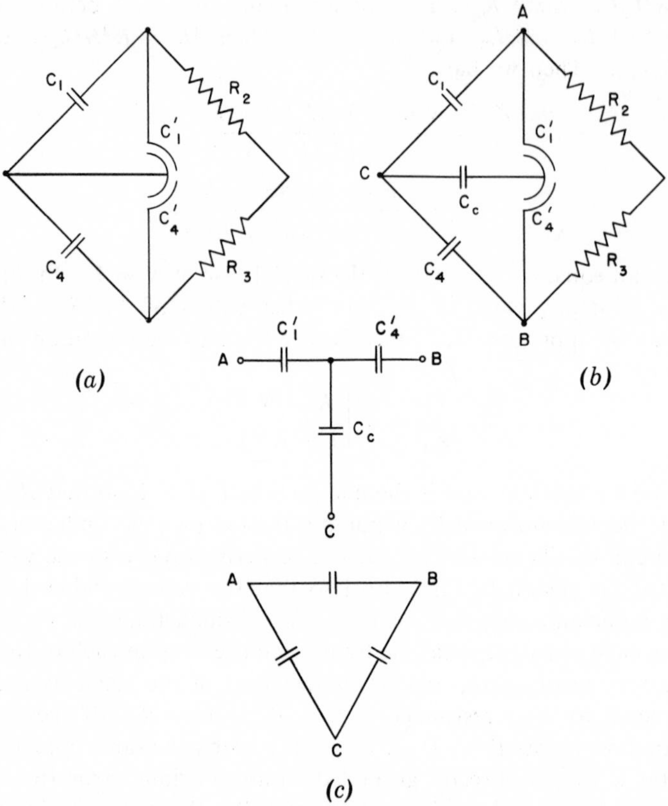

FIG. 45.

plates. Alternatively, two ordinary variable air capacitors may be arranged on a single shaft in such a way that one is increased when the other is decreased. A bridge arrangement employing a differential capacitor is shown in Fig. 45(*a*). We will assume that equal ratio arms are used. Then at balance $R_2 = R_3$, and

$$C_1 + C_1' = C_4 + C_4', \quad \text{or} \quad C_1 - C_4 = C_4' - C_1'$$

Thus the difference between C_1 and C_4 may be read directly if the differential capacitor is calibrated to read $(C_4' - C_1')$ directly. To reduce the range of a differential capacitor, a fixed capacitor in series with the movable element may be used as shown in Fig. 45(*b*). The Y-connected capacitors C_c, C_1', and C_4' may be transformed to an equivalent Δ-connection as shown in Fig. 45(*c*). Then

$$C_{AB} = \frac{C_1'C_4'}{C_1' + C_4' + C_c}, \quad C_{AC} = \frac{C_1' \cdot C_c}{C_1' + C_4' + C_c}$$

and

$$C_{BC} = \frac{C_4' \cdot C_c}{C_1' + C_4' + C_c}$$

Since C_{AB} is in a diagonal arm of the bridge, balance occurs when

$$C_1 + \frac{C_1' \cdot C_c}{C_1' + C_4' + C_c} = C_4 + \frac{C_4' \cdot C_c}{C_1' + C_4' + C_c}$$

or when

$$C_1 - C_4 = (C_4' - C_1') \cdot \frac{C_c}{C_1' + C_4' + C_c}$$

i.e. the range of the differential capacitor has been reduced by the factor[73] $C_c/(C_1' + C_4' + C_c)$. It will be apparent that C_c can be chosen so that the reduction factor is 0.1, 0.01, etc.

Direct-Capacitance Bridge

A bridge incorporating both the inductive ratio arms and differential balancing elements has been described by Young[74] and built commercially as the Western Electric direct-capacitance test set (Model D-160939). Two differential elements, one of capacitance and one of conductance, are superposed as shown in Fig. 46(*a*). Transforming the Y-connected conductances, g_a, g_c, g_e, to the equivalent Δ-connected conductances, G_A, G_C, G_{AC}, of Fig. 46(*b*), we have

$$G_A = \frac{g_a \cdot g_e}{(g_a + g_c) + g_e}$$

and

$$G_C = \frac{g_c \cdot g_e}{(g_a + g_c) + g_e}$$

G_{AC} is across the bridge diagonal and need not be computed. Now in Fig. 46(*b*) we have the Y-connected admittances, Y_A, Y_C, Y_D, made up of parallel conductance and capacitance elements. Transforming to the

[73] Rosen, *J. Post Office Elect. Eng.*, **29**, 319 (1937).
[74] Young, U.S. Patents 2,309,490 and 2,326, 274.

equivalent Δ-connected admittances, Y_{AC}, Y_{AD}, Y_{CD}, of Fig. 46(*c*), we have

$$Y_{AD} = \frac{Y_A \cdot Y_D}{(Y_A + Y_C) + Y_D}$$

and

$$Y_{CD} = \frac{Y_C \cdot Y_D}{(Y_A + Y_C) + Y_D}$$

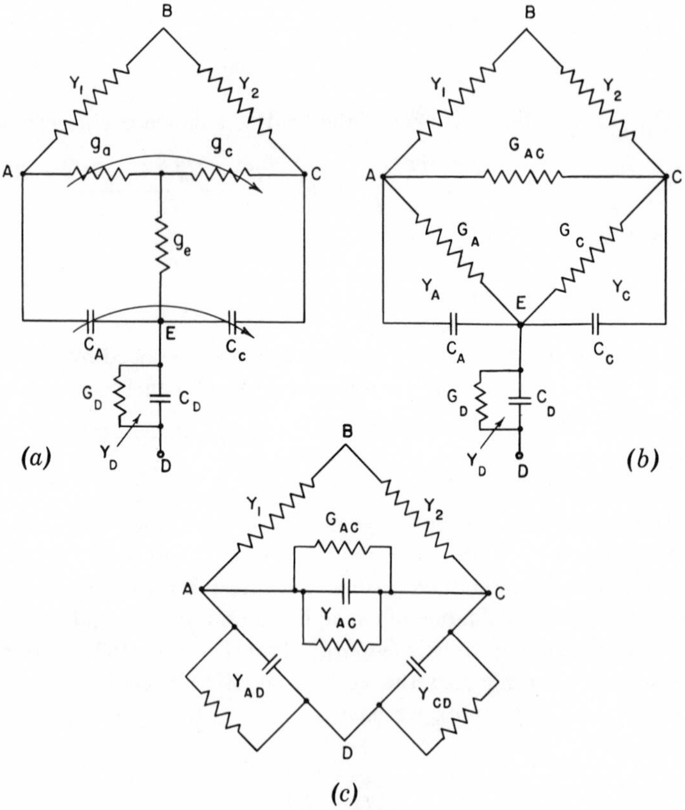

FIG. 46.

If an unknown admittance Y_x is connected in parallel with Y_{CD} (i.e. between junctions *C* and *D* of the bridge), the balance condition is

$$Y_x = Y_{AD} - Y_{CD} = (Y_A - Y_C)\frac{Y_D}{(Y_A + Y_C) + Y_D}$$

if the ratio arms, Y_1 and Y_2, are assumed to be equal (1:1 ratio). $(Y_A + Y_C)$ can be separated into real and imaginary components

$$Y_A + Y_C = G_A + G_C + j\omega(C_A + C_C)$$

where

$$G_A + G_C = \frac{g_e(g_a + g_c)}{g_e + g_a + g_c}$$

Since the sum of the differential elements $(g_a + g_c)$ is constant by construction, $(G_A + G_C)$ is also constant. Also by construction $(C_A + C_C)$ is constant. Hence $(Y_A + Y_C)$ is constant and has a constant phase angle. Then, if Y_D is adjusted to have the same phase angle,

$$\frac{Y_D}{(Y_A + Y_C) + Y_D} = F$$

is a pure number, and our equation of balance may be written $Y_x = F(Y_A - Y_C)$. (Actually F is adjusted to have the values 0.1, 0.01, etc., in discrete steps.) The balance equation may be rewritten as

$$Y_x = G_x + j\omega C_x = F[(G_A - G_C) + j\omega(C_A - C_C)]$$

where

$$G_x = F(G_A - G_C) = F \cdot \frac{g_e(g_a - g_c)}{(g_a + g_c) + g_e} = FF'(g_a - g_c)$$

and

$$C_x = F(C_A - C_C)$$

Both the conductance and capacitance components of the balance setting can be made direct-reading in terms of the settings of the differential conductance and capacitance elements together with the factor F.

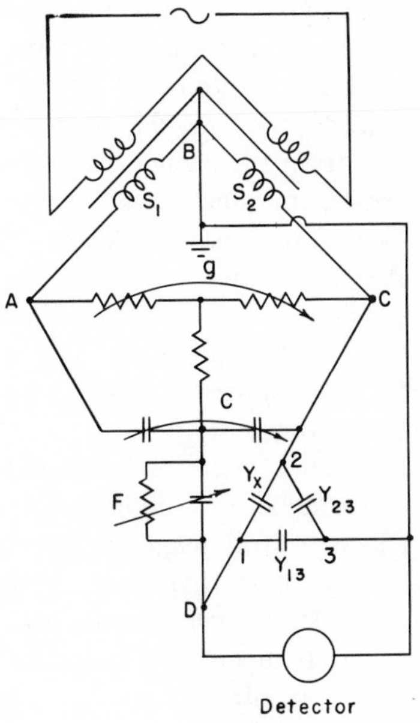

FIG. 47.

Figure 47 shows the bridge arranged for the measurement of direct admittances. The secondaries of the transformer, S_1 and S_2, constitute 1:1 inductive ratio arms of the type described above. The transformer core is toroidal, and S_1 and S_2 are a twisted pair in order that their coupling be as nearly perfect as possible. Since, at balance, the impedances of these arms reduce to the small resistances of the matched windings, capacitance of reasonable size shunting either of these arms has a negligible effect on the balance condition. The direct admittance (Y_x) to be measured is connected as shown between terminals 1 and 2 in the C–D-arm of the bridge, and stray admittances Y_{13}, Y_{23} are connected to terminal 3 at ground potential. It will be seen that Y_{13} is directly across the detector and does not influence the balance. Y_{23} is connected across the inductive S_2-arm and does not affect the balance to an appreciable extent because of the low impedance of S_2 at balance. Young has stated that a stray capacitance of as much as 300 $\mu\mu$f disturbs the balance by an amount which is "barely perceptible" in a bridge designed to measure direct admittances between vacuum-tube elements. This bridge, with an oscillator and tuned detector operating at 465 kc/sec, is arranged to be direct-reading for capacitances from 0.0005 to 110 $\mu\mu$f and for conductances from 0 to 10 μmho. It has been used by Moon[75] for the comparison of small capacitors (< 5 $\mu\mu$f) by a substitution method with an estimated accuracy of better than 0.1% when measuring a capacitance of 0.1 $\mu\mu$f. In this work the stray admittances across the B–C-arm of the bridge were kept constant during the substitution in order that the slight departure of the coupling in the ratio arms from 100% would not introduce any error.

Stray Admittances in Bridge Circuits

In most of the preceding discussion of bridge circuits, the elements used in the network were considered as simple impedors of various types. Although such a simplifying assumption may be justified in describing the essential features of a particular bridge circuit or in developing its balance equations, in setting up and using a bridge one must always consider the stray admittances between the various elements of the bridge and from the elements to ground or to neighboring objects. Ideally, if these admittances were sufficiently small, they could be neglected. However, care must be taken in arranging the components of the bridge so that the stray admittances are as small as possible. In most cases it is possible so to arrange the bridge that stray admittances will not affect the balance conditions or, if they must be taken into account, to fix their values independently of balance manipulations and external conditions.

Usually, with properly constructed components, insulation can be made sufficiently good that stray conductances are negligible. But the effects of stray magnetic and electric fields must frequently be considered. At very high frequencies both magnetic and electric fields may appear together in such magnitudes as to be of considerable importance, but generally at low and moderate frequencies the effect of one or the other will predominate.

[75] Moon and Sparks, *NBS J. Research*, **41**, 505 (1948).

MAGNETIC COUPLING. In order to keep the magnetic coupling small between circuit elements a number of precautions should be observed. (1) Connecting leads should be arranged in twisted pairs, or coaxially, or in some other way which will minimize the area of open loops. (2) Inductive elements should be placed at considerable distances from one another with their axes mutually perpendicular to minimize the coupling resulting from their stray fields. It is better, where possible, to use inductors which are wound as closed toroids or whose coils are arranged astatically.[76] (3) Magnetic shielding should be employed where practicable, particularly for transformers in the supply and detector branches of the bridge. Two types of magnetic shielding are effective. The element may be enclosed in a shield of high-permeability material in order to by-pass stray fields, or in a non-magnetic shield of very low resistance (such as a copper box), in which case the counter mmf resulting from the induced eddy currents tends to cancel the effects of the stray field. The latter method is quite effective with air-core inductors at high frequencies. It is often of advantage to use a bridge method in which only one inductive element is present, in order to avoid mutual coupling between inductive elements. In some cases, where stray field is present as a result of near-by equipment, it is possible to alter the test frequency sufficiently to eliminate any effect of coupling on the balance conditions, particularly where the detector can be so sharply tuned that it will not respond at the frequency of the stray field.

CAPACITIVE COUPLING. Such coupling, both between bridge elements and from them to ground, is a problem which is nearly always important. Here, spacing of the apparatus is of little help and orientation is of no assistance whatever. The method generally used to control the effects of stray capacitance is the enclosure of bridge elements in conducting shields which are so connected (or are maintained at such potentials) that the resulting capacitance either does not affect balance conditions or becomes a fixed and known quantity. It is true that enclosing a resistance element within a conducting shield will increase its time constant somewhat, since the distributed capacitance will be greater in the presence of the shield. However, this capacitance will be a fixed and measurable quantity, and, if the shield is connected to one end of the resistance element, the capacitance from shield to ground is localized at that point in the circuit.

If we consider the ground capacitances as concentrated at the four corners of a bridge, as in Fig. 48(*a*), their admittances can be transformed to the equivalent system of Fig. 48(*b*). Of these stray admittances Y_{BD} and Y_{AC} shunt the detector and source respectively, and therefore cannot

[76] Among available adjustable standards of inductance the Brooks inductometer is one of the best because of its low external field and its excellent astatic arrangement.

affect the balance conditions. The balance equation, written to include the stray admittances, becomes

$$(Y_1 + Y_{AB})(Y_3 + Y_{CD}) = (Y_2 + Y_{BC})(Y_4 + Y_{AD})$$

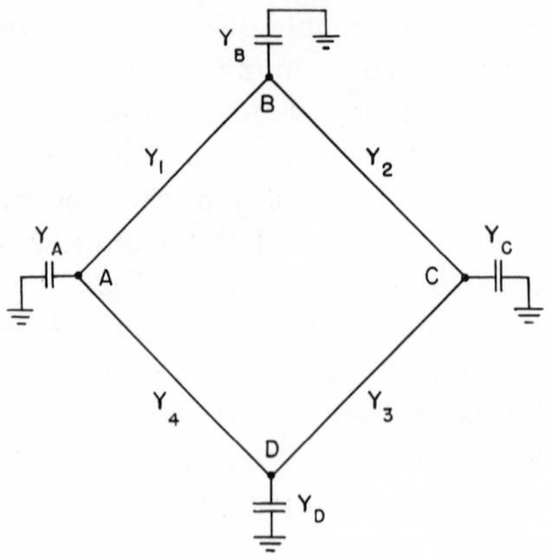

(a)

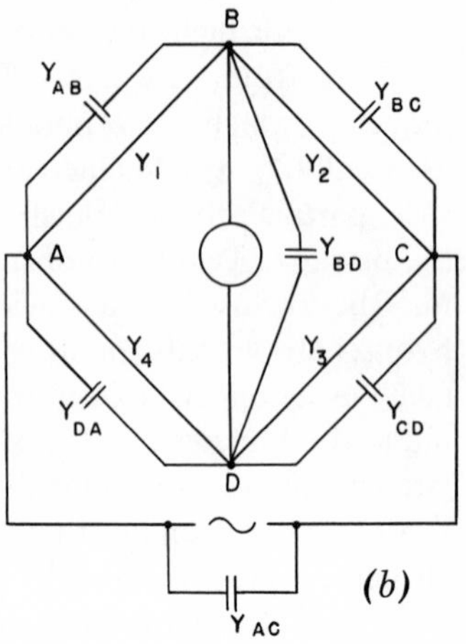

(b)

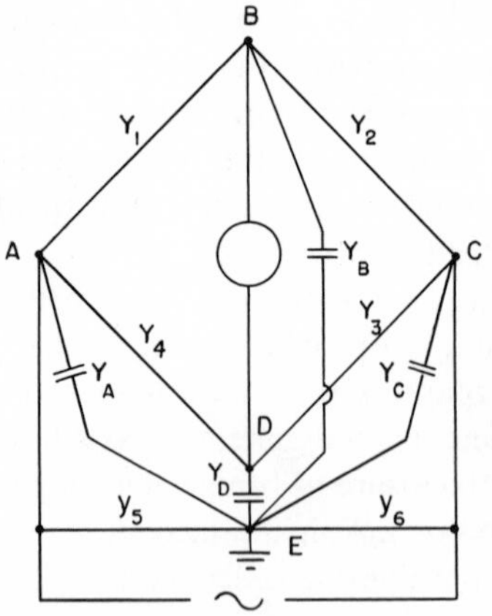

(c)

FIG. 48.

Now

$$Y_{AB} = \frac{Y_A \cdot Y_B}{Y_A + Y_B + Y_C + Y_D}, \text{ etc.}^{77}$$

so that the balance equation becomes

$$(Y_1 Y_3 - Y_2 Y_4) + \frac{(Y_1 Y_C Y_D + Y_3 Y_A Y_B - Y_2 Y_A Y_D - Y_4 Y_B Y_C)}{Y_A + Y_B + Y_C + Y_D} = 0$$

[77] Rosen, *J. IEE*, **62,** 916 (1924); or Hague, *op. cit.*, p. 61.

and if the ground admittances are to have no effect on the balance, then we must have

$$Y_1 Y_C Y_D + Y_3 Y_A Y_B - Y_2 Y_A Y_D - Y_4 Y_B Y_C = 0$$

This condition will be satisfied if $Y_B/Y_D = Y_2/Y_3 = Y_1/Y_4$, or if $Y_A/Y_C = Y_4/Y_3 = Y_1/Y_2$. These equations impose conditions on the ground admittances at opposite ends of one diagonal of a bridge in terms of the admittances of the pairs of elements shunting the diagonal.[78] It should then be possible to eliminate the effect of ground admittances concentrated at the corners of a bridge by the adjustment of suitable ground admittances at the opposite ends of one of the bridge diagonals.

Wagner Auxiliary Bridge Arms. Another method of eliminating the effect of ground admittances is the use of the *Wagner ground,* shown in Fig. 48(*c*). This method is usually simpler to apply and is frequently employed for this purpose. The Wagner[79] ground was originally devised to eliminate the effect of capacitance between telephone receivers (used as detector) and the observer's head (presumed to be at ground potential), by reducing to zero the voltage across this admittance so that no current will enter or leave the circuit at this point. Consider the impedance bridge of Fig. 49, consisting of the usual four-arm network, but having in addition the auxiliary arms 5 and 6 with a ground connection at their junction *E*. Also consider that the detector can be connected between *B* and *D* to indicate balance in the main four-arm bridge, Z_1, Z_2, Z_3, Z_4, or alternatively between *B* and *E* to indicate balance in the four-arm bridge Z_1, Z_2, Z_5, Z_6. Now we will make a series of balancing adjustments, first adjusting elements of the main bridge (1–2–3–4) with the detector connected between points *B* and *D*, then adjusting element 5 or element 6 in the auxiliary bridge with the detector connected to points *B* and *E*, then making a second adjustment

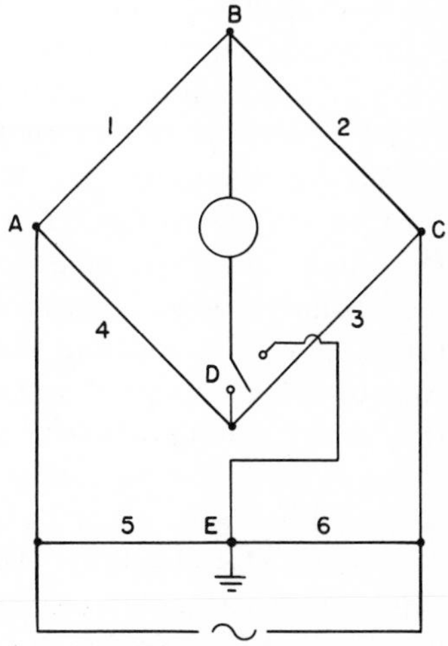

FIG. 49.

[78] Carvallo, *Rev. gén. de l'élec.*, **17,** 337 (1925).

[79] Wagner, *Elektrot. Zeits.*, **32,** 1001 (1911). For a general treatment of grounding systems for bridges, see Ogawa, *Researches Electrotech. Lab., Tokyo*, No. 254 (1929) and No. 277 (1930) (both in English).

in the main bridge, and, if necessary, a second adjustment of the auxiliary arms. This process is continued until no further adjustment is required for a balance indication with the detector connected to either D or E. When this is accomplished points B, D, and E will all be at the same potential, that of ground, and no current will flow in the ground admittances of B or D since no voltage exists across them.

It may be seen from Fig. 48(c) that, with the balance conditions as stated, and with B, D, and E all brought to ground potential, not only are the effects of admittances Y_B and Y_D eliminated from consideration, but also neither Y_A nor Y_C has any effect on balance conditions in the main bridge, since it shunts Y_5 or Y_6 rather than Y_4 or Y_3, Y_D being in effect infinite because it carries no current. Thus all ground admittance effects have been eliminated from the main bridge. The simultaneous balance conditions are (1) $Y_1Y_3 = Y_2Y_4$ for the main bridge; and (2) $Y_1(Y_6 + Y_C) = Y_2(Y_5 + Y_A)$ for the auxiliary bridge. Since both magnitude and phase relations are involved in the balance equation of the auxiliary bridge, just as they are in the balance equation of the main bridge, it will be apparent that a phase balance as well as a magnitude balance will be required when auxiliary elements 5 and 6 are adjusted. In general it is not possible to realize complete balance with only resistance elements in 5 and 6, unless 1–2–5–6 is a bridge of one of the types described by Fig. 30(a) (a ratio-arm bridge having $\phi_1 - \phi_2 = 0$, in Ferguson's classification). Hence it is generally to be expected that inductive or capacitive elements will be needed in the Wagner arms.[80] Practically it will usually be found that the balance in the Wagner arms need not be made as closely as that in the main bridge and that, since the auxiliary balance need be only approximate, resistance elements in the auxiliary arms will suffice in many cases where the phase angle $(\phi_1 - \phi_2)$ between the elements of arms 1 and 2 is not large. Wagner-ground arms can serve to advantage with most bridges, whether the bridge is being used for a direct determination of the characteristics of a bridge element, or indirectly in a substitution method, since the auxiliary balance stabilizes the balance of the main bridge by making it independent of ground admittances.

[80] The rate at which successive adjustments converge toward a balance condition is a function of the ground admittances as well as of the admittances in the arms themselves, and the approach to balance is subject to the same conditions as have already been discussed. (See p. 696.) Where convergence is slow it may be improved by connecting an appropriate admittance (most easily determined by trial) between ground and one of the detector junction points of the main bridge.

BRIDGE ACCESSORIES

Bridge Transformers

It is frequently advantageous to use transformers to connect the bridge to a source of power, and to the detector, both for impedance matching and to isolate the bridge electrically from the source and the detector.

Impedance Matching. It is quite generally true that *maximum* power can be transferred from a source to an absorber of energy if the impedances of the two are of equal magnitudes.[81] It follows then that the maximum power will be available for operating the bridge from a given source when impedances are matched.[82] If the impedances of the generator and bridge are different they can be brought more nearly to equality by a suitable coupling transformer, since the effective value of an impedance is changed through transformer coupling by a factor equal to the square of the transformer turn ratio. Thus a generator having a particular impedance could be matched to a bridge having an impedance 100 times as great by coupling them with a step-up transformer having a 1:10 turn ratio. Similarly a high-impedance source could be matched to a low-impedance bridge by using a step-down transformer of appropriate ratio. The relation between bridge and detector is precisely the same. Here the bridge may be considered the source of the voltage of unbalance which operates the detector, and an impedance match will in this case also make maximum power available for operating the detector. In practice it is not essential that the impedances be closely matched since the available power decreases rather slowly with the departure from unity of the ratio of impedances.[83]

[81] A precise statement of the theorem of maximum power transfer requires that the impedances of the generating and receiving networks be conjugate for maximum transfer. However, when only the magnitude of the load impedance can be varied while its phase angle remains fixed (usually the case in bridge circuits), maximum power transfer occurs when the magnitudes of the generator and receiver impedances are equal.

[82] Maximum availability of power is usually of concern only if the impedance of the generator is high. The output of a low-impedance generator is often limited by its permissible I^2R losses (without overheating) before the impedance of the power absorber is reduced to a value equal to that of the generator. This is quite generally true of generators and absorbers that are of interest in power engineering, so that in this case the theorem of maximum transfer is of no use. On the other hand, where generator impedance is so high that its I^2R loss does not determine its operating level, it is frequently of advantage to adjust circuit conditions for maximum transfer. This is rather often the case for communication circuits and for impedance bridges which are supplied by electron-tube oscillators.

[83] If we assume that the generator emf and impedance are both constant, the function

Distributed Capacitance. Transformers have distributed capacitance between windings and from each winding to ground which must be considered when the transformer is used in either the source or the detector arm of a bridge. If we consider only the secondary of the transformer connected to the A–C diagonal of the bridge in Fig. 50, the distributed capacitance of the secondary winding to ground can be considered to be

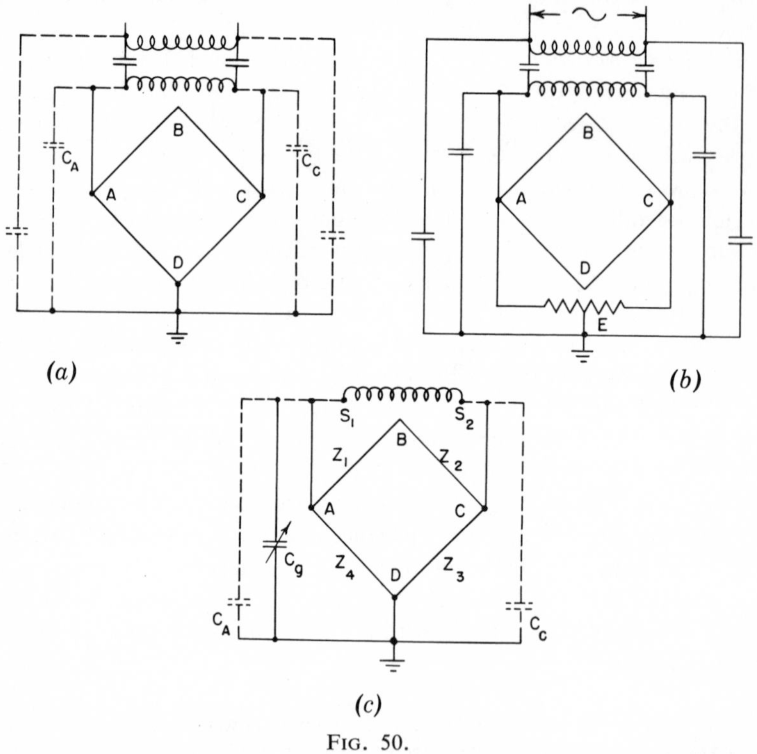

FIG. 50.

concentrated in C_A and C_C at the ends of the winding. If we assume the bridge to be grounded at D, these capacitances act as shunt admittances on arms A–D and C–D respectively. If we consider also the distributed capacitance between windings and from the primary winding to ground,

---

describing available power is of precisely the same form as that discussed previously for bridge sensitivity. (See p. 695.)

$$\frac{\text{Power available}}{\text{Maximum power}} = \frac{4K}{(1 + K)^2}$$

where K is the ratio of impedances of the generator and absorber; and we have seen that this function decreases rather slowly from its maximum value (i.e. when $K = 2$ or $\frac{1}{2}$, $P/P_{max} \approx 0.89$; and when $K = 10$ or $\frac{1}{10}$, $P/P_{max} \approx 0.33$).

it will be seen that the primary ground admittances are in series with the interwinding capacitances (approximated in each case by lumped capacitances at the ends of the windings), and that this series combination is also in parallel with the same bridge arms. In general these shunt admittances will influence the balance condition and cause errors, but their effects can be completely eliminated by the use of Wagner arms as shown in Fig. 50(*b*), when D is brought to ground potential by an auxiliary balance with the detector between D and E (or B and E) and the adjustment of arms A–E and C–E. In an equal-ratio bridge the effect of these capacitances can be eliminated with junction D directly grounded, by connecting an adjustable capacitor between junction A (or C) and ground as in Fig. 50(*c*). We will suppose that $Z_1 = Z_2$ and $Z_4 = Z_3$, but that $C_C > C_A$. When the bridge is balanced we must have

$$\frac{1}{Z_4} + j\omega(C_A + C_g) = \frac{1}{Z_3} + j\omega C_C$$

or, since $Z_4 = Z_3$, $C_g = C_C - C_A$. We have added capacitance in parallel with C_A until the ground admittances from A and C are equal. This can be accomplished by a preliminary balance, adjusting C_g with Z_3 and Z_4 disconnected from junction D. The main balance is then made with Z_3 and Z_4 reconnected to D, in the usual way. If the ground admittances are correctly adjusted, there will be no change in balance if the connections from the transformer to the bridge are reversed, S_1 being connected to C and S_2 to A.

Transformer Shielding. Shielded transformers may be used to advantage in both the supply and detector branches of a bridge. If the windings of the transformer are enclosed within separate isolated shields and the entire assembly is enclosed within an outer shield to which the transformer core is connected, the transformer-bridge connections and shield connections can be varied as desired. For example, in Fig. 51(*a*) the detector is coupled to the bridge through a doubly shielded transformer. Capacitance from the primary winding to the inner shield has no effect, since at balance there is no potential difference across it. The outer shield is connected to ground at D, and the capacitance between shields is a *fixed*, measurable quantity which is in parallel with arm C–D of the bridge and can be taken into account in the balance equation or compensated by a suitable capacitance shunting arm A–D. The secondary of the transformer and the detector are shown as enclosed within a grounded shield and have no effect on balance conditions. The shield of the supply transformer is connected to ground. Capacitance from the upper end of this winding to the shield is shunted across the supply (between B and D) and does not affect the balance. The bridge elements are also shown as shielded, with their shields connected to corners B and D of the bridge. The ground admittance from B is in the supply branch and does not affect balance; and since the shields connected to D are at ground potential their ground admittance has no effect. It will be noted that the effect of the doubly shielded transformer in the detector branch (the ungrounded diagonal of the bridge) is to place a fixed capacitance across one arm of the bridge where it may be taken into account, and to eliminate the effect of ground admittance to the remainder of the detector system, which will be of uncertain magnitude and will usually be much larger. It will, of

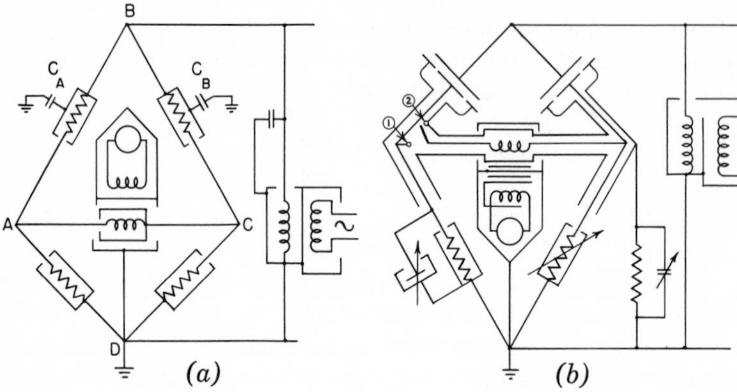

FIG. 51.

course, be necessary to take into account the effect of distributed capacitance between the bridge elements and their shields. An identical shielding system having the same effect could be used if the source and detector were interchanged; i.e. if the source were in the ungrounded bridge diagonal. The intershield capacitance of the transformer in the ungrounded diagonal can be eliminated from balance conditions by supplying the shield at a suitable potential from an auxiliary bridge arm. This can be illustrated with the completely shielded Schering bridge of Fig. 51(*b*). It will be noted that the intershield capacitance is shunted around the auxiliary arm and therefore affects the auxiliary balance, but does not affect the main balance if the shields are at the correct potential, i.e. if the detector indicates balance for both positions (1 and 2) of the detector switch.

Power Sources

Sources of power required for the operation of a-c bridges vary widely with the type of bridge and with the restrictions which are imposed by various conditions of measurement. If only a very small amount of power is required at a low voltage in the audio range, and the bridge balance is not sensitive to frequency, a simple buzzer or vibrating reed interrupter operated from dry cells is a convenient source. The buzzer will generate a rather loud audio signal and should be placed in a padded enclosure to deaden its sound, so that it will not interfere with the use of a telephone receiver as a detector. The signal frequency from such a source will usually not be very steady and its wave form will have a large

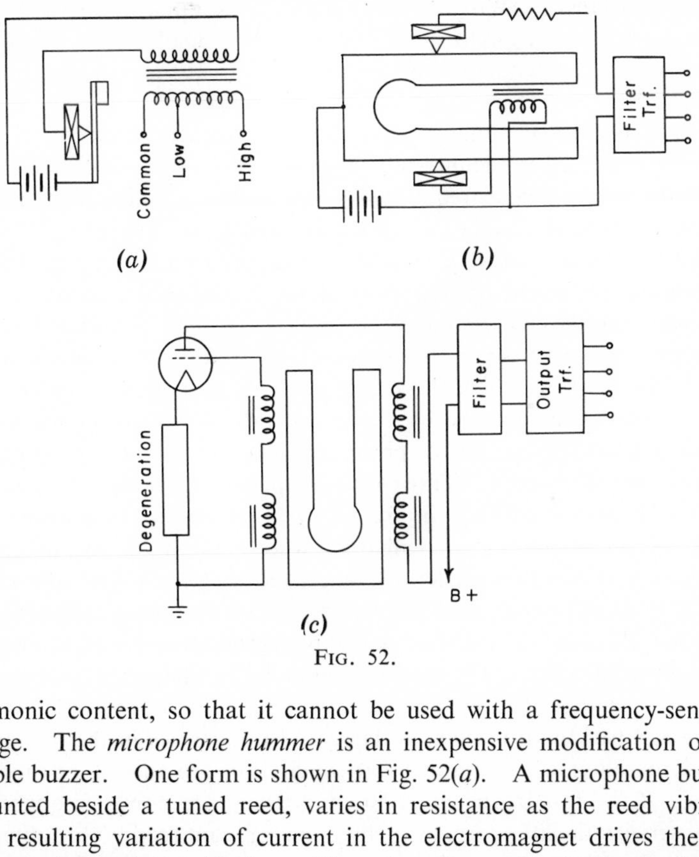

FIG. 52.

harmonic content, so that it cannot be used with a frequency-sensitive bridge. The *microphone hummer* is an inexpensive modification of the simple buzzer. One form is shown in Fig. 52(*a*). A microphone button, mounted beside a tuned reed, varies in resistance as the reed vibrates. The resulting variation of current in the electromagnet drives the reed and continues the oscillation. The microphone circuit is transformer-coupled to the output circuit, and taps on the output transformer permit its use with various impedances.[84] Wave-form distortion varies with mechanical adjustment, driving voltage, and output. A further modification [Fig. 52(*b*)] incorporates a tuning fork and ensures better frequency

[84] A General Radio Type 572–B microphone hummer is supplied by a $4\frac{1}{2}$-volt battery and has an output of 15 mw at 1000 cps $\pm$ 10%, with output impedances of 10 and 300 ohms.

stability. A source of this type, made by General Radio,[85] has two microphone buttons located at the points of maximum flexure of the fork so that they load the prongs of the fork equally and affect its free vibration only slightly. One microphone button is in the driving circuit and the other in the output circuit. Since the microphone produces considerable harmonic content a filter is incorporated in the output circuit to improve the wave form. The secondary of the output circuit is tapped for various output impedances. With a 6-volt drive the output is 20 to 30 mw having a harmonic content of 1% or less into a load whose impedance is matched. The temperature coefficient of frequency of the fork is $-0.008\%/°F$, and it is only slightly affected by the driving voltage ($< 0.01\%$ per volt). Figure 52(*c*) shows a further modification of a tuning-fork drive, for vacuum-tube operation.[86]

A power source whose frequency is controlled by a tuning fork or some similar mechanical resonating device is capable of delivering a small amount of power at a very constant frequency (limited at best by the temperature coefficient of frequency of the mechanical resonator), and the small output can be increased if necessary by a suitable power amplifier. However, since the frequency is fixed, such a source is not suitable for work in which the frequency must be varied. Under these circumstances, vacuum-tube oscillators provide a convenient means for obtaining a limited amount of power and may be coupled to amplifiers if more power is required. Three general types are available: (1) *resonant-circuit* oscillators, in which the frequency is established by a tuned *L-C* circuit; (2) *beat-frequency* oscillators, whose output is the difference frequency between two oscillators, one fixed and the other adjustable; and (3) *resistance-capacitance* oscillators, whose frequency is established by an *R-C* filter in a circuit that is highly degenerative except at the pass frequency of the filter. The reader should refer to Chapter 14, where such oscillators are described in some detail.

Where power requirements are large and frequencies in the low audio range are required, a motor-driven alternator provides a satisfactory source. If the test frequency is 60 cps (or another power frequency at which service facilities are available), power can readily be obtained either directly at the bus voltage or through a suitable transformer. In many types of bridge work constancy of supply voltage is not important in arriving at balance conditions, and voltage regulation is not essential. Where a supply voltage at power frequency must be regulated, two general types of stabilizers are commercially available in capacities up to several

[85] Lamson, *G.R. Experimenter*, **9** (May 1935).

[86] General Radio's Type 723 vacuum-tube fork has an output of 50 mw into a matched load, with a harmonic content $< 0.5\%$.

kilowatts. The simpler of these, the transformer type, operates as a magnetic stabilizer and makes use of a saturable-core reactor and a capacitor under conditions approaching resonance. Voltage stabilization to within perhaps $\frac{1}{2}\%$ is achieved under constant-load conditions, and within 2 to 3% when the load is varied. (Regulation is better on high- than low-power-factor loads.) The output wave form usually has considerable harmonic content (particularly the third harmonic), and must be filtered if purity of wave form is essential. Commercially available stabilizers, making use of vacuum-tube circuits, have considerably better regulation (to within perhaps 0.1%) even under conditions of varying load, and generally have a lower harmonic content than the transformer type. However, even as well as odd harmonics may be expected in the output, so that filters for improving wave form must be designed to take into account a substantial second harmonic as well as the third and higher harmonics. Where purity of wave form is essential, at the available power frequency, a well-designed sine-wave alternator driven by a synchronous motor provides a satisfactory supply unless the frequency must be held within very close limits. As has already been noted, it must be expected that the frequency of power available from commercial power sources may vary within a few tenths of a per cent around the nominal value, and may on occasions depart from nominal by as much as 1%. Such frequency variations may be serious if a sharply tuned detector is in use, whose response decreases rapidly when the frequency is altered by small amounts.

If the frequency of the source must be held within very narrow limits at power frequencies, and a source of considerable power is needed, an alternator may be driven by a d-c motor whose speed can be controlled. In general, whatever system is used for monitoring frequency, two types of speed control are possible. The motor field or the load may be altered to change the speed. If the shunt field of a motor is increased, its speed will decrease, or if the load on a shunt motor increases, its speed decreases. Both types of control have proved effective in various systems that have been devised for holding frequency constant. Perhaps the simplest method for monitoring frequency is the use of a frequency-sensitive bridge. An observer, noting the unbalance of such a bridge, can make the necessary adjustment of load or field current to bring the bridge back to balance and restore the frequency to the desired value. Such a system requires observing time and frequently an additional observer. Also considerable skill is required in applying adjustments to hold the frequency close to the required value. At best, the frequency sensitivity of the monitoring bridge and the reaction time of the observer act as limiting factors on the constancy of the controlled frequency. It is better, if possible, to use an automatic system of frequency monitoring and control that will sense small changes in speed and quickly apply the necessary adjustment.

One such system[87] consists of an adjustable centrifugal governor attached to the motor shaft, in which the centrifugal force on a weight is opposed by tension in spiral springs so that a particular equilibrium position is established corresponding to each speed of rotation. If the speed exceeds a certain value determined by the weight and the initial spring tension, the weight position is such that a contactor is closed, short-circuiting a resistance in series with the shunt field of the motor and increasing the field, so that the speed decreases. Thus the motor speed will oscillate about its mean value. In Giebe's arrangement,[88] the equilibrium position of the weight tends toward unstable equilibrium for speeds beyond a certain critical value. If the governor is adjusted so that the speed to be maintained is very near this critical value, the device becomes extremely sensitive in sensing small changes in frequency, and variations about a mean value of frequency can be held within 0.001%.

A number of systems of frequency control have been devised in which an electrically driven tuning fork is used to monitor speed. In one such system[89] a contact was arranged on the tuning fork so that it remained closed during one half-oscillation and open during the other half-oscillation. In series with the fork contact, another contact was made by means of a half-ring mounted on the motor shaft. When both contacts were closed current was supplied by the motor-driven alternator to a lamp load. The contacts were so arranged that the lamp load was on during $\frac{1}{4}$ cycle and off during $\frac{3}{4}$ cycle if the alternator frequency was synchronous with that of the fork. For a phase shift in the alternator, corresponding to a momentary change in speed, the load circuit was closed during a larger (or smaller) part of the cycle, the load duration increasing with increasing speed (advancing phase of the alternator). This increase in load would tend to slow down the motor and return it to correct speed. Other tuning-fork arrangements have made use of Thyratron tubes to regulate field current or load.[90] In one of these arrangements voltage from the alternator was applied to the plate of the Thyratron while voltage from the tuning fork was applied to the grid. If the alternator was at synchronous speed no current was passed by the

[87] Giebe, *Zeits. für Instrumentenk.*, **29,** 205 (1909); **52,** 345 (1932).

[88] See Laws, *Electrical Measurements*, 2nd edition, p. 455, McGraw-Hill, 1938, or Hague, *op. cit.*, p. 213, for details of this arrangement and theory of its operation.

[89] Hough and Wenner, *Phys. Rev.*, **24,** 535 (1907).

[90] Bearden and Shaw, *Rev. Sci. Inst.*, **5,** 292 (1934); Orkney, *Electrical Rev.*, **117** 669 (1935); Frazier, Eisler, and Frantz, *Electrical Engineering*, **54,** 307 (1935).

Thyratron. If the speed of the alternator changed, resulting in a phase shift between grid and plate signals, current in the Thyratron circuit was introduced into an auxiliary field winding of the driving motor in such a direction as to correct the speed.[91]

Detectors

A number of characteristics are desirable in null detectors used to indicate the approach to balance conditions in a-c bridges. (1) Ideally, the *sensitivity* should be sufficient but not too high for whatever precision is required in the bridge balance. Too much sensitivity is not only economically unsound but is undesirable in that it increases the difficulty of the balancing operation, by requiring very close adjustment of the bridge parameters that are altered to achieve a balance. Also it frequently implies a troublesome degree of instability in the response to bridge adjustments and in the operation of the detector. However, the response of an overly sensitive detector can be reduced by shunting or by other devices to improve operation. It is equally unsatisfactory to attempt to use a detector whose sensitivity is insufficient for the job at hand, since there will be a range of adjustment of the bridge-balancing parameters for which no response can be detected. The approximate midpoint of this range must then be accepted as the best balance. Detector sensitivity can frequently be improved by matching the impedance of the detector to that of the circuit to which it is connected, by a suitable coupling transformer.[92] In many instances a suitable vacuum-tube amplifier will augment the power available from the unbalanced bridge, permitting the use of a less sensitive and more rugged instrument for detecting balance

[91] An extremely accurate method of speed control, developed at the National Bureau of Standards, makes use of a Thyratron tube, and a commutator on the motor shaft. From a crystal oscillator, 1000-cycle voltage is impressed on the grid of the Thyratron through a contactor on the shaft, and d-c impulses are superposed by means of the rotating commutator. If the 1000-cycle emf at the instant of contact is greater than the voltage at which the tube fires, plate current will flow and a load is imposed on an alternator driven by the d-c motor, reducing the speed. If the phase of the signal is such that the voltage is below the critical value, the tube does not fire. This speed-control circuit was developed for switching operations used in absolute ohm determinations by the Wenner method, and is stated to hold the average speed (over a 1-min interval) constant to within 1 or 2 parts in 10^7. It is described in a paper by Thomas, Peterson, Kotter, and Cooter, *op. cit.*

[92] In general, the power interchange is maximum if the impedance of the absorber is equal to that of the source. In this case the effective input impedance of the detector should be matched to the impedance of the circuit which it sees from its terminals. If the detector and bridge impedances are not equal their ratio can be used to determine the optimum turn ratio of the coupling transformer by means of the formula $Z_L/Z_S = (N_L/N_S)^2 = N^2$.

than would otherwise be necessary. (2) The ideal detector should be *easy to use*. If the bridge is operated for long periods of time, the observation of unbalance and any necessary detector manipulation should not be unduly fatiguing to the operator. (3) *Frequency selectivity* in the detector is essential to balance in bridges that are frequency-sensitive, if the wave form of the supply voltage is impure. In bridges where frequency sensitivity is not a factor, frequency selectivity in the detector will tend to suppress those background emf's that are present and that tend to mask the balance point but have no significance with regard to balance. (Such background disturbances, which do not convey useful information, are generally designated as noise.) (4) *Phase selectivity* in the detector will permit separate adjustment of the in-phase and quadrature elements of the balance. This will frequently permit somewhat faster and easier balancing procedures than would otherwise be possible. However, phase selectivity is a feature whose desirability is frequently overrated. Experience shows that in many bridges an experienced operator can achieve balance almost as quickly by alternate manipulation of the quadrature components, using a detector that has no phase selectivity, as with a phase-selective detector. (5) *Logarithmic response*, achieved in some vacuum-tube circuits, is advantageous, i.e. increase in the sensitivity of the detector as balance is approached. (6) A detector that *will not be damaged by overloads* is desirable. When a sensitive detector is used, it may easily be overloaded by unbalance conditions. If the detector is of such a type that it may be injured by overload it should be shunted or its sensitivity otherwise reduced during preliminary balancing operations. (7) *Response time* of the detector should be short. If the detector is sluggish in its response to changes in the circuit conditions, the operator is likely to overrun the balance point and thus to require more time in the balance adjustment. (8) *Freedom from false balances* or spurious indications is most important. Such indications can occur through stray pick-up, as a result of inadequate or improper guarding and shielding, and, under certain conditions, from distortion in amplifiers.

The Telephone Receiver. This is much used as a detector in the audio range, between 200 and 10,000 cps. Beyond these limits the sensitivity of the human ear to sound becomes so small as to render the combination of telephone and ear a rather insensitive detector. Generally a "headset," consisting of a pair of "watch-case"-type receivers or "phones" connected in series and mounted on a headband and placed over both ears, is used. This not only is of advantage in helping to shut out extraneous sounds but also leaves both the observer's hands free, and is reasonably comfortable unless the headset has to be worn for long periods. The diaphragm of the ordinary telephone receiver has definite modes of vibration, and its amplitude of vibration may increase greatly for a given power input as the frequency approaches one of these natural frequencies. Both the amplitude of vibration of the diaphragm and the acuteness of hearing of the observer must be combined to determine the sensitivity of the telephone receiver as a detector of bridge unbalance. Neither of these factors can be stated in general terms, since diaphragms vary considerably in response and observers also vary widely both in general acuteness of hearing and in the frequency range to which their auditory response is greatest. However, it may be expected that maximum sensitivity will be found by a normal observer, using the ordinary telephone receiver, between 1000 and 2000 cps.[93] It is well to determine the sensitivity of available headsets and to select one which is best suited to the job at hand. An audio-frequency signal generator that can be operated throughout the audio range is convenient for this purpose. Such a generator can be used to introduce a known voltage into a circuit containing the headphones in series with a known high resistance, and the current sensitivity can then be determined directly as a function of frequency.

In matching the *effective impedance* of the telephone to the impedance of the circuit in which it will be used, either directly or through a coupling transformer, it must be remembered that it is the impedance and not the d-c resistance of the telephone which must be considered. This impedance is made up of two parts, the *static* impedance which the instrument would have at the given frequency if the diaphragm were stationary, and the *motional* impedance resulting from the generator action of the moving diaphragm. In the neighborhood of resonance the motional impedance may be many times greater than the static impedance, and the total can best be determined in a bridge suitable for inductance measurements.[94] If the operating frequency of the bridge cannot be selected to coincide with the maximum sensitivity of the receiver, considerable gain in sensitivity can be realized by acoustically tuning the receiver to resonance at the desired frequency with a closed air column of adjustable length.[95] With this method of tuning the effect of body capacitance between detector and observer can be simultaneously eliminated (without bringing the detector to ground potential) by coupling the acoustic resonator to the observer's ears by a flexible tube and stethescope-type earpieces.

[93] For two observers, using five sets of headphones of various makes, the point of maximum sensitivity ranged from 1200 to 2000 cps in a series of experiments. At maximum sensitivity the signal produced by 0.005 μa was audible with all phones in a quiet room, and for currents of as much as 0.1 μa the signals could be heard from 200 to 4000 cps in most cases.

[94] The question of motional impedance of receiver diaphragms is thoroughly discussed by Kennelly, *Electrical Vibration Instruments*, Macmillan, 1923.

[95] Kennelly, *op. cit.*, pp. 173 and 187.

Although the receiver diaphragm usually resonates at certain frequencies, the telephone cannot be considered a frequency-selective detector, since the resonance bands are usually rather broad and the response outside the bands is still relatively high. However, most observers have the ability to pick out sounds of a definite pitch and hence to adjust the balance to a minimum for some particular frequency even against a background of other frequencies.

The Vibration Galvanometer. This instrument, used at low frequencies, is one of the more sensitive types of bridge detectors. Although such instruments can be constructed for operation at frequencies as high as 1000 cps, their principal application is at frequencies below 300 cps, where their sensitivity may be expected to be greater than that of the telephone receiver. At power frequencies, (i.e. 60 cps) the sensitivity of well-designed vibration galvanometers may approach that of good d-c galvanometers. The vibration galvanometer is always operated with a moving system which may be tuned to mechanical resonance at the operating frequency. Since the damping is made very small the forced vibrations of the moving system are very much greater in the neighborhood of resonance than at any other frequency.[96] Thus a vibration galvanometer may be used as a detector whose response is limited to a narrow range of frequencies, and which discriminates sharply against other frequencies. This is of particular advantage where the wave form of the supply voltage is impure, since a vibration galvanometer tuned to the fundamental will have an extremely small response to any of the harmonics.

The moving element of the vibration galvanometer may be a small magnet suspended between the pole pieces of an electromagnet by taut suspensions (moving-magnet galvanometer),[97] a vibrating reed or wire driven by an electromagnet (Agnew's galvanometer),[98] or a tautly suspended moving coil in the air gap of a permanent magnet (d'Arsonval galvanometer).[99] The third form of vibration galvanometer is quite generally used and will be discussed in some detail. In appearance it resembles the usual type of moving-coil galvanometer but has a taut suspension which is usually under considerable tension, and a very narrow coil. Thus the moment of inertia is kept small and the moment of restoration very large. Generally the suspension is rigidly held by small movable clamps or bridges, and the active length of the suspension is varied by sliding the clamps along the suspension to alter the natural response frequency. Frequently the tension is made adjustable. Coarse

[96] See also the galvanometer oscillograph, Chapter 14.

[97] Hague, *op. cit.*, p. 255; Zollich, *Arch. für tech. Mess.*, J852–2 (May 1933).

[98] Agnew, *Sci. Papers Bur. Standards*, **16**, 37 (1920).

[99] Wenner, *Bull. Bur. Standards*, **6**, 347 (1910); *Proc. AIEE*, **31**, p. 1073 (1912).

tuning is accomplished by changing the active length of the suspension, and fine tuning by adjusting its tension. A mirror is mounted on the moving system, and the image of a line source of light is broadened into a band by the vibration.

THEORY. If we consider the moving-coil vibration galvanometer as a system having one degree of freedom (rotation about an axis), its equation of motion is identical with that previously discussed for the d'Arsonval galvanometer.[100]

We will assume for the present that the driving force is supplied from a sine-wave source and may write

$$P\frac{d^2\theta}{dt^2} + K\frac{d\theta}{dt} + U\theta = GI\sin\omega t$$

where P is the moment of inertia, K is moment of damping, U is moment of restoration, and G is moment of deflection. Since the coil is in motion in a magnetic field a back emf $G(d\theta/dt)$ is generated, so that in a closed circuit in which a driving emf ($E\sin\omega t$) is applied, the equation of motion becomes

$$P\frac{d^2\theta}{dt^2} + \left(K + \frac{G^2}{Z}\right)\frac{d\theta}{dt} + U\theta = \frac{GE}{Z}\sin\omega t$$

The impedance of the circuit will in general consist of both resistance and reactance, but in our initial discussion we will assume that there is only resistance present and will write $K + (G^2/R) = A$. Also we will divide our equation by P and, since

$$\frac{U}{P} = \frac{4\pi^2}{T_0^2} = 4\pi^2 f_0^2 = \omega_0^2$$

(f_0 being the *undamped* natural frequency of the moving system), we may write

$$\frac{d^2\theta}{dt^2} + \frac{A}{P}\frac{d\theta}{dt} + \omega_0^2\theta = \frac{GE}{RP}\sin\omega t$$

If we omit consideration of the *transient* response[101] and confine our

[100] See Chapter 3.

[101] The complete solution of this equation is

$$\theta = \frac{GE\sin(\omega t - \psi)}{R\sqrt{\omega^2A^2 + P^2(\omega_0^2 - \omega^2)^2}} - C\varepsilon^{-At/2P}\sin\left(\sqrt{\omega_0^2 - \frac{A^2}{4P^2}}\cdot t + \alpha\right)$$

where C and α are constants of integration, and

$$\psi = \tan^{-1}\frac{P(\omega_0^2 - \omega^2)}{A\omega}$$

attention to the *steady-state* response, this equation can be conveniently handled in the complex operational form.[102]

$$\left[(\omega_0^2 - \omega^2) + j\frac{A}{P}\omega\right]\bar{\theta} = \frac{G\bar{E}}{PR}$$

Then

$$\bar{\theta} = \frac{G\bar{E}}{PR}\cdot\frac{1}{(\omega_0^2 - \omega^2) + j\dfrac{\omega A}{P}} = \frac{GE\sin(\omega t - \psi)}{PR\sqrt{(\omega_0^2 - \omega^2)^2 + \dfrac{A^2\omega^2}{P^2}}}$$

i.e. the amplitude of oscillation is

$$\theta_{\max} = \frac{GE}{PR}\cdot\frac{1}{\sqrt{(\omega_0^2 - \omega^2)^2 + \dfrac{A^2\omega^2}{P^2}}}$$

and its angle of lag behind the applied voltage is

$$\psi = \tan^{-1}\frac{A\omega}{P(\omega_0^2 - \omega^2)}$$

Now the relative damping is $\gamma = A/A_c$, where $A_c = 2\sqrt{UP}$, the damping moment corresponding to critical damping. Making this substitution and rearranging, we have[103]

$$\theta_{\max} = \frac{GE}{RU}\cdot\frac{1}{\dfrac{1}{\omega_0^2}\sqrt{(\omega_0^2 - \omega^2)^2 + 4\gamma^2\omega_0^2\omega^2}}$$

[102] The transformation used is $d^n\theta/dt^n = (j\omega)^n\bar{\theta}$, which arises from the following considerations. If we have a sinusoidally varying expression $a(t) = a_1 \sin \omega t = \bar{a}$, in which a_1 is not a function of t, then

$$\frac{da}{dt} = \omega a_1 \cos \omega t = \omega a_1 \sin\left(\omega t + \frac{\pi}{2}\right) = j\omega a_1 \sin \omega t = (j\omega)\bar{a}$$

Similarly

$$\frac{d^2a}{dt^2} = (j\omega)\omega a_1 \cos \omega t = (j\omega)\omega a_1 \sin\left(\omega t + \frac{\pi}{2}\right) = (j\omega)(j\omega)a_1 \sin \omega t = (j\omega)^2\bar{a}$$

and in general $d^na/dt^n = (j\omega)^n\bar{a}$. In the case under consideration θ will be such a sinusoidal expression after the transient effects have disappeared, so that we may write

$$\left[(j\omega)^2 + (j\omega)\frac{A}{P} + \omega_0^2\right]\bar{\theta} = \left[(\omega_0^2 - \omega^2) + j\omega\frac{A}{P}\right]\bar{\theta} = \frac{G\bar{E}}{PR}$$

[103] Thus in the special case where no reactance is present in the circuit ($Z = R$), our equation reduces to

$$\theta_{\max} = \frac{\theta_{dc}}{\sqrt{1 + 2(2\gamma^2 - 1)\eta^2 + \eta^4}}$$

or, if we let $\eta = \omega/\omega_0$,

$$\theta_{\max} = \frac{GE}{RU} \frac{1}{\sqrt{(1-\eta^2)^2 + 4\gamma^2\eta^2}}$$

If the frequency is varied until the deflection attains its greatest value we have (on setting $\partial\theta_{\max}/\partial\eta = 0$)

$$\theta_{\max} = \frac{GE}{RU} \cdot \frac{1}{2\gamma\sqrt{1-\gamma^2}}$$

at a value of $\eta = \sqrt{1-\gamma^2}$ corresponding to a frequency somewhat less than the *undamped* resonance frequency.

DISCRIMINATION AGAINST HARMONICS. It is evident from the expression for amplitude of deflection that, if the relative damping is very small, the response will be very much greater for frequencies in the neighborhood of resonance than for any others, as is shown in Fig. 53. Thus we have a detector that can be sharply tuned (by varying U) to respond to a single frequency, and that will effectively discriminate against all others. The responses to second and third harmonics of the resonant frequency are given in the table accompanying Fig. 53 for some values of relative damping. The relative response at various harmonics, of a galvanometer tuned to the fundamental frequency, can be approximated if we make the following assumptions: (1) that the relative damping is small; and (2) that the operating circuit has a constant impedance.[104] Under these conditions, since $\eta \approx 1$ at resonance, we can write

$$M_p = \frac{\theta_p}{\theta_1} \approx \frac{2\gamma}{\sqrt{(1-p^2)^2 + 4\gamma^2 p^2}} \approx \frac{2\gamma}{p^2 - 1}$$

where p is the order of the harmonic. Thus

$$M_2 \approx \frac{2\gamma}{3}; \quad M_3 \approx \frac{\gamma}{4}; \quad \cdots$$

for a galvanometer whose relative damping is $\gamma = 0.003$, $M_2 = 0.002$,

---

Similarly,

$$\psi = \tan^{-1} \frac{2\eta\gamma}{1-\eta^2}$$

It will be noted that these expressions are identically those which were found for the steady-state response and lag angle of the galvanometer oscillograph. (See Chapter 14.)

[104] The assumption of small damping will be valid in any practical situation where the use of a vibration galvanometer is justified. The assumption that the total impedance of the circuit is independent of frequency is never precisely true, as we shall see later. However, it may serve as a rough approximation in many cases.

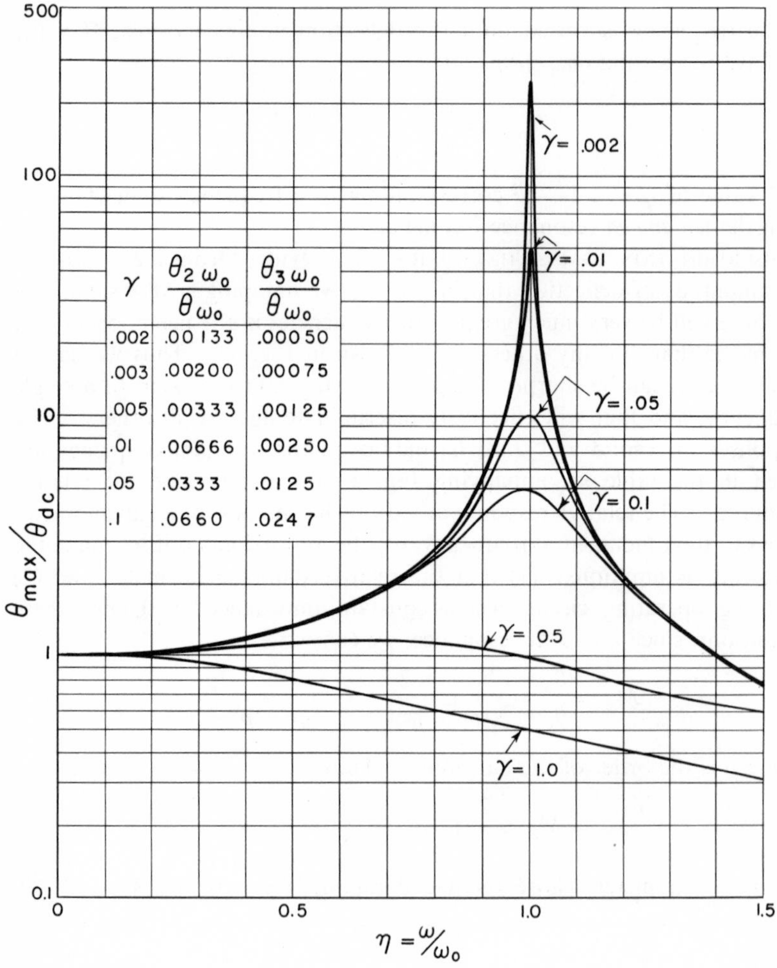
500
100
10
1
0.1
0
0.5
1.0
1.5
θ_{max}/θ_{dc}
$\eta = \omega/\omega_0$
γ = .002
γ = .01
γ = .05
γ = 0.1
γ = 0.5
γ = 1.0
γ | $\frac{\theta_2 \omega_0}{\theta \omega_0}$ | $\frac{\theta_3 \omega_0}{\theta \omega_0}$
.002 | .00133 | .00050
.003 | .00200 | .00075
.005 | .00333 | .00125
.01 | .00666 | .00250
.05 | .0333 | .0125
.1 | .0660 | .0247

FIG. 53.

and $M_3 = 0.00075$; i.e. the response to the fundamental is 500 times the response to a second harmonic of equal magnitude, and is 1333 times the response to an equal third harmonic. (The response is down 54 db for the second and 62 db for the third harmonic.) In computing the *resonance range* of a vibration galvanometer (i.e. the change in frequency, in proportional parts, needed to reduce the response to half-value) a much better approximation is possible. Here we can write

$$\frac{1}{2\gamma} \approx 2 \cdot \frac{1}{\sqrt{(1-\eta^2)^2 + 4\gamma^2\eta^2}}$$

since the response at resonance is twice the half-value response and the impedance may be considered constant; or $(1-\eta^2)^2 = 4(4-\eta^2)\gamma^2$. Then, since the resonance range is so narrow that η will not be very different from unity at the frequency corresponding to half-value response, we have approximately $1-\eta^2 = 2\sqrt{3}\gamma$; from which $\eta \approx 1-\sqrt{3}\gamma$, or $1-\eta = (\omega_0-\omega)/\omega_0 = \sqrt{3}\gamma$. In the example cited above ($\gamma = 0.003$), a change of 0.5% in frequency from resonance will reduce the response to half-value. The *time constant* of a vibration galvanometer (i.e. the time required to reduce the *transient* response to 37% of its initial value) can be written directly from the exponential term in the general solution stated above for the equation of motion. Thus $\tau = 2P/A = 1/\gamma\omega_0$ seconds.

MOTIONAL IMPEDANCE. In the preliminary survey of vibration-galvanometer performance given above we have made the simplifying assumption that the impedance of the circuit in which the galvanometer operates is constant. In general, this will not be precisely true, and in many applications the circuit impedance will vary strongly with frequency. We will now consider the actual impedance encountered by the galvanometer and some of the modifications in performance that will result. The equation of motion may be written in terms of the galvanometer current as

$$\left[(\omega_0{}^2 - \omega^2) + j\omega\frac{K}{P}\right]\bar{\theta} = \frac{G}{P}\bar{\imath}$$

In terms of the applied and back emf's, the current is

$$\bar{\imath} = \frac{\bar{E} - j\omega G\bar{\theta}}{Z}$$

where the back emf is

$$-G\frac{d\theta}{dt} = -j\omega G\bar{\theta}, \quad \text{and} \quad Z = R + jX$$

the total circuit impedance, i.e. the impedance of the circuit seen from the galvanometer terminals plus the impedance that the galvanometer would have if its coil were stationary. Then

$$\bar{\imath}Z = \bar{E} - j\omega \frac{G^2}{P} \left[\frac{1}{(\omega_0^2 - \omega^2) + \dfrac{j\omega K}{P}} \right] \bar{\imath}$$

so that

$$\bar{e} = \bar{\imath} \left\{ Z + j\omega \frac{G^2}{P} \left[\frac{1}{(\omega_0^2 - \omega^2) + \dfrac{j\omega K}{P}} \right] \right\}$$

$$= \bar{\imath} \left\{ R + jX + \frac{j\omega G^2}{P} \frac{\left[(\omega_0^2 - \omega^2) - j\dfrac{\omega K}{P} \right]}{(\omega_0^2 - \omega^2)^2 + \dfrac{\omega^2 K^2}{P^2}} \right\}$$

$$= \bar{\imath} \left\{ \left[R + \frac{\omega^2 K G^2 / P^2}{(\omega_0^2 - \omega^2)^2 + \dfrac{\omega^2 K^2}{P^2}} \right] - j \left[X + \frac{\omega G^2 (\omega_0^2 - \omega^2)/P}{(\omega_0^2 - \omega^2)^2 + \dfrac{\omega^2 K^2}{P^2}} \right] \right\}$$

$$= \bar{\imath}(R' + jX') = \bar{\imath}[(R + R_m) + j(X + X_m)]$$

It will be noted that the effective impedance of the circuit is increased as a result of the galvanometer motion. The *motional impedance* has the components

$$R_m = \frac{\omega^2 K G^2 / P^2}{(\omega_0^2 - \omega^2)^2 + \dfrac{\omega^2 K^2}{P^2}}, \quad \text{and} \quad X_m = \frac{\omega G^2 (\omega_0^2 - \omega^2)/P}{(\omega_0^2 - \omega^2)^2 + \dfrac{\omega^2 K^2}{P^2}}$$

From the latter expression it is apparent that at frequencies below resonance ($\omega < \omega_0$) the *motional reactance* of the galvanometer is inductive; at resonance ($\omega = \omega_0$) it is zero; and at higher frequencies it is capacitive. The *motional resistance* is always positive and at resonance is

$$R_m = \frac{\omega_0^2 K G^2 / P^2}{\omega_0^2 K^2 / P^2} = \frac{G^2}{K}$$

OPTIMUM RESPONSE. The damping of a vibration galvanometer, as of any other type of galvanometer, results in part from the dissipation of energy by air friction and in part from the energy returned to the circuit by the generator action of the coil moving in the field of the magnet, i.e. the galvanometer current $\times$ back emf. The amplitude of deflection in the steady state will be such that the average power received from the circuit is just equal to the total of the average power returned to the circuit by generator action and that dissipated in friction. This statement was implied in the equation of motion which we have already examined. We will now separate the components of damping and re-examine the equation of motion. If we say that the total impedance of the circuit (including the static impedance of the galvanometer itself) is $Z = R + jX$, we can write

$$P\frac{d^2\theta}{dt^2} + \left(K + \frac{G^2}{Z}\right)\frac{d\theta}{dt} + U\theta = \frac{GE}{Z}\sin\omega t$$

In terms of the transformation previously used the equation of motion becomes

$$\left\{(\omega_0^2 - \omega^2) + j\omega\left[\frac{K}{P} + \frac{G^2}{P(R + jX)}\right]\right\}\bar{\theta} = \frac{G\bar{E}}{P(R + jX)}$$

which reduces to the form

$$\left\{\left[R(\omega_0^2 - \omega^2) - \frac{\omega KX}{P}\right] + j\left[X(\omega_0^2 - \omega^2) + \frac{\omega}{P}(KR + G^2)\right]\right\}\bar{\theta} = \frac{G\bar{E}}{P}$$

Then

$$\theta_{max} = \frac{GE}{P\sqrt{\left[R(\omega_0^2 - \omega^2) - \dfrac{\omega KX}{P}\right]^2 + \left[X(\omega_0^2 - \omega^2) + \dfrac{\omega}{P}(KR + G^2)\right]^2}}$$

at a lag angle behind the applied voltage

$$\psi = \tan^{-1}\frac{X(\omega_0^2 - \omega^2) + \dfrac{\omega}{P}(KR + G^2)}{R(\omega_0^2 - \omega^2) - \dfrac{\omega KX}{P}}$$

The galvanometer may be tuned by changing the moment of restoration U, leaving all other parameters unchanged; i.e. we will adjust ω_0 until the deflection (θ_{max}) has its maximum value. Under these conditions $\partial\theta_{max}/\partial\omega_0 = 0$, and we have

$$\left[R(\omega_0^2 - \omega^2) - \frac{\omega KX}{P}\right]R\omega_0 + \left[X(\omega_0^2 - \omega^2) + \frac{\omega}{P}(KR + G^2)\right]X\omega_0 = 0$$

or

$$(\omega_0^2 - \omega^2) = \frac{-\omega XG^2}{P(X^2 + R^2)}$$

For maximum response with fixed values of R, X, G, P, ω we have

$$\omega_0^2 = \omega\left[\omega - \frac{XG^2}{P(X^2 + R^2)}\right]$$

If, as is usually the case, the static reactance of the galvanometer coil is negligible, the response will be greatest in an inductive circuit if the galvanometer is tuned to a frequency somewhat above the undamped resonance frequency. In a capacitive circuit the frequency for maximum response is somewhat less than the undamped resonance frequency. For the value of ω_0 given above we have

$$\theta_{\max} = \frac{GE}{\omega\sqrt{\left[\dfrac{RXG^2}{(R^2+X^2)} + KX\right]^2 + \left[KR + G^2 - \dfrac{X^2G^2}{(R^2+X^2)}\right]^2}}$$

$$= \frac{GE}{\omega\left(K\sqrt{R^2+X^2} + \dfrac{G^2R}{\sqrt{R^2+X^2}}\right)} = \frac{GE}{\omega\left(KZ + \dfrac{G^2R}{Z}\right)}$$

at a lag angle

$$\psi = \tan^{-1}\left(-\frac{R}{X}\right) = \pi - \tan^{-1}\frac{R}{X}$$

In this expression K (the moment of frictional damping) is a fixed parameter of the galvanometer, but in one way or another X, G, and R may be varied to obtain optimum response. For a variation of X, we have $\partial\theta_{\max}/\partial X = 0$, or $K(R^2 + X^2) = G^2R$. For a variation of G, we have $\partial\theta_{\max}/\partial G = 0$, or again $K(R^2 + X^2) = G^2R$. Thus the response can be brought to an optimum value by introducing inductance in series with the galvanometer or by varying G. The latter adjustment is possible if the galvanometer is provided with an adjustable magnetic shunt to alter the air-gap field. In case either X or G is adjusted to give optimum response the deflection is

$$\theta_{\max} = \frac{GE}{2\omega K\sqrt{R^2+X^2}} = \frac{GE}{2\omega KZ} = \frac{GE\cdot R}{2\omega\gamma_0\cdot 2\sqrt{UP}\cdot RZ} = \frac{\theta_{dc}}{4\gamma_0\eta}\cdot\frac{R}{Z}$$

where $\theta_{dc} = GE/RU$ is the d-c response for the d-c voltage E, and γ_0 is the relative damping on open circuit. A third method of adjusting the galvanometer to its optimum response is to couple the galvanometer to the measuring circuit by means of a transformer. This method of adjusting response has the further advantage that, if suitable shielding is used in the transformer, it permits the isolation of the detector from the measuring circuit.[105] If the turn ratio of the transformer is N, we have $\bar{\imath}_g \cdot Z_g + \bar{\imath}_g \cdot N^2Z_c + \bar{E}_b = N\bar{E}$, where subscripts g and c refer to the galvanometer and measuring circuit respectively. Then

$$\bar{\imath}_g = \frac{N\bar{E} - \bar{E}_b}{Z_g + N^2Z_c} = \frac{N\bar{E} - j\omega G\bar{\theta}}{Z_g + N^2Z_c}$$

[105] This feature has been discussed above under Shielded Transformers: see p. 737.

and we have as the equation of motion

$$\left[(\omega_0^2 - \omega^2) + j\frac{\omega}{P}\left(K + \frac{G^2}{Z_g + N^2 Z_c}\right)\right]\bar{\theta} = \frac{N\bar{E}G}{Z_g + N^2 Z_c}$$

If we observe that $Z_e = Z_g + N^2 Z_c$ is the equivalent impedance, as seen from the galvanometer, of the entire circuit including the galvanometer, we can write

$$\left[(\omega_0^2 - \omega^2) + j\frac{\omega}{P}\left(K + \frac{G^2}{Z_e}\right)\right]\bar{\theta} = \frac{N\bar{E}G}{Z_e}$$

which is identical in form with the equation of motion previously found. Now, if the galvanometer is tuned for maximum deflection, we can write by analogy to the previous case

$$\theta_{\text{max}} = \frac{NEG}{\omega\left[K|Z_e| + \dfrac{G^2 R_e}{|Z_e|}\right]}$$

We could, of course, find the optimum transformer ratio by setting $\partial\theta_{\text{max}}/\partial N = 0$ and solving for N in the general expression above. However, since it will not generally be practical or worth while to make an exact impedance match, we can simplify the problem greatly and arrive at a sufficiently good approximation of the optimum transformer ratio by making the following assumptions: (1) the galvanometer will be tuned so that $\omega_0 = \omega$; (2) we will consider that the circuit into which the galvanometer is coupled has negligible reactance ($Z_c \approx R_c$); and (3) the reactance of the galvanometer itself is negligible ($Z_g \approx R_g$). Under these circumstances we have

$$\theta_{\text{max}} = \frac{NEG}{\omega_0[(R_g + N^2 R_c)K + G^2]}$$

Then for the condition $\partial\theta_{\text{max}}/\partial N = 0$, we have $R_g K + G^2 = N^2 R_c K$, so that

$$N^2 = \frac{R_g}{R_c} + \frac{G^2}{KR_c}$$

But $G^2/K = R_m$, the motional resistance of the galvanometer at resonance, and we have[106]

$$N^2 = \frac{R_g + R_m}{R_c}$$

[106] The d-c resistance of the galvanometer can be determined by one of the usual d-c methods. The motional resistance R_m may easily be determined. First, the current sensitivity of the galvanometer is measured by noting the deflection when a known voltage at the resonance frequency is introduced into a circuit whose known resistance is so high that the galvanometer resistance is negligible. The galvanometer can then be used as a microammeter in a circuit of moderate resistance at the resonance frequency to determine R_m.

GENERAL CONSIDERATIONS. In using the vibration galvanometer it is essential that it be tuned to the frequency of the applied voltage. In preliminary adjustments it is very convenient to have available a voltage source whose frequency can be varied. The resonance frequency can then be determined after each adjustment of suspension length or tension, by varying the frequency of the source until resonance is observed. Thus the effect of the adjustment can be seen and the magnitude of the next adjustment estimated in advance. A good optical system for observing deflections and a bright light source are essential, since the deflection is observed as a broadening of the image of the source into a band whose brightness decreases rapidly as the deflection increases. A straight filament incandescent lamp, a plane mirror on the moving system, and a convex lens which will give a sharp image of the filament on a ground-glass screen at a distance of about a meter will usually form a satisfactory optical system. If possible the lighting of the room should be subdued or the screen shielded from stray light in order that the contrast be as great as possible between the screen and the band of light which forms the deflected image. It will usually be necessary to protect a sensitive galvanometer from mechanical vibrations at its resonant frequency in order to avoid false indications. In many cases a stone slab or a heavy board or metal plate set on sponge rubber will effectively absorb mechanical vibrations and prove to be a satisfactory base for mounting the galvanometer. In surroundings where mechanical vibrations are very severe a special mounting may have to be devised. In instances of this sort a massive concrete block suspended from steel springs and having a mechanical resonance frequency very much lower than that of the galvanometer has been used as a sub-base. The galvanometer is then mounted on a heavy slab or plate on sponge rubber or felt pads. Such mounts have proved very effective at the National Bureau of Standards under severe vibration conditions.

For preliminary balance adjustments of a bridge, when a vibration galvanometer is used as a detector, the emf of unbalance will frequently be so large as to require that galvanometer sensitivity be greatly reduced. This is most conveniently done with a low-resistance shunt across the galvanometer terminals. The shunt resistance can be increased in steps and the shunt finally removed to increase sensitivity as the balance is more closely approached. It should be noted that the relative damping of the galvanometer is increased by shunting it, and consequently not only is its response decreased but also its resonance range is increased. In the presence of a shunt the galvanometer will be less sharply tuned than in its absence. Because of the very small damping at which the galvanometer is normally used its resonance range will be quite small, and it is essential that the frequency of the supply voltage be very stable, since a relatively small departure of frequency from the resonance value will result in a large decrease in the galvanometer response.

The A-C Galvanometer. This is a separately excited iron-cored electrodynamic instrument which can be used as a detector. Sensitivities comparable with those of good d-c galvanometers are attainable.[107] If the field circuit is supplied from the bridge source through a phase-shifting network, the response can be made phase-selective and the components of the bridge balance separately adjustable. The moving coil of such an instrument must be enclosed in an electrostatic shield that is maintained at the coil potential. Coupling between the field circuit and the moving-coil circuit of an a-c galvanometer may induce an emf in the moving coil by transformer action, and necessitate working from an electrical zero which is different from the mechanical open-circuit zero and which corresponds to the deflection produced by this emf in the closed galvanometer circuit.[108] This emf can be balanced out by means of a suitable mutual inductor whose primary is in series with the field coils and whose secondary is in series with the moving coil of the galvanometer. If the instrument is used with non-sinusoidal voltage it must be kept in mind that, as in any electrodynamic instrument, deflecting torque may be produced by any harmonic component that is common to the field and moving-coil currents.

The Cathode-Ray Tube. This can be utilized as a detector of bridge unbalance, but, since the voltage sensitivity of such a device is very low, it is essential that it be used in conjunction with a suitable amplifier. Many commercial cathode-ray oscillographs incorporate a suitable amplifier, and such a combination can be employed directly as a detector in many bridge applications. Although the oscillograph is not phase-selective in itself, its sweep circuit can be coupled through a phase-shifting network to the generator supplying the bridge, and, by suitable adjustment, the unbalance voltage of the bridge can be made to appear on the oscillograph screen as an elliptical figure whose minor axis is affected by one component of the unbalance voltage, and which is tilted from the horizontal by the quadrature component of the unbalance voltage.[109] Alternatively, a synchronized linear sweep may be used, and the unbalance voltage then appears as a standing wave pattern on the screen. This type

[107] The theory and design of a-c galvanometers have been very thoroughly treated by Weibel, *Bull. Bur. Standards*, **14**, 23 (1919).

[108] The coupling between the moving coil and the field will, of course, change with the moving-coil position but will be constant at the established reference position.

[109] Lamson, *Rev. Sci. Inst.*, **9**, 272 (1938). Such a detector is commercially available in the General Radio Company's Type 707–A cathode-ray null detector.

of display is sometimes very useful when the effects of harmonic components in the bridge voltage must be studied, although some skill is required in the interpretation of the patterns. Most cathode-ray oscillographs are so constructed that they are not injured by severe overload (unbalance) conditions, and there is no frequency selectivity other than that which may be built into the amplifier.

The Electron-Beam Tube. This tube, sometimes called the "electric eye," can also serve as a null detector. It has a cylindrical cathode surrounded by a conical anode coated with fluorescent material on the side facing the cathode, so that it becomes luminous under electron bombardment. On one side is a control electrode which is operated at a potential intermediate between those of the cathode and anode. The arrangement is shown in Fig. 54(a). If the potential of the control electrode is very nearly that of the anode, it has little influence on the interelectrode field and the anode screen is uniformly illuminated. When it becomes more negative with respect to the anode, it repels the electrons and thus casts a shadow on the fluorescent screen; i.e. a sector-shaped area of the screen remains dark. This arrangement is enclosed in the same envelope with a triode. The signal voltage (e) is applied to the grid of the triode, as shown in Fig. 54(b), causing plate current to flow. The triode plate is connected to the control electrode of the electron-beam arrangement and, through a resistance R, to the target anode. The difference of potential produced by the plate current flowing through R drives the control electrode negative with respect to the target anode and forms a sector-shaped shadow on the fluorescent screen. The biasing resistance (r) is adjusted so that with no signal voltage present the shadow sector is closed. The dark sector then opens out with increasing signal voltage, and the angle it subtends indicates the magnitude of the signal. Such an indicator, preceded by a suitable amplifier, is quite rugged and is much used as a detector,[110] particularly where only moderate sensitivity is required.

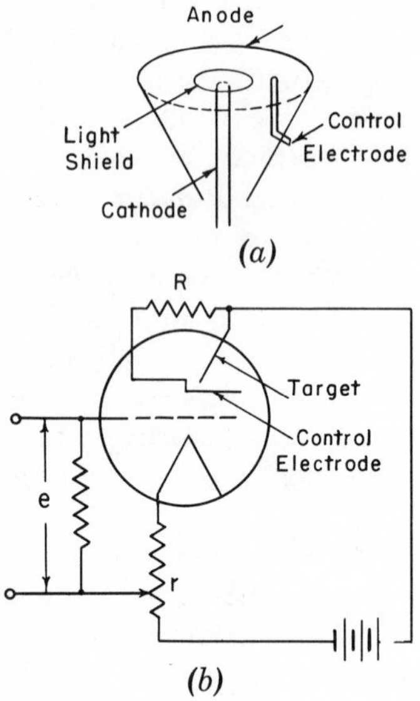

FIG. 54.

[110] Breazale, *Rev. Sci. Inst.*, **7**, 250 (1936); Garman, *Rev. Sci. Inst.*, **8**, 327 (1937); Koehler, *Rev. Sci. Inst.*, **8**, 450 (1937).

Rectifiers. These can be employed in conjunction with d-c indicating instruments as null detectors. Use has been made of three types of mechanical rectifiers: (1) brushes bearing on a synchronously driven commutator, (2) reversing contacts operated by a synchronously driven cam,[111] and (3) a vibrating-reed contactor driven from an electromagnet.[112] Spurious emf's and other contact difficulties are often very troublesome in the operation of a rotating commutator and stationary brushes, and care must be taken to avoid combinations of materials which show any appreciable contact difference of potential or thermal emf. Make and break contacts in which only a very slight wiping action is present are much more trouble-free and can be designed to be free from parasitic emf's. In the first two types of rectifier it is possible to introduce a phase-selective arrangement, by adjusting the angular position at which the circuit is opened and closed, with respect to the driving motor shaft. In the vibrating-reed detector a polarized steel reed is driven from an electromagnet which may be excited through a phase shifter. This device functions as a half-wave rectifier.

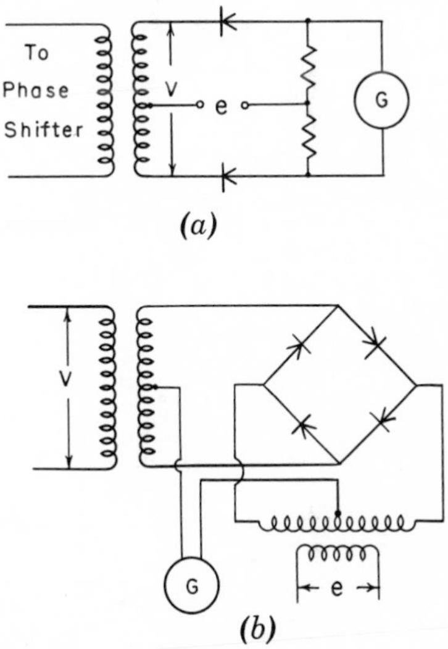

FIG. 55.

Copper oxide rectifiers[113] have also been much used. Four rectifier units can be connected in a rectangular array to form a full-wave rectifier in which the a-c input is impressed across one diagonal and the rectified direct current is taken at the opposite diagonal. Such a rectifier can be used throughout the a-f range with very little change in sensitivity, but is very inefficient as a rectifier at voltages much below 0.1 volt and shows almost no rectification at 0.01 volt, since the ratio of forward to reverse resistance approaches unity at low voltages. Performance can be improved at low voltage, and the feature of phase selectivity incorporated by polarizing the rectifier with an auxiliary voltage as shown in Fig. 55(*a*).[114] The signal voltage (e) to be rectified is applied between center taps of a transformer and a resistor. The auxiliary polarizing voltage (V) is

[111] Sharp and Crawford, *Trans. AIEE*, **39**, 1518 (1911).
[112] Pfannemüller, *Arch. für Elektrot.*, **28**, 356 (1934).
[113] See discussion of copper oxide rectifiers in Chapter 10.
[114] Walter, *Zeits. für tech. Phys.*, **13**, 363, 436 (1932).

applied to the transformer through a phase-shifting network, and the d-c indicating instrument is connected across the resistor. If we assume that the polarizing voltage is large compared to the signal voltage and that the current in the d-c instrument is small, the instantaneous polarity of the voltage V will determine at any moment which of the rectifier elements will operate, and the detector current will be proportional to $(V/2) \cdot e \cos \alpha$, where α is the phase angle between the polarizing and signal voltages. Since during one half-cycle the voltage is $(V/2 + e)$ in the operating

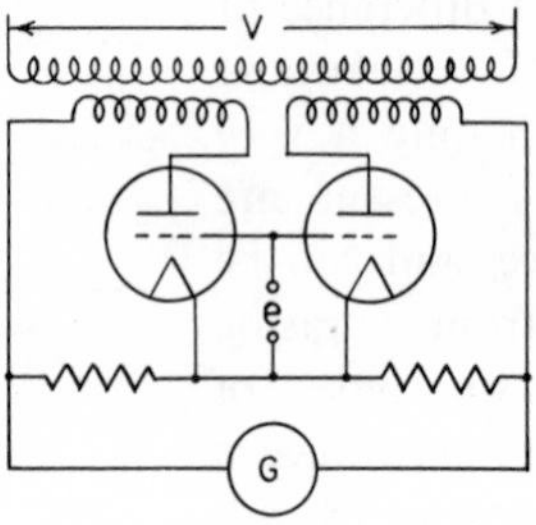

(*a*)

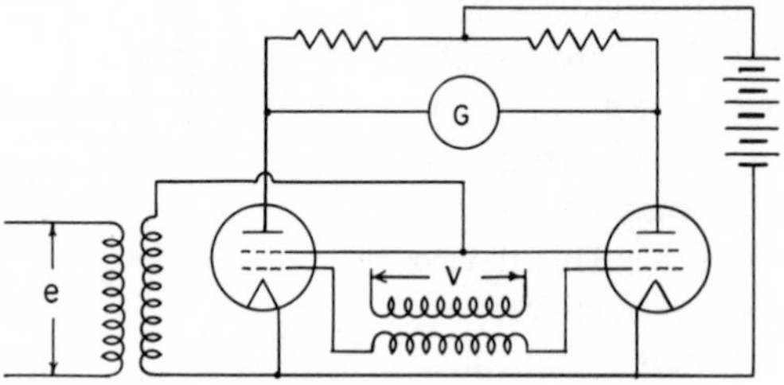

(*b*)

FIG. 56.

rectifier circuit, and during the opposite half-cycle the operating voltage is $(V/2 - e)$, the voltage V can be made large enough that the rectifiers will function efficiently. Also, since the phase of V can be varied with respect to e, the detector can be made phase-selective. Figure 55(*b*) shows a modification of the polarized rectifier in which full wave rectification is accomplished.[115]

Phase-selective rectifiers can also be constructed in a similar way, using vacuum tubes. The vacuum-tube analogue of Walter's rectifier is shown in Fig. 56(*a*). The plates of the triodes are supplied by an auxiliary voltage (V) through a transformer connected so that one plate is positive and the other negative during each half-cycle. The grids are connected

[115] Morton, *Trans. Faraday Soc.*, **33**, 474 (1937).

together, and the bridge unbalance voltage (*e*) is impressed between the grids and cathodes through a phase-shifting network.[116] A center-zero d-c instrument indicates both the magnitude and the direction of unbalance. The use of triodes requires a large polarizing voltage and may limit the application of the device at high audio-frequencies. If tetrodes are used, a comparatively low polarizing voltage can be applied to the space-charge grids.[117] This arrangement is shown in Fig. 56(*b*).

Amplifiers

Any of the detectors described above can be used with a suitable amplifier to increase its response to small unbalance voltages. An amplifier may be particularly advantageous where a relatively insensitive detector is to be used because of its ruggedness, freedom from overload damage, ease of operation, or some other desirable characteristic. Furthermore certain characteristics, such as logarithmic response, protection against overload, and frequency selectivity, can be built into amplifiers. Whatever type of amplifier is used, certain precautions must be observed. Because of its large capacitance to ground, the amplifier should be operated with one side at ground potential. This is especially true of a-c-powered amplifiers, but battery-powered amplifiers may also have higher capacitance to ground than can be tolerated. If the bridge is such that the detector branch cannot be operated at ground potential, it may be coupled to the grounded amplifier through a shielded transformer.[118] Wherever transformers are used, either to couple elements of the measuring circuit or in the amplifier itself, they should be as small as practicable, of balanced-coil construction, and magnetically shielded to minimize their coupling with any magnetic field that may be present. In addition it is sometimes necessary to orient the transformer for minimum pick-up, when working with a high-gain amplifier. The amplifier should also be completely shielded electrostatically, including input and output lines, which may be either a twisted pair inside a shield or a coaxial cable. Loops should be avoided since they might couple inductively with some other circuit element, giving rise to a spurious emf and a false indication of balance conditions. It is well to check an amplifier for inductive pick-up before using it in balancing a bridge. The bridge should be excited during this test but not connected to the amplifier input. If the amplifier is to be used with a high-impedance input, the input terminals

[116] Cosens, *Proc. Phys. Soc.*, **46,** 818 (1934).
See also Michels and Curtis, *Phys. Rev.*, **57,** 1065 (1940); and Macnamara, *Rev. Sci. Inst.*, **2,** 343 (1931).
[117] Morton, *op. cit.*
[118] See p. 737.

may be left open during this test. If the input impedance is low, a non-inductive resistor having a value approximately equal to the impedance of the bridge should be connected to the input terminals during this test.

In applications where the balance condition is a function of frequency, precautions must be taken against errors resulting from harmonics. If neither the amplifier nor the detector discriminates against harmonics, an indication of unbalance may be obtained from the detector response to harmonics even though the fundamental is balanced. This cannot generally be entirely corrected by using a filter between the amplifier and the detector, for, if the amplifier is not linear, sum and difference frequencies are produced by its operation. Since the difference between any successive even and odd harmonic is equal to the fundamental frequency, such a beat frequency would be passed by a filter tuned to the fundamental and would result in a false indication of unbalance.[119] It would therefore appear desirable to insert the filter in the amplifier input. However, if the filter contains inductive elements, any "pick-up" emf resulting from coupling would be amplified and passed through to the detector, resulting in a false indication. In amplifiers which have two or more stages, such filter elements are usually inserted between stages so that any inductive pick-up will receive less amplification; i.e. a compromise is made between the necessity for keeping harmonics out of the amplifier-detector system and the undesirability of amplifying spurious signals that would result from inductive pick-up. Trouble from spurious fundamental signals which arise from difference frequencies is minimized if the amplifier can be operated in its linear range, so that no stage is overloaded. Great care must be observed to avoid pick-up if a filter[120] containing an inductive element is required in the input stage of an amplifier.

A very effective method of obtaining frequency selectivity without inductive pick-up is by means of a degenerative amplifier using a tuned resistance-capacitance feedback network.[121] A frequency-selective network such as the Wien bridge, which has been discussed above, or the

[119] The production of sum and difference frequencies from harmonics, and hence the production of subharmonic frequencies, are general characteristics of nonlinear circuit elements and are not confined solely to amplifiers. The general case has been discussed by Goodhue, *J. Franklin Inst.*, **217,** 87 (1934).

[120] The design of filters cannot appropriately be considered here. For information on this subject the reader should refer to a textbook on circuit theory, such as Kerchner and Corcoran, *op. cit.*, Chapter 13, or a textbook on communications such as Everitt, *Communication Engineering*, Chapter 6, McGraw-Hill.

[121] Scott, *Proc. IRE,* **26,** 226 (1938). Also see *Vacuum-Tube Amplifiers*, Vol. 18 of the Radiation Laboratory Series, p. 406, McGraw-Hill, 1948.

twin-T network shown in Fig. 57(*a*) can be used for this purpose, as shown in the block diagram of Fig. 57(*b*). The frequency selectivity of the twin-T is slightly better than that of the Wien bridge, and it has other advantages in the present application.[122] Since the output of the selective network is zero at the frequency for which it is tuned, there is no feedback and hence no degeneration at this frequency. The magnitude of the signal passed by the selective network increases rapidly as the frequency departs from the critical value, and this signal is used to degenerate the amplification. As a result the full amplification is available at the selected

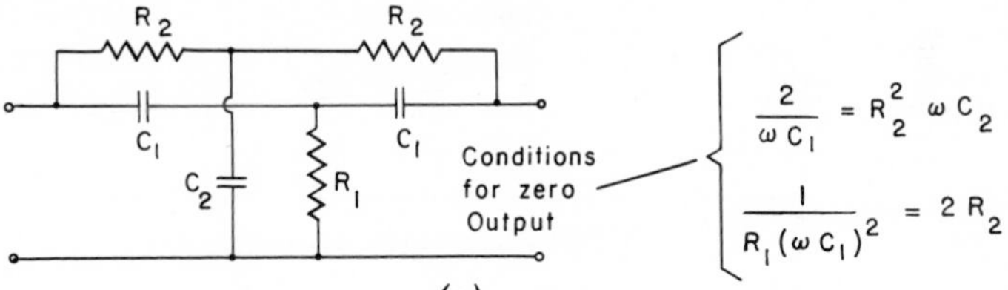

(*a*)

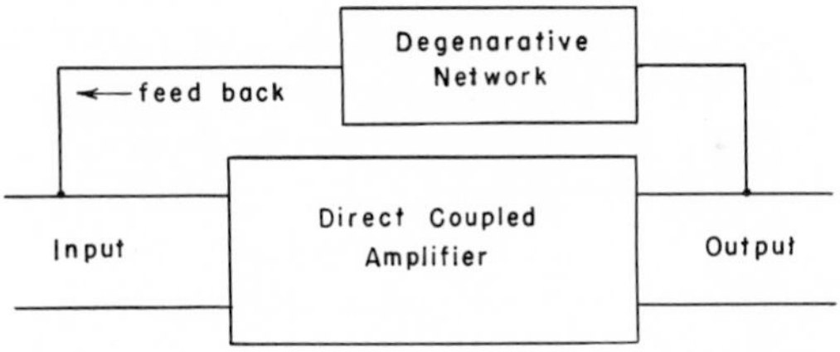

(*b*)

FIG. 57.

frequency but falls off rapidly for changes in frequency, being down by as much as 40 db at the second harmonic. Such an amplifier can be used with a rectifier-detector or some other type of detector which is not frequency-selective. However, where very great sensitivity is needed at low frequencies a vibration galvanometer may be employed to advantage with the amplifier. Since both the amplifier and the galvanometer may be quite sharply tuned, the frequency of the supply voltage must be held quite closely to the selected value to make the best use of the combination.

When the bridge balance is not frequency-dependent, a high-gain amplifier having a flat response over a wide frequency range will increase sensitivity. It is usually advantageous to have available a means for controlling the amplifier gain, which should be reduced during preliminary balances. Early multistage amplifiers were often transformer-coupled,

[122] In applications involving frequency selection over a wide range the Wien bridge may sometimes be preferred, as it has fewer parameters that must be adjusted together.

but with the advent of high-mu triode and pentode tubes, resistance-capacitance coupling has been generally adopted. Alternating-current-powered amplifiers have the feature of convenience to recommend them, but where freedom from background noise at high amplification[123] is essential, battery operation is usually preferable. The power requirements of modern amplifiers are small enough that battery replacement does not usually present a serious problem.[124] Most high-gain amplifiers have more than one stage of amplification, but there are many applications

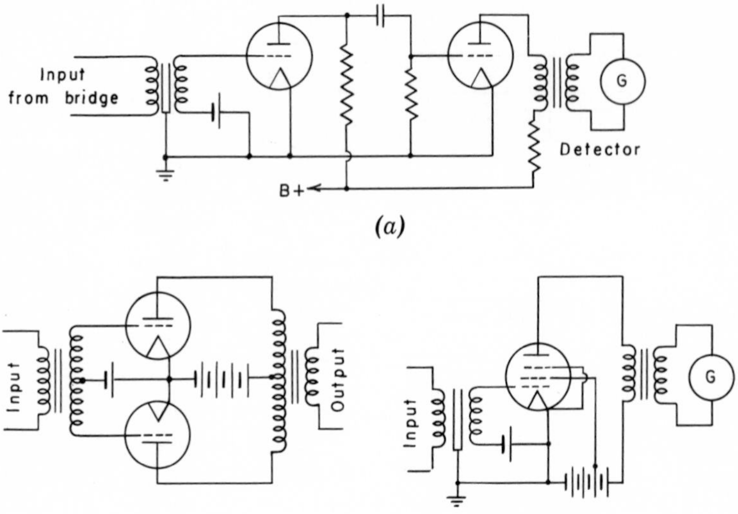

(a)

(b) (c)

FIG. 58.

in which a simple, single-stage amplifier is sufficient (particularly if it is used with a sensitive detector such as a telephone receiver or a vibration galvanometer). Difficulties of avoiding instability, self-oscillation, and undesirable interaction between stages are multiplied as the number of stages is increased. It is very rarely that more than three stages of amplification are used with bridge detectors.

A two-stage resistance-capacitance coupled amplifier is shown schematically in Fig. 58(*a*). This type of amplifier may be expected to have a flat response over a wide range of frequencies. It is indicated in the figure that the bridge is coupled to the input and the detector to the output

[123] It is also very difficult to eliminate completely 60-cycle effects from an ac-powered amplifier having a high gain.

[124] It is well to keep in mind that the shelf life of replacement batteries can be greatly increased by keeping them under moderate refrigeration.

terminals through transformers. Direct coupling is possible in many cases, but if the bridge and detector impedances are not matched reasonably to the input and output impedances respectively of the amplifier the capabilities of the combination will not be fully utilized. Generally speaking, if the impedances are at least as closely matched as a ratio of 2/1, the use of an impedance-matching transformer does not result in any net increase in sensitivity since the transformer losses are greater than the theoretical gain. Of course, even when the impedance match is close enough that a coupling transformer is not justifiable on this account

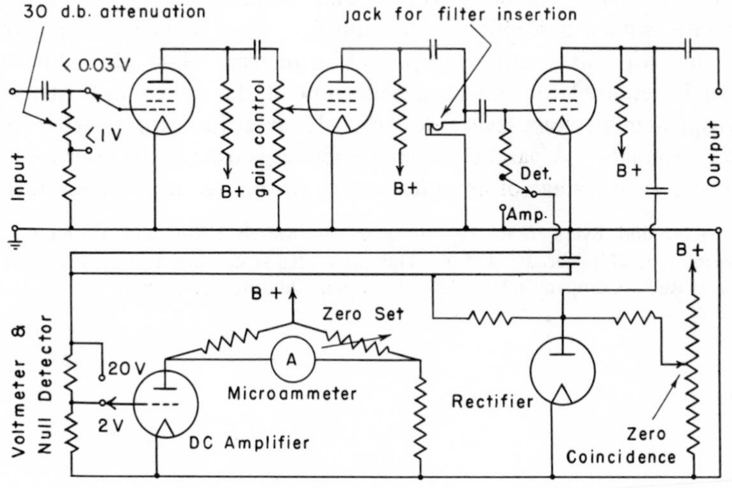

FIG. 59.

alone, other considerations may require the use of a shielded transformer in order that the circuits may be isolated from each other and operated at different potentials.

The push-pull amplifier of Fig. 58(*b*) may be expected to operate linearly over a larger power range than a simple amplifier, since if the tubes are well matched the curvatures of their grid-plate characteristics will be compensated. Figure 58(*c*) shows schematically how a pentode tube can be used to obtain high gain in a single stage of amplification. The control grid (next to the cathode) is operated in the usual way. The intermediate screen grid is maintained at a positive potential slightly less than that of the plate and acts as a shield between plate and control grid. The suppressor grid (nearest the plate) is connected to the cathode and counteracts the effect of secondary electron emission at the plate. It also improves the shielding between control grid and plate and makes the action of the control grid virtually independent of plate potential. The use of pentodes permits high amplification with freedom from distortion or instability.

The circuit of a modern general-purpose audio-frequency amplifier and detector[125] is shown schematically in Fig. 59. It is battery operated and has a built-in vacuum-tube voltmeter which also functions as a null detector. Alternatively the arrangement can be used as a three-stage linear amplifier. It has a flat characteristic from 50 to 5000 cps with an open-circuit gain of 83 db. (The gain is 45 db at 100 kc.) The input impedance is a resistance of 1 megohm in parallel with 20 $\mu\mu$f, and the output resistance is 50,000 ohms. The null detector has a semi-logarithmic response, with a perceptible indication for 15 μv input (with maximum gain and with no external filter), and an increase of 55 db in the input signal is required for full-scale deflection of the indicating instrument. The open-circuit noise level is less than 15 μv at full gain, referred to the input terminals. A parallel resonance circuit is used as the insertion filter after the second stage of amplification to further reduce random noise.

[125] Scott and Byers, *G.R. Experimenter*, **20** (March 1946), and Thurston, *G.R. Experimenter*, **22** (February 1948). This apparatus is commercially available as the General Radio Company's Type 1231–B amplifier and null detector.

INDEX